SCIENCEPLUS

Technology and Society

Annotated Teacher's Edition

Project Directors

International: **Charles McFadden**
Professor of Science Education
The University of New Brunswick
Fredericton, New Brunswick

National: **Robert E. Yager**
Professor of Science Education
The University of Iowa
Iowa City, Iowa

This new United States edition has been adapted from prior work by the Atlantic Science Curriculum Project, an international project linking teaching, curriculum development, and research in science education.

 Holt, Rinehart and Winston
Harcourt Brace Jovanovich

Austin • Orlando • San Diego • Chicago • Dallas • Toronto

ACKNOWLEDGEMENTS

Project Advisors

Herbert Brunkhorst
Director, Institute for Science
    Education
California State University, San
    Bernardino
San Bernardino, California

David L. Cross
Science Consultant
Lansing School District
Lansing, Michigan

Jerry Hayes
Associate Director, Scientific Outreach
Teacher's Academy, Mathematics
    and Science
Chicago, Illinois

William C. Kyle, Jr.
Director, School Mathematics and
    Science Center
Purdue University
West Lafayette, Indiana

Mozell Lang
Science Education Specialist
Michigan Department of Education
Lansing, Michigan

Project Authors

Earl S. Morrison (Author in Chief)
Nan Armour
Allan Hammond
John Haysom

Alan Moore (Associate Author in Chief)
Elinor Nicoll
Muriel Smyth

Project Associates

We wish to thank the hundreds of science educators, teachers, and
administrators from the scores of universities, high schools, and middle schools
who have contributed to the success of *SciencePlus*.

ATE Writers

Nancy Straus (Writer in Chief)
David Stienecker
Sharon Kahkonen
Iris Kane

ATE Consultants

Shirley Gholston Key (Multicultural Advisor)
Allan Cobb (Content Reviewer)

Field-Test Teachers and Sites

Charles Bissell
Gompers Secondary School
San Diego, California

Leslie Blanscet
Olive Peirce Middle School
Ramona, California

Steven E. Byrd
Florida State University School
Tallahassee, Florida

Suzette Carroll
Edison Junior High School
Los Angeles, California

Daisy Century
Sulzberger Junior High School
Philadelphia, Pennsylvania

Sharon Cox
Stidwell Junior High School
Sandpoint, Idaho

Ken Crease
White Mountain Junior High School
Rock Springs, Wyoming

Matt Keller
Rancho Cotate High School
Rohnert Park, California

Frank Lucio
Olive Peirce Middle School
Ramona, California

Naomi Lyall
Sunnyvale Junior High
Sunnyvale, California

Kim McConathy
Deep Water Junior High School
Pasadena, Texas

Bruce Metz
White Mountain Junior High School
Rock Springs, Wyoming

Nancy Miller
Bell Junior High School
San Diego, California

David Mooney
Upland High School
Upland, California

Mary Mund
Priest River Junior High School
Priest River, Idaho

Cindy Murray
Upland High School
Upland, California

Sally Pisani
Olive Peirce Middle School
Ramona, California

David Reynolds
Olive Peirce Middle School
Ramona, California

June Turnquist
Fremont High School
Sunnyvale, California

We also wish to acknowledge the contributions of the many Canadian field-test teachers who have helped to shape the *Scn SciencePlus* program.

SourceBook Consultants

Robert H. Allers
Earth Science Teacher
Vernon-Verona-Sherrill
    High School
Verona, New York

Linda Butler
Lecturer, Division of
    Biological Sciences
The University of Texas at Austin
Austin, Texas

Christopher J. Chiaverina
Physics Instructor
New Trier Township High School
Winnetka, Illinois

Juan Cotera
Architect
Austin, Texas

Edmund J. Escudero
Chemistry Teacher
Summit Country Day School
Cincinnati, Ohio

Roger H. Kolar
Architect
Austin, Texas

Maureen Lemke
Biology Laboratory Instructor
Goodnight Jr. High School
San Marcos, Texas

Contents

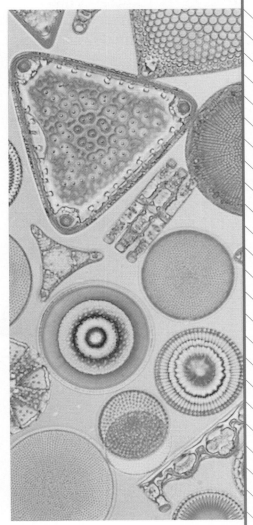

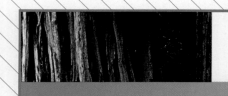

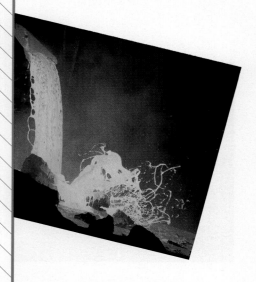

SCIENCEPLUS

Owner's Manual

The SciencePlus Philosophy

Welcome to SciencePlus, an innovative approach to science education. SciencePlus is unlike any science program you have used before. It is designed from the ground up to teach science in precisely the way that students learn best—by thinking, talking, and writing about what they do and discover. SciencePlus is activity- and inquiry-based. In other words, it is both hands-on and minds-on. SciencePlus is lively, engaging, and relevant to the student's world. SciencePlus is loaded with thought-provoking activities designed to challenge students' thinking skills while introducing them to realistic methods of science.

SciencePlus works for students and teacher alike. Students enjoy and benefit from its active, varied approach, while teachers find it to be teachable under real conditions. Laboratory-type activities require about 30–40 percent of class time. The remainder of class time is taken up by a rich variety of learning activities.

SciencePlus is tailored to meet the needs of middle school-aged students. It accommodates every type of student you are likely to encounter: the basic student, who requires substantial guidance; the average student, who is not yet fully-equipped with abstract-thinking skills; and the advanced student, who needs only to be pointed in the right direction to succeed.

At every stage, the SciencePlus program emphasizes concept and skill development over memorization of facts. By doing science activities and then thinking about the results, students learn the whys and hows, not just the whats and whens, of science. Ultimately, students come to see science as a system for making sense of the world.

Origins

The SciencePlus program was originally developed by the Atlantic Science Curriculum Project (ASCP) of Canada to replace the traditional recall-based curriculum, which had proven to be ineffective. SciencePlus represents a ground-breaking effort, the culmination of many years of labor by dozens of talented, dedicated science educators.

The SciencePlus development team was guided every step of the way by the latest insights into how children actually learn. The SciencePlus program has been thoroughly tested on real students in realistic settings, refined, and then retested. The result is a program that works! Teachers using SciencePlus have reported dramatic gains in student comprehension and retention of scientific concepts. Above all, students enjoy using SciencePlus and develop a heightened interest in science.

A Continuing Tradition

The American Edition of SciencePlus continues the tradition of excellence begun in Canada. Many of the recommendations of Project 2061 and NSTA Scope, Sequence, and Coordination have been employed in order to make the program even better. In addition, SciencePlus has been made easier to follow and more culturally and regionally relevant. Exciting new features have also been added to highlight the linkages among science, technology, and society.

SciencePlus is lively, engaging and relevant to the student's world.

An Interactive, Effective Program

Science*Plus* employs proven teaching strategies: guided and open-ended investigations, small-group discussions, exploratory writing and reflective reading tasks, games, picture and word puzzles, and independent long-range projects. This variety helps motivate and maintain the interest of students and teachers alike.

Science*Plus* develops scientific process skills as an essential goal. As the curriculum progresses, the students will gradually master increasingly complex tasks. For example, students will move from directed to open-ended inquiry, and from reading and completing tables and graphs to constructing them from experimental data they have collected on their own.

In general, each of the units in Science*Plus* is self-contained and may be taught as a separate instructional module. Science*Plus* contains a balance of physical, biological, earth/space, and environmental science topics.

Guiding Principles

The guiding principles of Science*Plus* are simple and few:

❖ Anyone can learn science

The popular image of science as the private domain of the super-intelligent is wrong and damaging. Science is for everyone. Children exposed to science for the first time take to it naturally. It is only later, after the science kits and fun activities have been abandoned in favor of fill-in-the-blank worksheets and recall drills, that love for science is replaced by fear and dread. Science*Plus* can rekindle the sense of wonder and fascination that lies dormant within your students.

❖ Science is a natural endeavor

Whether we realize it or not, each of us applies science nearly every day. Hardly a day passes that we don't ask ourselves "How does this work?" or "Why does that happen?" or "What happens if...?" Scientists differ from other people only in that it is their profession, rather than their avocation, to figure out "how," "when," and "why."

Unfortunately, stereotypes about science and scientists abound. Many students feel that only "nerds" or "geeks" enjoy science. This falsehood may do as much to turn people away from science as any curricular shortcoming. Science*Plus* actively refutes these stereotypes. It portrays science as a rewarding, quintessentially human undertaking. Scientists are portrayed as normal people, not aloof geniuses who talk in equations.

❖ Science is its own reward

There is no feeling quite like the thrill of discovery or the sense of accomplishment that comes from rising to a difficult challenge. Science can be thought of as a voyage into the unknown. This voyage can be exciting and rewarding for all.

Aims

Science*Plus* is designed to help you further develop each of the following in your students:

- Understanding of the interrelationships among science, technology, and society.
- Understanding of important science concepts, processes, and ideas
- Use of higher-order thinking skills
- Ability to solve problems and apply scientific principles
- Commitment to environmental protection
- Interest in independent study of scientific topics
- Social skills
- Communication skills

To accomplish these goals, a wide variety of teaching strategies are employed. The common denominator among these is their emphasis on *doing*. At all times, students are to be active and involved.

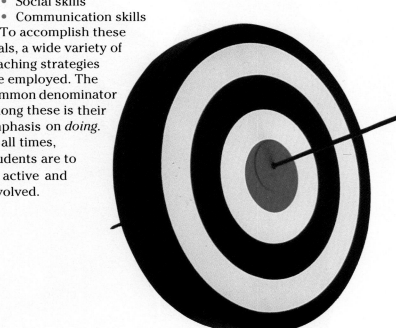

*Science*Plus* can rekindle the sense of wonder and fascination that lies dormant within your students.*

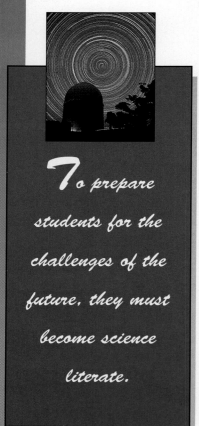
Science, Technology, and Society

Science and technology are flip sides of the same coin; each supports the other. Neither should be studied in isolation. Science*Plus* explores the relationship between science and technology, and the effect of both on our society as a whole. Even people who never again set foot in a laboratory after leaving school can benefit from an understanding of science and technology and how both relate to each other and to society at large.

Our society, complex as it is, will become even more so in the years to come. Science and technology will play roles in every aspect of life. In the future, "high-tech" will be more than a catch phrase, it will permeate every aspect of life. To prepare students for the challenges of the future, they must become science literate. They must be given the tools to become responsible and productive individuals in a highly technological world.

Science for All

Science*Plus* is designed to put the "process" back into science education and, in so doing, provide students with the intellectual skills they need to truly understand and apply science. Now, as never before, a thorough grounding in science is absolutely essential; without it, students—the citizens of tomorrow—cannot expect to be fully conversant in and responsive to the complex issues of the twenty-first century.

No program can teach itself. You, with your energy, enthusiasm, and ability, are the key to a successful outcome. Science*Plus* will help you help the students develop all the skills they need to learn independently. Science*Plus* fosters a spirit of joint exploration—students with teacher and with one another. **Let the journey begin.**

The SciencePlus Method

Building a Better Understanding of Science

The *SciencePlus* program is based on the Constructivist Learning Model (CLM). Constructivism is based as much on common sense as on the results of research. With the CLM, students "construct" an understanding of concepts step by step. Students begin by identifying what they already know about a topic. Any misconceptions they may have about a topic are exposed at this point. Identifying these misconceptions is a critical part of the process. Next, students do hands-on activities to experience the subject matter directly. Their experiences cause them to amend, add to, or scrap altogether the mental model they already have of the subject in question.

Constructivism is based on a few key steps:

1. Invitation

The Invitation stimulates students' curiosity and engages their interest. At this stage, students note the unexpected, pose questions, or define a problem.

2. Exploration

Explorations engage students in the search for solutions or explanations. Students look for alternative sources of information, collect and evaluate data, and clarify their findings through discussion and debate.

3. Proposing explanations and solutions

At the conclusion of the Explorations, students propose their response to the problem or question posed in the Invitation. The class is exposed to a variety of possible responses, and students have the opportunity to consider each.

4. Taking action

Students make decisions about a course of action based on the various proposals offered. If the class reaches consensus, then this stage may bring about closure of the lesson. It may happen, though, that this stage identifies new questions to explore.

▯▯▯▶ **For an in-depth discussion of Constructivism, see "The Constructivist Learning Model," by Bob Yager, The Science Teacher, September 1991**

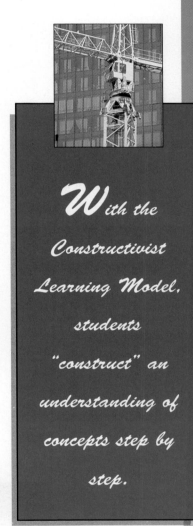

With the Constructivist Learning Model, students "construct" an understanding of concepts step by step.

Themes in Science

The traditional division of science into three branches—life, earth, and physical sciences—often leads students to believe that nature is similarly arranged. Too often, students view science as a system of separate, nonrelated abstractions, or as a compilation of facts and difficult-sounding terms. But science is simply the study of nature, and there are certain underlying principles, or themes, that unite the study of all areas of science. The themes provided here are not meant to replace the traditional teaching of scientific disciplines, but rather to create a framework for the unification of these disciplines.

The themes are intended to integrate facts and ideas, and to provide a context for discussing the textual matter in a meaningful way. You can employ these themes as an organizational tool to reinforce understanding of the subject matter, rather than the rote memorization of facts. The following six themes are emphasized in Science*Plus*.

One subject can be addressed from the viewpoint of many different themes.

Energy

Energy is the ability to put matter into motion. Energy is what makes the universe and everything in it dynamic and ever-changing. The study of dynamic systems in any field of science requires an understanding of energy: its origins, how it flows through systems, how it is converted from one form to another, and how it is conserved. Energy provides the basis for all interactions, whether chemical, biological, or physical. Thematically, energy connects all disciplines.

Evolution

Evolution can be broadly described as change over time. In the evolutionary sense, change is not a simple alteration, but rather a progression of such alterations over the continuum of time. The entire universe and all of its inhabitants can thus be studied from the viewpoint of historical change. This theme can be used to understand why things exist as they do today by understanding how they were in the past.

Patterns of Change

Change through time can be analyzed in connection to its rates and patterns. Changes can be predictable or unpredictable, regular or irregular, cyclical or unidirectional. Change can affect both simple and complex systems. Knowing different patterns of change provides students with an understanding of natural systems and their underlying mechanisms, and can help them predict what will happen in the future based on this understanding.

Scale and Structure

Scale and Structure provides a means for understanding the nature of matter and systems within the natural world. Structure defines how matter, a system, or a process fits together; scale determines the level at which this structure is examined. Scale and structure provide a means for understanding the underlying framework that gives order to matter.

Stability

Stability is constancy within a system. It can refer to the way in which systems as a whole do not change, or it can refer to a state of static equilibrium in which the forces causing change within a system are balanced. Stability also relates to the predictability of change within nature.

Systems and Interactions

Systems and Interactions provides a basis for the study of all matter from the simplest level to the most complex forms. A system can be defined as an interacting group of forces, bodies, or substances. How these systems interact gives vital information about the individual components of the system being studied.

The following table summarizes the application of themes throughout the Science*Plus* program.

UNIT	THEME					
	Energy	Evolution	Patterns of Change	Scale and Structure	Stability	Systems and Interactions
Level Green						
Science and Technology			◆		◆	
Patterns of Living Things		◆	◆	◆	◆	
It's a Small World			◆	◆		◆
Investigating Matter	◆			◆	◆	
Chemical Changes			◆	◆		◆
Energy and You	◆		◆			◆
Temperature and Heat	◆			◆		◆
Our Changing Earth		◆		◆	◆	
Level Red						
Interactions	◆		◆			◆
Diversity of Living Things		◆	◆	◆		
Solutions			◆	◆		◆
Force and Motion	◆				◆	◆
Structures and Design				◆	◆	◆
The Restless Earth		◆	◆	◆		
Toward the Stars		◆	◆	◆		
Growing Plants			◆	◆		◆
Level Blue						
Life Processes	◆			◆	◆	
Machines, Work, and Energy	◆				◆	◆
Oceans and Climates		◆	◆			◆
Electromagnetic Systems	◆			◆		◆
Sound	◆	◆				◆
Light	◆		◆		◆	
Particles	◆		◆	◆		
Continuity of Life		◆	◆	◆		

Using the Themes

A major strength of the thematic approach is that seemingly different processes, structures, or systems can be shown to have underlying similarities. Although many thematic organizations are possible, each Unit Interleaf in this *Annotated Teacher's Edition* suggests at least two major themes that can be discussed in relation to the unit material. Focus questions are also provided that can be used to promote discussion and an understanding of how the themes relate to the text material.

Although major themes have been identified in each Unit Interleaf, it is up to you to decide which themes you feel are most appropriate. The direction that your class discussion takes will most likely guide you in your choices.

In your class discussions, use the themes to provide a framework of understanding for your students. For example, whether you are studying photosynthesis or the way in which the forces of nature have shaped the physical appearance of the earth, the theme of energy can be discussed. Similarly, one subject can be addressed from the viewpoint of many different themes. For example, in discussing an organism such as a zebra, energy can be applied in a discussion of how the zebra takes in food from the environment; evolution can be discussed in relation to how the zebra's structures are adaptations to its environment; and patterns of change can be introduced by a discussion of how the zebra's migration habits are based on the seasons.

At the end of a unit, the themes can provide a helpful source of review and a way to consolidate the material presented. In addition, questions provided within the text as well as in the *Teacher's Edition* are thematically based.

In your class discussions, use the themes to provide a framework of understanding for your students.

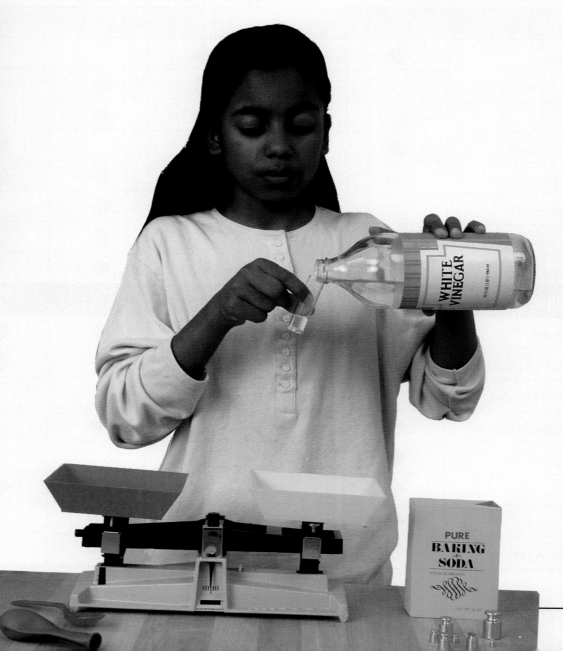

Components of SciencePlus

The Pupil's Edition

SciencePlus is no ordinary textbook. SciencePlus is a student-friendly text; lively, abundantly illustrated with clever, colorful illustrations, and loaded with engaging activities. Every effort has been taken to make this text the sort of book that students will actually want to use.

Units, Sections, Lessons

SciencePlus contains eight units, which are further divided into sections and lessons on closely related subject matter. Each lesson includes a wide variety of activities and explorations designed to develop the lesson content.

Explorations

Scattered throughout each unit are a series of Explorations—hands-on, inquiry-based activities. These Explorations allow students to see scientific principles in action. The Explorations are essential for inducing real learning in students. As students do the Explorations, they have the opportunity to compare their mental models of scientific principles to the real things. As weaknesses are exposed, students adjust their thinking to accommodate what they have learned.

Most of the Explorations are designed to be done cooperatively in small groups. In this way, the Explorations model real scientific experiences, in which scientists work together to solve problems. By working in cooperative groups, students also develop important skills

such as communicating ideas and sharing responsibility. In addition, the cooperative groups not only make science more interactive and more fun, but also provide valuable opportunities to develop socialization skills.

> ➡ **For more information on cooperative learning, see pages T34 and T35 of this *Annotated Teacher's Edition.***

Many Explorations can be completed within a single class period. Others are more involved and may require several class periods to complete. Most of the supplies needed for the Explorations consist of very common equipment and materials. In most cases, they can be easily gathered from the home. For help in gathering supplies, the second page of each parent letter in the TRB provides a listing of the materials you will need to teach the unit. This page makes it easy for you to ask parents to donate materials. This will help you keep your budget low and at the same time get parents involved in the SciencePlus experience.

Assessment

Science*Plus* contains a variety of methods for checking student learning.

◆ Challenge Your Thinking

To make sure your students comprehend the new information, each section concludes with *Challenge Your Thinking* questions. These questions challenge students to apply newly learned material in a variety of ways. Many of the questions are like brain-teasers in that they are unusual and highly creative. Because the questions are not simply recall, students actually find them fun to figure out.

◆ Making Connections

Each unit concludes with *Making Connections*, the Science*Plus* equivalent of a chapter review. The *Making Connections* pages consist of four parts:

- *The Big Ideas*
- *Checking Your Understanding*
- *Reading* Plus
- *Updating Your Journal*

Making Connections differs in a number of key respects from a traditional chapter review. To begin with, ***The Big Ideas*** asks students to formulate their own summary of the unit, using a list of questions as a guide. Following this, ***Checking Your Understanding*** poses a selection of comprehensive questions designed to gauge students' understanding of the unit's subject matter.

The third part of the review pages consists of a short description of the corresponding unit in the *SourceBook*. This part, called ***Reading* Plus**, refers students to the appropriate pages in the *SourceBook* and whets their appetite for further exploration.

The review pages conclude with an invitation to students to rewrite their answers to the ***For Your Journal*** questions located at the beginning of the unit. This part, called *Updating Your Journal*, gives students the opportunity to confront and discard any misconceptions they may have had at the outset of the unit.

All answers to the *Challenge Your Thinking* and *Making Connections* questions are located in the extended margins of this Teacher's Edition.

Special Features

A common complaint among students is that the material they learn is not relevant. The end-of-unit features in Science*Plus* help show students how science is an integral part of their lives.

In keeping with the spirit of Science*Plus*, each of the features are interactive, with thought-provoking questions and research ideas that encourage students to explore the topic further.

◆ *Science in Action*

The *Science in Action* features consist of interviews with scientists and other science-related professionals. As students read the interviews, they learn a lot more than just the requirements of each career. They learn that scientists are likable and interesting people, very much like themselves. They also learn about how and why the people got involved in their careers in the first place. Students will learn about real experiences and what the scientists like most—and least—about their work. They may even learn about the scientists' personal career aspirations as well as their greatest disappointments.

◆ *Science and Technology*

New developments in science-related technologies are showcased in the *Science and Technology* features. Written in language that students can easily understand, *Science and Technology* is designed to captivate student interest at the same time that it informs. The impact of these new technologies on our everyday lives show students how relevant scientific research can be, both from a scientific standpoint as well as a social standpoint.

◆ *Science and the Arts*

People tend to think of art and science as polar opposites, when in fact they have much in common. The connection between science and society is reinforced by the *Science and the Arts* features. These features show students how artists have been inspired by nature and how scientific methods or principles have enhanced or empowered their work. *Science and the Arts* also demonstrates how disciplined, orderly thinking can be a useful asset to creative individuals in many different fields.

The SourceBook™

As an added resource, each level of the Science*Plus* program includes a *SourceBook*, which provides additional information related to the units of Science*Plus*. The *SourceBook* is available in two formats. It is either bound into the back of the *Pupil's Edition*, or it is bound as a separate booklet.

Regardless of which format you choose, the intended use of the *SourceBook* is the same. It is designed as a companion to the Science*Plus* textbook. Each *SourceBook* unit should be used only after the unit in the textbook has been successfully completed. This sequence will ensure that the students will have mastered the fundamental concepts before they start adding details.

The Science*Plus SourceBook* consists of eight units of resource information that corresponds to the eight units of the text itself. Each *SourceBook* unit extends beyond the material presented in the text, providing an excellent resource with which students can add depth to their understanding of the topics presented in Science*Plus*.

Students are directed to use the *SourceBook* in each *Making Connections* review. A brief summary of the corresponding *SourceBook* unit is included under the heading Reading *Plus*. Page numbers are also provided for ease of use.

Once students refer to the *SourceBook* unit, they will find a brief introduction that includes an activity such as writing a newspaper article, constructing a model, or making a collage. Several questions are then provided to help direct the students' thinking as they read the unit.

The Annotated Teacher's Edition

The Science*Plus* Annotated *Teacher's Edition* will help you achieve the full potential of Science*Plus*. The *Teacher's Edition* consists of two major parts: the Unit Interleaf and the Extended Margins. Each Unit Interleaf consists of a four-page insert preceding each unit. The Extended Margins provide on-page annotations and teaching suggestions.

Using the Unit Interleaf

For ease of use, each Unit Interleaf is divided into three parts: *Teaching the Unit*, *Meeting Individual Needs*, and *Resources*. The information provided under these headings will help you make the best use of your time in planning and organizing your instruction.

Teaching the Unit

This portion of the Unit Interleaf is devoted to giving you the necessary background and planning information about the unit. Extensive information is also provided about incorporating themes into the unit instruction.

❖ **Unit Overview**
To quickly bring you up to speed, the *Unit Overview* provides a section-by-section synopsis of what the students will be asked to do in completing the unit.

❖ **Using the Themes**
Suggestions are provided here for relating the unit information to the appropriate science themes. For each theme emphasized in the unit, a focus question is provided to help you stimulate your students to think along thematic lines.

❖ **Using the *Science Discovery* Videodiscs**
Each Science*Plus* unit is correlated directly to *Science Discovery*, a videodisc program that has been designed specifically for Science*Plus*. The *Using the Science Discovery Videodiscs* section of the Unit Interleaf provides information on the videodisc resources that apply to the unit. The *Science Discovery* videodisc program is discussed in greater detail beginning on page T28.

❖ **Using the Science*Plus* SourceBook**
Here you will find a brief overview of what is contained in the corresponding unit of the *SourceBook*. For more information about the *SourceBook,* see page T23.

❖ **Planning Chart**
The extensive *Planning Chart* provides a graphic overview of the unit, making it easy to prepare lesson plans, set realistic schedules, and preview and select materials from the ancillary package. The *Planning Chart* provides the following information for each section and lesson of the unit.

- Page numbers for easy reference
- Estimated completion time in class periods
- Process skills emphasized
- Exploration and assessment items
- Ancillary materials and features, including *Science Discovery* videodisc resources

Meeting Individual Needs

Today's classrooms are places of diversity—populated by students with different ability levels and from a variety of ethnic backgrounds and cultures. The information and suggestions provided here will help you meet the challenge of individualizing your instruction to meet the needs of all your students. The information and suggestions are organized under the following headings.

❖ Gifted Students

Here you will find suggestions on how to keep your advanced and gifted students actively engaged in learning. Suggestions include long-term projects, open-ended activities, research projects, and challenges to students' creativity.

❖ LEP Students

Here you will find suggestions on how to teach students who may be just beginning to learn English.

❖ At-Risk Students

Suggestions are provided for helping you tailor your lessons to provide a successful experience for students who, for any of a number of reasons, are not motivated to learn about science. Recommendations are provided on how to keep such students motivated in their learning of science.

❖ Cross-Disciplinary Focus

Under this heading you will find activities that cross the boundaries between the various specialties of science, as well as between science and other disciplines such as art, history, and geography. By doing these activities, students will experience the inter-relatedness of science and other areas of study. These activities will help students see the significance of science to many areas of study.

❖ Cross-Cultural Focus

Your classes probably have students from many different cultural backgrounds. This, of course, has a major impact on how students learn and what they are able to relate to. Under this heading you will find activities and suggestions that serve to highlight cultural diversity and show its positive influence on science as well as other disciplines. These activities will help you add depth to your instruction by showing students how culture and science are integrated to the benefit of us all.

Resources

A list of teacher and student resources are provided for the unit, including appropriate software and media.

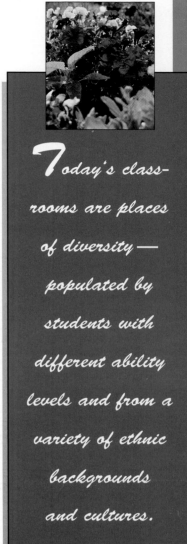

Today's classrooms are places of diversity—populated by students with different ability levels and from a variety of ethnic backgrounds and cultures.

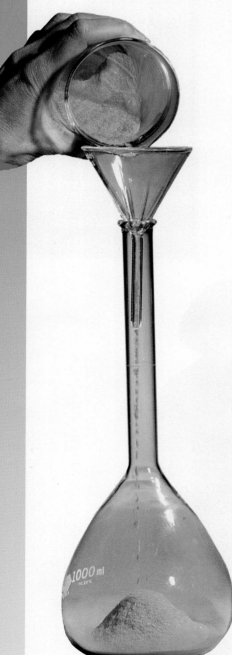

Using the Extended Margins

The entire *Pupil's Edition* of Science*Plus* has been reduced in size and placed on the pages of this *Annotated Teacher's Edition*. The margins around the reduced pages have been filled with many teaching suggestions and extensive commentary to help you teach each lesson with maximum effectiveness. The following headings will help you locate desired information quickly.

Unit Opener

Each unit opener has the following teacher's information to help you quickly engage your students in the subject of the unit.

❖ **Unit Focus** provides suggestions for introducing students to the unit in an active way. The *Unit Focus* poses thought-provoking questions that will help you crystallize your students' thinking.

❖ **About the Photograph** provides background information about the unit photograph: why it was chosen, how it represents the subject matter of the unit, and items of interest that it contains.

❖ **Using the Photograph** provides suggestions for challenging students to use their powers of observation and reasoning to derive knowledge from the unit opener photograph. Suggestions help you start your students thinking and asking questions about the unit topic.

❖ **About Your Journal** identifies the intent of the *For Your Journal* activity.

Lesson

Each Lesson of the unit has extensive commentary and teacher's notes to help you in planning and teaching the unit. The lesson information is divided into three parts: *Getting Started, Teaching Strategies,* and *Follow Up.* In addition a *Lesson Organizer* is provided at the beginning of each lesson.

❖ **Getting Started**
The *Getting Started* information provides a short summary of the lesson and a listing of the main ideas, or main concepts, that are covered in the unit.

❖ **Lesson Organizer**
A *Lesson Organizer* is also included at the beginning of each lesson. The *Lesson Organizer* gives a quick reference of the lesson objectives, process skills, new terms, materials needed, and estimated time requirement for completing the lesson. Resource information in the *Teacher's Resource Binder* and the *Science Discovery Videodiscs* is also listed here for easy reference.

❖ **Teaching Strategies**
Teaching Strategies provide helpful hints, highlight points of interest, suggest additional activities, and pose interesting questions for students to answer. *Teaching Strategies* also alert you to any special materials and preparation that might be required to carry out the lesson and to anticipate possible outcomes and questions.

❖ **Answers to Questions**
All questions that have been posed in the course of the lessons, either within the running text or in the review materials, are answered in the expanded margins for your convenience. In only a few instances, where the answer requires a graph or chart, will you have to turn pages to refer to the answer.

❖ **Follow Up**
The *Follow Up* provides closure to the lesson and consists of two parts: *Assessment* and *Extension.* The *Assessment* poses one or two questions or problems suitable for demonstrating mastery of the material in the lesson. The *Extension* provides problems or questions that complement and extend the subject matter of the lesson.

Review Pages

All questions appearing in each *Challenge Your Thinking* and *Making Connections* are fully answered in the Extended Margins.

Features

The end-of-unit features *Science in Action, Science and Technology,* and *Science and the Arts* are all accompanied by commentary designed to enhance the value of each feature.

The Teacher's Resource Binder

The *Teacher's Resource Binder (TRB)* contains a wide variety of useful resource materials that are designed to supplement and extend the subject matter of Science*Plus*.

Unit Worksheets are loose-leaf blackline masters conveniently organized by unit.

◆ *Home Connection* is a two-page parent letter that introduces the unit of study to the parents and includes home activities to encourage parents' participation. The last page lists the supplies needed to do the Explorations. This page makes it easy for you to invite donations in order to keep your budget low.

◆ *Worksheets* contain activities such as charts, graphs, puzzles, and games that clarify and reinforce concepts. *Activity Worksheets* provide additional activities to add depth to your instruction. *Resource Worksheets* provide blank charts, graphs, and puzzles directly from the textbook.

◆ *Sample Assessment Items* provide sample test items for each unit. Because they consist of a wide variety of question types, you will find items suitable for students of all ability levels. Sample answers are provided.

Videodisc Resources describes how *Science Discovery* videodiscs can be used in the Science*Plus* program. Written materials include lesson plans, barcodes, and student worksheets. For more information about the *Science Discovery* Videodisc program, see page T-28 of this *Annotated Teacher's Edition.*

Science Sites are maps that show scientific points of interest in each of the 50 states, Canada, Mexico, and other continents. Five questions on the back of each map help integrate the life, earth, and physical sciences.

ESL Spanish includes blackline masters that consist of translated parent letters, unit summaries, and a full glossary.

Posters provide two colorful reference sources that highlight safety and equipment in the laboratory.

Materials Guide provides a ready reference of all the supplies and equipment that are required to teach Science*Plus*. The *Materials Guide* contains unit by unit materials lists as well as a master materials list.

Other Teaching Aids

The Science*Plus* program includes the following support materials to make your teaching both effective and efficient.

Teaching Transparencies—which include approximately 20 four-color *Resource Transparencies* and *Teacher's Notes* and approximately 50 two-color *Graphic Organizer Transparencies*. The Graphic Organizer Transparencies consists of charts and graphs from the *Pupil's Edition.*

English/Spanish Audiocassettes—which provide important preview information for each unit in both English and Spanish.

Unit Tests—which include blackline-master tests for each unit of the *Pupil's Edition.* Four tests are included for each unit—three tests of increasing difficulty and one activity-based test for assessing student performance.

Test Generators (IBM®, Macintosh®)—which include test items, including graphics, for the *Pupil's Edition* and *SourceBook.* The *Test Generators* also allow you to add your own questions.

Science Discovery Videodisc Program

Science Discovery is a comprehensive videodisc program that blends imagination and state-of-the-art technology into an exciting program that will add a dynamic facet to your science teaching. The program includes:

- *Science Sleuths* videodisc
- *Science Sleuths Teacher's Guide*
- *Science Sleuths Resource Directory*
- *Image and Activity Bank* videodisc
- *Image and Activity Bank Directory*
- *Image and Activity Bank Quick Reference Card*

Science Sleuths

The *Science Sleuths* videodisc consists of 24 open-ended science mysteries, one for each unit of the *SciencePlus* textbook series. Each mystery begins with a dramatization in which a problem is presented and the students are asked to serve as consultants (sleuths) to figure it out. Problems include such mysteries as *Exploding Lawn Mowers, Dead Fish on Union Lake,* and *The Misplaced Fossil.* The videodisc then becomes a "videophone" that connects students to the laboratory, where they can request information such as the testing of samples, experiments, interviews, tables, newspaper clippings, news broadcasts, and many other bits of information from an extensive menu.

The students work as a class or in small groups to explore the mystery, develop hypotheses, and support their position using the data from the disc. They try to solve the mystery using as few of the video segments as possible. In this way they either challenge themselves or other groups to see who can solve the mystery most efficiently.

In working as Science Sleuths, students improve their problem-solving and reasoning skills while applying their science knowledge from the textbook. Students work in a realistic scientific mode in which information comes from a variety of sources. Students must also judge the accuracy of each source and separate raw data from interpretation and inference.

Science Sleuths Teacher's Guide

The *Science Sleuths Teacher's Guide* contains the teaching plans for using the videodisc.

Science Sleuths Resource Directory

The *Science Sleuths Resource Directory* contains the barcodes and frame numbers for using each mystery. There are five Directory sets so that you can have five working cooperative groups at a time.

Image and Activity Bank

The *Image and Activity Bank* videodisc consists of a still and motion image database designed to reinforce and extend concepts presented in *SciencePlus.* The still images include hundreds of photographs and computer graphics related to life, earth, and physical sciences. The motion images include demonstrations, experiments, and selected motion footage.

Image and Activity Bank Directory

The *Image and Activity Directory* provides descriptions, frame numbers, and barcodes for the *Image and Activity Bank* videodisc. A separate Reference Card provides barcodes and frame numbers for selected topics.

> ▶ *For complete directions on how to use Science Discovery with Science***Plus,** *open the Teacher's Resource Binder to the Videodisc Resource section.*

Using SciencePlus

Communicating Science

One of the most important skills that students can acquire is the ability to communicate what they have learned, both orally and in writing. Science*Plus* challenges students to develop and communicate their mastery of new ideas in novel ways—for example, by writing for one another or for some audience other than the teacher. Students' comprehension is enhanced when they are called upon to reformulate in their own words what they have learned.

Throughout Science*Plus*, students are called on to communicate what they have learned in many different ways. Students may be called on to interpret a passage, illustrate a paragraph, write a headline, label a diagram, or write a caption for a photo or drawing. These strategies complement the inquiry approach followed throughout Science*Plus*.

Reading and Writing in the Classroom

The time spent in helping students prepare to read is critical in fostering comprehension. Two strategies are particularly important in the pre-reading phase of instruction: building on prior knowledge and establishing a purpose for reading.

The Power of Prior Knowledge

The amount of prior knowledge that students have about a topic directly influences their comprehension of that topic. The more students know about something, the easier it is for them to grasp new information about it. Helping students identify the information they already have about a topic before reading assists them in relating the new information to existing knowledge.

Research strongly suggests that students tend to retain misconceptions they may have about a topic. If the text information seems to conflict with their preconceptions, students may ignore or reject new information. It is therefore extremely important to identify these misconceptions so that they may be dispelled.

Reading to Understand

One way to establish a purpose for reading is to make a study guide with questions that students can answer as they read. You can also help students learn to make their own study guides. First, teach students to preview a unit by looking at all the unit headings, illustrative material, and terms and phrases in boldface or italics. This technique helps students gain a feel for the unit and helps them build a basic structure for the new information. Then show them how to use the captions, headings, and highlighted words to devise study-guide questions to answer after reading the unit. Following this method, students will read with a purpose in mind, a purpose of their own devising.

Writing to Understand

Studies show that writing is an effective tool for improving reading. As students write, they are creating a text for others to read. The most important advice to give students about scientific writing is to strive for clarity and accuracy. These characteristics can often be achieved with simple vocabulary and short sentences. One useful approach might be to have them imagine that they are writing for a younger audience.

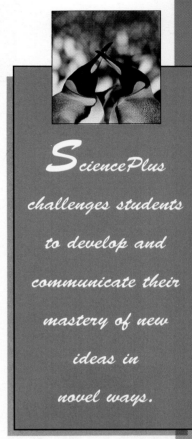

*Science*Plus* challenges students to develop and communicate their mastery of new ideas in novel ways.*

Keeping a Journal

One highly successful tool for improving students' performance in science is the Journal. The Science*Plus* approach to learning depends heavily on the Journal. The Journal has many functions. First and foremost, it is an ongoing record of students' learning. Students begin the study of a new topic by recording prior knowledge of that topic. Any misconceptions that students may have are thus exposed. As the lesson progresses, students record any and all new findings. In many cases, students find that what they learn through their activities contradicts their preconceptions.

Much of the work that students do is recorded in their Journals. The Journal is a constant reminder to students that learning is occurring. Students can look back and compare their early work with later work to see and take pride in the progress they have made. To supplement their other work, you may also want to ask students to briefly summarize what they have learned each week. This makes a very handy capsule history of their work.

What makes a good Journal? Insofar as is possible, the Journal should be neat and easy to follow. Students may organize their Journals in any of a number of ways, chronologically, by unit, or by lesson, to name a few. Some kind of heading should set off each major entry.

A spiral-bound notebook or hard-bound lab-type notebook makes a good Journal. Or you may make copies of the sample Journal pages in the *Teacher's Resource Binder* and distribute them to your students to use if you wish. These Journal pages are located at the beginning of the Unit Worksheets for Unit 1.

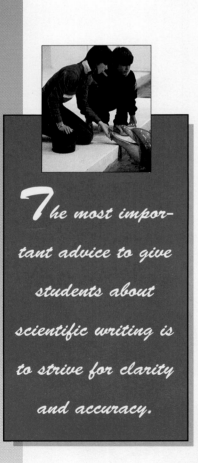

The most important advice to give students about scientific writing is to strive for clarity and accuracy.

Process Skills

Process skills are a means for learning and are essential to the conduct of science. For this reason, Science*Plus* is strongly process-oriented.

Perhaps the best way to teach process skills is to let students carry out scientific investigations and then point out to them the process skills they use in the course of the investigations. The teacher's *Planning Chart* at the beginning of each unit and the *Lesson Organizer* at the beginning of each lesson identify the process skills that are highlighted in the corresponding text.

Science*Plus* makes regular use of many different process skills as highlighted below. These and other process skills are called upon in Science*Plus* in virtually every lesson.

Observing

An observation is simply a record of a sensory experience. Observations are made using all five senses. Scientists use observation skills in collecting data.

Communicating

Communicating is the process of sharing information with others. Communication can take many different forms: oral, written, nonverbal, or symbolic. Communication is essential to the conduct of science, given its collaborative nature.

Measuring

Measuring is the process of making observations that can be stated in numerical terms. In Science*Plus*, all measurements are carried out in SI units.

Comparing

Comparing involves assessing different objects, events, or outcomes for similarity. This skill allows students to recognize any commonality that exists between seemingly different situations. A companion skill to comparing is contrasting, in which objects, events, or outcomes are evaluated according to their differences.

Contrasting

Contrasting involves evaluating the ways in which objects, events, or outcomes are different. Contrasting is a way of finding subtle differences between otherwise similar objects, events, or outcomes.

Organizing

Organizing is the process of arranging data into a logical order so it is easier to analyze and understand. The organizing process includes sequencing and grouping, and classifying data by making tables and charts, plotting graphs, and labeling diagrams

Classifying

Classifying involves grouping items into like categories. Items can be classified at many different levels, from the very general to the very specific.

Analyzing

The ability to analyze is critical in science. Students analyze to determine relationships between events, to identify the separate components of a system, to diagnose causes, and to determine the reliability of data.

Inferring

Inferring is the process by which conclusions are drawn based on reasoning or past experience.

Hypothesizing

Hypothesizing is the process of developing explanations for events that can then be tested. Testing either supports a hypothesis or refutes it.

Predicting

Predicting is the process of stating in advance the result that will be obtained from testing a hypothesis. A prediction that is accurate tends to support the hypothesis.

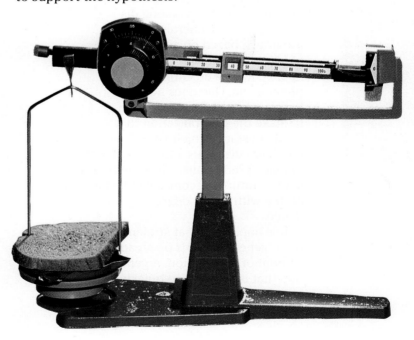

Critical Thinking

Critical-thinking skills are essential for making sense of large amounts of information. Too often, science lessons leave students with a set of facts and little ability to integrate those facts into a comprehensible whole. Requiring students to think critically as they learn improves their comprehension and increases their motivation.

Loosely defined, critical thinking is the ability to make sense of new information based on a set of criteria. Critical-thinking skills draw upon higher-order thinking processes, especially synthesis and evaluation skills. Critical thinking takes a number of different forms.

Validating Facts

This type of critical thinking involves judging the validity of information presented as fact. Too often, people will accept as valid almost any statement, no matter how outrageous, as long as it comes from a supposedly authoritative source. It is important for scientists to treat all untested data with suspicion, no matter how reasonable it may seem.

Students may validate facts in a number of ways: by observing, by testing, by rigorously examining the logic of the so-called fact. Science*Plus* presents students with many opportunities to critically evaluate facts and hypotheses.

Making Generalizations

A scientist must often be able to identify similarities among disparate events. Generalizations are drawn based on a limited set of observations but can be applied across an entire class of phenomena. One does not have to test every substance known to make the generalization that solid substances melt when heated. Generalizations allow scientists to make predictions. Once the rule is known, future outcomes can be forecasted with a high degree of confidence.

It is important that students base their generalizations on an adequate amount of information. A generalization that is formed too quickly may be wrong or incomplete, or could lead the student down a dead-end path.

Making Decisions

Many students would not regard science as a field requiring decision-making skills. But in fact, scientists must make decisions routinely in the course of their work. Any time a scientist works through a problem or develops a model, a whole series of decisions must be made. A single faulty decision can throw the entire process into disarray. Making informed decisions requires knowledge, experience, and good judgement.

Interpreting Information

Having all the information in the world is useless unless one also has the tools to interpret that information. Scientists must know how to separate the meaningful information from the "noise." Information can come in any form detectable by the five senses. It is important that scientists and students alike interpret information to determine its meaning, validity, and usefulness.

Requiring students to think critically as they learn improves their comprehension and increases their motivation.

Environmental Awareness

No species affects its surroundings as dramatically as does the human species. Thanks to recent highly publicized events—Chernobyl, destruction of the rain forests, the depletion of the ozone layer, and the greenhouse effect among them—people have come to realize the global impact that human actions can have. It is incumbent upon the educational system to promote environmental awareness among students. Science*Plus* addresses environmental issues in a way that students can easily grasp.

Environmental issues run the gamut, from global to local. While large-scale problems get headlines, they can be hard to grasp for many students, who may have never directly observed their impact. In most cases it is best to introduce your students to local issues to start building their awareness. Local issues are not only more relevant to their lives, but are more likely to lead to direct involvement.

Environmental awareness serves two purposes: it promotes understanding of the living world and the place of humans within it, and it produces a positive change in students' behavior toward the environment. Science*Plus* pursues both goals. You may involve students directly in environmental issues by using the suggested activities in the text and in this *Annotated Teacher's Edition*.

SciencePlus addresses environmental issues in a way that students can easily grasp.

Cooperative Learning

ooperative learning is a learning technique in which students work in heterogeneous groups and earn recognition, rewards, and sometimes grades based on the academic performance of their groups. Cooperative learning is the cornerstone of the Science*Plus* approach. Discussions, explorations, research projects, games and puzzles—all are designed to foster group participation.

Benefits of Cooperative Learning

One of the benefits of cooperative learning is that it models the real scientific experience in which scientists work together, not in isolation, to solve difficult problems. Students working in groups learn about the joys as well as the frustrations involved in scientific inquiry. With cooperative learning, the classroom becomes a hothouse of ideas and novel solutions.

Another benefit of cooperative learning is that students sharpen social skills and develop a sense of confidence in their own abilities. Students also channel their youthful energies into constructive tasks, while satisfying their fundamental need for social interaction.

Establishing cooperative learning in the classroom requires you to relinquish some control, for the students themselves become responsible for building their knowledge. Working in groups to probe and investigate ideas, answer questions, and draw conclusions about observations allows students to discover and discuss concepts in their own language. When students learn through cooperation, the knowledge derived becomes their

own, not just a loan of your ideas or those from the textbook.

Cooperative learning is also a good icebreaker for students of different ethnic or socioeconomic backgrounds. When students join forces to achieve a common goal, they almost invariably feel more positively about each other. Students come to recognize the commonality that cuts across all boundaries of class, race, and gender.

Cooperative learning also provides an excellent vehicle for students of differing ability levels to work together in a positive way. Basic students can interact successfully with average and advanced students, and in so doing, learn that they, too, have something to offer.

Cooperative learning empowers and involves students. It raises thier self-esteem because they are learning something on their own through cooperation rather than being handed pre-packaged knowledge. It helps students become self-sufficient, self-directed, lifelong learners. In a cooperative learning environment, students are less dependent on you for knowledge.

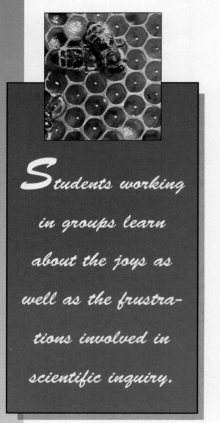

Students working in groups learn about the joys as well as the frustrations involved in scientific inquiry.

Using Cooperative Learning

In preparing for a cooperative learning activity in your class, consider the following guidelines.

Group size Cooperative learning groups may vary in size. Use small groups (2–4 members) for students unaccustomed to this learning style. Use larger groups for experienced students.

Group goals Students need to understand what is expected of them. Identify the group goal, whether it be to master specific objectives or to create a product such as a chart, report, or illustration. Identify and explain the specific cooperative skills required for each activity.

Individual accountability Each group member should have some specific responsibility that contributes to the learning of all group members. At the same time each group member should reach a certain minimum level of mastery.

Positive interdependence A learning activity becomes cooperative only when everyone realizes that no group member can be successful unless all group members are successful. This encourages positive interdependence: students working with one another to achieve group goals. Assign each student some meaningful role, or allow students to do this themselves. Or have each student in a group become an "expert" on some topic. Each member could then prepare and teach a lesson to the other group members or to the entire class.

Concept Mapping

Too often, students are able to master the individual elements of a topic without truly grasping the "big picture." If students fail to understand how the elements fit together or relate to one another, they cannot truly comprehend the topic. Concept mapping is a very effective method of helping students see how individual ideas or elements connect to form a larger whole. Concept maps are a highly effective tool for helping students make those logical connections.

The most effective concept maps are those that students construct on their own. Used in this way, concept maps are both a self-teaching system and a diagnostic tool. To construct a proper concept map, the student must first examine closely his or her mental model of the topic at hand. Any flaws or shortcomings in that model will be reflected in the concept map.

Concept maps are flexible; they can be simple or highly detailed, linear or branched, hierarchical or cross-linked, or can contain all of these major elements. Students can construct their own maps from scratch or can finish incomplete maps. Concept maps can take almost any form as long as they are logically arranged.

Concept maps are a highly effective tool for helping students make logical connections.

Making Concept Maps

▸ *The steps involved in making a concept map are outlined below. To provide guidance to your students in making concept maps, direct them to page 484 in the* **Pupil's Edition.**

1. Make a list of the concepts to be mapped. Concepts are signified by a noun or short phrase equivalent to a noun.

2. Choose the most general—the main—idea. Write it down and circle it.

3. Select from the list the concept most directly related to the main idea. Place it underneath the main idea and circle it. If two or more concepts bear the same relationship to the main idea, they should be placed at the same level.

4. Draw a line between the related concepts, leaving a space for a short action phrase that shows how the concepts are related. These are linkages.

5. Continue in this way until every concept in the list is accounted for.

The simple concept map below shows the relationship among the following terms: *plants, photosynthesis, carbon dioxide, water,* and *sun's energy.* More detailed maps are shown on the facing page.

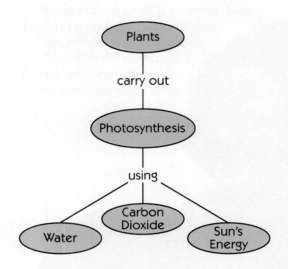

For any given topic, there is no single "correct" concept map. Not all maps are equally valid, however. Good concept maps have most or all of the following characteristics:

- start with a single, general concept—a big idea—and work down to more specific ideas

- represent each concept with a noun or short phrase—each of which appears only once

- link concepts with linkage words or short phrases

- show cross-linkages where appropriate

- consist of more than a single path

- include examples where appropriate

Using Concept Maps

Concept maps can be applied in many ways.

- to gauge prior knowledge of a topic
- end-of-lesson/section/unit evaluation
- pre-test review
- to help summarize special presentations such as films, videos, or guest speakers
- as an aid to note-taking
- for reteaching

You may also want to use partially completed concept maps as pop quizzes or as devices for summarizing particularly difficult class sessions. Also, be sure to use the concept map in each *Making Connections* review.

Evaluating Concept Maps

Again, there is no single correct concept map. However, you should consider the following criteria as you evaluate your students' concept maps.

- how comprehensive the map is (are all relationships shown?)
- how clearly concepts are linked (proper relationship between concepts, use of linkage terms between all concepts)
- overall clarity of presentation (could the map be simpler? is it redundant? is it logically arranged? are linkage terms used properly?)

Used properly, concept maps can increase comprehension, improve retention, and sharpen study skills in your students. They are a valuable addition to any student's arsenal of learning strategies.

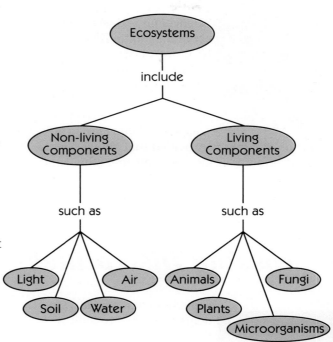

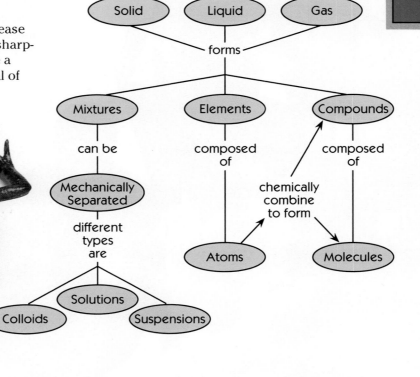

The most effective concept maps are those that students construct on their own.

Multicultural Instruction

Science is for everyone, and Science*Plus* is designed to serve the multiethnic and multicultural classrooms of today. Students, regardless of their ethnic backgrounds, will not have to look hard to find positive role models on the pages of Science*Plus*. In addition, content is provided that shows events, concepts, and issues from diverse ethnic and cultural perspectives. As students work through Science*Plus*, they will come to understand that science is a human endeavor that has been advanced by the contributions of many cultures and ethnic groups.

To add depth to your multicultural instruction, each Unit Interleaf contains a section called Cross-Cultural Focus. This information provides activities to help you focus on cultural diversity, and in so doing help you highlight the individuality and contributions of different ethnic groups.

Crossing Disciplines

Throughout Science*Plus*, students are asked to look at things from many different viewpoints. For example, students are asked to write a headline for a science story, to write advertising copy highlighting geological features for a travel agency, and even to make dioramas of animal habitats and ways of life. In so doing these activities, students see first-hand the connections between science and a variety of other disciplines including history, geography, social studies, and others. And the students even have fun making these connections.

Connections are also made naturally between the various science disciplines. Since Science*Plus* is not organized according to life, earth, and physical sciences, these disciplines are integrated throughout the program. Each discipline comes into play as needed in covering the main concepts in Science*Plus*. In this way, science disciplines are blended together so the emphasis is on student comprehension of the "big picture," rather than isolated components of different areas of science.

Additional cross-disciplinary suggestions are provided in each Unit Interleaf of this *Annotated Teacher's Edition*. The suggestions include a variety of activities that span science as well as non-science disciplines.

Meeting Individual Needs

Obviously, to teach effectively you must be able to reach every individual in your class. This is seldom easy, given the diverse nature of most of today's classrooms. In addition, certain students present special challenges. Dealing adequately with these students requires special preparation and strategies. In many cases a minimal amount of preparation is sufficient to make the classroom a place where all can learn. Some of the more common situations you are likely to encounter are discussed below.

At-Risk Students

At-risk students are those who, for any of a number of reasons, are liable to perform poorly and who have a high probability of dropping out. Science*Plus* is engaging and interesting throughout, appealing to all students. Throughout Science*Plus,* clear, easy-to-read prose and straightforward, attractive graphics reduce the potential for students to grow bored. The style of Science*Plus* is intentionally friendly and unintimidating. Field-testing has shown that the performance of at-risk students in science increases substantially when working with Science*Plus.*

Additional activities and teaching suggestions for at-risk students are provided in each Unit Interleaf of this *Teacher's Edition.*

LEP Students

Because Science*Plus* places so much emphasis on *doing* science, rather than reading about it, the program is ideal for students who are not wholly proficient in English. Science is a universal language—the language of curiosity and logical reasoning. Many Science*Plus* activities are easy to follow and require a minimum of reading. Lengthy explanations are seldom called for. You need only to get students started in the right direction; thereafter their intuition and common sense take over. The cooperative approach emphasized in Science*Plus* helps to give LEP students the extra support they need.

Additional activities and teaching suggestions for LEP students are found in each Unit Interleaf of this *Teacher's Edition.* The *Teacher's Resource Binder* also contains ESL information, including blackline masters of parent letters translated into Spanish, as well as unit summaries and unit glossaries in Spanish.

Also available are *English/Spanish Audiocassettes,* which provide important preview information to assist ESL students and students who are auditory learners.

Gifted Students

The difficulty of teaching gifted students lies in keeping them interested, motivated, and challenged. Gifted students who are inadequately challenged may become bored, withdrawn, or even openly disruptive. Science*Plus* includes many activities suitable for even the highest-performing student. Open-ended activities, in particular, are especially suited for gifted students.

The Science*Plus* approach emphasizes creative problem solving. In many cases there is no single right answer to a problem or question, so students' answers can reflect their individual abilities. This approach is ideal for gifted students, as they may extend the activities to fit their interests and talents.

Additional activities and teaching suggestions for gifted students are included in each Unit Interleaf of this *Teacher's Edition.*

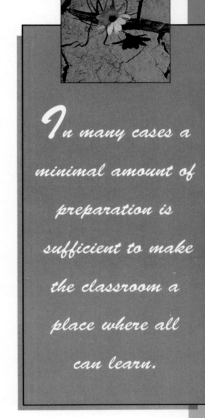

In many cases a minimal amount of preparation is sufficient to make the classroom a place where all can learn.

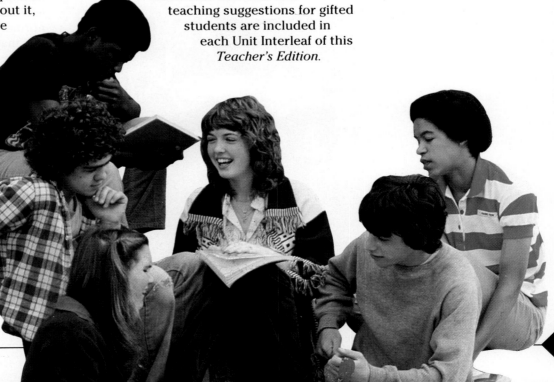

Physically Impaired Students

Make your classroom as easy to move about in as possible. Remove or bypass any obvious barriers. Encourage your students to physically assist impaired students. If the student uses a wheelchair, make the aisles wide enough to accommodate the chair. Make sure that the student can reach any equipment he or she needs. You may wish to enlist the aid of other students in the class to physically assist the disabled student as necessary.

As much as possible, adapt the classroom to make it possible for physically impaired students to engage in the same activities as other students. Use a mobile demonstration table so that it can be moved to different areas of the room for maximum visibility.

Visually Impaired Students

Seat students with marginal vision near the front of the room to maximize their view of both you and the chalkboard, or assign a student to make copies of what you write. You could also assign a student to explain all visual materials in detail as they are presented.

Students who are completely blind should be allowed to become familiar with the classroom layout before the first class begins. Promptly inform these students of any changes to your classroom layout. Whenever possible, provide blind students Braille or taped versions of all printed materials. Blind students may also use hand-held devices for converting written text into speech.

Hearing-Impaired Students

If you have partially hearing-impaired students in your class, remember to always face the class while speaking. Minimize classroom noise and arrange seating in a circle or semicircle so that hearing-impaired students can see others. This arrangement facilitates speechreading. Speak in simple, direct language and avoid digressions or sudden changes in topic. During class discussions, periodically summarize what students are saying and repeat students questions before answering them. Use visual media such as filmstrips, overhead projectors, and close-captioned films when appropriate. You might arrange a buddy system in which another student provides copies of notes about activities and assignments.

A student who is completely deaf may require a sign language interpreter. If so, let the student and the interpreter determine the most convenient seating arrangement. When asking the student a question, be sure to look at the student, not at the interpreter. If the student also has a speech impairment, group assignments for oral reports may be advisable.

Speech-Impaired Students

Mainstreaming speech-impaired students is generally not very difficult. Patience is essential when dealing with speech-impaired students, however. For example, resist the temptation to finish sentences for a student who stutters. At the same time, do not show impatience. Also pay attention to nonverbal cues, such as facial expression and body language. Be supportive and encouraging. You need not leave the speech-impaired student out of the normal classroom give-and-take. For example, you may call on a speech-impaired student to answer a question and then allow the student to write out his or her response on the chalkboard or overhead projector. Use multisensory materials whenever possible to create a more comfortable learning environment for the speech-impaired student.

Learning-Disabled Students

Learning disabilities are any disorders that obstruct a person's listening, reasoning, communication, or mathematical abilities, and range from mild to severe. An estimated two percent of all adolescents have some type of learning disability. Learning disabilities are the most common type of disability. Provide a supportive and structured environment in which rules and assignments are clearly stated. Use familiar words and short, simple sentences. Repeat or rephrase your instructions as needed.

Students may require extra time to complete exams or assignments, the amount of extra time being dependent on the severity of their disability. Some students may need to tape-record lectures and answers to exam questions. For those who have difficulty organizing materials, you might provide chapter or lecture outlines for them to fill in. Peer tutors, who work with learning-disabled students on specific assignments and review materials, can be effective.

Computer-assisted instruction is an extremely useful tool for some learning-disabled students. This mode of instruction can even help these students develop good learning skills. For learning-disabled students, computers serve as a tireless instructor with unlimited patience. In addition, students receive simplified directions, proceed in small, manageable steps, and receive immediate reinforcement and feedback with computerized instruction.

Students with Behavioral Disorders

Behavioral disorders are emotional or behavioral disturbances that hinder a student's overall functioning. The behaviorally impaired may exhibit any of a variety of behaviors, ranging from extreme aggression to complete passivity.

Obviously, no single teaching strategy can accommodate all behavioral disorders. In addition, behavioral psychologists disagree on the best way to deal with students who have behavior disorders. As a general rule, try to be fair and consistent, yet flexible in your dealings with behaviorally disabled students. Make sure to clearly state rules and expectations. Reinforce desirable behavior or even approximations of such behavior, and ignore or mildly admonish undesirable behavior.

Because learning disabilities often accompany behavior disorders, you might also wish to refer to the guidelines for learning disabilities.

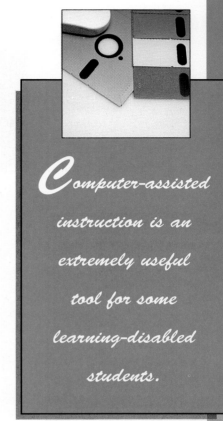

Computer-assisted instruction is an extremely useful tool for some learning-disabled students.

Science, Technology, and Society

STS is an approach to teaching science in which the impact of scientific, technological, and social matters on each other is explored. STS teaches science from the context of the human experience, and in so doing leads students to think of science as a social endeavor. STS emphasizes personal involvement in science. Students become active participants in the scientific experience. For this reason Science*Plus* incorporates an STS approach.

STS contrasts with the traditional "basic science" approach to science education, in which students follow a carefully sequenced program of the basic models, concepts, laws, and theories of science. The fundamental flaw of the basic science approach is that the student is more or less a passive participant in the learning process.

There are three parts to STS:

> **STS** | **science concept and skill development, and knowledge of the nature of science**

This component of STS introduces science as a system for learning about the natural world and gives students the foundation they need to actually practice science in and out of the classroom. The ultimate goal of STS, and of Science*Plus,* is to turn students into scientists, at least for the duration of their science education. To accomplish this, students first learn the methods of science and the skills that scientists draw on. Whenever possible, the major ideas of science are not simply presented, but are introduced from the standpoint of those who developed them. In this way, students come to see the reasoning that went into the development of these ideas.

> **STS** | **knowledge of the relationship of science and technology and engagement in science-based problem solving design**

Students who understand the real-world applications of science are better able to appreciate and enjoy it. This component of STS reinforces the practical value of science. Students see that science is a system for solving practical problems. Students themselves become practical scientists—first identifying problems and then developing solutions to them. Students learn to analyze, to plan, to organize, to design, and to refine models and designs.

> **STS** | **engagement in science-related social issues and attention to science as a social institution**

This component of STS deals with the ways in which science serves human needs. The benefits may be tangible or intangible, but either way, they are real. To emphasize the social responsibility of science, scientists are shown to be concerned about the impact of their work on society as a whole. It sometimes happens that advances in science and technology lead to thorny ethical issues. Such issues are often used as a focus for discussion and investigation. From these investigations, students draw conclusions and form reasoned opinions.

Studies have shown that students begin the study of science full of curiosity and enthusiasm. But after a few years of a traditional curriculum, the curiosity is squelched and the enthusiasm has all but vanished. By contrast, under the STS approach student interest builds through the years, and is maintained long after formal study ends. The key to this success is the active involvement in science that STS imparts. The end products of the STS approach are students who appreciate and understand science and who are equipped to deal sensibly with the complex issues that will become commonplace in the decades ahead.

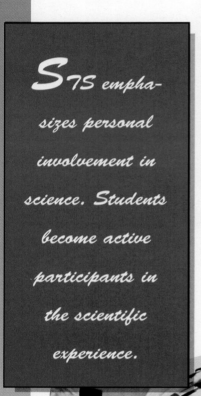

*S*TS *empha-sizes personal involvement in science. Students become active participants in the scientific experience.*

➤ *For a fuller discussion of STS, See the NSTA position paper, July 1990*

Materials and Equipment

SciencePlus is designed to be teachable even by those with a limited budget for materials. Most activities use common household items, which can be brought to class by students, parents, or otherwise easily obtained. The *Teacher's Resource Binder* contains a *Materials Guide*, which is a comprehensive guide to the materials and equipment you will need in carrying out the activities of SciencePlus. The *Materials Guide* features both a master list of materials and a unit-by-unit list. In addition, the second page of the parent letters contained in the *Teacher's Resource Binder* lists the supplies needed for each unit. This page makes it easy for you to invite donations from parents to keep your budget low.

SciencePlus Teacher's Network

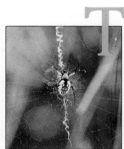

The *SciencePlus Teacher's Network (SPTN)* is part of the Atlantic Science Curriculum Project (ASCP), linking teaching, curriculum development, and research in science education. The ASCP, which produced the Canadian version of *SciencePlus: Technology and Society*, has existed for over fifteen years, beginning as a collaborative, grass-roots activity to improve science teaching in the middle/junior high schools. The goal of the SPTN is to continue this collaborative effort, linking teachers with teachers through newsletters, conferences, and small group and regional meetings.

The **Science*Plus* Communicator** is the official U.S. publication of the SPTN. The **Science*Plus* Communicator** offers opportunities for teachers to comment on science teaching and current issues, research, assessment, and science, technology, and society applications.

Assessing Student Performance

A Comprehensive Approach to Assessment

Developing a strategy for assessing student progress is an important step in realizing the goals of Science*Plus*. Students pay the most attention to those aspects of a lesson on which they know they will be graded. Teachers who want their students to be successful should therefore teach with continual assessment in mind.

In Science*Plus*, there is no distinct boundary between teaching and assessing. Every suggested assessment activity, including testing, is designed to teach. This emphasis can help correct the preoccupation with measuring and sorting students. The suggestions here are intended to aid you in your primary task: teaching.

You may use the assessment aids available with Science*Plus* to measure students' mastery of the concepts and processes of each unit. It is not recommended that you rely on these items alone, however. Assessment should be ongoing and should measure performance in every area. The quality of student class work, homework, lab work, and Journal entries should all be factors in assigning grades, in addition to performance on exams.

The authors strongly discourage relying on recall-based assessment strategies. Teachers who rely heavily on such assessment strategies may find it difficult at first to adopt new methods of assessment. However, once the transition is made, the reward—in the form of improved student performance and motivation—will have more than offset the inconvenience. As you work with Science*Plus*, you will find that it provides ample strategies and opportunities for assessing students in a variety of ways.

Assessing Understanding of Concepts

Throughout Science*Plus* are many opportunities for students to demonstrate their understanding of specific concepts. *For Your Journal*, at the beginning of each unit, encourages students to express through writing what they already know about specific concepts that will be covered in the unit. Then, after students work through the unit, they are given the opportunity to refine their journal entries in *Updating Your Journal*, at the end of the unit. By viewing their updated journal entries, you can get a good idea of the students' understanding of the main concepts of the unit.

Science*Plus* is generously supplied with questions and other activities that can serve to check students' understanding of the concepts developed by each lesson. *Challenge Your Thinking* is suitable for assessing student understanding of concepts at the section level, while *Making Connections* assesses students' understanding of concepts at the unit level.

Assessing Scientific, Psychomotor, and Communication Skills

In Science*Plus*, knowledge and understanding are tightly linked to the development of important process skills such as observing, measuring, graphing, writing, predicting, inferring, analyzing, and hypothesizing. All learning tasks are designed to help develop these skills. The teacher can assess such skill development by inspecting student work and by observing student performance.

The sample tables below are suitable as models for evaluating student performance.

Assessing Environmental Awareness

Science*Plus* is written with a commitment to environmental awareness. Many activities are included that promote such awareness. The teacher is provided with suggestions on extending this theme through creative projects, clean-up or recycling projects, and so on. Tasks such as these promote environmental consciousness. The care students take in carrying out these activities is a measure of their awareness of environmental issues.

Assessing Scientific Behavior

BEHAVIOR	Poor	Satisfactory	Good	Very Good	Excellent
Cooperates with others in small-group work					
Observes and records observations					
etc.					

Assessing Technical Skills

TASK	Yes	No	Uncertain
Is able to read thermometer correctly			
Is able to use spring scale to measure force			
etc.			

Assessing Scientific Attitudes

It can be useful to survey your students on the types of science-related hobbies and interests they pursue outside of class. In a direct way, this provides feedback on the success of your school's science program. A successful science program is reflected in a student body with outside interests in science. Ask your students to keep a tally of any science-related activities they undertake outside of class. These could include reading or writing about science and technology, science-related projects, visits to museums, attendance at lectures on science and technology topics, and viewing science programs on television.

For developing and assessing individual student interest and attitude in science, the assignment of elective reading and independent projects is essential. In addition to the numerous project ideas and extension activities included in the units of SciencePlus, the *Science in Action* feature provides a range of project ideas from which students may choose. Students may also want to read further about a topic in the *SourceBook* or other science-related book or magazine.

Student work on elective projects should count as a significant part of overall assessment. It provides the surest indication of a student's interest and proficiency in science, especially the student's ability to study, plan, and research independently.

A successful science program is reflected in a student body with outside interests in science.

A Balanced Assessment

The authors of Science*Plus* recommend achieving a balance between the different forms of assessment. As a general rule, the following proportions are suggested:

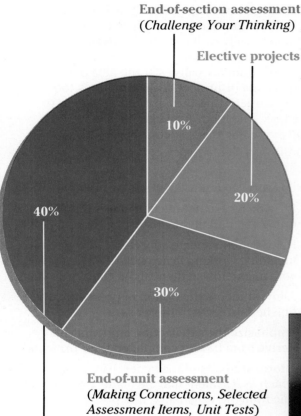

End-of-section assessment
(*Challenge Your Thinking*)

Elective projects

10%

20%

40%

30%

End-of-unit assessment
(*Making Connections, Selected Assessment Items, Unit Tests*)

Continuous assessment
of assigned work and
in-class performance

The Goals of Assessment

Obviously, tests should reinforce your instructional goals. Tests dominated by multiple-choice, matching, fill-in-the-blank, and short answer items have been very common in the past because of an emphasis on objectivity and ease in grading. However, such tests alone will not support the goals of Science*Plus*. By using various means to assess student progress, the teacher can test less frequently and more meaningfully.

Testing should be more than a means for assessing students' progress; it should also be an opportunity for students to learn. To reduce students' anxiety, give them ample time to prepare for and take the test. Careful, deliberate thought, rather than a superficial slapdash approach, should be encouraged in science. Quicker students and those who need additional challenge can be occupied with bonus questions while the others complete the required test items. Reviewing the test after it is completed provides yet another opportunity for students to learn.

$$V_a N_a = V_b N_b$$

Assessing Science Projects

*Science**Plus*** offers students abundant opportunities for independent investigation. Many open-ended, curiosity-stimulating questions are posed for students. Some of these questions are natural starting points for science projects. Students using *SciencePlus* have often developed successful science fair projects based on questions in the text.

The *Science in Action* feature is another source of possible project ideas. Many techniques are suggested for getting started, reporting results, and distributing the work of the projects in an efficient way. The *Teacher's Edition* is a source for project ideas as well.

Undertaking a major project provides students with a host of positive experiences. Students learn to organize, plan, and piece together many separate ideas and information into a coherent whole. Undertaking a major project also allows students to experience the sense of accomplishment that comes from tackling and completing a difficult task. It might even be argued that no science education is complete without having undertaken and completed a major project.

Many students will resist the idea of undertaking a major project, feeling that it is too much work or that they are simply not up to the task. The following suggestions may help you overcome this reluctance:

- Allow students to select their own project ideas.

- Encourage your students to be creative.

- Provide a clear set of guidelines for developing and completing projects.

- Help students locate sources of information, including workers in science-related fields who might advise them about their projects.

- Allow students the option of presenting their finished projects to the class.

- Emphasize the satisfaction students will derive from having completed their projects.

- Inform students of the general areas on which assessment may be made: e. g., scientific thought, originality, and presentation.

- Do not emphasize the details of assessment. "Scoring points" should not be a major incentive.

Do not allow preconceived notions about how the project should be done detract from the students' interest, enjoyment, and satisfaction in doing original work. Rather than forcing all students to fit their project work into a mold suited to scientific research, establish three sets of criteria described in the tables on pages T50 to T52.

> *Do not allow preconceived notions about how the project should be done detract from the students' interest, enjoyment, and satisfaction in doing original work.*

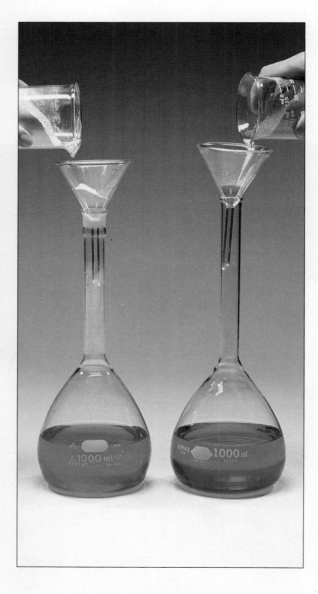

Developing Assessment Items

When developing tests, you should bear in mind the sort of skill required to answer each assessment item. The manner of testing determines what is learned: tests that require tick-mark responses teach tick-marking. Tests that require verbal, graphic, illustrative, and numeric responses develop writing, speaking, graphing, drawing, and mathematical skills. A superior test draws upon as many skills as possible.

The assessment/development model below is designed to help you construct the kind of comprehensive tests that will further the educational goals of Science*Plus*. The model features four categories (verbal, graphic, illustrative, and numeric) and twelve kinds of items. A set of test items, developed in accordance with the model, is provided in each unit of the *Teacher's Resource Binder*.

The manner of testing determines what is learned: tests that require tick-mark responses teach tick-marking.

✔ Assessment Item Development Model

✔ Verbal

Word Usage: Words given are to be used in a prescribed situation.

Correction/Completion: Incomplete or incorrect sentences and paragraphs are given for completion or correction.

Short Essay: Information is given and/or a question is posed for short essay response.

Short Responses: Answers to these questions require a tick mark, a line, a single word, phrase, or sentence.

✔ Graphic

Graphs for Interpretation: A graph of a relationship between two variables is given for interpretation.

Graphs for Correction or Completion: An incomplete or incorrect graph is given for completion or correction.

Graphing Data: Data are given to be graphed.

✔ Illustrative

Illustration for Interpretation: Illustrations (drawings or photographs) are presented for interpretation.

Illustrations for Correction or Completion: An incorrect or incomplete illustration is given for correction.

Answering by Illustrations: A question is asked for which a drawing is the expected answer.

✔ Numeric

Data for Interpretation: A data table is given for interpretation.

Numerical Problems: A problem is given for a numerical solution.

The tables below provide an objective approach to evaluating students' independent projects.

Criteria for Evaluating Student Reports and Presentations

Scientific Thought (possible 40 points)

Complete understanding of topic; topic extensively researched; variety of primary and secondary sources used and cited; proper and effective use of scientific vocabulary and terminology.	Good understanding of topic; topic well researched; a variety of sources used and cited; good use of scientific vocabulary and terminology.	Acceptable understanding of topic; adequate research evident; sources cited; adequate use of scientific terms.	Poor understanding of topic; inadequate research; little use of scientific terms.	Lacks an understanding of topic; very little research, if any; incorrect use of scientific terms.
40 39 38 37 36	35 34 33 32 31	30 29 28 27 26	25 24 23 22 21	20 15 10

Oral Presentation (possible 30 points)

Clear, concise, engaging presentation, well supported by use of multisensory aids; scientific content effectively communicated to peer group.	Well-organized, interesting, confident presentation supported by multisensory aids; scientific content communicated to peer group.	Presentation acceptable; only modestly effective in communicating science content to peer group.	Presentation lacks clarity and organization; ineffective in communicating science content to peer group.	Poor presentation; does not communicate science content to peer group.
30 29 28 27	26 25 24 23	22 21 20 19	18 17 16	15 10 5

Exhibit or Display (possible 30 points)

Exhibit layout self-explanatory and successfully incorporates a multisensory approach; creative use of materials.	Layout logical, concise, and can be followed easily; materials used in exhibit appropriate and effective.	Acceptable layout of exhibit; materials used appropriately.	Organization of layout could be improved; materials could have been chosen better.	Exhibit layout lacks organization and is difficult to understand; poor and ineffective use of materials.
30 29 28 27	26 25 24 23	22 21 20 19	18 17 16	15 10 5

Criteria for Evaluating Student Technology Projects

Scientific Technical Thought (possible 40 points)

Featuring an attempted design solution to technical problem; the problem is significant and stated clearly; the solution reveals creative thought and imagination; underlying technical and scientific principles are very well understood.	Featuring an attempted design solution to a technical problem; the solution may be a standard one for similar problems; underlying technical and scientific principles are recognized and understood.	Featuring a working model; underlying technical and scientific principles are well understood; model is built from a standard blueprint or design.	A model built from a standard blueprint or design or from a kit; underlying technical and scientific principles are recognized but not necessarily understood.	A model built from a kit; underlying technical and scientific principles are not recognized or understood.
40 39 38 37 36	35 34 33 32 31	30 29 28 27 26	25 24 23 22 21	20 15 10

Presentation (possible 30 points)

Clear, concise, confident presentation; proper and effective use of vocabulary and terminology; complete understanding of topic; able to extrapolate.	Well-organized, clear presentation; good use of scientific vocabulary and terminology; good understanding of topic.	Presentation acceptable; adequate use of scientific terms; acceptable understanding of topic.	Presentation lacks clarity and organization; little use of scientific terms and vocabulary; poor understanding of topic.	Poor presentation; cannot explain topic; scientific terminology lacking or confused; lacks understanding of topic.
30 29 28 27	26 25 24 23	22 21 20 19	18 17 16	15 10 5

Exhibit (possible 30 points)

Exhibit layout self-explanatory and successfully incorporates a good sensory approach; creative and very effective use of material.	Layout logical, concise, and easy to follow; materials used in exhibit appropriate and effective.	Acceptable layout of exhibit; materials used appropriately.	Organization of layout could be improved; materials could have been chosen better.	Layout lacks organization and is difficult to understand; poor and ineffective use of materials.
30 29 28 27	26 25 24 23	22 21 20 19	18 17 16	15 10 5

Criteria for Evaluating Student Experimental Research Projects

Scientific Thought (possible 40 points)

An attempt to design and conduct an experiment or project with all important variables controlled.					An attempt to design and conduct an experiment or project, but with inadequate control of significant variables.					
40	38	38	37	36	35	30	25	15	10	5

Originality (possible 16 points)

Original, resourceful, novel approach; creative design and use of equipment.		Imaginative, extension of standard approach and use of equipment.		Standard approach and good treatment of current topic.		Incomplete and unimaginative use of resources.		Lack of creativity in both topic and resources.	
16	15	14	13	12	11	10	9	8	7	6	5	4	2

Presentation (possible 24 points)

Clear, concise, confident presentation; proper and effective use of vocabulary and terminology; complete understanding of topic; able to extrapolate.	Well-organized, clear presentation; good use of scientific vocabulary and terminology; good understanding of topic.	Presentation acceptable; adequate use of scientific terms; acceptable understanding of topic.	Presentation lacks clarity and organization; little use of scientific vocabulary; poor understanding of topic.	Poor presentation; cannot explain topic; scientific terminology and vocabulary lacking or confused; lacks understanding of topic.
24 23 22 21	20 19 18 17	16 15 14 13	12 11 10 9	8 4

Exhibit (possible 20 points)

Exhibit layout self-explanatory and successfully incorporates a multi-sensory approach; creative and very effective use of materials.	Layout logical, concise, and can be followed easily; materials used appropriate and effective.	Acceptable layout; materials used appropriately.	Organization of layout could be improved; materials could have been chosen better.	Exhibit layout lacks organization and is difficult to understand; poor and ineffective use of materials.
20 19	18 17 16	15 14 13	12 11	10 8 6

SCIENCEPLUS

Technology and Society

To The Student

*T*his book was written with you in mind! There are many things to try, to create, and to investigate — both in and out of class. There are stories to be read, articles to think about, puzzles to be solved, and even games to play.

GET INVOLVED!

The best way to learn is by doing. In the words of an old Chinese proverb:

Tell me — I will forget.

Show me — I may remember.

Involve me — I will understand.

The authors of this book want **you** to **get involved** in science.

The activities in this book will allow you to make some basic and important scientific discoveries on your own. You will be acting much like the early investigators in science who, without expensive or complicated equipment, contributed so much to our knowledge.

What these early investigators had, and had in abundance, was **curiosity** and **imagination**. If you have these qualities, you are in good company! And if you develop sharp scientific skills, who knows, you might make your own contributions to science someday.

THE LEADING

EDGE

Scientists are usually interested in understanding things that happen in **nature**. However, the discoveries that scientists make are often used by inventors and engineers. The end result is our most sophisticated **technology**, including such things as computers, laser discs, nuclear reactors, and instant global communication.

There is an interaction between science and technology. Science makes technology possible. On the other hand, the products of technology are used to make further scientific discoveries. In fact, much of the scientific work that is done today has become so technically complicated and expensive that no one person can do it entirely alone. But make no mistake, the creative ideas for even the most highly technical and expensive scientific work still come from **individuals**.

GO FOR IT!

Science is a process of discovery: a trek into the unknown. The skills you develop as you do the activities in this book — like observing, experimenting, and explaining observations and ideas — are the skills you will need to be a part of science in the future. There is a universe of scientific exploration and discovery awaiting those who take the challenge.

Keep a Journal

A Journal is an important tool in creative work. In this book, you will be asked to keep a Journal of your thoughts, observations, experiments, and conclusions. As you develop your Journal, you will see your own ideas taking shape over time. This is often the way scientists arrive at new discoveries. You too may log some discoveries as you develop your own Journal.

About Safety

Science investigations and experiments should be both enjoyable and safe. If you follow the safety guidelines listed here, as well as any others mentioned in the explorations, you should have no problems. You should **always** follow these guidelines, even when you think that there is little or no danger.

The major causes of laboratory accidents are carelessness, lack of attention, and inappropriate behavior. These all spring from a person's **attitude**. With a proper attitude and **consistent** safety habits, you should be able to feel quite comfortable and at home in a science laboratory.

Safety Guidelines

● Eye Safety

Wear goggles when handling acids or bases, using an open flame, or performing any other activity that could harm the eyes. If a substance gets into your eyes, wash them with plenty of water and notify your teacher at once. Never place a chemical substance near your unprotected eyes. Never use direct sunlight to illuminate a microscope.

● Safety Equipment

Know the location of all safety equipment, such as fire extinguishers and first aid kits.

● Neatness

Keep work areas free of all unnecessary books and papers. Tie back long, loose hair and button or roll up loose sleeves when working with chemicals or near a flame.

● Chemicals

Chemicals and other dangerous substances can be dangerous if they are handled carelessly. When handling certain chemicals, such as acids or bases, you should protect your eyes and clothes with safety glasses and an apron.

Heat

Whenever possible, use an electric hot plate instead of an open flame. If you must use an open flame to heat a glass container, shield the flame with a wire screen that has a ceramic center. When heating chemicals in a test tube, do not point the test tube toward anyone.

Electricity

Be cautious around electrical wiring. When using a microscope with a lamp, do not place its cord where it can cause someone to trip. Do not let cords hang over a table edge in a way that will cause equipment to fall if a cord is pulled. Do not use equipment with frayed cords.

Sharp/Pointed Objects

Use knives, razor blades, and other sharp instruments with care. Do not use double-edged razor blades in the laboratory.

Never taste chemicals, unless you are specifically instructed to do so.

Never pour water into a strong acid or base. The mixture produces heat. Sometimes the heat causes splattering. The correct procedure is to pour the acid or base slowly *into the water*. This way the mixture will stay cool.

If any solution is spilled, wash it off with plenty of water. If a strong acid or base is spilled, neutralize it first with an agent such as baking soda (for acids) or boric acid (for bases).

If you are instructed to note the odor of a substance, wave the fumes toward your nose with your hand rather than putting your nose close to the source.

Glassware

Examine all glassware before using. Glass containers for heating should be made of heat-resistant material. Never use cracked or chipped glassware.

Cleanup

Wash your hands immediately after handling hazardous materials. Before leaving the laboratory, clean up all work areas. Put away all equipment and supplies. Make sure water, gas, burners, and electric hot plates are turned off.

The instructions for the explorations in this book will include warning statements where necessary. In addition, you will find one or more of the following safety symbols when a procedure requires specific caution.

 Wear Safety Goggles

 Wear a Laboratory Apron

 Flame/ Heat

 Sharp/ Pointed Object

 Dangerous Chemical/ Poison

 Corrosive Substance

Science and Technology

 Teaching the Unit

 ## Unit Overview

In this unit, students are introduced to the nature of science and what scientists do. In the section *Science Is . . .,* students act as scientists by participating in a number of hands-on experiments. They develop their own definitions of science, and they are encouraged to add to or change their definitions as they progress through the unit. In the section *Being Scientific,* students practice making careful observations, making inferences based on their observations, using a model to explain their observations, and setting up a controlled experiment. In the section *From Science to Technology,* students set up and carry out their own controlled experiment. The section concludes by introducing students to the concept of technology and how it demonstrates the use of science to solve practical problems.

Using the Themes

The unifying themes emphasized in this unit are **Patterns of Change** and **Stability.** The following information will help you weave these themes into your teaching plan. A focus question is provided with each theme as a discussion tool to help you tie the information in the unit together.

Patterns of Change is suggested in the workings of science itself: science is knowledge in the making; it is an active process in which facts are continually accumulated, reevaluated, and reprocessed.

Focus question: *What processes keep scientific knowledge constantly changing?*

Students should describe how scientists use research, generate hypotheses, and perform experiments to gain information. Each new piece of information alters the whole of scientific knowledge. Through controlled experiments, scientists are able to draw new conclusions about their observations and add support for existing theories.

Stability can be discussed in connection with experimental design and testing. Students are introduced to the idea that nature can be predictable. Students learn that, given a set of initial experimental conditions, results are expected to be reproducible.

Focus question: *Why is accuracy so important in carrying out experiments?*

Students should understand that when they act as scientists, they are using their observations to make predictions. Experiments are performed to test hypotheses. If variables are not carefully controlled and measurements are not accurately taken, it is impossible to know what variable is producing the outcome of the experiment. Accuracy produces stability in scientific knowledge.

 ## Using the *Science Discovery* Videodiscs

Disc 1 *Science Sleuths*, *The Traffic Accident*
A bicycle and an automobile have collided at an intersection. The driver claims to have been obeying the speed limit when a cyclist appeared out of nowhere. The cyclist claims to have braked when he saw the car approaching, but the driver swerved to hit him. The Science Sleuths must analyze the evidence for themselves to determine what really happened.

Disc 2 *Image and Activity Bank*
A variety of still images, short videos, and activities are available for you to use as you teach this unit. See the *Videodisc Resources* section of the **Teacher's Resource Binder** for detailed instructions.

 ## Using the *SciencePlus SourceBook*

Unit 1 focuses on science and its methods. Students are introduced to science as a search for answers to the many questions raised by our human curiosity. The major fields of science are highlighted, with attention to various careers available in each area. Finally, scientific methods are examined and illustrated by actual investigations done by working scientists.

PLANNING CHART

SECTION AND LESSON	PG.	TIME*	PROCESS SKILLS	EXPLORATION AND ASSESSMENT	PG.	RESOURCES AND FEATURES
Unit Opener	2		observing, discussing	For Your Journal	3	Science Sleuths: *The Traffic Accident* Videodisc Activity Sheets TRB: Home Connection
SCIENCE IS . . .	4			Challenge Your Thinking	15	TRB: Resource Worksheet 1–2 Graphic Organizer Transparency 1–1
1 The Nature of Science	5	3	observing, analyzing, experimenting, predicting			Image and Activity Bank 1–1 TRB: Resource Worksheet 1–1
2 Defining Science	12	2	analyzing, making a collage, writing a poem			Image and Activity Bank 1–2
BEING SCIENTIFIC	16			Challenge Your Thinking	34	
3 The Science of Observation	16	4 to 5	observing, classifying, inferring, drawing conclusions	Exploration 1 Exploration 2 Exploration 3	17 18 20	Image and Activity Bank 1–3 Graphic Organizer Transparencies 1–2 and 1–3
4 From Observations to Conclusions	22	4	observing, inferring, interpreting, drawing conclusions	Exploration 4	24	Image and Activity Bank 1–4 TRB: Resource Worksheet 1–3 Graphic Organizer Transparency 1–4
5 Is There a Gremlin in the Drink Machine?	28	1	observing, inferring, using a model, making a model			Image and Activity Bank 1–5
6 Testing Ideas	30	2 to 3	hypothesizing, identifying variables, predicting, controlling variables			Image and Activity Bank 1–6
FROM SCIENCE TO TECHNOLOGY	35			Challenge Your Thinking	47	
7 From Hypothesis to Experiment	35	5	designing experiments, controlling variables, collecting data, interpreting data	Exploration 5 Exploration 6	38 40	Image and Activity Bank 1–7 TRB: Resource Worksheet 1–4 Graphic Organizer Transparency 1–5
8 Technology— Brainchild of Science	42	2	reading, analyzing, inventing, researching			Image and Activity Bank 1–8 TRB: Activity Worksheet 1–5 Graphic Organizer Transparency 1–6
End of Unit	48		applying, analyzing, evaluating, summarizing	Making Connections TRB: Sample Assessment Items	48	Science in Action, p. 50 Science and Technology, p. 52 *SourceBook,* pp. S1–S20

*Time given in number of class periods.

✳ *Meeting Individual Needs*

☀ Gifted Students

1. To help students develop their critical-thinking, speaking, and leadership skills, have them present a debate to the class on a controversial issue such as, "Should we rely on nuclear power to meet our energy needs?" Have them review *Robert's Rules for Parliamentary Procedure* so that they are familiar with formal debating procedures. Tell students that to prepare for the debate, they should anticipate what their opponents' arguments will be. Then they should think of comments to discredit or weaken those points.

2. Have interested students read a report in a scientific journal. They should summarize the report by briefly stating the hypothesis that was being tested, the experimental set-up that was used to test the hypothesis, the observations that were made, and the conclusions that were drawn from these observations.

☀ LEP Students

1. To help students understand experimental set-ups, have them sketch all the variables in the experimental set-ups in this unit that they are asked to design themselves. Students should draw and label the controlled variables as well as those that are changed. Have the students label their drawings with words you have supplied for them on the chalkboard.

2. Have students make up word games, such as a word search, using these new terms: prediction, observation, quantitative observations, qualitative observations, properties, inference, interpret, model, variable, controlled experiment, hypothesis, and technology. Once students have finished making their word games, have them exchange papers with one another. Photocopy the word games for all the students in the class to enjoy.

3. At the beginning of each unit, give Spanish-speaking students a copy of the *Spanish Glossary* from the *Teacher's Resource Binder.* Also, let Spanish-speaking students listen to the *English/Spanish Audiocassettes.*

☀ At-Risk Students

This unit affords many opportunities for students to discover the excitement of acting as scientists as they plan, create, and test their ideas. Assemble a group of objects for students to investigate, observe, and take apart if they wish. These objects might include a flashlight, a stapler, a lawn sprinkler, a manual typewriter, and a zipper. After students examine each object, ask them to determine how each works. To get them started, suggest that they make a list of the different parts in each object or perhaps draw a diagram showing the different parts. They can then proceed by writing down the possible function of each part.

Exploration 4, Lights Out! #1, can be modified to give students further experience in controlling variables. For example, the size of the jar used can become the variable that changes. Ask students to see how changing a different variable affects the water level in the jar and the amount of time the candles stay lit. *(The larger the jar, the more oxygen there is available, and the longer the candle will stay lit. As oxygen is used up, the water level can increase to take up space previously occupied by oxygen. Remind students to change only one variable at a time.)*

☀ Cross-Disciplinary Focus

Social Studies

Ask students to find magazine and newspaper articles related to science and technology. Have students share their articles with the rest of the class and discuss them in terms of how science and technology affect society. For example, what are the implications of new medical technologies? Should research, such as that done in genetic engineering, be monitored or regulated? How can new technologies help to solve environmental problems? After the discussion, students could create a bulletin-board display with their articles.

Creative Writing

Invite students to write a science fiction story about how science and technology will affect them in the future. They should try to imagine what kinds of new technologies will be available and how new products will affect their everyday lives. Challenge students to let their imaginations run wild!

Mathematics

In Lesson 1, the death of a star is discussed. Students may not understand why the light from a star that exploded 15,000 years ago reached the earth in 1987. Explain that light travels at a speed of 300,000 kilometers per second. Ask students to calculate how far away the star actually was from the earth when it exploded. Suggest students begin by calculating how fast the light traveled per hour, per day, per month, and per year. Then have students multiply the number of kilometers per year times 15,000 years. *(9,460,800,000,000 km/yr × 15,000 yr = 151,912,000,000,000,000 km. This number is read as 151 quadrillion, 912 trillion kilometers.)*

 ## Cross-Cultural Focus

Appropriate Technology

For technology to be appropriate, it must be harmonious with the needs and lifestyles of people in the community, and with the natural world in which the people live. For example, in this country most people can get a drink of water by going to the sink and turning on a faucet to fill a glass. This may seem simple, but the faucets are connected by kilometers of underground pipes to pumping stations, water filters, and reservoirs. All of these together make up the technology that is used to supply water. It suits the needs of people who live in industrialized countries. In countries where the technology is different, people may use jars to carry the water to their homes and to store it until it is needed. Have students research and report on a technology used in another country. If possible, arrange for an ex-Peace Corps volunteer or member of a foreign consulate to speak to the class on technologies of a different country or culture.

Belief Systems

Scientific reasoning involves looking for direct evidence of cause and effect relationships in carefully controlled experiments. Many cultural groups, in their understanding of the physical world, have systems of belief that are not based on scientific reasoning or scientific methods. Have students do research on the belief systems of another culture. Suggestions include:
- The Yanomami Indians in South America
- The Dyak in Indonesia
- The Masai in Kenya
- The Aborigines in Australia or New Guinea

 # *Resources*

 ## Bibliography for Teachers

Caney, Steven. *Steven Caney's Invention Book.* New York, NY: Workman, 1985.

Driver, Rosalind. *The Pupil as Scientist?* Philadelphia, PA: Open University Press, Taylor and Francis, 1983.

Lowery, Lawrence. *The Everyday Science Sourcebook.* Palo Alto, CA: Dale Seymour, 1985.

Stanish, Bob. *The Unconventional Invention Book.* Carthage, IL: Good Apple, 1981.

Van Deman, Barry A., and Ed McDonald. *Nuts and Bolts: A Matter of Fact Guide to Science Fair Projects.* Harwood Heights, IL: Science Man, 1982.

 ## Bibliography for Students

Allison, Linda, and David Katz. *Gee, Wiz! How to Mix Art and Science; or, the Art of Thinking Scientifically.* Boston, MA: Little, Brown, 1983.

Lampton, Christopher. *Thomas Alva Edison.* New York, NY: Watts, 1984.

McKie, Robin. *Technology: Science at Work.* New York, NY: Franklin Watts, 1984.

Pollard, Michael. *The House that Science Built.* New York, NY: Facts on File, 1987.

 ## Films, Videotapes, Software, and Other Media

Botanical Gardens.
Software. Grades 6–9.
For Apple II.
Sunburst
Communication
101 Castleton Street
Pleasantville, NY
10570-3498
(800)228-3504

Careers in Math and Science: A Different View.
Film and Video.
Grades 5–9.
Walt Disney Educational Media
Distributed by
Coronet/MTI
108 Wilmot Rd.
Deerfield, IL 60015
(800)621-2131

Inferring in Science, Observing in Science, and Questioning in Science.
Videos. Grades 5–9.
Agency for Instructional Technology
1111 W. 17th Street
Bloomington, IN 47404
(812)339-2203

Rocky's Boots.
Software. Grades 6–9.
For Apple II.
The Learning Company
6493 Kaiser Drive
Fremont, CA 94555
(800)852-2255

✳ Unit Focus

Perform the "egg-in-the-bottle" trick. You will need a bottle with an opening slightly smaller than an egg; a peeled, hard-boiled egg; oil; matches; and a 10-cm square piece of paper. Smear oil around the mouth of the bottle. Fold the paper, light it with a match, and quickly drop it into the bottle. Place the egg in the bottle opening. The egg will eventually plop into the bottle. Ask students why this happens. *(The gases inside the bottle expand due to the heat. Some of the gases are forced out past the egg, which acts as a one-way valve. When the flame goes out, the gases in the bottle cool and contract, forming a partial vacuum.)*

Ask students if this was science and if they acted like scientists. Explain that, in this unit, they will learn more about what scientists do.

✳ About the Photograph

The twin space probes, *Voyager 1* and *Voyager 2*, were launched in 1977. This picture is of one of the probes passing by Jupiter in 1979.

Each space probe is about the size of a small car. A large, white radio dish antenna provides a link between the probe and Earth. On board, science instrument packages were used to study the planets, several of their moons, and billions of kilometers of space between planets.

Unit 1 Science and Technology

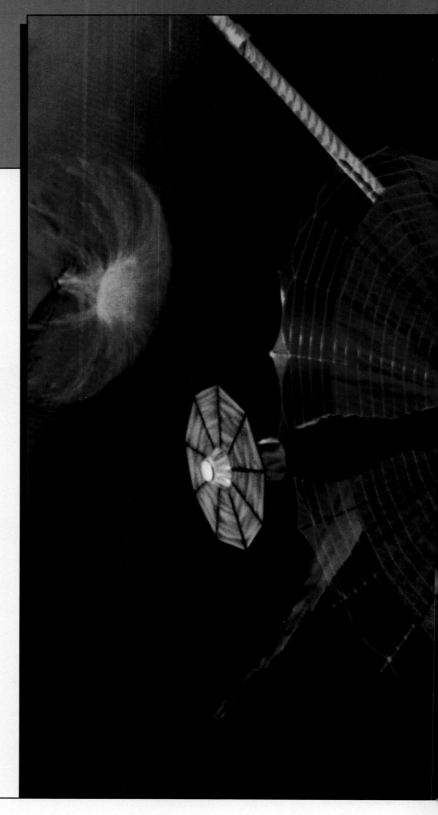

Ask students questions similar to the following.
- What is the object in the upper left-hand part of the picture? *(It is Io, one of Jupiter's moons.)*
- How are the Voyager space probes able to take pictures of Jupiter, Saturn, and Uranus, and send them back to Earth? *(Voyager cameras take pictures the way a TV camera does. Electrical signals are radioed to Earth in the form of numbers. These numbers are fed into a computer that produces an image based on this information.)*

Mention that the probes developed some serious problems after they were launched. By radio, scientists sent adjustments to the probes to correct the problems. Tracking stations maintained constant contact with the probes in order to receive data and to send instructions to the probes' computers.

For Your Journal

Write a paragraph summarizing your thoughts about each of the following:

1. What do you think of when you think of "science"?
2. What do scientists do?
3. Can ordinary people do science?
4. Have you ever done science? What did you do?
5. What connection does science have with inventions such as the space probe in the photograph?

✷ **About Your Journal**

Students should answer the Journal questions to the best of their abilities.

These questions are designed to serve two functions: to help students recognize that they do indeed have prior knowledge, and to help them identify any misconceptions they may have about the topic. In the course of studying the unit, these misconceptions should be dispelled.

Science Is . . .

Ask students what the quotation, on page 4 of their texts, means to them. Ask: Why is a scientist an explorer? Why does a scientist sometimes travel paths that have already been traveled before? Why does a scientist sometimes travel uncharted paths? *(Explain to students that this quotation is an example of a metaphor. You might point out to students that the scientist is not literally traveling down a path; rather, the path represents a course taken to gain knowledge of the world. A path also suggests a trail that has been traveled before, as scientists learn about the discoveries of others, and perhaps try to duplicate their findings. At other times, the scientist may travel unknown paths by undertaking original experiments that have never been tried before, and by making observations that have never been made before.)*

Tell students that in studying science, they will learn how to be explorers. They will take some paths that have already been traveled before, and they may even blaze a trail of their own and discover something new!

SCIENCE IS . . .

"I am an explorer. Some paths that I travel have been traveled before. Other paths are uncharted—leading to new insights and to new discoveries."

Who was the author of this statement? An early explorer? An astronaut? Actually, the statement was made by a scientist. It describes what you will be doing in this unit and throughout this book. This unit is about science: what it is, what scientists do, how they do it. More importantly, this unit is about how *you* become a scientist each and every day.

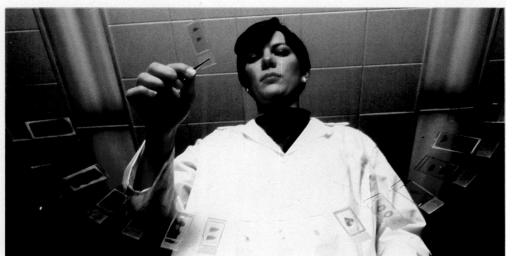

L E S S O N ① O R G A N I Z E R

Objectives

By the end of the lesson, students should be able to:
1. Describe who scientists are and what they do.
2. Discuss the nature of science.

Process Skills

observing, analyzing, experimenting, predicting

New Terms

Prediction—the expected outcome of a future event.

1 The Nature of Science

What is science? Who does science? How do they do it? Is science important? In the pages that follow are a number of activities that will help you answer these questions. You will find that doing these tasks with a partner or in a small group is more enjoyable than doing them by yourself.

Yes, No, or Maybe?

A science class made a list of statements about what they believed to be true about science. Which statement do you think is the best? Which one do you agree with least? In your Journal, list the numbers of the statements with which you agree, disagree, or about which you are not certain.

1. Science is what we know about everything around us.
2. Science is a job for men.
3. Science is a method for finding things out.
4. Scientific ideas never change.
5. Science is what you do in the laboratory.
6. Science is information about the world that will be useful later in life.
7. Science is exploring space.
8. Science is doing experiments.
9. Science is a collection of facts.
10. Scientists are different from most other people.

It's your turn! Create your own statement about science, and then share it with your classmates. Do they agree with your statement? Do you agree with theirs? After completing the next four activities, you may wish to change your statement about science in some way.

Materials

Making a Möbius Strip: 75-cm strip of adding machine tape, transparent tape, metric ruler, scissors, pencil

Teacher's Resource Binder

Resource Worksheet 1–1

Science Discovery Videodisc

Disc 2, Image and Activity Bank, 1–1

Time Required

three class periods

✴ Getting Started

This introductory lesson focuses on who scientists are, what scientists do, and on the nature of science. By being involved in a variety of readings, discussions, and activities, students are asked to think about the nature of science in terms of the activities scientists perform.

Main Ideas

1. Viewpoints about science vary a great deal from person to person.
2. Science encompasses the knowledge we have of the universe and also the ways in which this knowledge is acquired.

✴ Teaching Strategies

The five student activities that make up Lesson 1 can be done in any order. *Yes, No, or Maybe?* can be done in small groups. *Reading Science Case Histories* and listing the scientists' activities can be done individually by students in class or at home. *Making the "Best" Airplane* and *Cracking the Code* can be assigned as "do-at-home" activities. By the end of this lesson, students will be in a position to formulate their own definition of science. This definition will be modified as students progress through the unit.

Answers to

Yes, No, or Maybe?

1. Agree.
2. Disagree: Science can be a job for anyone who has the interest and determination.

(Answers continue on next page)

Answers continued

3. Agree.
4. Disagree: Scientific ideas are constantly evolving and changing.
5. Agree: Science includes what you do in the laboratory, as well as making systematic observations about the physical world. From these observations, scientists must then ask questions, formulate hypotheses, and design experiments to test hypotheses.
6. Agree.
7. Agree: Science is many things; exploring space is one part.
8. Agree: experiments provide the means for testing observations and theories and drawing conclusions. However, science is much more than just doing experiments.
9. Disagree: Science is not just a collection of facts, it is how these facts are collected and what scientists do with these facts that is important.
10. Disagree.

Science Case Histories

Before students read page 6, ask them to draw a picture of a scientist. Their pictures may reveal some common misconceptions about who scientists are. Have students discuss the contents of their pictures. At the end of the lesson, you may wish to have them look at their pictures again and discuss how their ideas about scientists have changed.

Death of a Star!

After students have read the page, ask them to discuss, either in small groups or as a class, the things that Shelton did that led to his discovery. *(Shelton quite unexpectedly **observed** a bright star; he **studied** a photograph of the star more closely; and finally he **concluded** that it was a supernova.)*

Science Case Histories

While reading about the activities of the scientists described below, make a list of the things these scientists did. Afterwards, share your list with your classmates.

Death of a Star!

An event that took place 15,000 years ago was first seen by an astronomer working in South America. At 11 P.M. on February 23, 1987, Ian Shelton was doing some routine work at a small observatory on a mountaintop in Chile. Unexpectedly, he noticed a surprisingly bright star in a photograph he had just taken. After a closer look, Ian concluded that the photograph showed a supernova—an exploding star. The star had exploded 15,000 years ago, but was so far away that its light was only now reaching the earth. Ian had discovered the largest recorded supernova in almost 400 years. Because Ian was the first to make the observation and to recognize its significance, the supernova was named after him.

Ian Shelton with his telescopic camera.

The Shelton supernova—three years before discovery (left) and shortly after discovery (right).

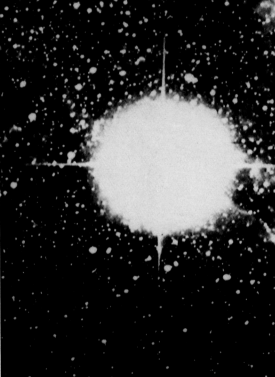

A Life-Saving Discovery

The year 1923 must have been a highlight in the life of Frederick Banting, for it was then that he shared the Nobel Prize in Medicine with J.J.R. Macleod for discovering insulin. Why was the discovery deemed important enough to win a Nobel Prize? Insulin is one of the many chemicals in the human body. It is so necessary for digestion that people whose bodies cannot produce it soon die. Lack of insulin causes the disease known as diabetes. Before Banting's discovery, there had been no effective treatment for diabetes.

Banting's involvement began three years earlier, while he was a doctor in private practice. He read about the possible connection between diabetes and a small gland called the pancreas. An idea for an experiment to test the connection came to him. To perform the experiment, Banting "borrowed" the laboratory of J.J.R. Macleod.

Banting and his assistant, Charles Best, tested Banting's idea, but the experiment did not support the original hypothesis. However, new observations suggested a new experiment. Finally, early in 1922, Banting announced the discovery of insulin. Today, diabetics the world over lead normal, healthy lives thanks to this vital discovery.

Banting and Best with a diabetic dog successfully treated with insulin.

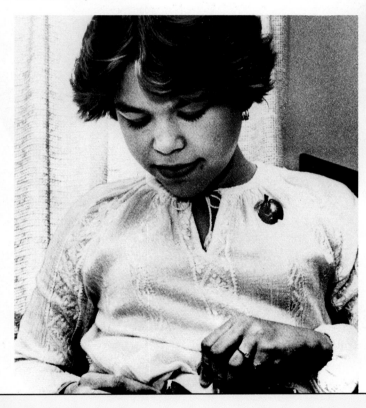

This girl, a diabetic since birth, sleeps with a pump strapped to her stomach. It gives her a continuous flow of insulin through a needle inserted just under the skin.

A Life-Saving Discovery

Have students compile a list of the things Banting and Best did to discover insulin. Ask them to share their lists with each other, either in small groups or as a class. *(Students may suggest that the scientists **read** about the connection between the pancreas and diabetes; **formed a hypothesis** about the connection; **experimented** to **test the hypothesis; made observations** that disproved the original hypothesis; **formed another hypothesis** based on their observations; and **tested this alternative hypothesis**, which led to the discovery of insulin.)*

Interested students may wish to find out more about the discovery of insulin and the latest developments in the treatment of diabetes.

Let's Do Some Science!

In these activities, students discover the peculiar nature of Möbius strips and the importance of design in making a model airplane.

Make Some Predictions

Encourage students to make a prediction in response to each of the questions asked, and then to test their predictions.

Answers to

In-Text Questions

Students will discover that:
- A Möbius strip has only one side. A pencil line drawn down the center will continue and eventually meet the starting point.
- If they cut along this line, they will end up with one large loop of paper but with an added twist.
- Cutting again, students will obtain two interlocking loops of paper.
  Students may suggest that they are doing what scientists do—making predictions, testing predictions, and discovering new ideas.

(Continues on next page)

Let's Do Some Science!
Making a Möbius Strip

First, make a Möbius strip by following the directions illustrated here.

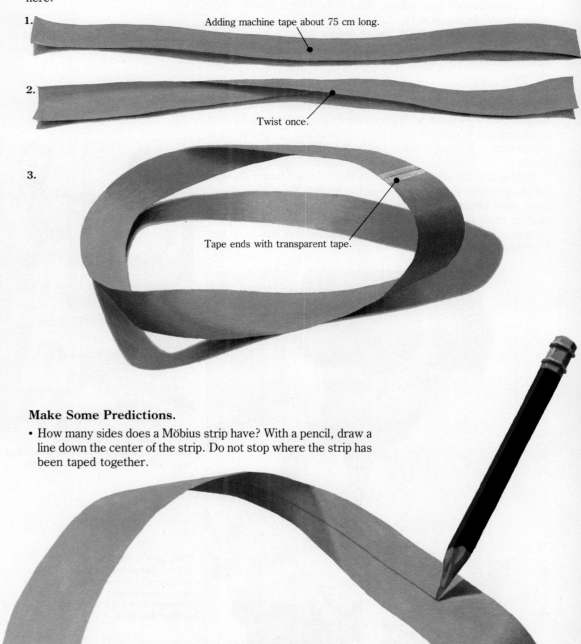

1. Adding machine tape about 75 cm long.

2. Twist once.

3. Tape ends with transparent tape.

Make Some Predictions.
- How many sides does a Möbius strip have? With a pencil, draw a line down the center of the strip. Do not stop where the strip has been taped together.

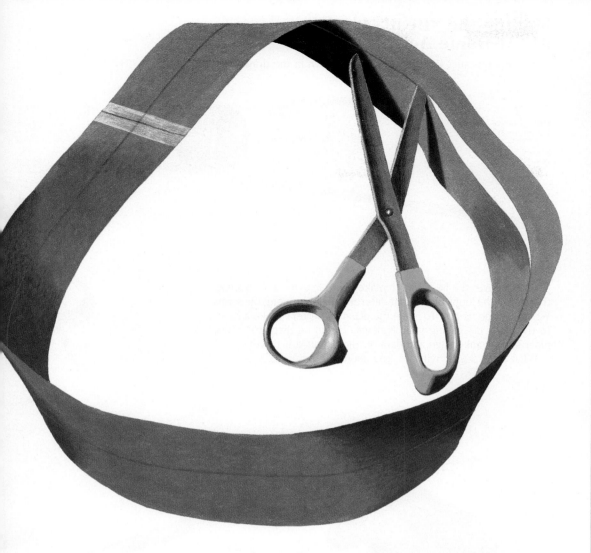

(Make Some Predictions continued)
Challenge students to experiment further with their Möbius strips. First, ask students to speculate about what would happen if the strip were cut one more time. They should then predict what would happen and test their predictions. After the students have designed and carried out their experiments, have them share their results with one another.

Students may be interested to know that the Möbius strip was named after a German astronomer and mathematician who lived from 1790–1868. August Möbius was the first to describe the mathematical properties of one-sided surfaces, such as the now-celebrated Möbius strip.

- How many pieces of paper do you think you will have if you cut along this line with a pair of scissors? Try it.

- How many pieces of paper do you think you will have if you cut once more along the center of the paper strip that you created above? Again, try it!

What does this activity tell you about science and about what scientists do?

Making the "Best" Airplane: An At-Home Activity

This plane works very well and is easy to make. Encourage students to do this activity at home. Ask them to write a report that includes diagrams of their designs and their data. Allow time for students to share their results.

Variables that students can try changing to make the "best" airplane include: the positions of the small and large loops (distances from the ends of the straw), the position of the straw when throwing it (loops on top or bottom, small loop in front or back), and the angle and force of the throw.

Ask students if they had difficulty controlling variables that they were not testing. For example, it may have been difficult to throw the model airplane at the same angle and with the same force each time. Ask students if they tested each change in variable a number of times, and if they found that the model airplane went the same distance each time. If not, they may have been unable to control the variables that were not being tested.

Answer to

In-Text Question

In answer to the last question, students may respond that:
- Scientists experiment and test their ideas.
- Scientists repeat the same experiment many times.
- Scientists conduct experiments in such a way that the results are reliable.
- Scientists control (keep constant) variables, other than the one being tested.
- Scientists keep records and communicate their ideas to others.

Making the "Best" Airplane: An At-Home Activity

At home, construct the model airplane shown in the drawing.

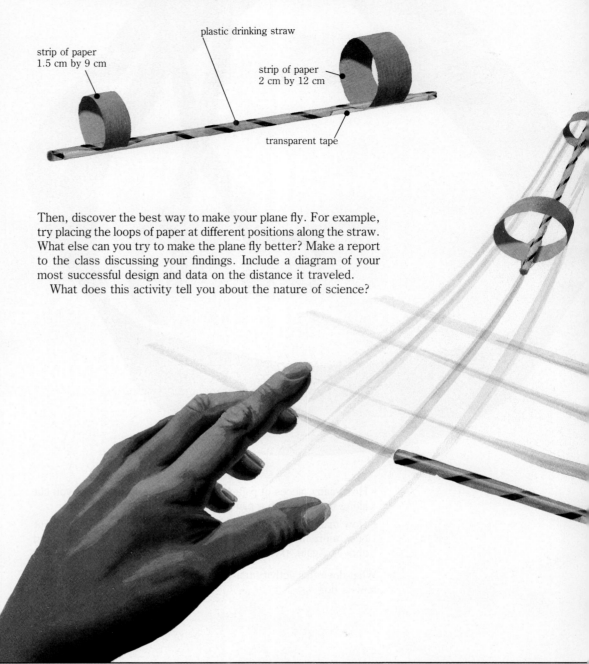

plastic drinking straw

strip of paper 1.5 cm by 9 cm

strip of paper 2 cm by 12 cm

transparent tape

Then, discover the best way to make your plane fly. For example, try placing the loops of paper at different positions along the straw. What else can you try to make the plane fly better? Make a report to the class discussing your findings. Include a diagram of your most successful design and data on the distance it traveled.

What does this activity tell you about the nature of science?

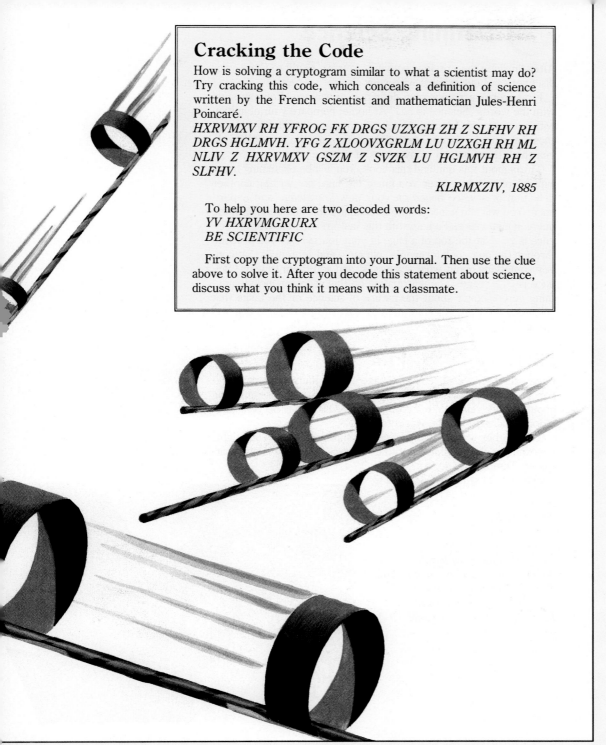

Cracking the Code

How is solving a cryptogram similar to what a scientist may do? Try cracking this code, which conceals a definition of science written by the French scientist and mathematician Jules-Henri Poincaré.

HXRVMXV RH YFROG FK DRGS UZXGH ZH Z SLFHV RH DRGS HGLMVH. YFG Z XLOOVXGRLM LU UZXGH RH ML NLIV Z HXRVMXV GSZM Z SVZK LU HGLMVH RH Z SLFHV.

KLRMXZIV, 1885

To help you here are two decoded words:
YV HXRVMGRURX
BE SCIENTIFIC

First copy the cryptogram into your Journal. Then use the clue above to solve it. After you decode this statement about science, discuss what you think it means with a classmate.

✳ *Follow Up*

Assessment

1. Identify each of the following statements as an observation, hypothesis, or prediction.
   (a) I got up at 7:00 A.M. today. *(observation)*
   (b) Tomorrow my brother is coming home. *(prediction)*
   (c) I am going to be a scientist when I finish school. *(prediction)*
   (d) I probably won't grow as tall as my father. *(prediction)*
   (e) I did not grow as tall as my father because I did not take vitamins. *(hypothesis)*
   (f) I think dinosaurs died out because of lack of food. *(hypothesis)*

2. You are building a kite and want to determine the best length of string to use for the tail. How would you find out? How would you be acting like a scientist? *(One possible answer might be to try several different tail lengths, each length tested several different times, and keep records of how the kite behaves with each different length. Students would be acting as scientists by conducting experiments, repeating their experiments several times, and keeping records of their results.)*

Extension

1. Challenge students to make a Möbius strip that if cut just once, will form two interlocking loops. *(The strip must be twisted 360° instead of 180°.)*
2. Invite students to create a cryptogram for their own definitions of science. Collect these puzzles, photocopy them, and share them with the class.

> **Primary Source**
> *Description of change:* excerpted from *Science and Method.*
> *Rationale:* excerpted to focus on the nature of science.

Answers to

Cracking the Code

The cryptogram says: "*Science is built up with facts as a house is with stones. But a collection of facts is no more a science than a heap of stones is a house.*" Poincaré, 1885

Students may suggest that the facts of science are organized; that the scientist (the builder) is important; that the process of gathering facts and ideas is as important as the ideas themselves. Science is not just a lot of facts, it is systematized knowledge.

Scientists propose hypotheses and experiment to test their hypotheses in order to find patterns or principles that govern the world. Most branches of science are organized around a few big ideas or themes. For example, biologists observe the characteristics of living things in order to classify them into groups and to identify relationships between them. Physicists study how things move to define the laws that govern motion. Earth scientists study the locations of earthquakes and volcanoes to determine the underlying structure of the earth's plates and how they move.

Science Is . . .

✳ Getting Started

In this lesson, students are asked to construct their own definitions of science. At this stage, you should resist providing them with a definition of science. Instead, encourage students to develop their own definitions. This lesson also emphasizes that science is a human activity, involving ordinary people from all walks of life.

Main Ideas

1. Science can be described in many different ways.
2. Science is a human activity.
3. Scientists are ordinary people.

✳ Teaching Strategies

Encourage students to think about their own definition of science, and then share it with the rest of the class. Then have a student read a dictionary definition of science and compare it with their own definition.

As students read the unit, they are asked to record in their Journals words, phrases, and sentences that convey what science is. At the end of the unit, ask students to create a new definition of science, and to compare it to their original definitions. Discuss with them how their definitions have changed.

❷ Defining Science

After finishing the previous activities you are ready to share your discoveries about science with your class.

First, construct your own definition of science. You can start with the words "Science is . . ." At home, compare your definition with one from a dictionary. At school, compare your definition with those of your classmates. Are all the definitions the same? Why do you think there are so many views of science?

Throughout this unit and this book, you will be examining many aspects of science. After you finish the unit, try writing another definition of science based on your new knowledge and experience. You will find it interesting to compare this definition with the one you just wrote. To help with this task, record the words "Science is . . ." at the top of a page in your Journal. As you proceed through the unit, look for words, phrases, and sentences that convey something about what science is, and add them to your "Science is . . ." page. The information on this page can include anything you discover about the nature of science or the tasks that scientists do. Here is a statement to start with; let's hope that you agree with it.

"Science Is . . . Fun"

Create another "Science is . . ." page in your Journal. From newspapers and magazines, collect pictures that convey something about science, and make a collage. This collage will be your definition of science for the world to see.

Yet another way to define science is through verse. You might, for example, write a poem entitled "Science Is." Here is one written by Tammy Doane, a middle school student:

Science is
Things to learn
Leaves to burn
Trees, flowers and all
The first snowflakes to fall
An opening flower, a croaking frog
The moss growing on a log
The sun sets at what time?
How much metal in a dime?

LESSON ❷ ORGANIZER

Objectives

By the end of this lesson, students should be able to:

1. Talk about the human qualities of a scientist.
2. Discuss what scientists do.
3. Formulate their own definition of the nature of science.

Process Skills

analyzing, making a collage, writing a poem

New Terms

Science Is People

Here are some questions that middle school student Nancy Leven asked Ursula Franklin. Ursula Franklin was one of the first women to be appointed a professor in Engineering at a major university. She is well known throughout the world for her work in science as well as her efforts for peace.

Nancy: Why did you become a scientist?

Ursula: *Because I enjoyed science, both in school and out of it, and because I was reasonably good at it. Although I was interested in and enjoyed many things, there was nothing I was more interested in doing for the rest of my life than science.*

Nancy: What do you do?

Ursula: *I study the relationship between the structure and the properties of materials—both ancient and modern materials. By "materials" I mean simply* stuff *of all kinds: metals, ceramics, textiles, wood, and other things. I also teach, consult with students, convene scientific meetings, sit on committees, and when I get time, try to write papers on my research.*

Ursula Franklin,
scientist and peace activist

Materials

Defining Science: Journal
"Science Is . . . Fun": newspapers, magazines, scissors, glue, Journal

Time Required

two class periods

"Science Is...Fun"

The poem written by Tammy Doane illustrates some important characteristics of science, including:
- things to learn
- things to do
- things to investigate

Explain to students that a collage is an art form in which bits of objects, such as newspaper, photos, cloth, pressed flowers, and so on, are combined to obtain a symbolic effect. You may wish to have students display their collages on the wall, and ask students to comment on the ones that they think best suggest the nature of science.

Science Is People

As an exercise in critical thinking, have students consider these questions while reading the interview:
- How are scientists similar to and different from you or me?
- If you were Nancy, what questions would you have asked Ursula Franklin?
- What is one thing about scientists you learned from this interview?
- Do you agree with everything Ursula Franklin said? Explain your answer.

Continue the discussion by asking students the following questions.
- What characteristics should a person have in order to become a research scientist? *(A natural aptitude for science, an inquiring mind, the ability to look at things critically, a willingness to endure several years of study and sometimes very long hours of experimental work, and the ability to be motivated by the possibility of discovering something new, thus adding to an understanding of the world.)*
- Do you think you have an aptitude and the desire to become a scientist? Explain your answer.
- Why is the study of science important for a person who does not intend to become a scientist? *(By understanding more about how science works, students will be better prepared for the technology of the future. Science teaches students the ability to think critically, a skill that can be useful in other disciplines and in everyday life.)*

Assessment

Ask students to summarize the personal characteristics that they have (or lack) that would be important if they were to become scientists.

Extension

1. Invite a scientist to your class to talk to students about what he or she does. Have students write questions for the scientist on slips of paper in advance. You may wish to have students put their questions in a box. Then the guest scientist can choose questions from the box to answer while giving the talk.
2. Ask students to find a science magazine, either at the library or at a newsstand, and read it. They should review the contents of the magazine, including columns, regular features, and types of articles, and explain what they liked or disliked about their magazine.

Nancy: How does a person get a job as a scientist?

Ursula: *Well, it is not necessarily easy to do. In addition to the long period of training involved (sometimes it takes 10 years of university education to reach the point where one is qualified to teach in a university), there are often few positions open. But really, you should go into science because you enjoy it and would rather do it than anything else, not because it is a way to get a good job. There are easier ways of making money! With respect to what subjects it is important to study, the answer is that everything is important. Any subject that prepares an inquiring mind and teaches you how to learn is important. You can always look up extra facts, but the discipline of learning and the ability to look at things critically are the skills you really have to acquire to be a scientist.*

Nancy: Are scientists different from other people?

Ursula: *No! In no way are scientists different—nor are they more clever. Just as a dancer or a musician requires some natural ability, encouragement, discipline, and good teachers to be successful, so too does a scientist. Scientists might benefit from having a certain natural gift for one activity rather than another, but they are not more gifted. It is just that their gifts lie in a certain area.*

Nancy: What other things are you interested in besides science?

Ursula: *People and politics, art and music. I also like to knit and cook. I am, of course, interested in my family (I have a son who is a professional photographer and a daughter who works in a legal clinic). Beyond my personal family, I am interested in the human family. I don't really think that you can be a scientist and not be concerned with peace and the continuation of human activity. One of the nice things about science is that whether you discover a little or a lot of new knowledge, it contributes to the sum total of knowledge. This knowledge must not only be preserved and enlarged, it must be used for the betterment of the whole planet and all its creatures—not just humans. This knowledge should not be used to destroy things. Anyone who is doing science as a vocation—because he or she loves it and feels that it needs to be done—cannot help but work for peace.*

1. Solve the cryptogram below to reveal a quote. To help you get started, the word *paths* appears twice. Solving this quote may give you a case of *déjà vu.*

   V NZ NA RKCYBERE. FBZR CNGUF GUNG V GENIRY UNIR ORRA GENIRYRQ ORSBER. BGURE CNGUF NER HAPUN-EGRQ YRNQVAT GB ARJ VAFVTUGF NAQ GB ARJ QVFPBI-REVRF.

   Show your solution key.

2. Describe the process you used to solve the cryptogram in the previous question. In what ways did your solution method use scientific thinking?

3. When was the last time you used scientific thinking (aside from the previous exercise, of course)? Describe the circumstances and the type of problem you were trying to solve.

1. The solution key is as follows:

   A = N
   B = O
   C = P
   D = Q
   E = R
   F = S
   G = T
   H = U
   I = V
   J = W
   K = X
   L = Y
   M = Z

   The solution to the cryptogram is the quote that appears on page 4 of Lesson 1.

2. One possible method for solving the puzzle would be to use the clue given that the word *paths* appears twice. Locate a word with five letters that appears twice. This is "CNGUF." Because it is the only word with 5 letters that appears twice, it must spell "paths." Use these known letters to replace other letters in the puzzle.

   Some scientific skills used might be logic, imagination, memory, testing, and hypothesis.

3. Answers will vary, but encourage students to compare their actions with the actions of the scientists discussed in the text.

LESSON 3

✳ *Getting Started*

This lesson begins with a science fiction story that introduces the term *observation*. Students are invited to make two kinds of observations—*qualitative* and *quantitative*. By making observations, they identify the characteristics of wax in *Exploration 1* and deduce the properties of the materials observed in *Exploration 2*. The lesson concludes with tasks that raise questions about the reliability of observations and about the differences in the abilities of people to observe.

Main Ideas

1. We learn about the world around us through observations.
2. Observations involving measurements are called quantitative observations.
3. Observations of the properties of a material, which can be used to identify it, are called qualitative observations.
4. Observations can involve all of the senses—sight, touch, taste, smell, and hearing.

③ The Science of Observation

Like science itself, many science fiction stories are based on facts. In the story that follows, you will read about Kriavalinan Z (known to his friends as Zed), who has just arrived on Earth from the planet Hephaistos.

A Stranger Has Landed

After the complicated maneuvers that were necessary to avoid detection, Zed finally landed on Earth. He stretched himself to his full height of 198 cm and yawned, relaxing after the difficult journey. Next came a quick meal. He began eagerly preparing to leave the spacecraft that had been home for the past three and a half years.

As Zed collected his belongings, he felt a thrill of excitement. Would Earth be similar to Hephaistos, thirty thousand light-years distant? Would it be a refuge or a place of danger? Now Zed was ready to leave. He proceeded toward the door slowly, his face a picture of concentration, wonderment, and anticipation. Zed pressed the door activator with the six fingers that made up his left hand. The door slid open and Zed saw Earth close up for the first time.

The first thing Zed noticed was all the color—the vivid reds and yellows of flowers; the waving greenery of the trees; and the pale, delicate blue of the sky, very much like the color of his skin. "Before venturing farther," Zed thought, "I must observe and try to make sense of this world. Later—perhaps much later—I will make contact with the beings who populate this lovely planet."

In these introductory paragraphs of a science fiction story, you have read about someone who explored an unfamiliar world in a scientific way. Making sense of something first involves making observations—seeing, feeling, hearing, tasting, and smelling.

In Exploration 1, imagine that you are Zed observing a strange object for the first time. What can you discover about a candle by making observations?

LESSON 3 ORGANIZER

Objectives

By the end of the lesson, students should be able to:
1. Distinguish between qualitative and quantitative observations.
2. Distinguish between an observation and a property.
3. Describe an object in terms of its properties.
4. Discuss reasons why people do not always make the same observations.

Process Skills

observing, classifying, inferring, drawing conclusions

New Terms

Observation—making sense of something by seeing, feeling, hearing, tasting, and smelling.
Quantitative observation—an observation involving measurements or numbers.

Qualitative observation—an observation that does not involve measurements or numbers.
Properties—characteristics that distinguish one thing from another.

Materials

Exploration 1: matches, modeling clay, birthday candle, ruler, metal lid or Petri dish, watch or clock, safety goggles, Journal

Test Your Powers of Observation

You Will Need

- matches
- modeling clay
- a birthday candle
- a ruler
- a metal lid or Petri dish

What to Do

1. Before lighting the candle, make as many observations as possible. Can you list five? ten? twenty? Your time limit is 7 minutes. Write your observations in your Journal.

2. Now place the candle on the lid. Modeling clay can be used to hold the candle in place. Light the candle. In the time it takes the candle to burn down (or 10 minutes, whichever comes first), make as many more observations as possible. Use the ruler to help make some observations. Do not, however, burn the ruler or anything besides the candle!

Remember to use caution around open flames!

For Discussion

1. Share your observations with your friends. Did they make observations that you didn't? Classify each observation as to whether it was made by sight, touch, hearing, taste, or smell.

2. Did you make any observations using the ruler? Observations of this type are called **quantitative observations.** Quantitative observations involve measurements and numbers. Perhaps you measured the shortest distance at which you could comfortably hold your hand over a flame, or timed how long it took for the candle to burn down. These are examples of quantitative observations. On the other hand, if you observed the color of the candle, the way the flame flickered, or noted the smell of burning wax, you were making **qualitative observations.** Qualitative observations *do not* involve measurements or numbers.

Decide which observations made by your class were quantitative and which were qualitative. Perhaps you can suggest some more quantitative observations that you could have made.

3. Reread "A Stranger Has Landed," and find statements that express quantitative observations, as well as those that give qualitative observations.

4. Many of your observations of the candle may have described the wax that makes up the candle. Characteristics that help distinguish wax from other materials are called its **properties.** For example, wax can be distinguished from ice by its ability to burn: wax will burn; ice will not burn.

   (a) What other properties of wax would help distinguish a piece of wax from a piece of ice?

   (b) Actually, ice and wax have many properties in common. For example, they are both solids. Can you find other examples

   of properties they share?

   (c) You can make quantitative observations about the properties of wax that would help distinguish it from ice. What would you suggest?

   (d) Is there a difference between an observation and a property? Explain your reasoning.

5. Write a description of an object as seen through Zed's eyes. Include both quantitative and qualitative observations. Have your classmates guess what you are describing. ❑

Exploration 2: scissors, 3 toothpicks, 3 pieces of aluminum foil (about 5-cm square), ruler, 3-mL measuring spoon, 3 beakers, confectioner's sugar, baking powder, plaster of Paris, water, baking soda, corn starch, vinegar, iodine solution (10 drops to 25 mL of water), masking tape, safety goggles
Exploration 3: metric ruler, matches, test-tube clamp, ring stand, Journal, watch or clock with second hand

Teacher's Resource Binder

Graphic Organizer Transparencies 1–2 and 1–3

Science Discovery Videodisc

Disc 2, Image and Activity Bank, 1–3

Time Required

four to five class periods

Teaching Strategies

Exploration 1

Use the science fiction story *A Stranger Has Landed* to set the stage for *Exploration 1*. Discuss with the class how Zed is being scientific. *(by observing)* Have students complete this Exploration in groups of three or four. Caution students to be careful when using an open flame.

Answers to

For Discussion

1. Observations should be classified according to the sense used.
2. Quantitative observations may include:
   - length of flame
   - length of candle
   - length of wick
   - rate of burning
   - the distance away from candle at which heat can still be felt

   Qualitative observations may include:
   - color of candle
   - smell of burning wax
   - the way the flame flickered
3. Quantitative observations may include:
   - 198 cm tall
   - length of journey
   - 6 fingers

   Qualitative observations may include:
   - reds and yellows of flowers
   - green of trees
   - blue sky
   - blue skin
4. **(a)** Properties that help distinguish ice from wax:
   - wax can be scratched easily with your fingernail; ice is harder to scratch
   - wax can burn; ice cannot
   - wax does not melt when placed on your desk; ice does
   - you cannot see through solid wax; you can see through solid ice
   - wax is not cold to the touch; ice is

(Answers continue on next page)

Answers continued

(b) Properties ice and wax have in common:
  - both melt when heated
  - both float on water
  - both break easily
  - both stay solid below 0 °C

(c) Some quantitative properties that would help to distinguish wax from ice:
  - the melting point of each
  - how high each floats in water
  - the hardness of each object (Each could be scratched with different objects to test for hardness.)

(d) Yes, there is a difference. For example, one could observe that a candle is red. This is not a property of wax. Wax could be many other colors as well. A property is a characteristic, such as a melting point or an ability to burn, that all things made of the same material have in common.

5. Encourage class members to write their description as a riddle—keeping the name of their object a secret. Have the class participate in a guessing game to determine what each object is and indicate whether the observations used are qualitative or quantitative.

Exploration 2

In this activity, students will be using observations in a more scientific way to distinguish three mystery powders from each other. Milliliters are used to measure both liquids and powders. Exact quantities are not essential.

After students see the different reaction each powder has with water, point out the following properties that can be used to distinguish the powders:
- Confectioner's sugar dissolves in water.
- Baking powder fizzes in water.
- Plaster of Paris may feel warmer after adding water and will eventually harden.

Answer to

In-Text Question

The way powder reacts with water is the most important property for distinguishing the powders.

Using Observations to Identify Mystery Powders

Three beakers labeled A, B, and C each contain a white powder. One powder is confectioner's sugar, one is baking powder, and one is plaster of Paris.

The following activity will help you determine which is which. But do not try to distinguish them by taste! Scientists never taste unknown substances, because doing so could be dangerous, even deadly.

You Will Need
- 3 toothpicks
- 3 pieces of aluminum foil, each about 5 cm square
- a small measuring spoon with a capacity of about 3 mL

What to Do

1. Bend up the edges of the foil to make 3 shallow dishes, and label them A, B, and C.
2. Put about 3 mL of powder A into dish A, powder B into dish B, and powder C into dish C.
3. Add about 3 mL of water to each dish.
4. Stir each mixture with a toothpick.
5. Observe carefully, and write your observations. Can you tell from these observations which powder is which? If you can, you are using some additional information that you already have about the powders and how they should react. If you can't, ask your teacher for labeled samples of each substance. Repeat the activity, and then try to identify the mystery powders.

What is the most important property that enables you to distinguish the powders from one another?

Extension

You can make this task more challenging by adding more powders to those mentioned above. Two possibilities are baking soda and corn starch. Besides testing each powder with water, try using vinegar and an iodine solution.

Now test a classmate's powers of observation. Prepare a mixture of any two powders. Can he or she name the powders in your mystery mixture?

How does this Exploration tell you about what science is?

Extension

Students should obtain the following results:
- Vinegar causes both the baking soda and the baking powder to bubble.
- Iodine turns both corn starch and baking powder black (indicating that both contain starch).

Hint: When using iodine, prepare a solution of about 10 drops to 25 mL of water. This is a good concentration for doing this activity. (This dilutes the iodine enough so that it will not stain hands and clothes.)

Answer to

In-Text Question

Students might respond that this Exploration helps to explain what science is because it encourages following directions, observing carefully, recording observations, drawing conclusions, repeating experiments, drawing more conclusions, and finally, solving the mystery of the identification of the powders.

Do You See What I See?

Why is it that several people can observe the same event and often not agree on what they saw? Witnesses to crimes or traffic accidents frequently disagree on the details they give to the police. Why is this so? One explanation is that witnesses see the event from different angles or perspectives, depending on their position when the event occurred.

Another important reason is simply that most people have not developed the skill of accurate observation. For example, can you make an accurate sketch of the steering wheel of the family car? Do you know the color of the car's upholstery? Just as a baseball player has to develop ball-handling skills and a pianist must work on instrumental and performing skills, developing good observation skills takes time and practice.

Sometimes there are other factors that prevent you from making good observations. Can you always rely on your eyes? Think about this question as you do the first three tests in Exploration 3. The final test will give you an opportunity to compare your observational skill with that of your classmates.

Do You See What I See?

Draw a box on the chalkboard. Inside the box, write this sentence:

Paris
in the
the spring.

Show this to students and then quickly erase it. Ask them to write what they have read. Many people read, "Paris in the spring," rather than "Paris in the the spring." Explain that the very best scientists have a keen sense of observation, and that they observe things that are often missed by others.

Exploration 3

The purpose of this Exploration is to investigate situations in which our observational skills may not be reliable. The need for making quantitative observations is demonstrated as well. Have students work in pairs to do *Tests 1, 2, and 3.* It is suggested that *Test 4* be done as a demonstration.

Answers to

Eyeball Benders

Test 1

In all cases, A and B are of equal length.

Test 2

1. Lines are parallel.
2. Circles in the center are the same size.
3. Segments of the arrow are the same length.

Eyeball Benders

Test 1

Which is longer—A or B? After recording your answers in your Journal, check by using a ruler to measure A and B.

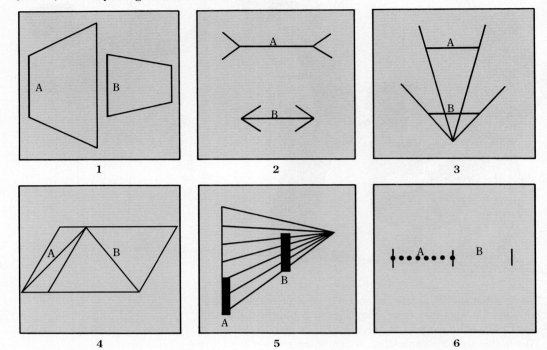

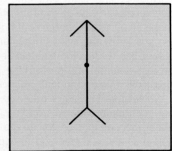

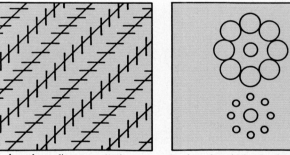

Test 2

1. Are these lines parallel?
2. Are the circles in the centers of the figures the same size?
3. Are the line segments above the dot and below the dot equal?

Test 3 (Just for Fun!)

You have probably seen these optical illusions before. How are they used in drawings? Examine other pictures to discover how artists have used different methods to create the illusion of depth, height, and distance.

The figures below reverse. Gaze steadily at each one to "see" what happens.

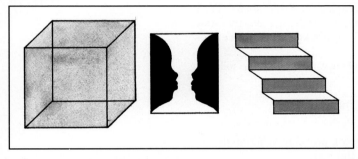

Are these figures below possible? What is wrong with each one?

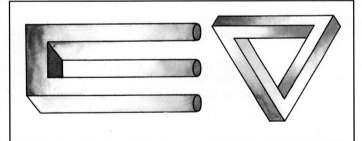

Test 4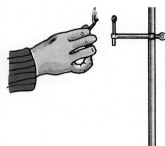

A match is held, head up, in a test tube clamp as shown. Another match is lit and brought near the first one. As the first match bursts into flames, observations begin.

The rules of the exercise are as follows:

1. Everyone makes observations while seated, except for the person who lights the match.
2. Observations begin at the instant the match bursts into flame and end 1 minute after the match goes out.
3. The exercise may be repeated three times.

Make brief notes on your observations. What do you see? hear? smell? How many observations can you make? How many different observations were made by others? Why didn't everyone make the same observations? What observations did the people sitting near the front make that those farther back missed?

✴ *Follow Up*

Assessment

Share the following description of snow with your students, and then ask them to answer the questions that follow.

"Snow—it's cold, white, fluffy, and slippery. If you examine it closely, you may be able to see single snowflakes, each one with six points. Each flake may be only 4 mm across, but billions of them can form a snowdrift. If the temperature goes above 0 °C, the flakes melt. You could be left with a puddle."

- Write three qualitative observations about snow. *(snow is cold; snow is white; snow is fluffy; snow is slippery)*
- Write three quantitative observations. *(snowflakes have six points; snow melts at 0 °C; each flake is about 4 mm across)*
- Suggest three properties of snowflakes. *(snowflakes have six points; snowflakes come in different shapes and sizes, but most are about 4 mm across; snowflakes melt at 0 °C; snowflakes are white)*

Extension

Challenge students to write a science fiction story about what a creature from outer space would observe during its first visit on earth. Their stories should include details of the things the creature sees, feels, hears, tastes, and smells. The creature's observations should be both qualitative and quantitative.

Test 3 (Just for Fun!)

These optical illusions are fun and demonstrate the fact that things are not always what they appear to be. You might explain to students that artists often use perspective to create the illusion of depth on a flat piece of paper. By making something smaller, for example, it appears to be farther away. You may wish to demonstrate other optical illusions. Perhaps students know of other optical illusions, or tricks based on illusions, that they can share with the class.

Test 4

This test should be done as a teacher demonstration. Collect observations from those at the front of the room (near the demonstration) and from those farther away. Those closest to the demonstration should be better able to observe the many colors in the flame, the smell of the burning match, and the sound of the match bursting into flame.

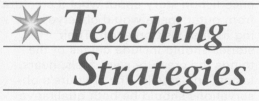

Getting Started

Making sense of your surroundings involves observing and then making explanations or inferences. This lesson begins by encouraging students to discern the difference between observations and inferences. These skills are reinforced by examining common sayings and through activities in which students make observations and offer explanations (inferences) for these observations. This lesson also introduces the concept of a scientific attitude.

Main Ideas

1. Making inferences is a way of making sense of what we observe.
2. Investigative questions often lead to solutions.
3. Being scientific implies having a scientific attitude.

Teaching Strategies

You might want to point out to students that there are subtle shades of difference between the use of the terms *to infer* and *to conclude*. *To infer* usually implies theorizing or predicting from what may be incomplete evidence. *To conclude* implies an inference that is the final, logical result in the process of reasoning, after the facts are observed. In a scientific experiment, an inference could be considered an initial explanation based on available evidence. A conclusion is made after the experiment is completed, and the results have been carefully observed and evaluated. *(Answers to In-Text Questions follow on next page)*

---

4 ## From Observations to Conclusions

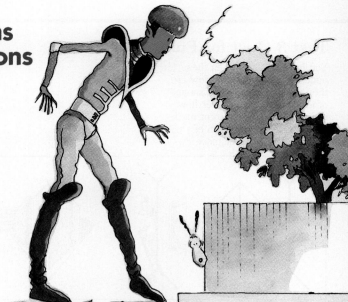

Zed approached the object with caution. What on Earth could it be? Whatever it was, there it sat by the edge of the road— taller than it was wide, and circular, with bumps on it. By standing next to it, Zed estimated the object to be 5 zks high (60 cm, in metric). "Nice colors," Zed thought, "red and silver. Perhaps it's a piece of art. Or maybe it's for sitting on—although it doesn't look very comfortable!"

Can you guess what Zed saw? Here's another clue: You wouldn't want to park a car in front of one.

The description you just read includes six observations. Try to identify them. Which one is quantitative? There are also two statements that are not observations. They are known as **inferences**. Try to identify them.

How do inferences differ from observations? Use the following examples to help you decide.

Observation	**Inference**
Marie is away today.	Perhaps Marie has the flu.
Erik didn't do as well on this test as he usually does.	Erik probably didn't study for the test.
My flowers grew better at this end of the garden.	The soil must be richer at this end of the garden.

Is each of the inferences the only possible explanation for the observation? Suggest at least three more observations and some possible inferences for each one.

Inferences are not observations; rather, they are statements that attempt to explain or make sense of observations. Now you know that making observations is not the same as *interpreting* them and arriving at conclusions.

LESSON **4** ORGANIZER

Objectives

By the end of the lesson, students should be able to:
1. Distinguish observations from inferences.
2. Classify questions according to whether or not they lead to scientific discoveries.
3. Suggest investigative questions.

Process Skills

observing, inferring, interpreting, drawing conclusions

New Terms

Inference—a statement that attempts to explain or make sense of an observation.
Interpret—to explain the meaning of an observation.

Confusing Observations with Inferences

What we see is often determined by what we expect to see. For example, suppose you hear behind you the roar of an engine and the squeal of tires. What do you expect to see when you look around? A hot rod? A police car? An accident? Unless you turn around and look carefully, you may never really know whether your expectations are correct.

Scientists too have expectations of what will happen in their experiments. But expectations can result in inaccurate observations if scientists are not trained to make complete and careful observations. Here is a good set of rules to follow when making observations.

1. List what is to be observed.
2. Record the observations made in each experiment at the time they are made.
3. Repeat experiments to check the observations made in each one.
4. Have others repeat the same experiment.

Here are three more inferences.

- Lightning never stikes in the same place twice.
- It seems to rain more on weekends than on weekdays.
- Whenever something can go wrong, it does.

Do you think they are based on careful observations? Try to suggest a few reasons why observations that led to these inferences may be inaccurate. Do you think that accepting these inferences will affect the accuracy of future observations?

Now try to list some more inferences similar to the ones above; that is, list statements that are likely to be based on inaccurate observations. Compare your list with those of others.

Materials

Exploration 4
The Dancing Dime: empty bottle, cold water and sink, dime or plastic disk
Ice Heist: ice cubes, beaker, salt, piece of string, watch or clock with second hand
The Curious Cup: water, drinking glass, paper, bucket or sink
The Reappearing Coin: coin or plastic disk, shallow dish, transparent tape, water

Lights Out! #1: aluminum pie pan, candle, large jar, matches, modeling clay, water, safety goggles
Lights Out! #2: large beaker or jar, candle, matches, modeling clay, 30 mL baking soda, 15 mL vinegar, 1-L container, watch or clock with second hand, safety goggles
Classifying Statements: cork, meter stick

(Organizer continues on next page)

In-Text Questions

The brief reading at the top of page 22 describes a fire hydrant. The six observations are:
- It was situated by the side of the road.
- It was taller than it was wide.
- It was circular.
- It has bumps on it.
- It was 5 zks (60 cm) high. (This observation is quantitative.)
- It was red and silver.
  The three inferences are:
- It's a piece of art.
- It's for sitting on.
- It looks uncomfortable. (If Zed had made this conclusion after sitting on the object, this would be an observation.)

Confusing Observations with Inferences

Ask students if they have ever jumped to conclusions. Ask: Was it because you did not make enough careful observations? Discuss the three inferences on page 23, and the reasons why they are probably incorrect. Some sample reasons follow.
- The inference that lightning never strikes the same place twice is based on poor observations. In fact, people use lightning rods to ensure that it *will* strike in the same place. The expression is used since lightning strikes are rare; it seems as if the unusual occurrence of a lightning strike could not occur more than once.
- It probably seems to rain more on weekends than on weekdays because most people are not in school or at work on weekends, and are outside where they are more aware of the weather.
- Things may seem to go wrong whenever they can because when things go wrong, they disrupt what we are doing. When we are doing something important, interruptions become more obvious to us.

Encourage students to write some of their own incorrect inferences. Sayings, superstitions, and prejudiced beliefs are good examples. When students complete the assignment, have them discuss and compare their lists with each other.

Exploration 4

This series of activities could be set up at six different work stations around the room. Divide the class into groups, and let each group spend a specified amount of time at each station. For more dramatic results in *The Dancing Dime* activity, a circular disc, cut from a plastic lid, or a Canadian dime can be used. Caution students to be careful around the flame in the *Lights Out!* activities.

The purpose of this Exploration is not to arrive at the correct inference or conclusion, but for students to attempt to make inferences. Accept all answers if they are genuine attempts at an explanation. Be careful that students do not provide the same observation twice by simply using different words. The correct inferences for each observation follow.

The Dancing Dime
Observation: The coin bounces on top of the bottle.

Inference: The hand warms the bottle and the air inside it. The air expands and, as it escapes, causes the coin to move.

Ice Heist
Observation: When the string is pulled up, the ice cubes are attached to it.

Inference: The salt causes the ice to melt. The water then refreezes, thus freezing the string to the ice.

The Curious Cup
Observation: When the glass is turned upside down, the water stays in the glass.

Inference: Air pressure on the outside of the glass holds the paper in place and holds the water in the glass.

The Reappearing Coin
Observation: As water is poured into the dish, the coin becomes visible.

Inference: Light entering and leaving the water is bent (refracted), allowing one to "see" the coin again.

It's Your Turn to Be Scientific

By now you should be an expert on making observations and inferences. In the following activities you will observe some unusual things. For each activity, record two or three observations and at least one inference. For each activity, make a table like the one below. Do not write in the book.

Activity	Observations	Inferences
The Dancing Dime		

The Dancing Dime

Fill an empty bottle with cold water. After a minute, pour out half of the water. Quickly put a dime on top of the bottle. Then, carefully pick up the bottle in both hands, holding it tightly. Observe what happens to the dime. Make an inference to explain your observations.

Ice Heist

Drop the end of a string into a beaker half-filled with ice cubes. Sprinkle some salt onto the ice cubes and wait 30 seconds. Pull on the string. What happens? Make an inference to explain your observations.

The Curious Cup

Fill a glass completely with water. Place a piece of paper that is slightly larger than the mouth of the glass over the mouth. Holding the paper in place, turn the glass upside down over a container, then remove your hand. What do you observe? What can you infer?

The Reappearing Coin

Tape a coin (using transparent tape) to the bottom of a shallow dish such as a margarine container. Place the container on the table. Now move backwards just far enough that you cannot see the coin over the rim of the dish. Have a friend pour water into the dish. What do you observe? What inferences can you make about your observations?

(Organizer continued)

Teacher's Resource Binder

Resource Worksheet 1–3
Graphic Organizer Transparency 1–4

Science Discovery Videodisc

Disc 2, Image and Activity Bank, 1–4

Time Required

four class periods

Lights Out! #1

Stand a candle in an aluminum pie plate or a Petri dish, using modeling clay. Fill the plate half full with water. Light the candle, then quickly place an empty jar over the flame. What do you observe? What can you infer?

Lights Out! #2

This time, place a candle in a large beaker or jar and light it. Add 30 mL of baking soda to a 1-L container. Pour in 15 mL of vinegar. Wait 1 minute. Hold the container almost horizontally over the candle. What happens? What can you infer?

Follow-up

1. Combine your observations and inferences with those of your classmates to make a class chart like the following for the six activities you just did. Place a check mark (√) beside the best inference. Do not write in the book.

Activity	Observations Made by the Class	Inferences Made by the Class
The Dancing Dime		
Ice Heist		
The Curious Cup		
The Reappearing Coin		
Lights Out! #1		
Lights Out! #2		

2. Inferences often raise new questions and suggest more experiments. Consider the activity "The Curious Cup." What new questions might be raised by it? What experiments might you try to answer these questions?

3. "Inferences are not necessarily true." Do you agree or disagree with this statement? Use the activities in this Exploration to support your answer.

4. What do you consider to be the value of making inferences?

Lights Out! #1

Observation: Bubbles may be seen escaping from the jar. When the flame is extinguished, the water level rises in the jar.

Inference: The heat from the candle expands the air, and some air escapes, causing bubbles. When the flame is extinguished, the air in the jar cools. The cooling air contracts, allowing water to enter the jar.

Lights Out! #2

Observation: When the air in the 1-L container is "poured" over the candle, the flame is extinguished.

Inference: The gas produced in the container (carbon dioxide) is heavier (denser) than air. It flows into the jar with the candle, extinguishing the flame.

Answers to
Follow-Up

1. Student responses will vary and selection of the best inference will depend upon class opinion.
2. New questions could include:
   - Will the experiment work if the glass is half full?
   - How long will the paper remain on the glass?
   - How large a glass can I use?
   - What would happen if cardboard was used instead of paper?

   New experiments:
   - Have students set up the equipment to find answers to these new questions.
3. Have students use the table they completed for question 1 to search for inferences that they feel are not true.
4. Making inferences helps us to make sense of what we observe. New questions and experiments are often suggested by an inference.

Investigative Questions

Choose one of the activities from *Exploration 4,* and have each student write a question about it. Record the questions on the chalkboard. Then have students read the section entitled *Investigative Questions.* When students are finished reading, have them classify the questions that are on the chalkboard as similar to either *Set 1* or *Set 2,* as shown on page 26.

Answer to caption: The viewer does not have a scientific attitude because she is simply accepting information given to her. If she had a scientific attitude, then she would make her own observations to base her inferences on.

Investigative Questions

Think back to the questions that you and others have asked and the statements you made while doing the activities in Exploration 4. Were any of them like these?

Set 1

- Why don't we try . . . ?
- What happens if you . . . ?
- Why doesn't it . . . ?
- Perhaps the reason it does that is . . .

Questions and statements like these lead to scientific investigations and discoveries. But not all questions and statements are investigative. Perhaps you have heard questions or made statements such as the following.

Set 2

- Who cares if . . . ?
- If you say so, I guess it's true . . .
- Nobody will ever understand that!
- I heard it on TV, so it must be right.
- You know, it just happens that way.

Does this television viewer have a scientific attitude?

Questions and statements like those in Set 1 help when searching for answers. They suggest activities such as these:

- Learning more about something
- Finding a reason or an explanation
- Repeating an experiment
- Collecting further observations
- Trying something else

Asking questions is part of being scientific. *Why . . .? How . . .? What if . . .? When . . . ? Will it ever happen again?* Such questions guide scientists as they seek answers to scientific problems. Do you think the questions and statements in Set 2 would help in your search for answers? Why or why not?

Classifying Statements

1. State whether or not each of the following statements or questions shows that the speaker is being scientific. (Remember that investigative questions or scientific statements ask about things, try to explain things, or suggest other experiments to try.)

   (a) That's impossible!

   (b) Would you show me that again?

   (c) Do you expect me to believe that?

   (d) How should I know?

   (e) Could we try it a different way?

   (f) What would happen if we dropped it from a greater height?

   (g) What was supposed to happen?

   (h) I don't think it would work with cold water.

2. Write three questions or statements that show an unscientific attitude. Refer to one or more of the activities in Exploration 4 for help with this task.

3. Now write three questions or statements that show a scientific attitude, again referring to Exploration 4.

4. If you drop a cork from a certain height, it will almost always come to rest on its end. Try it. What is the height at which this happens? Now write another investigative question about this experiment.

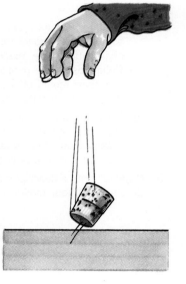

Assessment

1. Show a picture, photograph, or slide to the class. Have students make a list of observations about the picture.

2. Place a couple of raisins in a glass of club soda. Have students observe the raisins rising and falling. Ask them to list some observations, inferences, and scientific questions based on the demonstration. *(Observations might include: bubbles collecting on raisins, raisins rising to the surface, bubbles escaping from raisins, and raisins sinking. Inferences could include: the carbon dioxide bubbles are collecting on the surface of the raisins, which makes them float until the bubbles escape. Scientific questions might begin: "What would happen if . . ." or "Let's try . . .")*

Extension

To demonstrate that observations can often be biased by what we expect to see, try the following experiment. Have a student run toward a target on the floor while holding a ball. Have the student let the ball drop straight down so that it falls and hits the target on the floor. Ask other students to observe the direction the ball falls relative to the floor, backward or forward. *(Most will observe the ball falling backward, since this is what they expect to see. Actually, the ball falls forward relative to the floor, due to the forward momentum it has when it is dropped.)*

Answers to

Classifying Statements

Have students work in small groups to answer the questions.

1. Items *(b)*, *(e)*, *(f)*, and *(h)* indicate a scientific attitude.

2. Answers may vary, but possible responses might include: "It's magic!" "It's a trick!" "Who cares?" "The teacher will explain it to us." "I don't know enough to explain why this happens." "That's a stupid explanation."

3. Answers may vary, but possible responses might include: "What would happen if . . ." "Why do you think . . ." "Let's try . . ."

   Allow time for students to discuss the merits of their suggestions.

4. The height depends on the size of the cork.

   Other investigative questions:

   - What if I held it this way when I dropped it?
   - Does it depend on the surface on which it is dropped?
   - What happens if I use a smaller cork?
   - Does it land more often on its large end?

Is There a Gremlin in the Drink Machine?

What would you think if you were asked this question? Ms. Garcia's class was equally puzzled. Let's listen in on her interpretation of how a drink machine works.

This is what I think happens when you drop your money into the machine. A gremlin grabs the money, counts it, then drops it into a tin box. If there is not enough money, the gremlin keeps it. If there is too much, the gremlin makes change, then pushes out the change through a slot in the wall of the machine. There are a number of paths the gremlin can follow, each one blocked by a gate. When you make your selection, a gate is lifted, the gremlin scurries along the path, grabs a bottle, and throws it down the chute. And what if the gremlin falls asleep on the job? Then a sign automatically appears on the outside of the machine saying "OUT OF ORDER," and no more money will enter the gremlin's tin box.

The Gremlin Model

Ms. Garcia's explanation takes into account many observations and inferences about the operation of a drink machine. In science, such an explanation is called a **model**. A model is a picture or representation of the real thing, and it is supported by observations and inferences.

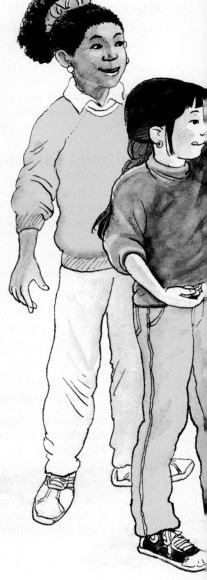

1. Make a list of the observations and inferences that support Ms. Garcia's model, using a table with the headings "Observation" and "Inference (Suggested by Observation)."

   Suggest an observation that does not support the gremlin model.

2. (a) Models help us make sense of what we observe. But sometimes a model may prove to be incorrect as more observations are made. For example, at the time of Columbus, some people thought the earth was flat. This was their model of the earth. What observations do you think supported this model?

   (b) There are people today who still claim that the earth is flat. They belong to the Flat Earth Society. Would you join this organization? What would you say to convince a member of the Flat Earth Society that the earth is really spherical?

3. Draw or write a description of *your* model of a drink machine. Be sure that your model is supported by observations.

LESSON 5

✳ Getting Started

In this lesson, students discover that a model includes many observations and inferences.

Main Ideas

1. Models are representations of the real thing.
2. Models are useful because they help us to understand and investigate the real thing.

✳ Teaching Strategies

Working in small groups, have students read Ms. Garcia's model and make a list of the inferences made, and the observations that must have led to these inferences.

Answers to

The Gremlin Model

1. **Observation/Inference (Suggested by Observation):**
   - Money put into machine/Gremlin takes the money
   - Change returns/Gremlin makes change
   - Sound of coins on metal/Gremlin drops the money in a tin box
   - You make a selection/Gate is lifted to allow gremlin up the path
   - A few seconds elapse/Gremlin is scurrying up the path
   - Sound of bottle or can of drink rolling/Gremlin throws the drink down the chute
   - You receive your drink or an "empty" sign appears/Gremlin is ready to receive more money

(Answers continue on next page)

LESSON 5 ORGANIZER

Objectives

By the end of the lesson, students should be able to:
1. Discuss the meaning of a model.
2. Create a model that can explain the operation of a machine.

Process Skills

observing, inferring, using a model, making a model

New Terms

Model—a picture or representation of the real thing, supported by observations and inferences. It is often used to help visualize something that cannot be directly observed.

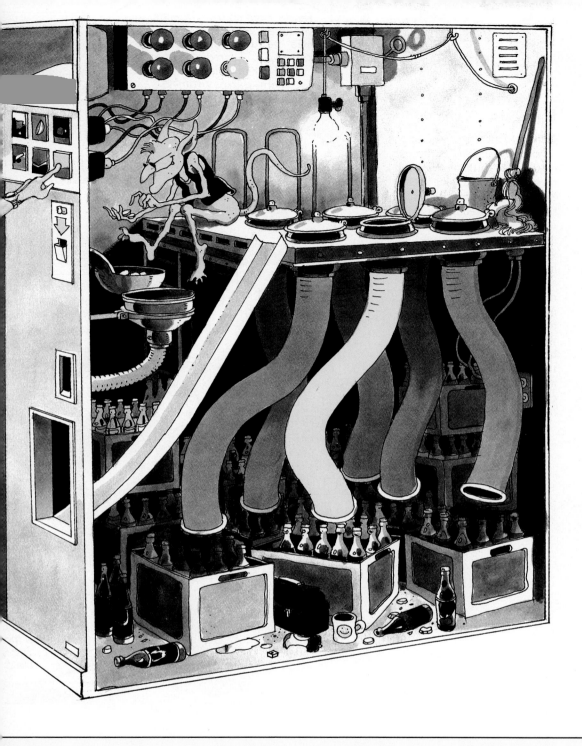

Observations that do not support the Gremlin Model:
- No sound of scurrying feet.
- No one is ever observed feeding the gremlin.
- When door of machine is open, no gremlin is seen.

2. **(a)** Those who believed in a flat earth probably based their belief on the observation that the earth appears flat when standing on its surface. If the earth were not flat, they reasoned, you would end up upside down if you walked far enough.

   (b) Perhaps you could point out how a ship slowly disappears over the horizon, or exhibit a photograph of the earth taken from space.

3. Have students create their own model to explain how a drink machine works. They might begin by listing all of the observations that they can about the machine.

✳ *Follow Up*

Assessment

Ask students to construct a model of the sun and the earth that makes it easier to understand why there is night and day. Have balls and flashlights available for students to use. *(Possible answer: The flashlight (the sun) could be held so that it shines on the ball (the earth), which could be turned to show how a particular location is sometimes lit by the flashlight and at other times is in shadow.)*

Extension

Have students research the models of the solar system that were accepted before and after the time of Copernicus.

Materials

Time Required

one class period

Getting Started

This lesson introduces students to the scientific methods of predicting, conducting fair tests, controlling variables, and creating hypotheses. By means of a story, students begin thinking about and discussing these concepts, and then proceed to devise their own hypotheses and experiments.

Main Ideas

1. A fair test is a controlled experiment in which all variables are controlled (or kept constant), except the one being investigated.
2. Variables are factors in an experiment that can influence the outcome of the experiment.
3. A hypothesis is a possible explanation for an observable event. It is a statement that can be tested by simple observation or by a controlled experiment.
4. A hypothesis includes the variable that changes and the expected outcome of changing this variable.

Teaching Strategies

A Tale of Two Kittens

This story is about two students who are being scientific by designing an experiment to prove a point. It provides an excellent opportunity to look again at the nature of science and to introduce the concepts of a controlled experiment, a hypothesis, and a variable. Remind students that a hypothesis is a type of inference, as discussed earlier. It is an ''educated guess,'' used to explain an observable event. Have students read the story with this question in mind, ''How are the Quinns being scientific?''

6 Testing Ideas

A Tale of Two Kittens

Jane and Larry Quinn loved cats. Both Jane and Larry even talked to them as though they were people. Jane and Larry also experimented with their cats—not in a way that would harm them, of course—just the opposite! They wanted them to be as healthy as possible. They reasoned that if people often need extra vitamins, then so might cats. Therefore they predicted that added vitamins would improve their cats' health. To test this **prediction,** they created their own mixture of cat food with a special vitamin supplement.

1 People need extra vitamins sometimes, and I bet cats sometimes need extra vitamins, just like people. I predict our cats will be healthier if we give them extra vitamins.

Let's mix vitamins with the cat food. They'll love it!

To test their prediction, the Quinns created a special vitamin supplement which they mixed with the ordinary cat food their cats ate.

3 The Quinns had just received two new kittens. They fed the special food to the Persian, and they fed the food with no extra vitamins to the Siamese cat. When they showed the cats to Wu Feng three months later, he seemed convinced, but only for a moment.

Wait! Your results prove nothing! Even if you hadn't used your supplement, the Persian would have been larger; Siamese cats don't grow as large as other cats

5 These two are almost twins! They're the same size, the same sex, and since they come from the same litter, they're the same age. Even their fur color is the same.

Let's prove we're right this time. We'll give them the same amount of water each day keep them in the same place

LESSON 6 ORGANIZER

Objectives

By the end of the lesson, students should be able to:

1. Write a hypothesis that can be investigated.
2. Identify the cause and effect in a hypothesis.
3. Identify the variables that must be controlled in order to conduct a fair test (controlled experiment).

Process Skills

hypothesizing, identifying variables, predicting, controlling variables

New Terms

Controlled experiment—an experiment in which all variables but one are kept constant. Also called a *fair test.*

Look at how big and healthy our cats are, Wu Feng. This vitamin supplement really works

But how do you know? Your cats might have grown just as well with ordinary cat food.

Oh, no! He's right! We can't tell how the cats might have compared without the supplement.

Let's try again. Mrs. Simpson's cat had a litter a month or so ago.

Let's go and see if there are two left.

Larry and Jane stuck to their procedure and recorded the mass of each kitten every week. Jane even took pictures to record the experiment.

WOW!

... This time I'm convinced! Kitten A looks better and feels heavier. You two even have figures to support your hypothesis! Your special vitamin supplement really works.

We were sure it worked!

The Moral of the Tale

1. How did the Quinns demonstrate the traits of a good scientist?

2. What mistakes did they make at first? How did they avoid them later?

3. Jane and Larry conducted a **controlled experiment.** What do you think this means? What is being controlled in a controlled experiment?

4. Could their experiment be repeated? Why is it important for an experiment to be repeatable?

5. In the Quinns' experiment, a number of factors were kept the same, or *controlled*, in order to keep the experiment fair and reliable. Such factors are called **variables.** Which variables did the Quinns control?

6. Toward the end of the tale, it was said that the Quinns had the figures to support their hypothesis. What does the term **hypothesis** mean?

Variable—a factor that can affect the outcome of an experiment.
Hypothesis—an explanation for an observable event.
Prediction—the expected outcome of a future event. Predictions can be made based on a hypothesis.

Materials
none

Science Discovery Videodisc
Disc 2, Image and Activity Bank, 1–6

Time Required
two to three class periods

The Moral of the Tale

1. The Quinns share many traits with scientists:
   - They are observant.
   - They are curious.
   - They experiment.
   - They collect and record data.
   - They try not to jump to conclusions.
   - They draw conclusions based on a controlled experiment.
   - They have a scientific attitude.

2. Initially, they jumped to conclusions. They expected the vitamin supplement to improve their cats' health. Since their cats were healthy, they inferred that the supplement was responsible. In their first experiment, they did not control all the variables. They failed to compare cats who received no vitamins with those that did. In their second attempt, they had more than one changing variable because they compared two different kinds of cats. Also, the cats may not have received the same amounts of food. The story does not say whether the Quinns were careful on this point. In their third experiment, they successfully controlled all the variables but one.

3. A controlled experiment is one in which only one variable—the one being tested—changes. In this case, the variable that changed was a vitamin. The amount of food, water, exercise, and the kind of cat used were controlled.

4. Yes, their experiment could be repeated. It is important for an experiment to be repeatable because that means the experiment was originally performed correctly.

5. The controlled variables were: the kind of cat used; the amounts of food and water; similar living conditions; the amount of exercise; the age of the cats.

6. A hypothesis is a statement that answers a question about nature. The question here might be "What makes a kitten grow to be healthier and larger?" Their answer, or hypothesis, was that vitamins make kittens grow larger and healthier. They then tested this hypothesis with a controlled experiment.

Science Snapshot

Lewis H. Latimer (1848–1928)

Collaboration in Discovery

Few inventions are perfect when they are first made. For example, Thomas Edison's first light bulbs did not last very long because their carbon filaments were quite fragile. This problem was tackled by Lewis H. Latimer, a black engineer and draftsman. His experiments resulted in major improvements in the ways the carbon filaments were manufactured and connected. The Latimer lamp was widely used for some time.

Latimer also played an important role in the development of the electric industry. He supervised the installation of electric lights for the cities of New York, Philadelphia, and London, England. He wrote the first textbook on electrical lighting systems. His published writing, which ranges from patent applications to poetry, is refined and precise.

Lewis Latimer was the son of George Latimer, a slave who escaped from Virginia and fled to Boston in the 1830s. Famous abolitionists such as William Lloyd Garrison and Frederick Douglass supported George Latimer's fight for freedom. Four hundred dollars were raised to purchase his freedom from his owner who had come to Boston looking for him.

Research Topic

Lewis Latimer had very little formal education. And yet, because of his strong determination, he became an extremely well educated man. Find out more about Latimer and write a paper on his life and accomplishments.

Hypothesis—A Link Between Cause and Effect

Mr. Kumar gave his class the following task.

1. Write an investigative question.
2. Suggest a hypothesis for the question.
3. List the variables that should be controlled in order to test the hypothesis.

Here is what Don's group did in response to this task.

Investigative Question

What affects plant growth?

Hypothesis

Using more fertilizer makes plants bigger.

Controlled Variables:

- Use the same type of plant.
- Start with the same size of plant.
- Use the same kind of soil.
- Give all plants the same amount of sunlight.
- Give all plants the same amount of water.

Now Answer These

1. Identify the *cause* and the *effect* in the hypothesis of Don's group.
2. Is this the only hypothesis they could have stated? If not, write another one, making certain that it includes a cause and an effect.
3. For your hypothesis, what variable(s) should be controlled in order to make this a fair test?
4. Jenna's group suggested this hypothesis for another investigative question: "Brand X soap powder removes stains better than Brand Y."
   (a) Does their hypothesis have a cause and an effect?
   (b) What could have been their investigative question(s)?
   (c) What variable(s) would you control in order to test their hypothesis?
5. What is your definition of "hypothesis"?
6. Now it's your turn! In small groups, suggest
   (a) an investigative question;
   (b) a possible hypothesis;
   (c) variables that should be controlled.

3. Any factors that can affect the outcome of the experiment are the variables that need to be controlled.
4. (a) Yes. Cause: different brands of soap; effect: amount of stains removed.
   (b) Answers may vary, but possible responses include:
   - Do all soap powders remove stains equally well?
   - What affects the ability to remove stains?
   (c) Variables to control:
   - Temperature of water
   - Kind of stain
   - Size of stain
   - Amount of water
   - Amount cloth is shaken while in the water
   - Amount of soap powder used
5. A hypothesis is a testable statement that explains the relationship between a cause and an effect.
6. Answers will vary.

Follow Up

Assessment

Michael made some lemonade using this recipe:
- 2 L ice water
- 2 lemons
- 500 g sugar
- 20 mL carbonated water

Then someone told him that the fizziness depends on the amount of sugar. He decided to test if this was true.

(a) Identify the cause and effect in his hypothesis. *(cause: amount of sugar; effect: more fizziness)*
(b) In testing his hypothesis, what should he change? *(Change the amount of sugar.)*
(c) In testing his hypothesis, what should he not change? *(Don't change the amount or temperature of water, the number of lemons, or the amount of carbonated water.)*

Extension

Have students think of a practical problem they would like to solve. For example, they may wish they could find out what dish soap cuts grease the best or what laundry detergent removes stains the best. Ask them to design a controlled experiment to solve the problem. If possible, have them carry out their experiments.

Hypothesis—A Link Between Cause and Effect

After discussing the task Mr. Kumar gave to his class, place students in small groups to respond to questions 1 to 6. After a certain amount of time, gather the class back together to share and to clarify their ideas.

Answers to

Now Answer These

1. Cause—using more fertilizer; effect—plants grow larger.
2. Several examples of hypotheses are:
   - Garden soil will produce bigger plants than field soil.
   - Less sunlight will produce plants with smaller stems.
   - Too much water will produce small plants.
   (Note: each of these can be written to express the opposite effect.)

Answers to

Challenge Your Thinking

1. **(a)** Probably not because her measurements are not precise and therefore are difficult to replicate exactly. For example, her "handful" and someone else's would probably be different.

   (b) Both are quantitative, but Grandma's measurements are based on one of her handfuls, rather than a known unit of measure. To make her measurements more accurate, you could measure, metrically, the amount that her hand can hold. Then it is more likely that her results could be replicated.

2. Answers will vary. If students have difficulty deciding who is being described, discuss with the class what is lacking in the traits given. For example, qualitative traits often cannot be measured, and therefore may vary according to who is making the observation.

3. Answers will vary, but should stress that being scientific means doing what scientists do: observing, inferring, measuring, devising experiments, and gaining new knowledge.

1. Read the two recipes below for making a blueberry pie, then answer these questions:

   (a) If you follow Grandma's recipe, will your pie taste the same as hers? Explain.

   (b) Are Grandma's recipe and the cookbook recipe qualitative or quantitative? Explain.

Grandma's Recipe

SIMPLY MIX THREE HANDFULS OF BERRIES WITH TWO HANDFULS OF SUGAR, A HANDFUL OF FLOUR AND A PINCH OF SALT.

Cookbook Recipe

Line a 23-cm pie plate with pie crust.

Combine in a mixing bowl:
200 mL sugar
 60 mL flour
  6 mL tapioca
 25 mL lemon juice

Stir mixture gently into 950 mL fresh blueberries. Pour mixture into pie crust and dot with 15 mL butter.

2. On an index card, make a table with the following headings: Quantitative Trait and Qualitative Trait. Use this table to describe yourself. Choose one person to read the cards (but not the names) aloud to the class, so that other students can try to guess who is being described. The best description wins!

3. On page 4 this statement is made: "This unit is about how *you* become a scientist each and every day." Do you feel it is true? Support your position with examples.

7 From Hypothesis to Experiment

Being scientific involves observing, measuring, inferring, hypothesizing, classifying, and more! Being scientific involves doing experiments in order to answer questions and test hypotheses. Throughout this book, you will be asked to be scientific by designing experiments. Here's the place to start. Join Alexander's group as they discuss a problem.

What determines how long it takes for objects to fall through water?

Well, here is our set-up—one tall container of water and a stop watch.

I think objects of greater mass will sink faster.

It may depend on the shape of the object.

And on what the object is made of—or even on the temperature of the water.

The group decides to try Ralph's hypothesis; they will test whether mass affects how fast an object sinks.

In groups of three, examine the plan made by this group of students, which you will find on the next page. Decide whether it is a good plan. Is the test they designed a fair one—that is, a controlled experiment? What are the variables being controlled? Are the results reliable? Can they be repeated?

LESSON 7

✳ Getting Started

In this lesson, students follow the development of an experiment from forming the initial hypothesis, to designing an experiment, to gathering data, and finally, to drawing conclusions. The lesson concludes with several highly motivating investigations.

Main Ideas

1. A fair test is an experiment in which all variables are controlled, except the one being investigated.
2. Variables are factors in an experiment that can influence the outcome of the experiment.
3. A hypothesis is a statement that is being investigated. The statement includes the variable that is changed and the expected outcome of changing this variable.

LESSON 7 ORGANIZER

Objectives

By the end of the lesson, students should be able to:
1. Design an experiment to test a hypothesis.
2. Perform an experiment according to a suggested format.

Process Skills

designing experiments, controlling variables, gathering data, interpreting data

New Terms

(Organizer continues on next page)

✳ *Teaching Strategies*

Investigating Objects Falling Through Water

This reading presents an actual experimental design for students to observe how a hypothesis, a plan, a data table, a graph, and conclusions are used. Students should use this as a model to follow when designing their own experiments. This lesson is set up as a discussion task. Ask students to discuss the hypothesis, the experimental plan (including variables tested, variables controlled, and measurements made), the results, and the conclusions.

Answers to

In-Text Questions

Hypothesis

Heavier objects fall faster through a liquid than lighter objects. Mass is the variable mentioned in the hypothesis that will be changed in the experiment.

Our Plan

Variables being controlled are:
- height of liquid (45 cm)
- kind of liquid (water)
- volume and shape of the balls
  Measurements being made are:
- height from which the balls fall
- mass of each ball
- time it takes to fall 45 cm

Our Results

Doing more than one trial is good scientific technique. It verifies results, shows that results can be repeated, and allows results to be averaged to obtain the "best" answer. The fact that the results can be repeated is illustrated by the four trials.

A graph is a "picture" of the results. It is easier to see relationships, and a graph can be used to make predictions for values of mass not measured in the experiment.

(Answers continue on next page)

Investigating Objects Falling Through Water

Hypothesis

Objects of greater mass fall through a liquid faster than objects of lesser mass.

Our Plan

For the test to be fair, we made sure that all of the objects to be dropped were of the same volume, but of different mass. To do this, we covered a ball bearing and a marble in enough modeling clay to make them the same size. Then we made a third ball having the same volume from modeling clay alone. This meant that all the objects had the same kind of surface.

We measured the time it took for each object to fall through 45 cm of water.

Which variable mentioned in the hypothesis is changed in the experiment?

What variables are controlled?

Our Results

Time Required for Balls of Different Masses to Fall Through 45 cm of Water

	Ball 1 (26.6 g)	Ball 2 (41.1 g)	Ball 3 (79.0 g)
Trial 1	1.0 s	0.6 s	0.2 s
Trial 2	1.2 s	0.5 s	0.2 s
Trial 3	0.8 s	0.7 s	0.2 s
Trial 4	1.0 s	0.6 s	0.2 s
Average	1.0 s	0.6 s	0.2 s

Why did they do more than one trial? Can their results be repeated?

(Organizer continued)

Materials

Exploration 5: paper, paper clips, scissors, metric ruler
Exploration 6: meter sticks, chairs, modeling clay

Teacher's Resource Binder

Resource Worksheet 1–4
Graphic Organizer Transparency 1–5

Science Discovery Videodisc

Disc 2, Image and Activity Bank, 1–7

Time Required

five to six class periods

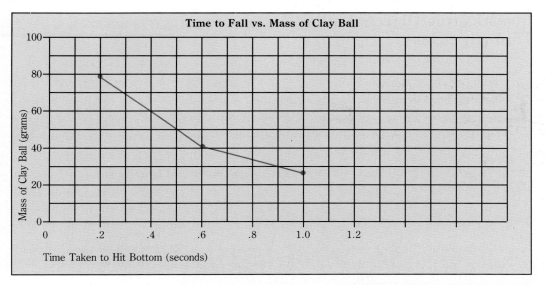

Time to Fall vs. Mass of Clay Ball

Mass of Clay Ball (grams) (y-axis: 0, 20, 40, 60, 80, 100)

Time Taken to Hit Bottom (seconds) (x-axis: 0, .2, .4, .6, .8, 1.0, 1.2)

Conclusion

Our data show that our hypothesis is correct. Perhaps the heavier object was able to overcome the resistance of the water better.

Now it's your turn to design an experiment investigating this problem. Think back to the discussion among the members of Alexander's group. They mentioned several variables that could affect the speed of objects falling through a liquid. Mass was the variable that Alexander's group investigated. Divide into groups and choose another variable to investigate. In doing so, follow these steps:

- State a hypothesis.
- Design an experiment.
- Collect observations and data.
- Summarize your findings by drawing a conclusion.

Following the experiment, compare your results with those of another group that investigated the same variable. Did each group conduct a fair test? Did each group arrive at the same conclusion?

What information does a graph provide that a data table does not?

Do their data support their conclusion? What inference was made?

Answers continued

Conclusion

As it turned out, the result does support the original hypothesis as stated. The more massive clay ball fell faster. The inference made is that the heavier object was better able to overcome the resistance of the water. Other possible hypotheses to investigate:

1. The rate of fall of an object will differ in different liquids. (Large graduated cylinders and liquids such as glycerine, water, and cooking oil can be used. Marbles may be used as the objects.)
2. The rate of fall depends on the shape of the object. (Portions of modeling clay of the same mass can be shaped and used.)
3. The rate of fall increases with the temperature of the liquid.
4. The rate of fall will decrease with an increase in the volume of the object. (To set up this experiment, use balls of the same mass but of different volume, such as a marble covered with clay and a clay ball of the same mass.)

Allow time for students to share the results from their experiments. Encourage discussion of the last two questions found at the bottom of page 37.

Investigating Objects Falling Through a Gas

This activity can be completed in groups of four to five students. The only materials needed are balls that have the same volume, but different mass. The heavier ball can be made by folding clay around an object like a large ball bearing or a marble. Mold another ball of the same size out of clay. By dropping these balls from the same height at the same time, students should be able to see that they hit the floor simultaneously. This observation disproves the hypothesis. Point out to students that there is some slight difference due to air resistance (similar to the water resistance of the previous experiment). However, the difference is so slight, it is difficult to detect.

Answers to

Exploration 5

3. Some variables that could affect its motion: height from which it is dropped, room temperature, size of paper clip, and weight of paper.

4. Changing the above variables could create new hypotheses.

Answer to caption: The hammer will probably win the race because the heavier mass can overcome air resistance better than the lighter mass.

Investigating Objects Falling Through a Gas

In many ways, liquids are similar to gases.

- Both have mass and volume.
- Both will flow. (Remember pouring a gas in the last activity of Exploration 4?)
- Objects can fall through both. (This led Sheila to wonder whether objects fall through air at different speeds.)

Now, using the materials employed by Alexander's group, investigate this hypothesis:

Heavier objects fall through air faster than lighter objects.

THE GREAT VERTICAL RACE
FEATHER VS. HAMMER
FINISH

Air and the "Paper Thing"

A "paper thing" (P.T.) is an interesting tool for investigating how certain types of objects fall through air.

What to Do

1. Make a P.T., as shown in the diagram on the next page.
2. Drop your P.T. and observe its motion.
3. List all the variables you can think of that could affect its motion.
4. On a piece of paper, write one hypothesis about how you could change the way in which the P.T. falls. Exchange your hypothesis with another group.
5. Design and then try an experiment to gather evidence that either supports or disproves the hypothesis that you received from the other group.
6. Share your plan and results with the group that gave you the hypothesis.

Which object will win? Why?

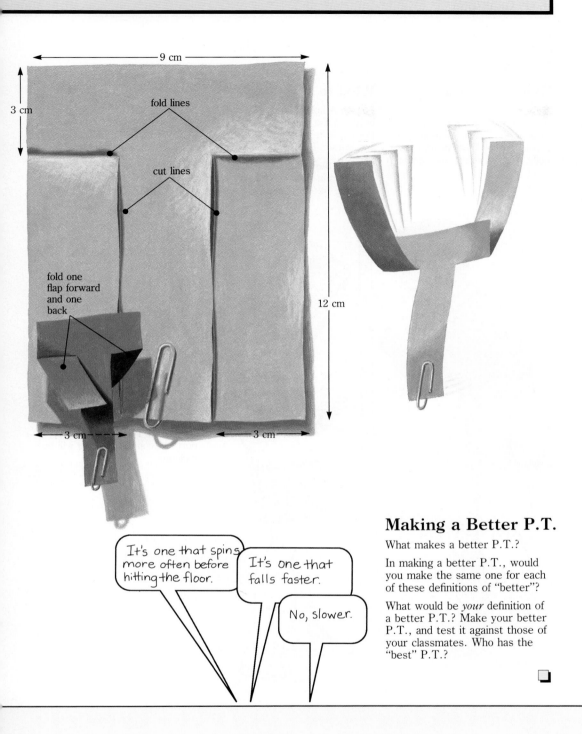

Students might try changing the weight of the piece of paper used to make the P.T., the size or shape of the P.T., or they may create an entirely new design. A smaller P.T. will fall faster and spin faster. Putting a larger paper clip on the P.T. will also make it fall and spin faster. A larger P.T. may not spin at all, but simply drop to the floor.

Making a Better P.T.

What makes a better P.T.?

In making a better P.T., would you make the same one for each of these definitions of "better"?

What would be *your* definition of a better P.T.? Make your better P.T., and test it against those of your classmates. Who has the "best" P.T.?

Answers to

Exploration 6

Experiment 1

Divide the class into groups of four or five students for this activity. Be sure to have students record their data and share their results. Some possible rules include:

- Hold your fingers at the same centimeter mark each time.
- Keep your fingers a certain distance from the meter stick.
- Do not make any distracting noises during a trial.
- Give each person a certain number of trials.
- Either average the results or use the best time.

Students may wish to test some other hypotheses, such as:

- Is reaction time better in the morning, after lunch, or in the late afternoon?
- Is reaction time better after vigorous exercise?
- Do people who play video games have a better reaction time than those who do not?
- Does reaction time vary with age?
- Reaction times between the right and left hand can also be compared.

(Answers continue on next page)

Meter Stick Experiments

Experiment 1

In the first part of this experiment, you are going to compare the reaction times of the people in your group. What factors might have an effect on reaction time?

What to Do

Person A holds the meter stick between the fingers of person B. Person A drops the meter stick, and Person B catches it.

How far the meter stick falls before Person B catches it will be a measure of that person's reaction time.

In groups of four or five, devise rules that should be followed in order to make this a fair test. These rules should include your controlled variables. Test the reaction times of the members in your group, using your set of rules.

Exchange your rules with another group. Try their rules. Do you like their rules better? Answer this question by writing how you would improve their set of rules.

Use your new, revised set of rules to test one or more of the following hypotheses:

- Reaction time is slower when the person is seated.
- Girls have a faster reaction time than boys.
- Right-handed people have a faster reaction time than left-handed people.

Be sure to record data to support the conclusions you will be making.

Experiment 2

What to Do

Place a meter stick on top of two fingers, as shown.

Now move your fingers toward the center of the meter stick. Can you move just one finger? Try this again, and carefully observe what happens. Where do your two fingers always end up?

A Problem to Solve

By adding modeling clay to the meter stick, think of a way for your fingers to end up (a) at the 20-cm mark on the meter stick, and (b) at the 40-cm mark on the meter stick. Devise a hypothesis for this experiment. What would be an appropriate conclusion?

Assessment

Share the following story with your students, and ask them for their evaluation.

A boy picks up a rock and sees several sowbugs scurry away under some dead leaves and other stones. He wonders if the sowbugs sense the light and always go toward darkness and away from light, or if they sense the dryness of the air and always go toward moisture and away from dryness. What experiment could he set up to test these hypotheses? *(To test whether sowbugs go toward darkness, he could capture several sowbugs and put them in a box that has a hole to let in light on one side. He could observe whether the sowbugs gather on the light or the dark side of the box. To test whether they go toward moisture, he could cover the hole in the box so that both sides of the box are dark. Then he could wet one side of the box, and again observe whether the sowbugs gather on the moist or dry side of the box.)*

Extension

If your school has a science fair, this would be an opportune time to discuss possible projects. Encourage a science fair project that includes a controlled experiment. (Students should follow the format in this lesson for setting up an experiment. They should not just write a report or make a collection.)

Answers continued

Experiment 2

Students should find that the two fingers always end up at the center of gravity of the meter stick. Both fingers must move toward the center of the meter stick to keep it balanced. If only one finger moves, the meter stick will eventually fall.

A Problem to Solve

Adding clay to one end of the meter stick changes the center of gravity and the position at which the two fingers will end up.

Hypotheses students could devise for this experiment:
- If just the right amount of clay is placed at the 0-cm mark, then your fingers will end up at the 40-cm mark.
- If half as much clay is placed at the 20-cm mark, then your fingers will end up at the 40-cm mark.
- If twice as much clay is placed at the 0-cm mark, then your fingers will end up at the 20-cm mark.

Students should conclude that their observations do or do not support their hypotheses.

✳ *Getting Started*

This lesson defines technology as the use of knowledge and innovation to solve practical problems. Examples of technology are everywhere in the students' environment. Science as the pursuit of knowledge is presented as neither good nor bad, right nor wrong. The use of science (technology) can be perceived, however, as being either good or bad. The students' concept of technology emerges through a discussion task, a reading task, and a research task.

Main Ideas

1. Technology is the use of knowledge and innovation to solve practical problems.
2. Technology plays a vital role in society.

✳ *Teaching Strategies*

Have students read page 42 to discover the meaning of the word *technology*. Discuss with students the importance of making scientific discoveries. *(for greater understanding and knowledge about the natural world; to assist in the development of technology to solve human problems)*

8 Technology—Brainchild of Science

Thousands of years ago, an unknown person made an important observation. Objects without sharp corners (what we call "round") can be moved more easily by being rolled than can objects with corners. This was a very valuable scientific discovery. Wouldn't that early scientist be surprised to see what use is now being made of that observation! There are wheels on almost everything that moves. Rollers and bearings, which are offshoots of the wheel, also make motion easier. The invention of wheels and rollers was a major technological advance that led to even more inventions.

In 1902, Marie Curie made another scientific discovery—a new element, which she called radium. Little did she know that her discovery would someday be used in the treatment of cancer!

In 1987, Ian Shelton noticed a supernova, as you read earlier. His scientific discovery may not lead to any new invention or solve any practical problem faced by humankind, but studying the supernova adds to our knowledge of the universe.

Science is a human activity that involves the pursuit of knowledge about the natural world. The application of knowledge to solve practical problems and to make new inventions is called **technology**.

LESSON 8 ORGANIZER

Objectives

By the end of the lesson, students should be able to:
1. Distinguish between science and technology.
2. Provide examples of technology in everyday life.

Process Skills

reading, analyzing, inventing, researching

New Terms

Technology—the use of scientific knowledge to solve practical problems and to make new inventions.

Now, discuss with a classmate your responses to the following questions. They all involve the idea of technology.

1. What are two technological advances that you have recently heard about? On what scientific discoveries are they based?
2. Does all new knowledge lead to the solving of practical problems—in other words, to new technology? Give examples to support your answer.
3. You might get rich if you were to invent a better mousetrap. But could you build one without science? What would you need to know about the habits and behavior of mice when designing your new mousetrap?
4. Have you solved a practical problem today? Perhaps you opened a can of juice without an opener. If so, you might have used your knowledge about levers and about the strength of metals. Perhaps you helped your parents build a garden shed. A great deal of knowledge and skill is needed to solve this practical problem. Are there any practical problems on which you are working right now? Name them.

The drawing below shows how a basic idea—the wheel—has been refined and readapted for different uses over the centuries. How might the wheel on the right have been used? How might wheels be improved in the future?

Answers to

In-Text Questions

1. Spark discussion by having students name some technological advances. Speculate openly about the scientific basis behind these advances, and then have each student do research outside of class to find out about at least one technological advance.
2. All knowledge does not lead to new inventions, but there is no telling what may happen in the future. When lasers were first studied, little application was envisioned. Now lasers are used:
   - in weapon systems
   - in art
   - to carry messages
   - as a tool in medicine
3. Information about the size of the mouse, what it prefers to eat, its ability to see in the dark, and the places where it likes to stay and build its home would be useful knowledge to have when trying to build a better mousetrap. You could build one without science, but only through trial and error. The use of science would greatly increase your chances of success by helping you understand what makes a better mousetrap.
4. Answers will vary.

Answer to caption: The wheel on the right was designed for use on the lunar rover. Future improvements might involve lighter and more durable materials, and changes in wheel shape and size.

Materials

Teacher's Resource Binder

Activity Worksheet 1–5
Graphic Organizer Transparency 1–6

Science Discovery Videodisc

Disc 2, Image and Activity Bank, 1–8

Time Required

two class periods

Technology That Keeps Us Talking

How often do you use the telephone? If you're like most people you use it nearly every day. You probably know that Alexander Graham Bell invented the telephone, but what else do you know about him? As you read this brief biography, make a list of the inventions that are described. Beside each invention, suggest the practical problem it was intended to solve.

Alexander Graham Bell— Scientist and Inventor

When Alexander Graham Bell was a boy in Scotland in the 1850s, he liked to experiment with sound. For instance, he built a model head, with a movable tongue, that could say "Mama." He could manipulate the throat of his dog, Skye, so that Skye sounded as if he were speaking. This interest in sound was passed on to Bell by his father and grandfather, both of whom were also named Alexander.

By the time he was 23, Bell's two brothers had died of tuberculosis, which was caused partly by the cold, damp Scottish climate. Bell was also showing signs of the disease, so in 1870 the family moved to Canada for the healthier climate. In 1872, Bell moved to the United States and opened a school in Boston for training teachers of deaf people. Bell also taught deaf students himself.

Alexander Graham Bell was interested in many things having to do with sound. For instance, after seeing lines of people waiting to use the telegraph, he invented a method of sending as many as eight signals over the same wire at the same time.

In 1881, when President James Garfield lay mortally wounded, Bell invented a metal detector in the hope of locating the bullet that was lodged in the president's body. But the metal bed springs interfered with the readings, and Garfield died before the bullet could be found.

Another invention was intended to add to Bell's personal comfort. When his room became too hot in the summer, Bell built an air cooling system—the first air conditioner!

However, Bell's major interests continued to be sound and its transmission over long distances. It is fitting that he became best known for inventing the telephone. In doing so, Bell drew from previous inventions and his own knowledge of sound, electricity, and the human ear. His reasoning might have been along these lines:

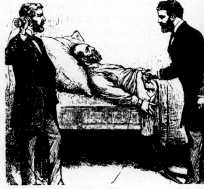

Bell examining President Garfield with his homemade metal detector.

"Sound waves can be turned into an electric current and carried along a wire. The telegraph shows me this."

"The electric current can be turned back into speech with the new receiver I have invented."

"I can use a device similar to an eardrum to pick up sound vibrations. In fact, a recent invention called a phonautograph does precisely that."

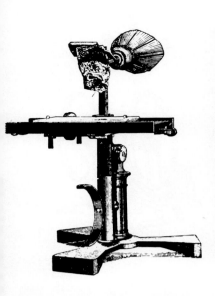

Above, two of Bell's many inventions. At left the phonautograph, a device for recording sound. At right, the photophone, which used light to create a visual record of sound.

The Phone Call Heard 'Round the World

Bell's reasoning worked. In a dramatic moment in 1876, he spoke his first words into his new invention, and the words were heard by his assistant in another part of the house.

Bell became famous and wealthy from the telephone and his other inventions. With the money, he continued to sponsor schools for the deaf and laboratories for hearing research. He died in 1922.

Bell, after making the first telephone call in 1876.

The Phone Call Heard 'Round the World

After students have read pages 44 and 45, ask: How might an inventor, like Bell, think? What kinds of qualities do inventors need? *(They must have active imaginations. They must be able to look at everyday objects in new ways. They must be curious about the world around them and about how and why things work. They must be able to identify problems and want to solve them. They must be able to picture things in their mind's eye, and to visualize the inner workings of gadgets.)*

Be an Inventor!

This activity could be designed as a class competition. Exhibited inventions could be examined for scientific knowledge and evaluated in terms of how well they perform the task for which they were designed.

Here are some guidelines to help students with their inventions:
1. **Identify.** Every successful invention solves a problem or fulfills a need. Think of something you need, or talk to friends and family members about what would make their jobs or their lives easier. What things do you use that you wish worked better?
2. **Brainstorm.** Think of as many ideas as possible for solving the problem or fulfilling the need. Let your imagination run wild.
3. **Research.** Learn everything you can about the subject related to the problem or need. Read books, and talk to people who know about the subject. For example, if you want to invent a new rattrap, you should find out all you can about rats and how and where they cause problems.
4. **Select.** Choose one idea for your invention. Ask yourself if your idea is really original and practical. If possible, use available tools and materials to make the invention.
5. **Evaluate.** Test your invention to see if it solves the problem. Invite potential users to try your invention. Ask for their opinions.

What Makes It Tick?

This activity could be set up as a "show-and-tell" (students make oral reports in front of the class), or as a research project (students turn in written reports).

Be an Inventor!

Julia invented a way to wash those hard-to-reach spots on her bicycle. She used a plastic bottle filled with soapy water. When the bottle was squeezed, the warm, soapy water squirted out and loosened the dirt. This invention solved Julia's problem.

You, too, can be an inventor and dream up an invention for a problem of your own. When you do, share it with your friends. Make a display that includes a written description of your invention. Tell how you constructed it, what it does, what problem it solved, and so on.

What Makes It Tick?

How does an aerosol can work? How does a light bulb work? Who invented these things? What practical problems did these inventions solve? Do research on an invention or a medical discovery, and report your findings to your classmates.

A Final Word

In a way, we are all like Zed, or the Quinns, or Alexander Graham Bell—observing, inferring, testing ideas, trying to make sense of the world.

- Joggers experiment with different running techniques and ways of getting into shape.
- Gardeners experiment with plants that best suit the local soil and climate.
- Musicians experiment with different musical instruments and techniques.
- Pet owners experiment with techniques for maintaining their pets in the best health possible.
- Cooks experiment with different techniques and ingredients to prepare the perfect dish.
- Teachers experiment with new ways to teach.
- Store owners experiment with ways of arranging merchandise to attract more customers.
- You, throughout this book, will conduct many experiments to satisfy your curiosity, discover new ideas, verify old ones, and arrive at conclusions.

So, whether they realize it or not, almost everybody does science. Throughout this book you too will do science many times. Who knows, within these pages you may even find an idea for an award-winning science fair project.

✳ Follow Up

Assessment

Indicate whether each of the following statements refers to science or technology:
(a) With the microscope, I can see smaller things than I can with the naked eye. *(technology)*
(b) Today, we performed an experiment to compare my reaction time with the reaction times of others in the class. *(science)*
(c) Astronomers believe that there are objects in space called black holes. *(science)*
(d) I use my bicycle to deliver papers. *(technology)*
(e) Scientists are learning more about the AIDS virus every day. *(science)*
(f) More uses for lasers are discovered every year. *(technology)*

Extension

One day a man named George de Mestral took his dog for a walk in the mountains near his home in Switzerland. He noticed the dog's fur was covered with burrs. As he struggled to pull off these seeds, he wondered what made the burrs cling so strongly. He looked at the seeds under a microscope, and what he discovered gave him an idea for an invention—Velcro!

Have students look at burdocks and Velcro under a compound microscope to see how they are similar. (Both have tiny hooks that cling to fur or cloth.) Often in nature there are models that inventive minds can use to ignite an idea. Challenge students to find some things in nature that could serve as models for inventions.

1. **Words of Wisdom**
   Most of our everyday expressions are based on observations. Not all of these observations are accurate. Which of the following expressions do you think are true or partly true? Which could be scientifically tested? What is the reasoning behind each expression?

   (a) You can't teach an old dog new tricks.

   (b) You can catch more flies with honey than with vinegar.

   (c) It's always darkest before the dawn.

   (d) You can't fight city hall.

   (e) A watched pot never boils.

   (f) You can catch a bird by putting salt on its tail.

   (g) There is always a calm before a storm.

   (h) A stitch in time saves nine.

   (i) A rolling stone gathers no moss.

   (j) You reap only what you sow.

2. Write an investigative statement for four of the expressions above.

3. Design an experiment to test one or more of the above sayings.

4. In 1900 the first crude automobiles were traveling the roads. Planes had not yet been invented, and radio and television were years away. What are some ways in which the technology of 1900 differs from that of today?

5. In the past century, technology has advanced as never before. What do you think are some of the reasons for this? Will technology continue to advance at the same rate in the future? Why or why not?

6. How might technology change in the next 100 years?

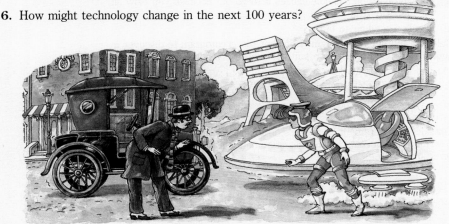

1. These sayings are presented in order to promote discussion. Although a saying may, at first glance, seem completely untrue, many of these sayings have a basis in fact.

   True or partly true:
   b, f, g, h, i, j
   Could be scientifically tested:
   a, b, c, e, f, g

   The reasoning behind some sayings could be discussed in a light-hearted manner. Remind students that appearances are often misleading. For example, when waiting for a pot of water to boil, staring at the pot makes the time to boil seem longer.

   Point out to students that scientific tests are helpful because they test our observations. Students may be confused by some of the sayings. For example, (f) is true because if you can get close enough to a bird to put salt on its tail, you are probably close enough to catch it. Saying (h) points out that if a tear in clothing is not mended, it will grow even larger, requiring more sewing.

2. Some investigative questions could be as follows:
   - Does the age of a dog affect its ability to learn a new task?
   - Are flies attracted by the smell of different substances?
   - Is the amount of light present at its lowest level just before sunrise?

3. Encourage students to use their imaginations to answer this question. Remind them to keep their variables constant. For example, several dogs of the same breed and of the same advanced age could be taught a skill. Their results could be compared to the success of younger dogs.

4. Answers will vary but a few examples are computers, televisions, radios, and sophisticated communication and transportation devices.

5. One technological breakthrough leads to another. Discoveries and ideas generated in one experiment can be used in the next experiment.

6. The obvious candidates for change are in the areas of computers, communication, and transportation.

Summary for

The Big Ideas

Student responses will vary. The following is an ideal summary.

Being scientific is a way of looking at the world. It includes observing, questioning, inferring, hypothesizing, testing, and drawing conclusions. It requires imagination, persistence, and curiosity.

An observation is something that is noted about the physical world. An inference is an idea, suggested by observations, that explains an occurrence in nature. A conclusion is an inference that seems to be true based on available evidence. These help people to act scientifically because they are steps in a process for understanding the physical world.

An investigative question is one that can be studied systematically to find out whether or not it is true.

In order to test a hypothesis, a controlled experiment is set up by allowing only one variable to change; the other variables remain constant.

Experiments are important in that they allow us to test the accuracy of our observations and the validity of relationships.

The steps involved in designing an experiment:

- Ask an investigative question
- Choose one variable to change
- Make sure that all other variables remain constant
- Set up several trials
- Report the results

Technology is the application of knowledge to solve practical problems. Science may provide the knowledge for technology. Science and technology help each other in that knowledge learned in the pursuit of each can be shared.

The Big Ideas

In Your Journal, write a summary of this unit, using the following questions as a guide.

- What does it mean to be scientific?
- What is an observation? an inference? a conclusion? How does each of these help people do science?
- How does an investigative question differ from a question that is not investigative?
- How are the words *hypothesis*, *variable*, and *controlled experiment* related?
- What is the purpose of experiments?
- What are some of the steps in designing experiments?
- How are science and technology related?
- How do science and technology help each other?

Checking Your Understanding

1. Yvonne's group made these statements as they did the candle activity in the beginning of this unit. Which statements are inferences? Which are observations?
   - (a) The candle is blue.
   - (b) The candle is 5 cm high.
   - (c) A pool of liquid forms on top of the candle as it burns.
   - (d) This liquid is made of the same substance as the candle.
   - (e) The candle flickers as it burns.
   - (f) Blowing hard on the candle causes it to go out.
   - (g) Blowing hard on a candle causes it to go out because you blow all the air away from it.
   - (h) Candles need air to burn.

2. Below is another cryptogram. Decipher the cryptogram to discover a quote. Hint: One of the words in the quote is "technology."

   VN VW NSZ UHVAVUA UK WUYZ, NSMN OVKZ UA ZMFNS
   JUEOB CZ CZNNZF VK AUN KUF WPVZAPZ MAB NZPSAUOUDL.

   After you crack the code, write a paragraph or two stating whether you agree or disagree with this statement and why.

3. Consider the statement "Scientists discover, inventors invent." Explain in writing the meaning behind this statement. Indicate whether you agree or disagree, and why.

Answers to

Checking Your Understanding

1. **(a)** Observation
   (b) Observation
   (c) Observation
   (d) Inference
   (e) Observation
   (f) Observation
   (g) Inference
   (h) Inference

2. The cryptogram reads "It is the opinion of some that the earth would be better if not for science and technology."

Answers will vary. Get students started by having them make a list of "pros and cons" for science and technology. For example: Technology can be used to stop or lessen pollution (pro); Technology causes pollution (con).

3. Scientists and inventors share many characteristics: they are both trying to solve a question or problem concerning the natural world. In their quest for answers, scientists use the tools of the inventor and inventors use the tools of the scientist.

(Answers continue on next page)

4. Once upon a time there was a young boy who lived in the country. This boy noticed that every morning, just before dawn, the roosters began to crow. He hypothesized that the roosters' crowing caused the sun to rise. Design an experiment to test this hypothesis.

5. If an experiment repeatedly disproves a hypothesis, which of the following responses would be correct for a scientist?

  (a) Ignore the results of the experiment.
  (b) Keep trying new experiments until the hypothesis is supported.
  (c) Reject the old hypothesis and form a new one.
  (d) Conclude that the experiment had some sort of flaw.
  Justify your response in writing.

6. Construct a concept map using the following terms: *scientists, conclusions, inferences,* and *observations.*

Reading *Plus*

Now that you have been introduced to the basics of science, let's find out just a bit more about who scientists are and what they actually do. By reading pages S1–S20 in the *SourceBook,* you will learn about the different branches of science—life science, earth science, and physical science—the type of problems each branch of science tackles, and the methods scientists use in their work. You will read an actual case study of two scientists who identified a gap in our knowledge of the natural world, and you will learn how they used a scientific method to expand our understanding of the natural world.

Updating Your Journal

Reread the paragraphs you wrote for this unit's "For Your Journal" Questions. Then rewrite them to reflect what you have learned in studying this unit.

Answers continued

4. The variable to change would be the crowing of the rooster.
5. A scientist should make sure that his or her experiment is sound. New experiments to test the hypothesis can be tried but eventually a new hypothesis will be formed. Therefore, choices (c) or (d) would be correct.
6.

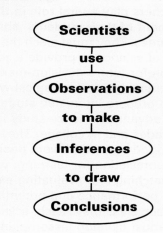

About Updating Your Journal

The following are sample ideal answers.
1. Answers will vary. Ask students to explain the ways in which their answers have changed since they began the study of this unit.
2. Scientists try to make sense of the world around them. They do this by asking investigative questions, thinking up possible answers, making observations, testing ideas, and thinking. *(The theme of **Patterns of Change** can be emphasized here as scientific knowledge is continually being added to, modified, and reassembled.)*
3. & 4. Point out to students that anyone, including the students themselves, who has ever wondered why something happens, made observations about the world, made tests and measurements, or speculated about the reason behind an occurrence, has acted scientifically.
5. The space probe in the picture points out one interaction between science and technology. Scientific knowledge provided the basis for the technology that created the probe.

Science in Action

Background

Middle school and high school science teachers play a vital role in the development of their students' abilities and aptitudes. They must teach the basic concepts of science to provide a sound foundation for future decision-making in our increasingly technological world. They also prepare interested students for more advanced science study in higher grades and in college. They try to instill good study and work habits and an appreciation for learning, while closely watching and evaluating each student's performance and potential.

For each class they teach, science teachers must develop lesson plans, gather needed materials, and design their presentations to meet the individual needs and abilities of their students.

All 50 states and the District of Columbia require public school teachers to be certified by the department of education in the state in which they work. To qualify for certification in most states, a teacher must have a bachelor's degree from a college with an approved teacher education program.

Spotlight on Science Teaching

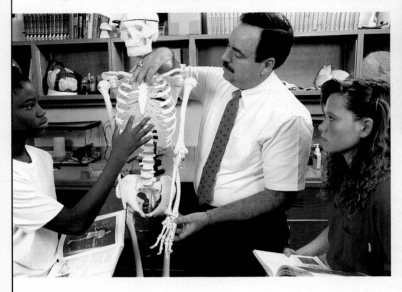

Middle School

John Mondragon teaches science to students in the seventh, eighth, and ninth grades.

Q: What aspect of teaching do you enjoy most?

John: I think just working in the classroom with the students and helping them learn is the most enjoyable aspect. It is stimulating to have them discover things for themselves and to help them understand new ideas.

Q. Are there any frustrations in teaching?

John: Yes. The most frustrating thing would be the lack of time to prepare adequately for classes. Another would be the lack of interest and response by some students.

Q. As a teacher, you constantly have to be learning yourself. What opportunities do you get for doing so?

John: Well, I have taken part in many courses and workshops. Recently, for example, I spent a summer studying geology. We went on many field trips, collecting samples of geological specimens. It was very interesting.

Q: Are there any socially important issues that you believe require special attention in science teaching?

John: I think one of the major issues of social importance is the environment, the need to live in harmony with nature. One of the objectives of education is to make people more aware of the need to protect the environment. While laws are needed, the main way of attacking the problem of environmental degradation is through education.

Q: What abilities and skills are most important in teaching?

John: Being able to relate well to people is the most important skill for any teacher. Also important, and closely related to this, is the ability to express your ideas clearly, to teach in a way that students will understand.

A teacher should also be well-organized. Teaching involves a lot of preparation and planning.

I think it is also useful for a teacher to know when to be quiet and let the kids learn for themselves, rather than tell them everything you want them to learn. A teacher needs to create an environment in which students do their own work to find answers for themselves.

Using the Interview

Students can role-play by having one student read the part of the interviewer and two other students read the parts of the two teachers. Use the following questions to promote discussion.

1. What interests, abilities, and skills does John Mondragon think are important for teaching? *(being able to relate to people, being able to express one's ideas clearly, being well-organized, being able to let students learn for themselves)*

2. What interests, abilities, and skills does Susan Harrigan think are important for teaching? *(having a profound interest in science, being willing to continue to learn, being prepared to change the way you teach a concept)*

3. Do you think there are differences in the interests, abilities, and skills required for middle school versus high school science teaching? Explain your answer. *(The high school teacher emphasized the need for a profound interest in the subject matter itself, whereas the middle school teacher emphasized being able to relate to people and to express ideas clearly.)*

4. Do you think you have the aptitude and interest necessary to become a science teacher? Why or why not? *(Answers will vary. Students who like science and people, and who have leadership capabilities are good candidates for future science teachers.)*

High School

Susan Harrigan is a high school biology teacher.

Q: How did you become interested in teaching?

Susan: I didn't decide to become a teacher until I had already completed three years of university study, but my mother tells me that as a child I used to play school a lot and, apparently, I always had to be the teacher. In any case, as soon as I started my first week of practice teaching required for my Bachelor of Education degree, I knew I had really found my niche. I liked it from day one!

I was also influenced by my own teachers. In particular, I had a university physics teacher who taught a class with well over 100 students and still seemed to have the knack of making each of us believe that he was really inter-

ested in each of us. I try to do the same with my students—helping to remove some of the fears they may have about what science in general is all about.

Q: What characteristic do you believe is particularly important for teaching?

Susan: I think people who want to be teachers, in particular teachers of science, must have a profound interest in the subject. They must find it exciting, so they can communicate their excitement to the students.

It is also important to continue to learn and to improve your teaching. There is always something new to be learned. You should be prepared to change the way you teach a concept. I find that I spend a lot of time with chemistry, physics, and math teachers discussing ways I can improve my own knowledge and teaching.

Q: Is there any particular social message that you try to get across in your teaching?

Susan: For one thing, I take every opportunity I can to discourage students from smoking. It is a personal commitment to the health of the students. I know they simply don't know all the implications of smoking, and I feel that, as a biology teacher and an adult, I owe it to them to at least present them with all the facts.

Some Project Ideas

Seek the advice and assistance of a teacher for these projects.
1. Pick a topic in which you have an interest, and propose to your teacher that you conduct a mini-lesson on it.
2. Start a science club for younger children in your neighborhood or at an elementary school. Your task, like that of a teacher, is to plan and organize the activities of the club so that the younger children learn something useful. Work with a friend or two if you wish, and seek the advice of one or more teachers.

✦ Going Further

1. Have students interview science teachers in the school about what they do and do not like about their jobs, what their workday is like, how they became interested in science teaching as a career, and so on. Have students prepare their questions ahead of time. They should take notes on the teacher's responses, or they may wish to tape-record the interview and play back parts of the recording to the class.
2. In many science classes, students are expected to dissect animals in order to learn about anatomy, biological systems, and development of organisms. Have students draw

up a pro-and-con analysis of this controversial classroom practice. Students should list at least five reasons why animals should be used for dissection and experimentation and five reasons why they should not be used in this way.
3. Students interested in a career in science teaching could write for more information to:
- National Science Teachers' Association, 1742 Connecticut Ave., NW, Washington, D.C. 20009
- American Federation of Teachers, 11 Dupont Circle, Fifth Floor, Washington, D.C. 20036

Background

This feature focuses on some of the unique materials that can honestly display the label "Made in Space." Once space travel and research became a reality, many scientists believed that the lack of gravity in space would provide the perfect environment for the production of certain materials that could not be made on earth. Experiments conducted in laboratories aboard space stations and the space shuttle have proven this prediction to be true.

Much of the research of manufacturing materials in space has been done aboard *Spacelab*. *Spacelab* is an onboard laboratory designed to fit into a space shuttle, and it can be used over and over again. Its maiden voyage took place in November, 1983, aboard the shuttle *Columbia*.

One of the most important and far-reaching applications of *Spacelab* research focuses on "materials" science, a branch of science that studies the properties of organic and inorganic substances. The *Spacelab* scientists engaged in this research are preparing the way for the zero-gravity factories that will one day orbit the earth.

Made in Space

In July 1985, the first product manufactured in space went on sale. For $385, a company could buy a 25-gram container of tiny plastic beads that had been manufactured on the space shuttle. These beads are used to calibrate delicate measuring instruments. The special environment of space makes possible the manufacture of these and many other unique materials.

The Microgravity Advantage

Why make plastic beads in space? Because in space these beads can be made with incredible precision. The microgravity environment (extremely low gravity) of the space shuttle affects the physical and chemical processes in several remarkable ways.

- Metals that will not mix on earth can be mixed in space to form alloys.
- Crystals—solids whose atoms are arranged in an orderly pattern— grow larger and purer in space than they do on earth.
- Lasers and optical fibers require extremely pure glass. While acceptable glass can be made on Earth, space provides a way to produce even purer materials.

Unbeatable Beads

In the case of the beads, the near-zero gravity of space yields a product that is much rounder and more uniform than that produced on earth. Their uniform size and shape makes the beads invaluable in producing tools that measure microscopic particles from talcum powder to air pollutants. The beads are made by a process similar to making a large sponge from a small one by soaking it in water.

The beads are made from bits of polystyrene, the same kind of plastic used in disposable coffee cups. The beads are increased in size by adding tiny particles of styrene to them. When the beads have attained the right size, the process is stopped by heating the liquid in which the beads have been forming.

These polystyrene beads are certified as made in space.

Discussion

To promote class discussion, you may wish to use questions similar to the following:

1. How do objects move in zero gravity? Don't they float up instead of falling down? *(It is a common misconception that objects float upward in the absence of gravity. In reality, objects will remain wherever they are placed unless a force acting upon them sets them in motion. Once in motion, the object will travel in a straight line unless something stops it or causes it to change direction.)*

2. How might a person who has spent several months in space be affected by the prolonged exposure to weightlessness? *(Most students should be able to predict that the person's muscles, including those of the heart, would probably grow weak because they do not have to work against the pull of gravity. Some students might correctly infer that the bones would also grow weaker. All of these, as well as other symptoms, have been verified by Russian cosmonauts who have spent many months in space. Current space programs provide activities to counteract the effects of weightlessness.)*

3. Why would the words *up* and *down* have little meaning in space? *(Up means away from the earth or against the pull of gravity. Down means toward the earth or in the direction of the pull of gravity. Since there is no gravity in space, there is no frame of reference to establish up or down.)*

When made on earth, the beads float as they get larger and then sink when the liquid is heated to stop their growth. The result is that either floating or sinking, they clump together. As a result, they are less uniform in size and shape than is desirable.

In space, where everything is weightless, differences in density do not cause floating or sinking. The beads made aboard the shuttle are almost perfectly spherical and uniform in size.

Growing Mega-Crystals in Microgravity

In June 1983, astronauts on the space shuttle used a furnace to heat a compound called mercuric iodide. The compound was contained in one end of a test tube. When heated, mercuric iodide produces a gas. As the gas cools, it forms crystals. The experiment was designed to find out how long it would take the gas to go to the other end of the tube and form crystals.

Surprise! The crystals were up to 100 times larger than crystals grown on earth. Why? In space, the tiny crystals that formed first were weightless and floated in the tube. Because the crystals did not stick to the walls of the test tube, they could grow in all directions.

The discovery that large crystals could be produced in space was quickly applied in the field of protein study. The structure of proteins can be determined using a technique called *X-ray diffraction analysis*. However, this technique requires fairly large crystals.

In space, protein crystals have been produced that are up to 1000 times larger than those grown on earth. These crystals make X-ray examination of some kinds of proteins possible for the first time.

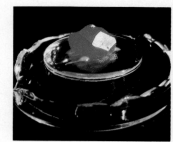

A large crystal of mercuric iodide made on Spacelab III

Materials with the Right Stuff

Find out about other "space age" materials with special properties. For example:

- Teflon nonstick coating
- Kevlar fibers
- Gore-Tex fabric
- graphite-fiber composites

What gives these materials their special properties? How are these materials manufactured? How are these materials used by consumers?

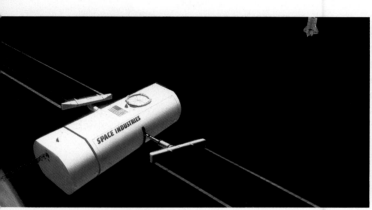

An artist's conception of the first space factory

◆ Critical Thinking

To promote logical-thinking skills, you may wish to ask questions similar to the following.

1. Imagine that you are in a spacecraft circling earth. You fill a balloon with helium and release it. What happens? Why? *(The balloon remains wherever it is placed or drifts in whatever direction it is pushed. Since there is no gravity, there is no such thing as buoyancy; therefore, the balloon does not float.)*

2. Imagine that you are riding in a jet airplane. You are climbing higher and higher. Suddenly you crest and begin to fall. For a few seconds you experience weightlessness before things return to normal. What happened? *(As the plane begins its descent, it actually free-falls for a few seconds. Since the plane, and you along with it, are both accelerating downward at the same rate, you do not feel the plane pushing you upward as it rises against the pull of gravity.)*

◆ Going Further

1. Ask students to imagine that they live aboard a special "space city" orbiting the earth. Within the "city" are homes, farms, and manufacturing facilities as well as other features that you would expect to find in an average town on earth. Challenge students to write a story about their experiences: the work they do, the home they live in, how they relax, what they do for entertainment, and so on. To obtain background information for their stories, suggest that students read about existing proposals for space stations planned for deployment in the future.

2. NASA prepares potential astronauts for the effects of weightlessness by taking them on special training flights. Ask students to do some research to find out about these flights and share what they learn with the class.

✳ *Teaching the Unit*

Unit Overview

In this unit, students explore some of the characteristics of living things. In Section 1, students classify objects into three groups—those that are living, those that are dead, and those that have never been alive. Then they are asked to compare and contrast the differences between plants and animals. In Sections 2 and 3, students study the different ways that animals and plants move, grow, and respond to stimuli. Students then read about actual experiments on animal behavior. The Section 3 concludes with students examining how animals are adapted to their environments. In Section 4, students are given the opportunity to use microscopes to observe some differences between plant and animal cells.

Using the Themes

The unifying themes emphasized in this unit are **Stability, Scale and Structure**, and **Patterns of Change**. The following information will help you weave these themes into your teaching plan. A focus question is provided with each theme as a discussion tool to help you tie the information in the unit together.

Stability can be presented in a discussion of the characteristics of living things. All living things are essentially different from nonliving things in very predictable, uniform ways. These characteristics and their uniformity are developed throughout the unit.

> **Focus question:** *Do the characteristics of living things vary in different organisms?*

Students should understand that although different organisms vary in their methods of carrying out the activities of life, stability is reflected in the sameness of their underlying characteristics. For example, plants and animals acquire food in different ways, but the end result of their actions is that the organisms gain their required nutrients.

Scale and Structure should be discussed in relation to Sections 1, 3, and 4, in which students learn how organisms use various bodily structures to survive in a particular environment. In Section 4, scale is emphasized as students investigate the structures of an organism at the microscopic level.

> **Focus question:** *How are the structures of living things related to their functions?*

The feature "Bird Adaptations" in Lesson 9 offers an excellent answer to this question in that bill size and shape, foot width and webbing, and body and wing conformation can all be discussed in relation to the bird's adaptation to its environment.

Patterns of Change can best be discussed in conjunction with Sections 2 and 3. Students are introduced to the many different types of growth in living things, particularly human growth. Students then learn about how changes in the environment cause changes within the life of an individual organism, as well as more long-term changes in groups of animals. The theme of **Evolution** can also be discussed in this context.

> **Focus question:** *What are some of the cycles of change that occur in nature?*

Possible answers could include the growth of an individual from conception to death, or the way in which seasonal cycles influence behaviors such as migration and hibernation.

Using the *Science Discovery* Videodiscs

Disc 1 *Science Sleuths, The Plainview Vandals*
Teenagers are accused of vandalizing an urban park. A park ranger gathers a variety of evidence that leads her to believe that the teenagers are the culprits. The Science Sleuths must analyze the evidence for themselves to determine the true cause of the vandalism.

Disc 2 *Image and Activity Bank*
A variety of still images, short videos, and activities are available for you to use as you teach this unit. See the *Videodisc Resources* section of the **Teacher's Resource Binder** for detailed instructions.

Using the *SciencePlus SourceBook*

Unit 2 focuses on the characteristics, structures, and functions of cells, and how cells are organized to form living things. A discussion of scientific classification follows. Students learn that the nature of classification is based on the way in which organisms are related. This leads to a discussion of the role of evolution and genetics in the modern system of classification.

PLANNING CHART

SECTION AND LESSON	PG.	TIME*	PROCESS SKILLS	EXPLORATION AND ASSESSMENT	PG.	RESOURCES AND FEATURES
Unit Opener	54		observing, discussing	For Your Journal	55	Science Sleuths: *The Plainview Vandals* Videodisc Activity Sheets TRB: Home Connection
ALIVE AND KICKING	56			Challenge Your Thinking	67	
1 Signs of Life	56	2	analyzing, classifying, making a chart, writing			Image and Activity Bank 2–1
2 Motion and Locomotion	58	1 to 2	observing, using a data table, measuring, comparing	Exploration 1	59	Image and Activity Bank 2–2 TRB: Resource Worksheet 2–1 Resource Transparency 2–1
3 Feet, Scales, and Bristles	61	3	observing, comparing, investigating, describing	Exploration 2 Exploration 3 Exploration 4	62 62 66	Image and Activity Bank 2–3
PATTERNS OF GROWTH	68			Challenge Your Thinking	81	Graphic Organizer Transparency 2–4
4 Human Growth	68	2	measuring, comparing, predicting, making a chart			Image and Activity Bank 2–4 Graphic Organizer Transparency 2–2
5 Other Growth Patterns	72	3	comparing, measuring, designing experiments, writing a report	Exploration 5	73	Image and Activity Bank 2–5 TRB: Activity Worksheets 2–2 and 2–3 Graphic Organizer Transparency 2–3
PATTERNS OF RESPONSE	82			Challenge Your Thinking	103	TRB: Resource Worksheet 2–6
6 Stimulus and Response	82	2	controlling variables, observing, recording, investigating	Exploration 6	82	Image and Activity Bank 2–6
7 You Be the Scientist	86	2	analyzing, drawing conclusions, evaluating, writing an article	Exploration 7	90	Image and Activity Bank 2–7
8 Seasonal Behavior of Animals	91	4	comparing, drawing conclusions, inferring, experimenting	Exploration 8	95	Image and Activity Bank 2–8 TRB: Activity Worksheets 2–4 and 2–5 Graphic Organizer Transparency 2–5
9 Adaptations of Structure	98	2	observing, analyzing, recognizing relationships, illustrating			Image and Activity Bank 2–9 TRB: Activity Worksheet 2–7 Graphic Organizer Transparency 2–6
BUILDING BLOCKS OF LIFE	104			Challenge Your Thinking	109	TRB: Resource Worksheet 2–11
10 Taking a Closer Look	104	4	manipulating equipment, observing, comparing, illustrating	Exploration 9	106	Image and Activity Bank 2–10 TRB: Resource Worksheet 2–8 Activity Worksheets 2–9 and 2–10 Resource Transparencies 2–7 and 2–8 Graphic Organizer Transparencies 2–9, 2–10, and 2–11
End of Unit	110		applying, analyzing, evaluating, summarizing	Making Connections TRB: Sample Assessment Items	110	TRB: Activity Worksheet 2–12 Science in Action, p. 112 Science and the Arts, p. 114 *SourceBook,* pp. S21–S40

*Time given in number of class periods.

53B

Meeting Individual Needs

 ## Gifted Students

1. Have students keep detailed records of birds seen in the vicinity of the school during each month of the year. Herbert Zimm's *Golden Nature Guides* and Peterson's guidebooks are both excellent identification sources. Have students keep a tally of the number of sightings of each bird on a large wall chart. Encourage them to illustrate their charts with drawings of the birds. From their records, they can determine which birds migrate, which ones are the first to return in the spring, and which ones stay all winter.

2. *Tenebrio* sp. is an excellent organism to study in the classroom because it is very easy to maintain. The larvae of this beetle are called mealworms. They can be purchased at bait and tropical fish stores. To start a culture, obtain about 10 mealworms and place them in a large jar with a screen cover. Moist oatmeal or bran and small pieces of raw carrot will maintain them. Challenge students to find out as much as possible about the mealworms, such as how they grow and change, how they move, and how they respond to stimuli. Have students design their own experiments to find out how *Tenebrio* larvae and adults respond to different stimuli. Students should then report their experimental results to the rest of the class.

 ## LEP Students

1. There are many opportunities for students to draw, rather than to describe in words, the concepts in this unit. For example, students could draw various types of movements in plants and animals, human growth patterns, the conditions necessary for seed growth, different plant and animal adaptations, and plant and animal cells. Ask students to label their illustrations.

2. Take students on a field trip to a local zoo. Give them the opportunity to practice their English by asking them to discuss the various animals they see and how they are adapted to their particular environments. Ask them to discuss how the zookeepers provide the appropriate food and a suitable environment for each of the animals.

3. At the beginning of each unit, give Spanish-speaking students a copy of the *Spanish Glossary* from the *Teacher's Resource Binder*. Also, let Spanish-speaking students listen to the *English/Spanish Audiocassettes*.

 ## At-Risk Students

Unit 2 offers many motivating activities for students to gain first-hand knowledge of the characteristics of living things. In Lesson 5, *Other Growth Patterns,* students are asked to conduct field research comparing leaf and stem sizes in young trees to leaves and stems of mature trees. *Exploration 5* gives students additional experience observing growth patterns, and the environmental factors affecting this growth, by designing and carrying out experiments that test seed growth in different conditions.

For special recognition, give students the opportunity to participate in a plant propagation project. A number of vegetables can be propagated from cuttings. For example, a sweet potato will produce dense foliage if placed in a glass of water, root-end down. A potato may be kept in position by pressing three toothpicks into its side and resting them on the rim of a glass. Keep the lower third covered with water and place it in a sunny window. The roots of carrots, beets and turnips, which contain a lot of stored food, can also be propagated. Remove the old leaves from the top and then cut off all the root except for 5–8 cm. Place this portion in a shallow dish of water. A few pebbles placed in the dish will hold the roots upright.

 ## Cross-Disciplinary Focus

Mathematics

When students are studying various modes of animal locomotion, have them look up the fastest animals, including the fastest land animal, the fastest bird, and the fastest marine animal, in the *Guinness Book of World Records*. Have them make a line graph of these speeds, with the time in seconds plotted on the y-axis and the distance in meters plotted on the x-axis.

Then have students calculate their own fastest running speeds. Measure a distance of 18 meters. Measure the time it takes each student to run that distance, and have them calculate their running speeds in meters per second. Their running speeds can then be plotted on the line graphs and compared with the fastest speeds of the animals.

Art

Interested students can construct dioramas to illustrate how different animals are structurally adapted to their habitats and ways of life. If possible, have them visit a museum of natural history first to observe dioramas of animals in their natural settings. They could construct mini-dioramas in boxes, using clay to model the animals and construction paper, paint, twigs, stones, and other materials to model the plants and the landscape. They could construct a diorama of a real habitat or a make-believe habitat, such as one that might be found on another planet. Emphasize that no matter what habitat they choose, the animals should be suitable to the habitat in which the animals are placed.

Cross-Cultural Focus

Nomadic Tribes

A nomad is a person who has no permanent home, and who has chosen to wander from one place to another as a way of making a living. Most nomadic peoples move through a certain area based on a cycle of activities or of the seasons. There are two different kinds of nomads: those who move in search of game, edible vegetation, and water, and those who move to find water and pasture for their herds. Ask students to do research on some of these peoples, such as the people of Lapland, the African Pygmies, the Australian Aborigines, or the Bedouins of Northern Africa and Arabia. Their research should include the reasons for migration, the possible preparations made, and the contributions that they have made to both the environment and to the culture of their homeland.

Philosophy

In the traditional Chinese belief system, life begins with the two opposite forces of yin and yang. Everything, from trees and water to animals and people, is composed of yin and yang. Even the hills and valleys are seen as living, and having yin and yang within them. The combined strength of these two powerful forces keeps a place in harmony. If one force becomes too powerful, chaos, in the form of floods or earthquakes, will result. Compare this view with the scientific view that states the importance of each living thing in the balance of an ecosystem, or a system of living things. You can also discuss yin and yang in relation to the loss of trees to build homes and the loss of land to commercial development.

✳ *Resources*

Bibliography for Teachers

Barrett, Katharine. *Animals in Action*. Berkeley, CA: Lawrence Hall of Science, 1986.

Challand, Helen J. *Activities in the Life Sciences*. Chicago, IL: Children's Press, 1982.

Elementary Science Study. *Earthworms*. Nashua, NH: Delta, 1971.

Outdoor Biology Instructional Strategies (OBIS). *Animal Behavior*. Nashua, NH: Delta, 1981.

Pranis, Eve, and Jack Hale. *Grow Lab: A Complete Guide to Gardening in the Classroom*. Burlington, VT: National Gardening Association, 1988.

Bibliography for Students

Burnie, David. *Bird*. New York, NY: Knopf, 1988.

Herberman, Ethan. *The Great Butterfly Hunt: The Mystery of the Migrating Monarchs*. New York, NY: Simon and Schuster, 1990.

Lauber, Patricia. *What Big Teeth You Have!* Minneapolis, MN: Carolrhoda, 1986.

Lerner, Carol. *Pitcher Plants: The Elegant Insect Traps*. New York, NY: Morrow, William & Company, 1983.

McClung, Robert M. *Mysteries of Migration*. Dallas, TX: Garrard Publishing Company, 1983.

Patent, Dorothy Hinshaw. *How Smart Are Animals?* San Diego, CA: Harcourt, Brace, Jovanovich, Inc., 1990.

Pope, Joyce. *Kenneth Lilly's Animals*. New York, NY: Lothrop, Lee, & Shepard Books, 1988.

Stidworthy, John. *A Year in the Life: Whale*. Needham Heights, MA: Silver Burdett & Ginn, Inc., 1987.

Films, Videotapes, Software, and Other Media

Adaptation & Identification. Software. Grades 7–12. For Apple II family, 48K. Scott, Foresman & Co. 1900 East Lake Avenue Glenview, IL 60025 (312) 729-3000

Adaptations of Plants. Film and Video. Coronet Film & Video 108 Wilmot Road Deerfield, IL 60015 (800) 621-2131

Bee-Cause. Software. Grades 7–12. For Apple II family. Q.E.D. Computing P.O. Box 5037 Kent, WA 98064-5037 (206) 432-2779

Botanical Gardens. Software. Grades 7–12. For Apple family, 64 K. Sunburst Comm. 39 Washington Avenue Pleasantville, NY 10570 (800) 431-1934

Imaging a Hidden World: The Light Microscope. Film and Video. Coronet Film & Video 108 Wilmot Road Deerfield, IL 60015 (800) 621-2131

The Wonder of Dolphins. Film and Video. Coronet Film & Video 108 Wilmot Road Deerfield, IL 60015 (800) 621-2131

Patterns of Living Things

Unit

2

✴ Unit Focus

Write the headings *living,* *dead,* **and** *nonliving* **on the board.** Ask students to name items in the classroom that would fall under each heading. Then ask students how they know whether an object is living, was once living, or was never alive. Encourage discussion about what makes something alive. Let them express their own ideas and do not attempt to correct them at this point. This exercise will give you an opportunity to find out their ideas on what makes something alive. Tell students that in this unit, they will learn about some of the characteristics that all living things have in common.

✴ About the Photograph

The zebra, a member of the horse family, is found in East and South Africa. The zebra can be distinguished from the horse by its striped coat, large head, small ears, and short, erect mane. Its hoofs are broad and more round like those of a horse, yet they are more narrow. The long tail, with a brush of whiplike hair at the tip, is used as a fly-swatter. The zebra is a sociable animal and travels in large herds. Since it tends to be very stubborn, it has not been domesticated.

✳ Using the Photograph

Tell students that these zebras live on grassy plains in East Africa.

- How do you think their teeth are adapted for eating grass? *(They have chisel-shaped incisors for chopping and large molars with convoluted surfaces for grinding.)*
- How are their feet adapted for running on hard ground? *(The foot has evolved into a tough hoof for ease in running.)*
- Why do you think zebras have stripes? *(The stripes help to camouflage a zebra. The stripes tend to hide the contour of a zebra's body so that it is less noticeable from a distance. Thus lions, the only natural enemy of the zebra, are less apt to notice it.)*

Have students examine the pattern of stripes on the zebras in the picture. Ask: Are the patterns on any two zebras alike? *(They should discover that no two zebra patterns are alike.)*

For Your Journal

Write a paragraph summarizing your thoughts about each of the following.

1. How do you tell something alive from something that is not?
2. What are some of the characteristics of living things?
3. How do living things interact with their surroundings?
4. How do the zebras in the photograph demonstrate "aliveness"?

✳ About Your Journal

Students should answer the Journal questions to the best of their abilities.

These questions are designed to serve two functions: to help students recognize that they do indeed have prior knowledge about the topic, and to help them identify any misconceptions they may have. In the course of studying the unit, these misconceptions should be dispelled.

☀ *Getting Started*

This introductory lesson first distinguishes between the terms *living, dead,* and *nonliving.* Students then investigate some of the characteristics of living things—movement, locomotion, growth and regeneration, reproduction, and response to stimuli.

Main Ideas

1. All living things share certain common characteristics.
2. Plants and animals are living things.

☀ *Teaching Strategies*

Divide students into groups of three or four to complete the classification activity on page 56. Explain that both living and nonliving things are pictured on some of the stamps. Every item on each stamp should be classified. Ask students to give reasons for their classification choices in their Journals.

1 Signs of Life

Do you know that there are over 2 million different kinds of animals and plants in the world? That is a large number of living things. But how can you tell whether everyday things are living or nonliving? What are the signs of life? Nonliving things, such as water or a rock, have never been alive. Something that is dead was once alive but no longer has any of the signs of life. A fish being cooked in a frying pan is dead, but the metallic pan in which it is cooked is nonliving. How would you classify a leather wallet—as living, dead, or nonliving?

Look at the object or objects pictured in each of the postage stamps on these pages. Are there any objects pictured that should be listed as "dead" things? If so, name them. Sort the stamps into two lists: living and dead/nonliving. Write down your reason(s) for classifying each picture as you did.

LESSON 1 ORGANIZER

Objectives

By the end of the lesson, students should be able to:
1. Classify objects as living, nonliving, or dead.
2. Compare the characteristics of living and nonliving things.
3. Distinguish between plants and animals.

Process Skills

analyzing, classifying, making a chart, writing

You Be the Judge

The following statements were made by some students who were discussing the differences between living and nonliving things. Do you agree or disagree with their ideas? Explain in writing how you would respond to each student.

Olga:
"Clouds and wind are living because they have energy, and energy makes things live."

Blair:
"A river is living because it moves; soil is nonliving because it does not move."

Velma:
"Smoke is alive because it can hurt you, and volcanoes are living because they rumble."

Paul:
"A candle flame is living because it gives heat and light. It wiggles around and can make new flames."

Roberto:
"Crystals are alive. I have seen them grow larger."

It is not a simple matter to explain how living, dead, and nonliving things differ. Living things share not just one but a number of common characteristics or signs of life. Write down the signs of life that you think are common to all living things.

Animal or Vegetable?

Look again at the list you made of the stamps that showed living things. Are all of the objects alive in the same way? Divide these living things into two further groups to show two different ways in which things may be alive.

Afterwards, with the help of your classmates, prepare a brief statement that explains how a plant differs from an animal.

You Be the Judge

Ask students to read the statements on page 57 and decide how they would respond to each one. *(Students should see that, although the characteristics mentioned are all qualities of living things, none of the examples are living. Many characteristics must combine to make a living thing.)* Encourage an open-ended discussion.

Animal or Vegetable?

Have students work together in small groups to prepare their statements. Statements might include:

- Plants are rooted in soil and cannot move quickly; animals can move quickly.
- Plants can only move parts of their bodies.
- Most plants have green leaves and make their own food; animals hunt for their food.
- Animals have nervous systems, digestive systems, and sense organs; plants do not.

✳ *Follow Up*

Assessment

1. Give small groups of students a set of pictures from magazines of a variety of plants, animals, and inanimate objects. Have them classify the pictures into categories that include Living, Nonliving, and Dead.
2. Choose one picture of a plant and one picture of an animal from the collection. Ask students to describe the characteristics, or signs of life, associated with each living thing.

New Terms

Living—those things that are alive, or have the signs of life (e.g., a worm, a tree).
Nonliving—those things that have never been alive or can never show the signs of life (e.g., water, rocks).
Dead—those things that were once alive, but no longer have any of the signs of life (e.g., timber).

Materials

Signs of Life: Journal

Time Required

two class periods

✳ *Getting Started*

In this lesson, students investigate motion in plants and animals, and locomotion in animals. Students observe locomotion in a variety of small invertebrates and other animals.

Main Ideas

1. Animals move on their own from place to place.
2. Plants and animals move in response to environmental changes.
3. Animals move in a variety of ways.
4. Many forms of animal locomotion have been used as models for human inventions.

✳ *Teaching Strategies*

If possible, start growing pea or bean seedlings near a window 14 days before beginning this lesson so that students can observe how the seedlings move toward light. Let students turn the seedlings several times to see how the plants respond to the change.

Also, try to obtain a *Mimosa pudica*, the sensitive plant, from a nursery. Then students can observe how the leaves close when they are touched. The mimosa's leaves also close up very rapidly in response to irritation, smoke, or darkness. The mimosa can be reused in Lesson 6 of this unit.

Ask: How is plant movement different from animal movement? *(Plant movement is usually much slower than animal movement. Also, only one part of a plant usually moves, and the entire plant does not move from one place to another under its own power. Animal locomotion involves the coordinated movement of many or all parts of the body, and the animal moves from one place to another.)*

One of the first things you may notice about an animal is that it is able to move about on its own. This is called **locomotion** (*loco* is from the Latin word meaning "place"). Most animals have skeletons and muscles, which work together to provide freedom of movement.

Plants move as well. This motion is the result of a plant's reaction to changes in its environment. Because plants usually move rather slowly, we do not easily notice it. Look at the pictures of a bean seedling. Can you suggest how the plant's surroundings might cause the plant's stem to bend to one side? The pictures at the bottom of the page are of a mimosa plant. This plant moves when there is a change in its surroundings. The leaves of the mimosa sometimes close up very suddenly. Can you give a reason for this kind of motion? (A clue: The mimosa is also known as the "sensitive plant.")

Bean seedling—same plant photographed several times over a few days

Mimosa plant—before (left) and after (right) a stimulus

LESSON 2 ORGANIZER

Objectives

By the end of the lesson, students should be able to:
1. Compare and contrast the movements of plants and animals.
2. Observe and describe the motion of several animals.
3. Identify several forms of animal locomotion that have been copied by humans.

Process Skills

observing, using a data table, measuring, comparing

New Terms

Locomotion—the ability of an animal to move about on its own.

Observing Locomotion

For the experiment below, you can use any of the following small animals: a spider, an ant, a sowbug, a fly, a grasshopper, an earthworm, a caterpillar, a millipede, a salamander, or a small fish. But be gentle to be sure you do not harm the animal. Record your observations in a table like the one below.

Put one of the animals in a small container with a transparent seal. Cover the container with something that will keep out light. (A cloth or piece of cardboard will do.) Remove the covering carefully and watch the animal closely. How does the animal move when the cover is first removed? Record your observation. Continue to observe the animal for 2 minutes. Describe the way the animal moved, clearly and in as much detail as possible. Estimate how far the animal moved during the 2 minutes.

Repeat the experiment using other animals, and compare the results. Using your data, fill out a lab report that includes the information in the table.

Questions

1. What do you think made the animals move when the cover was first removed?

2. What do you think made the animals continue to move?

3. Which body parts did each animal use for locomotion?

4. If all the animals you observed could be entered in a 2-minute race, which would win?

5. What characteristic of this animal would make it a winner in such a race?

6. According to your data, which animal would come in last? Can you suggest reasons why?

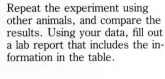

Piece of cloth

Container

Transparent seal

Name of Animal	How the Animal Moved When the Cover Was First Removed	Description of Animal Movement	How Far the Animal Moved in Two Minutes
○			

Exploration 1

Three days before the activity, ask students to collect a small animal, such as a spider, ant, sowbug, fly, grasshopper, caterpillar, millipede, salamander, or small fish. Instruct students to treat the animals with respect and to avoid harming them. Ask them to consider the environment in which the animal was found so that they can duplicate it in their containers.

Have students work in small groups and carefully observe four or five animals. Encourage students to make accurate estimates or measurements of the animals' locomotion. When the activity is over, animals should be released where they were found.

Answers to
Questions

1. They responded to the light.
2. They responded negatively by moving away from the light or positively by moving toward it.
3 & 4. Answers will depend on the animals used. Ask students to draw and label the different body parts used by the animal.
5. In general, animals that can fly or leap move the fastest.
6. The earthworm, which does not have legs, probably moves the slowest.

Materials

Exploration 1: small animals such as a spider, an ant, a sowbug, a fly, a grasshopper, an earthworm, a caterpillar, a millipede, a salamander, or a small fish; small containers, such as wide-mouthed jars and shoe boxes; cloth or pieces of cardboard to cover the containers; plastic wrap; string; metric ruler; watch or clock; Journal

Teacher's Resource Binder

Resource Worksheet 2–1
Resource Transparency 2–1

Science Discovery Videodisc

Disc 2, Image and Activity Bank, 2–2

Time Required

one to two class periods

Answers to

Animal Innovators

Have students work in small groups to make a list of human inventions that are similar to animal movements. Answers are:

- bat—hang gliders, airplanes
- cuttlefish—jet aircraft, rocket
- beaver—swim flippers
- hummingbird—hovercraft, gyrocopter, helicopter
- water beetle—hot-air balloon

✳ Follow Up

Assessment

Explain the following tasks to your students: Use one sheet of colored paper to design a device meant to travel well through the air. Explain why it is suited for air travel. Use a second sheet of paper to design a device meant to travel well in a liquid, like water. Again, explain why your device is suited to travel in a liquid. List examples of animals and human inventions that have the same features as your devices. *(Features appropriate for travel in air: streamlined, with pointed front; lightweight; and wide wings. Features appropriate for travel in water: streamlined, like a cone with a pointed front; fins.)*

Extension

Some of humanity's early attempts to fly involved attaching "wings" to a person's body. Have students do research to find out about one of these early attempts to fly, and write a report to explain what humans learned about the locomotion of animals from these attempts.

Animal Innovators

Can you imagine yourself flying through the air or swimming like a fish through the water? The animals shown here fly or swim in unique ways that make it look easy. In fact, the different ways their bodies work remind us of some of our own inventions.

On this page are pictures of animals that have different ways of moving in air or water. For each animal on this page, suggest human inventions that seem to imitate the animal's movement.

Cuttlefish—has special organs that draw in water and then force it out at high speed.

Bat—extends flaps of skin to catch the air.

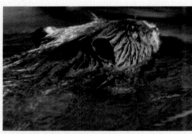

Beaver—webs of skin between its toes help to push the water.

Water Beetle—uses an air bubble to rise gently through the water.

Hummingbird—beats its wings so fast that they are only a blur; can hover and can even fly backwards.

3 Feet, Scales, and Bristles

Two-footed animal

Animals with Feet

Many animals rely on the use of limbs for locomotion. Some animals move about on many feet. Other animals have only one foot; slugs, snails, and periwinkles belong to this group. They move very slowly. Put a snail in a glass jar and observe how it uses its foot to move itself. Describe what you see.

Most animals that walk on land have four or more feet. Some of these animals (for example, bears, rabbits, and squirrels) can stand for a time on their hind feet to feed. Gorillas, chimpanzees, and other "great apes" can stand and walk on either two or four feet.

Birds have four limbs, however, the two front limbs have developed into wings. Birds stand and walk on their two hind limbs. Did you know that not all birds can fly? Try to name three such flightless birds.

The kangaroo stands on two feet, using its heavy tail to keep its balance. People stand and walk on two feet. This is called an erect posture. Human babies take time to develop this skill. See if you can find out from your parents how old you were when you were able to balance on two feet for the first time.

Insects have six legs. Imagine how much more complicated locomotion is on six legs than on two legs. There are hundreds of thousands of different kinds of insects, so obviously insects are able to get around without too much trouble.

Spiders are fascinating eight-legged animals. A spider's feet can walk on the thin threads of the web it spins. An oily substance on the spider's legs keeps it from sticking to its own web. Watch a spider and see if you can figure out the order in which it moves its feet.

Where is the snail's foot?

LESSON 3 ORGANIZER

Objectives

By the end of the lesson, students should be able to:
1. Observe different forms of animal locomotion.
2. Describe the locomotion of a variety of animals, including snakes, earthworms, horses, and certain insects.
3. Compare the locomotion of animals that have different numbers of feet.

Process Skills

observing, comparing, investigating, describing

New Terms

(Organizer continues on next page)

✳ Getting Started

Lesson 3 provides an opportunity for students to sharpen their observational skills by observing how several animals move, including those with feet, such as insects and spiders, and those without feet, such as earthworms and snakes. Also, students observe a series of illustrations of a moving horse to analyze its motion.

Main Ideas

1. Some animals are able to move without using legs and feet.
2. Locomotion can also be accomplished with two, four, six, eight, or more legs.

✳ Teaching Strategies

Animals with Feet

If possible, have a number of spiders in jars for students to observe. Ask students to count how many legs a spider has, and to figure out the order in which the spider moves its legs. (Spiders can be refrigerated for 30 to 60 minutes to slow down their leg movements.)

Also try to obtain a snail for students to observe. If it is placed in a jar, students can observe how it uses its foot to move. *(The foot is under the mantle, behind the head. Mucus, produced by glands in the foot, provides a slimy layer on which the snail moves. Muscles in the foot contract in a wavelike rhythm, pulling the snail along.)*

Tell students that there are a number of flightless birds including the ostrich, cassowary, emu, rhea, kiwi, and penguin.

Exploration 2

Tell students to follow the same procedure for capturing, holding, and releasing the insects as they did in *Exploration 1*. Students should discover that while an insect is moving, it always has three legs supporting its body. The supporting legs are always on opposite sides and positioned like a triangle. For example, during a step an insect may move legs 1, 4, and 5 forward while supporting itself with legs 2, 3, and 6. Legs 2, 3, and 6 will move first in the second step. Therefore, statement *(i)* is true.

Exploration 3

It is very difficult to observe a horse in motion. Students might be interested to know that not until 1877 was it proven that when a horse gallops, all four legs leave the ground simultaneously. Photographer Edweard Muybridge arranged 24 cameras with very rapid shutter speeds to photograph a moving horse. He attached strings to the camera shutters. These strings were tripped by the horse as it passed through them. The images on this page are derived from his photographs.

Answers to

Questions

1. Two legs usually touch the ground during a walk. At no time during walking are all four legs off the ground.
2. When a horse gallops, either none or all four feet touch the ground at one time.
3. During a walking gait, two legs are always touching the ground; during a running gait, all or none of the horse's feet are touching the ground.
4. Walking sequence: right foreleg, left hind leg, left foreleg, right hind leg.
5. Running sequence: the same as for walking.
6. The horse flexes its leg muscles much more when it is running than when it is walking.
7. A horse's walking gait is similar to that of a crawling baby: front right limb moves with left back limb, front left limb moves with right back limb.

Solve the Insect Movement Mystery

Put an insect on a piece of paper. Watch carefully to see how the insect moves. Decide which of the following things happen:

(a) The front legs both move forward at the same time.
(b) The middle legs both move forward at the same time.
(c) The hind legs both move forward at the same time.
(d) All three legs on one side move forward at the same time.
(e) On one side, the front and middle legs move forward at the same time.
(f) On one side, the front and back legs move forward at the same time.
(g) The legs all move at different times.
(h) Three legs move forward at the same time: the front and middle legs on one side, and the back leg on the other side.
(i) Three legs move forward at the same time: the front and hind legs on one side and the middle leg on the other side.

How's Your Horse Sense?

Below is a sequence of pictures showing a horse walking. On the facing page is another sequence of pictures showing a horse running. The pictures are arranged to show the order in which steps are taken. Study each set of pictures carefully. Then answer the questions that follow.

Questions

1. As the horse walks, how many feet touch the ground at a time? At any time are all of the horse's feet off the ground?
2. As the horse runs, how many feet touch the ground at a time?
3. How does the horse's running gait differ from its walking gait?
4. Describe the way the horse moves its legs throughout the walking sequence—for example, "right foreleg first, left hind leg second," and so on.
5. Repeat the description for the running sequence.
6. How does the horse flex its legs in the running sequence compared to the walking sequence?
7. Have you ever seen a baby crawl? How does the horse's walking gait compare to the movements of a crawling baby?

Walking

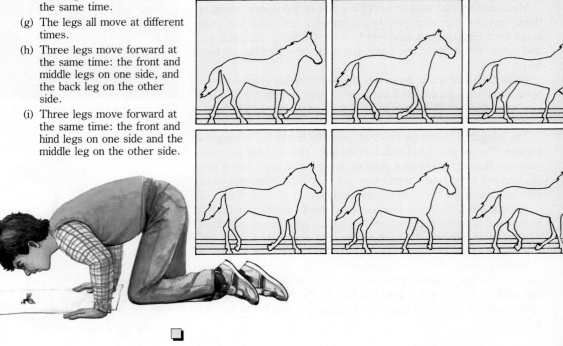

(Organizer continued)

Materials

Exploration 2: live insects, paper
Exploration 4: earthworms, stiff paper, water

Science Discovery Videodisc

Disc 2, Image and Activity Bank, 2–3

Time Required

three class periods

Comparing Structures

1. The illustrations on the right show a horse's forelimb and its human counterpart. Find the equivalents of the fingernails, fingers, hand, wrist, forearm, elbow, and upper arm in the horse's leg.
2. How is each of the structures in each forelimb well suited to its function?

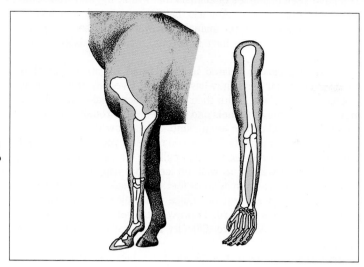

Running

Comparing Structures

To help students answer these questions, you may wish to have them trace the human and horse bones onto tracing paper and then color homologous bones the same color.

1. The horse equivalents of the human structures are as follows: fingernail—hoof; fingers—foot bones; hand—bones from foot to knee; wrist—knee; forearm—leg bones above knee; elbow—next joint above knee; upper arm—upper leg.
2. The structure of the human wrist and hand (gliding joints of the wrists, separate digits that bend in three places, and opposable thumbs) allow for a great deal of dexterity. The bones of the horse's upper leg are thicker and stronger to support weight. The hooves give the horse traction and support, and help absorb the shock when the hoof strikes the ground. The long legs of a horse allow it to run very fast.

Legless Wonders

Tell students to sit on the floor, take off their shoes and socks, and try to make their feet move forward by wiggling their toes. This will give them an idea of how snakes move by using their muscles. On smooth, flat ground, snakes move in a straight line by pushing their muscles against the ground. On rougher ground, snakes move in an S-shaped wave, pushing their bodies from side to side against small objects, such as pebbles and plants.

Have students read pages 64 and 65 and study the pictures. Then ask: Why don't pythons move in S-shaped curves? *(Their straight, forward motion is caused by the friction of the small plates, or scales, on their undersides pushing against the ground. These plates are connected to and controlled by the strong muscles surrounding the snake's body.)*

(Continues on next page)

Legless Wonders

You have seen examples of animals that swim, fly, and walk. Animals that fly have wings. Animals that swim have fins, and animals that walk have legs. Of the animals that walk, some have only two legs, while other animals have hundreds! Some animals even have no legs at all.

Snakes are closely related to lizards and alligators, yet they differ in one major way: they have no legs. Even so, they have no trouble moving about. With their sleek bodies, snakes are able to move easily through tunnels and crevices, or through thick vegetation. Many snakes can even climb trees. How do they do it?

Think for a moment about how you move as you walk. Your feet grip the ground, your leg muscles pull you forward, and then you push off. But if you try to walk on ice, what happens?

Snakes have scales instead of feet. The scales catch on rough surfaces just as your feet do. Once the scales have a grip, the snake then pushes forward. However, on very smooth surfaces such as glass, snakes have difficulty moving about. Why do you think this is so?

Some snakes move by first bending and then straightening their bodies. First they bend their bodies around an obstacle, such as a rock or plant stem. Then they straighten out and push off. As the snake moves it resembles an S-shaped wave in motion.

A snake moving along the ground, seen from above. Would this snake have any trouble moving along a glass tabletop?

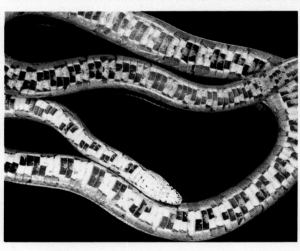

A snake's belly is covered with tough flaps of skin called scales.

A python moving along the ground, seen from above. Can you think of any reasons why pythons would move this way and not in S-shaped curves?

This side view of a python's skeleton helps to show how the python moves.

The scales on the python's belly are attached to muscles that can move the scales forward and backward. Use this knowledge and the drawings on the left to explain how the python moves forward.

The python's design allows it to move quickly and silently through tangled vegetation in search of prey.

(Legless Wonders continued)

If you feel comfortable handling snakes, have a snake available in the classroom for students to feel. They may be surprised to learn that snakes are not wet and slimy, but have tough, scaly skin that resists drying out. Have students notice how the snake moves, and how the snake's skin feels against their own skin, using its muscles to push itself along.

Exploration 4

Live earthworms can be caught in moist soil or purchased at a bait store. They should be obtained just before this exercise, and can be kept alive for a few days in a refrigerator.

If living earthworms are in short supply, movement can be demonstrated by placing a single worm on an overhead projector screen for a few minutes. Take care not to injure or dehydrate the earthworm. The sound made by an active earthworm moving on a stiff piece of paper may be loud enough to pick up with a microphone.

Introduce the terms *cross section* and *lengthwise (lateral) section* so that students can better describe the muscle action of the earthworm.

Have students close their books and write their own descriptions of how the earthworm moves before reading the description in their texts.

✳ *Follow Up*

Assessment

Ask students to classify the following animals according to their method of locomotion: turtle, sparrow, toad, grasshopper, rattlesnake, cat, giraffe, snail, housefly, perch, hawk, spider. Students should tell how each animal's structure is adapted to help it to move. *(turtle—has 4 legs, walks;*
sparrow—has 2 legs, hops, perches;
  has wings, flies;
toad—has 4 legs, hops;
grasshopper—has six legs, hops,
  crawls; has wings, flies;
rattlesnake—has no legs, crawls;
cat—has four legs, walks, runs,
  pounces;
giraffe—has four legs, walks, runs;
snail—has one foot, crawls;
housefly—has six legs, walks; has
  wings, flies;
perch—has fins, swims;
hawk—has 2 legs, perches, walks;
  has wings, flies;
spider—has 8 legs, walks, pounces)

Listening to an Earthworm!

Put an earthworm on a piece of stiff paper. Can you hear it make any noise as it moves?

Hold the paper up level with your eyes and try to look between the animal and the paper. Do you see the bristles? Rub your finger back and forth along the lower side of the earthworm. Do you feel the bristles? When the stiff bristles are extended, they hold the animal in place on the ground. When the bristles are pulled in, the animal can slide along. When the earthworm moves along paper, its bristles sometimes make a scraping noise.

Notice the rings on the body of the worm. The inside of an earthworm's body is divided into sections called *segments*, which show up on the outside as rings. There are four pairs of bristles for every segment. How many bristles does your earthworm have?

Now put the earthworm on damp paper. Watch it move. How does the earthworm use its bristles to propel itself? Write down your observations.

Like snakes, earthworms have muscles. How does the earthworm use its muscles to move? Look at the illustration. Locate the muscles. These muscles are very strong. One set of muscles goes around the worm in rings.

Now locate the muscles that run lengthwise along the worm's body. The two sets of muscles work against each other. What happens when one set of these muscles contracts and the other set relaxes? When the ring muscles contract, what happens to the length of the segment? When the lengthwise muscles contract, what happens to the length of the segment? See if you can piece together this information about the muscles and bristles and write a description of how earthworms move.

Inside and lengthwise look at an earthworm.

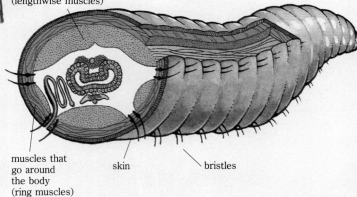

muscles that go the length of the worm (lengthwise muscles)

muscles that go around the body (ring muscles) skin bristles

Compare your description with the one provided below.

1. When the earthworm moves, the ring muscles in the segments at the front contract, while the lengthwise muscles relax. In this way, the earthworm is "squeezed" forward.

2. At the same time, the bristles at the front end are pulled in while the bristles at the back end hold the animal in place.

3. The bristles at the front end are now put out to keep the front end in place, while the bristles at the back end are pulled in.

4. The back segments now become shorter as the lengthwise muscles contract and the ring muscles relax. The rear part of the body slides forward.

Extension

1. Have students make a "flick-book" to illustrate the motion of a snake or another creature. Students should draw a separate diagram on each page, each diagram differing only slightly from the one before. When flicked steadily with the fingers, the diagrams illustrate the sequence of events that occur as the animal moves. (The diagrams will require the same scale.)

2. Search for detailed illustrations or photographs of a centipede and a millipede. Ask students to answer the following questions.
   (a) Count, or estimate, the legs on each animal. A magnifying glass will help.
   (b) How many legs are found on each body segment of each kind of animal? Read about it in a reference book in the library, if necessary.

1. What characteristics do living things have in common? Sometimes a nonliving thing has a characteristic of a living thing. How many examples of this can you list? Make a class list—Can you top 20 examples? If a nonliving thing has a characteristic of something that is alive, why is it classified as nonliving?

2. A biologist made the following classification of all objects:
   (a) Living—having all the signs of life
   (b) Dead—having once had all the signs of life
   (c) Nonliving—never having had all the signs of life

   Where does a wooden chair fit in? How about other things—water, mushrooms, a pie? Classify each of the following into one of the three groups:

   > oyster, moss, yeast cake, salt ,sugar, bones, hibernating bear, pencil, wool sweater, seaweed, sponge, pearl, volcano, kernel of corn, clams, barnacle on a rock, bean seed, baked beans, freshly picked strawberries, pine cone, lichens on a rock, electric fan, cactus, paper

3. Your class has just been asked to write the section in the *Book of Knowledge* called "Wonder Questions." Choose one question from the list below. The question should be answered clearly in a paragraph of 150 words or less and should be understandable to an 11- or 12-year old. If an illustration would help, draw one!
   (a) Why does a baby have to learn how to walk?
   (b) How do you tell a plant from an animal?
   (c) In how many different ways can animals move?
   (d) How does an insect use its six legs to move?
   (e) How does a horse use its four legs to move?

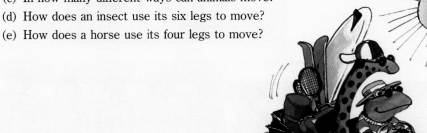

Answers to
Challenge Your Thinking

1. • Answers will vary, but some possible characteristics of living things are as follows: growth, reproduction, consume food, produce their own food, movement, response to stimulus, life span, ingestion, digestion, respiration, excretion
   • Answers will vary but some examples of non-living things with living characteristics include machines that move and mechanical devices that respond to stimuli, such as a smoke detector or a burglar alarm. For something to be alive, it must have *all* of the characteristics of living things.

2. **living:** mushrooms, oyster, moss, yeast cake, hibernating bear, seaweed, sponge (if natural and still living in water), kernel of corn (contains embryo), clams, barnacle, bean seed, seeds contained in a strawberry, seeds contained in pine cone scale, lichens, cactus
   nonliving: water, salt, pencil (lead), pearl, volcano, electric fan
   dead: pie, wooden chair, sugar, bone, pencil (wood), wool sweater, baked beans, paper

3. (a) A baby must learn how to walk because walking involves learning how to put together a pattern of muscle movements in a harmonious way.
   (b) Unlike animals, most plants make their own food and most contain chlorophyll, a green pigment necessary for making food. Also, plants are unable to move from place to place; they can only move parts of their bodies.
   (c) Swimming, burrowing, walking, running, hopping, crawling, soaring, and flying are some examples of animal locomotion.
   (d) Insects usually walk by moving a middle leg on one side at the same time that they move their front and hind legs on the other.
   (e) A horse walks by alternating its legs from front to back and side to side. One possible sequence could be: left front, right rear, right front, left rear.

LESSON 4

☀ Getting Started

Lesson 4 focuses on the growth rates of human beings, and provides an opportunity for students to observe, measure, and calculate the growth rates of various parts of their bodies.

Main Ideas

1. Growth is a characteristic of all living things.
2. Not all people grow at the same rate or reach the same size.
3. The proportion of the head to the total body size changes as a human develops from embryo to adult.

☀ Teaching Strategies

Measuring Human Growth

Ask students to work in pairs to do the activity. Have each student determine their measurements and fill them in on a data chart like the one shown on page 69. Ask each student to predict how tall he or she will be as an adult. (Be careful that this activity does not become embarrassing for any students.)

You may wish to demonstrate how to make accurate body measurements. To measure height, tape a large sheet of paper to the wall. Have a student stand up straight against the paper. Place a ruler on the student's head so that it is perpendicular to the wall. Make a mark on the paper where the ruler touches the paper. Measure leg length from the floor to the side hip joint, where the leg bends. Measure head height from the end of the chin to the crown.

4 Human Growth

Locomotion is vital to most animals, but growth is a fundamental characteristic of all living things—plants and animals. One thing you know for certain is that you are growing. But how much do you grow? Do all parts of your body grow at the same time or at the same rate? Do they grow in the same proportions?

Measuring Human Growth

With the help of a friend, find:

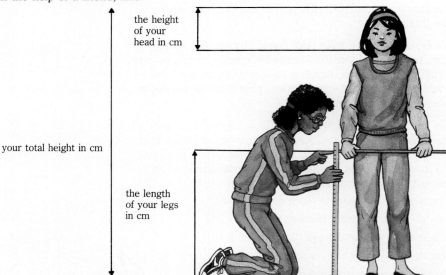

the height of your head in cm

your total height in cm

the length of your legs in cm

A. A few people

B. Most people

LESSON 4 ORGANIZER

Objectives

By the end of the lesson, students should be able to:

1. Compare growth rates in human beings.
2. Identify the parts of the human body that grow least or most during various growth stages.

Process Skills

measuring, comparing, predicting, making a chart

New Terms

What proportion of your total height is taken up by your legs? What proportion of your total height is taken up by your head? Record your results in a table like the one to the right. How do you think your results would differ if you were measuring a 6-month-old baby? Compare your measurements with those of an adult.

How tall will you be as an adult? Do you have a record at home of your height when you were very young? If you are a girl, double your length at 18 months. If you are a boy, double your length at 2 years. How old do you think you were when you were one-half the height you are now? You might be surprised to discover how long ago that was!

	Height/ Length (cm)	Proportion (%)
Total		
Legs		
Head		

Your Class Profile

Picture all the members of your class standing in line from the shortest to the tallest person, as in the illustration below. Compare the heights of all the members of your class. Is your class "profile" similar to the one in the illustration below? How many people are in A? B? C?

Not all people grow at the same rate, nor do all people reach the same height. There is nothing unusual about this. For any characteristic you could name, height or hair color, for example, each person differs at least slightly from every other person. In fact, such *variation* can be found in any group of living things. The amount of variation depends on the characteristic measured. If you made a class profile using shoe size, would you expect the shoe size profile to be similar to the height profile? Try it.

How to calculate %

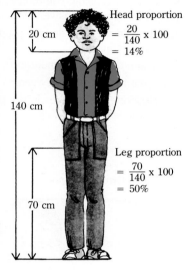

Head proportion
$= \frac{20}{140} \times 100$
$= 14\%$

Leg proportion
$= \frac{70}{140} \times 100$
$= 50\%$

20 cm
140 cm
70 cm

A Class Profile

C. A few people

Your Class Profile

It is important that students realize that a range of measurements is quite normal in any group of living things. Since many of the girls may have already had their growth spurt, they may be taller than the boys. Tell students that they will learn more about growth spurts in *Activity 3* on page 71.

Direct students' attention to the figure on the right side of the page that illustrates how to calculate proportion. Make sure students understand the meaning of the term proportion and how it is calculated. Ask: Why is a proportion expressed as a percentage? How else can a proportion be expressed? *(A proportion is a part in relation to its whole. Thus, it can be expressed as a fraction or as a percentage.)*

Materials

Measuring Human Growth: meter stick, measuring tape or metric ruler, Journal

Teacher's Resource Binder

Graphic Organizer Transparency 2–2

Science Discovery Videodisc

Disc 2, Image and Activity Bank, 2–4

Time Required

two class periods

Human Growth Patterns

Discuss why all the drawings of the human growth stages are exactly the same height. *(So that students can compare the growth of the different parts of the body.)*

Answers to

Activity 1

(a) From stages 1 to 7, the changes are:
- The head becomes smaller in relation to the total height.
- The legs get longer in relation to the total height.

(b) The legs undergo the greatest change from birth to 5 years. They develop slowly while the baby is still in the womb.

(c) The head grows fastest before birth. Many bodily functions are controlled by the brain, so the brain develops early in life.

(d) Tell students to consider the chart to be "40 parts" high with each of the 4 divisions containing an equal "10 parts."

Stage 1
Head proportion =
$20/40 \times 100\% = 50\%$
Leg proportion =
$7/40 \times 100\% = 17.5\%$

Stage 4
Head proportion =
$9/40 \times 100\% = 22.5\%$
Leg proportion =
$15/40 \times 100\% = 37.5\%$

Stage 7
Head proportion =
$5/40 \times 100\% = 12.5\%$
Leg proportion =
$18/40 \times 100\% = 45\%$

Human Growth Patterns

As you know, people grow to different heights and weights. But did you know that as we grow, the proportions of our head, body, and limbs change? This pattern of change is similar for everyone.

Imagine that you have been selected by a team of scientists to write a report on their findings about human growth patterns. The results of the scientists' study are shown on these two pages. The directions that follow will help you write your report.

Activity 1

The characters in the figure below show the human body in seven stages from before birth to adulthood. Each stage is drawn to the same height to allow you to compare the growth of the different parts of the body. Answer the following in your report:

(a) How do the head and leg proportions change through the different stages?

(b) When do the legs undergo the greatest change?

(c) What part of the body seems to develop the earliest?

(d) Describe the changes in the proportions of a developing person in stages 1 to 7.

Human Growth Stages

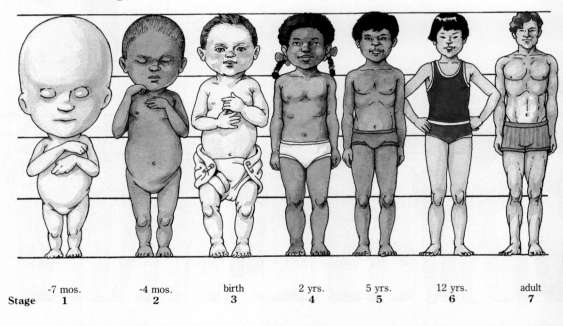

	-7 mos.	-4 mos.	birth	2 yrs.	5 yrs.	12 yrs.	adult
Stage	1	2	3	4	5	6	7

Activity 2

The table at right compares average height, head size, brain weight, and total weight at three different ages. The comparisons are shown as a percentage of the adult values. Answer the following in your report:

(a) Which feature develops earliest in life?

(b) Which feature develops the least in the first 5 years?

(c) An 18-year-old is 160 cm tall and has a body weight of 50 kg. Using the chart, figure the height and body weight of this person at birth and at 5 years of age.

Activity 3

The figure below compares the growth rate of girls and boys. Answer the following in your report:

(a) When do girls get a large growth spurt?

(b) When do boys get a large growth spurt?

(c) Who, on the average, is taller at adulthood?

Changes in Size and Height

Feature	At Birth	Age 5 Years	Age 18 Years
Head size	60%	90%	100%
Brain Weight	25%	90%	100%
Height	30%	65%	100%
Total body weight	5%	30%	100%

Growth Rates

Age in years

Answers to

Activity 3

(a) Girls have a large growth spurt between the ages of 11 and 15 years.

(b) Boys have a large growth spurt between the ages of 16 and 20 years.

(c) On the average, men are taller than women at adulthood.

✳ Follow Up

Assessment

1. Ask students to complete a class profile entitled "Our Class in 10 Years." (Refer to page 69 for instructions.) Students should use a bar graph to show what the expected heights of class members will be at that time. Ask students to then compare that bar graph to the present class profile to answer the following questions.
   (a) How do the profiles compare?
   (b) What changes do you notice?

2. Divide a long chalkboard into 30-cm sections. Label each section, counting by 5, up to 20. Each section will represent 5 years of age. This will serve as a time line on which students can place pictures. Have students cut out magazine pictures of people from ages 0 to 20. (This could include pictures of themselves at various stages of growing up.) Ask students to look at the people in the pictures and predict where they should be placed on the time line. Have students use characteristics such as head size, leg length, body weight, and head to body proportions to help them decide the ages of the people in the pictures.

Extension

Ask students to compare human life spans to those of some animals. For example, the human life span in the United States is, on the average, 75 years. The average life span of a lion is 23 years; a bear, 20 years; a cat, dog or monkey, 15 years. Have students make a bar graph showing the life spans of these animals and others they find out about.

Answers to

Activity 2

The table at the top of page 71 lists four features of the human body. It shows the amount of change that occurs with each feature as a percentage of the total adult value.
(a) Head size develops earliest in life.

(b) Total body weight develops least in the first 5 years.

(c) For the 18-year-old student who is 160 cm tall and weighs 50 kg, the height at birth was: 30/100 × 160 cm = 48 cm; the body weight at birth was 5/100 × 50 kg = 2.5 kg; the height at age 5 years was 65/100 × 160 cm = 104 cm; the body weight at age 5 years was 30/100 × 50 kg = 15 kg.

Humans are not the only things that grow. All plants and animals grow. Measuring their growth is not always as easy as you might think, though.

With a partner, compare leaves from a seedling with those of a full-grown tree of the same type. Think of the different ways you might measure the size of the leaves. Use the way you think best to measure the growth of the leaf.

Now compare the sizes of the stems of the seedling and the tree by measuring the distance around the stems (the circumference). As the plant grows to maturity, which changes most—the leaves or the stem? Which part of the plant do you think develops most at an early age? Why?

Compare the maple seedling to the fully grown maple tree. You can look at the leaves and stems to describe the maple's growth pattern. Do you think all trees have the same growth pattern?

☀ Getting Started

Lesson 5 explores different forms of growth in plants and animals, and the conditions that affect this growth. *Exploration 5* helps students discover some of the conditions necessary for seed germination. Growth patterns, re-generation of parts, reproduction, and some types of harmful growth are also discussed.

Main Ideas

1. Many different factors affect the growth of plants and animals.
2. Light, temperature, and moisture are factors that may affect the growth of seeds.
3. Large size can create special problems for an organism.
4. There are many different forms of growth, including tissue renewal and repair, regeneration of lost body parts, reproduction, cancer, and galls.

☀ Teaching Strategies

If possible, take students outdoors for the tree-comparison activity. They will need a measuring tape and graph paper. Have students measure five leaves from a seedling and five leaves (older leaves, not shoots) from the same type of fully grown tree. Students may outline the leaf on graph paper, then count the squares within the out-line.

The average size of the leaves from the seedling should be smaller. There should be a much greater difference be-tween stem circumferences of older and younger trees. Ask students to ex-plain this. *(At an early age, leaves de-velop faster than stems. This provides the plant with sites of photosynthetic activity to make food for growth.)*

L ESSON 5 ORGANIZER

Objectives

By the end of the lesson, students should be able to:
1. Design an experiment to test the effect of different conditions on seed growth.
2. Comprehend why large size may pose problems to living things.
3. Identify different types of growth pat-terns, including continued growth, re-newal, reproduction, regeneration, and harmful growth.

Process Skills

comparing, measuring, designing an experi-ment, writing a report

New Terms

Germinate—to sprout or grow from a seed or bud.
Regeneration—the growth of new body parts to replace those lost or damaged.

Conditions for Growth

If you were to fall into icy water, you would probably die within 10 minutes. An orchid dies when the temperature drops below 28°C overnight. Tropical fish suffer when the water temperature decreases suddenly. A cactus plant thrives in the parched desert. A rosebush blooms where the air is moist.

Many conditions affect the lives of plants and animals. Moisture and temperature are two such conditions, as the examples above indicate. What other conditions do you think influence the lives of plants and animals?

Ways of Growing Seeds

soil in egg cartons

seeds between moistened paper towels

seeds on moistened cotton wool

soil in a plastic-foam cup

jar

moist sawdust

seeds

paper towel

Changing Conditions

The labels on seed packages must be accurate and must describe the best methods and conditions for growing seeds. Improper conditions and sudden or extreme changes in the environment can damage the seeds and prevent growth.

Imagine that you are a botanist working for a seed company. You are responsible for testing different conditions for growing seeds and for developing directions to go on the label. Discover what conditions are needed to produce the best results. Some of the conditions that could be tested are light, temperature, and moisture.

Make a report for the company files and write a draft of the instructions needed for the seed package. In your report, include the following information: the sets of conditions you tested, what happened to each group of seeds, and which conditions were the best. One word you might find useful in writing the report is *germinate*. This means "to begin to grow from a seed." Another word sometimes used for this process is *sprout*.

In performing your tests, you have worked with conditions that you could change. You gave each group of seeds a set of conditions different from the conditions given the other groups of seeds. Remember that a condition that can or does change is called a variable. Describe the variables used in your experiments.

You might also want to mention any difficulties you had with your report. How did you solve them?

Conditions for Growth

Ask students: What other conditions affect the lives of plants and animals? *(Plants and animals may be affected by temperature, light, food supply, weather, pollution, population, type and number of predators, and shelter.)*

Exploration 5

Have students work in groups of three or four. Mung beans or alfalfa seeds from health food stores are excellent seeds to use. Allow at least 10 days for the experiment to permit complete germination. Explain to students that they should use several seeds in each group. They should make careful observations each day, record the number of days it takes for the seeds to germinate, and the percentage of germination for each group of seeds. Some possible variables:
- water vs. no water
- temperature
- light vs. darkness
- soil vs. cotton wool
- sand vs. soil mix
- depth of planting
- number of seeds in a given area
- oxygen vs. no oxygen (covered with oil vs. no oil)

Students should discover that seeds need water, oxygen, and warm temperatures to germinate. Once they have germinated, those in soil or soil mix will grow better than those in sand (which contains no nutrients and cannot hold water) or cotton wool (which contains no nutrients). The optimum depth for planting is about 5 times the size of the seed. If seeds are planted too close together, the seedlings will not get enough light or nutrients.

Cancer—a wild, uncontrolled growth within an organism.

Gall—a harmful growth found on the leaves, stems, or roots of a plant.

Reproduction—the process by which organisms produce offspring of their own kind.

Species—a group of closely related organisms that can mate and produce living young.

Materials

Exploration 5: quick-growing seeds (mung bean, alfalfa, radish, or mustard seeds); growth medium for seeds (soil mix, paper towels, sawdust, sand, or cotton wool); small containers for growing seeds (plastic cups, egg cartons, or jars); water

Other Growth Patterns: measuring tape or metric ruler, 2 leaves (1 from a seedling, 1 from a full-grown tree of the same type)

Teacher's Resource Binder

Activity Worksheets 2–2 and 2–3
Graphic Organizer Transparency 2–3

Science Discovery Videodisc

Disc 2, Image and Activity Bank, 2–5

Time Required

three class periods

Large vs. Larger

Discuss with students the disadvantages of extreme size in nature. For example, the food requirements of an animal depend upon the volume of the animal's body. On the average, an African elephant is 5 m tall and an Asian elephant is 3.5 m tall. Proportionally, the African elephant is 1.4 times taller than the other, but it is also 1.4 times longer and 1.4 times thicker. Its volume, therefore, is 1.4 × 1.4 × 1.4, or 2.7 times as great as its smaller relative. It is likely that it would require at least two and one-half times as much food to survive. *Human Growth Patterns, Activity 2,* similarly demonstrates that if a person's height at age 18 is 160 cm and total body weight is 50 kg, height increases about 3 times, while body weight can increase at least 8 times.

Answer to caption: Size is not the only difference between African and Asian elephants. If students observe the picture carefully, they will observe that the African elephant has much larger ears than the Asian elephant. Other differences not visible from the illustration are larger tusks on the African Elephant, and the Asian Elephant has two humps, rather than one, on its forehead. The skin of the African elephant is also much more wrinkled.

Large vs. Larger

Is bigger always better? Large size can have its problems. An African elephant grows to be much larger than an Asian elephant. The African elephant also eats much more than the Asian elephant. This means that the African elephant must spend most of its waking time finding food and eating, just to stay alive. The Asian elephant, on the other hand, spends only about half its time eating. Why does the African elephant need to eat so much more food? Is the African elephant twice as big as the Asian elephant?

Can you tell the Asian elephant from the African elephant? (Hint: Size is not the only clue.)

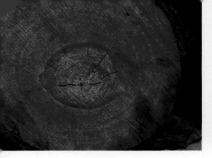  

How Old?

Some living things show their age in obvious ways. Tree rings, rings on a fish scale, and rings on an antelope's horn, all shown above, are examples of this. What part of each of the living things below would you examine to find out how old it is?

How Old?

To determine the age of the organisms shown,
- count the number of annual growth rings on tree trunks.
- count the ridges on clam shells.
- count the number of rings on the horn of an antelope.
- study the markings on the bill of a puffin.
- assess which of a horse's teeth have come in and the angle at which the teeth lie. (Horse teeth come in straight, but the angle changes as the horse matures.)

If possible, bring in the cross-section of a log and/or some clam shells. Explain that the rings of a tree are caused by seasonal differences in growth—in summer, the tree grows rapidly, resulting in a wide, light-colored band. During the colder seasons, tree cells do not grow as large or as fast, resulting in a narrower, dark-colored band. Similarly, the bands on a clam shell are caused by seasonal variations in growth. Challenge students to look at the specimens you brought to class and estimate the age of the tree and the clams by counting the bands. If it is known when the tree was cut down, they may wish to label significant years, such as the year they were born, on the tree cross-section.

Answers to

Continued Growth

- The fingernail that grows at a faster rate: the thumbnail.
- The other part of you that continues to grow: your hair.

Renewal

Ask students what happens when they have a cut, scratch, or burn that has removed part of the skin. Discuss how the skin is replaced as the wound heals. Explain that, in humans, parts of muscles and nerves also regrow, or regenerate, as long as the loss has not been too great. Tell students that all living things, both plant and animal, are able to regenerate some parts. But some animals, unlike humans, are able to regenerate major parts of their bodies. Have students read, on pages 76 to 79, about some animals that have amazing regenerative abilities.

Ask students if they have ever tried catching lizards or salamanders. They may have discovered that the tail falls off when grasped. They also might have noticed that the tails were more brightly colored than the rest of the bodies. Ask students how the ability of some lizards and salamanders to snap off their tails acts as a protective adaptation. *(The bright colors of the tail draw attention away from the vital parts of the animal. Then the tail can break off, allowing the animal to survive.)*

Continued Growth

The upper front teeth of mice and related animals, such as beavers and squirrels, continue to grow throughout the animals' lives. The teeth are kept sharp and at an appropriate length by the animals' gnawing. Parts of your body grow continuously too. It takes about one year for a fingernail to grow from the base to the edge at the tip of your finger. If it takes a year for each fingernail to grow, which one must grow at a faster rate, your thumbnail or your little finger nail? What other part of you continues to grow throughout your life?

Renewal

Another kind of growth is the renewal that follows an injury. When you skin your elbow, some of the skin is destroyed. Your body immediately begins a healing process to repair the damage. But there is a limit. After severe burns, for example, renewal may not occur naturally; skin grafting may have to be done.

Some animals have a remarkable capacity for renewal. For example, salamanders can replace a lost tail with a new one. This process is called **regeneration.**

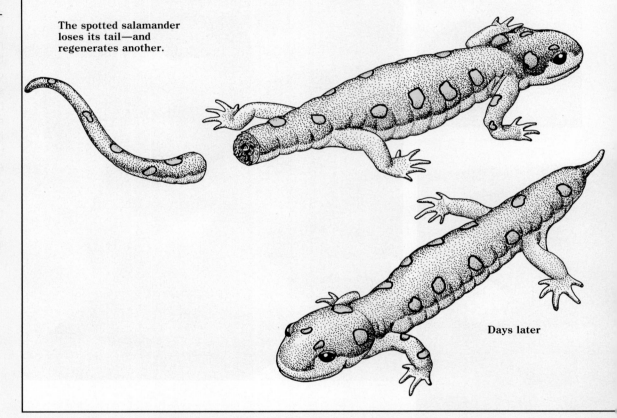

The spotted salamander loses its tail—and regenerates another.

Days later

Hercules and the Hydra

Hercules of mythical might,
  Hydra the serpent he slew
Off went Hydra's heads in the fight
  But in place of each, two new
  ones grew!
Our hero met with great frustration
From Hydra's swift regeneration.

Hercules and the Hydra

Students may need some background information about the poem on page 77. Hercules and the Hydra, pictured in the illustration, are figures from Greek mythology. The Hydra was difficult to kill because as soon as a head was cut off, a new head would regenerate. The necks had to be sealed with fire to prevent the heads from growing back.

Challenge students to find out information on the animal genus *Hydra*. Ask students to find out what similarities there are between this real-life *Hydra* and the Hydra from mythology. *(Both Hydras can regenerate parts of their bodies.)*

Lobster

Ask students if they have ever seen lobsters or crabs at the seashore with one claw smaller than the other. Some of these animals have lost their original claws and are in the process of growing new ones. Crustaceans, such as lobsters and crabs, have the ability to self-amputate their legs. The caught or injured leg is broken off at a specific breaking point at the base of the leg. A special muscle in the leg contracts excessively to cause a rupture at the breaking point. Wounds heal more quickly at this point, thus preventing blood loss.

Lobster

A lobster gets its claw caught in a rock crevice. As the lobster struggles to get free, its claw breaks off at a joint. Several months later, a new full-sized claw has replaced the one lost.

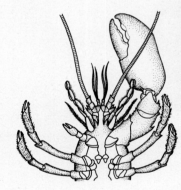

Tadpole

Tadpoles that lose a leg can grow a new leg in its place. Adult frogs cannot regenerate lost legs!

Planaria

Planaria are tiny flatworms found in fresh water under logs and stones. Some are about the size of a large ant. Cut them in half, and two planaria result. It is also possible to create two-headed planaria.

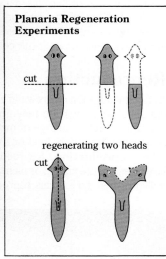

Planaria Regeneration Experiments

cut

regenerating two heads

cut

Starfish

Starfish invade clam beds to feed. Because of this, fishermen used to cut starfish into pieces and throw them back in the water to destroy them. Unfortunately, doing this caused a population explosion, since most of the chopped-up pieces grew back as complete starfish.

Sea Cucumber

If attacked, the sea cucumber may discharge some of its internal organs to distract the attacker. It later regenerates these lost parts.

Can you think of examples of regeneration in plants?

Starfish

Ask students why it is important for people who fish for a living to know as much as possible about the organisms that inhabit the area where they fish. *(They will be less apt to make mistakes such as cutting up a starfish.)* Ask: Why is it important for them to know about these animals' prey and predators? *(They will be able to harvest the most fish possible, without upsetting the balance of creatures in the system of living things.)* Tell students that an adult starfish can eat 8 to 10 clams or oysters a day. Thus, cutting up starfish and throwing them back in the water can quickly decimate a clam or oyster bed.

Planaria

If you wish the students to carry out the planaria regeneration experiments, planaria can be ordered from a biological supply company or caught in a pond. To catch them in a pond, stand on the shore or a dock and hang fresh bait of raw liver from a string. When the planarians come to feed, scoop them up with a dip net and transfer them to a jar filled with pond water. Planarians might also be found underneath rocks in ponds and streams.

Have the students do some library research to find out how to care for the planarians and which parts of the planarians regenerate. Then have students design their own experiments to investigate regeneration in planaria.

Answers to

Sea Cucumber

If you break off the top of a plant or the end of a branch, the plant will regrow from buds located lower on the stem or on the roots.

Harmful Growth

Ask students to look for and bring in samples of different kinds of galls on leaves or stems. These can be found during any season. (Oak trees often have leaf galls.) Galls can be caused by a variety of organisms, such as insects, fungi, and bacteria. After the infecting organism enters the plant, normal tissue is transformed into cancerous tissue, which undergoes rapid growth. The insect deposits an egg in the plant, and the plant responds by growing a gall. The galls provide the occupants with shelter, protection, and food. Open up a gall and look for the developing insect inside, or the hole that the insect used to leave the gall.

Reproduction

Explain to students that plants and animals reproduce in a variety of ways. These include:

- sexual, usually requiring two parents, results when two cells, from two distinct sexes, are joined. Examples of this are fertilized eggs in animals and seeds in flowering plants.
- asexual reproduction results from the division or multiplication of cells in a single parent. Examples include runners in plants and budding in yeast.

✳ *Follow Up*

Assessment

Have students design an experiment to test the effects of two other variables not already tested in *Exploration 5.* Students should describe their seed germination set-up. *(Answers will vary, but the experiment should be set up so that only one variable is changed; all other variables should remain constant. The variable changed could be depth of planting or amount of oxygen present. Or, the effect of low moisture level could be compared among different seed types. The moisture present would stay the same low level; the seed type would be the changing variable.)*

Harmful Growth

Can growth ever be out of control and harmful to living things? Under usual circumstances, how often cells divide is carefully controlled. But sometimes, cells can lose these controls and divide more often than normal. If these dividing cells damage or destroy surrounding tissues, the condition is called **cancer.** Not all rapidly dividing cells cause cancer, though. A wart is an example of a non-cancerous growth.

Another kind of harmful growth, called a **gall,** is found on the stems of many plants and on tree leaves. These "sores" are caused by insects that have put their eggs onto a plant and irritated the plant's cells, making the cells grow to form a gall.

Reproduction

All plants and animals grow old and eventually die. The place of the old generation must be taken by a new generation. Each animal and plant reaches a stage of maturity when it is able to produce a new generation of its kind or *species*. This kind of replacement is called **reproduction.** Reproduction is made possible by special structures of the animal or plant. Can you think of different ways in which plants and animals reproduce?

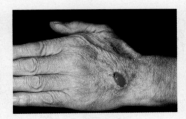

Two forms of harmful growth: above, a gall on a plant stem; below, a human skin cancer.

Through reproduction, species produce more of their own kind.

Extension

Turn your classroom into a mini-jungle. Have students bring in cuttings, and see how many different plants they can successfully propagate. They will need small containers with drainage, a light-weight soil mix (a 50:50 mix of peat moss and vermiculite works well), and plastic bags. In general, cuttings should be about 10 cm long. Gently plant them in a moistened soil mix and keep them in plastic, out of sunlight, for about a week. Then place them in sunlight and keep the soil moist. Plants that are easy to propagate include: spider plants, *Sansevieria*, African violets, Wandering Jew, jade plants, *Coleus*, and Swedish ivy.

Challenge Your Thinking

1. As a researcher at the museum, you have discovered three ancient carvings in a drawer. You and your colleagues are discussing how to label these carvings:

Dr. Ruiz: "These appear to be alien."
Dr. Chan: "Hardly, they are just carvings of humans from different parts of the world."
Dr. Artwell: "No, no, no, you can see that they are just primitive carvings of people in this country."
You: "Here is what I think . . . ."

In a paragraph, convince Drs. Ruiz, Chan, and Artwell of your opinion.

2. Look at the bar graph illustrating the height of students in Ada's class, and then answer the questions. Ada is 130 cm tall.

   (a) How many students are there in Ada's class?

   (b) How many boys are shorter than Ada?

   (c) How many girls are as tall as Ada or taller?

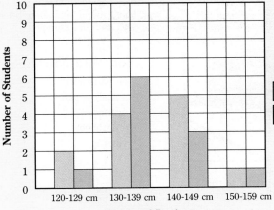

3. Add the answers to the following "Wonder Questions" to the *Book of Knowledge* that you worked on earlier in the unit.

   (a) Do boys grow faster than girls?

   (b) Why does a baby have such a big head?

   (c) Is bigger always better?

   (d) How can you tell the ages of plants and animals?

   (e) Can an animal lose a part and grow a new one?

   (f) Do all parts of humans grow at the same rate?

Answers to
Challenge Your Thinking

1. Answers will vary considerably, but some students might notice the similarity between the proportion of the body parts of the statues pictured in the illustration and the proportions shown in *Human Growth Stages* on page 70.

2. (a) There are 23 students in Ada's class.
   (b) Two boys are shorter than Ada.
   (c) One girl is shorter than Ada; the rest are as tall or taller.

3. Accept a wide variety of student answers, but the following are possible responses.
   (a) Boys and girls both experience growth spurts; these growth spurts usually occur earlier in girls.
   (b) The brain develops rapidly and early on because of its importance in carrying out bodily functions.
   (c) When an organism is bigger, it usually requires a greater amount of energy to sustain itself.
   (d) In animals: size, proportion of body parts; in plants: total size of plant, leaf size, circumference of stems and branches, number of rings in trunk.
   (e) Some animals can, including the planaria, lizard and salamander, crab and lobster, starfish, and tadpole.
   (f) Different parts of the body grow at different rates depending on the stage of growth.

LESSON 6

✳ Getting Started

This lesson helps students identify response to a stimulus as a characteristic of living things. Responses are identified as positive or negative.

Main Ideas

1. A stimulus can cause a response in a living organism.
2. Responses to stimuli may be positive or negative.
3. Most plants respond slowly to a stimulus, but some can respond very quickly.

✴ Teaching Strategies

Have students read page 82. Ask them to name examples of animals reacting positively and negatively to different stimuli.

Answers to

In-Text Questions

- The common meaning of irritability is where a person is quick to anger. This is similar to the scientific definition which defines irritability as a response to a situation.
- The stimuli depicted on page 58 are *amount of light* and *pressure from touch.*

Answer to caption: Have students share their drawings of a cat responding negatively.

Anything that causes living things to react is called a **stimulus.** The reaction to a stimulus is called a **response.** All living things respond to stimuli. The scientific term for the ability to respond to stimuli is *irritability.* How does the scientific meaning of this word compare to the common meaning? What were the stimuli that caused the responses depicted in the photos on page 58?

Animals respond to a number of stimuli—for example, odors, temperature, light, taste, touch, gravity, and electric shock. In order to test the responses of living things, you should experiment with one stimulus at a time. That stimulus will be the variable in the experiment.

There are two ways of responding to stimuli: positively and negatively. A living thing responds *positively* by moving toward a stimulus. It responds *negatively* by moving away from a stimulus.

The mouse responds *positively* to the cheese, *negatively* to the cat. The cat responds *positively* to the mouse. Suggest or draw a scene in which the cat is responding *negatively* to something.

Experimenting with Stimulus and Response: An Earthworm Responds

It is easy to test an earthworm's response to a number of stimuli. As you carry out these experiments, record your findings on a data sheet similar to the one on page 84.

The earthworm has no eyes, ears, or nose. Can it still sense light, sound, and some odors, as well as other stimuli?

You Will Need

- an earthworm
- a shallow pan
- water
- a flashlight
- vinegar

LESSON 6 ORGANIZER

Objectives

By the end of the lesson, students should be able to:

1. Recognize the relationship between a stimulus and a response.
2. Design an experiment to determine an organism's response to a stimulus.
3. Observe an organism's response to a stimulus, and classify this response as positive or negative.

Process Skills

controlling variables, observing, recording, investigating

New Terms

Stimulus—anything that causes a living thing to react.
Response—the reaction to a stimulus.
Irritability—the ability of a living thing to respond to stimuli.

What to Do

Observe and record all responses.

You are going to observe and investigate the earthworm's response to touch (pencil test), light (flashlight test), and smell (vinegar test).

1. Place the worm on damp paper towels in the shallow pan. (The worm will die if it is not kept moist.)

2. Gently touch (do not poke!) the front end of the worm with the tip of a pencil.

3. Gently touch the worm along its side several times, and then at its back end.

4. Let the earthworm rest for a while under a damp towel. Remove the towel, and shine a beam of light on the front end of the worm. Give the worm another rest, and shine the light on other parts.

5. Soak a piece of paper towel in vinegar. Uncover the worm and bring the towel near it. Do not touch the worm with the towel.

Exploration 6

This Exploration provides another opportunity for students to conduct an experiment with controlled variables. For best results, divide the class into small groups.

Encourage students to treat the earthworms, and all living things, with respect. The earthworms should be returned to their natural environment when the activity is completed.

Tell students to be sure to let the earthworms rest between stimulations, since they may not react if they receive too many stimulations in too short a time span.

Your attitude about touching the earthworms will be noticed by the students. Be sure you are comfortable handling the earthworms before the lesson begins. Some students may feel squeamish about touching the earthworms, but they should soon get used to it.

Materials

Exploration 6: earthworm, shallow pan, water, flashlight, vinegar, pencil, paper towels, Journal

Science Discovery Videodisc

Disc 2, Image and Activity Bank, 2–6

Time Required

two class periods

Answers to

Data Sheet

Touch: Students should observe that when the sides and back end are touched, the worm recoils and squirms more vigorously than when the front end is touched.

Light: When the light shines on its head, the worm slowly moves away. It does not respond when the light shines on the back end and sides.

Vinegar: The worm slowly moves away when the vinegar is brought near it.

Answers to

Questions

1. (a) No, some parts are more sensitive to touch than others.
   (b) The sides and back end of an earthworm seem to be more sensitive to touch than the front end.
2. (a) The front part of the worm seems most sensitive to light.
   (b) The worm responds negatively to the light.
3. Earthworms are not found on the surface of the ground since they respond negatively to light. Also, the soil is drier on the surface than below.
4. Worms are likely to be found on the surface at night because there is no sunlight. The earthworm "breathes" through its moist skin; however, after a hard rain, worms will come to the surface because there is not enough oxygen available below the surface.
5. The outer layer of an earthworm's skin possesses chemical receptors that supply important information about the worm's environment.
6. Since earthworms respond negatively to light, they remain underground during the day. This is useful because at night the sun cannot dry their skin, and birds and other predators cannot see them. Wriggling to avoid a touch might also help the worm elude predators.

Data Sheet: **An Earthworm Responds**

Purpose: In your Journal under this heading, write a statement outlining your reasons for doing these tests.

Stimulus: **Touch**

Response: Describe how the earthworm responds to touch. Determine whether the response is positive or negative. What happens when you touch
(a) the front end;
(b) the back end; and
(c) the sides?
Did you make any other observations?

Stimulus: **Light**

Response: Describe how the earthworm responds to light. Is the the response positive or negative? What happens when you shine a light on
(a) the front end;
(b) the back end; and
(c) the sides?
Did you make any other observations?

Stimulus: **Vinegar**

Response: Describe how the earthworm responds to having the towel soaked in vinegar brought near it.

Questions

1. (a) Are all parts of an earthworm equally sensitive to touch?
   (b) If there is a difference, which parts respond to touch more than others?
2. (a) Which part of the worm seems most sensitive to light?
   (b) Did the worm move toward the light (positive response) or away from the light (negative response)?
3. Give two reasons why earthworms are not usually found on the surface of the ground.
4. When are you likely to find worms on the surface? Why are they there at that time?
5. How could the earthworm sense the vinegar without touching it?
6. How are the worm's responses useful for its way of life?

Plant Responses

Ideally, one or more of the plants mentioned in the text should be available for the class to see. The leaves of the mimosa quickly close up when they are touched, due to the collapse of certain cells when they lose water. The leaves of the Venus flytrap snap shut when touched by an insect. Once shut, the leaves secrete digestive juices that break down the soft parts of the insect's body. This plant lives in marshy areas where the supply of soil nitrogen is severely limited. Feeding on insects provides them with a source of nitrogen. The prayer plant and wood sorrel respond to light levels in their environment. Morning glories also respond to light by opening their blossoms in the morning and closing them at night.

Plant Responses

Plants also respond to certain stimuli. You saw in the section "Motion and Locomotion" that plants bend toward the light when they are placed near a sunny window. The movement of plants is, in most cases, very gradual.

However, some plants show surprisingly quick responses. You may have watched the leaves of the mimosa plant droop in response to touch. The leaves of the Venus flytrap snap suddenly shut when insects (or anything else) touch sensitive hairs on the leaf surface. Wood sorrel, a common plant, folds its leaves in the evening. The prayer plant is a house plant that also folds its leaves in the evening. What stimulus are the wood sorrel and the prayer plant responding to?

Wood sorrel—Can you think of other plants that respond to the same stimulus as the wood sorrel?

Venus flytrap—Why does this plant respond to an insect's touch? (Hint: The soil of its native habitat is poor in certain minerals.)

Stimulating Things to Investigate

Now try to answer one or two of the following questions about stimulus and response. You may have to go to the library for the answer.

1. What are the sensitive parts of the mimosa?

2. If you watch a mimosa over a period of time, you will see the leaflets open in the morning and close together at night. If a mimosa were placed in a dark closet, do you think the leaflets would still fold and unfold?

3. Is wood sorrel sensitive to touch?

4. Is there a definite temperature that will cause a crocus flower to close or open?

5. How does an earthworm respond to food? to temperature changes?

6. Does a sow bug seek light or moisture?

7. How do fish respond to the stimuli of sound and light?

8. As seedlings grow, do their roots always grow downward and their stems upward?

9. How would a prayer plant respond if you kept it in the dark all day and in the light all night?

Answers to

Stimulating Things to Investigate

This page has nine ideas for optional independent study. Below are brief responses to the questions.
1. the leaves
2. no
3. no
4. The crocus plant responds to springtime temperatures.
5. An earthworm moves toward food and away from overly hot or overly cold temperatures.
6. moisture
7. negatively
8. yes
9. Eventually, it would switch its normal pattern.

Follow Up

Assessment

An experiment was done to test the responses of a mealworm to light. The apparatus was set up as shown in the illustration below. Reproduce this illustration for the students, and have them note the position of the mealworms after 4 hours of illumination. Then have them answer the following questions.

(a) Which variable is deliberately manipulated in this experiment? *(light)*

(b) Name three variables that should be controlled during this experiment. *(the temperature of the environment, the moisture on the container surface, the brightness of the light)*

(c) Make an appropriate observation for this experiment. *(The mealworms moved under the black paper.)*

(d) Draw an appropriate conclusion for this experiment. *(The mealworms prefer a dark area rather than a bright one.)*

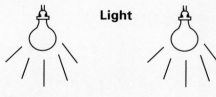

Light

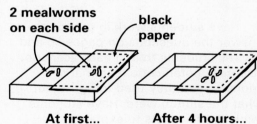

2 mealworms on each side   black paper

At first...   After 4 hours...

Extension

Ask students to set up the following experiment to find out what habitat earthworms prefer. Fill one jar half full with moist soil, the other with moist sand. Place three earthworms in each jar. Cover the earthworms in the soil-filled jar with sand, and those in the sand-filled jar with soil. Wait a day, and then carefully dig with spoons to find out in which layer the earthworms have settled. *(In both jars, the earthworms will be in the soil rather than in the sand.)* Ask students what they think might account for this behavior. *(The earthworms gain more nutrients from the soil than from the sand.)*

It is not always easy to explain how and why an animal behaves a certain way. Many stimuli are at work influencing an animal's behavior. Finding out which specific stimulus is causing the animal to behave in a particular way can take hours, days, and sometimes even years!

The following are short accounts of scientists who solved some riddles of animal behavior by looking at bees and flying squirrels. Imagine that you are the scientist. First read the account of an observation or experiment, and then explain the results. Use the questions provided to help you think about these results.

Main Ideas

1. Scientists ask questions, test ideas, and communicate results to other scientists.
2. Scientific knowledge may develop slowly over many years, as one scientist builds upon the work of another.
3. Plants and animals have an internal clock, a built-in sense of time.

Scientists Observe and Experiment.........with Bees

1906

In the summer of 1906, Forel, a Swiss scientist, noticed honeybees coming to share his breakfast jam when he ate outdoors.

Teaching Strategies

Thinking as a Scientist.............

How would you explain the arrival of the bees? Is your explanation the only one possible?

Have students work in groups to answer the questions on pages 86 and 87. Tell students that in each scenario, scientists noted certain animal responses, and they tried to figure out what the stimuli were. Have students think like scientists to explain:
- The different responses observed in the animals
- How to test what stimulus provoked a certain response
- What conclusions can be drawn from the test results

LESSON 7 ORGANIZER

Objectives

By the end of the lesson, students should be able to:
1. Infer the correct relationship between a stimulus and a response in animal behavior.
2. Comprehend how scientists may work cooperatively over long periods of time to solve scientific problems.
3. Investigate the biological clocks in living things.

Process Skills

analyzing, drawing conclusions, evaluating, writing an article

New Terms

1909

A few years after Forel's observation, a German scientist, von Buttel-Reepen, began studying the activity of bees. He noticed that bees always came for the nectar from buckwheat flowers in the morning and never in the afternoon. The bees somehow knew when the nectar flow started and stopped. Perhaps it was the fragrance of the flowers that attracted the bees.

How would you test whether or not it was the fragrance of the flowers that attracted the bees?

However, von Buttel-Reepen found the flowers as fragrant in the afternoon as in the morning. He might have suggested any one of these to explain why the bees arrived only in the morning:

(a) The bees kept some scouts to watch for and report the nectar flow.

(b) The bees responded to the sun's position.

(c) The bees had their own time sense.

How would you explain the bees arriving only in the morning? How would you test your explanation?

1906

Answers will vary, but the arrival of the bees can be explained by the odor or color of the jam, the odor of any of the other foods, or even the light reflected from the dining table.

Forel also noticed that the bees came to the outdoor table at breakfast time even when no food was present. It seemed to Forel that this behavior indicated that the bees had some type of internal clock.

1909

To test whether it was the fragrance of the flowers that attracted the bees, a scientist could try to detect any difference in the flower's scent at different times of the day, use flowers without a scent to see if the bees were still attracted, or use an extract of the flowers to see if it is the scent of the flowers (rather than the sight of the flowers) that attracts the bees.

If students chose explanation (c), they came to the same conclusion as von Buttel-Reepen. They could test choices (a) and (b) by observing if any scouts were seen arriving at the fragrant flowers before the other bees, or if any bees ever arrived on overcast and cloudy days.

(Answers continue on next page)

Materials

Time Required

two class periods

1927

From Beling's experiment a scientist could conclude that, in some ways, bees can tell time. Here are some of the things that might have helped the bees to do so:

- light (and darkness)
- temperature changes
- the sun's position
- humidity in the air
- cosmic rays
- electrical charges in the air

Five of these six were listed in 1927 by Beling herself.

1955

Renner and von Frisch's experiment showed that the bees were not using the sun's position to tell time, nor were they confused by other external conditions. It was inferred that the bees must indeed have an internal clock!

(Answers continue on next page)

1927

Beling, working in Germany in 1927, studied the problems that had earlier interested Forel and von Buttel-Reepen. She trained a group of bees to go to a feeding station at a certain time each day, and marked the bees with colored dots so that she could tell them apart. One day, Beling removed the food and watched. The bees still came to the empty feeding station at their usual time. This led her to test all of the possible stimuli that might help the bees tell time.

1955

In 1955 Renner and von Frisch conducted an unusual experiment to test the effects of other stimuli on bees. A hive of bees was trained to eat once every 24 hours in a special room in Paris. The hive of bees was then flown overnight to New York and placed in a room just like the one in Paris. The bees came out of the hive and began to eat 24 hours after their last feeding, as if they were still in Paris. They did not seem to react to the difference between the sun's position in New York and the sun's position in Paris. It made no difference to the bees that New York time is five hours behind Paris time.

What conclusion(s) do you draw from this experiment? Name things that you think might have helped the bees tell time. (Beling listed six different things.)

What did this experiment tell about the bees' sense of time?

feeding station

New York   Paris

...with Flying Squirrels
1955–1960

From 1955 to 1960, DeCoursey studied the behavior of flying squirrels at the University of Wisconsin. She put them in cages outdoors and observed their daily activity in the cages. The exercise wheel was the center of most of the squirrels' activity. DeCoursey found that the squirrels began their daily run on the exercise wheel around the time of sunset.

In another experiment, flying squirrels were kept in a darkened room below ground level. They received no light from the sun. Their activity over a period of 25 days is shown in the figure at the right below. The dark line indicates the time of day when the squirrels began to run on the exercise wheel.

DeCoursey concluded that flying squirrels had their own sense of time, controlled by a response to a particular stimulus. In fact, it may be that all living things have such "built-in clocks."

Did the squirrels begin running

(a) at any time at all;

(b) regularly, but earlier each day;

(c) regularly, but later each day; or

(d) at the same time each day?

What stimulus were the squirrels responding to?

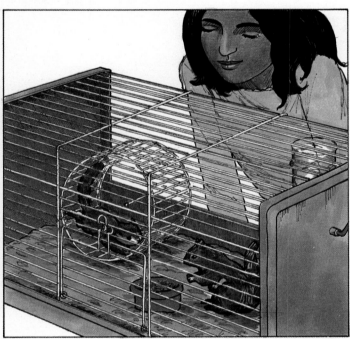

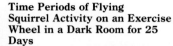

Time Periods of Flying Squirrel Activity on an Exercise Wheel in a Dark Room for 25 Days

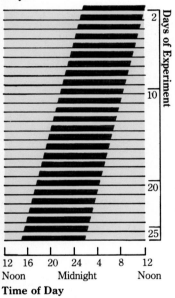

Days of Experiment

2
10
20
25

12 16 20 24 4 8 12
Noon   Midnight   Noon

Time of Day

Answers continued
1955–1960

In her experiments with flying squirrels, DeCoursey observed that the squirrels began running regularly but earlier each day. This, in turn, indicated to her that the squirrels had an internal clock based on sunlight, for without the light, they gradually lost their sense of time.

Exploration 7

Besides using the information in their texts, suggest that students do some library research on biorhythms to help them write their articles. Also, they may wish to conduct some of their own experiments to learn about biorhythms. For example, they could measure their own temperatures and pulse rates at different times during the day and night to find out:

- when they have their lowest and highest temperatures
- when their pulse rates are at a minimum and a maximum

(They should discover that there are daily rhythmic patterns, not only in activities such as sleep and wakefulness, but in things such as body temperature and heart rate as well.)

✳ *Follow Up*

Assessment

1. The graph below shows the daily activity level of the red fox. Copy the graph on the board. Ask students to answer the following questions based on the graph.

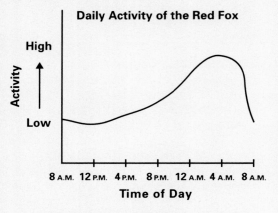

Daily Activity of the Red Fox

High

Activity

Low

8 A.M. 12 P.M. 4 P.M. 8 P.M. 12 A.M. 4 A.M. 8 A.M.

Time of Day

(a) At what time of day is the fox most active? *(from 1 A.M. to 5 A.M.)*

(b) What environmental conditions might regulate the fox's daily clock? *(The fox is probably most active when food is most plentiful.)*

2. Many insects show daily variations in their level of activity. Ask students

to perform the following investigation. Collect a cricket and leave it in a terrarium or in a small container for a few days. (Gather the materials needed to make the container as similar to the cricket's natural environment as possible.) Note any evidence of daily rhythms or sense of time. Release the animal when the experiment is completed.

EXPLORATION 7

Animal Time-keeping

You have been asked to make a contribution to the school's monthly newspaper. Your topic is "Biorhythms."

The scientific research you have just been reading about is a good source of information to draw on.

Here are some things to think about as you write your article:

- Do humans have built-in clocks?
- What are some animals with built-in clocks?
- What stimuli do you think control an animal's clock?

❑

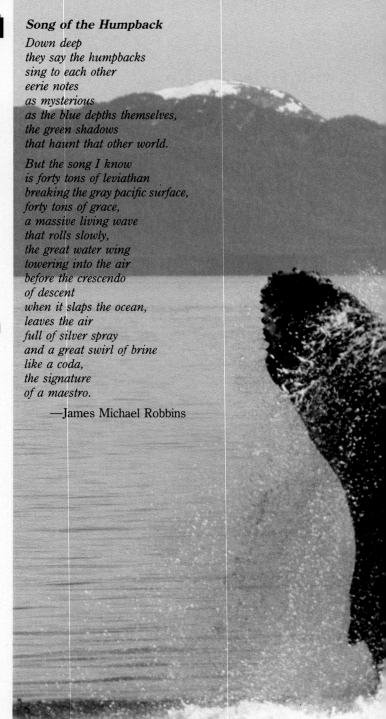

Song of the Humpback

*Down deep
they say the humpbacks
sing to each other
eerie notes
as mysterious
as the blue depths themselves,
the green shadows
that haunt that other world.*

*But the song I know
is forty tons of leviathan
breaking the gray pacific surface,
forty tons of grace,
a massive living wave
that rolls slowly,
the great water wing
towering into the air
before the crescendo
of descent
when it slaps the ocean,
leaves the air
full of silver spray
and a great swirl of brine
like a coda,
the signature
of a maestro.*

—James Michael Robbins

Extension

Have students do research on the sense of direction in migratory birds. Have students find out how scientists discovered this information. Students might want to compare the sense of direction in birds with other migratory animals, such as butterflies.

8 Seasonal Behavior of Animals

The poem on the previous page is about the humpback whale. Humpbacks are well known for their eerie, mournful-sounding "songs." These songs are thought to be some form of communication, but their exact function is not known. Throughout the season, humpbacks sing the same song again and again. The following year each will sing an entirely different song.

These graceful, gentle giants spend the summer in the cold waters of the far north. Come fall they travel south, eventually arriving in the warmer waters off California and Mexico.

Like the humpback whale, many animals move from place to place, often over long distances. They, or their descendants, return again and again to the same places. This type of behavior is called **migration**. For most migrating animals, one of these places is ideal for the young to hatch or be born, while another place is best for growing, maturing, or waiting out a cold winter. What other animals can you think of that migrate?

Questions

1. Why do you think the humpback whales travel from north to south every year?
2. What might be the purpose of the humpbacks' songs?
3. Why might humpbacks change their songs every year?
4. Why do you think animals migrate?
5. Do people ever migrate? Give examples.
6. Do you think that migration always has to take place over large distances? Why or why not?

LESSON 8

✷ Getting Started

In Lesson 8, students will learn that the migration of many types of animals is a response to seasonal changes in temperature. Also, they will learn to identify the difference between warm-blooded and cold-blooded animals and their respective responses to temperature changes.

Main Ideas

1. Migration in animals is a response to seasonal changes.
2. Warm-blooded animals maintain the same body temperatures even when surrounding temperatures change.
3. The body temperatures of cold-blooded animals change as the temperature of their surroundings changes.

✷ Teaching Strategies

Ask students to name as many migratory animals as they can think of. For example, some insects, such as monarch butterflies, migrate. Many birds and fish migrate, including waterfowl, robins, swallows, herons, hawks, salmon, and eels. Some mammals, the wildebeest and the mule deer for example, also migrate.

Answers to
Questions

Tell students they will need to do some library research to answer these questions.
1. Humpback whales travel from north to south every year to breed and
(Answers continue on next page)

LESSON ORGANIZER

Objectives

By the end of the lesson, students should be able to:
1. Describe instances of migration and the factors affecting it.
2. Identify how different animals maintain body heat.
3. Compare and contrast warm-blooded and cold-blooded animals and their responses to temperature changes.

4. Set up an experiment to determine the effect of body size on rate of heat loss.

Process Skills

comparing, drawing conclusions, inferring, experimenting

(Organizer continues on next page)

give birth to their young in warm waters. They then travel back north to feed in food-rich Arctic waters.

2. The function of the humpbacks' songs is still unclear. The songs of all individuals in one community are very similar, but the voices of particular whales are uniquely identifiable. Therefore, the songs may serve as locating signals, indicators of territorial claims to feeding grounds, or they may have some sexual function as well, since the songs are sung only by the males.

3. The songs may change every year to signal changes in sexual relationships or territorial claims to feeding grounds.

4. Animals migrate for a number of reasons: to find sources of food or water, to escape from cold weather, or to reproduce and raise young.

5. Some nomadic tribes, such as the Bedouins of Northern Africa, migrate with the change of seasons.

6. Most animals migrate by traveling great distances, but some animals migrate within a relatively short distance, for example, by climbing up a mountain.

Keeping Warm

The animals in these photographs all have a common need to keep warm in winter. Their body temperature must remain steady no matter what the air temperature may be. Even a small change in their body temperature has serious consequences. Animals with unchanging body temperatures (usually above the temperature of their surroundings) are called **warm-blooded** animals. Try to name at least six other warm-blooded animals.

In cold weather, warm-blooded animals have to work to maintain their body temperature. Before reading any further, look at the photographs and write down all the ways you think warm-blooded animals keep warm.

(Organizer continued)

New Terms

Migration—a pattern of behavior in which animals move from one place or climate to another, often over long distances, and then return periodically to the same places in order to mate, reproduce, or nurture the young.

Warm-blooded animals—animals with unchanging body temperatures, usually above that of their surroundings.

Perspire—to sweat; to secrete water from small glands in the skin.

Cold-blooded animals—animals whose body temperatures match the temperatures of their surroundings.

Keeping Warm

Students should work in small groups, following the text, looking at the photographs, and answering the questions.

Be sure students understand that all mammals and birds are warm-blooded; all reptiles and amphibians are cold-blooded. Some specific examples of warm-blooded animals are: bear, lion, cat, seal, penguin, beaver, wolf, whale, dog, bat, kangaroo, and hawk.

After students observe the photographs to look for ways the animals maintain their body temperatures, discuss their answers. Focus on the following points:

- Birds are covered with interlocking feathers, under which is a layer of fluffy down feathers. They fluff up their feathers to trap a layer of warm air close to their bodies. Birds also migrate to warmer climates.
- Mammals have dense fur, often thicker near the body, to trap heat.
- Raccoons that live in cold climates prepare for winter by eating extra food in the fall and building up a layer of fat under their skin, which acts as insulation.
- The thick hide and layer of blubber under the skin helps protect the walrus from the cold.
- Many bats hibernate or migrate during the winter.
- The bear seeks shelter where it can sleep for the winter.
- Warm-blooded animals can eat more food during cold weather, since they burn more energy.
- Warm-blooded animals can also move around more quickly to keep warm.

Dormancy—a sleep-like state during which an organism's bodily functions are suspended or greatly reduced.

Materials

Exploration 8: 2 glass bottles with lids—one twice the volume of the other, woolen cloth to wrap around each bottle, safety pins, 2 thermometers, water, heat source, watch or clock, safety goggles

Teacher's Resource Binder

Activity Worksheets 2–4 and 2–5
Graphic Organizer Transparency 2–5

Science Discovery Videodisc

Disc 2, Image and Activity Bank, 2–8

Time Required

four class periods

In-Text Questions

The three different North American hares show great variation in ear size. Students should infer that since the ears are thin and richly supplied with blood, much body heat can be lost there. Students should observe that the farther north the animal lives, the smaller its ears. The hare that lives on the hot, southern plains has large ears to help lose heat and keep itself cool. The Arctic hare has short ears to minimize heat loss and keep itself warm.

In winter, warm-blooded animals must eat more than usual to renew their energy supply. Moving around is another way to produce body heat. Some animals develop thicker coats. Birds may look plump on a cold winter day, because they '"fluff up" their feathers for added protection. How could this help them stay warm?

Have you ever had "gooseflesh" and shivered when you were cold? When the body of a warm-blooded animal shivers, the movement increases the heat produced in the body. Warm-blooded animals keep warm by other means as well. Their blood vessels near the surface contract, or become smaller. As a result, more blood is kept in the warmer inner parts of the body, reducing heat loss. You can imagine how useful this is for whales, dolphins, and other warm-blooded animals that live in water that is often quite cold.

Look at the pictures below of North American hares. Compare the ear length of the hare that lives in the Arctic with the ear lengths of its southern cousins. Use what you know about how animals stay warm to explain the differences between them. (Hint: The ears are thin and well-supplied with blood.)

Which Loses Heat Faster—a Mouse or a Mountain Lion?

What do you think? Make a prediction first, then test your idea.

You Will Need

- 2 glass bottles, one of which can hold twice as much as the other
- woolen cloth to wrap each bottle (or some other kind of insulator)
- 2 thermometers

What to Do

1. Fill each bottle with hot water at the same time.
2. Take the temperature of each. Cover their tops.
3. Measure the temperature of each bottle every 5 minutes for half an hour.

Was there any difference in the rate of cooling of the small and large containers? Try to explain the difference. Does the result support your answer about the mouse and the mountain lion?

Exploration 8

One or two activity centers can be set up for this Exploration. Within 20 to 30 minutes, the differing rates of temperature decrease should become noticeable. Students could graph this temperature loss.

Answers to

In-Text Questions

A good explanation for the difference in heat loss will take into account the fact that although the larger volume of water contained twice as much "heat energy" as the smaller volume, the surface area of the opening of the larger bottle is not twice as large as the surface area of the smaller bottle. Therefore, the rate of cooling in a larger animal will be slower than that in a smaller animal. In other words, heat content is a function of volume, but heat loss is a function of surface area.

Cooling Systems

After students have read this section, ask: Why does perspiring help to keep you cool on hot days? *(As the water evaporates, it takes heat away from your body.)*

To demonstrate the cooling effect of evaporating water, have students wet one hand and keep the other hand dry. Ask them to swing both hands in the air. Have them identify the hand that feels cooler. By blowing on the wet hand and not on the other, they can feel how a breeze could speed up the evaporation and cooling processes.

A Cold-Blooded Bunch

Before beginning this section, ask students what they think the terms warm-blooded and cold-blooded mean. Allow students to then read this section. Point out that cold-blooded does not mean that the animal has cold blood; instead, temperature of cold-blooded animals varies according to its environment. Body temperature is not constant in cold-blooded animals; it is held constant by internal controls in warm-blooded animals. (You may wish to point out that some warm-blooded animals, such as chipmunks, enter a dormant state in winter. During that time their body temperatures do not remain constant, but actually fall below normal.)

Ask students to interpret the graph at the bottom of the page. The graph shows that a cold-blooded animal, like the snake, experiences changes in body temperature on a seasonal basis. The snake's body temperature can be hotter or much colder than a human's, depending on the temperature of the environment.

Insects are cold-blooded and can be used to demonstrate the effect of heat on cold-blooded animals. Have students collect some flies and keep them in a jar in a cool spot for a few days. Ask students to make some observations. *(They should note how little the flies move about.)* Then have students place the jar of flies on an overhead projector. Ask them to observe the change in the flies' movements in 5 or 10 minutes.

After students have read page 97, ask: Where do frogs and other cold-blooded animals spend the winter in the North? *(They spend the winter*

buried in the ground, well below the frost line where there is no danger of freezing.)*

Ask: Why does warm spring weather act as a stimulus for many dormant cold-blooded animals? *(The warm spring weather raises the body temperatures of cold-blooded animals, thereby acting as a stimulus for them to increase their activity. Frogs, toads, and other amphibians require a moist skin at all times, so it is natural for warm, wet, spring weather to increase their activity.)*

Cooling Systems

What are the different things that warm-blooded animals may do to keep cool in hot weather? First, think of yourself. When you get hot, you **perspire**—your skin secretes water from many tiny glands. As the water evaporates, it takes heat from your body, helping it to stay cool. This process is also called sweating.

A method some warm-blooded animals use to keep cool is panting. Think of a dog on a hot day. Every time a dog exhales, heat is removed from its body. Breathing rapidly removes heat more quickly. At the same time, evaporation from the tongue also helps to cool the dog.

A Cold-Blooded Bunch

Humans and many other animals are warm-blooded. But there is another group—**cold-blooded** animals. Cold-blooded animals react to the temperature of their surroundings very differently than warm-blooded animals do. For example, compare the body temperature of a snake with that of a human, shown in the graph below. What differences exist between snake and human body temperatures over a year? Why do you think the snake's temperature changes so much? The snake is an example of a cold-blooded animal. Other examples are frogs, toads, turtles, and fish. Can you guess what "cold-blooded" really means? In what circumstances would a snake's body temperature be higher than that of a human?

Dog trying to be "cool." What other warm-blooded animals pant? (Surprise: The cheetah, one of the big cats, pants.)

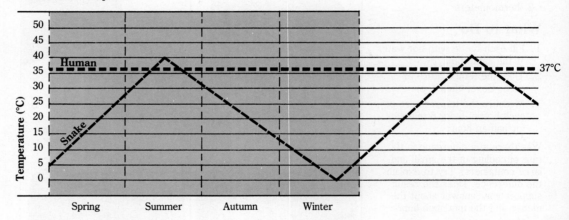

Body Temperatures of Humans and Snakes Compared

Answers to

Questions

1. The blood of a cold-blooded animal is not cold when the surrounding temperature is warm.
2. Answers will vary. For example, students might write about the mice that move about under the snow in tiny tunnels, invisible to the world above.

The body temperatures of cold-blooded animals closely match the temperature of their surroundings. As their body temperatures lower, animals such as frogs and salamanders begin to move more slowly. Their hearts beat fewer times per minute and their breathing rate slows down. As winter temperatures approach, they enter a sleep-like state called **dormancy**. During the northern winter, cold-blooded animals must find a place to rest undisturbed and away from the extreme cold that could kill them. Where do you suppose a frog spends the winter?

Cold-blooded animals, while dormant, need little food or oxygen. What food they do use comes from the energy that is stored up in their bodies. One danger is that this food could be used up too soon. If a dormant animal is disturbed before the arrival of warm spring weather, it faces the danger of using up its food supply and starving.

One winter, a scientist, Dr. Aleksiuk, found a snow-covered cavern in Canada containing hundreds of snakes huddled together. The snow provided insulation from the cold, and by huddling together the snakes produced enough heat to stay alive. On a winter day in Canada, it can be extremely cold!

In April, when warmer weather arrived, Dr. Aleksiuk watched the snakes come out of the cavern. He reported seeing as many as 15,000 garter snakes emerge from a cavern only 3 meters deep and 5 meters wide.

Come spring, snakes, frogs, toads, and salamanders "wake up." Warm rains and climbing temperatures signal these animals to become active again. Why do you suppose the warm rain acts as a stimulus to these animals?

Painted turtle (in dormancy)

Questions

1. When is a cold-blooded animal not a cold-blooded animal? Explain.

2. In the winter, after a snowfall, wooded areas often seem empty and silent. Write a newspaper article for children about the living things that live beneath the snow cover.

3. Small animals, such as mice, must usually work harder to survive the winter than do large animals. Why do you think this is so?

4. Try writing a poem entitled *"Why I Like/Why I Don't Like Being Cold-blooded."* Write as if you were the animal speaking. Try to use some scientific words in your poem.

Assessment

The chickadee is 14.5 cm long; the blue jay is 31 cm long. Both are winter birds; they do not migrate south for the winter. Ask students: Which bird do you think needs to eat more? *(Students should think back to the comparison of African and Asian elephants and realize that the blue jay will consume much more food.)*

Extension

Ask students to investigate one or more of the following questions.
1. Find out how some of nature's unusual animals survive the winter. For example, bees, bats, or whales.
2. Find the correct answers to the following questions: Which are the smallest animals that migrate? Which animals migrate the fastest? Which animals travel the farthest?
3. Find information on the migration of the Monarch butterfly. Determine how far it flies, how long it takes to migrate, and where it spends the winter.

3. Small animals have a large surface area compared to their body mass. Therefore, they lose heat much more quickly than larger animals.
4. Student poems will vary. Here is one student's poem you can share with your class.

The Limitations of Being Cold-blooded
My body temperature changes
I freeze in the winter and fall,
In the spring and the summer it ranges,
I'm never happy at all.

One minute I'm cold, and
The next I'm as warm as can be,
I'm ever so glad when the time comes,
When I sleep in the state of dormancy.
It's ever so peaceful and quiet,
I relax for the rest of the year,
When I wake I go search for my water and food,
But I really wish I could stay here.
　　　　　by Michelle Newman

LESSON 9

9 Adaptation of Structure

How well-suited are you to your surroundings? What if you moved farther south or farther north? How would you deal with tropical heat or polar cold? Humans can add clothing or invent air conditioning, but plants and animals do not have these options. In the previous lesson, you read about how other animals are able to adapt to seasonal changes in their environment. But how do plants and animals adapt to changes that occur slowly, over a very long time?

When long-term changes occur in the environment, plants and animals must adapt or risk dying out. For most kinds of animals and plants, this kind of adapting takes a long time and goes on as conditions change. Can you think of slow changes that might force a kind of animal or plant to adapt? Can you think of any kinds of animals that might have died out because they couldn't adapt?

Where would you find a cactus plant growing naturally? Where would you look for a frog? Frogs and cacti need very different conditions to survive. List the ways in which each is adapted to its environmental conditions. What adaptations would each need to have if their conditions were reversed?

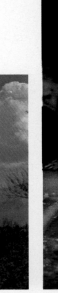

☀ Getting Started

In Lesson 9, students focus on animal adaptations. They examine how structural adaptations relate to an animal's survival and learn that such adaptations occur over a very long period of time.

Main Ideas

1. Groups of living things adapt very gradually to their environment over a long period of time.
2. An animal's bodily structures suit the special needs required to live in a certain environment.

☀ Teaching Strategies

In the previous lesson, students learned how individual animals respond to seasonal changes. In this lesson, they will learn that sometimes long-term changes in the environment trigger adaptations too. Students may be confused by the difference between adaptations that an individual can make during its lifetime and adaptations that occur in a group of organisms from generation to generation. For example, when winter arrives, individuals can migrate to warmer climates. However, if there is a long-term change in climate, such as a gradual decrease in temperature, succeeding generations of a *species* might eventually change so that they have thicker fur or a greater capacity to store fat.
(Answers to In-Text Questions follow on next page)

LESSON 9 ORGANIZER

Objectives

By the end of the lesson, students should be able to:
1. Recognize the relationship between an animal adaptation and the animal's ability to survive.
2. Compare the time of adaptation with the life span of an individual organism.

Process Skills

observing, analyzing, recognizing relationships, illustrating

New Terms

Adaptation—a trait in an organism that makes it better suited to its environment.

Insect Adaptations

Over time, the bodies of many animals have changed so that they are adapted to special conditions and needs. Many insects have special body parts for food gathering and defense. What special body parts do the insects pictured below have? How do these parts help the animals?

Leaf Katydid

Grasshopper

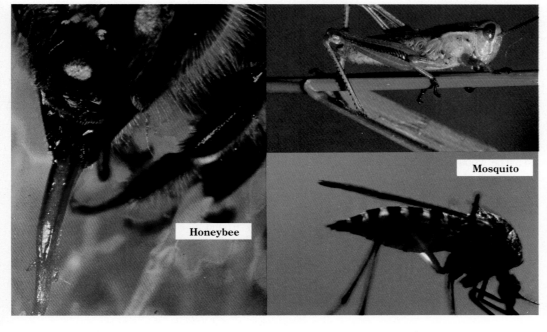

Mosquito

Honeybee

Materials

Teacher's Resource Binder

Activity Worksheet 2–7
Graphic Organizer Transparency 2–6

Science Discovery Videodisc

Disc 2, Image and Activity Bank, 2–9

Time Required

two class periods

Since the questions on page 98 are quite open-ended, many answers are possible.

- It could be expected that long-term changes in light, temperature, food supply, or water supply might force a group of organisms to adapt. It is possible that the dinosaurs died out because they were not able to adapt to a long-term change.
- To live in deserts, cacti have developed extensive root systems, massive and waxy trunks that store water, and tiny spine-like leaves that prevent water loss and protect the plant. To live in their moist habitat, frogs have developed thin skins through which respiratory gases can pass, and strong hind legs and webbed feet for swimming. If the frog and the cactus were to switch environments, succeeding generations of frogs would have to develop a tough, waterproof covering, and the species of cactus would need a thin skin and broad leaves to rid itself of moisture.

Answers to

Insect Adaptations

Ask students to carefully observe the pictures of the insects on page 99. Have them list the adaptations that each insect has, and explain how these structures help the animal to survive.

- The honeybee has a stinger for discouraging its enemies, a long coiled tube with which to suck nectar, and baskets on its hind legs for collecting pollen.
- The grasshopper has large hind legs for jumping, strong mouth parts for chewing, and a scraper on its hind legs to create a noise to communicate with other grasshoppers.
- The mosquito has a long hollow tube to pierce the skin of its prey and a chemical it injects to prevent blood from coagulating while it is sucking blood.
- The katydid has wings that look like leaves. When the katydid is sitting on a branch, it is well hidden from its enemies.

Bird Adaptations

Divide the class into small groups for this matching exercise. Encourage a friendly competition to determine which group can find all the correct answers in the shortest amount of time.

Explain that the task is to identify which bird beak, shape of foot, or wing best fits the lifestyle of the bird that is described.

Answers to

In-Text Questions

Discuss the correct answers, which are as follows: **1.** *(c)*; **2.** *(j)*; **3.** *(b)*; **4.** *(m)*; **5.** *(o)*; **6.** *(a)*; **7.** *(l)*; **8.** *(n)*; **9.** *(i)*; **10.** *(h)*; **11.** *(g)*; **12.** *(p)*; **13.** *(k)*; **14.** *(f)*; **15.** *(d)*; **16.** *(e)*.

Bird Adaptations

Birds have also adapted to their surroundings over time. A seemingly endless variety of adaptations make birds well suited to their environments. Match the descriptions below to the illustrations.

1. The owl has a short, sharp curved beak for piercing the skull or slashing the throat of its prey.

2. The feet of the curlew have three spread-out toes and a small hind toe. This design allows the bird to land and walk on very soft ground.

3. A duck's foot, with a tough membrane between the toes, is a natural paddle, making swimming a breeze.

4. The aptly named crossbill uses its beak to separate the scales of pine cones and get at the seeds underneath.

5. The ostrich cannot fly, but its two-toed feet help it to have tremendous running speed.

6. The golden eagle can soar for hours as it searches for prey, its wings catching the slightest updraft.

7. The osprey's feet are well adapted for grasping and carrying off prey.

8. The sandpiper's beak is long and slender, well suited for probing sand and mud for small animals.

9. The peregrine falcon can swoop down on its prey at over 300 kilometers an hour.

10. Although flightless, the penguin's streamlined body and short but powerful wings let it "fly" underwater.

11. The scissor-tailed flycatcher is an aerial acrobat. Its design gives it tremendous maneuverability, enabling it to chase and catch insects in flight.

12. The ptarmigan is found in the Arctic and other places that are snow-covered most of the year.

13. The flightless kiwi feeds by probing the leaf litter of the forest floor for insects and other tiny animals.

14. The woodpecker uses its sharp bill to bore holes in trees in search of insects.

15. The nighthawk feeds by flying through the air with its mouth open, catching insects in mid-flight.

16. The foot of the evening grosbeak can curl tightly around a branch, allowing the bird to perch securely in trees.

(a)

(e)

(i)
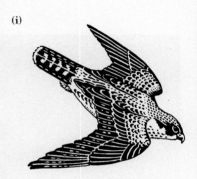

(m)

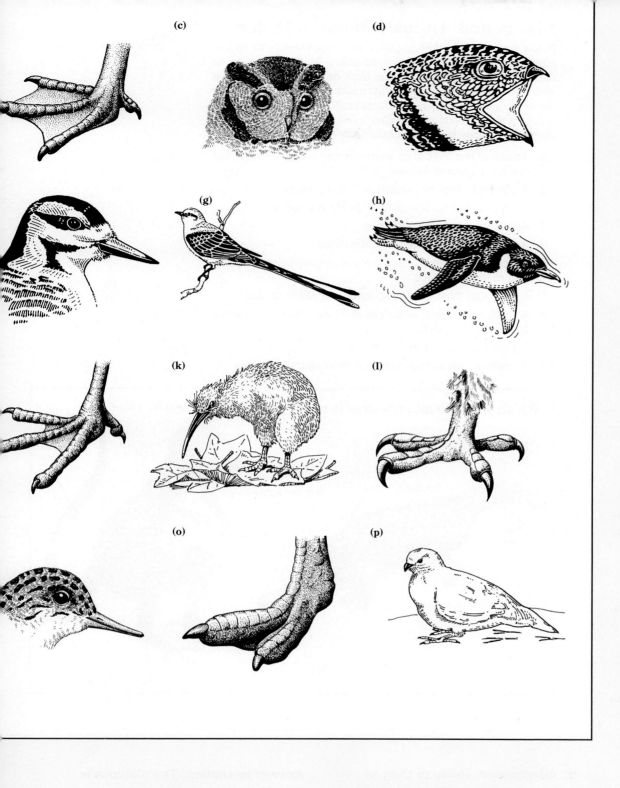

Plants and Animals Made to Order

You may wish to have students work in small groups to complete this exercise. Have each group describe and/or draw each of their animal or plant creations on a separate sheet of paper. Encourage students to use their imaginations. Be sure to remind them to relate the special adaptation to real plants and animals whenever possible.

Answers to

In-Text Questions

Here are a few examples of the many possibilities:

1. Adaptations: thick white fur or feathers, fat deposits; real-life examples: polar bear, snowshoe hare, lynx, ptarmigan

2. Adaptations: extensive root systems, massive waxy trunks that store water, thick waxy leaves; real-life examples: succulent, cactus

3. Adaptations: the ability to maneuver through trees, either by flying, which would require wings, or climbing, which would require dexterous limbs, hands and/or claws for grasping bark; real-life examples: monkey, squirrel, birds, sloth

4. Adaptations: wings, powerful muscles for flapping wings, lightweight; real-life examples: bat, most insects

5. Adaptations: leaves that can withstand freezing, such as evergreen needles, or leaves that drop off during extreme cold and then grow back; real-life examples: Arctic willow, Douglas fir

6. Adaptations: large, protruding eyes that can focus upward and downward; real-life examples: frog, water beetle, mud skipper

7. Adaptations: seeds adapted for dispersal by wind, ejection, or by getting caught in animal fur; real-life examples: touch-me-not, burdock, maple tree

8. Adaptations and examples: ability to escape from predators by burrowing into the ground (a mole); well-camouflaged or protective covering such as shell or spines (a porcupine, a turtle); the ability to spray a noxious subtance (a skunk)

Plants and Animals Made to Order

Below is a list of hypothetical plants and animals faced with special conditions that require the plant or animal to adapt in order to survive. Imagine that you are the plant or animal that must live with the conditions described. What might you look like? Describe and try to sketch your special adaptation(s). Try to think of adaptations real plants and animals have made to conditions similar to these. There may be many possibilities.

1. An animal that lives in an area with very heavy snowfalls but doesn't migrate or become dormant
2. A plant that lives in a region with little rainfall
3. An animal that spends most of its life in trees
4. An animal (not a bird) that flies
5. A tree that must withstand arctic climate
6. An animal that needs to see above water and below it equally well at the same time
7. A plant that must be sure to spread its seeds around
8. A small, slow animal with weak teeth and claws that needs a good defense system
9. A plant that lives in trees
10. A seashore animal that must stay moist during low tide

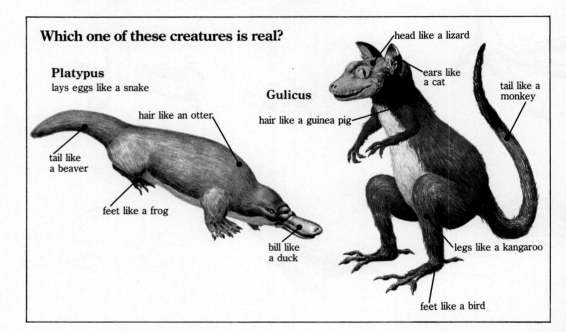

Which one of these creatures is real?

Platypus
lays eggs like a snake

tail like a beaver

feet like a frog

hair like an otter

bill like a duck

Gulicus

head like a lizard

ears like a cat

tail like a monkey

hair like a guinea pig

legs like a kangaroo

feet like a bird

9. Adaptations: ability to cling to trees (perhaps with aerial roots) and to extract minerals and water without roots that grow in the ground; may have the ability to catch and hold rainwater in their leaves; real-life examples: orchids, ball moss, some lichens

10. Adaptations: hard covering for protection against drying out and from predators, ability to cling to rocks or burrow into the sand to prevent being washed out to sea with the tides; real-life examples: periwinkle, barnacle, shellfish

Answer to caption: The platypus is the real animal.

Challenge Your Thinking

1. Each member of the class should choose a specific animal and tell a story, from that animal's point of view, about its preparations for winter. If you choose to migrate, tell the class how, when, and where you migrate and the reasons for your migration. If you choose to be an animal that stays put, tell about your preparations.

   You will have to do research. Look in books on the subject and ask informed persons. It is a good idea to write down what you are going to say in 150 words or less.

2. Copy the square below into your Journal. For each item in List A, select the best matching item in List B. Enter its letter in the appropriate box in the puzzle square. When you have completely filled the boxes, you will discover a "warm-blooded" message! Do not write in this book.

List A

1. Warm-blooded winter inhabitant
2. Southern migrant in winter
3. Dormancy
4. Panting
5. Feather fluffing
6. Sweating
7. Cold-blooded
8. Banding
9. Rabbit ears

List B

Y. Black-capped chickadee
O. Way of cooling off
U. Body temperature matches that of surroundings
R. Way of keeping warm
H. Slow breathing and heartbeat
E. Tracking migrating birds
A. Robin
T. Blood gives off heat

1.	2.	3.
4.	5.	6.
7.	8.	9.

✳ *Follow Up*

Assessment

Challenge students to design an animal. They should decide the following: what kind of feet it will have, and whether they will be webbed, clawed, or hoofed; if its arms, legs, and neck will be long or short; what shape its body will have, how many feet it will have, and whether or not it will have a tail; if the body will be covered by fur, feathers, scales, skin, or shell; what it will eat; how it will defend itself. Then students should draw an environment suitable for the animal. *(Answers will vary. The different animal adaptations should be appropriate for survival in the chosen environment.)*

Extension

Insects are noted for being well-suited to their living conditions. Have students choose one kind of insect and describe its specialized parts and behavior. Encourage them to include illustrations with their reports. Suggest that each student or group of students choose a separate group of insects on which to report.

LESSON 10

✳ *Getting Started*

In Lesson 10, students are introduced to the microscope and the tiny world of cells and microscopic organisms. They learn about the principle differences between plant and animal cells.

Main Ideas

1. The tiny units making up living things are called cells.
2. Microscopes magnify cells and tiny organisms and reveal some details of their internal structures.

When you approach a building from a distance, you first notice the shape of the whole building. As you draw nearer to it, you become aware of its different parts: walls, windows, doors, staircases, chimneys, and so forth. When you are only a few feet away, you realize that the walls are made up of bricks. Each brick forms part of the structure of the entire building.

1X   3X   60X

Likewise, animals and plants have an overall shape or structure, as well as different component parts. But when you examine their structure more closely, you see that they are made up of smaller units. These tiny "bricks" that make up the structure of living things are called **cells.** Cells are too small to be seen with the naked eye, but are clearly visible under a microscope.

Taking a closer look at an onion.

  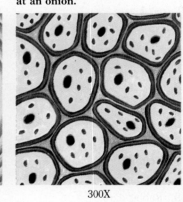

1X   3X   300X

LESSON 10 ORGANIZER

Objectives

By the end of the lesson, students should be able to:
1. Use a microscope properly to observe tiny objects, cells, and single-celled organisms.
2. Prepare wet mounts of several kinds of cells.
3. Identify the main parts of plant and animal cells.

4. Compare and contrast typical plant and animal cells.

Process Skills

manipulating equipment, observing, comparing, illustrating

New Terms

Cells—the smallest units that make up the structure of living things.
Wet mount—a thin sample in water of plant or animal cells, between a slide and a coverslip, that can be observed under a microscope.

How to Use a Microscope

The instrument that allows us to see cells and examine small objects is the microscope. Try to match the names of the parts of the microscope (in italics) with the labels on the diagram as you read the instructions for its use. The diagram below shows only one example of a microscope. The microscope you will be using may be slightly different. For example, it may have its own light source instead of a mirror.

1. Be sure the microscope is steady, its *base* sitting on a flat, stable surface. Look into the *eyepiece* at the top. This eyepiece fits into the *tube* or barrel of the microscope.

2. Adjust the *mirror* near the base of the microscope, so that the right amount of light is sent up the tube.

3. Place the microscope slide on the *stage,* with the material to be viewed over the hole in the stage. Use the stage clips to hold the slide in place.

4. There are two or three *objective lenses* attached to the *nosepiece* at the base of the tube: One is low power (e.g., 5X or 10X), one is medium power (e.g., 20X), and the others are medium or high power (e.g., 20X to 50X). Always use the low power lens first. Turn the nosepiece until the lens clicks into place.

5. Look from the side while you turn the *coarse-adjustment knob* to move the lowest power objective lens down close to the stage.

6. Look through the eyepiece and turn the coarse adjustment knob until your specimen is in focus.

7. Turn the *fine-adjustment knob* to make the focus clearer, if need be.

8. Change the objective lens from low to medium or high. Be sure that the objective lenses do not hit the stage when you rotate them into place. This could scratch the fragile lenses or break the slide.

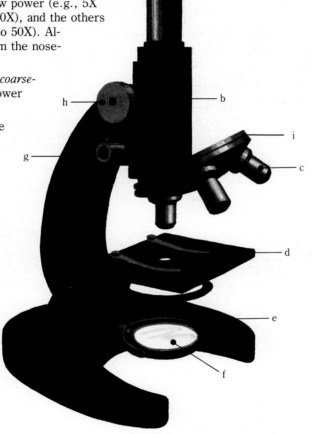

How to Use a Microscope

Each group of students should have access to a monocular microscope. Tell them to carefully follow the directions outlined on page 105. First, have them locate the important parts of the microscope and practice focusing and adjusting the light source. Tell students to pay particular attention to steps 6 and 7. Emphasize that they should always start with the lowest power lens, by snapping it into place and then winding down the coarse-adjustment knob while watching from the side. Then, wind the fine-adjustment knob up to focus the lens.

Answers to

In-Text Questions

(a) eyepiece
(b) tube
(c) objective lenses
(d) stage
(e) base
(f) mirror
(g) fine-adjustment knob
(h) coarse-adjustment knob
(i) nosepiece

Materials

How to Use a Microscope: microscope
Exploration 9: microscope, microscope slides and coverslips, eyedropper, newspaper, forceps, scissors, tissue, onion, toothpicks, iodine solution (10 drops in 10 mL of water), gloves, safety goggles

Teacher's Resource Binder

Resource Worksheet 2–8
Activity Worksheets 2–9 and 2–10
Resource Transparencies 2–7 and 2–8
Graphic Organizer Transparencies 2–9, 2–10, and 2–11

Science Discovery Videodisc

Disc 2, Image and Activity Bank, 2–10

Time Required

four class periods

Exploration 9
Part 1

Tell students that in *Part 1* they will make wet mounts of the letter "e" cut from a newspaper. Students should examine the slide under a microscope and a make a sketch of the microscopic view.

Students will observe that the microscopic image is both backwards and upside down as compared with the real object. The image is *laterally inverted*. Students will notice this because each time they move the slide downward on the stage, the image will appear to move upward, and each time the slide is moved to the right, the image will appear to move to the left.

Looking at Cells

When you examine the cells of a plant or animal through a microscope, the sample you use must be very thin—so thin that light can shine through it. Also, the sample must be kept moist. The illustrations on the right show how to make a **wet mount**.

You Will Need

- a microscope
- microscope slide(s)
- coverslip(s)
- an eyedropper
- a letter *e*—from a newspaper
- forceps
- an onion
- toothpicks
- iodine

Watch out for these

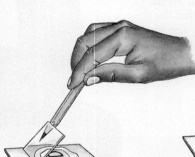

Dark, round circles are air bubbles.

Dark, jagged lines are coverslip edges.

Thin, irregular lines are from drying up of water.

What to Do
Part 1

In this activity, you will see that things look different, not just larger, under a microscope.

Making a Wet Mount

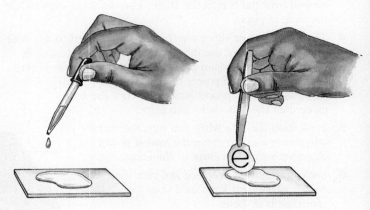

1. Put a drop of water on a slide.

2. Place a letter *e* from a newspaper on the water.

3. Lean a coverslip on a pencil.

4. Lower the pencil slowly and finally remove it. Avoid getting air bubbles under the coverslip. Absorb excess moisture around the coverslip with tissue. Now view the slide through the microscope. Draw what you see.

Part 2

Next, take forceps and peel a little of the transparent "skin" from the inside of an onion. Make a wet mount of the skin, then examine it under the microscope. Now, add a drop of iodine to the edge of the coverslip. Carefully draw what you see.

Part 3

Compare these plant cells with some animal cells. With a clean toothpick, gently scrape some soft material from the inside lining of your cheek. Make a wet mount of this material. Examine the slide under the microscope. Then add a drop of iodine as before. Draw what you see.

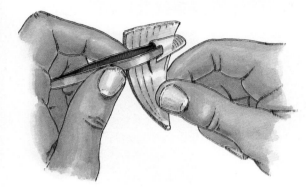

Did you notice any change after adding the iodine? What happened? What similarities were there between the plant and animal cells? What differences did you notice? The onion skin cells have a specific part to play in the life of an onion plant. They are only one of several kinds of cells in the plant. Your cheek cells are also special. Your body has many different kinds of cells; bone cells, blood cells, muscle cells, and nerve cells are just a few of the different types. Each type of cell has a special function.

Onion Cells

Cheek Cells

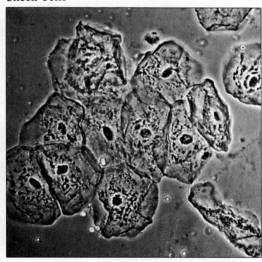

Parts 2 and 3

Tell students that in *Parts 2* and *3* they will be looking at typical plant cells (onion cells) and typical animal cells (their own cheek cells). (You may wish to demonstrate how to make the wet mounts for students.) Tell them to follow the directions carefully. Remind them to add the iodine solution before they make their drawings. Encourage students to make their drawings as accurately as possible. You may wish to give them diagrams of typical plant and animal cells so that they can look for the various cellular structures in the samples while observing their own wet mounts with the microscope.

Answers to

In-Text Questions

- Neither type of cell has much natural color. Both are more visible if the wet mount is made with a drop of a dilute iodine solution instead of a drop of water. The iodine solution will "stain" the cell, making it easier to see.
- **Similarities:** The typical animal and plant cells contain a cell membrane, cytoplasm, a nucleus, and a nuclear membrane.
- **Differences:** Plant cells contain a large vacuole and a thick cell wall. Green plant cells also contain chloroplasts. Animal cells lack these organelles.

  Each cell is a bit like a separate living thing. It uses food and oxygen and produces energy. In more complex animals and plants, each cell specializes to become a tiny part of a *tissue*, which is a large group of similar cells all helping to perform a particular function for the organism.

Answers to

In-Text Questions

A. Spirogyra algae—plant-like cells
B. Diatoms—animal-like cells
C. Root tip cells—plant cells
D. Plant cells
E. Smooth muscle cells—animal cells
F. Nerve cells—animal cells
G. Red blood cells—animal cells
H. Amoeba—animal-like cells
I. Elodea cells—plant cells
J. Plant vascular tissue—plant cells

✳ Follow Up

Assessment

1. Have each student or group of students perform a short exercise with the microscope. Inform students before class that this will be a practical laboratory test. Observe whether or not they use the microscope correctly: that they carry the microscope properly, that they start with the lowest power objective, that they adjust the diaphragm or mirror, and that they focus the course and fine adjustments correctly.

    Prepare slides of *Elodea* cells or other leaf surfaces. Ask students to look at the slides and draw what they see.

2. Obtain a water sample from the bottom of a pond or marsh. The sample should contain some plants from the pond or a bit of the material from the bottom. Many microscopic plants and animals will be visible. Several types of filamentous algae will appear, as will various protozoans and tiny roundworms. Ask students to find and draw, with the aid of the microscope, examples of plant cells and animal cells in the water sample. *(The one-celled organisms may show locomotion, appear to be hunting for food, and respond to stimuli. It is possible that students will see one of the unicellular organisms removing waste from its body. Students may also observe reproduction by division.)*

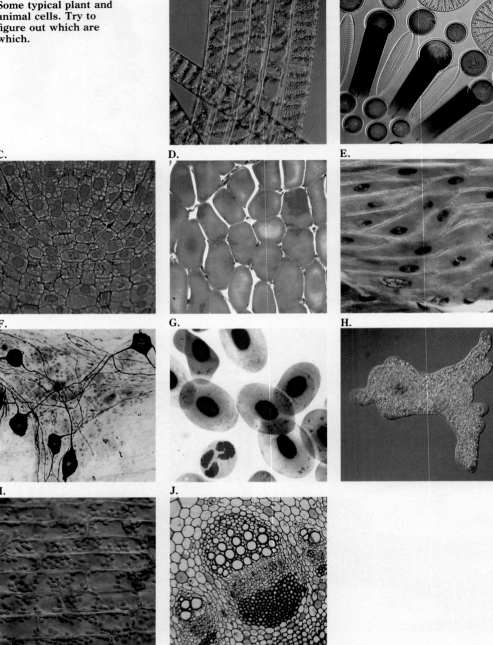

Some typical plant and animal cells. Try to figure out which are which.

Extension

1. When a great number of similar cells work together to serve a particular function in organisms, those collections of cells are called *tissues*. Ask students to use reference books to determine the shape of the cells making up muscle tissue, bone tissue, and nerve tissue. They should then make a sketch of a sample of the cells for each kind of tissue.

2. Students should find out the answers to these questions on microscopes, and then write a short report on the microscope as an important instrument of science.
   - When were microscopes invented?
   - Who invented this useful instrument?
   - How many kinds of microscopes are there?
   - How does each kind of microscope operate?

1. How are the cells that make up living things like bricks?

2. How are cells not like bricks?

3. How do microscopes aid in the study of living things?

4. Describe how microscopes change the way things look (other than just making them look larger).

5. Suppose that you are looking through a microscope at a tiny animal. It swims up and to the right out of your field of view. Which way do you move the slide to follow it?

6. Copy the table below into your Journal. Then rate yourself as a microscope user.

Activity	3 good	2 fair	1 could be better
(a) I carry the microscope carefully to my work area.			
(b) I begin observing with the lowest power objective lens.			
(c) I carefully adjust the light level.			
(d) I avoid touching the objective lens to the slide I am viewing.			
(e) I focus the microscope by first using the coarse adjustment knob and then using the fine adjustment knob.			
(f) I properly prepare the microscope for storage when my work is finished.			

Answers to

Challenge Your Thinking

1. Cells are like bricks in that they work together to form a structure. Many bricks can be joined together to form a wall; likewise, many cells can be joined together to form a tissue. Cell walls of plants are rigid and give support to the organism, just as bricks give support to a building.

2. Cells are unlike bricks in that each cell is made up of even smaller structures that carry out the function of the cell. These cell functions are the activities of life.

3. Microscopes are so important because they allow us to examine the structures that make up an organism.

4. The objects are also inverted.

5. To the left.

6. Answers will vary.

Summary for

The Big Ideas

Student responses will vary. The following is an ideal summary.

The characteristics of life are made up of the following: the ability to move, energy consumption, growth and development, response to stimulus, and reproduction.

Plant motion is usually very slow; animal motion can be slow or fast. Also, the entire plant does not move from place to place.

Plants and people have similar growth patterns in that they grow larger, develop, and become more complex. Their growth patterns differ in that plants can continue to develop throughout their lives depending on environmental conditions. Animal growth usually stops with the onset of adulthood.

Growth can be developmental, regenerative, or continuous. Developmental growth is important in that it gives rise to an adult; regenerative growth restores lost or damaged structures; continuous growth replaces structures that wear away, such as hair and nails. Uncontrolled growth, such as cancer, is harmful. Reproduction causes entirely new organisms to grow.

"Response to stimuli" refers to an organism's response to a change in the environment or within the organism itself. Responses are valuable because they help an organism protect itself from possible threats.

The recurring cycles of sleeping and waking, activity, and hunger in animals suggests that all animals may have an internal clock. Migration may also be triggered by an internal clock.

Every species represents the result of an ongoing evolutionary process. Adaptation in species occurs over long periods of time, driven by natural selection. For example, a species of fish might have evolved more efficient gills, desert species might have developed ways to extract water from the environment, etc.

The Big Ideas

In your Journal, write a summary of this unit, using the following questions as a guide.

- What are some signs of life?
- How do plant and animal motion differ?
- In what ways are the growth patterns of plants and people similar? In what ways are they different?
- What are some of the different forms of growth? Of what value is each?
- What does "response to stimuli" mean? Why is it valuable?
- What evidence is there that animals have a sense of time?
- What are some adaptations of plants and animals over long periods of time?
- How do plant and animal species adapt over long periods of time?

Checking Your Understanding

1. Would a seed be an example of a living thing? Why or why not?
2. Look at the illustration below showing the life cycle of a butterfly. How does the butterfly's growth pattern differ from that of a human?

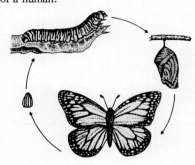

3. What are some of the reasons that animals migrate? Name at least three animals that migrate.
4. Construct a concept map using the following terms: *cold-blooded, bear, warm-blooded, animals,* and *frog.*
5. What are some of the different ways in which animals move?
6. Are all forms of growth useful? Explain.
7. Is bigger always better? Explain.

Answers to

Checking Your Understanding

1. A seed is a dormant plant embryo, waiting for the right conditions to begin development and the processes of living.
2. The life cycle of a butterfly consists of four distinct stages: egg, larva, pupa, and adult. These stages differ in appearance, movement, and feeding habits. The growth pattern of a human, from egg to adult, is a more gradual, ongoing process.

3. Reasons for migration include: to avoid unfavorable weather, to find food, or to reproduce. Three animals that migrate are whales, bats, and birds.
4. See concept map on page S168.
5. Animals can move in a variety of different ways: crawling, walking, swimming, and flying.
6. Uncontrolled growth is not useful. It is generally harmful and often fatal.
7. Large size has its disadvantages. Larger organisms, such as the African elephant, must spend more time than their smaller counterparts finding food and eating, just to stay alive.

(Answers continue on next page)

8. How do snakes demonstrate adaptation to their environment?

9. In your own words, compare the earthworm's locomotion to that of a snake.

10. How might a sense of time be helpful to animals? to plants?

11. Why do cold-blooded animals go dormant in the winter? How can warm-blooded animals survive the winter without going dormant?

12. Add the following to your list of "Wonder Questions." Suggest answers to each.

    (a) Where do snakes, frogs, and salamanders go in the winter?

    (b) How do warm-blooded animals keep their body temperature constant?

    (c) What advantages do warm-blooded animals have over cold-blooded animals?

    (d) What causes animals to start migrating? to stop migrating?

    (e) What cues do animals use to guide them as they migrate?

Reading *Plus*

Now that you have been introduced to living things, let's take a closer look at them. By reading pages S21–S40 in the *SourceBook,* you will learn more about the fundamentals of living things—how they are organized, how cells work, how living things hand down characteristics from generation to generation, as well as how scientists classify living things.

Updating Your Journal

Reread the paragraphs you wrote for this unit's "For Your Journal" questions. Then rewrite them to reflect what you have learned in studying this unit.

About Updating Your Journal

The following are sample ideal answers.

1. Something that is alive must exhibit all of the characteristics of life, not just some of them. *(The uniformity of these characteristics shows the **Stability** in living systems.)*

2. The characteristics of life include movement, growth and development, energy use, response to stimulus, and reproduction.

3. Living things interact with their surroundings by responding to conditions in the environment, which include temperature, amount of food, number of predators, shelter, and amount of living space. Responses to these conditions can be either positive or negative.

4. The zebras move, breathe, eat, interact with their surroundings, reproduce, and eventually die.

Answers continued

8. The scales of a snake help the animal grip the ground so that it can push itself forward. These scales also prevent their bodies from drying out.

9. A snake moves by either flexing its body in an S-shaped curve or by pushing off with its scales. An earthworm propels itself forward by alternately contracting ring muscles and lengthwise muscles.

10. A sense of time in animals and plants is important to help them survive the difficulties of their environments. For example, small creatures might sleep during the day to avoid predators; some birds migrate south in the winter to find food; some plants close up their leaves at night to conserve heat and water; some trees drop their leaves in the fall and become dormant to reduce the chance of freezing in the winter.

11. Cold-blooded animals enter a period of dormancy when their body temperatures drop too low to allow any activity. Warm-blooded animals have more options because they are able to maintain constant body temperatures.

12. (a) Some snakes, frogs, and salamanders become dormant in the winter.

    (b) Warm-blooded animals have an internal thermostat that regulates temperature. Most mammals have a layer of fat under their skin that serves as insulation. Animals with hair or feathers can fluff up this outer covering to trap air, which also acts as insulation.

    (c) Warm-blooded animals have the advantage of being able to function even when it is cold. They can also live in places that cold-blooded animals cannot.

    (d) Environmental cues, such as day length, cause animals to start migrating. A combination of learned and innate behavior signals the end of migration.

    (e) Animals take cues from the environment that include landmarks, wind direction, position of the sun, and magnetism.

✦ Background

Forests are one of our most important natural resources. We use forest products for building materials, paper, fuel, and for a variety of other uses. Forests help clean the air we breathe, help protect our water supplies and wildlife, and provide recreational opportunities.

Foresters are responsible for protecting, managing, and developing forest resources, both to make them more productive today, and also, to make them available for future generations.

One of the duties of foresters is to supervise the growing, protection, and utilization of trees. They make maps of forest areas, estimate the amount of standing timber and future growth, and manage timber sales. All of these responsibilities involve working successfully with other people. For example, managing timber sales involves dealing with landowners and supervising the work of loggers. Also, foresters protect the forests from fire, harmful insects, and disease. Foresters have several other responsibilities, too, such as wildlife protection, watershed management, and the development of parks and campgrounds.

Spotlight on Forestry

Jerry Blanco is forester responsible for providing information to the public about our forest resources.

Q: How did you become interested in forestry?

Jerry: Forests have always been a part of my life. I grew up in a remote community where most people earned their living from the forest somehow—logging, trapping, hunting, and so on. My father was a part-time trapper and over the years he developed a keen appreciation of the forest, something he managed to pass on to me. As a kid I spent a lot of my time knocking around in the woods with my friends or by myself. It wasn't all play, though. Gradually, I became a serious student of the forest. I came to realize what an incredibly complex, dynamic place it was. It seemed only natural to take my knowledge and appreciation of the forest and put it to work, so to speak, by becoming a forester.

Q: What does a forester do?

Jerry: The forester's job is to monitor the forest and to work to keep it in the highest possible state of health. Many foresters work for the government. Some work for private industry. Foresters also work to educate the public, as I do.

Q: There has been much controversy about using herbicides and pesticides in forest management. What are your views?

Jerry: As you know, the main problem with these chemicals is that they are terribly poisonous. Very nasty stuff. As a naturalist, I am not too thrilled with the idea of using poisons to "manage" the forest—it is perfectly capable of managing itself. But as a realist, I recognize that from time to time we must act assertively to protect our natural resources. The key is to use chemicals sparingly, and then only as a last resort.

✦ Using the Interview

You might consider having two students role play the parts of the interviewer and the forester. Use the following questions to promote discussion.

- Why is the forester's job becoming more and more important? *(Due to an increasing world population and the demand for forest products, there is a greater need now for more careful management of forest products so that forests will not be destroyed.)*
- Do you think pesticides should be used in forest management? Explain your answer. *(This controversial issue is debatable—pesticides can harm the environment, but if they are not used, people could not purchase forest products at a reasonable price.)*

- What are some things that you can do to decrease overusing our forests? *(Recycle newspapers, do not use paper bags at the grocery store, do not use herbicides and pesticides excessively, recycle wood products.)*
- Do you think you would like the job of a forester? Why or why not? *(Students' current interests will provide some clues. For example, if they enjoy science, being outdoors, and working with people, then the career of a forester could be suitable.)*

Some Project Ideas

The forest changes constantly. In a forest near you, look for evidence of recent (or not-so-recent) change. For example, a clearing in the process of re-growth. How do recently cleared areas compare to areas that were cleared longer ago? Look at individual trees for evidence of change, possibly a scar from earlier damage. Use your powers of observation to the fullest. Keep careful records of what you see. Look for evidence of seasonal changes. How does the forest in winter differ from the forest in summer? How do different kinds of trees differ? What kinds of conditions do different types of trees seem to prefer? How "climbable" are the different types of trees? How is this significant? How do the trees reproduce? What kinds of seeds do the trees produce? How are the seeds dispersed? What are the advantages and disadvantages of each type of seed dispersal method?

Another project is to organize a tree-planting campaign in your area. Be sure to use trees suitable for your climate and soil type.

For Assistance

For help with your project, use reference material or consult persons knowledgable about forestry. Ask your teacher for help in finding foresters in your area. State or federal agencies dealing with forestery-related matters are a good place to start.

✦ Using the Project Ideas

Ask students to choose one of the projects that are suggested. If possible, arrange to take your students to a forested area nearby to conduct field research. Students should plan their investigations ahead of time so that the field trip can be spent collecting data. Divide students into small groups or research teams. Topics they can investigate include cataloging the species of trees present, the size and number of these trees, and the types of other plant and animal species present. You will need to supply students with appropriate field guides for your area. Impress upon students that taking accurate and complete notes will produce the most accurate picture of the area they are studying.

If a field trip is not possible, students might enjoy researching the characteristics of different types of forests including temperate, tropical rain, and taiga. Another interesting area to investigate is the effect of fire on deforestation. Ask students to find out whether the effect on the forest is positive or negative.

✦ Going Further

Environmental concerns are often at odds with the wants and needs of mankind. For example, in the old growth forests of the Pacific Northwest, attempts to save the endangered northern spotted owl are perhaps endangering the jobs of people living there.

Do research to find out how you feel about this issue, using the following questions as a guide:
• Whose rights are more important, those of man or of nature?

• How do the terms *clear-cutting* and *old growth* relate to this problem?
• How can forestry management help to solve the problem?

For more information on forestry issues and careers, have interested students write to:
American Forest Institute
1619 Massachusetts Ave., NW
Washington, D.C. 20036

Science and the Arts

✦ Background

John James Audubon is known **first and foremost as an accomplished artist.** His work captured the essence of the wildlife in the America of his time. He was one of the first scientific artists to paint birds in their natural surroundings. In Audubon's paintings, birds are often posed dramatically on branches and among plants.

Audubon, the naturalist, has been overshadowed by Audubon, the artist. His accounts of North American bird species are still some of the most complete and accurate that have ever been published. Largely as a result of Audubon's influence, the birds of North America have been portrayed and described far better than those of most other parts of the world.

The name "Audubon" has been made famous by the National Audubon Society, an organization that has dedicated itself to preserving the birds that Audubon spent his life studying and interpreting.

Science and the Arts

John James Audubon

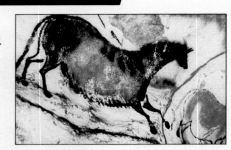

The natural beauty and variety of living things have inspired artists since humans first drew forms in the mud or on cave walls. For example, the horse on the right was painted 17,000 years ago in a cave in France. More recently, the diversity of life flourishes in the works of artists like Durer, Van Gogh, and Rousseau.

Audubon's Early Life

One artist, who you may already know about, became famous painting birds. That artist was the Frenchman John James Audubon (1785–1851). As a child, and throughout his life, John Audubon loved hunting and the outdoors, and drawing birds would be his lifelong passion. His father, who was generally supportive even when he didn't completely agree with him, eventually sent John to the best drawing school in Paris. Much to his family's disappointment, John failed in the school because he was impatient with the instruction and was only interested in drawing birds.

A New Start in America

In 1803 John was sent to America to escape military service under Napoleon. There he fell in love with his neighbor's daughter, a beautiful young girl named Lucy Bakewell. He determined at once to marry her, but before her father would give his consent, the young man had to be established in some kind of work. So, with the planning and support of his father, Audubon tried a number of businesses.

John and Lucy were married, but all their business enterprises were utter failures—Audubon was sought by a mob, assaulted by a business enemy, and even put in jail for debt. The sheriff took almost everything the couple owned. In fact, Audubon was left with only his drawings (which at the time were considered worthless), and his clothes, and his gun. However, this liberated him to pursue his true calling—the study and painting of birds. To make ends meet, Audubon painted portraits and gave drawing and music lessons, while Lucy worked as a governess.

✦ Promoting Observational Skills

Ask students to carefully study the paintings in order to answer the following questions.
- How realistic is the cave painting of the horse? What things about the painting seem particularly skillful or attractive in the work of the artist?
- Pretend you are an art critic. What would you say about Audubon's paintings of the Louisiana heron and the ivory-billed woodpeckers?

✦ Discussion

Promote discussion in the classroom by posing the following questions.
- The two bird species pictured on the pages are the Louisiana heron and the ivory-billed woodpecker. The latter is extinct. What might be the reasons for its extinction?
- Audubon worked as a scientist and an artist. What are some occupations that require a person to work in both capacities?
- What might be the value of a drawing or a painting over an actual photograph of a particular bird in a bird guide?

Creative Freedom

In this new phase of his life, Audubon made a number of flatboat expeditions on the Mississippi River to collect specimens of birds and to paint their pictures. Accompanying him on these expeditions was his assistant, a young man named Jo Mason, who was thirteen years old at the time of the first trip in 1820. This gifted young artist and student of botany would teach Audubon much about plants and would personally contribute some of the artwork in Audubon's paintings. The plant life in the finished works would be a major factor in the eventual success of Audubon's paintings, because the natural settings in which the birds were protrayed gave the paintings much of their interest and liveliness.

Success and Recognition

Audubon had the idea of publishing life-sized engravings of all the species of American birds in a huge work called *The Birds of America*. He was unable to find an American publisher who would undertake this work, so he went back to Europe in 1826. How this former business failure was able to promote and organize this enormous project is in itself a remarkable story. His paintings were published in installments to one thousand subscribers at the price of one thousand dollars per subscription. When he returned to America, John Audubon was hailed as a great artist and naturalist.

Find out for Yourself

John Audubon's most important works about birds are *The Birds of America* and *Ornithological Biography*. They were intended to be read together. Your library may have copies of them. See if you can find a painting that Audubon made of a bird you are personally familiar with. What did he write about the bird?

Do you like Audubon's paintings? Do you think he drew the birds realistically? Or do you think he drew them to give them more personality? Would you agree with such an approach? How does what Audubon wrote about birds show that he took a scientific as well as an artistic interest in his subjects?

✦ *Going Further*

- Have interested students research how other artists depict wildlife in their paintings. They could write a report comparing the styles of Durer, Van Gogh, and Rousseau.
- Invite the students to go on a bird walk to identify as many different species of birds as they can. Suggest that they take a field guide with them, such as Peterson's *Field Guide to the Birds.*
- Students with artistic interests might enjoy drawing live birds or other animals. They might try to use Audubon's style in their own drawings.

Answers to

Find Out for Yourself

- Student answers will vary according to their own personal favorites among the birds they had the opportunity to observe. Involve the students in a discussion of things they have personally observed in connection with their chosen bird—such things as the preferred habitats of the birds, their nests, the way they fly, their calls, their mating behavior, etc.
- Student answers will depend upon their individual tastes, as well as their conception of the purpose of Audubon's work. Audubon's admirers have often held that his work is superior because it captures the "spirit" of the animal. His critics complain that the work is too "artistic" and that the animals have expressions that give them human-like qualities.
- Audubon's scientific interest in his subjects is revealed by the accurate and detailed representations of such things as the lichens on the branches in the painting of the ivory-billed woodpeckers. Also, the students may point out that the woodpecker highest in the painting is represented in a way that is not only artistically appealing, but also shows some characteristic behavior of the species. By contrast, the Louisiana heron is portrayed with simple grace in a very beautiful setting. Students who research further into Audubon's biography may learn that as a young person Audubon worked in a museum and learned taxidermy. At this time he developed the scientific habits of including measurements on his sketches, as well as enlarged details of such critical features as beaks and feet.

Teaching the Unit

 ### Unit Overview

In this unit, students draw on their personal experiences to learn about the dynamic world of microorganisms. In the section *A Hidden World,* students learn about the diversity and classification of microorganisms by observing them in their natural environment and by growing cultures in the classroom.

In the section *Friend or Foe?* students examine both the beneficial and harmful relationships that exist between people and microorganisms. By studying the work and methods of Louis Pasteur, students learn how scientists approach problem solving.

In the final section, *Keeping Germs in Their Place,* students learn about mechanisms for controlling the growth of harmful microorganisms. By studying Alexander Fleming's work, students see how these mechanisms have protected people against the spread of disease. Then students learn how microorganisms cause food to spoil and how we can prevent this from happening.

 ### Using the Themes

The unifying themes emphasized in this unit are **Systems and Interactions, Scale and Structure,** and **Patterns of Change.** The following information will help you weave these themes into your teaching plan. A focus question is provided with each theme as a discussion tool to help you tie the information in the unit together.

Systems and Interactions is dominant because of the emphasis placed on interrelationships among microorganisms, food, and people. Students learn about how they benefit from and are harmed by this interaction. They also learn how to prevent unnecessary exposure to microorganisms by being aware of the conditions under which microorganisms grow and reproduce.

Focus question: *In what ways do humans and microorganisms interact?*

Lessons 3–5 discuss microorganisms that play a part in our lives every day, types of food formed through the action of microorganisms, and how we use helpful microorganisms and deal with harmful ones.

Scale and Structure is an integral part of the sections *Friend or Foe?* and *A Hidden World,* which both explore the size, structure, and function of microorganisms.

Focus question: *How might the size and structure of microorganisms help them survive?*

The size and specialized structures of microorganisms enable them to live and reproduce successfully in virtually every environment.

Patterns of Change is developed through discussions of how microorganisms affect food and people. Students come to understand that microorganism growth and reproduction rates, as well as the changes effected by microorganisms, are predictable when variables such as time and temperature are known.

Focus question: *What predictable changes occur in foods due to the action of microorganisms?*

When conditions are right, microorganisms that have been added to a particular food, either purposefully or by accident, begin to digest that food and multiply, causing chemical changes in the food. For example, milk contaminated by bacteria spoils, and the gas given off by yeast causes bread to rise.

 ### Using the *Science Discovery* Videodiscs

Disc 1 *Science Sleuths, The Biogene Company Picnic*
Many of the employees attending the Biogene company picnic have suddenly become sick. The emergency-room doctor needs to know the cause of the illness in order to treat the sick people and to alert public health officials in case of a possible epidemic. The Science Sleuths must analyze the evidence for themselves to determine the true cause of the illness.

Disc 2 *Image and Activity Bank*
A variety of still images, short videos, and activities are available for you to use as you teach this unit. See the *Videodisc Resources* section of the **Teacher's Resource Binder** for detailed instructions.

 ### Using the *SciencePlus* SourceBook

Unit 3 focuses on microorganisms and the various diseases they can cause in both animals and plants. Students learn how the structure and function of bacteria and viruses affect their interactions with other organisms. Finally, the unit details our natural defense against disease and major immune system disorders, including AIDS.

PLANNING CHART

SECTION AND LESSON	PG.	TIME*	PROCESS SKILLS	EXPLORATION AND ASSESSMENT	PG.	RESOURCES AND FEATURES
Unit Opener	116		observing, discussing	For Your Journal	117	Science Sleuths: *The Biogene Company Picnic* Videodisc Activity Sheets TRB: Home Connection
A HIDDEN WORLD	118			Challenge Your Thinking	131	Graphic Organizer Transparency 3–2
1 "But I Don't See. . . "	118	1 to 2	observing, analyzing, writing			Image and Activity Bank 3–1 TRB: Activity Worksheet 3–1 Resource Transparency 3–1
2 Our Tiny Neighbors	123	4	observing, using a microscope, drawing micro-organisms, analyzing	Exploration 1 Exploration 2	124 126	Image and Activity Bank 3–2 TRB: Activity Worksheet 3–2
FRIEND OR FOE?	132			Challenge Your Thinking	149	
3 Tall (but True) Tales	132	3	reading for understanding, writing, drawing, evaluating	Exploration 3 Exploration 4	134 134	Image and Activity Bank 3–3
4 A Balanced View	138	2	analyzing, inferring, comparing, writing	Exploration 5	142	Image and Activity Bank 3–4 TRB: Activity Worksheet 3–3 Graphic Organizer Transparencies 3–3 and 3–4
5 The Staff of Life	144	2	observing, using a data table, inferring, analyzing	Exploration 6 Exploration 7	144 148	Image and Activity Bank 3–5 TRB: Resource Worksheet 3–4 Activity Worksheet 3–5 Resource Transparency 3–5
KEEPING GERMS IN THEIR PLACE	150			Challenge Your Thinking	173	Graphic Organizer Transparency 3–8
6 Germ Warfare	150	2 to 3	predicting, inferring, critical thinking, preparing a data chart	Exploration 8	151	Image and Activity Bank 3–6 TRB: Activity Worksheets 3–6 and 3–7
7 Microorganisms and Food Preservation	156	2 to 3	calculating; analyzing; using graphs, tables, and diagrams; comparing			Image and Activity Bank 3–7 TRB: Activity Worksheets 3–8 and 3–9 Graphic Organizer Transparency 3–6
8 Surrounded by Microorganisms	162	1	reading, analyzing, evaluating, compiling a list			Image and Activity Bank 3–8 TRB: Activity Worksheet 3–10
9 Let's Eat Out Tonight	164	1	analyzing, evaluating, researching, writing			Image and Activity Bank 3–9
10 Food and the Law	167	2	analyzing, evaluating, summarizing, writing a letter	Exploration 9	170	Image and Activity Bank 3–10 TRB: Activity Worksheet 3–11 Graphic Organizer Transparency 3–7
End of Unit	174		applying, analyzing, evaluating, summarizing	Making Connections TRB: Sample Assessment Items	174	TRB: Resource Worksheet 3–12 Science in Action, p. 176 Science and Technology, p. 178 *SourceBook,* pp. S41–S56

*Time given in number of class periods.

✴ *Meeting Individual Needs*

☀ Gifted Students

1. Explain to students that microorganisms have *organelles* that carry out such life processes as digestion, locomotion, elimination, and energy production. Suggest that they choose a member of the kingdom Protista, such as a paramecium, and research the major organelles that make up its internal structure. Have students make a poster-sized diagram of the protist and label the organelles by name and function. Invite students to use their posters to present what they have learned to the class. Arrange the finished posters as part of a special classroom display on the kingdom Protista.

2. Suggest that students consider the following rule: "Food in lockers is no longer allowed for health safety reasons." Challenge them to write an opinion that either favors or opposes this rule and then present their ideas to the class.

☀ LEP Students

1. Provide students with pictures of several different kinds of food, such as a carton of milk, a container of yogurt, a package of meat or poultry, and eggs. Then have students write a simple sentence or phrase that states how the item should be stored to keep it safe from contamination by microorganisms. Allow them to use a bilingual dictionary if necessary. When students finish, review their work for science content, with only minimal emphasis on language proficiency.

2. Remind students that in this unit they have learned several rules to follow when preparing food to prevent contamination by microorganisms. For example, hands should be washed before handling food; food should be kept covered and refrigerated; damp sponges and cloths should not be used to wipe cutting boards; and dishes and utensils should be carefully washed and air-dried. Suggest that they make a bilingual poster to illustrate one or two of these rules. Invite volunteers to share their finished posters with the class by reading the information on their posters in English and in their native language.

3. At the beginning of each unit, give Spanish-speaking students a copy of the *Spanish Glossary* from the *Teacher's Resource Binder.* Also, let Spanish-speaking students listen to the *English/Spanish Audiocassettes.*

☀ At-Risk Students

Unit 3 offers many opportunities for students to take a hands-on approach to the study of microorganisms.

Students act as scientists as they collect, observe, and culture different groups of microscopic organisms. With the Explorations *Water Neighbors* and *Is Yeast Alive?* students explore their environment and discover that what looks ordinary from afar can become extraordinary upon taking a closer look.

Some students may have trouble understanding the importance of classification systems in science. Using photographs and illustrations that you have provided, challenge each student to make models of one representative from each group: Protista, Monera, Fungi, and Viruses. For materials, they can use modeling clay, pipe cleaners, string, and colored paper. Instruct students to pay special attention to internal structures and possible means of locomotion. Have students list similarities and differences between their models and then collectively devise a system for grouping the models. Compare their system to the one used by scientists, and discuss and resolve any differences.

☀ Cross-Disciplinary Focus

Creative Writing

Remind students of the *Tall (but True) Tales* they read in Lesson 3. Suggest that they write similar stories from the point of view of a microorganism and illustrate their stories with drawings. Have volunteers perform dramatic readings of their stories for the class. Then encourage students to organize their stories into a booklet.

Some students may enjoy writing poems about the hidden world they encountered in this unit. Encourage students to be creative. Suggest that their poems may be as serious or as funny as they like. Students could illustrate what they write with drawings of their own or with pictures cut from magazines. Have volunteers share their poems with the class and arrange their finished poems in a bulletin board display.

Drama

Have groups of three or four students write a short play set in the microscopic world of microorganisms. Provide them with time to cast the play, make props, rehearse it, and present it to the class.

Mathematics

Remind students of how quickly the microorganisms they observed through the microscopes in Unit 2 moved. Point out that the maximum speed reached by some microorganisms has actually been calculated.

Have them make bar graphs to compare the size and maximum speeds of the following microorganisms:

Organism	Length	Swimming Speed
Bacillus subtilus	2.5 μm	15 μm/s
Spirillum volutans	13.0 μm	110 μm/s
Euglena	38.0 μm	230 μm/s
Paramecium	220.0 μm	1000 μm/s

Display the finished bar graphs where other students may review and enjoy them.

Art

Suggest that students make papier-mâché models of microorganisms to represent each of the groups mentioned in the unit—protozoa, algae, fungi, molds, bacteria, and viruses. Have students label each one with its name and the group to which it belongs and then arrange their finished models in a display.

Students who enjoy drawing could make a cartoon poster illustrating one of the *Tall Tale* scenarios from Lesson 3 or a story of their own. Have volunteers share their cartoons with the class by relating the story it illustrates.

Cross-Cultural Focus

Using Microorganisms Around the World

Encourage students from other countries and cultures to share with the class how their culture uses microorganisms to make certain kinds of foods. For example: What kinds of bakery products that require yeast are common in their culture? What cheeses are made in their native country? How is yogurt used in cooking? Encourage students to share appropriate recipes with the class or organize them into a booklet for class members to read at their leisure.

Preserving Foods with a Cultural Difference

Many cultures preserve certain foods to store them for long periods of time. For example, many Asian cultures dry foods such as fish, fruit, and even poultry; some eastern European cultures pickle foods; and some Scandinavian cultures salt foods. Invite students from other parts of the world to describe how their native foods are preserved in ways not commonly used in this country. Have those students bring to class examples of such foods.

✳ *Resources*

Bibliography for Teachers

Aklcamo, I. Edward. *Fundamentals of Microbiology.* Reading, MA: Addison-Wesley, 1986.

Dube, H.C. *Textbook of Fungi, Bacteria, & Viruses.* New York, NY: Advent Books, Inc., 1986.

Jahn, Theodore L., et al. *How to Know the Protozoa.* Dubuque, IA: William C. Brown, 1978.

Kingsley, V. Vincent. *Basic Microbiology for the Health Sciences.* Philadelphia, PA: Saunders, 1982.

Sleigh, Michael. *Protozoa & Other Protists.* New York, NY: Routledge, Chapman & Hall, 1989.

Teasdale, Jim. *Microbes.* Morristown, NJ: Silver Burdett & Ginn, 1984.

Bibliography for Students

Bains, Rae. *Louis Pasteur.* Mahwah, NJ: Troll Books, 1985.

Cobb, Vicki. *Lots of Rot.* New York, NY: Harper & Row, 1981.

Dowdle, Walter, and Jack Lapatra. *Informed Consent: Influenza Facts and Myths.* Chicago, IL: Nelson-Hall, 1983.

Jacobs, Francine. *Breakthrough: The True Story of Penicillin.* New York, NY: Dodd, Mead, 1985.

McMahon, Thomas A., and John Tyler Bonner. *On Size and Life.* New York, NY: Scientific American Books, 1983.

Nourse, Alan E. *Viruses.* New York, NY: Watts, 1983.

Patent, Dorothy H. *Bacteria: How They Affect Other Living Things.* New York, NY: Holiday House, 1980.

Sabin, Francene. *Microbes and Bacteria.* Mahwah, NJ: Troll Books, 1985.

Films, Videotapes, Software, and Other Media

Algae and *Fungi.* Filmstrip and Videotape. American School Pub. Princeton Road, Box 408 Hightstown, NJ 08520

Classifying Microorganisms.

Microorganisms That Cause Disease. Film and Videotape. Coronet Film & Video 108 Wilmot Road Deerfield, IL 60015

Journey into Microspace. Videotape.

The Microorganisms Simulator. Software for Apple II Family. Focus Media, Inc. P.O. Box 865 Garden City, NY 11530

Living Things in a Drop of Water.

The Protists. Film and Videotape. Encyclopedia Britannica 425 North Michigan Ave. Chicago, IL 60611

UNIT
3

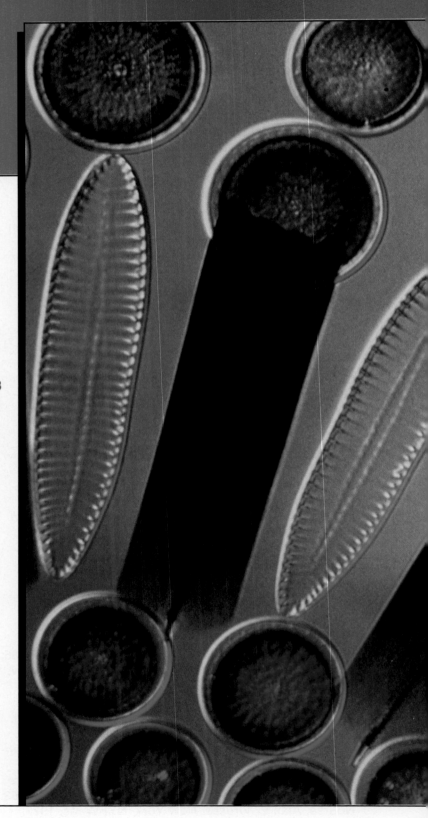

Unit 3   It's a Small World

Unit 3   **It's a Small World**

✳ Unit Focus

Ask students if they have ever had a cold or the flu. Call on volunteers to describe the symptoms. Then involve the class in a brief discussion of what causes colds and flu. Help students arrive at the primary cause of these diseases, accepting such terms as *bugs, viruses,* and *germs. (To avoid misconceptions, do not accept bacteria as a cause for either disease.)* Then ask students if they have ever seen a germ that causes colds or flu. Encourage them to explain why they cannot see these organisms. *(They are too small to be seen with the unaided eye.)*

✳ About the Photograph

This photomicrograph shows several species of diatoms at a magnification of about 2200 times. Diatoms are singled-celled plants that belong to the phylum Chrysophyta (golden-brown algae). They are found in both fresh and marine water and in moist soil.

Diatoms appear almost jewel-like because their cells are enclosed in a hard, glass-like shell made of silicon. Their shells have many pores and ridges of various designs, giving diatoms a special beauty. The markings of diatoms are so precise that they are used to test how well a microscope can focus.

✳ Using the Photograph

Have students study the photograph. To promote discussion, ask them questions similar to the following:
- What shapes do you see in the photograph?
- What colors do you see in the photograph?
- What are you looking at in the photograph?

If no one is able to identify the photograph, explain what *diatoms* are and tell students that they may see some diatoms as they complete the activities in the unit.

✳ About Your Journal

Students should answer the Journal questions to the best of their abilities.

These questions are designed to serve two functions: to help students recognize that they do indeed have prior knowledge, and to help them identify any misconceptions they may have about the topic. In the course of studying the unit, these misconceptions should be dispelled.

For Your Journal

Write a paragraph summarizing your thoughts about each of the following:

1. How small can a living thing be?
2. What kinds of living things can you see only through a microscope?
3. What do you think of when you think of "germs"?
4. What makes food go bad?
5. Do all microorganisms pose a threat to humans, for example the diatoms in this photograph? Explain.

LESSON 1

✳ Getting Started

This lesson introduces microorganisms in the context of proper food preparation and storage. It demonstrates the importance of knowing about microorganisms in order to ensure the safety of the food we eat. Students are given the opportunity to identify situations in which food can be contaminated by harmful microorganisms and to share what knowledge they may already have about the subject. The lesson concludes by having students review how to use a microscope.

Main Ideas

1. Improper preparation and storage of food can lead to contamination by microorganisms.
2. Knowledge about microorganisms is necessary in order to provide safe food.

✳ Teaching Strategies

Before students begin reading the lesson, ask them whether they have ever thrown away food because it was spoiled. Then involve students in a discussion of why they think food spoils and what can be done to prevent it.

If any students have experienced food poisoning, invite them to share what it was like with the class. Ask students what they think causes the symptoms of food poisoning. Accept all reasonable responses. Point out that they will learn more about what causes food to spoil as they read the lesson.
(Continues on next page)

 "But I Don't See . . ."

Jason was late getting home for dinner.

His mother was in the kitchen and said, "We ate, and Dad and Melanie went to a baseball game. Your plate's in the fridge. Why are you so late, anyway?" Then, upon seeing his expression, she added, "What's wrong?"

His mother always knew when something was wrong, especially when he really didn't feel like talking about something.

"You might as well tell me," she said.

"Bad day," he said, "Oh, not at school, at work." Work was helping old Pete run the local lunch counter called P.D.'s Place. Pete had been catering to the school kids of the community for years, and Jason was happily employed there three days a week after school and on Saturdays. He used his money to save up for that new electric guitar he'd been wanting.

"The health inspector came in this afternoon—he arrived before I got there, about three o'clock. He looked at everything and wrote down a lot of stuff. He even watched me wash my hands before making sandwiches." Jason hesitated. The next part was not easy to admit, especially to his mother.

"He said I didn't know how to wash my hands properly and gave me this," Jason groaned as he pulled a crumpled paper from his pocket and handed it to her. She looked at Jason with concern, smoothed the paper, and read:

> **GUIDELINES FOR FOOD SERVICE PERSONNEL**
> **Instructions for Washing Hands**
>
> Wet your hands with warm water.
> Cover your hands with soap.
> Rub your hands together in a circular motion for 30 seconds. Remember to rub the areas between your fingers, and to clean under your fingernails.
> Hold your hands with the fingers pointing down as you rinse them.
> Dry your hands well with fresh paper towels.

LESSON 1 ORGANIZER

Objectives

By the end of the lesson, students should be able to:

1. Describe what the word *microorganism* means.
2. Explain why it is important to have some knowledge of microorganisms in order to ensure that our food is safe to eat.
3. Identify some of the precautions that should be taken in order to keep microorganisms from contaminating the food we eat.
4. Describe how a microscope works and how to use one.

Process Skills

observing, analyzing, writing

"What else did the inspector have to say?" she asked.

Jason replied, "He told Pete a lot, I guess, and left a copy of his report with him. Pete's really upset because he thinks somebody complained and that's why the inspector came today. Mr. Grover, that's the inspector, says that's usually what happens when he's told to go out late in the day, like today. He generally drops by every few months and takes a quick look around, but this time he was really picky."

Now came the worst part.

"He said the public isn't safe in P. D.'s and that he'll give Pete only so long to fix up the Place—six weeks probably—or it will have to be closed for good. I'll lose my job. How will I get my guitar, then?"

His mother said quietly, "You will have to help Pete make things right."

Jason said, "There's a long list of things from what I saw him writing. He was muttering to himself, something about 'germs having a field day' there. He went over the list with Pete. I know the fridge doesn't work well, and the sliding door on the freezer comes off sometimes, but what's wrong with the way we wash dishes? And why shouldn't I make sandwiches on the cutting board—I always use the sponge to clean the board before and after. There are a lot of other things he said too that Pete and I don't understand. I wrote down some of them, and told Pete I'd try to find out about them. They are on the back of the sheet I gave you."

His mother looked at the scrawled words:

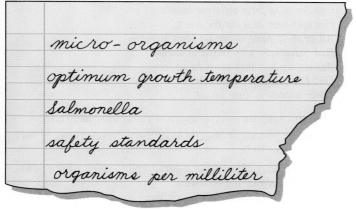

micro-organisms

optimum growth temperature

Salmonella

safety standards

organisms per milliliter

As Jason got his plate of dinner from the fridge and put it in the microwave oven to heat, he thought, "But I don't see the need for all this fuss. I wonder where I can get information on microorganisms . . ."

(Teaching Strategies continued)

Have students pause after reading page 118. Call on a volunteer to read the "Instructions for Washing Hands" aloud while another student demonstrates. Ask students to speculate about why the health inspector was concerned about the way Jason washed his hands. *(Answers may vary, but a possible response might be: His hands needed to be very clean so he wouldn't spread germs on the food he was preparing.)* Encourage students to express whether or not they agree with what the inspector did. Then have them continue reading page 119.

After students finish reading the page, assess their understanding by asking questions similar to the following:

1. What did the inspector mean by "the public isn't safe in P.D.'s"? *(P.D.'s is so unsanitary that people eating there might get sick.)*
2. What did the inspector mean when he muttered something about "germs having a field day"? *(The conditions at P.D.'s are perfect for germs to thrive and multiply.)*
3. Why did the inspector threaten to close P.D.'s if the place isn't fixed up quickly? *(because people's health is being jeopardized by the conditions at P.D.'s)*

Invite a volunteer to read the list on the back of the sheet Pete gave his mother. Challenge students to explain what the inspector meant by each of the items. Accept all reasonable responses.

New Terms

Microorganism—a tiny living thing, usually single-celled, that can be seen only with the aid of a microscope.

Materials

Microorganisms—Our Invisible Companions: Journal

Teacher's Resource Binder

Activity Worksheet 3–1
Resource Transparency 3–1

Science Discovery Videodisc

Disc 2, Image and Activity Bank, 3–1

Time Required

one to two class periods

Microorganisms—Our Invisible Companions

Have students pause after reading the first paragraph and provide them time to examine the picture on page 121. Ask students what they see in the picture that might contribute to health problems. *(Possible responses include: dirty dishes are stacked up all over the place; dirty wash rags and towels are lying around; cupboards containing cleaners and other chemicals are standing open; milk and other food products that should be refrigerated are sitting out where they can spoil; food is sitting in uncovered pots and dishes; cabinets containing clean dishes are left open; the cutting board is not covered; the chef is using his hands to put food on the grill; the garbage can is not covered tightly; a mop is standing where food is being prepared; the waitress does not have her hair covered.)*
(Continues on next page)

Primary Source
"The Microbe" reprinted without alteration from *More Beasts for Worse Children,* by Hilaire Belloc.

Microorganisms—Our Invisible Companions

How well did you understand the criticisms made by the health inspector in the story on the previous page? Examine the picture of P.D.'s Place, and see if you can find some of the problems not mentioned by Jason. How can Pete and Jason gain an understanding of the health inspector's criticisms in order to run the lunch counter safely?

Pete and Jason were unaware of their problem because they couldn't see it. The inspector mentioned **microorganisms.** They are the subject of this unit. *Micro* means very small, too small to be seen with the naked eye. *Organisms* are living things. Microorganisms are tiny living things that can be seen only if you use a microscope.

What did the inspector mean when he muttered "germs having a field day"? People commonly refer to some microorganisms as "germs." What are some other terms that are used to refer to microorganisms? You will find one in the following poem by Hilaire Belloc.

> *The Microbe is so very small,*
> *You cannot make him out at all,*
> *But many sanguine people hope*
> *To see him through a microscope.*
> *His jointed tongue that lies beneath*
> *A hundred curious rows of teeth;*
> *His seven tufted tails with lots*
> *Of lovely pink and purple spots,*
> *On each of which a pattern stands,*
> *Composed of forty separate bands;*
> *His eyebrows of a tender green;*
> *All of these have never yet been seen —*
> *But Scientists, who ought to know,*
> *Assure us that they must be so. . .*
> *Oh! Let us never, never doubt*
> *What nobody is sure about.*

1. Do you suppose microorganisms really look like this?

2. What do you know about any of the different types of microorganisms?

3. Use drawings, a poem, or a paragraph to show what you know and think about the following:
   (a) what microorganisms look like
   (b) how small they are
   (c) where you could find them
   (d) how they act

4. How important are microorganisms to you?

(Microorganisms continued)

After students have finished discussing the illustration, have them continue reading, pausing before the poem. Invite a volunteer to take apart the word *microscope* and explain its meaning. Provide help if necessary. (Micro *means small,* scope *means to look at. A microscope is an instrument used to look at very small things.*) Then have students suggest terms that are used to refer to microorganisms. Keep track of their suggestions on the chalkboard. *(microbe, germ, virus, bacteria, microscopic organism)*

Have students finish reading the rest of the page. You may wish to call on a volunteer to read the poem aloud and then have students discuss its meaning. Challenge students to write the answers to the questions at the bottom of page 120. Point out that they will have an opportunity to review and revise their answers at the end of the unit.

A Hidden World 121

Back to the Microscope

Encourage students to turn to the previous unit and review the information on microscopes. Be prepared to answer any questions they may have. As an alternative, you may wish to have volunteers or small groups of students present each of the topics to the class, providing demonstrations when appropriate.

Cells Together and by Themselves

Have students read the rest of the page. Challenge them to provide examples of multicelled organisms and single-celled organisms. Ask students why they might expect that most microorganisms are single-celled. *(Answers may vary, but a possible response might be: Since microorganisms are so small that they can be seen only with the aid of a microscope, they are likely to be single-celled.)*

✳ *Follow Up*

Assessment

1. Have students list ways in which food can be kept safe from harmful microorganisms. When they finish, have them compare and discuss their ideas and make a master list to display in the classroom.
2. Have students describe problems they have encountered that they think may have been caused by microorganisms. *(Their responses might include food spoilage, childhood diseases, and other illnesses.)*

Extension

1. Challenge interested students to do some research on microorganisms that spoil food. Have them share what they learn with the class. Encourage them to display pictures of some of the microorganisms they identify.
2. Have students present information on microorganisms that help in the preparation of food.

Back to the Microscope

Jason wanted to learn about microorganisms, so he attended a microscope workshop at the Discovery Center nearby. He learned many things about the microscope, just as you did in the previous unit, "Patterns of Living Things."

Take a moment to review the following topics pertaining to the microscope:

- the parts of the microscope and their names (page 105)
- operation and care of the microscope (page 105)
- making wet mounts (page 106)
- viewing plant and animal material (page 107)
- differences between plant and animal cells (pages 107–108)

Cells Together and by Themselves

As you know, plants and animals—indeed all living things—are composed of cells. Some living things are composed of only a few cells while others are composed of billions or even trillions of cells. Any living thing that is composed of more than a single cell is said to be *multicelled*—you, for example. There are some living things, though, that consist of only a single cell. As you might expect, many microorganisms fall into this category.

In the pages that follow you will have the opportunity to view many different kinds of microorganisms. Some of these microorganisms have little, if any, effect on humans, while others affect us in important ways. In the days ahead you will see and do many new things. Think of it as a voyage of discovery into a previously hidden world.

3. Have students try writing poems about microorganisms. Call on volunteers to share their poems with the class. Then suggest that students organize their poems in a book, make a cover, and decide on a title. The book may be displayed in the classroom or library.

2 Our Tiny Neighbors

At the Discovery Center, Jason saw a collection of old microscopes and read the information below, which was part of the display.

Meet the Pioneers

Imagine being able to go back in time almost 350 years. If you traveled to Italy, you might meet a group of scientists, including one named Galileo, who formed a club called the Academy of the Lynxes. The members of this club used glass lenses to study things either very small or very far away, and made detailed drawings of what they saw. Galileo and his friends conducted their studies with lenses made in the Netherlands, where the glass lens industry had first developed. It was there that Anton van Leeuwenhoek (LAY ven hook) became the first person to use lenses to study tiny living things (microorganisms) in water.

Anton van Leeuwenhoek

Anton van Leeuwenhoek (1632–1723), a linen merchant in Delft, Holland, taught himself to grind lenses. So skillful was he at this craft that his instruments had a magnification of up to 275 power. This is remarkable, since his instruments, which were simple microscopes, had only one lens. Leeuwenhoek came to be known as the founder of **microbiology**. Take the word *microbiology* apart and you can find its meaning.

Over a period of almost 50 years, Leeuwenhoek wrote hundreds of letters to the Royal Society in London describing his observations. He observed and drew an "abundance of very little and odd animalcules." In this unit you are going to investigate some of Leeuwenhoek's "animalcules."

Like many scientific pioneers, Leeuwenhoek was an amateur scientist, not a professional. This does not in any way diminish his accomplishments. Take the word *amateur* apart. It means "one who loves." Amateurs do what they do simply for the joy of it, not because they are paid to do so. We should recognize that many important contributions have been made to science by amateurs all over the world.

Front
View

Back
View

These drawings show one of the microscopes that Leeuwenhoek made. Look for the lens. Try to imagine where the object was placed, how the image was brought into focus, and how the instrument was held.

Exploration 1

The following is a list of the likely habitats of specific protozoa. You may wish to have students collect samples from several of these areas to increase their likelihood of observing the microorganisms pictured on page 125. CAUTION: Advise students not to go near a pond or body of water to collect specimens unless accompanied by an adult.

- *Euglena:* stagnant, contaminated pools; near manure piles; duck ponds.
- *Paramecium:* ditches; garden pools with plenty of decaying matter; neglected flower arrangements in vases.
- *Amoeba:* clear ponds; on water plants, such as water lilies, *Elodea,* and *Cabomba;* around sphagnum moss.
- *Vorticella:* clear ponds; dead sticks (white fluffy patches); undersides of duckweed; on bodies of water insects; on submerged stones.
- *Stentor:* clear ponds; around sphagnum moss; attached to aquatic plants in the springtime.

Since the results of this Exploration are unpredictable, it is a good idea to have students obtain a variety of samples from different locations. Suggest that students include a portion of sediment as well as some surface water in their samples. Point out that different kinds of microorganisms are likely to live in different parts of the source material.

Before students begin examining their samples, review the process of preparing a slide. Demonstrate the technique for students or call on a volunteer to perform the demonstration. Remind students to keep both eyes open as they look through the microscope.

(Continues on next page)

Water Neighbors

You Will Need

- a microscope
- slides
- coverslips
- droppers
- rice grains (boiled)
- several small containers
- a marker or tape

What to Do

1. A day before using the microscope, collect samples of water from several of these sources: a roadside ditch, a puddle, a pool formed from melting ice or snow, a pond, a moving stream, a mud puddle, and a neglected vase of flowers.

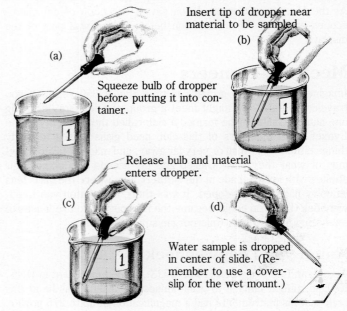

(a) Squeeze bulb of dropper before putting it into container.

(b) Insert tip of dropper near material to be sampled

(c) Release bulb and material enters dropper.

(d) Water sample is dropped in center of slide. (Remember to use a coverslip for the wet mount.)

cover on loosely

marked water level

Sample 3 Mac's farm

water sample

plant parts

bottom mud

2. Label the containers to identify the sources of the samples, and mark the water level in each container (with a marker or tape). Include some mud in the bottom of each sample, and plant parts, where possible.

3. Let the samples stand loosely covered in their containers, in soft light (not in direct sunlight). Add 2 or 3 grains of boiled rice to each sample.

4. Add water when necessary to keep the water level at the original mark. Tap water that has stood for several days can be used, but water from a well, pond, or spring would be better.

5. After one day, follow the technique illustrated above to gather material from the sediment on the bottom of each container to make a wet mount. Examine this material in the wet mount for the presence of microorganisms. Also, examine the upper and middle layers of the water in each container for microorganisms.

6. Examine your samples at high power. Notice that the thin film of liquid is like a deep pool for tiny organisms. If a microorganism you are watching "takes a dive" downward in the pool, you will have to make an adjustment in focus in order to see it clearly again. This shows the depth of the field of view.

7. Draw each kind of microorganism you discover in your samples. Pictures of some living things commonly found in such surroundings are shown on the next page. Be sure to label the drawing of each microorganism, indicating the sample and the magnification used. Keep the samples for the next Exploration.

8. Compare what you found with the discoveries made by others using different water samples.

(Organizer continued)

New Terms

Microbiology—the study of microorganisms.

Culture—to grow microorganisms by providing the living conditions that will allow them to grow best.

Algae (singular, alga)—plant-like (usually single-celled) organisms.

Protista—a kingdom consisting mainly of single-celled microorganisms; *Euglena, Paramecium,* and algae are protists.

Protists—certain one-celled organisms, such as the euglena and the paramecium, with plant-like or animal-like characteristics—or both.

Monera—a kingdom of microorganisms, mainly bacteria.

Virus—a microorganism that does not behave like a living thing unless it comes into contact with living material; must be viewed with an electron microscope.

Kingdom—the most general category scientists use to classify organisms.

Questions

1. Were the objects you drew living or nonliving? Explain your answer. Give evidence to support your answer.
2. Did all your samples contain the same kinds of microorganisms?
3. In what different living conditions do you find microorganisms?

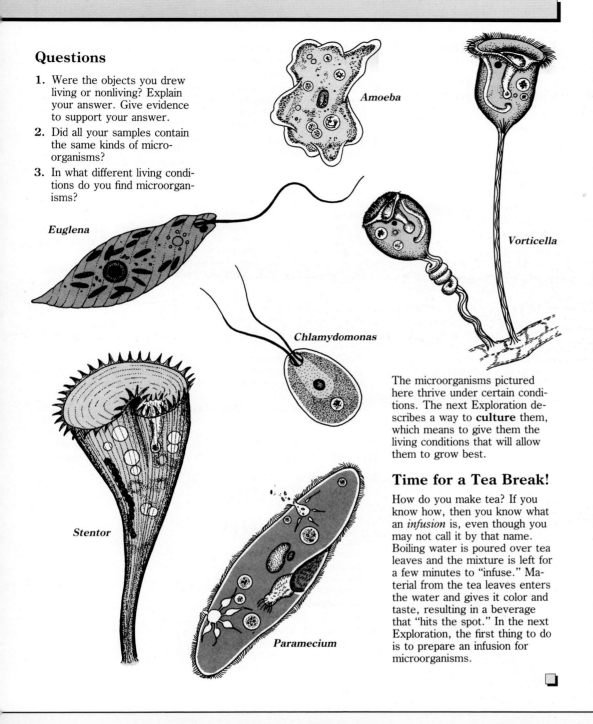

Euglena

Amoeba

Vorticella

Chlamydomonas

Stentor

Paramecium

The microorganisms pictured here thrive under certain conditions. The next Exploration describes a way to **culture** them, which means to give them the living conditions that will allow them to grow best.

Time for a Tea Break!

How do you make tea? If you know how, then you know what an *infusion* is, even though you may not call it by that name. Boiling water is poured over tea leaves and the mixture is left for a few minutes to "infuse." Material from the tea leaves enters the water and gives it color and taste, resulting in a beverage that "hits the spot." In the next Exploration, the first thing to do is to prepare an infusion for microorganisms.

(Exploration 1 continued)

As students begin examining their samples, have them watch for any movement. This will be the best indicator of the presence of microorganisms. Bacteria will no doubt be present and observed as tiny vibrating particles, but they are not very exciting to see, even at a magnification of 400X. If a student seems to have a particularly good sample, you may wish to have other students take a look at his or her slide. Encourage students to cooperate with one another so that they may observe as many different kinds of microorganisms as possible. You may wish to monitor what is happening by moving among students and taking a look through their microscopes.

Ask students to compare their drawings to the illustrations on page 125. Ask students if they think they observed any of the organisms shown there. If so, have some of the students describe how the microorganisms looked and moved, and identify the samples they were examining.

Answers to

Questions

1. Most students will probably agree that the objects they drew were living things. Evidence that they were living things may include: they moved under their own power, they reacted to other things in their microscopic environment, they fed on other microorganisms.
2. There will probably be a variation in the kinds of microorganisms that students observed from sample to sample. You may wish to have students elaborate on how the organisms differed.
3. Answers may vary, but possible responses may include: some microorganisms live in water, some live in sediments, others live on plants and decaying matter. Students may also describe the origins of the samples as a response to the question.

Materials

Exploration 1: microscope, microscope slides and coverslips, eyedroppers, rice grains (boiled), several small containers with covers, a marker, labeling tape, water from different sources, drawing paper
Exploration 2: microscope, distilled water, microscope slides and coverslips, eyedroppers, shallow glass dishes, a few fibers of lens paper or cotton batting, hay (dry grass or straw), containers with covers, heat source, pan, drawing paper, knife, safety goggles

Teacher's Resource Binder

Activity Worksheet 3–2

Science Discovery Videodisc

Disc 2, Image and Activity Bank, 3–2

Time Required

four class periods

Exploration 2

It is possible that during this activity, changes in populations of micro-organisms may take place. Encourage students to report any changes they observe and challenge them to explain why they occurred.

In step 2, furniture levelers (clear plastic or glass) make good substitutes for the shallow glass dishes. Caution students to be sure that they check the water level in the dishes every day and replace any water lost through evaporation. Replacement water should be taken from the infusion, if possible. If no infusion water is left, distilled water, spring water, or boiled tap water can be used.

In step 5, students may discover that the light needs to be decreased with the diaphragm when observing these microorganisms.

The lens-paper fibers (or cotton batting) used in step 7 slow down the movements of the microorganisms. This will make it easier for students to observe the microorganisms as they make their drawings.

Answers to

Thinking About Your Observations

1. Answers will vary depending on the particular set of conditions in your classroom. Amoeba, if present, will appear in greatest numbers after about two weeks. Changes in the number and kind of microorganisms in the infusion will depend on several factors, including temperature, light, and the type and amount of decaying plant material.

2. • The hay provided food for bacteria. The bacteria then became food for the other microorganisms.
   • Boiled tap water eliminated chlorine, which is poisonous to microorganisms.
   • infusion allowed to stand for two days—allowed bacteria to grow so that there would be a plentiful supply of food
   • dishes at room temperature in a well-lighted place out of direct sunlight—provided the conditions in which many protozoa thrive

Life in a Hay Infusion

You Will Need

- a microscope
- water
- slides
- coverslips
- eyedroppers
- shallow glass dishes
- a few fibers of lens paper or cotton batting
- dry grass
- containers
- covers

What to Do

1. Boil 4 to 6 g of the grass (spikes and stems, cut into 2-cm segments) in 1 L of water. If possible, use distilled water or spring water. If you must use tap water, boil it before adding the grass.

2. The water should become brown. Let the infusion stand for 2 days, then pour it into several shallow dishes.

3. Add material from selected containers used in Exploration 1. Label the dishes carefully.

4. Leave the dishes at room temperature in a fairly well lighted place, but not in direct sunlight. Cover them loosely.

5. Every day, if possible, remove and examine drops from the dishes for microorganisms. It is a good idea to look at drops taken from the top and the bottom of the liquid, or from near the pieces of grass. Remember to adjust the light level of the microscope to get the best image.

6. Draw any microorganisms you have not seen previously.

7. Put a few fibers of lens paper (or cotton batting) on a slide in a drop of sample, before adding the coverslip. Observe and record any effects.

8. Describe the movements and activities of any organisms that you see. Be especially careful to record how they move and how they get their food.

Thinking About Your Observations

1. Did the living conditions favor some living things more than others? Give evidence to support your answer.

2. You tried to create good living conditions for the cultures. Pick out from the directions in the "What to Do" section all of the conditions that encouraged the living things to thrive. Explain the purpose of each.

3. You probably would not want these organisms living and thriving in your tap water. How might you discourage their growth?

4. You have been growing cultures of microorganisms. What does *culture* mean? How is it related to the word *cultivate*? What do people cultivate or culture in their home environments?

5. Consider how you could use the cultures you started to answer the following questions.

   (a) What will be the effect of freezing on the microorganisms?

   (b) How will a salt solution or vinegar affect these living things?

   (c) What will happen if small pieces of lettuce or spinach are added to a culture?

   (d) What will happen if . . . ? (Add your own questions.)

Elise was asked question (5a) above, and she said, "Freezing will kill all the microorganisms." Her answer is called a **prediction**. Write your own predictions to answer the other problems in question 5. You might decide to design an experiment that would test one of your predictions.

• loosely covered dishes—prevented some evaporation and provided air

3. Answers may vary, but possible responses include: add chlorine to the water, change the amount of heat and sunlight, cut off the air supply.

4. As a verb, to *culture* means to provide an ideal environment in which to grow living things. As a noun, a *culture* is a population of living things grown in a laboratory setting. *Culture* as a verb and *cultivate* have the same meaning. People often culture house plants, for example, or plants in an outdoor garden.

5. (a) Freezing will kill most of these microorganisms.

   (b) A salt solution or vinegar will kill most of these microorganisms.

   (c) The lettuce or spinach would decay and become food for the microorganisms.

   (d) Accept all reasonable responses.

Plant, Animal, or . . . ?

You have seen that one-celled microorganisms move, take in food, and respond to stimuli such as temperature and light. In these and other ways, they fit our description of living things. When you were studying the unit "Patterns of Living Things," you discussed members of the plant and animal kingdoms. Using the microscope, you may have seen some things that you thought were like plants or like animals. In fact, deciding what to call them has sometimes caused problems.

Doctor Pro and Doctor Con are having an argument:

It's a plant. It's green and uses sunlight to make its own food.

No, it's an animal! It moves around, and sometimes uses food not made by itself.

Dr. Pro

Dr. Con

There *is* a way to settle the argument, yet, at the same time, to respect the opinions of both scientists. How would you settle this dispute?

At one time scientists actually debated this issue. Eventually it was agreed to put certain one-celled organisms into their own kingdom, separate from the plant and animal kingdoms. This kingdom is called **Protista.** *Euglena* and *Paramecium* are **protists.**

> **KINGDOM**—The most general category scientists use for classifying organisms. Members of the same kingdom share very basic similarities.

Plant, Animal, or . . . ?

After students have read page 127, you may wish to refer them back to page 125. Point out that the organisms shown in the illustration on page 125 are all protists. Ask students if they observed any of these microorganisms while doing *Explorations 1* and *2*. Have students who respond positively identify the protists they believe they observed. Then ask students which of the organisms on page 125 looks like the one the two scientists are arguing about on this page. (*Euglena*) You may wish to point out that the *Euglena* has a "tail" that it uses to propel itself through the water, enabling it to move around like an animal. But it also contains chloroplasts, with which it carries out photosynthesis, like a plant.

At this point you may wish to discuss the five-kingdom classification system. These five major groups are monerans (bacteria), protists (algae, Euglena, Protozoa, and Paramecium), fungi, plants, and animals. Make a chart on the blackboard and ask students to name as many members in the kingdom as they can.

Students may be interested to know that there are more than 50,000 species of protists. About 30,000 of these are protozoa, which are divided into four groups (phyla) based on their method of locomotion. They are the *Sarcodina,* which move by pseudopodia and include the amoeba; the *Ciliophora,* which move by means of cilia and include the paramecium; the *Mastigophora,* which move by means of flagella and include the trypanosoma; and the *Sporozoa,* which are nonmotile parasites.

Algae

Some students probably observed algae in *Exploration 2.* If so, ask them to describe what the algae looked like, and have them draw pictures of what they saw on the chalkboard. You may wish to point out to students that most algae are green. Challenge them to offer an explanation for why this is so. *(Algae contain chlorophyll and carry out photosynthesis.)*

If any of your students have an aquarium at home, they are probably very familiar with algae. Ask them to describe what problems algae can cause in an aquarium, what causes the algae to grow, and what they do to keep it from growing. Suggest that they bring a sample of their aquarium water to class for students to examine under a microscope.

Algae are usually classified as members of the kingdom Protista. They differ from other protists in that they contain chlorophyll and carry out photosynthesis. There are about 20,000 species of algae. They range from seaweeds to the green scum seen on ponds and lakes. Most algae are aquatic, but some grow in soil and on tree bark.

Algae

Was the water sample you used earlier from a pond? Did you observe what appeared to be microscopic plants? Did they look like any of the following pictures? You might obtain some green scum from the surface of a pond and make a wet mount of it, so you can examine its microscopic plants with a microscope. These tiny plants provide food for a variety of animals and are the first link of the food chain.

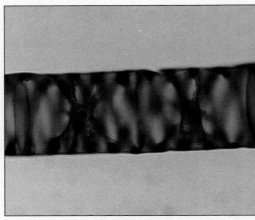

Spirogyra *Chlorella*

These plant-like organisms are called **algae** (singular, alga). Algae can be found in places other than ponds. Look at the following pictures to find out where. The photos show a few of the many forms that algae can take. One type of algae, *kelp,* even grows to a length of more than 50 m!

Protococcus (growing over a tree)

Green algae (covering rocks)

Bacteria—Also Our Neighbors

Bacteria are also microorganisms. What do you know about them? How large are they? How numerous are they? What do they look like?

The following photos show the main types of bacteria, described by shape:

- Round-shaped bacteria
- Spiral-shaped bacteria
- Rod-shaped bacteria

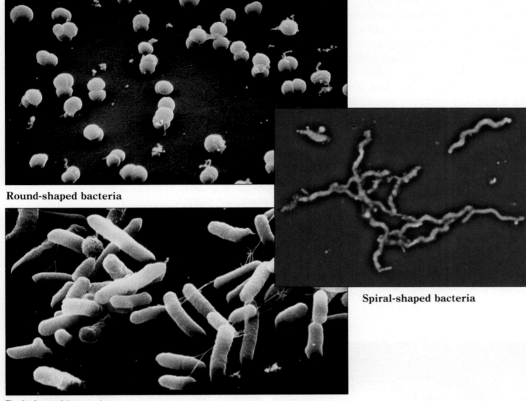

Round-shaped bacteria

Spiral-shaped bacteria

Rod-shaped bacteria

Looking at these pictures may make you suspect that you saw bacteria while you were looking at the wet-mount slides you prepared earlier. Bacteria are very small, even when magnified 400 times, and appear as tiny quivering shapes in the field of view.

Bacteria are not considered to be animals or plants. They are put into a separate kingdom called **Monera.** They can be cultured easily, but since some are disease-causing, you will not be culturing them. They can be easily viewed in prepared slides.

Bacteria—Also Our Neighbors

Bacteria live just about everywhere—in the air, water, soil, food, and even in and on the bodies of all living things. They have been found in the frigid polar regions of the Arctic and Antarctic, and in the near-boiling waters of hot springs. A single drop of pond water may contain over 50 million bacteria. A spoonful of soil may contain many billions. There are even billions of bacteria living on and in the human body. About 5,000 different species of bacteria have been identified by scientists. Many more have yet to be classified.

Bacteria are essential in the production of some foods, including many dairy products such as butter, buttermilk, yogurt, and cottage cheese. Vinegar is also a product that is the result of bacterial action. Bacteria are responsible for most food spoilage.

Some kinds of bacteria cause diseases in people by destroying healthy cells. These diseases include cholera, leprosy, gonorrhea, pneumonia, syphilis, tuberculosis, typhoid fever, whooping cough, and salmonella. Certain bacteria produce toxins that cause diseases such as diphtheria, scarlet fever, tetanus, and botulism.

Bacteria play a crucial role as one of the two major groups of decomposers (the other group is fungi). Without these organisms, dead animals, plants, and other organisms would accumulate and tie up valuable inorganic and organic resources.

Small but Not Simple

Call on a volunteer to read the first paragraph aloud. Then have students respond to the questions. Students should identify the microorganisms they observed in water samples as protists; the organisms in green pond scum as algae; and the organisms that are just barely visible even when magnified 400 times as bacteria, or Monera.

Have students read the rest of the page silently. Then direct them to the photographs of viruses. Point out that these were taken with an electron microscope because viruses are too small to be seen under a light microscope. Students may find it interesting to know that viruses are measured in nanometers (nm). One nanometer is equal to one millionth of a millimeter. Spherical viruses, for example, range in size from 15 nm to about 200 nm in diameter.

✳ *Follow Up*

Assessment

Have students make posters to show at least one representative microorganism from each of the groups discussed in the lesson—protists, bacteria, and viruses. Encourage students to be as accurate as possible with their drawings. Have them label each of the microorganisms they illustrate.

Extension

Some students may be interested in looking for a common alga called *Protococcus*. It frequently grows on tree trunks or concrete foundations. It may look like a green stain or moss. Instruct students to collect a sample of the alga by using a knife to scrape a little of the material onto a damp paper towel. Have them put a small amount of the collected material in a drop of water on a slide, stir it to make the cells move apart, and add a coverslip. Students should look at the cells with low power and high power and then add a drop of iodine solution to stain the cells. Ask students to draw a cell with as many details as they can see.

Small but Not Simple

What types of microorganism neighbors have you met so far? What are the names of those found in the water samples? in the green scum on the tops of ponds? in those that are just barely visible even when magnified 400 times?

There is another type of microorganism, far smaller than any you have seen so far. If an average bacterium (singular of bacteria) were the size of a watermelon, then one of these microorganisms would be about the size of an aspirin tablet. A special type of microscope—an *electron microscope*—is needed to see them. Have you guessed what microorganisms are being described? If you said **viruses,** you are correct.

The name *virus* literally means "poison" in Latin. Viruses cause many diseases: the common cold, influenza (flu), measles, chicken pox, and AIDS, to name a few. Viruses differ from bacteria and other microorganisms because they do not clearly behave like living things. Most viruses resemble crystals. Outside of living material, they are totally inactive: they do not move, eat, breathe, or show any other signs of life. When viruses come into contact with living material, though, they multiply, causing symptoms of disease.

So far, our work has involved microorganisms in water. They have been held in tiny ponds between glass pieces for our convenience and may have died in the process. The conditions were artificial for them. Can you imagine how microorganisms lead their normal lives? The next lesson will help you do this.

An electron microscope

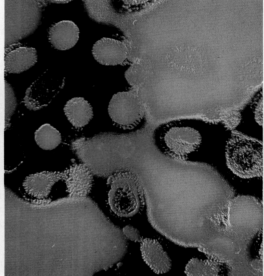

Electron micrographs of two viruses—left, HIV (the virus that causes AIDS); right, an influenza virus.

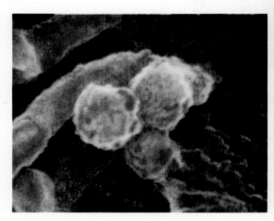

1. What techniques have you used so far to view microorganisms? How did the type of microorganisms you saw vary for each technique? Why?

2. Where might you look to find microorganisms?

3. What types of microorganisms have you cultured? Would all types of microorganisms be cultured in the same way? Why or why not?

4. A group of students watched the microorganisms in a hay infusion for 10 days. Each day they recorded the average numbers of paramecia and euglenas they saw.

   (a) Graph their data:

Day number	Number of Paramecia	Number of Euglenas
1	15	3
2	15	6
3	18	10
4	23	15
5	28	7
6	25	1
7	15	0
8	40	1
9	too many to count	0
10	too many to count	1

   (b) In explaining the changes in number of the different protists, the students wrote the following explanation: *"We think that maybe the euglenas were really old and at the end of their lives, or maybe they were sick or not given the right foods."* Do you think that their explanation could be right? Explain.

   (c) What other possible explanations could there be to account for the increase in paramecia and the decline in the number of euglenas?

   (d) Design an experiment to test the hypothesis you think has the best chance of explaining the data.

Answers to

Challenge Your Thinking

1. The techniques used so far involved culturing microorganisms and viewing them with the aid of a microscope under different powers. Some organisms, such as bacteria, are smaller than others and must be viewed with the higher-power lenses. Other organisms, such as algae and fungi, can form colonies that are visible with the naked eye.

2. Microorganisms can be found everywhere: in the air, in soil, in water, in foods, on or in plants and animals, and even on the head of a pin.

3. Bacteria and protists were cultured in this section. Organisms would be cultured according to their needs. Different organisms require different temperatures, shelter, and food supplies.

4. **(a)** See graph below.

   (b) Euglenas do not grow old in the way that we do. Instead, they divide and continue their lives as two new organisms. If, however, conditions are poor (such as when there is a lack of food), the euglenas may fail to divide or may even die from lack of nourishment.

   (c) Some explanations that might be suggested:
   - The conditions (such as light or temperature) might have favored Paramecia and not Euglena.
   - Paramecia might have eaten the Euglena.
   - Paramecia might be faster and more likely to get food than Euglena.
   - Paramecia might release poisons that kill Euglena.
   - Light was possibly too low to allow Euglena to photosynthesize.

   (d) Answers will vary, but one possible approach would be to separate the Euglenas from the Paramecia and then test the effect of changing different variables (such as food and light) on each.

Answer to graph, question 4(a).

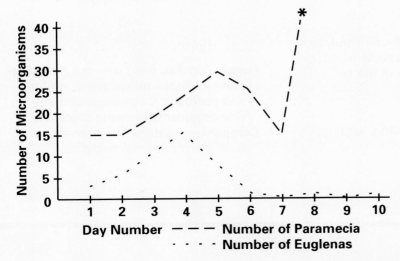

*the number of paramecia from Days 9 and 10 cannot be plotted because there were "too many to count."

LESSON 3

✳ *Getting Started*

In this lesson, students learn about the intimate relationship that exists between microorganisms and human beings. The lesson begins with three descriptions of microorganisms that fall into the "fact is stranger than fiction" category. A photomicrograph of dust mites helps to reinforce the fantastic nature of the microscopic world. In *Exploration 3,* students examine their hand (with a magnifying glass) from the point of view of a microorganism that might be living there. In *Exploration 4,* students use a microscope to look for microorganisms living in soil. The lesson concludes by having students consider both the beneficial and the harmful effects these organisms may have.

Main Ideas

1. Microorganisms live in a world that is uniquely their own.
2. Microorganisms are intimately involved in the lives of people.
3. Many different kinds of microorganisms live in soil.
4. Microorganisms that live in soil can be beneficial as well as harmful.

(Teaching Strategies follow on next page)

3 Tall (but True) Tales

"One can't believe impossible things," Alice said. "I dare say you haven't had much practice," said the Queen. . . . "Why, sometimes I've believed as many as six impossible things before breakfast."

Lewis Carroll, *Through the Looking Glass*

Read the passages below. Do they seem almost impossible? What do you think these living things are? Where might they live? You might try to illustrate each life situation with sketches.

A. *The inhabitants of this world number perhaps 72 million. They avoid oxygen and live sealed under a rubbery webbing, where they thrive in near-tropical heat and humidity. The living is easy, as their food comes from below, welling up through cracks. Sometimes, however, pieces of the surface break loose completely, carrying thousands of the dwellers, as if on rafts, to faraway places and almost certain death.*

B. *The creature lay, mouth up, in a forest of tall red stalks. It lay waiting, with large front claws ready to receive the small flakes of crunchy food that were drifting slowly downward toward its open mouth. Suddenly the stalks began to tremble, and the surface began to vibrate. A mighty force pulled the creature upward, so it lost its grip on the nearest stalk, and was taken into a whirling mass of particles and gas. When the motion stopped, the creature found itself in an even better place than before, with great stores of food, and so it started eating again peacefully.*

C. *The signal had been received. With food supplies depleted, it was time to move. Billions of bag-like creatures began to crawl, changing shape like blobs of partly-set jelly, all moving as one. They kept out of dark shadows if possible, but otherwise did not allow anything to affect their progress. Many died along the way, but their passing was unheeded by the others. Upon arrival, they climbed upon one another to form a pyramid, and then rested awhile. Then they began to re-form their group to form a taller structure, a tower.*
    To hold the tower firmly together, many individuals produced a kind of fast-acting glue, which hardened to cement their dying bodies together like bricks. From within the tower, some of the survivors crawled up over the others and reached the top. There they sealed themselves inside capsules with water and food, enough for a long journey, and were heaved from the tower

---

LESSON 3 ORGANIZER

Objectives

By the end of the lesson, students should be able to:

1. Explain the relationships that exist between microorganisms and human beings.
2. Describe the environment shared by humans and microorganisms.
3. Identify what some of the microorganisms that live in the soil look like.

4. Describe some of the harmful, as well as beneficial, effects of microorganisms that live in the soil.

Process Skills

reading for understanding, writing, drawing, evaluating

New Terms

Fungi (singular, fungus)—the fifth kingdom; includes mushrooms, molds, and puffballs; composed of many tiny organisms growing together.
Compost—a natural fertilizer made from decomposing matter.

into the air. Some of them would find a place to establish another colony.

All those left behind dried up and died, with all their energy used in making certain that a few would have the chance to begin life anew in another place. The whole population, threatened with starvation, sacrificed itself to permit a few of their kind to escape.

These may sound like creatures from science fiction, but they are real and are very close to us. Description A is about the micro-organisms found on a person's forehead. The tiny rafts are skin flakes, which are constantly falling off as new skin cells form below them. The food is perspiration, oils, and other substances the skin normally supplies.

The creatures of description B are called dust mites and are commonly found in carpets and mattresses—even in clean homes. They eat the skin flakes we shed. The dust mites in the paragraph are being drawn into a vacuum cleaner from a red carpet.

One of the many usually subvisible dust mites in your home, magnified here about 500X. Note the serrated (saw-toothed) front claws (for collecting flakes of human skin) and the protective body armor. Dust mites are the cause of most dust allergies.

A *slime mold* is described in C. This protist is quite common. You might even find them on your lawn. When a slime mold's food source is used up or destroyed, the whole group migrates to find new food supplies. Sometimes the colony sacrifices itself to allow a few individuals to escape and start new groups, or *colonies*.

Teaching Strategies

Materials

Exploration 3: magnifying glass (10×), Journal
Exploration 4: soil samples from a garden or pot containing a live plant, glass container (500 mL), distilled water, microscope, microscope slides and cover-slips, eyedropper, drawing paper, markers or colored pencils, graduated cylinder, plastic wrap

Science Discovery Videodisc

Disc 2, Image and Activity Bank, 3–3

Time Required

three class periods

Exploration 3

Challenge students to examine their hand from the point of view of a microorganism that might be living there. Encourage them to be creative as they write their descriptions. Suggest that they include drawings or poems. Some students may want to write seriously, while others may prefer a more humorous style. Some students may wish to turn their descriptions into comic strips. Others may wish to make a small book or a poster. If students are having difficulty getting started, suggest that they reread the descriptions on the two previous pages.

Exploration 4

To prevent the water used in step 1 from contaminating the soil, have students use distilled water or tap water that has been boiled.

You may want to tell students about some of the evidence of microorganisms that they may observe in the soil samples. For example, they may see strands of hyphae from fungi, the cell walls of diatoms, and spores of various kinds. Point out that they may observe things like pollen grains and insect parts that are not microorganisms but are, instead, microscopic parts of larger organisms.

Since it is very likely that students will observe parts of fungi, be prepared to talk about fungi. Draw on students' previous knowledge of molds, toadstools, and mushrooms. Point out to students that they will learn about the fungi kingdom later in the lesson.

As students examine the samples of soil, you may wish to monitor what they are doing by having individuals describe what they are observing. Encourage students to look through each other's microscopes, especially if someone observes something particularly interesting or unusual. When students finish the Exploration, encourage them to share and discuss their descriptions and observations.

An Up-Close View

You Will Need

• a magnifying glass (10×)

What to Do

1. Examine your hands with a magnifying glass. Note the different areas: the back, the palm, between the fingers, around and under the nails, and the knuckles.

2. Describe your hand as if you were a microorganism living on it. Include the following:

   (a) Favorable areas where the living is easy

   (b) Areas where you would have difficulties

   (c) How easy it would be to get from one area to another

   (d) Probable dangers

   (e) What might happen to you if the person touched her/his face, or put a hand on a dusty table

   (f) Your food supply

It seems amazing that these living things are so common, and so near, and that we are unaware of them. It suggests that not all microorganisms pose a problem for us. In fact, many microorganisms are actually helpful to us.

You have learned that microorganisms are easy to find in water. Are they also common in soil? If so, what types are you likely to find? The next Exploration will help you answer these questions.

Microorganisms in Soil

You Will Need

• a sample of soil from a garden or from a flowerpot that contains living plants
• a glass container (500 mL)
• water (not tap water)
• a microscope
• slides
• coverslips
• an eyedropper

What to Do

1. Mix about 50 mL of soil with about 300 mL of water in the glass container.

2. Leave the container loosely covered in a spot where there is dim light, at room temperature, for five or six days.

3. Use the microscope to examine the mixture for microorganisms. Carefully adjust the light level.

4. Look for moving organisms. You may also see objects that do not move, but have a definite shape or form a pattern in the field of view.

5. Draw examples of what you see. Remember to include the magnification used. Estimate the sizes of the organisms.

6. Write a description of each discovery you made.

Good Guys or Bad Guys?

People sometimes buy sterilized potting soil for their houseplants. In this soil, all the living things have been killed. Does it mean that all soil microorganisms are undesirable? How do farmers deal with this problem? Do we benefit from microorganisms, or should we fear them all? You will find answers to these questions as you proceed.

A Recipe for Soil

Rhea writes for a gardening magazine and needs your help. She has had time only to make rough notes for her column, "Answers to Readers' Questions." She asks you to write her column from her rough notes. Below you will find questions from readers.

1. *Dear Rhea,*
   I enjoy reading your column and have used a number of your ideas. In one of your replies you advised using good garden soil. When you mention "good" garden soil, what do you mean?

   (signed) An Inquirer

   Notes: Soil—not just small rocks—includes lots of living things: worms and insects (can see), microorganisms (need microscope to see)—also includes plant, animal remains—moisture very important, soil organisms need water (especially micros, they "swim" in it)—also need air spaces for roots, bugs, worms

   AMAZING BUT TRUE
   In 1 mL (a pinch) of soil there may be at least 2 billion microorganisms.

2. *Dear Rhea,*
   You recently described the potting of plants in sterilized potting soil. I know that sterilization kills microorganisms. Are there soil microorganisms that can harm me?

   (signed) Anxious

   Notes: Some can!—wash vegetables well—*Don't* eat soil particles—can have tetanus bacteria (lockjaw)—see photo—notice round ends and spores—these can live years—become active in right conditions (inside of us)—rusty nails can carry tetanus too—gardeners (also others) need tetanus shots, provide protection (immunity) from disease

Tetanus is caused by these rod-shaped bacteria.

Good Guys or Bad Guys?

Have students read the introductory paragraph silently or call on a volunteer to read it aloud. Encourage students to brainstorm for answers to the questions. Accept all reasonable responses without comment. You may wish to write some of their ideas on the chalkboard to refer to as students complete the lesson.

A Recipe for Soil

Call on a volunteer to read each of the "letters" aloud. Be sure that students understand the questions before they begin writing. After they finish, have several students read their letters to the class. Encourage discussion of the responses and help students resolve any differences.

Although students' letters will be different in style and organization, the following examples may serve as models.

1. Dear Inquirer,
   Good garden soil is not just small pieces of rock. It also contains the decaying remains of animals and plants, which help to keep the soil moist and full of nutrients. They also keep the soil particles loose, creating air spaces around them. Good soil also contains many living things. Some of them, such as worms and insects, are visible to the naked eye. Others, called microorganisms, are only visible with the aid of a microscope. They "swim" in the thin film of water that surrounds the soil particles.

2. Dear Anxious,
   Some microorganisms that live in the soil can be harmful to people. The kind of bacteria that causes tetanus, or lockjaw, is an example. Its spores can live in the soil for years. When the conditions are just right, such as when it enters a person's body, the bacteria come alive. Rusty nails are one place where the tetanus bacteria may live. Gardeners and others who work outdoors should be inoculated to protect themselves from the disease.

   To avoid ingesting soil particles and the harmful microorganisms they may contain, it is important to wash all vegetables well before eating them.

Another Microorganism

In this activity, students are asked to read a passage and identify two or three main ideas. When students finish writing, have them share their ideas with each other. Be prepared to help resolve any differences.

Encourage students to write their responses in their own words. Although students' responses will vary, the following may serve as a model.

To help prevent molds and fungi from growing on garden flowers, cut back the leaves of very thick plants and any leaves that show signs of mildew (gray, powdery spots). Allow air to circulate freely around the plants, and keep the area from getting too moist. Pick up any dead leaves so that they won't provide a place for fungi to grow.

Microorganisms to the Rescue

By writing short titles for each of the paragraphs, students are given the opportunity to identify the main idea in each one. Although student responses will vary, some possibilities include:
First paragraph:
"Microorganisms Enrich the Soil"
"Microorganisms, Fertilizer, and the Air"
"Take Advantage of Microorganisms"
Second Paragraph:
"From Plant to Compost"
"Making Compost"
"Microorganisms Turn Plants into Fertilizer"

When students complete the activity, call on volunteers to share their titles with the class.

You may wish to direct students' attention to the information about fungi in the marginal note. Point out that the molds and mildews discussed on this page, as well as many of the organisms that help plants to decay and eventually become compost, belong to this kingdom.

Another Microorganism

Rhea has the following information about keeping garden flowers free of molds and mildew. She asks you to be her editor and cut it down to two or three sentences. Pick out the main ideas, and rewrite the information in your Journal, using your own words and making certain to include what is important:

Good gardening methods help to prevent problems with molds and other fungi on the leaves of flowering plants (such as phlox). These microorganisms have less chance to grow if the plants are kept neat and trimmed. Cut leaves out if the plants are very thick, or show signs of mildew (gray, powdery spots). Let the air move freely around the plants, and see that the area is not too damp. Be sure to pick up any dead leaves, so they do not become a place where fungi can grow.

Microorganisms to the Rescue

Rhea is writing an article, "Microorganisms—Make Use of Them." She wants suitable short titles for the paragraphs. Practice on these two paragraphs. Note also what she says about the benefits of microorganisms. Do not write in this book.

_____?_____
(paragraph title)

Take advantage of the help that soil microorganisms can give. They help break down dead plant and animal matter, returning substances to the soil for plants to reuse. Also, important gases (like carbon dioxide needed by plants) are released into the air. Dead leaves and other plant materials can be used to produce a natural kind of fertilizer.

_____?_____
(paragraph title)

Many gardeners put unwanted plant materials (such as vegetable peelings) in a special area to be broken down over a period of time by the action of microorganisms. They may add packages of bacterial culture to help the decaying action. This pile of decomposing matter is called **compost** *and is a natural kind of fertilizer. Heat is produced as the material decays. The temperature of a compost heap may reach 75 °C.*

> **FUNGI—THE FIFTH KINGDOM**
> Fungi (singular, fungus) include mushrooms, molds, and puffballs. Fungi are different enough from other living things to be classified as a separate kingdom. They play an important role as decomposers of dead material. Fungi are especially abundant in soil, but are also found almost everywhere else as well—and it's a good thing too. Without fungi, the world might soon become crowded with dead matter.

Answers to

A Study on Sterilizing Soil (page 137)

1. If you heated the soil to between 77°C and 82°C, most of the harmful organisms would be killed, but the helpful bacteria would survive.

2. The advantage: the seedlings that grow from seeds will not become infected with any plant diseases already in the soil. Weed seeds in the soil would also be killed.

3. Once the tiny plants form, it is necessary to add something, such as compost, to put helpful microorganisms back into the soil. In good compost, harmful microorganisms have been killed by the heat.

A Study on Sterilizing Soil

As mentioned previously, people often germinate seeds in sterilized soil. This is soil that has been heated to kill all the living things in it. Look at the chart to the right to see the temperature needed to kill various kinds of organisms.

1. If you were preparing your own soil, what procedure for heating the soil might you follow?

2. How would it be an advantage for seeds to germinate in sterilized soil?

3. Once the tiny plants formed, what would the gardener have to add? How could this be done?

Decision Please—Good Guys or Bad Guys?

1. A noted scientist once said something like this:
   "The role played by very small things in nature is very great."
   Would you agree? Support this statement by as many instances as you can—drawing from the examples you have examined recently.

2. Prepare the pro and con arguments for a debate:
   "Resolved, that microorganisms are bad guys."
   Add to these arguments after you have finished the next two lessons.

Organisms	Temperature Required to Kill (°C)
nematode worms	50
dangerous bacteria, fungi	65
soil insects, most viruses	70
most weed seeds	77
helpful bacteria, some viruses	82

Assessment

1. Have students make posters to show how microorganisms can be helpful and harmful. Display the posters around the classroom or in the school library.

2. Have students write articles about what their world would be like if they were microorganisms. What kind of environment would they like? Encourage them to be creative. When they finish, have volunteers share their articles with the class.

Extension

1. As an extension of *Exploration 4,* have students examine soil from different areas, such as: under a tree or shrub where many leaves have fallen and rotted; in an area where the soil is hard and dry; along a roadside; in a field of grain; and in a damp area such as near a pond or drainage ditch. Have students record the differences they find, especially in the types and abundance of each microorganism. Challenge students to make inferences about the differences they observe.

2. Have students design an experiment to determine whether microorganisms will decompose paper. Make the following suggestion to get students started: Place small pieces of paper in a dilute solution of plant fertilizer dissolved in water. (The fertilizer will provide nitrogen for the bacteria.) Then add a little unsterilized soil. Be sure to have students set up a control. Have them observe and record what happens over a period of one to two weeks and then report their findings.

This fungus sends out coils to trap a nematode worm pest in the soil. The fungus strangles and then digests the worm.

Answers to

Decision Please—Good Guys or Bad Guys?

1. Most students will probably agree with the statement. Supporting evidence may include: microorganisms decompose substances, release gases into the atmosphere, produce heat, and make fertilizer for plants. Some students may also point out that many diseases are caused by microorganisms.

2. Answers may vary, but possible responses include:
   Pro—microorganisms cause many plant and animal diseases. They cause food to spoil.
   Con—microorganisms help plant and animal material to decay, add important gases to the atmosphere, are necessary for some food production, provide fertilizer for plants, and help maintain good soil conditions.

LESSON 4

✷ Getting Started

This lesson provides students with the opportunity to examine some of the experimental work of Louis Pasteur. As students analyze the steps Pasteur used to solve problems, they gain an understanding of how the scientific method can be applied to real-life situations. A close look at the process of pasteurization demonstrates to students how harmful microorganisms can be controlled without destroying those that are beneficial. Students learn how certain microorganisms are necessary in order to produce foods such as yogurt and cheese. By making yogurt in *Exploration 5,* students are given the opportunity to put beneficial microorganisms to work, while controlling harmful ones. The lesson concludes with a discussion of the delicate balance that exists between helpful and harmful microorganisms in the production of cheese.

Main Ideas

1. Scientists approach problem solving in an organized and systematic manner.
2. Our understanding of microorganisms can be used to control them for our use.
3. Harmful microorganisms can be controlled without harming those that are beneficial.

✷ Teaching Strategies

Ask students if they have ever heard of Louis Pasteur. Call on students to share their knowledge with the class. Some students will know that Pasteur is responsible for the process of pasteurization. Some may also be aware of his work developing a rabies vaccine.

 ## A Balanced View

You have certainly been increasing your knowledge of microorganisms. You know something of their beneficial and harmful effects in the soil. You have discovered ways to avoid the possible harmful effects they may have. You have also learned that some microorganisms are needed. Methods of dealing with harmful microorganisms and of using helpful microorganisms became possible only through knowledge. Louis Pasteur (1822–1895), a notable French scientist, was one of the pioneers whose discoveries advanced our knowledge of microorganisms. His work laid the foundation for dealing wisely with microorganisms, especially with those found in foods.

A System for Problem Solving

Louis Pasteur was a chemist and a problem solver. People in the silk and the wine industries often called for his help in solving problems. Pasteur himself was interested in the problem of food spoilage. He came to the belief that food spoilage might be the work of microorganisms.

Louis Pasteur was a good problem solver. Study the diagram below, which suggests how he sometimes approached problems. Have you ever tackled problems in a similar way?

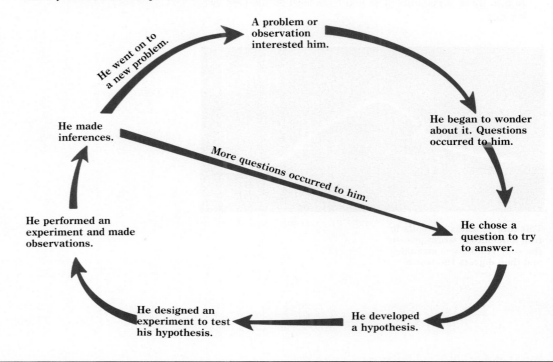

LESSON 4 ORGANIZER

Objectives

By the end of the lesson, students should be able to:
1. Identify the processes of observing, inferring, and hypothesizing in the descriptions of experiments.
2. Explain how society depends on the technology of pasteurization.
3. Explain the difference between a substance that is pasteurized and one that is sterilized.
4. Describe how knowledge of microorganisms can lead to their control and use.

Process Skills

analyzing, inferring, comparing, writing

Investigations

Four of Louis Pasteur's investigations are outlined below. Read them, and use the diagram on the previous page to identify which part of the problem-solving process he used in each step below.

1. (a) Pasteur found bacteria in the slime at the bottom of a jug of sour milk.
   (b) He put a drop of the slime into a sugar solution.
   (c) The solution turned sour, and bacteria developed in it.

2. (a) Pasteur boiled sugar solutions and then covered them tightly.
   (b) These solutions did not spoil.

3. (a) Pasteur covered flasks of boiled broth and opened them in four places: in Paris, in the open country, on a hillside, and on a glacier.
   (b) Results:

Number of Flasks of Broth	Place	Number of Flasks in Which the Broth Spoiled
20	Paris (dusty, crowded yard)	20
20	open country	8
20	high on a hillside	5
20	mountain glacier	1

4. (a) Pasteur found large numbers of microorganisms in wine that had developed an unpleasant flavor.
   (b) He heated additional wine gently to between 55 °C and 60 °C.
   (c) The microorganisms were not present in the wine that had been heated, and the wine tasted as it should.

Conclusions

Four of Pasteur's discoveries are listed below. Read them. Look again at the investigation outlines above. Choose the investigation that most likely helped him make each discovery.

1. Bacteria can enter food from the air.
2. Gentle heating may be enough to kill unwanted bacteria in food, but not enough to kill bacteria that give food its flavor.
3. Bacteria in food come from somewhere else and can be killed by heating.
4. Bacteria can cause food to spoil.

New Terms

Pasteurization—a method of gently heating a substance to kill unwanted microorganisms, while sparing the beneficial ones.

Materials

Exploration 5: 1 L of milk (whole, 2%, or skim), 1 envelope of yogurt culture, heat source, pan, container with cover, thermometer, thermos (1-L size, with a wide mouth, if possible), refrigerator, water, safety goggles

(Organizer continues on next page)

A System for Problem Solving

Have students read the paragraph silently. When they finish, direct their attention to the diagram. Call on volunteers to read each of the steps aloud. Pause after each step has been read to provide students an opportunity to discuss it. Be sure they understand each step before going on to the next. When the diagram has been reviewed to your satisfaction, encourage students to discuss the way they solve problems. Help them to decide if their methods are similar to Pasteur's.

Investigations

Be sure students understand that they are to use the diagram on page 138 to identify the stage of problem solving that each step in the outline represents. You may wish to have students complete and discuss one outline before going on to the next.

Answers to

In-Text Questions

1. (a) A problem or observation interested him.
   (b) He designed and performed an experiment to test his hypothesis.
   (c) He made observations.
2. (a) He designed and performed an experiment to test his hypothesis.
   (b) He made observations.
3. (a) He designed and performed an experiment to test his hypothesis.
   (b) He made observations.
4. (a) A problem or observation interested him.
   (b) He designed and performed an experiment to test his hypothesis.
   (c) He made observations.

Answers to

Conclusions

1. Investigation 3
2. Investigation 4
3. Investigation 2
4. Investigation 1

Answers to

Now You Know

A *simple* answer might be: "Germs get into the milk and cause it to turn sour." A more *scientific* answer might be: "Microorganisms called bacteria get into the milk from the air or through contamination of the milk container. When the conditions are right, they begin to digest the milk and multiply, causing the milk to sour."

Pasteurization

Before students begin reading, direct their attention to the illustration of Pasteur and involve them in a discussion of what Pasteur is doing and how his laboratory might have differed from a modern laboratory.

Have students read the rest of page 140. Then ask: Why do you think the method of gently heating a substance to kill unwanted microorganisms is called pasteurization? *(It is named after Louis Pasteur, the scientist who discovered the process.)* How does pasteurization differ from sterilization? *(Sterilization kills all living things in a substance. Pasteurization only kills harmful organisms, allowing beneficial organisms to survive.)*

Answer to

In-Text Question

At P.D.'s Place, this technology had broken down because food that should have been refrigerated was left sitting out, the refrigerator did not work properly, and the freezer door was broken.

Now You Know

If you were asked why milk goes sour, how would you answer the question in a simple way? in a more scientific way?

Pasteurization

Pasteur's method of gently heating a substance to kill unwanted microorganisms, while sparing beneficial ones, has been given the name **pasteurization.** Its use in treating milk has protected generations of people from serious diseases. The treatment kills most of the harmful bacteria that may be in milk, but does not damage those that give milk its desired flavor.

We depend upon technology to pasteurize dairy products. We also depend upon technology to keep the pasteurized dairy products safe until we consume them. You should be able to name some inventions used for that purpose. At P.D.'s Place, how had this technology broken down?

(Organizer continued)

Teacher's Resource Binder

Activity Worksheet 3–3
Graphic Organizer Transparencies 3–3
and 3–4

Science Discovery Videodisc

Disc 2, Image and Activity Bank, 3–4

Time Required

two class periods

140   It's a Small World

Problems to Ponder

1. Fresh milk from healthy cows starts out free of infectious microorganisms. How can it become contaminated with disease-causing microorganisms and microorganisms that cause its spoilage?

2. After pasteurization, how must milk be stored in order to keep it safe to drink?

3. In the last lesson, you learned about sterilization of soil. Soil can also be pasteurized. How might you pasteurize soil?

4. Why might someone choose to use pasteurized soil, rather than untreated soil or sterilized soil?

5. Ultraviolet radiation is used to pasteurize milk. What is ultraviolet radiation? How does it do the job? You may need to research these questions.

*Lait de la Vie Eternelle**

The nomadic Mongols who moved across Asia and Europe in the thirteenth century ate it. Galen, a doctor who lived during the second century, recommended it highly to his patients. In India, where it was introduced about 2500 years ago, it was considered food fit for the gods. In 1902, Elie Metchnikoff, a microbiologist who later won a Nobel Prize, declared that people could hope for longer lives if they ate it. In France, it has been called "lait de la vie éternelle."

What is this wonder food? The answer is *yogurt*. Even today, it is considered healthful and is very popular. Have you ever eaten frozen yogurt? Some people prefer it to ice cream. Yogurt is digested in about 1 hour. Regular cow's milk takes about 3 hours to digest. Yogurt is recommended for people who cannot digest milk.

Yogurt is made from milk by the action of certain microorganisms. An average-sized container of yogurt actually contains helpful bacteria. These bacteria are helpful because they either destroy or weaken almost all the harmful bacteria that are likely to come into contact with them.

When you make yogurt, you put microorganisms to work for your benefit. The next Exploration will show you how.

*milk of eternal life

Answers to

Problems to Ponder

1. As soon as it leaves the cow, milk may be contaminated by many sources, including the cow itself, the milking equipment, the air, the people handling the milk, and the containers in which the milk is stored.
2. Milk needs to be covered and stored at a cool temperature.
3. Soil can be pasteurized in two ways. A compost pile with good bacterial action will produce enough heat to kill most harmful organisms, but not enough heat to kill the beneficial ones. Also, soil may be heated in an oven at 75 °C.
4. Pasteurized soil wouldn't contain the harmful organisms of untreated soil, yet it would contain the helpful bacteria that sterilization would destroy.
5. Ultraviolet radiation is an invisible form of light energy. The sun is a major source of ultraviolet radiation. The energy of ultraviolet radiation kills living cells, so it can be used to kill harmful microorganisms.

Lait de la Vie Eternelle*

Have students read this introduction for the Exploration that follows. When they finish, ask them to respond by a show of hands if they have ever eaten yogurt. Call on several volunteers to describe how yogurt tastes and whether or not they like it.

Exploration 5

Depending on your particular classroom situation, this Exploration may be done by small groups or by the entire class. It may be advisable to avail yourself of the services and equipment of the home economics department. Or you may feel that this Exploration is more suitable as a homework assignment. If so, encourage students to share the results of their efforts with the class. NOTE: Some people are allergic to milk and milk products. Caution students before they sample any yogurt made during this Exploration.

As students follow and analyze the directions, challenge them to look for evidence of the manipulation of bacteria.

Answers to

Points to Ponder

1. Washing your hands, washing and scalding utensils, and heating the milk to 82°C are all done to kill harmful bacteria.

   Allowing the milk to cool to 48°C, adding the yogurt culture, and incubating the mixture at 40°–46°C are done to provide temperatures at which helpful yogurt-making bacteria thrive.

   Incubating the mixture for 4 hours is done to provide time for the bacteria to work.

   Removing the yogurt from the thermos and storing it in the refrigerator is done to quickly halt the bacterial action and preserve the taste of the yogurt.

   Making another batch of yogurt from the first batch is done to prove that bacteria are still alive and only need the right conditions in order to begin acting again.

2. The bacteria in your yogurt will remain alive indefinitely if they are not contaminated. They can, therefore, be used to start new batches.

3. Answers will vary depending on individual results, but homemade yogurt can be just as creamy and thick as commercial yogurt, and it costs much less, especially if one batch is used to make another.

Making Yogurt

You Will Need

- 1 L of milk (whole, 2%, or skim)
- 1 envelope of yogurt culture
- a heat source
- a pan
- a container with cover
- a thermometer
- a thermos (1-L size, with a wide mouth, if possible)

What to Do

1. Wash hands well. Wash all utensils, and rinse them with boiling water.
2. In a pan, heat the milk to 82 °C.
3. Let the milk cool to 48 °C.
4. Add the yogurt culture and mix well.
5. Pour into the thermos. The mixture should be between 40 °C and 46 °C for the incubation period.
6. Incubate for 4 hours. If the yogurt still seems thin, let it stand awhile in the thermos, and then check it again.
7. Remove the yogurt from the thermos and store it in a clean, covered container in the refrigerator.
8. To make the next batch of yogurt, simply add 45 mL of the yogurt you just made to lukewarm milk and incubate. You do not need to use another envelope of culture.

   (**Note:** To make a firmer yogurt, add 45 mL of skim milk powder and 5 mL of unflavored gelatin, mixed with a little water, to the milk before heating.)

Points to Ponder

Along with others who made yogurt, discuss and record answers for some of these items:

1. Suppose you are using this method to make yogurt at home. A 9-year-old neighbor is visiting and wants to know what you are doing. Explain why each step of the method is necessary in terms of what is happening to microorganisms.

2. Why do you need to buy only one envelope of bacterial culture, even if you want to continue making batches of yogurt?

3. (a) How much did it cost to make the yogurt?
   (b) How much would it cost to buy that much yogurt in the supermarket?
   (c) How do the smoothness and taste compare with that of store-bought yogurt?

4. Look at the labels on yogurt containers from the store.
   (a) Pure yogurt contains only milk and bacteria. List other contents (additives) in commercial yogurts.
   (b) Have commercial yogurts been pasteurized? If so, what effect do you think this has on the healthful quality of the yogurt? Would it be possible to make a good-quality yogurt by using some of the pasteurized yogurt as "starter"? Why or why not?

Making home-made yogurt is easy.

4. (a) Additives, especially if fruits are added, may include corn syrup, fruit pectin, sorbic acid, potassium sorbate, stabilizers, flavoring, coloring, and citric acid.
   (b) Many commercial yogurts are pasteurized. Because some bacteria may be destroyed, commercial yogurts may not be as good to use as "starters."

Cheese

What kind of cheese do you like best? Name as many different kinds of cheese as you can. How is cheese made?

As you read the following informative article about cheese, look for answers to these questions:

1. How can cheese be made from pasteurized milk?
2. What health precautions must be taken?
3. What causes some cheeses to be harder than others?
4. What kinds of microorganisms help to make cheese?
5. How do cheese makers keep out unwanted microorganisms?

Natural bacteria present in milk can be used to make cheese, but today it is normal to pasteurize the milk first for safety. Then, specially cultured bacteria must be added to the milk. If nonpasteurized milk is used, some countries require the cheese to remain in storage for at least two months before it can be sold to the public. This protects the public from disease-causing organisms.

The hardness of cheese varies. The longer the bacteria work, the harder the cheese. Cheese is said to "ripen" as bacteria continue to work, and the flavor and the odor change. You may have heard of "processed" cheeses. Processed cheeses are made by blending various natural cheeses together to achieve a desired taste. The resulting blend is then pressed into shape.

Molds are important in the manufacture of some cheeses, such as Roquefort, blue cheese, and Gorgonzola. Brie is mold-ripened from the outside, and must be eaten within a few days of ripening, so it cannot be stored for long.

Dairies and cheese plants must keep unwanted microorganisms out, while keeping the needed bacteria healthy. For example, certain molds that are necessary when making a few special cheeses would spoil other cheeses. Control of these molds and their spores is very important. Extreme care and cleanliness are necessary. Dairies do not welcome visitors throughout their plants because the cultures are likely to be contaminated with undesirable microorganisms. The successful operation of dairies and yogurt and cheese-making plants depends upon maintaining a delicate balance between helpful and harmful microorganisms.

A modern cheese-making operation

✳ *Follow Up*

Assessment

1. Suggest that students visit a local grocery store and make a list of all the dairy products that are made with the help of microorganisms, including different kinds of yogurts and cheeses. Have students share what they discovered with the class. Also, have students see how many products they can find that are pasteurized.
2. Have students write a summary of the lesson. Remind them that a summary is a shortened version of what they have read. It should include the main ideas and the most important facts, presented in their own words. It should be kept short and to the point.

Extension

1. Have students choose one of the people from the following list and do some research to find out how they contributed to the study of microorganisms. Suggest that they present their findings to the class by making an oral report.
   - J. Lister
   - Martinus Beijerinck
   - Robert Koch
   - E.J. Cohn
   - Theodor Schwann
   - H.L.F. von Helmholtz
   - W.D. Miller
2. Have students do some research to discover how people kept food from spoiling before modern packaging and refrigeration techniques. Have them use their information to make a mural or bulletin board display.

Cheese

Keep track of the kinds of cheeses students are familiar with by listing their responses on the chalkboard. Then have students read the article. Encourage them to write the answers to the questions as they read. When they finish reading, check their understanding of the article by involving them in a discussion of their answers.

Answers to

In-Text Questions

1. by adding specifically cultured bacteria to the pasteurized milk
2. Pasteurize the milk first, or if unpasteurized milk is used, store the cheese for at least 2 months. Extreme cleanliness is also necessary.
3. The longer the bacteria work, the harder the cheese.
4. bacteria and molds
5. Extreme care and cleanliness are necessary. Dairies do not allow visitors to wander through their plants.

LESSON 5

✴ Getting Started

In this lesson, students are given the opportunity to take a close look at some members of the fungi kingdom. The lesson begins by having students analyze a simple bread recipe to determine if any of the ingredients might be alive. In the Exploration that follows, students examine yeast cells and perform experiments to determine the conditions that are most suitable for their growth. The lesson concludes with an Exploration in which students are given prepared slides of bread molds to examine under a microscope. As students study the molds, they learn about their structure and function. They also learn about some of the adverse effects molds can have on people.

Main Ideas

1. Yeast is an important ingredient in some food products.
2. Yeasts and molds require specific growing conditions.
3. The growth of yeasts and molds can be controlled by controlling factors in their environment.

✴ Teaching Strategies

Have students read the lesson introduction silently, pausing after the second paragraph. Call on a volunteer to explain why he or she would not expect to find living microorganisms in baked bread. *(The heat required to bake the bread would kill all microorganisms.)* Some students may correctly point out, however, that microorganisms in the air, from people, and from baking utensils might quickly contaminate the bread.

(Continues on next page)

---

⑤ The Staff of Life

What could be a more basic meal than milk, cheese, and bread? We have learned about the connections between microorganisms and milk, cheese, and yogurt. But what microorganisms would you find in bread?

Actually, in baked bread we would not expect to find living microorganisms. Why not? Look at the recipe for "Best White Bread." Which ingredients of this bread recipe might be alive?

Best White Bread
1 package of dry yeast
60 mL of warm water
500 mL of milk, scalded
30 mL of sugar
10 mL of salt
15 mL of shortening
1.5 L of sifted all-purpose flour

Is Yeast Alive?

You Will Need
- 5 to 6 mL of dry yeast
- a graduated cylinder, or container marked to measure 5 mL
- 6 test tubes or similar containers
- 7 mL of white sugar
- 3 thermometers
- 3 containers (250 mL)
- ice cubes
- water
- a heat source
- a marker or masking tape
- a microscope
- slides
- coverslips
- an eyedropper

What to Do

1. Prepare three containers as shown on the next page.
2. The temperature of the water in beaker B must be between 30 °C and 35 °C.
3. Label the test tubes 1, 2, 3, 4, 5, and 6.
4. Divide the yeast into 6 parts (about 1 mL each). Put 1 part into each test tube.
5. To tube 1, add 5 mL of water. Put tube 1 into container A.
6. To tube 2, add 5 mL of water. Put tube 2 into container B.
7. To tube 3, add 5 mL of water. Put tube 3 into container C.
8. To tube 4, add 5 mL of water and 2 mL of sugar. Put tube 4 into container A.

L E S S O N ⑤ O R G A N I Z E R

Objectives

By the end of the lesson, students should be able to:
1. Describe the conditions necessary for the active growth of yeast cells.
2. Explain how molds grow and reproduce.
3. Identify some of the harmful effects of molds.

Process Skills

observing, using a data table, inferring, analyzing

New Terms

Hyphae (singular, hypha)—thread- or stem-like parts of a mold.
Spore cases—swellings or spheres at the ends of the hyphae.

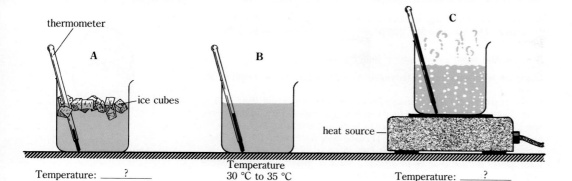

thermometer

A

ice cubes

Temperature: ___?___

B

Temperature
30 °C to 35 °C

C

heat source

Temperature: ___?___

9. To tube 5, add 5 mL of water and 2 mL of sugar. Put tube 5 into container B.

10. To tube 6, add 5 mL of water and 2 mL of sugar. Put tube 6 into container C.

11. Let the tubes stand (do not shake them) in the water baths for at least 10 minutes. Observe.

12. Remove tubes from the baths and observe them closely. Record all observations.

13. Examine a drop from each test tube under the microscope. It may be necessary to dilute the drop with a little water of the same temperature to view the yeast best. Do you see what appear to be yeast cells?

14. Draw several yeast cells.

15. Record in a chart, like the one below, any observations about the differences in the yeast cells from the various test tubes. Do not write in this book.

In your Journal, copy and complete the following chart (for all 6 tubes).

Test Tube	Substances in Tube	Temperature of Water Bath	Time of Testing	Observations
1	1 mL of yeast 5 mL of water			
2				
etc.				

Thinking About Your Experiment

Using the information you have recorded in the table, consider the following questions:

1. What variables did you work with in this Exploration?

2. In what ways did you try to make the testing "fair"; that is, how did you control all other possible variables?

3. Is there any evidence that yeast is a living microorganism? If so, what conditions seem to be good for its survival and growth?

Materials

Exploration 6: 5–6 mL dry yeast, 5-mL graduated cylinder, 6 test tubes or similar containers, 7 mL white sugar, 3 thermometers, three 250-mL containers, ice cubes, water, heat source, marker and masking tape, microscope, slides, coverslips, eyedroppers, watch or clock, safety goggles, Journal
Exploration 7: prepared wet-mount slides of mold, a microscope

Teacher's Resource Binder

Resource Worksheet 3–4
Activity Worksheet 3–5
Resource Transparency 3–5

Science Discovery Videodisc

Disc 2, Image and Activity Bank, 3–5

Time Required

two class periods

(Teaching Strategies continued)

Call on a volunteer to read the "Best White Bread" recipe to the class. Involve students in a discussion of which ingredient might be alive. *(the yeast)* Encourage students to speculate as to why yeast is used in bread. *(Yeast causes the bread to rise. It also adds flavor to the bread.)*

Exploration 6

This Exploration is best performed by groups of three or four students or as a class demonstration. You may wish to have students gather and set up the materials (except for the water and ice) the day before they actually perform the Exploration. Dry yeast can easily be obtained from a supermarket. The "quick-acting" variety will produce more dramatic results. CAUTION: students should be particularly careful working around the heat source and hot water.

Students may observe some yeast cells in the budding stage. If so, ask students what they think is happening. Help them to form the conclusion that this is the way yeast reproduces.

Answers to

Thinking About Your Experiment

1. *Manipulated variables* include: the amount of sugar (added to 3 test tubes); the temperature of the water baths (0°C, 30°C–35°C, 100°C). *Controlled variables* include: the quantity of water and yeast; testing time; type and size of containers.

2. The same amount of water and yeast were put into each of the test tubes; the testing time was the same for all the tubes; the containers that were used were the same type and size.

3. The bubbles indicate that the yeast is giving off a gas (carbon dioxide); the yeast seems to be growing by producing new cells.

The best conditions for the growth and survival of yeast include a moist environment with a temperature of 30°C–35°C and a food supply such as sugar.

(Answers continue on next page)

4. Students may have observed budding and the grouping of yeast cells into colonies. Gas bubbles should be visible. The bubbles are trapped by dough in bread-making, which makes the bread rise.
5. Details of the yeast cells will not be visible, but the general shape and their apparent size in the field of view should be recorded.

Answers to

Research

1. The date by which yeast should be used is on the package. The viability of yeast can be checked by placing it in some warm water with a little sugar. If it is usable, it will begin to grow and produce gas bubbles within a few minutes. Old yeast will not do this, and therefore, the bread will not rise or will rise only a little.
2. Foods that are made with sugar are most likely to suffer yeast spoilage. Examples include fruit juices and preserved fruits, jams, and jellies.
3. There is a peculiar "yeasty" odor, bubbling, and discoloration of the food.
4. Use clean utensils and keep foods in airtight containers. Store food in cool, dry areas.

Molds

Ask students to name the different places they have seen molds in their homes. Have students prepare some bread mold, since it is easy to grow and can be used in *Exploration 7*. Simply place some moist bread in a plastic bag. Seal the bag and place it in a warm area. In a few days, you should have a healthy colony of mold.

CAUTION: Avoid any contact with molds or inhaling their spores. They can cause allergic reactions and other health problems.

---

4. Did you observe any special characteristics of yeast when it was active? Did you see any gas produced? Might this gas be valuable?
5. Describe yeast as you saw it under a microscope.

Compare what you have discovered with the following description of yeast.

Yeasts are single-celled fungi. They cannot manufacture their own food. They live on sugar. As they consume the sugar, they produce carbon dioxide gas as a waste product in such amounts that they cause bread dough to swell up or "rise." Yeasts grow best at 25–30 °C. The highest temperature that yeast cells can stand is 37 °C to 40 °C. Since yeast spores are likely to be in anyone's kitchen, yeasts can contaminate and spoil some foods if care is not taken.

Sourdoughs

Gold prospectors in the West were once called "sourdoughs." This is because wherever they went, they carried a *sourdough* with them. A sourdough is a mixture of flour, water, and yeast that has been soaked in warm water. This is "fed" with a little sugar and milk, and then kept cool for later use. The same culture can be kept for years, if fed now and then. Prospectors could use their sourdough cultures to make bread—a useful skill at a time when bakeries were few and far between.

Research

1. The length of time a product can last before becoming unusable is called its *shelf life*. How long is the shelf life of dry yeast? Check at the grocery store. Find out how you can tell if the yeast is too old to be usable. What might be the result if you used yeast that was too old?
2. What types of food do you think would most likely spoil because of yeasts?
3. What signs would make you suspect that a food product had been spoiled by yeast growth?
4. Suggest how to prevent spoilage of food by yeasts.

Molds

You read about molds earlier in connection with gardening. However, you are probably more familiar with molds around the home. In what different places have you see them? Mold is a microorganism that grows very quickly once it starts. You have probably seen this happen with food. What does a mold look like up close? The next Exploration will show you.

New yeast cells form by a process called budding.

A single yeast cell.

A bud begins to form.

The bud grows.

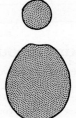

The new bud breaks away from the original cell.

Yeast Cells—Can you spot the new buds?

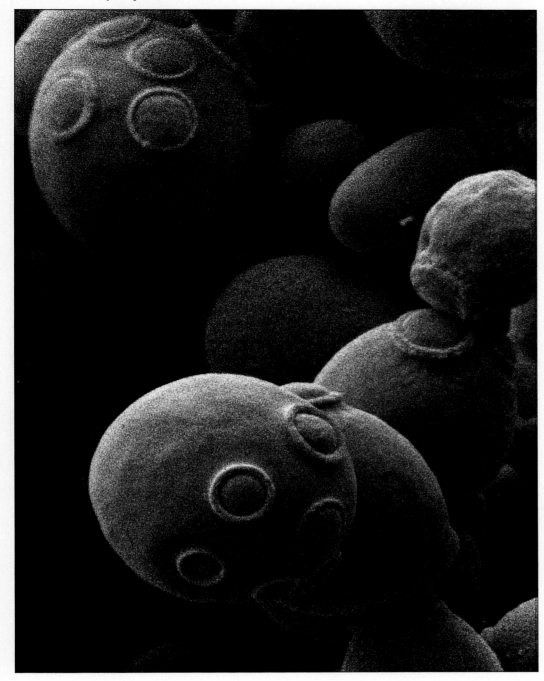

Yeast Cells

Direct the students' attention to the photomicrograph of yeast cells on page 147, and involve them in a discussion of whether or not the yeast cells in the picture look like the cells they observed in *Exploration 6.* You may wish to point out to students that this picture was taken with an electron microscope, which magnifies things many times larger than the light microscopes they use. These yeast cells, for example, are magnified 8,000 to 10,000 times.

Point out to students that several of the yeast cells have formed buds. Identify one so that all students can see what it looks like. Explain that the circular areas on some of the yeast cells are places where buds will eventually form. Involve students in a discussion of why yeast cells form buds. Help them to understand that most yeasts grow new cells by putting out buds, which increase in size and then break away from the parent. You may wish to review the illustrations of budding on page 146.

Students may be interested to know that there are about 350 different species of yeasts. Some cause infections in animals and people, while others are used in medicine, in baking, and in making wine, beer, and cider. The most-used species of yeast is probably *Saccharomyces cerevisiae.* A strain of this species is used in making bread.

Exploration 7

CAUTION: To safeguard against any allergic reactions to the molds, slides should be ready and molds covered. If students have made the bread mold, place a small portion of the covered mold under a stereo microscope so that students can observe the three-dimensional structure.

You may wish to have students read *"Why You Need to Be Careful"* at the bottom of the page before they begin the Exploration. When all students have had a chance to participate in the Exploration, dispose of the molds properly. Be sure no molds are left in the classroom.

✳ *Follow Up*

Assessment

1. Have students draw and label pictures to show what yeasts and molds look like. Then have them write a short article explaining how yeasts and molds are alike and how they are different.

2. Have students design a hypothetical experiment in which they must culture a bread mold. Ask them to think of all the variables involved and to designate those variables that will be changed.

Extension

1. Some students may enjoy doing the following activity to demonstrate how yeast cells produce gas. Place one package of yeast in a bottle with some warm water and a little sugar. Place a balloon over the top of the bottle and tie it securely with a piece of string. Place the bottle in a warm location and observe what happens. Students should notice the balloon gradually filling with gas. Have them explain what is happening and identify the gas that is in the balloon.

2. Suggest to students that they make some bread. There are easy-to-follow directions on most bags of flour. If you have a home economics department in your school, get permission to use their baking facilities. If not, suggest that students make the bread at home and bring a loaf to class. Encourage students to describe how they made the bread and to explain the role yeast played in the process.

Bread Mold

You Will Need

- a prepared wet-mount slide of mold
- a microscope

What to Do

1. The slide will be prepared for you. Observe the mold under low power and high power.

2. Draw and label the parts of the mold. Label these parts if you see them:
   - thread-like or stem-like parts—**hyphae** (singular, hypha)
   - swellings or spheres at the ends of the hypha—**spore cases.**

3. Do you observe some hyphae going into the bread and others with spore cases? Can you suggest the functions of the hyphae and the spores inside the spore cases?

4. Compare your discoveries with the photos and information that follow.

> **CAUTION:** Some molds are harmful. Molds must be grown in sealed containers and disposed of safely. Molds should never be grown without adult supervision.

The photo at the top right shows the stem-like hyphae. Like yeast, mold does not make its own food. This is one way that Fungi differ from members of the plant kingdom, which are able to produce food. The hyphae absorb

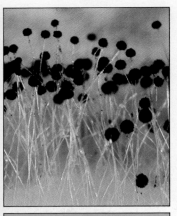

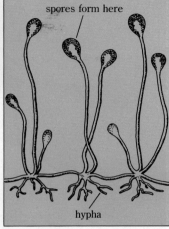

the food they need from whatever the mold is growing on. The spores found in the spore cases are the reason for the mold's fast growth. Each spore can start a new mold if the conditions are right. There are millions of spores in a bit of mold that you see with the naked eye. Molds can be of many colors. What are the colors of the molds you have seen on food?

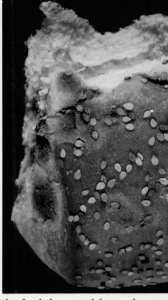

Bread Mold

Why You Need to Be Careful

Allergic reactions due to molds are quite common. As molds grow, they produce *toxins*, or poisons. Some infections and a few cases of blindness have been blamed on contact with molds. It is wise to avoid any contact with molds and to avoid inhaling their spores.

1. Look at the picture below, which shows the activity of a paramecium over a period of time.

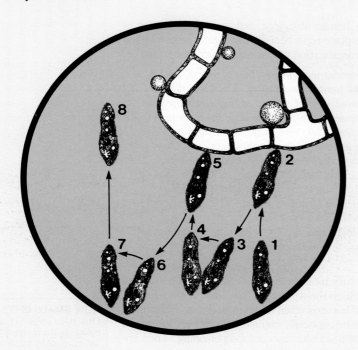

(a) What is the paramecium doing?

(b) What characteristic or characteristics of living things is the paramecium demonstrating?

(c) Is the paramecium responding positively or negatively? Explain.

2. Louis Pasteur showed that wine was damaged by microorganisms found within it. He described the wine as "diseased," and suggested that in a similar way, people and other animals could be infected by microorganisms as well.

From the paragraph above, pick out and write down:

(a) an observation made by Pasteur

(b) a conclusion made by Pasteur

(c) an inference he made

3. Some molds produce chemicals that kill bacteria. How might this be useful to them? How might this be useful to humans?

Answers to

Challenge Your Thinking

1. **(a)** The paramecium is maneuvering around or avoiding an obstacle in its way.
   (b) movement, response to stimulus
   (c) The response is negative because the paramecium is attempting to avoid an obstacle.
2. **(a)** observation: the wine was damaged
   (b) conclusion: the wine was damaged by microorganisms found within it
   (c) inference: people and other animals could be infected by microorganisms in a similar manner
3. Bacteria-killing chemicals are used by the molds as a defense against bacterial attack. Antibacterial agents can be used to control human diseases.

LESSON 6

✳ Getting Started

In this lesson, students take a closer look at harmful bacteria and explore nature's way of controlling them. In *Exploration 8,* students are given opportunities to suggest how to control bacterial contamination in the average home. Students are then introduced to the concept of antibiotics. By examining the work of Alexander Fleming, students learn how antibiotics can be used to control bacteria and bacterial infections. Next, students learn about some of the natural ways in which food is protected from bacterial contamination. The lesson concludes with an activity in which students are asked to research and prepare a chart on food-related illnesses.

Main Ideas

1. There are naturally occurring mechanisms that control the growth of harmful microorganisms.
2. Antibiotics are important substances produced by microorganisms.
3. If left alone, microorganisms establish a balanced environment of their own.

✳ Teaching Strategies

Read the description of the "battle" aloud or call on a volunteer to read it. Then ask students what they think the description is about. Who or what are the participants in the battle? Where is the battle taking place? Provide students with time to discuss their ideas. Then have them read the rest of the page to discover if they were correct.

6 Germ Warfare

We think of wars as human struggles, but every day battles of terrible violence take place right beneath our eyes, unseen by us. The following is a dramatization of one such microscopic battle.

> *Invading "S" brigades were met by the defenders, and a battle raged over the limited food supply. The blind defenders, many half-starved, moved as fast as they could over the rough terrain. They moved to do battle with the newcomers, the "S" brigades, shaped like tiny submarines, and each fitted with 15,000 or more wriggling hairy extensions. Once within reach, the defenders took the "S" troops by surprise and sprayed them with murderous streams of poison. The "S" brigades suffered many casualties, but returned the fire—they had their own brand of poison.*
>
> *When not busy with the actual battle, members of both sides ate any food they came across to gain an advantage, or they divided into two to replace slaughtered members of their groups.*

The battle in this story took place on a human hand. It involved the bacteria normally found on a person's hand and *Salmonella* (the "S" troops), a type of bacteria often found in kitchens. *Salmonella* bacteria are known to be especially common on chicken, eggs, and turkey, and can cause a serious type of food poisoning. They are about 2 μm long—about one tenth the size of a tiny dust particle you might barely be able to see in a shaft of sunlight. *Salmonella* bacteria need moisture in order to thrive, and will die after a week without it.

Do you think the health inspector approved of Jason's use of a sponge in P.D.'s Place? You may have to look again at the story before you decide.

HOW SMALL IS IT?
One micrometer (1 μm) is one millionth of a meter. One millimeter is equal to 1000 μm!

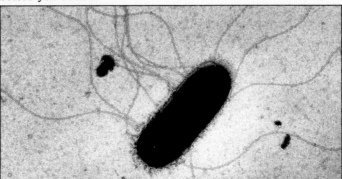

A *Salmonella* bacterium, commonly found in kitchens and on food. The extended strands spin like a twirling lasso to propel the creature.

LESSON 6 ORGANIZER

Objectives

By the end of the lesson, students should be able to:
1. Identify ways in which soil microorganisms are beneficial.
2. Explain the function of antibiotics for the microorganisms that produce them and the importance of antibiotics to humans.
3. Describe how food is naturally protected from bacterial contamination.
4. Recognize that people can safely coexist with microorganisms.

Process Skills

predicting, inferring, critical thinking, preparing a data chart

Harmful Invaders

What to Do

1. Assemble in small groups to discuss the following questions. Record the results of your discussion.

   The chart below shows the results of a study made of several hundred "clean" homes. The percentage of homes found to have dangerous bacteria on certain objects in the kitchen is shown. *Salmonella* would probably be the most important type of all, but there are likely to be a dozen other types present as well.

   (a) What condition is liable to be common to all these objects?

   (b) According to this study, which object is least likely to be contaminated? Why do you think that might be?

   (c) Which object was contaminated in every home? Why do you think this was so?

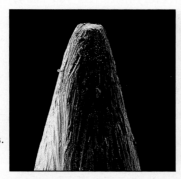
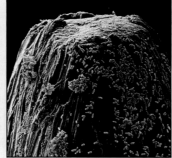
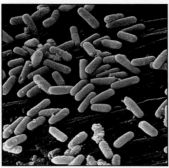
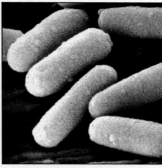

The point of a pin has numerous places for life. Here are close-ups of a "clean" pin, revealing clusters of household bacteria.

Bacteria in a Kitchen

Object	Percentage of Homes
dish towel	97.5
hand towels	98.6
sink faucets	94.0
sink surface	97.2
drain board	99.4
washing machine	89.6
refrigerator	90.4
cloth or sponge for wiping counters	100.0

2. Assume that *Salmonella* bacteria are on people's fingers while they prepare food. Predict what might happen when:

   (a) Jack rubs his forehead while he is checking to see if the roast is done.

   (b) Anne uses a finger to push a piece of carrot back into the boiling stew.

   (c) Cindy's fingers touch a mound of mashed potatoes, fluffy with milk and butter, as she spoons it into a bowl. She then leaves the bowl to cool on the kitchen counter.

   (d) Max drums his fingers on the countertop, while he waits for the microwave signal.

   (e) Carlos opens the fridge door again.

3. In which of the situations (a) to (e) of question 2 could food possibly be contaminated the most? the least?

4. When people suffer from *Salmonella* food poisoning, what do you think it is that probably makes them sick?

5. In 1987, between 400 and 1000 Honolulu Marathon runners got sick after eating lettuce contaminated with *Salmonella*. Almost 300 had to drop out of the race. How could the lettuce have become contaminated?

6. Look at the pictures above. Aren't they surprising! You may be relieved to know that more bacteria are helpful than harmful. However, you have to be concerned about how to minimize the dangers from the harmful ones. What suggestions can you make to do this? □

New Terms

Antibiotic—a term that means "against life," a substance produced by one kind of microorganism that has a harmful effect on or kills other kinds of microorganisms.

Materials

Teacher's Resource Binder

Activity Worksheets 3–6 and 3–7

Science Discovery Videodisc

Disc 2, Image and Activity Bank, 3–6

Time Required

two to three periods

Exploration 8

Allow student groups time to discuss and record their answers to the questions. When they finish, have them reassemble as a class to share and discuss their ideas and responses.

Answers to

In-Text Questions

1. (a) All of the objects are likely to be moist.
   (b) the washing machine, because of the repeated use of hot water, detergent, and possibly chlorine bleach
   (c) the wiping-up cloth or sponge, because it is likely to remain damp from one meal to the next, to be stored in a warm place, and to not be disinfected after it is used

2. (a) *Salmonella* are transferred to Jack's forehead, where they will encounter other bacteria.
   (b) *Salmonella* are transferred to the carrot. If the stew boils long enough, the heat will probably kill the *Salmonella*.
   (c) The *Salmonella* will be transferred to the potatoes, where they will encounter excellent growing conditions—slow cooling with an excellent food supply. The *Salmonella* may also penetrate deep into the potatoes as they multiply.
   (d) Some *Salmonella* are killed while others are transferred to the table top.
   (e) More *Salmonella* are transferred to the door handle.

3. Food would be contaminated the most in situation (c). Situation (d) is least likely to contaminate food.

4. The poisons, or toxins, that are given off by *Salmonella* make people ill.

5. Sample answers: *Salmonella* from uncooked meat juices may have gotten on the lettuce. The lettuce may have been placed on a contaminated cutting board or washed in contaminated water. The person handling the lettuce may have had *Salmonella* on his or her hands.

6. Student responses should demonstrate an understanding of the conditions favorable to the growth of harmful bacteria—moisture, warmth, and food supply.

Battling Germs with Antibiotics

Before students begin reading this section, ask them to respond with a show of hands if they have ever heard of antibiotics. Most students will respond yes. Call on several of them to share their knowledge with the class. Most will probably know that antibiotics are used as medicines to treat certain diseases and infections.

Have students read the first section on page 152 silently. When they finish, provide them with an opportunity to discuss what they have read and ask questions that they may have. Be sure students understand that antibiotics are produced by many different kinds of microorganisms, not just bacteria.

You may wish to point out that the most commonly used antibiotics in medicine come from bacteria and molds. Some students may have heard of one of the most prominent bacterial antibiotics, bacitracin. Bacitracin was isolated in 1945 from the bacteria in a contaminated wound. The class of bacteria known as *Actinomycetes* have produced many of the most important antibiotics, among them tetracycline, streptomycin, and erythromycin. Among antibiotics produced from molds, perhaps the most important and well-known is penicillin, which is produced by several species of *Penicillium* mold.

Antibiotics—An Amazing Discovery

Have students read the story of Alexander Fleming silently. When they finish, involve them in a discussion of the main points of the story listed on page 153. You may wish to have the points read one at a time, with students addressing each of the questions as they occur. Encourage students to honestly express what they think they would have done if they had been in Fleming's position. Help students recognize that Fleming and Pasteur were similar in that they were both problem solvers, and both carefully followed a problem-solving process. They asked questions and were quick to draw conclusions and inferences from experimental data. They both exhibited a scientific attitude. (Remind students of that discussion in Unit 1, *Science and Technology*.)
(Continues on next page)

Battling Germs with Antibiotics

Microscopic battles occur almost everywhere. As you know, many microorganisms live in pores in the soil. They eat one another in a kind of food chain, the smallest bacteria becoming food for slightly larger protists, and so on. They also squirt fluids to kill some others that come too close to them. These fluids include the **antibiotics** (*antibiotic* means "against life") that we have come to depend upon to fight bacterial infections. Although antibiotics kill bacteria, they are of no use against viruses.

The potential of soil microorganisms as a source of antibiotics is great. There are many thousands, if not millions, of different types of soil microorganisms. Only a few have been tested for their antibiotic potential. Often a certain kind of microorganism is found in only a small area. Scientists collect and investigate microorganisms from the far corners of the earth when the opportunity arises. This is one reason why scientists are concerned about the destruction of the vast rain forests of South America.

Antibiotics—An Amazing Discovery

How long have antibiotics existed? The first widespread use of these "wonder drugs" occurred during World War II. However, antibiotics were discovered years before, in 1928. The discoverer was Alexander Fleming. Here are the main points of the Fleming

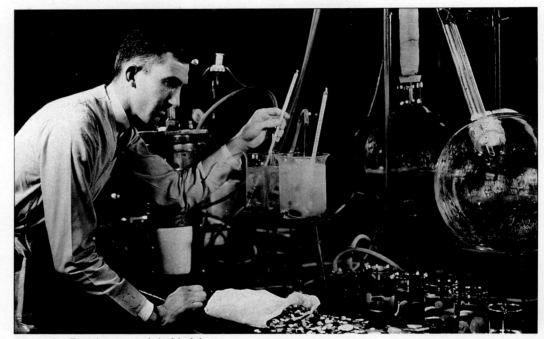

Alexander Fleming at work in his lab

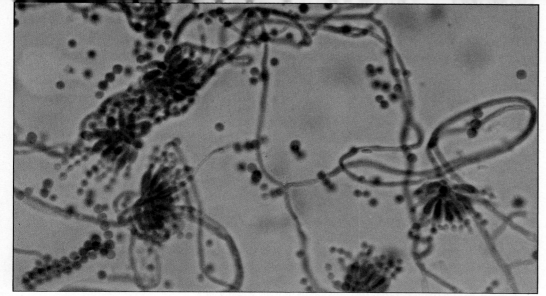

Penicillium notatum—Do you recognize the parts of this mold? The antibiotic penicillin is produced in the round spores.

story. Would you be as quick to draw conclusions as he was?

- Alexander Fleming was working in a hospital lab growing cultures of bacteria.

- One of his cultures was very poor—the well-rounded bacterial colonies appeared in only one part of the dish. See the picture below.

- What would you have done with the culture? Would you have thrown it out? Many scientists would have. Would you have saved it? What for?

- Fleming looked at it closely, wondering about it. Examine it closely, as he did. What do you notice? Do you see a bit of mold growing at the top with no colonies of bacteria growing near the mold?

- So, do you suppose he solved the problem by concluding, "Somebody left the cover off the dish and ruined the culture and so it should be disposed of. Problem solved."?

- Maybe the culture was ruined. But it also posed an interesting problem. Fleming asked himself, "Did the mold have something to do with killing the bacteria?"

- Fleming identified the mold as *Penicillium notatum,* somewhat like a type of mold that grows on cheese. What would you have tried next if you had been Fleming?

- Fleming grew the mold in other bacterial cultures and found that it was able to kill other types of bacteria.

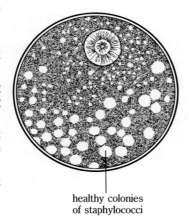

healthy colonies of staphylococci

(Antibiotics continued)

Direct students' attention to the photomicrograph of *Penicillium notatum* at the top of the page. Be sure students understand that this is the same kind of mold that Fleming observed in his experiment. Point out that this mold is related to the common greenish molds that grow on bread, cheese, and citrus fruits.

Students may find it interesting to know that Fleming had actually thrown away his contaminated culture dishes. When a lab assistant passed by, Fleming retrieved the dishes to show the assistant what had happened. This second look sparked Fleming's curiosity, and it was then he realized that in the areas invaded by the mold, the bacteria no longer grew. Fleming began testing molds of all kinds and eventually discovered the one that contaminated his original cultures. However, the technology of the day prohibited him from isolating the substance he called penicillin. As a result, little attention was paid to his discovery for nearly a decade.

The beginning of the second World War prompted a renewed interested in finding natural substances that attacked bacteria. A team of scientists at Oxford University headed by Howard Florey and Ernst Chain began experimenting with some samples of Fleming's original cultures. By then, the technology was available to isolate penicillin from the mold. Because of the war raging in Europe, large-scale production of the antibiotic was carried out in the United States. By 1943, penicillin was being used to help save the lives of men wounded in battle. In 1945, Fleming, Florey, and Chain were awarded the Nobel Prize in physiology and medicine.

Natural Bacterial Control

After students have read the paragraph, involve them in a discussion of how they can "help" food take advantage of its natural defenses against invading microorganisms. *("Help" can be achieved by providing the right storage conditions, including cleanliness, proper storage containers, and the proper temperature.)*

Answers to

Points to Ponder

1. Answers may vary, but possible responses may include: sour, sharp, pungent, acidic, spoiled, bad, rancid, fermented, tainted, off.
2. Look at the freshness date (sell-by date) on the milk container. Some students may correctly point out that one should check to be sure the milk is refrigerated and that the container is cool to the touch.
3. At home, milk should be stored in a clean, closed container in the refrigerator. It should be placed in the refrigerator as soon as possible.

Answers to

Thinking Things Over

1. a, c		**8.** b	
2. b		**9.** b	
3. a		**10.** b	
4. b		**11.** d	
5. a		**12.** b	
6. a		**13.** a, c	
7. b		**14.** a, b	

The microorganisms referred to in each statement are as follows:
Protists—statement 11
Bacteria—statements 1, 4, 5, 6, 9, 10, 11, 12, 13, 14
Viruses—statement 7
Yeast—statement 3
Molds—statements 1, 2, 5, 6, 8, 11, 12

How would you say Alexander Fleming and Louis Pasteur were similar to each other? Sometime later the chemical penicillin was discovered. It is made by the mold *Penicillium notatum*. It is a valuable antibiotic that is effective against many disease-causing bacteria.

Natural Bacterial Control

Even after pasteurization, a liter of milk may contain several million bacteria, but these bacteria are controlled by certain properties of the milk. For example, milk contains a natural antibiotic. The tiny particles that make up milk are also very difficult for the bacteria to feed on. After a week or so, however, the growth of bacteria begins to get out of control. The bacteria cause substances in the milk to form little lumps (curds), and waste material from the bacteria changes the milk's taste.

Points to Ponder

1. Suggest words that describe the new taste of milk when it has been changed by bacteria.
2. You go to the store for a carton of milk. How can you tell if the milk on the shelf should still be expected to have its bacteria under control?
3. What can you do once you get the milk home to help it keep the growth of bacteria under control?

Thinking Things Over

Here are some principles you have learned recently:
(a) Some microorganisms can be used to help us.
(b) We need to control some microorganisms to prevent them from causing harm.
(c) Some of microorganisms' natural activities (without human control) are helpful to us.
(d) The system of microorganisms in nature seems to keep itself in balance.

Which of the above principles apply to each of the specific examples below?

1. Antibiotics may kill naturally occurring bacteria.
2. The spread of athlete's foot may be decreased with the use of footbaths in swimming facilities.
3. A little bit of sourdough can make good bread.

4. Naturally occurring microorganisms are found in large numbers on human hands.

5. Yogurt and cheese result from the action of microorganisms on milk.

6. Soil microorganisms are the source of many antibiotics.

7. Measles is caused by a type of microorganism that cannot be killed by an antibiotic.

8. Many molds are poisonous. Mold cultures should never be handled directly.

9. *Salmonella* bacteria on chicken, eggs, and turkey often cause food poisoning.

10. Refrigeration is necessary to keep dairy products from spoiling.

11. Soil microorganisms are part of food chains.

12. Dishcloths and sponges in most homes contain dangerous microorganisms.

13. Naturally occurring bacteria help control disease-causing bacteria.

14. Curds form in milk after a week or so.

Some of the microorganisms you have studied are protists, bacteria, viruses, yeasts, and molds. Identify which microorganisms are likely being referred to in each statement.

An International Concern

Form groups of four. Divide your forces to obtain information from the library, consumer groups, doctors and nurses, departments of health, and the food industry.

Suppose that a large international event is going to be held in your area. You are a member of the organizing committee. You have been asked to prepare information (in the form of a chart) for members of visiting foreign groups. The chart should show details about the main sources in North America of food poisoning and illness due to microorganisms in food. Include in the chart:

(a) The types of microorganisms

(b) The foods likely to be involved

(c) The conditions to guard against (and conditions to provide)

(d) The symptoms of illness they cause

> Add the information to your list of pro and con arguments for the debate, "Resolved: microorganisms are bad guys."

An International Concern

Encourage students to share and discuss their information before they compile their charts. Be prepared to help resolve any differences that arise. NOTE: *Salmonella, Staphylococcus aureus,* and *Clostridium botulinum* together cause 80% to 90% of the food poisoning cases in North America. Yeasts and molds very rarely cause illness.

Assessment

1. Set up microscope stations for students to identify the following:
   (a) parts of molds
   (b) bacteria (prepared slides only)
   (c) yeast cells
   (d) protists (*Paramecium* or *Euglena* would be good choices)
   (e) algae
   As an alternative, use drawings and/or photos instead of microscope stations. Have students identify the kingdom to which each organism belongs.

2. Have students make a "dictionary" of terms that describe microorganisms. Suggest that they include drawings to help explain some of the more difficult terms. Display the "dictionaries" in the classroom or library.

Extension

1. Have students draw a cartoon strip to illustrate the following paragraph. "Eggs have many tiny holes in their shells through which the egg 'breathes.' Bacteria can enter in this way. Once inside, however, the bacteria encounter an elaborate defense system. A thick membrane keeps out the bacteria until they dissolve a portion of the membrane to make a tiny opening in it. The egg white then attacks the bacteria, killing many with liquids that tear the bacteria apart. The egg white also has a way of 'wrapping up' food substances that could otherwise have nourished the invading bacteria. The bacteria that survive the poison attack, therefore, starve to death and never reach the egg yolk with its rich supply of food."

2. Bacteria are sometimes attacked by a kind of virus called a bacteriophage. Challenge interested students to do some research on these organisms. Have them present their information to the class in the form of a "chalk talk," a poster, or a written report. The following questions might help students get started:
   • What do bacteriophages look like?
   • When were bacteriophages discovered?
   • How do bacteriophages destroy bacteria?

7 Microorganisms and Food Preservation

Divide to Multiply

When microorganisms have the right conditions, they multiply rapidly. Many have the ability to multiply by division, which sounds impossible, but simply means that one cell can divide in two, to form two new cells (sometimes called *daughter* cells). What do you think happens to the parent? For a glimpse of what this means in terms of quantity, try the following:

Suppose you were offered work for 30 days. You were to receive one cent for your first day's work. For the second day, your pay would be two cents, which would be doubled for the third day, and so on. Each day you would get double the pay you received the day before. Would you take the job? How much would you be paid on the thirtieth day?

This is the kind of math that bacteria are good at. Try these:

1. If a cell of Bacterium X divides in two every 15 minutes, how many cells could there be in 1 hour? in 3 hours? in 6 hours?

2. If there were 100,000 Bacterium X individuals to start with, how many would there be altogether in 6 hours?

Why is it important to understand the idea of multiplication by division? The situation below will give you an idea of what can happen if this is not understood.

Suppose a stew is served at P.D.'s Place for dinner. The stew is cooked, at 100 °C, long enough to kill most (but probably not all) of the microorganisms in it. There is some stew left over. It has

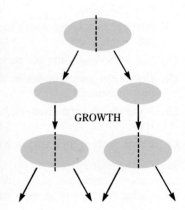

GROWTH

GENIUS at work

Objectives

By the end of the lesson, students should be able to:

1. Describe the relationship between temperature and the multiplication rate of microorganisms.
2. Analyze the methods of food preservation that are used to maintain the health and safety of the food human beings eat.
3. Describe the influence of technology on the development of food preservation techniques.

Process Skills

calculating; analyzing; using graphs, tables, and diagrams; comparing

---

LESSON 7

✳ Getting Started

This lesson focuses on how microorganisms cause food to spoil and on the methods that have been developed to prevent food spoilage from occurring. The lesson begins by having students calculate just how rapidly microorganisms can multiply in food. By using a series of data graphs, tables, and diagrams, students learn about the optimum temperatures at which microorganisms grow and the temperatures at which they are destroyed. The lesson then focuses on the technology of food preservation. Students follow the development of this technology from the beginning of the nineteenth century to the present. The lesson concludes with a series of food preservation miniprojects for students to complete.

Main Ideas

1. Microorganisms multiply rapidly in the proper growing conditions.
2. Temperature and time are important variables to consider when controlling the growth of microorganisms.
3. Many methods of food preservation have been developed with the advancement of technology.

✳ Teaching Strategies

Before students begin reading, remind them of how quickly the yeast cells that they observed in Lesson 5 multiplied. Ask them if they think other microorganisms multiply just as quickly. *(Most students will probably agree that they do.)* Then involve students in a discussion of how quickly food can spoil.

cooled a bit and a few airborne microorganisms fall into it. They find perfect growing conditions. These microorganisms, and the ones left over after cooking, start to multiply.

Imagine, for example, that 10 bacteria get into the stew from Jason's thumb as the stew is lifted from the stove, put on the counter, and covered at 7 P.M. Suppose these cells divide every half hour, (even though this could actually happen every 15 minutes in a really warm room). By 8 P.M. there will be 40 bacterial cells, by 9 P.M. 160, by 11 P.M. 2560, and so on. By the next day at 11 A.M., there will be over 40,000,000,000 bacterial cells in the stew. This many would probably not change the appearance of the food. If the stew is warmed up for lunch, it might taste a bit "off" to some, and it might give an upset stomach to others. But since it is heated (if boiled long enough) before eating, at least the bacteria will be killed, and any problem would be caused mainly by toxins (poisons) made by the bacteria while they were living.

1. What did you learn from the situation just described?
2. How might you have altered this situation so that it posed less of a health hazard?
3. Construct a similar scenario, based either on your own experience or your imagination.

Temperature and Food Spoilage

Temperature is an extremely important factor in food preservation. There are three sets of data supplied below in table and graph form. What information can you discover from each?

Data Set 1

Two of the most important temperatures related to food spoilage are the following: the temperature above which organisms cease to grow, and the temperature that best suits the organisms for growth. Match the following terms, which scientists use, with the temperature descriptions above: *optimum* (best) *growth temperature* and *maximum growth temperature*. Now can you explain what *minimum growth temperature* is?

The graph on the right shows what happens to the growth rate of microorganisms (how fast they multiply) as the temperature rises. Refer to points A to F as you answer these questions.
1. Can you identify the three growth temperatures named above, and show their location on the graph?
2. During what temperature interval is the increase in growth rate greatest (A–B, B–C, etc.)?
3. During what temperature interval is there a dramatic decrease in growth rate?

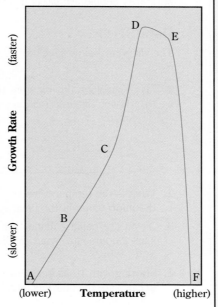

Temperature vs. Growth Rate

Growth Rate — (faster) / (slower)

Temperature — (lower) / (higher)

Divide to Multiply

Because of the size of the numbers involved and the number of calculations needed to find the answer, suggest that students work with calculators.

Answers to

In-Text Questions (page 156)

- On the thirtieth day, there would be 536,870,912 pennies ($5,368,709.12).
1. Bacteria in 1 h = 16,
   in 3 h = 4,096,
   in 6 h = 16,777,216
2. 16,777,216 × 100,000 = 1,677,721,600,000

Answers to

In-Text Questions (page 157)

1. Most students will probably agree that it is important to store food properly in order to keep it from spoiling.
2. The leftover stew should have been covered and placed in the refrigerator. Jason should have been wearing rubber gloves or should have been very careful not to get his thumb in the stew.
3. Student responses should demonstrate an understanding of how food can spoil and what can be done to prevent it.

(Answers to Temperature and Food Spoilage follow on next page)

New Terms

Maximum growth temperature—the temperature above which microorganisms stop growing and die.
Optimum growth temperature—the ideal temperature for the growth of microorganisms.
Minimum growth temperature—the temperature below which microorganisms stop growing.

Materials

Teacher's Resource Binder

Activity Worksheets 3–8 and 3–9
Graphic Organizer Transparency 3–6

Science Discovery Videodisc

Disc 2, Image and Activity Bank, 3–7

Time Required

two to three class periods

Answers to

Temperature and Food Spoilage

Data Set 1

1. The *maximum growth temperature* is the temperature above which microorganisms stop growing and die.

   The *optimum growth temperature* is the ideal temperature for the growth of microorganisms.

   The *minimum growth temperature* is the temperature below which microorganisms stop growing, *but do not necessarily die.* For example, food that has been chilled might still contain microorganisms that could become active when the food is warmed. Also, any toxins present in the food before it was chilled would still be harmful. On the graph, *A* is the minimum growth temperature. *D* is the optimum growth temperature. *F* is the maximum growth temperature.

2. Increase in growth rate is greatest during interval *C–D*.

3. A dramatic decrease takes place during interval *E–F*.

Data Set 2

The data in the table is based on results from experimental work with *E. coli,* a bacterium that is common in human intestines. Its presence is also used as an indicator of the amount of sewage present in wells and other water supplies.

According to the table, the optimum growth temperature is 37°C. That is the temperature at which the microorganisms multiply in the least amount of time.

Maximum growth temperature is between 45°C and 50°C. The microorganisms stop growing at some temperature between these two.

Minimum growth temperature is at some point below 10°C.

Room temperature is usually considered to be 20°C. According to the table, the microorganism does not multiply very rapidly at this temperature. Your body temperature, however, is 37°C—the optimum growth temperature for the microorganism.

Data Set 2

This table refers to the growth of a type of microorganism that is common in your intestinal tract. The "time to double" refers to how long it takes for one microorganism to divide and become two microorganisms.

Temperature (°C)	Time to Double (minutes)
10	130
20	60
25	40
30	29
37	17
40	19
45	32
50	no growth

For this microorganism, what is the optimum growth temperature? the maximum growth temperature? The information for the minimum growth temperature is not provided, but approximately what would this temperature be? How would room temperature and our body temperature affect the growth of this microorganism?

The maximum, optimum, and minimum growth temperatures are not the same for all microorganisms. But, it is important to know that, in general, the ones that spoil food or cause food poisoning grow over a wide range of temperature, including any temperatures people are likely to experience.

Data Set 3

The diagram below gives information for storing and preparing food.

1. (a) What does this diagram tell you?
   (b) How is this information useful? What might be a good title for it?

2. What is the temperature inside your refrigerator? Relate it to the information in the diagram.

3. If you are holding dinner for someone who is going to be at least 2 hours late, what should you do with the food while you wait? Why?

4. Starting with 10 bacteria, use the information from Data Set 2 to calculate the possible increase in numbers of bacteria over a 2-hour period. How does this show the need to take precautions when preparing and storing food?

Data Set 3

Provide students with time to review the diagram. Then involve them in a discussion of the questions.

1. (a) The diagram shows the dangerous and safe temperature ranges for preparing and storing food.
   (b) Remembering this information could help prevent serious illness from food poisoning. Accept all reasonable title suggestions.

2. Most refrigerator temperatures fall below 5°C, within the "safe" range on the diagram.

3. You should cover the food and place it in the refrigerator until the person arrives. Then take it out of the refrigerator and reheat it. Otherwise, the warm food will provide an ideal place for bacteria to grow. It could become contaminated and cause food poisoning.

4. Suggest to students that they use the 37°C or 40°C temperature from the data table in *Data Set 2* to make their calculations. Call on one or two volunteers to share their results with the class. The rapid rate of bacterial reproduction shows the need to be careful when handling food.

Food Preservation

Food does not usually come to our tables directly from the garden or farm. Because we like to eat a variety of foods all through the year, food has to be stored and preserved.

Think about the food you ate yesterday and today. What, if anything, has been done to preserve it for storage over a period of months? List all the food preservation methods you can think of.

Ask your older relatives, family friends, and neighbors about food preservation techniques of the past. As an alternative, you could do some research in the library.

Technology and Food Preservation

Food is a big business. Technology plays an important part in developing new techniques for food preservation. Look at the table below showing new developments from 1809 to 1929.

Developments in Food Processing Industry	
1809	Food preserved by canning, with heat, by Nicolas Appert.
1812	A factory opened to produce "tinned" food.
1838	Ice used to preserve fish.
1853	Time to sterilize food reduced by addition of salt to water.
1861	Ice and salt used to freeze fish.
1864	Heat used by Pasteur to kill bacteria.
1874	The refrigerator is invented.
1879	Sterilizers (autoclaves) used to preserve food.
1898	Pasteurization of milk made compulsory.
1906	Freeze-drying used.
1910	Commercial food-drying began.
1929	Quick-frozen foods produced by Clarence Birdseye.

Questions

1. How do you think salt helps to preserve food?
2. Do some research to find out what an autoclave is. How do you think it helps sterilize food?
3. Further progress has been made in food preservation technology since 1929. Do research to bring the table up to date.

Food Preservation

Have students read the two paragraphs silently or call on a volunteer to read them aloud. Provide students with time to make a list of the food preservation methods with which they are familiar. *(These may include freezing, canning, freeze-drying, pasteurization, vacuum-sealing, UHT processing, refrigeration, and so on.)* Then have students share and discuss their ideas. Make a composite list of their suggestions on the chalkboard to help students recognize how many different methods of food preservation there are.

Technology and Food Preservation

Provide students with time to look at the table. Then have them discuss the answers to the questions.

Answers to

Questions

1. In 1853, salt dissolved in water was used to raise the boiling point of water. The higher temperature sterilized the food faster. In 1861, salt was used to lower the freezing point of water so food could be frozen more quickly and at a lower temperature.
2. An autoclave sterilizes by super-heated steam under pressure.
3. Students' research may uncover some of the following methods of food preservation: freeze-drying, additives, aseptic packaging, irradiation, fumigation, controlled atmosphere storage, UHT processing.

Early Nineteenth-Century Technology

Call on a volunteer to read aloud the preservation method for peas taken from an 1819 cookbook. Challenge students to determine the purpose and assess the value of each of the steps. Ask them to write this information in a chart. The following is a suggested list of steps and purposes:

- shell the peas—removes the outer covering
- put them in a colander—drains excess water
- lay a cloth four or five times double on a table—provides a surface on which the wet peas can dry out, since the cloth absorbs remaining drops of moisture on the outside of the peas
- spread peas out—permits moisture inside the peas to evaporate over a period of time
- have bottles ready—allows time for cleaning, sterilizing, and drying bottles
- cover with mutton suet fat—fills the spaces between and above the peas to eliminate air and moisture
- cork them—keeps out air, moisture, and dirt
- set in a dry, cool place—discourages the growth of microorganisms

Have students read the last paragraph on page 160. Then direct them to the illustration at the bottom of the page. Ask students what they think the people are doing. *(They are cutting blocks of ice from a lake.)* Students may find it interesting to know, but difficult to believe, that large blocks of ice were cut from frozen lakes in the winter and stored in ice houses, where they were packed in sawdust. This kept the ice frozen from February through August. The ice was used in iceboxes, to make ice cream, and to cool drinks throughout the summer. Direct students' attention to the picture of the icebox. Call on a volunteer to read the caption and involve students in a discussion of the question. *(The icebox had to be insulated to keep out the heat and keep in the cold. The ice was placed in the top of the icebox. As warm air rose, it encountered the ice and was cooled.)*

Early Nineteenth-Century Technology

The preserving recipe below is from *Mrs. Whiting's 1819 Cookbook,* a collection found in a museum and reprinted in 1987.

To Keep Green Peas till Christmas
Take young peas, shell them, put them in a colander to drain, then lay a cloth four or five times double on a table, then spread them on, dry them very well, and have your bottles ready, fill them, cover them with mutton suet fat when it is a little soft, fill the necks almost to the top, cork them, tie a bladder and a leather over them and set them in a dry cool place.

Consider the steps in this method. Explain what you think their effects would be. In other words, in what ways does this procedure help to preserve the peas?

An Icebox—**What important knowledge was used when designing an icebox?**

Iceboxes appeared in the early nineteenth century, but they did not make ice—they held it. Large blocks of ice were chopped from frozen lakes and rivers in the winter and stored in warehouses until needed in the summer. How was it possible to keep ice from February until August?

Food Preservation Miniprojects

Select one that you are really interested in.

1. Look at foods in the home. What preservation method is used for each? Include packaged foods, unpackaged foods, and foods being cooled. For a single food, can there be more than one preservation method? Give examples.

2. Do the same as for project 1, but this time look at foods in the supermarket. Also, find out how they are able to sell fresh produce from Mexico, South America, Spain, etc.

3. What foods are used on space flights? Find out what you can about the quantities of food and drink that are needed and how they are preserved.

4. Plan the foods that you would take for a week of hiking and camping in the mountains in the summer.

5. As a class project, make a display such as a picture collage showing advances in food processing and preservation. Research and include the following: UHT processing, aseptic packaging of liquids, freeze-drying, and vacuum packaging.

6. Research arguments against food preservatives being added to foods. Sometimes preservatives are branded as "poisons in our food."

7. Look at the list of ingredients shown below from a box of crackers. Can you imagine the purpose of each ingredient? Collect labels from other foods showing the substances contained in them. Materials added as preservatives or for color or artificial flavor are called *additives*. From your collection, pick out the names of additives. Try to find out more about these substances, especially the ones that are used as preservatives.

> INGREDIENTS: UNBLEACHED FLOUR, WHEAT GERM, COCONUT OIL, VEGETABLE SHORTENING (MAY CONTAIN ONE OR MORE OF THE FOLLOWING: PARTIALLY HYDROGENATED SOYBEAN, PALM OR COTTONSEED OILS), SUGAR, SALT, SKIM MILK POWDER, AMMONIUM BICARBONATE, BRAN, HYDROLYZED SOYA PROTEIN, BAKING SODA, BAKING POWDER (CONTAINS SODIUM ACID PYROPHOSPHATE, BAKING SODA, CALCIUM SULPHATE, CORN STARCH, MONOCALCIUM PHOSPHATE), SODIUM METABISULPHITE (AS A PRESERVATIVE), PROTEASE

Food Preservation Miniprojects

Have students select the project that interests them the most. You may wish to have students present their information in some form that can be displayed in the classroom, such as posters, murals, fact sheets, booklets, and bulletin board displays.

✳ *Follow Up*

Assessment

1. Ask students to imagine that they have made a large pot of chili for a backyard party to be held the next day. Suggest that they write some instructions on what to do with the chili to protect it from contamination by microorganisms and to ensure that it is safe to eat.

2. Challenge students to use the data table in *Data Set 2* on page 158 to make a graph. (You may wish to suggest that the horizontal coordinates show temperature, and the vertical coordinates show the time in minutes it takes the microorganism to divide.)

Extension

1. Some students may enjoy thinking of a way to show how rapidly microorganisms can multiply. Possibilities include making a diagrammatic poster, creating a mural or bulletin board display, or making a model using clay figures or other manipulatives.

2. Suggest that students use the data in Data Set 2 on page 158 to make a table that shows how many microorganisms exist after 5 hours at each temperature. (Headings may include *Number at Start, Temperature, Number of Microorganisms after 5 Hours.*)

You know that microorganisms are found in water and soil. You also know from your reading that microorganisms are sometimes found in the air. In fact, microorganisms are all around us. Without precautions, food can easily become contaminated.

Microorganisms in the Air

"Empty" air can be teeming with microorganisms, as the three accounts below will show.

1. Fungus spores are always around us. They can be carried by atmospheric currents from state to state, even across entire continents, in only a few days. They enter buildings easily. The spores stick to damp areas. There, the spores germinate, hyphae grow, and feeding begins. Some fungi feed on substances in concrete, others feed on paint or the glue on wallpaper. One type of fungus even feeds on the poisonous preservatives used in wood.

   As fungi feed on house materials they may absorb substances they cannot use. Some of these will be released into the air as gases. Have your ever heard someone describe a building as smelling "musty"? This is a typical result of fungal growth—the smell comes from the gases released. You might notice this smell at a damp time of the year, or in a building that has not been aired out for a while.

2. When a vacuum cleaner is used, not only are dust particles, dust mites, and many other microorganisms picked up, but the tiniest particles are blasted out of the back of the machine at high speed. The person pushing the vacuum cleaner is hit with these tiny dust particles, which travel like shots from a cannon. All the particles small enough to come through the filter are put back into the air. Some soar to the ceiling and fall slowly down again. One scientist who studies microorganisms in the air considers home vacuum cleaners to be just about the best dust-spreaders around.

3. A sneeze can travel at about 60 km/h (that's about the same rate as a gale force wind, which can break branches off trees). A tissue held over the nose fails to contain the viruses that are shot out, partly because the tissue is full of tiny holes (its softness depends upon the fact that the fibers are so far apart).

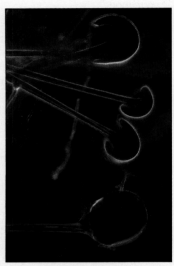

The photo shows several fungi seen after emerging from a spore. The rounded part is the main body; the long tube is the hypha arm that will dig into materials like the plaster or brick of a house wall in search of food.

Getting Started

This lesson provides students with a close look at how microorganisms are spread through the air. The conclusion drawn from this lesson is that microorganisms are all around us and can easily contaminate our food.

Main Ideas

1. Microorganisms travel through the air.
2. Simple personal habits can help protect people against the harmful effects of microorganisms.

Teaching Strategies

Before students begin reading, provide some time for them to discuss and review what they know about where microorganisms live.

Microorganisms in the Air

Have students read the three scenarios, pausing after each one to discuss its implications in their daily lives. Ask students questions similar to the following:

- If fungal spores are all around, how can you keep them inactive? *(by making their environment unfavorable to their survival, e.g. by keeping surfaces dry)*
- When should you try to avoid using a vacuum cleaner? *(before dusting; when people who are allergic to dust are around)*
- Will knowing a little more about the effects of sneezing help you to change any of your habits? Explain your answer.

LESSON **ORGANIZER**

Objectives

By the end of the lesson, students should be able to:
1. Describe how microorganisms travel through the air.
2. Explain the importance of using proper hand-washing techniques.
3. Describe the function of soap in the cleaning process.
4. Identify a satisfactory set of rules to use when preparing food.

Process Skills

reading, analyzing, evaluating, compiling a list

New Terms

One second after the blast, the viruses, in globules of spray, will be about 30–40 cm away from the nose. The liquid evaporates quickly, but the viruses continue to drift slowly through the air. If someone is standing in their flight path, the viruses may land on them. A sneeze propels viruses in all directions. No area of a room is safe from viruses.

It is thought that viruses actually *cause* sneezes. This adaptation allows viruses to spread themselves very rapidly. Fortunately, we often seem able to resist viral attacks because of immunity, which is a result of previous exposure.

So you see that microorganisms cannot be avoided. This doesn't mean that we should just give up trying to control them. There are ways to reduce the chance of contamination and infection, and most of them are quite simple.

Washing Your Hands

You probably never realized before how easily foods are contaminated. Keeping your hands as clean as possible probably makes a lot of sense to you now. You should have no difficulty in agreeing with the rules given to Jason at the beginning of the unit.

Everyone realizes the importance of soap in the cleaning process. But just what does it do? Dirt, bacteria, and other microorganisms do not dissolve in water. Also, water alone does not easily penetrate the many tiny folds in our skin. This is where soap comes in. Soap makes water "wetter," that is, more able to penetrate into tiny spaces to pick up dirt and microorganisms. Soap also dissolves oil and grease, so that water can carry it away.

Making Rules for Life

In your Journal, compile a list of rules you think should be followed by yourself and others when preparing food. Give reasons for your rules. Take into account all that you have learned in the unit or know from your own experience. Talk to others to get ideas. Organize your rules into groups according to the situations to which they may apply.

Washing Your Hands

After students have read the section, have them review the hand-washing technique described previously in Lesson 1.

Making Rules for Life

If students are having difficulty organizing their rules, you may wish to suggest categories similar to the following:
- how to avoid spreading illnesses
- how to prevent contamination of one food by another
- how to keep microorganisms in food from multiplying
- how to kill microorganisms already present in food
- how to avoid contaminating food during handling
- how to avoid contamination of food by pets

Assessment

Suggest the following scenario to students. Then have them respond to the questions that follow.
"Paula scraped mold from the surface of a piece of mozzarella cheese and at once ate some of the cheese. The rest she grated for use in a pizza."

Explain why eating the rest of the cheese might not have been a good idea. *(Microorganisms or their toxins might be in the remaining cheese.)* Would the cheese cooked in the pizza be safe to eat? Why or why not? *(Some microorganisms might still be alive.)*

Extension

Suggest to students that they try the following activity. Smear a thin layer of petroleum jelly on a microscope slide. Place the slide on a shelf or windowsill for a day or two. Then examine the slide with a magnifying glass and a microscope. Ask: What do you observe? Based on what you saw on the slides, what conclusions can you draw about the way microorganisms travel through the air?

Materials

Teacher's Resource Binder

Activity Worksheet 3–10

Time Required

one class period

Let's Eat Out Tonight

Whether you go to a fast-food restaurant or to an elegant dining establishment, aren't you concerned about the cleanliness of the place and the care the employees take to control microorganisms? Sometimes eating-out experiences are quite unpleasant. Have you had any such experiences?

Here are some eating-out situations. For each situation, choose what your response would be. If none of the responses apply, add your own. Explain your responses in your Journal.

What Would You Do If . . .

1. You saw a piece of cream pie, uncovered, sitting on a counter, and it was served 20 minutes later as part of your order?
   (a) Take a chance and eat it.
   (b) Refuse it and leave.
   (c) Ask for another piece from the enclosed, refrigerated display case.
   (d) Ask for the manager.
   (e) Other (describe).
2. You saw the serving spoon resting (handle and all) on the potato salad at a salad bar?
   (a) Ask for a clean spoon.
   (b) Go home and make your own salad.
   (c) Avoid the potato salad but take other foods from the salad bar.
   (d) Speak to someone in charge.
   (e) Other (describe).
3. You went to an ice cream stand on a warm summer day, and saw the scoop dipped in the same container of water, time after time, between uses?
   (a) Go somewhere else.
   (b) Ask if there is a clean scoop.
   (c) Eat the ice cream and hope for the best.
   (d) Buy a packaged ice cream treat.
   (e) Other (describe).

Getting Started

In this lesson, students are given the opportunity to respond to several imaginary situations in which they encounter unsanitary conditions in public eating facilities. The choices customers have in responding to such conditions are discussed, including how to file a complaint with the appropriate government agency. Students are challenged to discover the various levels of government responsible for food safety in their area. They are then asked to write an imaginary letter of complaint to the appropriate authority.

Main Ideas

1. People can protest the unsafe preparation and handling of food in public eating establishments.
2. There are government agencies that are responsible for overseeing the safety of food prepared in public eating facilities.

Teaching Strategies

Have students read the introductory paragraphs silently. Then ask them to respond with a show of hands if they can recall a time when they ate out and the food was either prepared or served in a way that was unsanitary. If some students respond, call on a few to share their experiences.

Objectives

By the end of the lesson, students should be able to:

1. Explain what they would do if they encountered unsanitary conditions in a public eating establishment.
2. Describe how to register a complaint about the unsafe preparation of food by a public eating facility.
3. Identify government agencies responsible for maintaining sanitary conditions in public eating facilities.

Process Skills

analyzing, evaluating, researching, writing

4. You saw a waiter/waitress trying to cover a sneeze when passing the warm foods at the buffet table?

    (a) Hurry to get some food before the microorganisms have time to multiply.

    (b) Speak to the manager.

    (c) Warn everyone in your group to avoid the foods on that table.

    (d) Eat and enjoy.

    (e) Other (describe).

5. Your waiter/waitress wiped the table with a damp cloth and then put the cutlery on the table before going for some clean place mats?

    (a) Ask for clean cutlery.

    (b) Wipe the cutlery with a clean napkin.

    (c) Leave.

    (d) Forget it—a few germs won't hurt you.

    (e) Other (describe).

6. You see several flies in the restaurant?

    (a) Wave your arms when they approach your plate.

    (b) Ask if someone can get rid of them.

    (c) Look for another restaurant.

    (d) Look for other signs of carelessness.

    (e) Other (describe).

These are all imaginary events, but they could happen. What responses did you choose? In such situations, people have choices

New Terms

Materials

What Would You Do If . . .: Journal

Time Required

one class period

Answers to

What Would You Do If . . . ?

Encourage students to think of their own responses to expand on those listed in the text.

1. Because cream pie is made from dairy products, it can easily become contaminated with microorganisms if left unrefrigerated. So choice (a) is the least acceptable. Choice (c) is questionable since the refrigerated pie may have been left out earlier. Choices (b) and (d) are the most reasonable.

2. Because any number of people have used the serving spoon, its handle is contaminated with microorganisms. Since it is resting on the potato salad, it is likely that the salad has been contaminated too. So choice (a) is the least acceptable. It is better to avoid the potato salad altogether. The remaining choices are reasonable, although choice (b) seems extreme.

3. Each time the scoop is dipped into the water, it leaves behind a residue of melted ice cream that will provide food for microorganisms, especially in the heat of the day. So choice (c) is the least acceptable. Choices (a) and (d) are the most reasonable. Choice (b) is questionable since this establishment is obviously careless about the way it handles food.

4. A sneeze will spread microorganisms some distance from their source, so choice (d) is the least acceptable. Choice (a) is not as reasonable as it may sound since the microorganisms can multiply in a person's body. Choices (b) and (c) are the most reasonable.

5. The cloth is likely to contain microorganisms that will contaminate the table and any cutlery placed on it. So choice (d) is unacceptable. Wiping the cutlery with a napkin, choice (b), would not eliminate many of the microorganisms. Choice (a) is reasonable. Choice (c) seems extreme.

6. Flies spread many kinds of harmful microorganisms, so choices (a) and (b) are unacceptable. Choice (d) is advisable if you want to stay at the restaurant, but it won't eliminate the flies. Choice (c) is the most acceptable.

Keeping Germs in Their Place   165

Another Choice

Invite students to comment on writing a letter of complaint to a government agency. Do they think it is fair to the owner of the restaurant? Should they talk to or write the restaurant owner before writing a letter of complaint to a government agency? Encourage students to support their opinions with reasons.

Get Involved!

Encourage students to complete the activity. Ask the school librarian to supply a list of names and addresses that students can use to write their letters. If the school library has material on the subject, ask the librarian if you can use it to set up a reading center in your classroom.

It's Not All Bad!

It's important for students to realize that most public eating facilities comply with sanitary codes and that their compliance is enforced by regular government inspections. Now is the time to encourage students to discuss some of the pleasant experiences they have had at restaurants.

Follow Up

Assessment

Tell students to imagine that they are in charge of a food sale to raise money for a class trip. Ask them to draw up a list of reminders about food safety for the students who will be helping in the sale.

Extension

Remind students of the hand washing technique described in Lesson 1. Suggest that they ask a nurse or doctor to describe either the 3-minute hand-washing technique or the 7-minute scrub that is required for personnel in operating rooms of hospitals. Invite students to share what they learn with the class.

to make. They can accept the situation as it is and ignore the possible results. They can leave and go somewhere else to eat. They can demand something better and improve the present situation for themselves and for others. They can attempt to point out the problem to someone in charge, with the hope that a change for the better will occur for future customers.

If the welfare of others concerns you, then you might want to speak to those in charge to encourage them to make changes. To fail to act is to be passive.

Another Choice

There is another choice open to a customer who is concerned about food safety in a restaurant. The person could make a written complaint to a government department that inspects eating establishments. This happened at P.D.'s Place. There had been a complaint (or more than one, perhaps).

Get Involved!

1. Find out the names and addresses of government departments that look after food safety at the various levels of government—local, state, and federal.

2. Find out what each department looks after (or if they all have the same purposes).

3. Write a letter of complaint that a dissatisfied customer *might* write about one of the situations discussed above or about one from your own experience.

It's Not All Bad!

Even though there are many unpleasant or unhealthful things that can happen when you eat out, it would be a mistake to dwell on this. After all, bad dining experiences really are few and far between. Most people in the restaurant business are trained professionals and are as worried about cleanliness as you are. Their livelihood depends on keeping their customers happy and healthy.

Think about the last time you went to a restaurant. Did you get the impression that care was taken to keep conditions clean and healthful? What, in particular, gave you this impression?

10 Food and the Law

1. Are you concerned about the quality of the chicken you eat at a restaurant?
2. Do you think that the milk you buy is really safe to drink?
3. When you purchase bread, can you be certain it is fresh?
4. When you eat from a plate in a restaurant, are you concerned that someone else ate food from the same plate previously?
5. When you eat a piece of pie, do you think it might be contaminated from standing around for hours?
6. Are you worried about the unwrapped doughnuts that are packaged by a clerk for you?

These and many other concerns that you may have are covered by food laws. If you read some of these laws, it might relieve your mind of concerns like those mentioned above!

Federal Food Laws

We are protected by food standards (a body of rules) against the dangers of unsafe food. In the United States, the Food and Drug Administration regulates the food industry. The FDA ensures the quality and cleanliness of food products and also prevents food sellers from making false claims about their products.

Read the following examples of federal food regulations. The first deals with contamination by microorganisms:

> *No person shall sell directly to the general public any poultry, poultry meat, or poultry meat by-product that has been barbecued, roasted, or broiled on his premises and intended to be ready for consumption unless that poultry, poultry meat, or poultry meat by-product (a) has, at all times prior to sale, been stored at a temperature of 4 °C or lower or 60 °C or higher.*

Another type of regulation controls the quality of perishable foods, where shelf life is important:

> *Milk may contain not more than 50,000 bacteria per cubic centimeter as determined by the official method.*
>
> *(1) The following information shall be shown on any part of the label:*
> *b. where the durable life of a prepackaged product is 90 days or less,*
>   *i. the durable life date, and*
>   *ii. instructions for the proper storage of the prepackaged product if it requires storage conditions that differ from normal room storage conditions.*

LESSON 10

✳ *Getting Started*

This lesson directs students' attention to the laws and regulations that govern the food industry, including a discussion of the FDA (Food and Drug Administration) and examples of the kinds of federal regulations that control food standards. The lesson continues with examples of state and local regulations that cover food service personnel, food safety, and the role of the inspector in enforcing these laws and regulations. By completing *Exploration 9*, students are given the opportunity to role-play as they explain a food inspector's report. The lesson concludes with students composing a letter to the Department of Health.

Main Ideas

1. The food industry is controlled by laws and regulations.
2. Food safety regulations exist at all levels of government.
3. The laws and regulations governing food processing facilities are enforced by inspectors from all levels of government.

(Teaching Strategies follow on next page)

LESSON 10 ORGANIZER

Objectives

By the end of the lesson, students should be able to:
1. Explain how government agencies regulate the food industry.
2. Describe the importance of the inspector in enforcing food-industry regulations.

Process Skills

analyzing, evaluating, summarizing, writing a letter

New Terms

ppm—the abbreviation for *parts per million;* a measure of the strength of a solution.

Materials

Teacher's Resource Binder

Activity Worksheet 3–11
Graphic Organizer Transparency 3–7

Science Discovery Videodisc

Disc 2, Image and Activity Bank, 3–10

Time Required

two class periods

Have students read the list of questions that introduces the lesson. Provide time for them to share any anxieties they may have had at some point about the quality of their food.

Federal Food Laws

Call on a volunteer to read the first regulation aloud. Encourage students to recall what they learned earlier by asking them why the regulation sets these temperature requirements for storage. *(Microorganisms will not grow on these food products below 4 °C or above 60 °C.)* Ask: What terms could you use to describe these two temperatures? *(The minimum growth temperature is 4 °C, and the maximum growth temperature is 60 °C.)*

Call on a volunteer to read the second group of regulations aloud. Ask students why the regulation allows for a certain number of bacteria to be present in the milk. *(It would be almost impossible to kill all of the bacteria and still maintain the flavor of the milk.)* Ask: Why isn't this number of bacteria harmful to people who drink the milk? *(The human body can protect itself against this small number of bacteria.)*

State Regulations

Have students read the dish-washing instructions on pages 168 and 169. Then check their understanding by asking questions similar to the following:

- How might the utensils be sorted? *(One way would be to sort them into glasses, plates, and cutlery.)*
- Why should the wash water in step 2 be changed frequently? *(Food and grease will accumulate in the wash water and make the detergent less effective.)*
- Why do you think the sanitizer must have a temperature of 82°C or more? *(to kill any microorganisms still left on the dishes)*
- How can proof be offered that a temperature of 82°C is maintained in the sanitizer? *(by keeping a thermometer in the sanitizer)*

State Regulations

The following is an example of directions given in one state to guide personnel in the food service industry:

Dish Washing by Hand

Where manual equipment is used, utensils shall be washed and disinfected as follows: The manual equipment shall consist of not less than three sinks of corrosion-resistant material and shall be of sufficient size to ensure thorough cleansing and disinfecting of utensils. Only draining racks of noncorrodible material should be used. The three-compartment sink procedure is outlined below:

1. Sort, scrape, and pre-rinse utensils.

2. *First Compartment*
   Wash utensils in warm water with a good detergent to remove all food matter. Change wash water frequently.

3. *Second Compartment*
   Rinse before sanitizing, since any remaining film or food matter must be removed before the sanitizer can perform effectively. Change rinse water frequently.

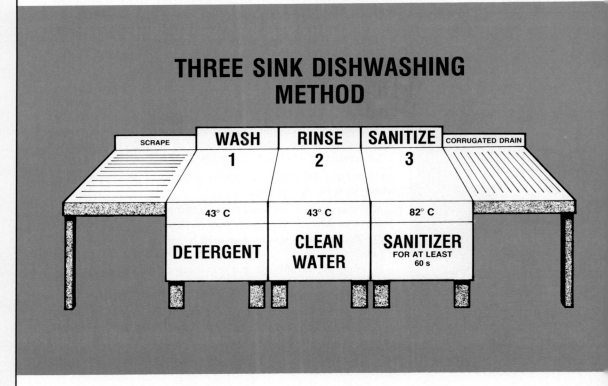

THREE SINK DISHWASHING METHOD

- Why can the temperature of the sanitizer be lower if chlorine is added to the water? *(Chlorine is a chemical that kills microorganisms, too, so the water temperature does not have to be as high.)*
- Why do you think the utensils are air-dried instead of towel-dried? *(Damp towels could harbor microorganisms that could contaminate the utensils.)* Invite students to discuss their opinions about the necessity and value of rules like these.

4. *Third Compartment*

Sanitize by immersion in the third sink for at least 60 seconds at a temperature of 82 °C or more. A basket or rack must be used for immersion purposes and proof must be offered that 82 °C will be maintained.

or

Sanitize in the third sink in a chlorine solution of not less than 100 ppm of available chlorine, at a temperature not lower than 43 °C, for at least 60 seconds.

5. The utensils should be examined. Recycle any found to be unclean and reject any found to be damaged.

6. Allow utensils to air dry.

> **ppm**—Short for *parts per million;* a measure of the strength of a solution.

City Regulations

In a city, the Board of Health generally approves regulations that deal with food safety. For example, a group of regulations in one city reads as follows:

50. **(1)** All cakes, pastries, and other bakery products not individually wrapped shall be stored in glass cases or other protective places so as to protect such products from contamination at all times.

(2) All such unwrapped foodstuffs referred to in Section (1) shall be handled with tongs, forks, or other utensils.

(3) All cream, cream substitutes, milk, milk products, filled cakes, pastries, or other foods shall be stored at a temperature of no more than 4 °C.

(4) All cream, cream substitutes, and milk products shall be served in the original container or from a satisfactory container.

Inspectors

There are food inspectors at all levels of government—federal, state, and local. Sometimes restaurants or food processing facilities may be inspected by more than a single agency. Inspectors make routine calls on all eating establishments, and they also go out in response to complaints. Each inspector has to know all the regulations and has to judge whether they are being followed properly.

City Regulations

Have students read the regulations silently. Then involve them in a discussion of how the regulations help protect the food from contamination by microorganisms. You may wish to use the following questions to help guide the discussion:

- How does storing bakery products in glass cases protect them from contamination by microorganisms? *(It reduces their exposure to microorganisms in the air and from people.)*

- Why is it a good idea to handle bakery products with tongs or forks? *(to prevent microorganisms on people's hands from contaminating the food)*

- Why do the foods referred to in regulation (3) need to be refrigerated at all times? *(Bacteria begin to grow in them at room temperature.)*

- In regulation (4), what might be a "satisfactory container"? *(one that is sterilized and covered)*

Inspectors

Have students read the paragraph silently. Be sure they understand that inspectors are responsible for enforcing the laws and regulations that govern food safety. In this way, they function much like police officers.

Exploration 9

This Exploration is designed to be done by pairs of students. One student should play the role of the "expert," and the other student the role of "Pete." Explain to students that they should become involved in a discussion as they role-play the situation.

Call on a volunteer to read the introduction to the class. Be sure students understand what they are to do. You may wish to suggest that students review the situation at P.D.'s Place in Lesson 1 (pages 118 to 121) before they begin.

Direct students' attention to the Inspection Report on page 171, and ask them to read it. Be prepared to answer any questions students may have. Be sure they understand that each of the violations checked at the top of the report is explained in detail at the bottom of the report. When you are satisfied that students understand the report, have them complete the Exploration.

(Continued on next page)

You Be the Expert

Here is the situation:

Pete would like your help. He has just received the inspector's report shown on the next page. The letter that came with it suggested that unless some dramatic changes were made immediately, in all likelihood P.D.'s Place would soon be closed permanently by the Department of Health.

Pete wants you to go over the report with him. He wants to know the reason for each of the criticisms. He wants to make whatever changes are necessary and wants to make them quickly. He wants assurance from the Department of Health that P.D.'s Place will stay open. He wants also to convince the department officials that his place provides a valuable service to the community.

What to Do

1. Go over the inspector's report.
2. Explain why each criticism is on the inspector's list. Decide whether the criticisms are valid or not.
3. Decide how to respond to each item on the list of violations. Which violations can be fixed easily? Which may take more time?
4. Compose a letter to the Department of Health to indicate what immediate or long-range actions will be taken. Give any other relevant information that will show the cooperative action being taken.

What steps could you take to help ensure that problems will not occur again in the future?

Eating Establishment Inspection Report

RECORD 1 TYPE 3	FACILITY NUMBER 4 9	10 INSPECTION DATE 15 DD MM YY	RE-INSPECTION DATE 16 MM YY 19	INSPECTION TIME 20 HRS MIN 23	REGION 24 25	EMPLOYEE CODE 26 30
0 0 1						

TYPE OF FACILITY	31	CODE 33	MUNICIPALITY 34 NO 35	QUALITY RATING 36

RECORD 1 TYPE 3	FACILITY NAME 10
0 0 2	P. D.'s PLACE 34

FACILITY ADDRESS – STREET 35 59	60 FACILITY ADDRESS – TOWN OR CITY 77

Sir Madam: The following are findings from a recent inspection of your premises by Department of Health staff. Areas where deficiencies exist are indicated and explained below. We would appreciate your co-operation in correcting any deficiencies noted.

	SATISFACTORY	UNSATISFACTORY		SATISFACTORY	UNSATISFACTORY
1. Licensing	☑	☐	8. Personnel:		
			(a) Hygiene	☐	☑
2. Construction:			(b) Dress	☑	☐
(a) Operation	☑	☐	(c) Habits	☐	☑
(b) Floors, Walls, Ceilings	☐	☑	9. Washroom Facilities	☑	☐
(c) Lighting	☑	☐	10. Handwashing Facilities	☐	☑
(d) Ventilation	☑	☐	11. Garbage Disposal	☐	☑
3. Equipment:			12. Rodent and Insect Control	☑	☐
(a) Design	☑	☐	13. Dry Goods Supplies	☑	☐
(b) Construction	☑	☐	14. Miscellaneous (identity):		
(c) Maintenance	☐	☑	(a) _____	☐	☐
4. Cleaning and Sanitizing of Equipment and Utensils:			(b) _____	☐	☐
(a) Mechanical	☐	☐	(c) _____	☐	☐
(b) Manual	☐	☑			
5. Water Supply	☑	☐			
6. Sewage Supply	☑	☐			
7. Food Protection:					
(a) Storage	☐	☑			
(b) Covered	☐	☑			
(c) Refrigeration	☐	☑			
(d) Handling	☐	☑			

EXPLANATION OF DEFICIENCIES AND RECOMMENDATIONS #2: new window screens needed; and another light over sink; dusty floor (corners).
#3: no thermometer in fridge (temperature 6°C – too high).
#4: dirty dishes on counter; need 3 sinks.
#7: open milk carton on counter; sandwich on wooden block; damp dish towels hanging under counter; chipped dishes; food spilled on refrigerator shelf; open mayonnaise bottle on counter; cracked wooden meat block; drops of liquid on counter; must not dry-sweep the floor; keep disinfectants out of food storage area; also keep mop out of food area; #8) personnel must wash hands properly; hang outer clothes away from food area.
#7: Cover all baked goods on display.

OTHER COMMENTS It is most important to eliminate any use of damp sponges for wiping up; and use of dish towels (dishes will air-dry quickly when washed properly).

2/5/92
Date of Inspection

G. Grover
Inspector

FORM 140

OWNER/OPERATOR COPY

(Exploration 9 continued)
Remind students that they should work together in pairs. For example, the "Pete" character should ask questions, and the "expert" should explain the report. Both students may want to keep notes on their discussion in their Journals. They should work together to write their letter to the Department of Health and to answer the follow-up question at the bottom of page 170.

When students finish the Exploration, call on several volunteers to share their letters and ideas for the follow-up question with the class. Encourage class members to discuss any differences of opinion and help them resolve any conflicts.

Science Snapshot

Ask students to put themselves in Lloyd Hall's place to solve the problem of meat contamination. Challenge them to formulate questions to answer, possible hypotheses, and experiments to test these hypotheses.

✳ *Follow Up*

Assessment

1. Have students choose one or more of the regulations presented in the lesson and write an explanation of how it protects food from contamination by microorganisms. Invite students to share their explanations with the class.

2. Ask students to imagine that they are the owner of a restaurant. Have them make a list of rules that their employees should follow to help prevent food from becoming contaminated by microorganisms. When students finish, have them share and discuss their ideas.

Extension

1. Suggest to students that they interview a local restaurant owner to discover what regulations he or she must follow, and what licenses and permits were needed in order to open the restaurant. Have students share what they learn with the class.

2. Some students may be interested in doing some research on the FDA or the state or local agency responsible for the regulation of food safety in their area. Suggest that they use what they learn to prepare a report for the class.

3. Have students do some library research on Hall's gas sterilization process. Find out what gas is used, how the process is implemented, why microorganisms are killed by the process, and any possible disadvantages of the process.

Science Snapshot
Lloyd A. Hall (1894–1971)

Most food is perishable. This means that sooner or later it will be contaminated by microorganisms and become inedible. Of course the longer that food stays safe to eat, the better. In 1925 a young black man named Lloyd A. Hall introduced a process of chemical sterilization, which helped keep food safe and healthy.

Before Hall's research on chemical sterilization, meat packers added spices to their meat products, but in the process contaminated their meats with molds, yeast, and bacteria. In Hall's sterilization process, these spices were exposed to a gas that was poisonous to microorganisms. The treated spices could then be added to the meats without fear of contamination. Hall's process was also used to sterilize drugs, medicines, hospital supplies, bandages, cosmetics, and many other products. Hall's chemical sterilization method is still in general use today.

Hall's interest in chemistry began at East Side High School in Aurora, Illinois where he was an outstanding student. He graduated among the top ten in his class. He attended Northwestern University on a scholarship and graduated in 1916. He went on to do graduate work in chemistry at the University of Chicago.

In 1925, Hall started work with Griffith Laboratories as chief chemist and director of research, a position he held until he retired in 1959. While at Griffith Laboratories, he specialized in food preservation techniques and developed processes for curing meats, seasonings, and bakery goods.

Hall was granted over 100 U.S. and foreign patents on products and methods that he had invented. Hall also authored dozens of scientific papers.

Research Topic

Find out more about Dr. Lloyd A. Hall, and write a paper on one of the food preservation processes he developed.

Challenge Your Thinking

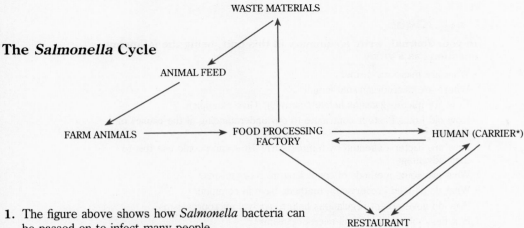

WASTE MATERIALS

The *Salmonella* Cycle

ANIMAL FEED

FARM ANIMALS → FOOD PROCESSING FACTORY → HUMAN (CARRIER*)

RESTAURANT

A carrier is not necessarily sick with the disease, but remains infected and can pass the infection on.

1. The figure above shows how *Salmonella* bacteria can be passed on to infect many people.
   (a) If you were an inspector, where would you look for a possible source of *Salmonella* bacteria in a restaurant?
   (b) How might a human carrier cause farm animals to become contaminated with *Salmonella* bacteria?
   (c) *Salmonella* bacteria are very common, but we can avoid becoming ill from them. How?
   (d) Why is this figure called a cycle?

2. (a) Describe a sandwich you would take with you for an outing on a summer day when you had no way to keep food cold. Tell why you would choose this.
   (b) Name two foods you would not recommend taking because of danger from food poisoning. Explain why you named these foods.

3. Examine the following pairs of foods, and choose from each pair the food that is more likely to become a source of poisoning from microorganisms. Give your reason for the choice in each case.
   (a) ground meat or a piece of steak
   (b) a baked potato or potato salad
   (c) mustard or salad dressing
   (d) coleslaw or cabbage and carrots cooked for dinner
   (e) milk or whipped cream

Summary for

The Big Ideas

Student responses will vary. The following is an ideal summary.

Microorganisms are tiny living things that can be best seen by using a microscope. There are many different kinds of microorganisms: bacteria, algae, protists, fungi, and viruses (although viruses are not usually classified as living things).

Microorganisms can be found everywhere: in soil, in air, in water, on nonliving things, on living things, and even inside living things.

Microorganisms are beneficial in many ways. They function as decomposers; they provide food for other organisms and are thus a vital link in the food chain; their waste products create foods such as cheese, bread, vinegar, and yogurt; and their natural defense systems provide substances humans can use to combat disease. Microorganisms are harmful because they can spoil food and can cause disease in plants and animals.

Louis Pasteur's experiments showed that bacteria can cause food to spoil and that although bacteria live everywhere, their growth can be controlled by altering components of their environment. For example, Pasteur demonstrated that bacteria can be killed by heating.

Bacteria thrive in a range of temperatures known as the optimum growth temperature range. Above and below these temperatures, bacteria either die or fail to grow and reproduce. Knowing this, we can keep the temperature of our foods out of the optimum growth temperature range.

Methods for controlling microorganisms include sterilization, pasteurization, personal hygiene, and temperature control of foods.

All food preservation methods have in common the elimination of microorganisms or the control of their growth.

Government regulations are important because they set standards for cleanliness, food storage, and preparation so that we are protected from dangers in our food. These regulations are then enforced by government inspectors.

Although there are many harmful microorganisms, most are beneficial to us. Therefore, control of all microorganisms is not necessary.

The Big Ideas

In your Journal, write a summary of this unit, using the following questions as a guide.

- What are microorganisms?
- Where are microorganisms found?
- How are microorganisms helpful? harmful? Give examples.
- How did Louis Pasteur contribute to our understanding of the causes of diseases?
- How are bacteria affected by temperature? How can people use this to their advantage?
- What are some methods of controlling microorganisms?
- What do all food preservation methods have in common?
- How do government regulations help to control microorganisms?
- Is it desirable to control all microorganisms?

Checking Your Understanding

1. Refrigeration does not kill most microorganisms, so how can it be possible to preserve foods simply by keeping them cold?

2. Imagine that you have made a large pot of stew. Naturally, you would like to prevent spoilage. Would it make any difference if you:

   (a) kept the stew in one large pot or several smaller ones?

   (b) placed the pot in the refrigerator immediately after turning off the stove, or waited until the stew had cooled?

   (c) stored the stew covered or uncovered?

   (d) froze the stew, rather than refrigerated it?

3. The illustrations below show three bacterial cultures that were once healthy but that have since become contaminated by mold. Each culture has been contaminated by a different type of mold. Which mold might be worth investigating for its special properties? Explain.

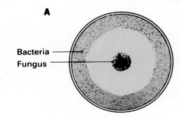 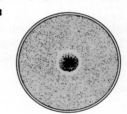 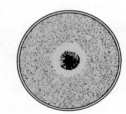

A B C

Bacteria
Fungus

4. Make a concept map using the following terms or phrases: *viruses, bacteria, molds,* and *antibiotics.*

5. Most people do not consider viruses to be living things. Decide for yourself whether viruses are living or nonliving and then make an argument to support your position.

6. Below are a few statements about microorganisms. Indicate whether you agree, disagree, or are uncertain about each statement. Then briefly explain your choice. Do not write in this book.

Statement	Agree	Disagree	Uncertain	Reason
(a) Microorganisms cause more harm than good.				
(b) If microorganisms were to vanish, you probably wouldn't notice.				
(c) Microorganisms are indispensable to us.				
(d) Without microorganisms, you couldn't make a pizza.				
(e) Gardeners benefit from microorganisms.				

Reading *Plus*

Now that you have been introduced to microorganisms, let's find out more about them. By reading pages S41–S56 in the *SourceBook,* you will learn more about the various microorganisms—how they cause disease, how they live and multiply, how they differ, and how they are classified. You will also learn about the human body's defenses against microorganisms, as well as what happens when these defenses break down.

Updating Your Journal

Reread the paragraphs you wrote for this unit's "For Your Journal" questions. Then rewrite them to reflect what you have learned in studying this unit.

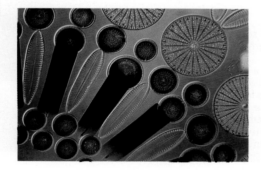

About Updating Your Journal

The following are sample ideal answers.
1. Living things, such as microorganisms, are so small that they are best viewed under a microscope. *(Their answer should reflect an understanding of the **Scale and Structure** of the world that microorganisms inhabit.)*
2. Answers will vary, but responses could include bacteria, viruses, germs, protozoans, fungi, and molds.
3. The word "germ" brings to mind an organism that causes disease. However, students should understand that most microorganisms are beneficial to humans.
4. Food "goes bad" when conditions permit the rapid growth of microorganisms, and the toxins that they produce are able to build up.
5. Not all microorganisms pose a threat to humans, but some do. Among these are viruses and bacteria, which can cause diseases in animals and plants. The diatoms shown in the photo are an important part of many food chains and are not a threat to humans.

Answers to
Checking Your Understanding

1. The small number of microorganisms in food will be unable to reproduce because of the temperature. The effect of toxins produced by this small number of bacteria will probably be minimal.
2. **(a)** no difference
   (b) If you wait until the stew cools, microorganisms will have a good chance of multiplying and producing toxins; if you refrigerate the stew immediately, the microorganisms will not have a chance to grow.
   (c) The stew should be stored covered so that microorganisms in the air will not be able to contaminate the stew.
   (d) Whereas refrigeration will slow the growth of many microorganisms, freezing might actually kill them.
3. The mold in culture A appears to be producing a substance that has a negative effect on the growth of the bacteria. Knowing what type of mold this is and what substance it is producing might help in fighting harmful bacteria.
4. See concept map on page S168.
5. In most ways, viruses do not exhibit the characteristics of living things. They show no signs of life unless they have invaded a host cell and are using the host's structure to reproduce; they do not grow, consume energy, respire, or release waste products.
6. **(a)** and **(b)** Students should disagree with these statements for many reasons: microorganisms form the basis for all food chains; they help with digestion; they decompose waste products in our environment; they help in food production; their products are also used in making some drugs.
   (c) Students should agree with this statement for the reasons outlined above.
   (d) True. Bacteria are used in making cheeses. Yeast is used to make the dough.
   (e) True. Bacteria that live in soil recycle many chemical elements used by living things.

Science in Action

✦ Background

Biology is the science of life and living systems. Since it is such a broad field, it is divided into many branches. Some of the major ones include: anatomy, bacteriology, biochemistry, biophysics, botany, ecology, genetics, marine biology, medicine, microbiology, molecular biology, physiology, and zoology.

The growth of modern biology began at the beginning of the 1900s when the emphasis of study shifted from theory and speculation to experimentation and applied mathematics. As a result, the biological sciences experienced rapid growth, especially in the areas of biochemistry and molecular biology.

Anyone interested in a career in the biological sciences should take biology, chemistry, mathematics, and physics—in both high school and college. Many careers are available to people with bachelor's degrees. Advanced areas of biological research, however, require graduate degrees.

Spotlight on Biology

Lila Colburn is a biologist and university teacher whose main area of study concerns how organisms evolve. We met her in her laboratory.

Q: What aspects of your work do you find most stimulating?

Lila: I love being in the laboratory. I love trying to solve problems about living things—and there is no shortage of interesting problems. In recent years I have become interested in cellular processes; how does this incredibly complicated, tiny chemical factory we call a cell keep itself running so smoothly?

My second love is teaching. I enjoy the give-and-take of working with sharp young minds. Working with students keeps my thinking fresh. I must say that I am continually amazed at the talent among our young people today.

Q: Are there any frustrations in your work?

Lila: Oh, yes, certainly. Not having enough time for everything I want to do. So many challenges, so little time!

Q: What social issues especially concern you as a scientist?

Lila: As a biologist, I am acutely aware of the harm our species is causing to life on this planet. I fear for the future if we do not learn to temper our destructive, short-sighted impulses. Our planet is under an all-out assault on a mind-boggling scale. We cloud our skies with carcinogens and greenhouse gases; we lace our streams and rivers with poisons; we cut and burn down our forests and cover our most productive agricultural lands with condominiums and shopping malls. And as if that were not enough, we have built enough nuclear weaponry to destroy every city on earth a dozen times over. I am somewhat hopeful on this issue, because of the recent developments in the USSR, but a nuclear war could still easily happen, and probably will unless we can somehow get the nuclear genie back into the bottle. I am not fearful for myself, because I am coming to the end of my life, but I am concerned for the future. A nuclear war would destroy civilization as we know it. That which has taken thousands of years to build would be shattered in a few fiery seconds.

Q: What direction do you see science taking in the future?

Lila: Who knows? Things are moving so fast now that it makes my head spin trying to keep up. More science will happen in the next 50 years than in all of history so far.

✦ Using the Interview

Before students begin reading, invite them to express their ideas about what biology is and what a biologist does. Some students may be familiar with different branches of biology, such as botany, zoology, and microbiology. Encourage them to share whatever knowledge they have about these areas of study with their classmates. Then have them read the interview silently, or call on a volunteer to read it aloud.

When students finish reading, you may wish to evaluate their understanding of the interview by asking questions similar to the following:

- Why does Lila Colburn like being a biologist? *(She likes trying to solve problems about living things.)*
- What has she been studying in recent years? *(what controls certain kinds of activities in the cell)*
- Why does she like teaching? *(She finds it stimulating to talk to young people about the same things that she is interested in.)*
- What social issue is Lila Colburn interested in as a scientist? *(the prospect of nuclear war and the proliferation of nuclear weapons)*
- How would you evaluate this interview? *(Accept all reasonable responses.)*
- What other questions do you wish the interviewer had asked Lila Colburn? *(Challenge students to find answers to additional questions they would have liked the interviewer to ask.)*

Suggest that interested students work in groups of 2 or 3 to complete one of the *Drosophila* research projects. Ask each group to design a plan for carrying out their project. (NOTE: different strains of *Drosophila* may be obtained from biological supply houses.)

When students finish, have a spokesperson from each group explain the group's project to the class—what they hoped to discover, what the results were, and what conclusions they drew from the results.

Some Project Ideas

One project idea is to do a survey of the microorganisms that can be found in the soil of your area. For this you will need a microscope and an identification key. Another project could be culturing *Drosophila* (fruit flies). You could compare how *Drosophila* develops under different conditions, for example, a cold location versus a warm one, or a dry environment versus a damp one. Or you could determine the type of fruit or other food the fruit flies seem to prefer. Be sure to house your fruit flies so that they don't escape.

For Assistance

Ask a biologist or your teacher for help in getting started. Biologists work for universities, for government agencies, with consulting firms, and other private companies. Your teacher can assist you in finding a biologist willing to help.

✦ *Going Further*

To help students gain a greater appreciation of what a biologist does, suggest they work in small groups to find answers to one or more of the following questions.
- What is biology and what do biologists study?
- What are the major branches of biology?
- How is biology alike and different from the other sciences?
- What are the most challenging problems in biology today?
- How do you feel about the use of animals in laboratory testing? Do some research to help you make your decision.

Have students share their information with the class by making a bulletin-board display or mural entitled "Biology Today."

Science and Technology

Bacteria at Your Service

What do you think of when you hear the word *bacteria?* If you're like most people, you think of disease. It's true that some bacteria cause disease. But did you know that many kinds of bacteria provide valuable services? For example, when bacteria decompose the dead remains of plants and animals, they return nutrients to the soil. Taking natural processes like these as clues, scientists have begun to use bacteria to solve some of our toughest technological problems.

Alaskan oil spill victim

Cleaning Up Our Act

Some of the greatest successes in using bacteria have come in cleaning up the environment. By taking advantage of bacteria's ability to decompose matter, scientists have had some success in cleaning up oil spills and toxic wastes.

When oil spills occur, they often cause severe damage to the environment. Plants and animals are killed as their habitats and food sources are poisoned. The good news is that scientists have discovered bacteria that actually feed on oil! As they eat oil, they break it down into harmless substances.

Other kinds of bacteria are able to decompose toxic wastes that cause diseases or birth defects in humans. Scientists have even cultured bacteria that break down explosive wastes.

Oil spill near Galveston, Texas

◆ Background

Bacteria are simple, single-celled organisms. Most are no more than 0.2 to 0.3 micrometers in diameter, which makes them among the smallest living things. There are thousands of kinds of bacteria, and they exist almost everywhere. Fortunately, most of them are harmless to people, and relatively few kinds cause disease.

Bacteria play an important role in the field of genetic engineering. For example, a gene for a desired trait may be implanted into a particular strain of bacteria. As the bacteria reproduces, it also reproduces the implanted genetic material. This material can then be extracted from the bacteria and implanted into animal or plant cells.

Bacteria are currently used to help clean up oil spills and to produce such substances as insulin and interferon. Another promising area for the use of bacteria is in the production of bioplastics. In 1989 an experimental factory in Billingham, England, was producing 45 metric tons a year of biodegradable plastic made by bacteria. The biological function of the plastic, called PHB, is to store energy for the bacteria, just as fat does for animals and starch does for plants. At first, the researchers discovered that the plastic was stiff and brittle. Another drawback was that it melted at a temperature of 170°C. This high melting point made the plastic difficult to work with.

The researchers found that they could solve the problem by feeding the bacteria a mixture of glucose and organic acids. This new diet gave the plastic a lower melting point and also made it stronger and more flexible. The main drawbacks of bioplastic production is the time and cost needed to extract it from the bacteria.

◆ Discussion

When students have finished reading the feature, involve them in a discussion of what they have read. You may wish to use questions similar to the following:

1. What are some valuable services that bacteria provide? *(Bacteria decompose the dead remains of plants and animals, and they return nutrients to the soil.)*

2. How can the ability of bacteria to decompose matter be used to help clean up the environment? *(Some kinds of bacteria are being used to help clean up oil spills and toxic wastes. The bacteria are able to eat oil and toxic wastes and break them down into harmless substances.)*

3. What would be the advantages of using plastics made by bacteria? *(Plastics made by bacteria can also be decomposed by them. The characteristics of these plastics can be manipulated by changing the diet of the bacteria.)*

The Plastics of the Future?

Our landfills are overflowing with plastic garbage that doesn't decompose. We may find a solution to this problem in certain bacteria, which actually produce biodegradable plastic! These amazing bacteria store their energy as plastic, just as animals store their energy as fat, and plants as starch. Their plastic is normally quite brittle, but when certain substances are added to the bacteria's diet, the plastic they produce is flexible and can be made into consumer products.

Biodegradable plastic produced by bacteria

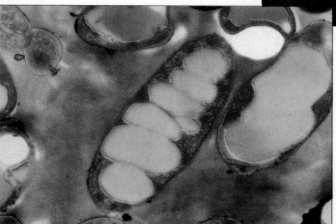

These bacteria store energy as plastic granules.

Perhaps the best thing about this plastic is that the same bacteria that manufacture it can also decompose it. So in the future, we may be able to put plastic garbage in a landfill, add bacteria, and then just wait for the garbage to disappear.

Unfortunately, this kind of plastic is much more expensive to produce than others, so it hasn't been used much. But if scientists can figure out a way to make it cheaply, it could help us reduce the amount of garbage taking up space in our already overburdened landfills.

More Hard-Working Bacteria

You've learned about just a few of the ways that bacteria have been put to work. See if you can find out about others on your own.

- How do genetic engineers use bacteria?
- How are bacteria used in processing some types of food?
- Can you imagine any other ways we could use bacteria to our advantage?

◆ Going Further

Have students research how scientists manipulate bacteria's genetic material and then use that material in other organisms. Suggest that they make a poster diagram illustrating the steps in the process.

Ask students to do some research on bacteria that are used in cleaning up oil spills and toxic wastes. Have them investigate the following questions:

- What kinds of bacteria are used?
- How are they grown?
- Why aren't the bacteria killed by the toxic waste?
- What are the problems with this procedure, and how are researchers trying to solve them?

✴ *Teaching the Unit*

 ### Unit Overview

In this unit, the concept of matter and its properties are developed in ways that allow students to draw from the experiences and knowledge they bring with them to class. In the section *Meet Matter*, students formulate a working definition of matter and use creative thinking skills to observe, analyze, and describe the properties of matter. In the section *Measuring Matter*, students review the metric system and are asked to apply what they have learned to the quantitative analysis of mass and volume. In the final section, *More About Matter*, students investigate the different states of matter. The unit concludes with a discussion of the particle model of matter and challenges students to develop models of their own.

 ### Using the Themes

The unifying themes emphasized in this unit are **Stability, Scale and Structure,** and **Energy**. The following information will help you weave these themes into your teaching plan. A focus question is provided with each theme as a discussion tool to help you tie the information in the unit together.

Stability may be applied to the first and second sections by discussing with students that although matter's properties can be changed by physical and chemical processes, certain fundamental properties remain: namely, that matter always takes up space and has mass.

> **Focus question**: *Why will a certain type of matter always show the same physical and chemical properties?*

Students should understand that the chemical and physical properties of matter are determined by the underlying structure of matter; a certain type of matter always has the same structure, and this structure controls how the matter will behave.

Scale and Structure may be discussed from two points of view. First, call students' attention to the connection between matter's gross physical properties (for example, its state) and its underlying structure. Secondly, show that some of the apparent oddities in the way that matter behaves (for example, the ability to dissolve a substance in a liquid without noticeably changing the volume of the liquid) are explained by the structure of matter at its most fundamental level.

> **Focus question**: *How does the structure of matter influence its state?*

In general, gases are energetic, noninteracting particles separated by large amounts of space; liquids are closely spaced particles able to move about freely with respect to each other; and solids are closely spaced particles in a fixed position with respect to one another.

Energy can be explored by discussing the relationship between a substance's state and its energy level. Although this particular point is not discussed in the text, it is the next logical step in understanding the differences between the various states of matter.

> **Focus question**: *Which state of matter, solid, liquid, or gas, do you think has the most energy? the least?*

Students should be able to infer that solids probably have the least energy because they consist of tightly packed particles in fixed positions. Gases, on the other hand, are free to move about, and therefore probably have the most energy.

 ### Using the *Science Discovery* Videodiscs

Disc 1 *Science Sleuths, The Blob!*
A mysterious blob has washed up on a public beach. Since the authorities cannot identify it, and because they fear it is a dangerous substance, they decide to close the beach. The Science Sleuths must analyze the evidence for themselves to determine the true nature of the mysterious substance.

Disc 2 *Image and Activity Bank*
A variety of still images, short videos, and activities are available for you to use as you teach this unit. See the *Videodisc Resources* section of the **Teacher's Resource Binder** for detailed instructions.

 ### Using the *SciencePlus SourceBook*

Unit 4 of the *SourceBook* can be used to provide a theoretical framework for the topics covered in *Investigating Matter*. The *SourceBook* unit includes discussions of molecules; the molecular basis of the states of matter; mixtures, compounds, and solutions; and elements and atoms. Throughout the unit, the molecular basis of the properties of matter is emphasized.

PLANNING CHART

SECTION AND LESSON	PG.	TIME*	PROCESS SKILLS	EXPLORATION AND ASSESSMENT	PG.	RESOURCES AND FEATURES
Unit Opener	180		observing, discussing	For Your Journal	181	Science Sleuths: *The Blob!* Videodisc Activity Sheets TRB: Home Connection
MEET MATTER	182			Challenge Your Thinking	189	
1 About Matter	182	2 to 3	observing, inferring, classifying, writing	Exploration 1	184	Image and Activity Bank 4–1 TRB: Resource Worksheet 4–1 Resource Transparency 4–1 Graphic Organizer Transparency 4–2
2 Matter's Useful Properties	186	1	observing, classifying, analyzing	Exploration 2	187	Image and Activity Bank 4–2 TRB: Resource Worksheet 4–2
MEASURING MATTER	190			Challenge Your Thinking	205	
3 SI: The Metric System of Measurement	190	2 to 3	sequencing, analyzing, comparing, recognizing number relationships			Image and Activity Bank 4–3
4 Volume	193	3 to 4	measuring, calibrating, collecting data, drawing conclusions	Exploration 3 Exploration 4	194 197	Image and Activity Bank 4–4 Resource Transparency 4–3
5 Mass	201	3	measuring, graphing, collecting data, predicting	Exploration 5 Exploration 6 Exploration 7	201 202 204	Image and Activity Bank 4–5 TRB: Resource Worksheets 4–3 and 4–4 Graphic Organizer Transparencies 4–4, 4–5, and 4–6
MORE ABOUT MATTER	206			Challenge Your Thinking	219	
6 States of Matter	206	1 to 2	observing, classifying, interpreting data, analyzing			Image and Activity Bank 4–6
7 Changes of State	209	3	observing, designing experiments, analyzing, controlling variables	Exploration 8	211	Image and Activity Bank 4–7 TRB: Resource Worksheets 4–5 and 4–6
8 A Model of Matter	214	2	using models, inferring, interpreting poetry, writing			Image and Activity Bank 4–8 TRB: Activity Worksheet 4–7
End of Unit	220		applying, analyzing, evaluating, summarizing	Making Connections TRB: Sample Assessment Items	220	Science in Action, p. 222 Science and Technology, p. 224 TRB: Activity Worksheet 4–8 Graphic Organizer Transparency 4–7 *SourceBook,* pp. S57–S72

*Time given in number of class periods.

Meeting Individual Needs

Gifted Students

1. Pose the following hypothetical questions for students to think about:
   - What would the world be like if there were no such thing as the liquid state of matter?
   - How would your life be affected if matter did not change states—liquids did not freeze to form solids or evaporate to form gases, solids did not melt or sublimate, and gases did not condense to form liquids?
   - What would society be like if there were no standard form of weights and measures? What problems would this create? How would scientific research be affected?
   - What would the world be like if the boiling point of water were 50°C and the freezing point 10°C?

   Have students select one of the questions and then write a response. Their ideas can be presented as an oral report to the class.

2. Propose the following scenario for students to consider:

   Suppose you have invented a method to communicate with dolphins. You discover in your conversations with them that they are highly intelligent beings much like ourselves. As a step toward establishing an organized society, the dolphins want to formulate a system of measurement. How would you suggest they proceed? What system would you suggest they use? Suggest to students that they write an interview with one of the dolphins in which they discuss and resolve the problem.

LEP Students

1. Students may enjoy playing the "List the Properties" game. Group students into two or more teams. Then write the name or show a picture of an example of matter, such as an apple. Instruct each team to write as many words or terms as they can to describe the properties of the object. Allow them to use a bilingual dictionary if necessary. Help resolve any conflicts about the words or terms chosen. The team with the greatest number of descriptive words wins.

2. Have students select and describe objects (examples of matter) that are relevant to their particular culture and native land, for example, fruits and vegetables that are unique to the individual's homeland, plants that are not found in the United States, household items that are uniquely cultural, and so on. This activity provides an excellent opportunity for the rest of the class to learn something about another culture and, at the same time, lets them apply what they learn to the concepts of matter.

3. At the beginning of each unit, give Spanish-speaking students a copy of the *Spanish Glossary* from the *Teacher's Resource Binder.* Also, let Spanish-speaking students listen to the *English/Spanish Audiocassettes.*

At-Risk Students

This unit is filled with many attention-grabbing activities for your students. For example, the games *Metric Concentration* and *Metric Spin* are ideal ways for students to grasp the concepts behind metric conversion while playing an exciting game. This unit also provides many activities that require making something—a graduated cylinder, a device for measuring lung capacity, a featherweight balance—all of which give students concrete examples of concepts covered in the unit. With the activity *Fifteen Hypotheses,* students are given the chance to use their imaginations and design their own experiments to reinforce what they have learned.

For students who need more practice understanding the properties that define the different states of matter, the *At-Home Investigation* on page 206 is a fun activity your students can do at home or in class. In the activity, students are asked to make a cornstarch putty, which they can manipulate by rolling, cutting, or putting in a container. Ask students to examine and list the properties of the substance carefully, and to determine whether the putty is a solid or a liquid. This is a good opportunity to reinforce the particle nature of matter with your students.

Cross-Disciplinary Focus
Creative Writing

In the past several decades, scientists have developed a large number of synthetic materials that have proven to be highly useful and even indispensable. Ask students to imagine that they could wave a magic wand and cause all of the synthetic materials invented in the last 100 years to disappear. How would life be different? How would it be the same? Would people be better or worse off? Challenge students to write a short story from the point of view of someone who wakes up one morning to find that all of these synthetic materials have suddenly vanished. To help students get started, you may wish to work with them to assemble a list of common synthetic materials. Display the stories where class members may read them at their leisure.

Art and Design

Architects use their knowledge of the properties of materials when they design buildings and other structures. Some of the variables they must consider include strength, durability, appearance, cost, and weight. Have students imagine that they have been asked to design a house. The first thing they must do is to decide on all the materials they want to use. What factors would they have to consider? What properties would they look for in the materials they choose? Suggest that they list in a table the materials they would use. The table should show how each material will be used and why it was chosen. Some students might enjoy including a drawing of the house they would build. When students finish, have them present their ideas to the class. Involve the class in a discussion of whether or not the materials chosen were the best for the job.

Cross-Cultural Focus

Other Measures of Matter

With the notable exception of the United States, most of the world uses the metric system of measurement. In the past, however, many different systems of measuring matter were used. For example, the ancient Egyptians used the *cubit* as a unit of length. The cubit was defined as the length of a man's forearm from the elbow to the fingertips. In more recent times, the Scots measured mass in *stones*, a unit of measure equal to about 6.4 kg. The Swahili of East Africa measured length with units based on the *shibiri*, a distance equal to the span of a hand. Have students work in groups to do research and prepare a presentation on the systems of measurement used by different cultures of the past. Ask them to find out how the measuring system fit the technology of the time. Encourage students to be creative. Suggest that their presentations include diagrams, posters, murals, demonstrations, cartoons, and so on.

Physicists from Around the World

Each year Nobel Prizes are awarded to people, regardless of nationality or cultural background, who have made valuable contributions for the "good of humanity." The awards are given for physics, chemistry, physiology or medicine, literature, and peace. Have students make a table of the Nobel Prize winners in physics for the past 25 years. Their tables should show the person's name, country of origin, and achievement. As an extension, have students write a biography on one of the physicists listed in their table. Encourage students to select people from various parts of the world. Finished biographies could be organized into a book entitled *Physicists from Around the World.*

✳ *Resources*

Bibliography for Teachers

Ardley, Neil, and Robert Matthews, eds. *Physics Today.* Chicago, IL: World Book, 1985.

Barber, Jacqueline. "Chemical Reactions." *Great Explorations in Math and Science.* GEMS Series, ed. by Lincoln Bergman and Kay Fairwell. Berkeley, CA: Lawrence Hall of Science, 1986.

Barber, Jacqueline. *Solids, Liquids, and Gases: A School Assembly Program Presenter's Guide.* GEMS Series, ed. by Lincoln Bergman and Kay Fairwell. Berkeley, CA: Lawrence Hall of Science, 1986.

James, H. J., and S. L. Nelson. "Classroom Learning Cycle: Using Diagrams to Classify Matter." *Journal of Chemical Education*, June 1981, pp. 446-77.

Bibliography for Students

Asimov, Isaac. *The Measure of the Universe.* New York, NY: Harper & Row, 1983.

Bishop, Owen. *Yardsticks of the Universe.* New York, NY: Peter Bedrick, 1984.

Cotterill, Rodney. *The Cambridge Guide to the Material World.* New York, NY: Cambridge University Press, 1985.

Gaskin, Carol. *Journey to the Center of the Atom!* New York, NY: Scholastic, 1987.

Films, Videotapes, Software, and Other Media

Basic Units of Matter.
Videotape.
Great Plains
Instructional TV Library
University of Nebraska
P.O. Box 80669
Lincoln, NE 68588

The Behavior of Matter.
Videotape.
Encyclopedia Britannica
425 North Michigan Ave.
Chicago, IL 60611

Measurements: Length, Mass, and Volume.
Software. Grades 7–12.
For Apple II and
Commodore 64.
Focus Media, Inc.
P.O. Box 865
Garden City, NY 11530
(800) 645-8989

Particles in Motion: States of Matter. Film.
National Geographic
Society
Educational Services
Department 79
Washington, DC 20036

What's a Matter?
Software. Grades 7–9.
For Apple II, IIe, IIc.
Orange Juice Software
338 S. Arch Ave.
New Richmond, WI
54017
(715) 246-3588

Unit 4 Investigating Matter

✳ Unit Focus

Write the following question on the chalkboard:

What can be heavy or light, soft or hard, visible or invisible, colored or clear, smooth or rough, and living or nonliving?

After students have had a chance to respond, point out that matter is the only thing that could have all of these qualities. Write the word *matter* on the chalkboard and challenge students to make up a definition of their own. Accept all reasonable responses. Then have students suggest an example of matter to illustrate each of the qualities in the question. Keep a list of their ideas on the board.

✳ About the Photograph

The photograph shows a winter scene near one of the thermal areas in **Yellowstone National Park.** Yellowstone, located in the northwest corner of Wyoming, is the oldest national park in the United States. It is known for its deep canyons, magnificent waterfalls, clear lakes, evergreen forests, and rolling meadows.

Most of Yellowstone's landscape was created by volcanic eruptions more than 60,000 years ago. The large mass of molten rock that still lies beneath its surface furnishes the heat for the park's 200 active geysers and thousands of hot springs.

For Your Journal

Write a paragraph summarizing your thoughts about each of the following:

1. What do water, ice, and steam have in common?

2. Imagine that you could divide a liter of water in half, again and again, more than a hundred times. What do you think would eventually happen?

3. How are all of the things in this picture related?

4. Is all the matter in this picture visible? Explain.

✳ Using the Photograph

All three states of matter can be identified in the photograph. Ask students to name any examples they can see of solids, liquids, and gases. Then ask students:

- What substance is shown as a solid, a liquid, and a gas? *(water)*
- How is the solid form of this substance shown? *(as ice, frost, and snow)*
- How is the liquid form shown? *(as water in a lake or hot spring)*
- How is the gaseous form shown? *(as mist and clouds)*
- Which object supplies the energy that makes life on earth possible? *(the sun)* Is this object a form of matter? *(yes)*

Involve students in a discussion of how the photograph shows the changing nature of matter. *(Ice is melting; water is turning into steam and mist; mist is turning into frost; water is turning into snow; the sun is heating the air.)*

✳ About Your Journal

Students should answer the Journal questions to the best of their abilities.

These questions are designed to serve two functions: to help students recognize that they do indeed have prior knowledge, and to help them identify any misconceptions they may have about the topic. In the course of studying the unit, these misconceptions should be dispelled.

✳ Getting Started

This introductory lesson makes **the point that matter is all around us.** A series of riddles is used to set the stage for the first Exploration. Here students are asked to examine a number of examples of matter and to identify as many characteristics, or properties, of matter as possible. These properties are then classified as either chemical, physical, or biological. The physical properties of matter are examined in greater detail in later lessons. The biological and chemical properties of matter are investigated in depth in later units. The lesson concludes with a discussion of how matter can be defined by its properties.

Main Ideas

1. Matter is all around us.
2. Matter can be identified and characterized by its properties.
3. The properties of matter can be classified as chemical, physical, or biological.
4. The chemical properties of matter are determined by its chemical structure. Chemical changes generally transform matter into a totally different form.

(Continues on next page)

MEET MATTER

1 About Matter

Matter. The word is used in so many different ways. In this unit, you are going to use the word *matter* in yet another way. You will find that . . .

- Indeed it does matter. . .
- That you use your gray matter. . .
- To learn many facts about matter. . .
- In order to discover what is matter. . .

For this unit is about matter.

LESSON 1 ORGANIZER

Objectives

By the end of the lesson, students should be able to:
1. Identify some chemical, physical, and biological properties of matter.
2. Specify whether a particular property of matter is biological, physical, or chemical.
3. Recognize that each type of matter has a unique set of properties.

Process Skills

observing, inferring, classifying, writing

New Terms

Matter—anything that has mass and occupies space.
Physical properties—characteristics of matter that do not involve chemical changes; examples include size, shape, color, and texture.

Chemical properties—characteristics of matter that describe how a substance behaves in chemical changes.

Materials

Exploration 1: water, vinegar, 4 beakers, ice cube, egg, balloon, 2 sugar cubes, candle, matches, earthworm (or any insect), geranium (or any plant), air freshener, safety goggles

The Riddle of Matter

In the book *The Hobbit,* by J. R. R. Tolkien, the hero is a hobbit named Mr. Bilbo Baggins. Hobbits are little people, like elves, who populate Middle Earth, the magical world of *The Hobbit.* At one point in the story, Bilbo is lost in a dark cave. He encounters a creature of the deep named Gollum. Gollum agrees to show Bilbo the way out of the cave if Bilbo can guess all of Gollum's riddles and ask him one that Gollum cannot solve. However, if Bilbo fails, he may end up as Gollum's next meal.

Bilbo asks Gollum to go first. So Gollum hisses:

*What has roots as nobody sees
Is taller than trees,
Up, up it goes
And yet never grows?*

What has these characteristics or **properties?** Bilbo guessed right—mountains.

Bilbo also answers Gollum's second riddle correctly:

*Voiceless it cries,
Wingless flutters,
Toothless bites,
Mouthless mutters.*

While you think about this riddle, here is another one. (This one isn't from Gollum or Bilbo.)

*Can be tasted or not tasted,
Can be seen or not seen,
Can be changed, can be wasted,
Of every color—from black to green.*

The answer to the last riddle is all around you: the air you breathe, the pencil you hold, and even you. Now do you know the answer? It is **matter.** In Exploration 1, you will observe 12 more examples of matter. For each one, write down several observations and inferences about matter that you feel to be true. You may discover an answer to this final riddle: What is matter?

(Main Ideas continued)

5. The physical properties of matter (e.g., color, shape, and mass) may be observed without altering the underlying structure of the matter. Some physical changes take the form of changes of state (e.g., melting, freezing, and evaporating). However, the underlying identifying properties of the matter are not affected.

6. A substance's specific physical and chemical properties may make it useful to people.

✳ *Teaching Strategies*

The cartoon on page 182 introduces the term *matter* in a lighthearted way. Ask students to identify the meaning of the word as it is used by the cartoon characters. Then encourage them to suggest other phrases that they may have heard that use the word *matter.* (*vegetable matter, matter of years, for that matter, no matter*)

The Riddle of Matter

These riddles offer a unique way to focus the students' interest on the properties, or characteristics, of matter. It also sets the stage for *Exploration 1,* in which students are asked to make observations and/or inferences about different types of matter.

> **Primary Source**
> *Description of change:* excerpted.
> *Rationale:* excerpted to focus on properties of matter mentioned in *The Hobbit.*

Teacher's Resource Binder

Resource Worksheet 4–1
Resource Transparency 4–1
Graphic Organizer Transparency 4–2

Time Required

two to three class periods

Exploration 1

Distribute the examples of matter listed in the table among several activity stations. Have students work in groups of two or three at each station for 3 to 5 minutes. You may want to include your own examples of matter to make the activity more challenging.

Possible observations and inferences to complete the table are included in the answers below.

Answers to

A Matter for Discussion

1. **(a)** The earthworm and the geranium are examples of living matter. The egg is an example of matter that was once living. All of the other examples are nonliving.

   (b) Solids: candle, ice cube, egg, sugar cube, air freshener
   Liquids: water, vinegar
   Gases: air inside the balloon, bubbles on the egg submerged in vinegar
   Note: students may argue correctly that:
   - An egg is made up of solids, liquids, and gases. (There is air inside an egg.)
   - The balloon is composed of both a solid and a gas.
   - Living things are made up of solids, liquids, and gases.

   (c) The air freshener and the vinegar have an odor.

   (d) Kinds of changes: the candle burning, the ice cube melting, the sugar cube and the eggshell dissolving.

   (e) Original matter is destroyed when the candle burns and when the eggshell dissolves; the sugar cube and the ice cube seem to disappear.

   (f) Answers may vary, but possible responses include:
   - Sight: all examples can be seen except the air in the balloon.
   - Hearing: none of the examples are audible, but students should be able to provide examples.
   - Taste: vinegar, water, sugar cube

   - Touch: temperature, texture, wetness
   - Smell: vinegar, air freshener

   (g) Whether an ice cube is frozen or melted, it is still water; when a sugar cube dissolves, it is still sugar; as the air freshener disappears into the air (sublimes), it is still the same kind of matter.

   (h) Students should recognize that the classification of matter is based on its properties. Any two examples of matter that have

the same properties are the same kind of matter.

2. The biological properties of living things include growth, motion, the ability to reproduce, and adaptability.

Answer to caption: The properties shared by the wheat and the deer, but not by the quartz, include growth, movement, the ability to reproduce, and use of energy from the environment.

What Is Matter?

In your Journal, make a data table like the one below. Observe the examples of matter listed and record your observations or inferences in your table. Indicate with a letter *O* or *I* whether you are making an observation or an inference. See if you can record at least five observations for each example of matter. What inferences about matter do these observations suggest? Do this Exploration in groups of three. Do not taste any material unless specifically instructed to do so by your teacher.

Example of Matter	Observations/ Inferences
a beaker of water	
a beaker of vinegar	
an ice cube	
an egg	
a balloon filled with air	
a sugar cube	
a sugar cube in a beaker of water	
a burning candle	
an earthworm	
a geranium	
an egg in a beaker of vinegar	
an air freshener	

Afterwards, share your observations and inferences with your classmates. Have you solved the riddle "What is matter?"

A Matter for Discussion

1. After much discussion, Ms. Chester's class came up with this list of inferences about matter. Write an observation to support each of these inferences.
   (a) Matter may be either living or nonliving.
   (b) Matter may be either solid, liquid, or gas.
   (c) Matter may have an odor or no odor at all.
   (d) Matter can undergo many kinds of changes.
   (e) Often, the original matter changes so much that it appears to be destroyed.
   (f) Matter can be detected using your senses—sight, hearing, taste, touch, and smell.
   (g) In some types of changes, although the matter may look different, it is really still the same.
   (h) Each kind of matter has its own distinctive characteristics or properties that identify it.

2. Living things are examples of matter. In the unit "Patterns of Living Things," you studied their properties, or characteristics. Review what you did and suggest four properties that distinguish living things from nonliving things. These properties are sometimes called *biological properties*.

What properties are shared by the wheat and the deer, but not by the quartz?

3. When you examined the sugar cube in Exploration 1, you made two kinds of observations. First, you observed the shape and color of the sugar cube. You may also have made quantitative observations about it by measuring its length and its mass. These observations describe **physical properties** of a sugar cube. Second, you observed a change—something happened to the sugar cube when it was placed in water. This observation also describes a physical property of sugar: Sugar is not destroyed by water; it can still be tasted in the water. You can thus make two kinds of observations about physical properties: observations describing the matter itself and observations describing how the matter changes.

   (a) Describe the physical properties of an ice cube. In your description include examples of both types of observations about physical properties.

   (b) Describe the physical properties of water, including examples of both types of observations about physical properties.

4. In some physical changes, the **chemical properties** of matter do not change. For example, we say that water is still water if it is changed to a solid (ice) or to a vapor (steam). Also, sugar is still sugar if it is dissolved in water. However, in two examples of changes in Exploration 1, you observed actual changes of chemical properties.

   (a) What two examples of chemical properties did you observe?

   (b) What chemical property of iron causes millions of dollars worth of damage every year to objects made of iron?

   (c) List three physical properties of wax and one chemical property of wax.

5. List as many properties of an apple as you can. Include biological, physical, and chemical properties.

6. Create your own definition of matter. The next section may suggest a way of improving your definition.

Be a Riddlemaster

You've had a while to guess the answer to Gollum's second riddle. Did you guess "wind"? Do you think wind is an example of matter? (By the way, Bilbo *does* find his way out of the cave, and he goes on to further adventures.)

Now it's your turn. Make a riddle about one of the examples of matter in Exploration 1. As clues to your riddle, use the properties of that example of matter—but don't make it too easy! On the right is a riddle that almost stumped Bilbo. The answer is one of the examples of matter in Exploration 1.

A box without hinges, key, or lid
Yet golden treasure inside is hid.

Follow Up

Assessment

1. Have students list the properties, both chemical and physical, of an example of matter not covered in the lesson, such as a nail, a lump of coal, a piece of paper, a food product, an animal or plant, or a beverage.

2. Have students analyze and list the properties of matter referred to in their riddles. Ask them to classify the properties as either biological, physical, or chemical.

Extension

Have students imagine that they are taking a hike in a forest. Challenge them to make a list of some of the chemical and physical changes of matter they might observe.

> **Primary Source**
> *Description of change:* excerpted.
> *Rationale:* excerpted to focus on qualities of matter mentioned in *The Hobbit.*

---

3. **(a)** Observations describing an ice cube include: clear, cold, solid, has size and shape. An observation describing a change in an ice cube: melts.

   (b) Observations describing water include: clear, flows, wet, liquid, takes the shape of its container. Observations describing a change in water: freezes, evaporates.

4. **(a)** Chemical properties: burning candle, dissolving eggshell.

   (b) Chemical property: rusting.

   (c) Physical properties may include: solid, can be scratched with a fingernail, melts, can have color, has no odor. Chemical property: burns.

5. Physical properties may include: color, odor, shape, size, texture, composition (solid or liquid), mass, density, and hardness. Biological properties include: it grows and reproduces. Chemical properties include: decays, turns brown when exposed to air, will ferment under the right conditions.

6. Accept all reasonable answers. The following lessons will expand the concept to include mass, volume, and states of matter.

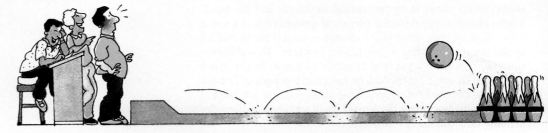

2 Matter's Useful Properties

Imagine a house made of air, a bowling ball made of paper, a bicycle made of glass. These ideas are ridiculous. Air, paper, and glass do not have properties that are useful in making these objects. They do, however, have other useful properties.

- Air works well in an air mattress. What properties of air are being used here?
- Paper is useful for making a wide range of products, from bathroom tissue to cardboard boxes.
- Glass is found everywhere. Its properties make it useful in windows, bottles, insulation, light bulbs—the list goes on and on.

The properties of materials—physical, chemical, and biological—determine how the materials are used.

Here is a short list of materials. With a classmate, suggest a use for each, then name a property that is important for this use. Which type of property is it? Record your ideas in a data table like this one. Do not write in the book.

Material	Use	Important Property	Type of Property
corn			
gold			
oil			
aluminum			
plastic			
coal			
nickel			
wool			
(your choice)			

✳ Getting Started

In this lesson, students are asked to complete a data table in which they identify the useful properties of everyday items and then classify them as either physical, chemical, or biological.

Main Idea

The properties of a material determine its use.

✳ Teaching Strategies

Have students form small groups and ask each group to examine a different consumer product. Ask: What properties make this product useful? What properties make it salable? Follow up by having a member from each group present his or her group's ideas to the class.

Have students work individually or in groups to complete the table on page 186. Answers may vary, but possible responses are included in the table shown on the next page.

LESSON 2 ORGANIZER

Objectives

By the end of the lesson, students should be able to:
1. Identify the properties of materials that make them useful.
2. Classify the properties that make materials useful as either physical, chemical, or biological.

Process Skills

observing, classifying, analyzing

New Terms

Materials

Teacher's Resource Binder

Resource Worksheet 4–2

Science Discovery Videodisc

Disc 2, Image and Activity Bank, 4–2

Time Required

one class period

A Class Project: Properties and Uses of Paper

For this project, you will prepare a report and present it to your class. Work in groups of three or four. Decide which tasks each person in the group will do. Perhaps some tasks will be done by the whole group. Later, in preparing your report, decide who will present the different parts of the report. Will you use a poster to help you? The overhead projector? Perhaps you can make a display.

Here are some suggestions about what to include in your presentation.

Taking the logs to the sawmill

Part 1

This part involves doing library research, talking to people, visiting offices and factories, and/or simply thinking. Consider these questions:

(a) How is paper made? Where is it made? How many uses of paper are there? What properties make paper suitable for each use?

(b) How many trees does it take to make the Sunday edition of a major newspaper? Is there a danger of running out of trees? What can be done to conserve this resource?

(c) What jobs depend on the manufacture and use of paper? Are there jobs in your community that depend on paper? Do any members of your class deliver newspapers?

A forest—where it all begins

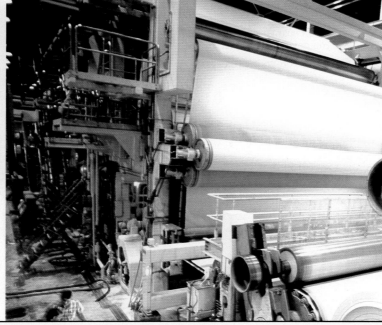

Manufacturing newsprint

Exploration 2

The following is background material that you can share with your students. The word *paper* comes from *papyrus,* which is a reed used by the ancient Egyptians to make writing material. But paper, as we know it today, was invented in China in A.D. 105 by Ts'ai Lun, an official of the Imperial Court. Ts'ai Lun made his paper from the fibers of the mulberry tree. Later, he also used fish nets, old rags, and hemp for his raw material.

Since 1850, most paper has been made from wood pulp. Its strong, cellulose fibers make it the ideal raw material. The properties of paper depend on various factors, such as the type of pulp used and the amount of refining done to the pulp.

Part 1

Before students begin reading *Part 1,* call on them to suggest ways in which paper and paper products are used. Write the list on the chalkboard to demonstrate how important paper is in our everyday lives. Then ask students to look at the list and identify at least one property for each item that makes it useful.

Suggest that students work in groups of three or four to do their research projects. To help students get started, you may wish to have each group consider the following questions:

• What information do you want to present?

• What resources (libraries, interviews, professional organizations, and so on) will you use to gather the information you need?

• How will your group present its findings? Will they make an oral report to the class, compile their findings in a book or in fact sheets, make a bulletin board display or mural, or decide on some other way of presenting their information?

• Which members of the group will be responsible for the research? for making charts, graphs, and other visual materials? for presenting the report?

Answers to Table, Properties of Matter

Material	Use	Important Property	Type of Property
corn	corn flakes	nutritious	chemical
gold	jewelry, electronics	does not corrode	chemical
oil	lubricant	reduces friction	physical
aluminum	building material	lightweight	physical
plastic	building material	can be molded	physical
coal	fuel	burns	chemical
nickel	coating	resists corrosion	chemical
wool	clothing	traps heat	physical

Part 2

This class project is ideal for groups of four to five students. Each group investigates a property for several brands or types of paper. Suggest that each group decide on how they want to proceed. You may wish to use the following questions to help students get started:

- What brands or types of paper do you want to test?
- What property of the paper do you want to investigate?
- Who will be responsible for the different parts of the project?
- How will you present the results of your investigations?

The following are some suggested procedures for students to use in their investigations of the properties listed in *Part 2.*

(a) Each student may bring in three or four sheets of the brand of paper towels they use at home. Have them examine the properties that all the brands have in common. What properties or characteristics distinguish one brand from another? Two suggestions for testing the strengths of different brands are as follows:

- Strength may be defined as the ability to hold up during scrubbing. Suggest that students design a fair test in which each brand of paper towel is used to scrub an abrasive surface.
- Strength may also be defined as the ability to support a weight. Suggest that students pour sand into the center of a wet paper towel until it tears. They can keep track of the amount of sand used for each trial for each brand of paper towel. Then the final amount each wet paper towel was able to hold before tearing can be compared.

(b) Many varieties of paper can be used in this investigation: newspaper, brown paper, wax paper, freezer paper, paper towels, typing paper, and so on. The test can be as simple as timing how long a water drop will remain intact on each kind of paper.

(c) This is probably the most desirable property of paper towels. Again, students can bring in samples from home. A simple test might involve:

- Finding the mass of a container with a dry paper towel inside.
- Submersing the paper towel in water.

Part 2

This part can be done by devising experiments to investigate a property of paper. Here are four suggestions:

(a) *Strength.* Compare the strength of a variety of brands of paper towels. What would be your test for strength? Is it a fair test? When is strength important?

(b) *Ability to repel water.* Develop a test to compare how well different papers repel water. What is done to make paper more water-repellent?

(c) *Ability to absorb water.* Test at least three brands of paper towels to determine which absorbs water best.

(d) *Ability to disintegrate in water.* Bathroom tissue should have this property so that it will not clog drains and sewer pipes. Are all bathroom papers equally good? How could you find out? Did you develop a fair test?

Good luck on your project!

Preparing to print a newspaper

Pulp and paper are used to make school supplies and a wide variety of other products.

- Reweighing the container with the wet paper towel inside. Students may suggest several variations for this experiment, including measuring the volume of the water absorbed.

(d) A simple test could involve placing a set length of tissue in a large bottle filled with water and vigorously shaking the bottle. To make this a fair test, students would need to control:

- the amount of water
- the number of shakes
- the vigor of the shakes

Students may wish to compare one property for different brands of the same product. The following are some suggestions:

Product: thread, Properties: flammability, strength, ability to stretch; Product: powdered detergents, Properties: amount of suds, ability to clean a stain; Product: liquid detergents, Properties: amount of suds, ability to clean grease; Product: powdered drinks, Properties: taste, ability to dissolve.

1. Here is a description of Mario's pencil. List as many properties of the pencil as you can, and group them according to whether each is a physical property or a chemical property.

   "My pencil is painted red and is 10.5 cm long. It is made of four materials. One is wood. By itself, wood floats. A pencil does not float as well. When I chew on my pencil, it leaves marks in the wood. Wood is soft enough to grind away in the pencil sharpener. You can recognize my pencil by a burn mark near one end.

   Enclosed in the wood is a rod made of graphite. Graphite is soft. It can easily mark a piece of paper.

   The eraser is held in place with a small piece of metal. Metal is used because it can be easily bent. My eraser is pink and is now only 0.25 cm long. When rubbed on paper, it leaves part of itself behind. But it does remove the pencil mark. That is my pencil, and if anyone sees one like it, please return it. Pencils have the property of being able to disappear."

2. How many quantitative observations are included in Mario's description? List them.

3. Your friend Marsha has the hardest time remembering the names of things, even common household items. Fortunately she can usually describe them very well. What common examples of matter is she describing?

   (a) "Pass me that stuff that forms tiny colorless cubes and flows pretty well unless it's wet, in which case it sticks together. Oh yes—it also has a strong taste. The oceans are loaded with the stuff."

   (b) "Oh no—I've spilled some of that stuff that's wet and clear; it has hardly any taste, and when it's really cold it becomes solid; sometimes it falls from the sky."

   (c) "Look, up in the—oh, what's that stuff called—it's transparent and you hardly know it's there; it doesn't have any taste or smell by itself; when you run or ride your bike you can feel it; you can actually float through it if you have the right equipment."

...Well, you see, it looked like... with big blue ...very, very... wide ... with eighteen... ...and.....

Answers to
Challenge Your Thinking

1. Physical properties include: pencil is red; 10.5 cm long; is soft; will float; is made of wood, rubber, graphite (which is soft and leaves marks on paper), and metal, (which can be bent easily); and has a pink eraser that wears away easily and is 0.25 cm long. Chemical properties include: pencil will burn.

2. If necessary, explain to students that quantitative observations relate to the size, quantity, or amount of an object. The two quantitative observations made about Mario's pencil are: the pencil is 10.5 cm long; the eraser is 0.25 cm long.

3. (a) salt
   (b) water
   (c) air

Follow Up

Assessment

Have students select an object in the classroom and make a list of its useful properties. Then have them identify the properties as either physical, chemical, or biological.

Extension

Have students continue the riddle theme from Lesson 1 by writing riddles that identify only the useful properties of an object. Challenge the class to solve the riddles.

LESSON 3

Getting Started

The two card games in this lesson are designed to help students gain an understanding of the prefixes used in the metric system and the relative magnitudes of these prefixes. The game *Metric Concentration* gives students the chance to practice sequencing metric units in order of magnitude. The game *Metric Spin* allows students to practice changing one metric quantity to another.

Main Ideas

1. The metric system is based on multiples of ten.
2. The magnitudes of metric units are identified by prefixes.
3. Converting from one metric unit to another is relatively easy.

Teaching Strategies

Before students begin the lesson, ask them to name any metric units with which they are familiar. Keep track of their responses on the chalkboard. Then ask students where they have seen metric units used. *(product labels, speedometers, road signs)* If possible, bring in a product that lists a metric unit on its label to show to students. Then ask them to indicate with a show of hands how often they use metric units—never, once in a while, or often. Point out that metric units are almost always used in science.

After students have read the lesson introduction, direct their attention to the *Metric Prefixes* table. Allow time for students to review the multiple that each prefix represents. Then tell students to close their books. Name a metric prefix and call on a volunteer to identify its meaning. Continue until each student has had a chance to respond.

3 SI: The Metric System of Measurement

Imagine what the world would be like if every country used its own system of measurement! To facilitate trade and communication, most countries use the **Système International d'Unités,** the international system of metric units, or **SI.**

Three of the most familiar units in the metric system are given in the table at the right. You will use them many times throughout this book.

Obviously, these three units are not suitable for all measuring needs. The metric system expands the use of these units by using prefixes.

Quantity	Unit	Symbol
length	meter	m
volume	liter	L
mass	gram	g

Metric Prefixes

kilo	1000	k	kilogram (kg)
hecto	100	h	hectoliter (hL)
deca	10	da	decameter (dam)
—	1	—	meter (m), gram (g), liter (L)
deci	0.1	d	decigram (dg)
centi	0.01	c	centimeter (cm)
milli	0.001	m	milliliter (mL)

Not all of these prefixes are used equally often, but you should still know about them in case you encounter them. Notice that it is easy to convert from one unit to another; metric units are in multiples of 10. Here are two games that will help you to become more familiar with SI metric.

Metric Concentration

Use index cards to make a deck of 21 cards of identical size. Set aside three of them to be key cards. The three cards should be marked with the key units: meter, liter, and gram. Then make six cards based on each of the three key units. These cards will show prefixes along with the units. A sample deck has been started on the next page.

Once you have prepared all 21 cards, shuffle them well and spread them out face down on a table. One after the other, players will turn over a card for 4 or 5 seconds. If the card turned over is one of the key cards, it is set to one side to start a series. If it is not the key card, after 5 seconds it is turned back over and the play goes on to the next player.

LESSON 3 ORGANIZER

Objectives

By the end of the lesson, students should be able to:
1. Recognize that metric units are based on multiples of 10.
2. Sequence metric prefixes in order of magnitude.
3. Convert from one metric unit to another.

Process Skills

sequencing, analyzing, comparing, recognizing number relationships

New Terms

Système International d'Unités—the international system of metric units, or SI.

Key Cards

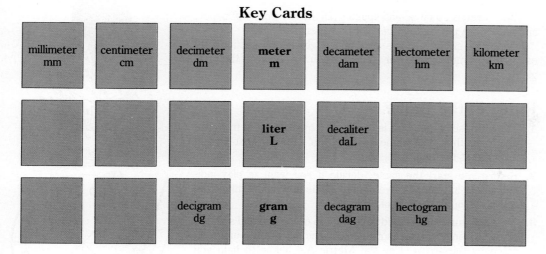

millimeter mm	centimeter cm	decimeter dm	**meter m**	decameter dam	hectometer hm	kilometer km
			liter L	decaliter daL		
		decigram dg	**gram g**	decagram dag	hectogram hg	

Once a key card has been located, players have the opportunity to start building the series for that unit. As they are picked out, the cards are placed in order on either side of the key card until all the cards have been located and placed in their proper position. The winner is the person who manages to place the most cards face up in the proper place.

Metric Spin

Again, use index cards to make a deck of 21 cards. This time include a number with each unit. Use a variety of numbers. The cards shown below are examples of cards you might use.

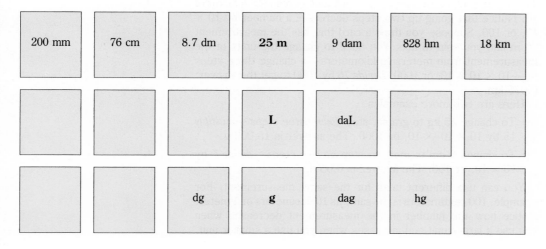

200 mm	76 cm	8.7 dm	**25 m**	9 dam	828 hm	18 km
			L	daL		
		dg	g	dag	hg	

Metric Concentration

The purpose of this game is to help students become familiar with metric prefixes and the multiples they represent. The game is well-suited for two to four players.

You may wish to make the cards ahead of time or have students make their own. Suggest to students that they review the rules carefully to be sure everyone is in agreement before play begins. Some students may wish to refine the rules or add rules of their own. Others may wish to come up with different versions of the game. Students who are having trouble remembering what the metric prefixes stand for may wish to use the deck to practice sequencing the cards on their own.

Metric Spin

The purpose of this game is to provide students with practice converting from one metric unit to another. The game is well-suited for two to four players.

You may wish to have students make the cards and spinner ahead of time, or you can make them yourself. Note that the cards shown on this page are examples. Any metric quantities may be used as long as they represent a variety of metric units. Suggest to students that they review the rules carefully to be sure everyone is in agreement before play begins. Be available to help resolve any disputes.

Materials

Metric Concentration: 21 index cards
Metric Spin: 21 index cards, stiff paper, scissors, paper fastener

Science Discovery Videodisc

Disc 2, Image and Activity Bank, 4–3

Time Required

two to three class periods

Metric Aid

You may wish to review the *Metric Aid* diagram before students play *Metric Spin.* Call on a volunteer to identify the meaning of each of the metric prefixes. Then provide students with practice by asking a metric conversion question: Ten meters is how many kilometers? *(0.01)* Provide time for students to figure out the answer. Then call on volunteers to share their results with the class. If necessary, review how to use *Metric Aid* to solve the problem.

If your students are accustomed to using decimals, you may wish to point out that each step in the diagram represents a change in the decimal point of the original number. As you move down the diagram, you move the decimal point one place to the right for each step. As you move up the diagram, you move the decimal point one place to the left for each step.

 *Follow Up*

Assessment

1. Have students measure familiar objects with a meter stick (their height, the width and length of a door, the height of a table, or the length and width of the classroom). Then ask them to convert each of the measurements to other metric units. Let students refer to *Metric Aid* if they need help.

2. Divide the class into two teams. Have a member from Team A call out a metric conversion question: How many milligrams is in 10 centigrams? *(100)* Any member from team B may respond. If the response is incorrect, another member from Team B can respond. If the response is correct, Team B asks a question and Team A responds. Continue the game until each member has had a chance to ask and respond to a question.

Then construct a circle and spinner (an arrow) from stiff paper, and fasten the pieces together with a paper fastener.

Divide the circle into a series of wedge-shaped sections. In each, write a metric prefix or an instruction, as shown in the margin.

Rules of the Game

1. The purpose of the game is to change a measurement from one unit to another. The winner is the player with the most correct answers at the end of the game.

2. Before you start the game, decide if you want to play individually or in teams of two. Then decide how many times you will go through the pile of cards.

3. To take a turn, pick a card from the top of the pile and spin the arrow. Change the measurement on the card to the unit indicated by the arrow. Use the Metric Aid below to help you make the conversion.

4. Write your answer on a piece of paper. Check your answer by discussing it with the other players.

5. Players or teams continue to take turns until all have gone through the pile the agreed number of times.

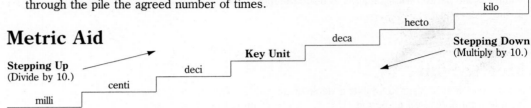

Metric Aid

Stepping Up (Divide by 10.) — milli — centi — deci — **Key Unit** — deca — hecto — kilo — **Stepping Down** (Multiply by 10.)

The metric prefixes are shown as steps that increase by a factor of 10. Notice that going up two steps decreases a number by 10×10, or 100. Suppose you draw a card that has the measurement 76 m and you spin to kilo. You need to change the units of the measurement from meters to kilometers—a change three steps *up*—$10 \times 10 \times 10$, or 1000. *Divide* 76 by 1000 to get the answer: 0.076 km.

Here are two more examples.

(a) To change 15 kg to grams, step *down* three steps—*multiply* 15 by $10 \times 10 \times 10$, or 1000. The answer is 15,000 g.

(b) To change 5 cm to meters, step *up* two steps—*divide* 5 by 10×10, or 100. The answer is 0.05 m.

You can use different units for the same measurement. For example, 100 centimeters is the same as 10 decimeters or 1 meter. Notice how the number in the measurement decreases when you use a larger unit and increases when you use a smaller unit.

Extension

Display a variety of packaged consumer items that list metric units on their labels. You may wish to collect the items yourself or ask students to bring them to class. (Note: use only empty or unopened containers.) Identify each item with a letter or number. Then beside each one, place a conversion question. For example, the question beside a 1.89-liter milk carton might be: How many milliliters is this? Have students record their answers to the questions. When they are finished, encourage them to share and discuss their responses and resolve any differences.

4 Volume

How large a furnace is needed to heat a home?

- The answer depends, in part, on how much space, or volume, there is to be heated in the house or apartment.

How much electrical energy can be produced by a dam's hydroelectric generator?

- The amount depends, in part, upon the volume of water that flows over the dam.

How many goldfish can Lynne put in her aquarium?

- One of the factors determining the answer is the volume of the aquarium; another is the volume of the goldfish.

How much weight can a hot-air balloon support?

- Again, the answer depends upon the volume of the balloon.

As you can see, each of these situations involves a common factor, volume. What is volume, then? **Volume** is the amount of space taken up by something. When Lynne puts her goldfish into the aquarium, the fish pushes a certain amount of water out of the way. The volume of water *displaced* by the fish is equal to the volume of the fish.

At times, though, people use the word *volume* to mean the space inside a hollow object, such as a bottle. Volume, in this sense, is a measure of how much a container will hold. For example, the volume of Lynne's aquarium is the amount of space inside her aquarium.

Volume is one property of all matter—gases, liquids, and solids. The next Exploration will look at this property of matter.

✹ Getting Started

In this lesson, students are introduced to volume as a property of matter, and they gain an understanding of volume by measuring it. Students learn to use a graduated cylinder to measure the volume of a liquid; make and calibrate their own graduated cylinders; and use graduated cylinders to discover that solids and gases occupy space. Through a series of cooperative-learning experiences, students collect and share data on body and hand size, and use the data to compile statistics for the entire class. The lesson concludes with students performing an activity to determine and compare lung capacity.

Main Ideas

1. Volume has two meanings: the amount of space occupied by matter and the amount of space inside a hollow object.
2. A graduated cylinder is used to measure the volume of liquids and powders.
3. The liter and milliliter are units of volume.
4. Volume is a property of all matter.

✹ Teaching Strategies

Encourage students to brainstorm a definition for volume. Keep a list of their ideas on the chalkboard and accept all responses without comment. Have them compare the definition of volume in the text with the ideas they come up with. Finally, hold up an object such as a book or pencil and ask: Does this have volume? *(yes)* How do you know? *(It occupies space.)* Does all matter have volume? *(yes)* Why? *(All matter occupies space.)*

LESSON 4 ORGANIZER

Objectives

By the end of the lesson, students should be able to:

1. Use a graduated cylinder to measure volume.
2. Identify milliliters and liters as units of volume.
3. Demonstrate that matter occupies space and therefore has volume.
4. Use data to calculate statistics.

Process Skills

measuring, calibrating, collecting data, drawing conclusions

(Organizer continues on next page)

Exploration 3

The five activities in this Exploration are ideal for small group participation. The first three activities have been designed to help students develop their measuring skills by using and making a graduated cylinder. The last two activities are designed to help students prove to themselves that solids and gases occupy space.

Using a Graduated Cylinder

Be sure that students carefully read the rules for accurately determining the volume of the water in their graduated cylinders. You may wish to have students exchange cylinders and determine the volume of water in the cylinder they receive. Have students discuss and resolve any discrepancies.

When students finish the activity, make sure that they recognize that the volume of the liquid in their graduated cylinders is measured in milliliters. Ask students what other metric unit might be used to measure the volume of a liquid or powdered solid. *(liter)*

Volume Excursions

You Will Need

- a graduated cylinder
- a 2-L milk carton
- a pill bottle
- masking tape
- a marble or pebble

What To Do

Using a Graduated Cylinder

A graduated cylinder is used to measure the volume of a liquid. In this part of the Exploration, you will practice using a graduated cylinder to measure the volume of a liquid.

First, add water to your graduated cylinder until it reaches the 25 mL mark. Are you certain you have exactly 25 mL? Here are a few rules to follow:

(a) A piece of white paper held behind the graduated cylinder makes the liquid level easier to see.

(b) Always read the volume by examining the cylinder at eye level.

(c) If the surface of a liquid is curved, use the bottom of the curvature for your reading. This curvature is called the **meniscus** of the liquid.

What is the volume of the liquid in your graduated cylinder?

(Organizer continued)

New Terms

Volume—the amount of space occupied by matter or the amount of space inside something that is hollow.
Meniscus—the curved surface of a liquid.
Displacement method—a method that measures the volume of an object by measuring the liquid it displaces in a container.
Lung capacity—the amount of air that lungs can hold.

Materials

Exploration 3: graduated cylinder, water, white paper, empty 2-L milk carton (plastic), masking tape, empty pill bottle, marble or pebble, metric ruler, beaker
Exploration 4
Activity 1: 2-L plastic container, crayon
Activity 2: 1000-mL beaker, metric measuring cup, bowl, water, crayon
Activity 3: large jar, large pan, 2 blocks of wood or bricks, rubber tubing, water

Teacher's Resource Binder

Resource Transparency 4–3

Science Discovery Videodisc

Disc 2, Image and Activity Bank, 4–4

Time Required

three to four class periods

Making a Graduated Cylinder . . .

. . . from a Milk Carton

Use your graduated cylinder to add 1000 mL of water to an empty milk carton. Now you have 1 L of water. Mark this level on the carton. To complete your homemade graduated cylinder, divide the distance from this level to the bottom of the carton into 10 equal divisions. Pour out the water, and then ask someone to add more water to your homemade graduated cylinder. Make a reading to the nearest division markings. Have someone check your results.

. . . from a Pill Bottle

Run a strip of masking tape along the length of a pill bottle (or other small bottle). Add 5 mL of water to the pill bottle and mark the level. Repeat this until the bottle is full.

What volume of water will your new graduated cylinder hold? How accurate is your pill bottle graduated cylinder? Is it accurate to the nearest 5 mL, 2 mL, or 1 mL? How can you make it more accurate?

Making a Graduated Cylinder

For best results, have students use 2-L milk cartons. When students make their 10-mL marks on the carton, suggest that they press just hard enough to make a dent. That way, they will be able to see where the marks are by looking for the dents on the inside of the carton.

The pill bottles that students use may hold different volumes of water. Encourage students to compare the volumes of their bottles. Help students recognize that their bottles are accurate to the nearest 5 mL because that is the amount they used to calibrate the bottle's scale. To make their graduated cylinders more accurate, students would have to calibrate their scale to smaller and smaller amounts.

Proving That a Solid Occupies Space

Encourage students to compare their results to discover if the solid objects they used have the same or different volumes. To extend the activity, have students make a table to show the volumes of each of the objects they used.

When students have completed the activity, have them discuss what happened when they placed an object in the graduated cylinder. *(The level of water rose in the cylinder.)* Why did this happen? *(The object occupied some of the space previously taken up by the water.)* Help students recognize that the volume of a solid that floats on water or dissolves in water could not be measured by this method.

Proving That a Gas Occupies Space

Caution students not to tip the bottle as they immerse it into the water. Help students recognize that the air in the bottle occupies space, preventing the water from rushing in and getting the paper wet. By tipping the bottle and releasing the air, an empty space is created that is then filled by the water.

Proving That a Solid Occupies Space

Fill a graduated cylinder half-full with water. Read the volume of water in the cylinder.

Place a marble, a pebble, or some other solid object in the cylinder. Slide the object in, using the technique illustrated here.

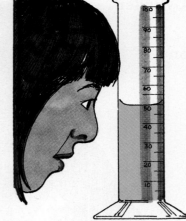

Proving That a Gas Occupies Space

Push a piece of paper to the bottom of your pill bottle graduated cylinder. Then immerse the cylinder in a beaker of water, open end first, as shown below. Why didn't the paper get wet? What must you do in order to get water to enter the cylinder?

Now read the volume of water again. What is the volume of the solid object? What kind of solid could not have its volume determined by this method?

Body Volumes

The famous football player William "The Refrigerator" Perry, who weighed about 7.5 kg when he was born, said, "I was big when I was small!" Some people are large; some people are small. Some have large hands; others have large feet. In this Exploration, you will measure your total body volume and the volume of your hands, feet, and lungs.

You Will Need

- a 2-L plastic container
- a crayon
- a 1000 mL beaker
- a graduated cylinder or measuring cup
- a bowl
- a large jar
- a large pan
- a piece of rubber tubing

What to Do
Activity 1

What Is Your Total Volume?

Here is a way to find out. Take an empty 2-L plastic container and a crayon with you the next time you take a bath. Have enough water in the tub so that you can submerge yourself up to your chin. **Caution:** *Do not submerge your head.* The water level will rise according to your volume. Use the crayon to mark the level of the water when you are completely submerged. Now get out of the tub. Of course, the level will go down.

While you are out of the tub, bring the water level back up to its previous mark. You can do this by filling the container with water and pouring it into the tub. Count how many times you empty the container into the tub, and then multiply that number by two. (Why?) This is your volume in liters.

Activity 2

How Big Is Your Hand?

You may have heard that most people have one foot that is larger than the other. Is this true of hands as well? Here is a way to find out.

You can use the same method as before. Instead of a tub, however, use a container just large enough to submerge one hand in.

Exploration 4

These two activities further develop student awareness and understanding of volume and how it can be measured. To encourage analysis and math skills, have students work collectively to present their data in a table and evaluate the results.

Activity 1

To prevent the possibility of choking, caution students not to submerge their heads while performing the activity. They should be careful not to fill the tub so high that it overflows, and they should remove the crayon mark when they are finished. Tell students to brush off excess water from their bodies before leaving the tub. Help students recognize that they must multiply the number of times they fill the container by 2 because the container holds 2, not 1, liters. Remind students to record their results to bring to class.

To extend the activity, have students discuss the variables that affect the accuracy of their results. For example, the volume of their heads will not be included, and the water on their bodies and any water splashing out of the tub will be added to their total volume. Ask students how they could make the activity more accurate. *(For example, they could estimate the volume of their heads, be careful not to splash any water out of the tub, and let as much water as possible drain off of their bodies.)*

Activity 2

Suggest to students that they may wish to try both displacement methods and then compare the results. If the results are slightly different, they may wish to calculate the average and use that as the final figure.

(Continued on next page)

(Activity 2 continued)

Discuss with students the possible reasons for obtaining different results from the two methods. Ask students to determine where experimental error could have occurred. *(For example, in the second method, some water could cling to the sides of the container and thus not be accounted for.)* If students use a measuring cup marked in cubic centimeters, point out that 1000 cm³ = 1 L.

Examining Your Data

Remind students to make accurate records of their results. As a class, calculate the statistics asked for in this section. Students should follow along by recording these statistics in their Journals.

Submerge the first hand to be measured to the first wrinkle on the wrist. Mark the level reached by the water, and then remove your hand. Because the amount of water involved is smaller, you won't use a 2-L container to bring the water level up to the mark. Instead, use a metric measuring cup or graduated cylinder. The measuring cup may be marked in either cubic centimeters or millimeters. (Note that 1 mL = 1 cm³. How many cubic centimeters are there in a liter?) Do the same thing to find the volume of your other hand.

Another way to make the same measurements is to fill the container to the top so that it would spill if anything were added. Have a bowl underneath to catch water that spills over as you dip in each hand. Pour this water into a measuring cup or graduated cylinder to determine the volume of each hand.

Both methods enable you to measure the volume of your hands by finding out the volume of water each hand displaces. For this reason, each is a type of **displacement method** for finding volume. Try both displacement methods to measure the volume of other objects as well.

Examining Your Data

If everyone in your class did the last two activities, you now have a large amount of data about hand and body sizes. Using this data, calculate the class statistics suggested below.

(a) Average volume of female bodies; average volume of male bodies

(b) Total volume of students in the class

(c) Amount of classroom air displaced by the class

(d) Number of people with a bigger right hand than left hand

(e) Average volume of the right hand; of the left hand

(f) Average volume of the male hand; of the female hand

Activity 3

Who Has the Largest Lung Capacity?

Measuring volume can be more difficult if you can't use any of the methods just discussed. One situation in which this is the case is in determining **lung capacity**—the amount of air your lungs hold. Is there any way of telling who might be best at blowing out candles on a birthday cake? Is it tall people, young people, males, or females who have the largest lung capacity? You can calculate lung capacity if you have the equipment shown below.

Get a large jar and fill it with water. Hold your hand over the mouth of the jar and turn the jar upside down in a large pan half-filled with water. Insert a rubber tube into the opening of the jar. Using only one breath, blow as much air into the tube as you can.

Compare your lung capacity with that of your classmates. Do you think exercise can increase lung capacity? Explain.

> Be sure to sterilize mouthpiece between uses.

rubber tube

Activity 3

Have students use a china marker, crayon, or piece of tape to mark the level of water in the jar after it has been turned upside down in the pan. They can then determine the amount of water displaced by measuring the distance between the mark and the new water level. **Caution**: Make sure that the mouthpiece is sterilized with rubbing alcohol after every use.

Involve students in a discussion of what happens when they blow into the tube. *(The air from their lungs displaces the water in the jar. The water is forced out, and the air takes its place.)* If several students complete the activity, suggest that they organize their results in a table and then use the table to arrive at some statistics about the lung capacities of the students in their class.

To extend the activity, suggest that groups of students do some research on asthma, a lung disease affecting about 10 million Americans. The following questions may help students get started:

• What causes asthma?
• How is asthma treated?
• How does asthma affect lung capacity?

Students might also want to do research to find out how exercise can increase lung capacity. Have students present their findings to the class.

Answers to

Are You a Volume Whiz?

(a) Correct.

(b) Incorrect. The volume is constant no matter what the physical shape.

(c) Incorrect. The amount is a fact if the volume has been measured; it is an estimate if it has not.

(d) Incorrect. The sugar will dissolve in the water. (There will be some increase in volume, but it will be very slight.)

(e) Answers will vary depending on the size of the thumb being measured.

(f) Correct. This can be demonstrated by compressing the air in a sealed syringe.

(g) Both. Some students will agree and others will disagree.

(h) Incorrect. Gases are matter and therefore, by definition, occupy space.

(i) Incorrect. A liter is exactly 1000 mL.

(j) Both. Most students will agree that shampoo is measured in milliliters.

(k) Correct. Milliliters can be used for measuring powders.

(l) Correct. 1000 mL and 1 L are the same volume.

(m) Incorrect. A milliliter of gasoline will not take you far!

✳ Follow Up

Assessment

Display several classroom items on a table (an eraser, a book, a pencil, a jar). Ask students to determine a method for finding the volume of each one. (Answers will vary. Students should display an understanding of the methods discussed so far in the unit.)

Extension

1. Challenge students to solve the following problem: In a container of sand, how much space is occupied by the air between the grains of sand? (Have students demonstrate their methods to the class. One possible method: fill a pill-bottle "graduated cylinder" with sand. Cover the bottle with a piece of plastic wrap.

Are you a Volume Whiz?

How well do you understand the concept of volume? Join two other classmates and discuss whether the following statements are correct, incorrect, or a bit of both. Keep down the volume in your discussion!

(a) No two objects can occupy the same space at the same time.

(b) A piece of modeling clay has a larger volume when it is rolled flat than when it is rolled into a ball.

(c) Saying that a marble has a volume of 8 mL is an inference.

(d) The volume of sugar can be determined by the displacement method.

(e) Your thumb has a volume of less than 10 mL.

(f) The volume of a gas can change.

(g) Fifteen milliliters of milk on your cornflakes is plenty.

(h) Gases do not occupy space.

(i) A liter is exactly 500 mL.

(j) An appropriate unit for measuring shampoo is a liter.

(k) In recipes, baking soda is measured in milliliters.

(l) A solid object with a volume of 1 L will displace 1000 mL of water.

(m) It is more appropriate to buy gasoline by the milliliter than by the liter.

Turn the bottle upside down in a container of water and remove the plastic wrap. The sand will fall to the bottom of the container and the water will rise into the "graduated cylinder." The volume of air that was in the sand can now be measured. It can be observed as a pocket of air inside the graduated cylinder.) Students may discover other solutions to the problem.

2. Set up a display of consumer items. Using a game-show format, have student teams take turns estimating the volume of each item. The team with answers closest to the actual volumes wins.

5 Mass

We buy milk and gasoline by volume. The liter is one unit for measuring volume. As you have seen, all matter has volume.

We purchase meat, sugar, and cheese by the gram (g) or kilogram (kg). These are units of mass. All matter has mass. **Mass** is the measure of the amount of matter. In Exploration 5, you will do four activities that will help you understand more about mass.

Becoming a Mass Expert

What to Do
Activity 1

Mass is measured with a balance. Examine a classroom balance.

- What does it do?
- How does it work?
- Why is it called a "balance"?

Next, form a ball that has a mass of 100 g, or 1 hectogram (1 hg). Again, check your estimate.

Finally, place 10 of the 1-hectogram masses made by your classmates together. You now have 1000 g, or 1 kilogram (1 kg).

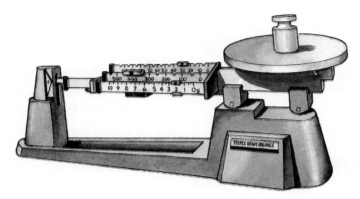

Is the mass of this object more or less than 10 g?

Activity 2

How large is a gram (g) of modeling clay? a milligram (mg)? a kilogram (kg)?

From a piece of modeling clay, make a ball that you think has a mass of 1 g. Check your estimate with the balance.

Now form a ball that you think has a mass of 10 g, or 1 decagram (1 dag). How close was your estimate?

If you could subdivide your 1-g sample of modeling clay into 1000 equal parts, each part would have a mass of 1 milligram (1 mg). Now that's small!

Choose several objects from around your classroom. Estimate the mass of each one, and then check your estimate with the balance. Record your data in a table like the one below:

Object	Estimated Mass	Actual Mass

LESSON 5 ORGANIZER

Objectives

By the end of the lesson, students should be able to:
1. Identify mass as a property of matter that can be measured.
2. Use a balance to measure mass.
3. Compare the relative size of a gram to a kilogram.
4. State a rule that identifies the relationship between the mass and the volume of a substance.

Process Skills

measuring, graphing, collecting data, predicting

New Terms

Mass—a measure of the amount of matter.

(Organizer continues on next page)

LESSON 5

✴ *Getting Started*

In this lesson, students investigate mass as a property of matter and gain experience in measuring it. Students are introduced to the units of mass (mg, g, kg) and learn to use a balance to measure it. They then compare the masses of materials with equal volumes. Finally, students are challenged to make their own featherweight balance.

Main Ideas

1. Mass is measured by using a balance.
2. Units for mass include the milligram, the gram, and the kilogram.
3. The standard for comparing masses is water: 1 mL of water has a mass of 1 g.
4. A relationship exists between the mass of a material and its volume.

✴ *Teaching Strategies*

Have students name items they would purchase by volume and items they would purchase by mass. Keep a list of their suggestions on the chalkboard under the appropriate headings.

Exploration 5
Activity 1

Display a balance in a convenient part of the classroom. Allow three or four students to work and experiment with the balance at a time. Help students recognize that a balance works by comparing unknown masses to known masses or to the force of the object upon masses built into the beams.

Answer to caption: the mass of the object is less than 10 g.
(Continues on next page)

(Exploration 5 continued)

Activity 2

Allow two or three students to work together. Encourage them to confer and agree on the mass of the clay before they place it on the balance. After students finish, ask them why they did not estimate a milligram of clay. *(The amount of the mass is too small.)* When might such a unit be important to use? *(when measuring the ingredients of medicine or other chemicals, jewels, or precious metals)*

Activity 3

Students should recognize that the only comparison of mass they could make (without using a known mass) is who has a greater mass and who has a lesser mass. Students who know their weights can become the standard against which other students can measure themselves. A log could be used as a fulcrum for the board—in see-saw fashion—to make a primitive balance.

Activity 4

If a display of completed balances is set up in the classroom, encourage students to discuss the relative effectiveness of each balance and why some designs might work better than others.

Exploration 6

Activity 1

By comparing the masses of an equal volume of different materials, students should discover that the masses of the materials are different. Students should conclude that even if different kinds of matter have equal volumes, they may have different masses.

Activity 2

After completing the data table on page 202, have students compare their values. Any differences that arise will offer an excellent opportunity to discuss errors, both avoidable and unavoidable, in measuring.

Answers to

In-Text Questions

- One liter of water has a mass of 1000 g.

(Answers continue on next page)

Activity 3

Here's some food for thought. Suppose you wish to compare your mass with that of your classmates. You have a long board. How can you use it to compare your masses? Explain how your method would work.

Activity 4

This is an activity to do at home. Examine the picture of the homemade balance. Your challenge is to make your own homemade balance. Instead of paint cans, you can use pails or similar containers. Or perhaps you can think of another type of homemade balance to make. When you are finished, have a balance display in your classroom.

Comparing Masses

You Will Need

- a balance
- a 1-L container
- 250 mL each of some of the following materials: sand, soil, cereal, grain, powdered detergent, and sawdust

What to Do
Activity 1

Comparing Volumes and Masses

If you have equal volumes of two substances (say, 250 mL of each), do you have equal masses as well? Test your prediction by placing equal volumes of some of the materials listed above in a 1-L container, one at a time. Find the mass of each with a balance. If the masses of the equal volumes are different, arrange them from smallest to largest.

Activity 2

Comparing Masses

If you had to choose a standard for comparing masses—that is, a substance whose mass you could use to compare all other masses—what would it be? The metric unit of mass is defined in terms of water. In other words, water is the standard for comparing masses. One milliliter (1 mL) of water has a mass of 1 g. By this definition, what must be the mass of 1 L of water?

Now compare the mass of 1 L of water to the masses of 1 L of at least three other materials. First, find the mass of your empty container. Then pour 250 mL of water into the container and find the mass of the water and the container. (What must you do with the mass of the container in order to find the mass of just the water?) Pour out the water and, one at a time, add 250 mL of other materials to the container. (First be sure to wipe it dry.) You might try the substances listed below, other liquids, or anything else you wish. Determine the mass of each, and then record your findings in a data table similar to this one.

Material	Volume of Material (in mL)	Mass of Material (in g)	Mass of 1 L of Material
water	250 mL	250 g	1000 g
alcohol	250 mL	?	?
detergent	250 mL	?	?

(Organizer continued)

Materials

Exploration 5: classroom balance, modeling clay, several small classroom objects, Journal
Exploration 6: classroom balance; 1-L container; 250 mL each of sand, soil, cereal, grain, powdered detergent, alcohol, and sawdust; water; paper towels; Journal
Exploration 7: large index card, straight pin, paper clips, thread, lightweight object

Teacher's Resource Binder

Resource Worksheets 4–3 and 4–4
Graphic Organizer Transparencies 4–4, 4–5, and 4–6

Science Discovery Videodisc

Disc 2, Image and Activity Bank, 4–5

Time Required

three class periods

Some Problems to Solve

1. When Kathy did Exploration 6, using her homemade balance, she found that 1 L of sawdust was balanced by 600 mL of water.

   (a) What is the mass of 1 L of sawdust (from Kathy's data)?

   (b) What would be the mass of 2 L of sawdust? 500 mL of sawdust? 100 mL of sawdust?

   (c) Suppose Kathy could find the mass of exactly 1000 mL (1 L) of the wood from which the sawdust came. Would it weigh less than 600 g, or more than 600 g? Why?

   (d) When Mike did the activity, he found that 1 L of sawdust was balanced by 828 mL of water. Did Mike make a mistake? He examined the sawdust a little more closely and found that it was somewhat different in color from the sawdust used by Kathy. Can you explain the different results?

   (e) Using your data from the activity, which has the greater mass: 1 L of sawdust or 1 L of sand? How much greater?

2. Danny had three colorless liquids to identify. He used a balance to find the mass of 200 mL of each of the liquids. By referring to the table in the margin, he was able to identify the three liquids correctly. What did Danny find?

Substance	Mass of 1 L
alcohol	810 g
ethylene glycol (antifreeze)	1100 g
glycerine	1250 g
seawater	1040 g
vegetable oil	900 g
vinegar	1010 g
water	1000 g

162 g   250 g   202 g

3. Complete the table below in your Journal. Then plot the measurement for each substance on a copy of the graph at the right. How are the patterns of points for different substances similar? How do they differ?

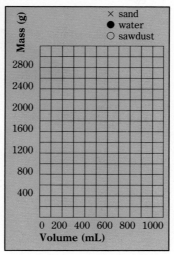

× sand
● water
○ sawdust

Volume	Mass of Sand	Mass of Water	Mass of Sawdust
1000 mL	2800 g	1000 g	700 g
500 mL	1400 g	500 g	
200 mL	560 g		
100 mL			

Answers continued

- To find the mass of just the water, subtract the mass of the container from the combined mass of the container and water.

Answers to

Some Problems to Solve

1. (a) 1 L of sawdust has a mass of 600 g. (600 mL of water has a mass of 600 g.)

   (b) 2 L of sawdust has a mass of 1200 g; 500 mL of sawdust has a mass of 300 g; 100 mL of sawdust has a mass of 60 g.

   (c) The wood would weigh more than 600 g because 1000 mL of wood would have a greater mass than 1000 mL of sawdust. The sawdust occupies a greater volume than the same mass of wood.

   (d) Mike's and Kathy's sawdust may have come from two different types of wood, such as a hardwood and a softwood, that had different masses for the same volume of wood. Mike's sawdust may have been more compact than Kathy's, thereby creating more mass for the volume.

   (e) 1 L of sand has a greater mass and, therefore, weighs more than 1 L of sawdust. The difference in weight depends upon the sand and the sawdust used.

2. To find the answer to this question, multiply the mass of liquids A, B, and C by 5 to find the mass of 1 L of each. Then compare these values to those in the table. Danny figured out that:
   - liquid A was alcohol
   - liquid B was glycerine
   - liquid C was vinegar

3. See table and graph on page S168. The lines on the graph are similar in that they all show an increase in volume. They differ in the amount of increase they show for each substance.

Exploration 7

This interesting activity can be done at home or in the classroom. Instead of paper clips, the balance could be calibrated with very small washers.

Answers to
Questions

1. To *calibrate* means to mark an instrument with reference points that correspond to a known quantity. The featherweight balance was calibrated with paper clips. When using this balance, the mass of an object will be measured in paper clips.

2. All balances are similar in that one part or side balances another part or side. With the featherweight balance, the card balances the mass of the paper clip(s). On a classroom balance, known masses will balance an object placed on a pan resting on the opposite end of the beam, or masses built into the beams respond to the force with which the object pushes down.

 ***Follow Up***

Assessment

Set up several stations where students can demonstrate that they can use and read a balance. The stations could include the following:
- Determining the mass of an object using a balance.
- Determining the mass of a specified volume of water or other liquid using a balance.
- Comparing the masses of several objects and/or liquids.

Extension

Have students make a list of all the consumer products measured in metric units that they use during the day. Have them bring their lists to class to compare. Then involve students in a discussion of whether or not they think the metric system should be used in place of the customary system. Encourage students to support their ideas with reasons.

Making a Featherweight Balance

You Will Need
- a large index card
- a pin
- paper clips
- thread

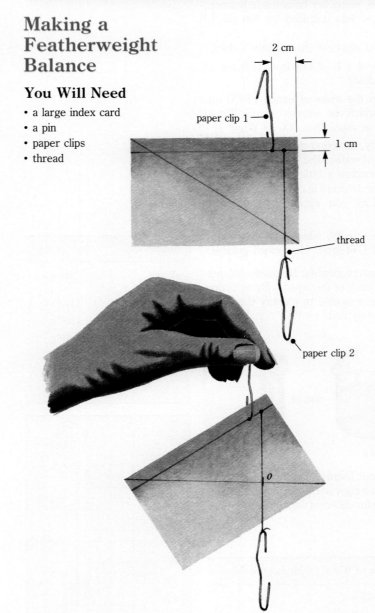

What to Do

1. Using a pin, make two holes in the index card, as shown in the diagram.

2. Make hooks out of two paper clips and attach them to the card as shown. (Paper clip 1 anchors the balance; paper clip 2 dangles.) Draw a line from one corner of the card to the opposite corner.

3. To calibrate your balance, follow these steps.
    (a) Hold on to paper clip 1.
    (b) Make a mark where the thread crosses the line. Label this mark *0*.
    (c) Add paper clips, one at a time, to paper clip 2. For each added paper clip, mark where the thread crosses the line. You now have a calibrated balance. Each division indicates the mass of one paper clip.

4. Measure the mass of a very light object by hooking it onto paper clip 2. Record your results.

Questions

1. What is meant by "calibrate"? With what did you calibrate your featherweight balance?

2. How is your featherweight balance similar to your classroom balance?

1. The table on the right shows the masses of five different volumes of glycerine. Plot these figures on a graph.

Mass	Volume
62 g	50 mL
125 g	100 mL
250 g	200 mL
500 g	400 mL
1000 g	800 mL

2. Metric Puzzle
Eva made balls of clay of different masses.
   18   g
    2   dag
    0.5 hg
   1000 mg

Arrange them from the largest mass to the smallest mass.

3. A Fable
A thirsty crow needed water and the only source available was a pitcher. But the crow could not reach the water. After much thought it started to drop pebbles, one after the other, into the pitcher. Soon the water level was high enough for the crow to take a drink. The moral of this story is, "Where force fails, patience will often succeed."

What scientific idea did the crow use in order to get water?

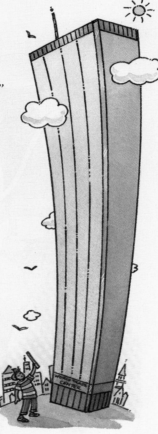

4. Would you measure the mass of an elephant in milligrams? Would you want to? Suggest the appropriate metric unit for each of the following measurements. The first one has been done for you.

Measurement	Units
(a) height of the World Trade Center	meters
(b) distance to China	
(c) width of the Mississippi River	
(d) volume of a penny	
(e) mass of an elephant	
(f) mass of a bag of potatoes	
(g) volume of an ice cube	
(h) volume of Lake Michigan	
(i) volume of a perfume bottle	
(j) mass of a fly	
(k) your height	
(l) your mass	
(m) your volume	

Answers to
Challenge Your Thinking

1. See graph below.
2. First convert all of the measurements to grams:
   18 g = 18 g
   2 dag = 20 g
   0.5 hg = 50 g
   1000 mg = 1 g
   Then it is an easy matter to arrange them from largest mass to smallest mass:
   0.5 hg > 2 dag > 18 g > 1000 mg
3. The crow is thinking scientifically by realizing that all matter has volume and that no two objects can occupy the same space at the same time.
4. **(a)** meters
   (b) kilometers
   (c) meters or kilometers
   (d) milliliters
   (e) kilograms
   (f) grams or kilograms
   (g) milliliters
   (h) kiloliters
   (i) milliliters
   (j) grams or milligrams
   (k) centimeters or meters
   (l) kilograms
   (m) liters

Primary Source
Description of change: excerpted from Aesop's Fables.

Rationale: to focus on the nature of matter.

Answer to graph, question 1

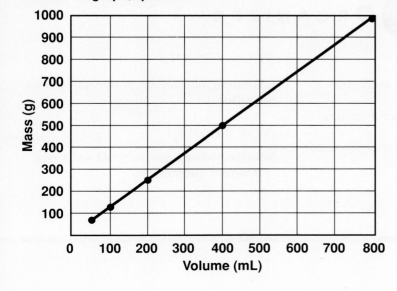

☀ Getting Started

Students have been using the terms solid, liquid, and gas since Lesson 1. In this lesson, students are given the opportunity to formulate definitions for these terms.

Once again, students meet Zed, the visitor from outer space, who poses some perplexing questions about matter. Through a series of simple activities, students attempt to explain to Zed the differences between solids, liquids, and gases.

Main Ideas

1. Matter can be classified into three states: solid, liquid, or gas.
2. Solids are rigid, cannot be noticeably compressed, and may have distinct boundaries.
3. Liquids flow, cannot be noticeably compressed, and may have a boundary with air.
4. Gases flow, can be compressed, and have no boundary with air.

☀ Teaching Strategies

While students are reading the lesson introduction, write the headings *solid*, *liquid*, and *gas* on the chalkboard. When students finish reading, ask them to suggest items for each of the categories and write their responses under the appropriate headings. Then involve students in a discussion of the differences between solids, liquids, and gases.

6 States of Matter

Water is a liquid, ice is a solid, the air you breathe is a gas. You can point to many examples of solids, liquids, and gases around you. But how would you explain solids, liquids, and gases to someone who knows nothing about them? On this and the next page, you will be the teacher and do just that.

Solid, Liquid, or Gas? (Or, Zed's Perplexing Questions)

By now Zed, whom you met in Unit 1, has been on Earth for several days. He is just getting to know something about the different kinds of materials here and wants someone to explain the difference between solids, liquids, and gases. You do your best to explain this to him in just three simple lessons. However, Zed is a good student and after thinking over your lessons carefully, he poses some difficult questions. Read each lesson and do the activity it describes. Then discuss with a classmate how you would answer each of Zed's questions.

LESSON 6 ORGANIZER

Objectives

By the end of the lesson, students should be able to:
1. Classify matter as either a solid, a liquid, or a gas.
2. Discuss the properties that characterize each state of matter.

Process Skills

observing, classifying, interpreting data, analyzing

New Terms

Interface—the boundary between two different substances.

Lesson 1

Solid or Liquid?

You put a nail in one test tube and water with food coloring in another. You explain to Zed that the nail is solid and the water is liquid. (How would you explain the difference?) Zed listens intently. "Ah," he says, "so liquids flow and take the shape of their containers, while solids don't." Then he takes a box of salt, pours it into another test tube, and says, "Salt is a liquid because it flows and takes the shape of its container, right?" Now you have a problem. What do you say to Zed to convince him that salt is not a liquid, but is a solid?

Lesson 2

Liquid or Gas?

You have two plastic syringes, one filled with water, the other with air. You show Zed how to close the bottom of each syringe. Then you try to push down on the plunger. The gas is easily *compressed*, that is, squeezed into a smaller space. But the water cannot be compressed easily. You explain that this is an important difference between liquids and gases. Gases can be compressed noticeably, but liquids cannot.

Zed has been listening very closely. He picks up a sponge nearby and squeezes it. Then he says, "This sponge is a gas because it is easily compressed." Is he right? What do you say to Zed now?

Lesson 3

Solid, Liquid, or Gas?

You have three test tubes. You put some salt in the first one, some water in the second, and a few drops of perfume in the third. Once again, you explain to Zed the differences between a solid, a liquid, and a gas. What do you tell him now?

This time, you also explain to Zed that at the sides of a solid, and at the top of a liquid, there is a boundary. This boundary is called the **interface**. For solids and liquids the interface is easy to see. It is sharp and clear. But the perfume just spreads out in the air, forming no boundary. Soon you can smell it throughout the room.

Zed thinks about what has been said. Then he takes a test tube of water and puts a drop of red food coloring in it. He watches the food coloring spread out. There is no sharp boundary between the food coloring and the water. He exclaims, "Food coloring is a gas because it spreads out, forming no boundary!" What do you say to him?

Before reading any further, make sure you have clear answers to each of Zed's three perplexing questions. Then compare your answers with Zed's conclusions in the rest of the story.

Solid, Liquid, or Gas?

Have students complete the three lessons individually or in pairs. As an alternative, have two students role-play each of the lessons for the class, one student taking the role of Zed and the other performing the activity. Involve the entire class in answering the questions.

Lesson 1: Solid or Liquid?

Help students recognize that while salt is similar to liquids in some ways, it is actually made up of many solid grains or particles. Individual grains neither flow nor take the shape of a container. To further reinforce this idea, you might point out that salt, unlike water, can be piled up. You may wish to provide students with a magnifying glass to examine a small portion of the salt.

Lesson 2: Liquid or Gas?

Students should conclude that a sponge is composed of an elastic solid with many holes in it. As the sponge is squeezed, the air is forced out of the spaces giving the impression that it can be compressed. Under ordinary conditions, however, the sponge maintains its shape and does not flow like a liquid or disperse like a gas. It is the gas inside the sponge that is dispersed.

Lesson 3: Solid, Liquid, or Gas?

Students should recognize that although the food coloring dissolves in the water, it is still a liquid. It cannot spread out beyond the liquid into which it is placed—it forms an interface with the boundaries of the liquid. A gas can spread out indefinitely.

Materials

Solid or Liquid?: 3 test tubes, nail, water, food coloring, salt, magnifying glass
Liquid or Gas?: 2 plastic syringes, water, sponge
Solid, Liquid, or Gas?: 3 test tubes, salt, water, perfume or cologne

Science Discovery Videodisc

Disc 2, Image and Activity, 4–6

Time Required

one to two class periods

Answers to

What Have You Learned?

1. See table on page S168.
2. Most students will probably identify glass, ice, and some plastics as solids that they can see through. One liquid that cannot be seen through is liquid mercury.
3. Smoke is made up of tiny pieces of carbon. Each piece is a solid—it is rigid and does not flow. However, all the pieces together act like a gas when they spread out and seem to have no boundary with air. However, smoke is not a gas but tiny particles of a solid. Unlike a gas, each particle of smoke forms a boundary with the air.
4. **(a)** Ice is rigid and flows very slowly. Water flows easily and takes the shape of its container.
   (b) Both ice and water can be clear. Both feel wet to the touch. Neither can be easily compressed.
   (c) Water has a distinct boundary with air; steam does not. Water is not easily compressed; steam can be compressed.
   (d) Both water and steam can flow.

At-Home Investigation

When doing the investigation, students should observe that the water is absorbed by the corn starch. When compressed, the mixture behaves like a solid. However, when there is no pressure on the mixture, it starts to flow (slowly) and behaves more like a liquid.

Zed goes away, after thanking you for the explanations. He knows that solids, liquids, and gases are the three states in which matter exists. He also knows that if a solid is ground into a fine powder, you may have to examine one particle to discover its rigidity.

Zed also thanks you for explaining that solids and liquids are not easily compressible, and that it was the gas in the sponge, not the solid part, that was compressed. He is intrigued by the fact that solids and liquids have an interface with air, whereas gases do not. At the same time, while gases and liquids both flow, solids do not.

Yes, Zed now understands much more about the three forms (or states) of matter—solid, liquid, and gas. Do you?

What Have You Learned?

Characteristics of States

	Has a boundary with air and cannot be noticeably compressed	Has no boundary with air and can be noticeably compressed
Apparently rigid		
Flows		

1. Copy this table into your Journal. Fill in the words "liquid," "gas," and "solid" in the table under the appropriate heading.
2. After Lesson 1, Zed might have said, "You can see through liquids but not through solids." Give him an example or two to show that this is not necessarily the case with solids, or with liquids.
3. Smoke is made of millions of tiny pieces of carbon. But, as it comes out of a chimney, smoke seems to spread out and disappear. Do you think smoke is most like a solid, a liquid, or a gas? Give reasons for your answer.
4. Water can be changed into a solid or a gas.
   (a) List some ways that ice and water differ.
   (b) List some ways that ice and water are similar.
   (c) List some ways that steam and water differ.
   (d) List some ways that steam and water are similar.

At-Home Investigation

Try this activity at home, after asking permission first.

Mix 80 mL of corn starch with 50 mL of water. Stir the mixture well. When fully mixed, it should be difficult to stir.

Now try these investigations:

1. Form a small ball of the mixture by rolling it around in your hand. What happens when you stop?
2. Pour some water on a table top. Try to cause a splash by hitting the water sharply with a ruler. Pour some of the mixture onto the table and try to make a splash.
3. How would you describe this material to Zed—as a solid or a liquid? Support your decision with observations you have made.

✸ Follow Up

Assessment

Tell students to imagine that they are explaining the differences between a solid, a liquid, and a gas to a second grader. Have them write down what they would say. Encourage students to include some examples and to be creative in their presentation.

Extension

Suggest that the students research to find out at what temperatures water changes from a liquid to a solid and from a liquid to a gas. Then have students select three other solids (almost any metal will do) and find out the same information about them. Have students report their findings in class.

7 Changes of State

In the fairy tale "Cinderella," a pumpkin and some mice were changed into a carriage and horses by means of a magic wand. In the classroom, you can bring about great changes without magic. For example, paraffin wax, a rigid, white solid, can easily be changed into a clear, runny liquid. This transformation is called a change of state. Later you will be devising experiments to find out more about changes of state—but first it will be useful to investigate the language you need to describe such changes.

The Language of Changes of State

1. How many words are used to describe changes of state? As you can see from Column 1, there is a surprising number! For each change of state in Column 1, try to find a matching description in Column 2. You may need to look up some of the terms. Record the results in your Journal.

Column 1	Column 2
A. melting	(a) Over time, mothballs disappear into the air as gas.
B. condensation	(b) After a summer rain, puddles gradually disappear.
C. freezing	(c) If air is cooled to a low enough temperature, the oxygen in the air will become a liquid.
D. evaporation	(d) A meteorite hitting the ocean could produce enough heat to rapidly turn large amounts of water into water vapor.
E. solidification	(e) Solder is a useful alloy because it changes into a liquid at lower temperatures than most metals do.
F. vaporization	(f) In making homemade ice cream, coarse rock salt and ice are mixed in a churn to create low enough temperatures to harden the cream.
G. liquefaction	(g) Last night, water vapor in the air changed into dew on the grass.
H. sublimation	(h) As lava cools, it hardens into rock.
I. boiling	(i) As the candy mixture was heated, it suddenly bubbled over.

Which changes of state are shown in these photos?

LESSON 7

✳ Getting Started

In this lesson, students are introduced to the changing states of matter. Several language activities introduce students to the vocabulary used to describe these changes. In *Exploration 8*, students investigate two changes of state—the melting and solidification of paraffin wax, and the condensation of water from air. The lesson concludes with students designing their own experiments to discover more about the changing states of matter.

Main Ideas

1. A change of state is a physical change.
2. There are three states of matter and six possible changes of state.
3. The melting point of a substance is the temperature at which a solid changes to a liquid. The melting point is also the freezing point.
4. The boiling point of a substance is the temperature at which a liquid changes to a gas.

✳ Teaching Strategies

Ask students to describe things they have seen change from one state to another. Keep track of their responses on the chalkboard. Then direct students' attention to the photographs. Challenge them to describe in their own words what change of state is happening in each one. *(Accept all reasonable responses.)*
(Answers follow on next page)

LESSON 7 ORGANIZER

Objectives

By the end of the lesson, students should be able to:
1. Use the terms relevant to changes of state in their correct context.
2. Provide examples of each change of state.
3. Define melting point, freezing point, and boiling point.
4. Explain how the dew point of a vapor (gas) can be found.

Process Skills

observing, designing experiments, analyzing, controlling variables

New Terms

Freezing Point—the temperature at which a liquid changes to a solid.
Melting point—the temperature at which a solid changes to a liquid.
Boiling Point—the temperature at which a liquid rapidly forms a vapor.
(Organizer continues on next page)

Answers to

The Language of Changes of State (on page 209)

Use this lesson as a basis to help students review and consolidate what they may already know. You might point out that several terms may be used to describe the same process.

1. **A.** melting—(e)
   B. condensation—(g)
   C. freezing—(f)
   D. evaporation—(b)
   E. solidification—(h)
   F. vaporization—(d)
   G. liquefaction—(c)
   H. sublimation—(a)
   I. boiling—(i)
2. Melting—freezing or solidification; Condensation—evaporation or vaporization; Freezing—melting; Evaporation—condensation or liquefaction; Solidification—melting; Vaporization—condensation; Sublimation—solidification, as when water vapor solidifies as frost on a window pane. A better term might be "crystallization."
3. At this point, the appropriate term would be solidification. However, you may wish to introduce the term "crystallization." If you do, be prepared for some confusion with the use of the term "crystallization" as it applies to growing a crystal from a solution. The poem, "Crystallization," at the end of this unit could help to clarify the use of the term.
4. See table on page 211.
5. Evaporation is a specific type of vaporization, in which a non-boiling liquid gradually becomes a gas.
6. After students finish, have them exchange papers and complete the one they receive.

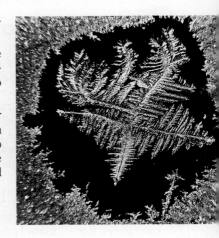

2. Many of the terms that describe changes of state are opposites. Pair up as many opposites as you can.
3. Can a gas change directly into a solid? The answer is yes. The next time you see frost forming on a window, you are observing this process. What would be an appropriate term to describe this process?
4. Complete the table. Note that some of the terms have similar or identical meanings. Use the descriptions in Column 2, from question 1, to determine the type of temperature change (up or down) that causes each change of state. Assume that the substance is water. Again, do not write in this book. Record your answers in your Journal.

Change of State	Terms	Change in Temperature
solid to liquid		
liquid to solid		
liquid to gas		
gas to liquid		
solid to gas		
gas to solid		

5. The change from liquid to gas that occurs when a puddle disappears is called *evaporation*. The process of vaporization is similar to evaporation, but not quite the same. What is the difference between them?
6. Teachers are forever making up quizzes and worksheets for their students. With a partner, make up a quiz or a worksheet of your own that involves the vocabulary of changes of state. You could design:
   - a fill-in-the-blanks test
   - a word search
   - a crossword puzzle
   - a game
   - your choice

(Organizer continued)

Dew Point—the temperature at which water vapor condenses into the liquid state to form dew.

Materials

Exploration 8
Activity 1: water, small can (100 mL), 5 g paraffin wax, thermometer that goes to 100 °C, electric kettle, oven mitt, safety goggles
Activity 2: tin can, ice cubes, water, thermometer

Teacher's Resource Binder

Resource Worksheets 4–5 and 4–6

Science Discovery Videodisc

Disc 2, Image and Activity Bank, 4–7

Time Required

three class periods

Temperature Wizardry

You will now observe many of the changes of state that you have just studied.

Activity 1

Changing Paraffin

In this activity, paraffin wax will be melted and then solidified. Work in groups.

You Will Need

- water
- a small tin can, such as a 100-mL soup can
- paraffin wax
- a laboratory thermometer that goes to at least 100 °C
- an electric kettle (No burners are used here because of the danger of fire. Paraffin burns easily.)
- an oven mitt

What to Do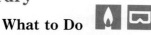

1. Boil water in the kettle.
2. Fill the can about one-quarter full of hot water.
3. Put 5 g of paraffin pieces into the can with the water.
4. Put the thermometer in the can. Thermometers are easily broken, so handle them carefully.
5. Observe the paraffin as it melts.
6. As the water and paraffin cool, take the temperature of the water and record it once every minute. Note the temperature at which the paraffin appears to solidify.

Questions

1. (a) Describe the appearance, feel, and smell of the solid paraffin.
   (b) Describe the appearance and smell of the melted paraffin.
2. At what temperature did the paraffin solidify? Compare the temperature at which your sample solidified with those obtained by other groups.
3. If the paraffin samples for different groups solidified at the same temperature, your class has discovered the **freezing point** of paraffin. This is the temperature at which paraffin changes from a liquid to a solid. The temperature at which paraffin changes from a

Exploration 8
Activity 1

This activity explores the processes of melting and freezing. Have students work in groups of three or four. Supply each group with only a small quantity of paraffin. This will reduce the mess that can result if paraffin wax is dropped. To speed up the activity, use water no hotter than 65 °C to melt the paraffin wax.

Answers to

Questions

1. (a) Answers may vary, but possible responses include: solid paraffin has a waxy appearance, is soft enough to be scratched with a fingernail, and has a greasy feel. It has little, if any, odor.
   (b) Melted paraffin is clear and has an oily odor.
2. Paraffin appears to solidify at 54 °C.
(Answers continue on next page)

Answers to Table, page 210

Change of State	Terms	Change in Temperature
solid to liquid	melting	increase
liquid to solid	freezing	decrease
liquid to gas	evaporation, vaporization, or boiling	increase
gas to liquid	condensation or liquefaction	decrease
solid to gas	sublimation or vaporization	increase
gas to solid	solidification or crystallization	decrease

Answers continued

3. **(a)** You could heat the water gradually and note the temperature at which paraffin melts. Then compare this temperature to the one obtained earlier for the freezing point.

   (b) If you place ice cubes into water, the water will eventually reach a temperature of 0 °C. Water cannot be cooled below this temperature using only ice cubes. Another test would be to place ice cubes into a beaker and allow them to partially melt. The temperature of the melted water would be 0 °C.

   (c) Possible responses include:
   - Gasoline has a freezing point far below that of water; therefore, gasoline does not freeze in the gas tanks of cars on cold days.
   - Antifreeze is used in cars partly because it lowers the freezing point of the water in the car's cooling system.
   - The melting points of the metals used to make cooking pots are high enough so that the pots will not melt when they are used.

   (d) Antifreeze is used as a coolant in car radiators. It remains liquid at temperatures well above those at which water would boil away.

Activity 2

This activity explores the process of condensation by having students observe moisture condensing out of the air. Students may work individually or in pairs. The temperature at which the water will condense will depend on the relative humidity on the day the activity is performed. The more humid it is, the higher the dew point.

Answers to

Questions

1. Dew condenses out of the air in the same way as the moisture condenses on the can. The temperature at which condensation occurs is known as the *dew point*. At the dew point, the air is saturated and can no longer hold any more moisture.

solid to a liquid is its **melting point.**

(a) The melting and freezing points of a substance are the same temperature. How would you prove this for paraffin?

(b) The freezing point of water is 0 °C. What is its melting point? How can you prove it?

(c) The melting or freezing point is an important physical property of a substance. Suggest a use for a substance where this property is an important consideration.

(d) Another important physical property of a liquid is its **boiling point.** This is the temperature at which a substance in its liquid state changes rapidly into a gas. Rapid formation of bubbles is evidence that the liquid is at its boiling point. You may have observed water, for example, at its boiling point. Antifreeze, used in automotive cooling systems, has a higher boiling point. Why is this an important property of antifreeze?

Activity 2
Making Dew

Can you get a liquid out of air? If air is cooled to a low enough temperature, or subjected to a high enough pressure, the gases in it will condense into liquids. Here are a few gases and the temperatures at which they condense.

oxygen	−183 °C
nitrogen	−196 °C
helium	−269 °C

But there is yet another liquid that you can get out of air. This one can be made to condense in your classroom. Here is how.

You Will Need

- a tin can
- ice cubes
- a thermometer

What to Do

1. Fill the can half-full with water. Add two or three ice cubes and stir continuously with your thermometer. Be careful not to break the thermometer.

2. Observe (by both looking and feeling) the sides of the can. At what temperature do you first observe moisture forming on the can?

Questions

1. The temperature at which moisture first forms on the can is called the *dew point*. Why do you think it has this name?

2. Scott was mowing the lawn one evening. Suddenly he thought, "The temperature must be at the dew point." How did he know?

3. List at least three places around your home where you have noticed water condensing. For each one, give the reason why condensation occurred.

4. You have seen water come out of the air, but how does it get into the air to begin with? What is this process called?

2. Scott noticed that dew was forming on the grass.

3. Answers may vary, but the following provides a few examples. In each case, the object on which the dew forms is cold enough to cool the surrounding air to the dew point, causing condensation to form.
   - on a mirror after a shower
   - on cold water pipes
   - on a bottle just removed from the refrigerator
   - on eyeglasses after walking indoors on a cold winter day.

4. Water can get into the air through evaporation or boiling. Evaporation is a form of vaporization, in which gaseous particles escape from the surface of a non-boiling liquid. Water evaporates from bodies of water such as oceans, seas, rivers, and lakes. Trees and other plants add large quantities of water to the air through evaporation of water from their leaves. Animals give off water vapor when they breathe, and they are cooled when perspiration absorbs body heat and then evaporates. Also, when a liquid boils, it becomes a gas and enters the surrounding air.

Still More Experiments!

One class made a list of hypotheses about changes of state. Each student then chose one hypothesis to investigate at home. Each student made a poster of his or her findings. The teacher encouraged everyone . . .

- to make the poster neat and interesting
- to include his or her
  - hypothesis
  - plan
  - results
  - conclusions
- to make both qualitative and quantitative observations
- to use graphs and data tables when possible

Test one of the following hypotheses yourself, and report to the class in a similar way. Remember, you may find that a hypothesis is *not* supported by your findings. Sometimes an experiment will prove a hypothesis to be incorrect.

Fifteen Hypotheses

1. Hot water will cool at a faster rate than cool water.
2. Hot water freezes in a shorter time than cold water.
3. Different amounts of water freeze at the same temperature.
4. The mass of an ice cube is the same as the mass of an equal volume of water.
5. Water boils at the same temperature every day.
6. The more salt that is added to water, the cooler the salt water can be made with ice cubes.
7. The lowest temperature that liquid water can be is 0 °C.
8. Water with sugar dissolved in it evaporates slower.
9. Water always evaporates at the same rate.
10. The larger the quantity of water, the higher the temperature at which the water will boil.
11. The dew point changes from day to day.
12. The longer the air conditioner is on, the lower the dew point will be in your home.
13. The rate of evaporation of water depends on the amount of surface exposed to the air.
14. The melting point of ice is the same as the freezing point of water.
15. You can make matter change state by adding heat to it.

Follow Up

Assessment

1. Divide the class into two teams. Team A describes an event when matter changes from one state to another. *(Water begins to bubble and becomes a vapor.)* Team B should name the term that is used to describe the event. *(boiling, vaporization)* If all agree that Team B's response is correct, then Team B describes an event for Team A to identify. Play continues until a predetermined number of events have been described. The team with the most correct answers wins.
2. Have students look for examples of the changing states of matter in their everyday lives. Suggest that they write a brief description of each example they find. Have students share their descriptions in class.

Extension

1. Have groups of students make a mural to illustrate the terms listed in *The Language of Changes of State.* Encourage students to be creative. For example, they may want to illustrate their murals with drawings of their own or pictures from magazines. They may enjoy writing original poetry or riddles as well.
2. Have students keep track of the dew point and the relative humidity for a week. This information can be found in newspapers or by calling a local weather service. Then have them graph both sets of data and use the graphs to show the class how relative humidity and dew point are related.

Answers to

Fifteen Hypotheses

The following hypotheses are *not* correct.

2. It takes longer for hot water to freeze because more heat has to be removed.
4. As water freezes, it expands about 10 percent, so it becomes less dense. That's why ice floats in water.
5. The atmospheric pressure changes from day to day, and from place to place. Water boils at different temperatures depending on this pressure.
9. The evaporation rate depends on the surface area, the temperature, and the relative humidity. Water evaporates faster at higher temperatures, with a larger surface area, and at lower relative humidities.
10. Unequal masses of water boil at the same temperature as long as the conditions are identical.

Getting Started

This lesson builds on students' understanding of models to introduce the particle model of matter. The particle model of matter can be used to explain the many properties of matter. The model and its implications are developed without introducing the concepts of atoms and molecules. The lesson provides students with opportunities to use the particle model of matter to explain the properties and behavior of solids, liquids, and gases.

Main Ideas

1. A model is a representation of an object or phenomenon in the real world.
2. Scientists believe that all matter is made up of particles.
3. The properties of solids, liquids, and gases can be explained by using the particle model of matter.

Teaching Strategies

Ask students to identify models with which they are familiar. Encourage students to identify scientific models, such as models of the solar system, the earth, and organs of the body, as well as the more familiar models of cars, trains, and airplanes. After several suggestions have been made, involve students in a discussion of how models are useful. Point out that in this lesson they will learn about a model for matter.

A Model of Matter

Have you ever compared the clouds overhead to cotton balls? If so, you were using a model in which the cotton balls represented the clouds. When you look at a globe, you are using another model; the globe represents the earth.

Some models are not objects, but rather ideas. Scientific models are examples of this type of model. Below you can read about Jason's observation, and how it leads to a scientific model.

Jason's Model

Jason made an important discovery just after doing the Explorations on volume. If he had not done these activities, it is doubtful that he would have made the observation at all.

In school, he measured the volume of his hand by placing his hand in a beaker of water. The water rose by an amount equal to the volume of his hand. At home, he helped his mother make pickles. First, they had to soak the cucumbers in salted water overnight. But when they added the 500 mL of salt to the water and stirred it, Jason observed that the volume of the liquid hardly increased. If matter has volume, what happened to the volume occupied by the salt?

LESSON ORGANIZER

Objectives

By the end of the lesson, students should be able to:
1. Explain why models are useful.
2. Identify why scientists use the particle model of matter to explain the behavior of matter.
3. Use the particle model of matter to explain some properties of solids, liquids, and gases.
4. Describe several models to identify the properties of different states of matter.

Process Skills

using models, inferring, interpreting poetry, writing

Scientists have a model of matter that explains this observation. If you could magnify a single drop of water until it was as large as the Empire State Building, what would you observe? Scientists think that you would observe the tiny particles making up the water, and in between the particles, empty spaces. Are you beginning to see why adding salt to water does not increase the total volume as much as expected?

In this model, all matter is made up of particles. It is known as the **particle model of matter.** The particle model is useful because it can be used to explain many of the things you observed about solids, liquids, and gases.

As you can see, a model is seldom perfect, but it does help us to understand by providing a "picture" for us to see. How can you use the particle model to picture these observations?

(a) Solids and liquids cannot be compressed noticeably, but gases can.

(b) Liquids can flow, but solids are rigid.

(c) Gases do not have an interface with air; solids and liquids do.

New Terms

Particle model of matter—a model in which all matter is shown to be made up of particles.

Materials

Pause for Thought (1): salt, test tube and stopper, water

Teacher's Resource Binder

Activity Worksheet 4–7

Science Discovery Videodisc

Disc 2, Image and Activity Bank, 4–8

Time Required

two class periods

Answers to

Pause for Thought (1)

By doing this activity, students will notice that the sum of the separate volumes of water and salt before shaking are greater than the volume of water plus salt after shaking.

Answers to

Pause for Thought (2)

• You can add water to sand without increasing its total volume.
• Sand can be poured like water.
• Sand takes the shape of its container.
• Sand interfaces with air.
• Sand can be easily separated into individual particles, while individual water particles cannot be seen with the naked eye; sand does not feel wet to the touch; sand neither freezes nor boils; sand does not evaporate.
• You can make a very small "water castle" by adding several drops of water together. But you cannot "pile" water to the degree that you can pile sand.
• Water does not feel gritty. One might infer that the particles are so small that you are unable to feel their grittiness.

Answers to

In-Text Questions

(a) In solids and liquids, the particles are very close together. In gases, the particles are farther apart and can be pushed, or squeezed, closer together.

(b) In solids, the particles are held in position and are not free to move. In liquids, the particles are free to slip and slide over each other.

(c) In solids and liquids, the particles stick together. In gases, the particles are free to roam and spread out. Therefore, no interface forms between a gas and the air.

From Sandra's Journal

The feature *From Sandra's Journal* challenges students to use their imaginations to compare the particulate nature of solids, liquids, and gases to familiar items and situations and to suggest additional models based on these comparisons.

Provide time for students to study the comparisons made by the photographs to the particulate nature of solids, liquids, and gases. After students have looked at the pictures and read the captions, ask them if they think the pictures represent good comparisons. Accept all reasonable responses. Then invite students to finish Marsha's comparison. *(Answers may vary, but a possible response might be: The bees represent the particles making up a gas. These particles, like bees, can spread out—and go their own way.)*
(Continues on next page)

From Sandra's Journal

Today we compared solids, liquids, and gases to things we are familiar with.

Tom compared a solid to the audience at a stadium, where people don't get up and roam around, but sit in one spot.

I compared a liquid to basketball players on the court. They are moving around, but staying within the boundary of the court.

Marsha compared a gas to a swarm of bees. She said . . .

What do you think Marsha's comparison was going to be? Think of other good models for a solid, a liquid, and a gas.

(From Sandra's Journal continued)
Challenge students to suggest comparisons of their own. Encourage them to support each comparison with an explanation. Some suggestions follow.
A gas is like:

- sand blowing in a sandstorm
- leaves blowing in the wind
- dust dancing in the air
- balloons floating in the sky
  A liquid is like:
- powders such as flour or corn starch
- a crowd moving through a street
- a platoon of marching soldiers
- runners in a marathon
  A solid is like:
- books arranged on shelves
- cars in a traffic jam
- a floor made of boards
- a mosaic picture made of tiles

To extend the activity, have students use their comparisons to make posters. Display the posters around the classroom or use them to make a mural.

Writing About Matter

Lead students in a discussion of what Updike is describing in each verse of the poem "January." Then have students evaluate the poem in terms of how it makes them feel, the images it creates, and the use of metaphors.

Observations about the changes of matter alluded to in the poem include:
- snow melts
- milk freezes
- water freezes
- snow forms crystals of ice on trees

Help students recognize that the poem "Crystallization" is describing a snowy winter landscape as seen early in the morning. The two changes of state alluded to in the poem are crystallization (solidification) and melting.

Be a Writer

Point out to students that they may choose any form of writing—essay, poetry, short story, letter, cartoon, and so on. Encourage them to be creative. Suggest that they include drawings to illustrate what they write. When students finish, call on volunteers to share their work with the class.

 Follow Up

Assessment

1. Choose one or more of the papers composed by students in the *Be a Writer* activity on page 218. Have students identify the various changes of state referred to in the papers. *(Answers will vary.)*
2. Set up a demonstration showing:
   - an ice cube melting in water
   - a sugar cube dissolving in water
   Have students use the particle model of matter to discuss and explain the differences between the two processes. *(Students might infer that when the sugar dissolves, particles of solid sugar mix with water particles. When the ice melts, particles of solid ice become liquid particles of water.)*

Writing About Matter

Writers often include observations in their works that are very much a part of everyday experience. In the poem "January," what everyday observation about matter and its changes does poet and novelist John Updike make?

January

The days are short
The sun a spark
Hung thin between
The dark and dark.

Fat snowy footsteps
Track the floor
Milk bottles burst
Outside the door.

The river is
A frozen place
Held still beneath
The trees of lace.

The sky is low
The wind is gray
The radiator
Purrs all day.

In the poem below, "Crystallization," what is being described? Which changes of state are observed?

Crystallization

It's early—and through the window I gaze
At castles and clouds and far away days
At enchanting places of shadow and light
This magic, crafted by the cold of the night

From water to ice, wispy tentacles spring
From eyes to mind, imagination takes wing
Making reality of these shimmering things

The sun now rises and with its cold rays
My fantasies melt for another day.

Be a Writer

Choose one of the changes of state listed on page 209 and include it in a piece of writing of your own. Or, write about yourself as a particle of matter. What would you be doing and feeling as you went through various changes of state?

Extension

1. Have students discuss the differences between the language of science and the language of poetry. Encourage them to consider such questions as:
   - Which language is better at expressing the feeling and mood of natural phenomena?
   - Which language is more precise?
   - How can the two languages be used together to explain an idea?
   - When would you use the language of poetry? the language of science?

2. Have students present a talk to the class in which they explain the particle model of matter. Their talk should describe the particulate nature of solids, liquids, and gases, and include everyday comparisons to help explain the behaviors.

Primary Source
"January" reprinted without alteration from *A Child's Calendar*, by John Updike.

Challenge Your Thinking

1. Here are the melting points of a few substances. State at what temperature the substance is a solid, a liquid, and a gas.

Substance	Melting Point	Boiling Point
hydrogen	−259 °C	253 °C
ethyl alcohol	−117 °C	78 °C
oxygen	−218 °C	−183 °C
mercury	−39 °C	357 °C
aluminum	660 °C	2467 °C
water	0 °C	100 °C

2. Bill thought that using ball bearings made a better model of water than using sand. How could this be a better model?

3. After he took a shower, Dominic's bathroom was in quite a state! In fact, he noticed many changes of state. What are three changes he may have noticed?

4. Many of the words that describe changes of state are used every day. Compare the "science meaning" with the common meaning of the following statements.

   (a) He *melted* into the crowd.
   (b) He was *boiling* mad.
   (c) *"Freeze!"* shouted the sheriff in the movie.
   (d) "I was following him and he *evaporated* into thin air."
   (e) It took a lot of thought, but suddenly the ideas *crystallized*.
   (f) "You should *solidify* your position by deciding now."
   (g) "Here is a *condensed* version of the report."

Answers to
Challenge Your Thinking

1. See table below.
2. Ball bearings may make a better model for water because you cannot pile them up as you can sand. Also, each particle is identical in size and appearance.
3. Possible responses include:
   Vaporization—steam forming rapidly
   Condensation—water condensing on the mirror, tap fixtures, etc.
   Evaporation—mirror clearing up as the room cools and humidity drops
4. See table on page S169.

Answer to Table, question 1

Substance	Solid	Liquid	Gas
hydrogen	below −259 °C	−259° to 253 °C	above 253 °C
ethyl alcohol	below −117 °C	−117° to 78 °C	above 78 °C
oxygen	below −218 °C	−218° to −183 °C	above −183 °C
mercury	below −39 °C	−39° to 357 °C	above 357 °C
aluminum	below 660 °C	660° to 2467 °C	above 2467 °C
water	below 0 °C	0° to 100 °C	above 100 °C

Summary for

The Big Ideas

Student responses will vary. The following is an ideal summary.

Matter is anything that takes up space and has mass. Everything in the world is made of matter. Matter can have many different properties: for example, texture, taste, odor, hardness, and so on. Matter is categorized by the types of properties that it has. Each type of matter has a collection of properties all its own.

Matter can undergo different types of changes. A physical change is one in which physical properties—such as color, size, or state—are altered; but the actual substance remains unchanged. For example, when sugar is placed in water and the water is stirred, the sugar seems to disappear, but in fact it has only broken up into tiny particles too small to be seen. A chemical change, on the other hand, actually alters the structure of the matter. Burning and rusting are examples of chemical changes.

Mass is the measure of the amount of matter in an object. Volume is the amount of space an object takes up. It is also the amount of space within a hollow object. Mass is measured using a balance, in units called grams. Volume can be measured in liters, using a graduated cylinder.

The metric system is based on different base units—gram, meter, and liter. These base units are paired with prefixes that are based on powers of 10. The different prefixes make it possible to make very large or very small measurements in units that make sense. For example, large objects or distances may be measured using units with a prefix corresponding to 1000 or more. Small objects or distances may be measured using a prefix corresponding to 1/1000 or less.

The Big Ideas

In your Journal, write a summary of this unit, using the following questions as a guide.

- What is matter?
- What are some properties of matter?
- How do we make use of the properties of matter?
- What types of changes may matter undergo? How is matter affected by these changes?
- What is mass? What is volume?
- How may mass and volume be measured?
- Why does the metric system use different prefixes for a given base unit?
- What is meant by "state of matter"?
- What causes matter to change states?
- How do *rigidity, boundary with air,* and *compressibility* explain solids, liquids, and gases?

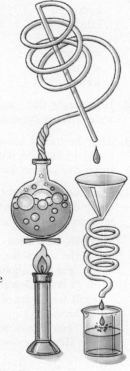

Checking Your Understanding

1. Jack collected the data below during an experiment to test the following hypothesis: The time it takes 100 mL of water to freeze decreases as the temperature of the freezer is lowered.

Temperature of Freezer (°C)	Time to Freeze (min.)
−27	14
−20	20
−13	30
−8	43
0	65

(a) Graph his data.

(b) Explain what Jack would have to do to make this a fair test.

(c) Explain what would be an appropriate conclusion to draw from this experiment.

Objects or distances close in size to the base unit need no prefix.

The three states of matter—solid, liquid, and gas—are physical properties. Solids are rigid, do not flow, and cannot be compressed. Liquids cannot be compressed either, but they do flow and take the shape of their containers. Gases expand to fill their containers and can be easily compressed.

Adding heat to matter or taking heat away causes matter to change states.

Rigidity, boundary with air, and compressibility help to explain the particle nature of solids, liquids, and gases. Particles of solids are so close together that they are rigid; particles of gas are far apart and can be compressed; the particles in solids and in liquids are close together, so they form an interface with gas.

Write a paragraph to answer each of the following.

2. On a cold morning you see "steam" rising from the surface of a pond. Does this mean that the pond is at the boiling point? What do you think is happening to cause this?

3. Matter is often defined as anything that has mass and takes up space. Is this a good definition? Why or why not?

4. Make a concept map using the following words or phrases: *matter, physical changes, chemical changes,* and *new types of matter*. One word or phrase is used twice.

Reading *Plus*

Now that you have been introduced to the properties of matter, let's take a closer look at what matter is actually made of. By reading pages S57–S72 in the *SourceBook*, you will learn about the parts of matter—atoms and molecules—and how they combine to form the natural world around you.

Updating Your Journal

Reread the paragraphs you wrote for this unit's "For Your Journal" questions. Then rewrite them to reflect what you have learned in studying this unit.

About Updating Your Journal

The following are sample ideal answers.

1. Water, ice, and steam are different phases of the same substance.
2. If a volume of water is divided in half enough times, you would expect to eventually reach a fundamental water particle, which could not be divided further.
3. All are examples of matter: they take up space, have mass, and are composed of very small particles. *(Thus, matter illustrates the theme of **Stability** in its underlying characteristics.)*
4. No, the air is invisible. Dust particles and tiny living creatures are also unseen parts of the scene.

---

1. **(a)**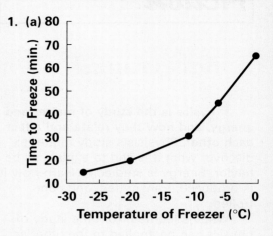

(b) All variables other than the one being tested (temperature) would have to be the same for each trial. For example, the starting temperature of the water, the container holding the water, and the concentration of solutes in the water would all have to be the same from trial to trial.

(c) The time required for water to freeze varies directly with the temperature; the lower the temperature, the shorter the time required to freeze.

2. The water releases water vapor. When this water vapor comes in contact with the cold air, it condenses and forms a cloud of tiny droplets.

3. Answers will vary, but students should note that all other common properties of matter (such as color, density, hardness, brittleness, flexibility, and so on) vary enormously for each type of matter, and may not even apply to certain examples. But all matter has mass and takes up space.

4.

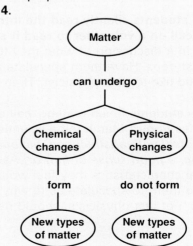

Science in Action

Background

Physics is the study of matter and energy, and how they relate and affect each other. Physicists study matter to discover what it is and to explain its behavior. Energy is studied to learn how it is produced, transmitted, and controlled.

What is learned from the study of physics can be applied to the other sciences, including chemistry, biology, medicine, astronomy, and geology. Physics also plays an important role in engineering and technology. Engineers design buildings, automobiles, spacecraft, and airplanes according to the principles of physics. The theories and principles of physics are also used to develop such modern devices as microwave ovens, compact-disc players, computers, and vacuum cleaners.

Experimental physics involves the careful design and execution of experiments, the results of which are compared to a predicted outcome. The predictions are based on the laws and theories developed by theoretical physics. Mathematics is the language and basic tool of theoretical physics.

A person who wants to become a physicist should study science and mathematics courses in high school. In college, physics students must study chemistry and higher mathematics. Most people who have careers in physics have advanced degrees.

Science in Action

Spotlight on Physics

Robert March is an experimental physicist. He teaches at a university, where he also does research. Because of his early interest in mechanical things and his ability in mathematics, his high school teachers encouraged him to study physics at a university. In order to qualify for the job he now holds, he completed a bachelor's, a master's, and finally a doctoral degree at a university—altogether about eight years of study after graduating from high school. But he has no regrets about the long period of study because he is doing work that he loves.

Q: What abilities are most important in your occupation?

Robert: I happen to be a physicist, but I think most scientists would answer this in the same way. It is most important to be able to deal with abstractions.

Q: What do you mean by abstractions?

Robert: Force is an abstraction. If I push you, that is not an abstraction. If a magnet pulls on a nail, that is not an abstraction. And yet, both are examples of force, which is an abstraction.

Another ability that a scientist must have is patience. Suppose you have spent three days doing a very complicated experiment, and the result is negative. You have tested a little hypothesis, and it is wrong. You have to say,

"Well, that hypothesis was wrong." It is even worse, and this is by far the usual case, when the test says "maybe" to your hypothesis. So then you have to design further experiments to see whether "maybe" is a yes or a no.

Another ability that is important to an experimental scientist is hand-eye coordination. You have to have some kind of mechanical skills. For example, a clumsy scientist would be spending all of the time cleaning up.

But a person can be a good theoretical physicist or theoretical chemist or theoretical biologist and not know which end of a screwdriver to pick up. These people work with ideas, using the results of other people's experiments.

Q: What personal characteristics are common to physicists?

Robert: I don't know that there are any personal characteristics which are all-embracing. Scientists are just ordinary people, and they have weaknesses and strengths like everybody else. I don't see a personal characteristic which is mandatory. However, when your three-day experiment has just gone for naught, a sense of humor comes in handy.

Some Project Ideas

The list of experiments you can do by yourself is endless. And many of these experiments may never have been done before. Who knows what you might discover. Many scientific careers began with such experiments.

A physicist readies a subatomic particle detector for an experiment.

Using the Interview

Have students silently read the introduction to the interview, or call on a volunteer to read it aloud. Then involve students in a discussion of what they think physics is and what a physicist does. Have them speculate as to whether or not they would like to be a physicist. Then have students read the interview.

When students finish reading, call on a volunteer to identify the abilities Robert March felt a scientist should have. *(an ability to deal with abstractions, patience, good hand-eye coordination, a good sense of humor)* Ask students to add any additional characteristics they feel would be important. Challenge them to speculate as to why Robert March felt all scientists, not just physicists, should have these abilities.

If some students seem to have trouble understanding what is meant by an abstraction, you may wish to use this example. Ask students to define the number *2* with words only. After several attempts have been made, point out that the number *2* is an abstract concept. You can demonstrate what *2* is, but it is very difficult to describe what is meant by the number *2.* Then challenge students to think of examples of abstract scientific ideas or concepts. *(gravity, density, mass, the particle model of matter)*

After students have finished discussing the interview, ask them to reevaluate whether or not they would like to be a physicist. Encourage them to support their opinions with reasons.

Naturally, some of the ideas below will be new to you. You have not yet studied a lot of physics. So ask your teacher what the unfamiliar words mean. Or, better still, look them up in a dictionary.

Truth in Advertising

Often a person wants to know what brand of a product works best before making a purchase. In this case, the price is also important. Sometimes advertisers' claims can be misleading. Valuable experiments can be done to test the claims of products to be stronger, more absorbent, fire-resistant, insulating, unbreakable, long-lasting, water-repellent, and so on. Take a look at advertisements in a newspaper or magazine to find claims that could be tested.

Recording the Unknown

Some simple experiments can be very important when done on unfamiliar things. Are the densities of the different kinds of rocks that are found in your area known? A record of how rocks differ in density from one location to another can be very important to a geologist who is looking for valuable mineral deposits or who wants to know more about the geological history of an area.

The recording of weather is also important. The study of the weather involves many simple physical measurements, including

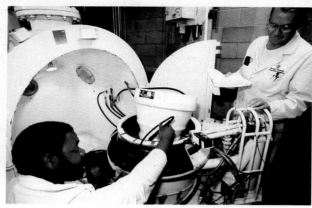

Using ultrasound to check a rocket nozzle for hidden flaws

temperature, air pressure, humidity, wind speed and direction, and the amount of sunshine and precipitation. Some of this information is valuable for predicting the weather. Records are normally kept at only a few selected locations. There is a good chance that no one has yet kept a careful record of the weather near your home or school.

For Assistance

Physicists are usually very willing to help interested young people with physics-related projects. The best place to locate a physicist is in the physics department of a university or college near you. Also, some government and private research laboratories employ physicists. Check with your teacher about these.

Physical experiments usually involve other sciences. For example, if your experiment concerns weather, you might wish to consult a meteorologist (weather scientist). Or, if it concerns rocks, you could talk about it with a geologist.

The most important and often the most difficult part of an experiment is to state the problem to be solved (or idea to be tested). The next step is to design the experiment. Your teacher can help you or can give you the name of a physics teacher to consult. Be sure to consult someone. Even the most experienced scientists have to ask the advice of other people about their experiments.

◆ **Using the Project Ideas**

Have students read *Some Project Ideas* and choose the one that interests them the most. You may wish to have students who choose the same project work together. As an alternative, give students the opportunity to plan a research project based on an idea of their own.

Ask students to design a plan for carrying out their project. For example, students who undertake the project for comparing different rock densities might consider the following questions:
• What materials would be needed?
• How should the sites from which samples are taken be chosen?
• By what method would the densities of the rocks be measured?
• How could procedural errors be avoided?
• How should the information be presented?

Explain to students that their plans should be complete enough so that a person who knows nothing about science can carry out the project using their instructions.

When students finish, have volunteers share their plans with the class and explain how they found the necessary information to complete their projects.

◆ Going Further

To help students gain a greater appreciation for what a physicist does, suggest they work in small groups to discover the answers to one or more of the following questions:
• What are the major branches of physics?
• How is physics similar and different from the other sciences?
• Who are some important physicists from the past and present? What were their major accomplishments?
• What does a superconducting "supercollider" do? Do you think that the amount of money spent on research and development in this area is justified? Explain.

Have students share their information with the class. Suggest that they use the information to make a bulletin board display entitled "What Is Physics?"

Background

The development of plastics began in the late 1860s with a competition. A prize of $10,000 was to be awarded to anyone who could find a cheap substitute for ivory billiard balls. The winner was John Wesley Hyatt, an American inventor, who made a ball from a substance he called *celluloid*. Hyatt had made his plastic by combining camphor with cellulose nitrate, a substance obtained from cotton fibers. Celluloid was quickly put to use in the manufacture of such items as knife handles, frames for eyeglasses, and photographic film. In fact, it is likely that the film industry would never have gotten started without celluloid.

During the 1920s and 1930s, advances in chemistry led to the commercial production of three new kinds of plastic—polystyrene, acrylics, and cellulose acetate. During World War II, further advances in plastics research resulted from the shortage of many kinds of raw materials. Some of the new plastics to emerge during this period included polyethylene, silicones, and epoxy.

The continued progress of space and nuclear research in the 1950s and 1960s required the development of new plastics and new uses for existing ones. During this period, plastics became increasingly important in medicine, industry, and architecture.

Plastics Everywhere

Imagine that you are an inventor. You need a material that is strong enough to stop a bullet, heat resistant enough to withstand the re-entry temperatures of a spacecraft, crack resistant—and lightweight. Would you consider plastic for the job? It might surprise you, but plastics have been used for nose cones for rockets and for automobile engine parts.

A complete list of all the uses of plastics today would be very long. How many different plastic objects can you find in your classroom? Plastics can be hard and tough, as in a football helmet. Or they can be soft enough to make nylon stockings or to fill a pillow.

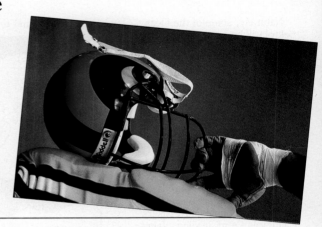

The Early Days of Plastics

Plastics are made from **resins,** which are thick substances whose colors range from clear or white to yellow or brown. The earliest plastics made in the United States were molded from resins that came directly from nature.

The first widely used plastic that was made from a synthetic, or human-made, resin was *Celluloid.* This substance was produced in 1869 by a printer in Albany, New York, as a substitute for ivory in making billiard balls. It was used for many other things, as well, including the first photographic roll film. Unfortunately, Celluloid was hard to mold. Also, it caught fire easily.

Billiard balls are made of plastic.

Building Giant Molecules

The synthetic resins from which plastic is made today are created by building giant molecules called **polymers.** (Molecules are tiny particles that make up matter.) For example, one very important synthetic resin is made by linking together individual molecules of *styrene* into long chains. The result is *poly*styrene. (The Greek word *poly* means "many.")

Discussion

Ask students to make a list of all plastic objects in the classroom. Call on a volunteer to read his or her list aloud and invite other class members to add to it. Encourage students to identify some of the properties the objects have. For example, solid, colorful, hard, heat-resistant, flexible, and so on. Help students to recognize that the many properties of plastics makes them ideal substances for many different kinds of uses.

Promote discussion in class by posing the following questions.
1. Could an oil shortage affect the production of plastics? Why or why not? *(A critical oil shortage could affect the production of plastics because synthetic resins from which plastics are made use petroleum.)*
2. What property of plastics make them both desirable and a danger to the environment? *(Students should recognize that the durability of plastics is what makes them both desirable and an environmental hazard.)*

Synthetic resins are made, for the most part, from petroleum or coal products. For example, to make the resin polystyrene, you would first need to make styrene. To do this, you would start by combining *ethylene*, a gas which comes from petroleum, and *benzene*, a strong-smelling poisonous liquid that comes from petroleum or coal. This would give you *ethylbenzene*, which can be converted to styrene by a process that removes some hydrogen from the ethylbenzene.

Finally, to get the styrene molecules to polymerize, you would add certain chemicals to the styrene and then heat and pressurize the mixture. This would cause the styrene molecules to link together as long-chain molecules of polystyrene.

A modern plastics plant

From Manufacturer to Processor

Polystyrene is a solid. The material manufacturer who produces it as just described grinds it into grain-like particles to be sold to a processor or fabricator who will make it into plastic products.

Landfill

An Enemy of the Environment?

The problem of disposing of plastics has caused concern among environmentalists. Much plastic cannot be recycled by melting it down and reusing it. Futhermore, the plastics that are available for use today cannot be biodegraded by microorganisms. The result is that we are accumulating plastic waste at an extremely rapid rate. Some plastics have been designed to be *photodegradable*—that is, to break down in sunlight. However, the problem is far from being solved.

Find Out for Yourself

The list of products made of plastic is very long and continues to grow even longer. Do some research to find out what new uses are being made of plastics in one of the areas listed below.

- Architecture
- Industry
- Medicine
- Sports

◆ Critical Thinking

To promote logical-thinking skills, you may wish to ask questions similar to the following.

1. Suppose you have a choice of using either a plastic container or a paper-product container. Which would you choose? Explain your answer. *(Answers will vary depending on the proposed use of the container. Many students will probably agree that they would choose containers made from paper products because paper is biodegradable. Some students, however, may feel that the added strength and durability of plastic containers make paper a poor substitute.)*

2. Imagine that all plastic products had to be photodegradable. What might some of the problems be? *(Students should recognize that plastic products that were photodegradable could not be stored or used in sunlight for long periods of time because they would break down.)*

◆ Going Further

1. All plastics are classified as either *thermosetting* or *thermoplastic*. Suggest that students do some research to find out what these two terms mean. Then have them make a chart to show some uses and properties of each kind of plastic and its major properties.

2. Discarded plastic containers and other objects have become a major threat to marine and aquatic wildlife. Suggest that students do some research to discover the magnitude of the problem, and how scientists are trying to solve it.

3. To emphasize how dependent our society has become on plastic products, suggest that students walk through a grocery store or a department store and make an inventory of all the items that are made in part or entirely from plastic.

 *Teaching the Unit*

 Unit Overview

In this unit, students are introduced to the chemical nature of the substances they encounter in everyday life. In the section *Chemicals and You,* students are encouraged to explore and analyze their prior knowledge of chemicals, and chemical safety is reviewed. In the section *The Name of the Game Is Change,* students observe changes in substances and relate those changes to the chemical and physical properties of matter. In the final section, *The Basics of Chemistry,* students explore elements, compounds, the periodic table, acids and bases, and combustion and corrosion. The unit concludes with students examining their opinions about chemical changes.

 Using the Themes

The unifying themes emphasized in this unit are **Patterns of Change, Scale and Structure,** and **Systems and Interactions.** The following information will help you weave these themes into your teaching plan. A focus question is provided with each theme as a discussion tool to help you tie the information in the unit together.

Patterns of Change can be used to help students organize their knowledge as they observe the chemical changes presented in the unit. In understanding these changes, students will begin to understand how science can help us predict what will happen next.

Focus question: *What happens when substances undergo a chemical change?*

After completing this unit, students should understand that certain substances, because of their chemical properties, react with other substances in predictable, uniform ways. For example, at room temperature, vinegar mixed with baking soda will always produce carbon dioxide.

Scale and Structure can be discussed by focusing on the relationship between the properties of matter and its structure. By observing matter from a chemical viewpoint, the physical characteristics, as well as the way a substance will behave in a given situation, can be understood.

Focus question: *How does chemical structure determine the physical and chemical properties of matter?*

Students should discover that the differences and similarities displayed by different substances actually reflect differences and similarities in chemical structure. For this reason, chemical structure is used to classify chemical substances.

Systems and Interactions can be developed in a discussion of the relationships between the elements listed in the periodic table. These relationships can be further explored in the reactions between acids and bases.

Focus question: *When two chemicals are combined, what are the clues that a chemical reaction has taken place?*

Students should realize that a chemical reaction has occurred when: there is a color change, gas is given off, a new substance has formed, or the change is not easily reversible.

 Using the *Science Discovery* Videodiscs

Disc 1 *Science Sleuths, Exploding Lawn Mowers* Homeowners at Printer's Green, a new housing development, experience small explosions when they mow their lawns and a slightly larger explosion when they try to smoke out a gopher. The Science Sleuths must analyze the evidence for themselves to determine the true cause of the explosions.

Disc 2 *Image and Activity Bank*
A variety of still images, short videos, and activities are available for you to use as you teach this unit. See the *Videodisc Resources* section of the **Teacher's Resource Binder** for detailed instructions.

 Using the *SciencePlus SourceBook*

Unit 5 focuses on the development of atomic models. Students learn how the structure of atoms affects chemical activity and how structure is related to the periodic properties of the elements. Finally, chemical bonding is introduced, and chemical reactions are discussed.

PLANNING CHART

SECTION AND LESSON	PG.	TIME*	PROCESS SKILLS	EXPLORATION AND ASSESSMENT	PG.	RESOURCES AND FEATURES
Unit Opener	226		observing, discussing	For Your Journal	227	Science Sleuths: *Exploding Lawn Mowers* Videodisc Activity Sheets TRB: Home Connection
CHEMICALS AND YOU	228			Challenge Your Thinking	238	TRB: Resource Worksheet 5–4
1 Chemicals in Our Lives	228	3	observing, inferring, formulating hypotheses, analyzing	Exploration 1	230	Image and Activity Bank 5–1 TRB: Resource Worksheets 5–1 and 5–2
2 Safety First!	236	1	observing, Illustrating a poster, classifying, applying knowledge			Image and Activity Bank 5–2 TRB: Resource Worksheet 5–3
THE NAME OF THE GAME IS CHANGE	239			Challenge Your Thinking	259	
3 Changes All Around	239	2	observing, comparing, interpreting data, classifying			Image and Activity Bank 5–3 TRB: Resource Worksheet 5–5 Graphic Organizer Transparency 5–1
4 Signs of Chemical Change	244	3	observing, inferring, comparing, analyzing	Exploration 2 Exploration 3	244 247	Image and Activity Bank 5–4 TRB: Resource Worksheet 5–6 Graphic Organizer Transparency 5–2
5 Classifying Changes	249	1 to 2	analyzing, summarizing, interviewing, researching			Image and Activity Bank 5–5 TRB: Resource Worksheet 5–7 Graphic Organizer Transparency 5–3
6 Chemical and Physical Properties	252	3	analyzing, investigating, summarizing, writing a report	Exploration 4	254	Image and Activity Bank 5–6 TRB: Resource Worksheet 5–8 Graphic Organizer Transparency 5–4
THE BASICS OF CHEMISTRY	260			Challenge Your Thinking	273	
7 The Nature of Chemicals	260	2	analyzing, identifying, comparing, researching			Image and Activity Bank 5–7 TRB: Resource Worksheet 5–9 Resource Transparency 5–5 Graphic Organizer Transparency 5–6
8 Acids and Bases	265	2	observing, comparing, classifying, researching	Exploration 5	266	Image and Activity Bank 5–8 Resource Transparency 5–7
9 The Nature of Burning—A Chemical Change	268	2 to 3	inferring, analyzing, comparing, investigating	Exploration 6 Exploration 7 Exploration 8	269 270 271	Image and Activity Bank 5–9 TRB: Activity Worksheets 5–10 and 5–11 Graphic Organizer Transparencies 5–8 and 5–9
10 Chemical Changes and You	272	1	analyzing, communicating, summarizing, writing			TRB: Activity Worksheet 5–12
End of Unit	274		applying, analyzing, evaluating, summarizing	Making Connections TRB: Sample Assessment Items	274	Science in Action, p. 276 Science and the Arts, p. 278 *SourceBook,* pp. S73–S98

*Time given in number of class periods.

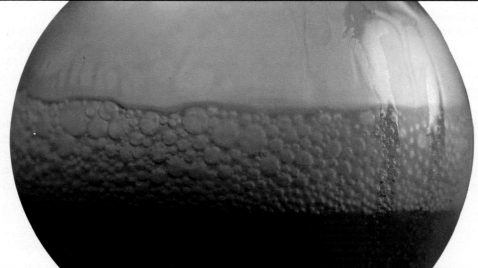

✳ *Meeting Individual Needs*

☀ Gifted Students

1. Pose one or more of the following hypothetical questions for students to think about:
   - What would the world be like if there were no chemical changes, only physical changes?
   - How would you prepare food if the chemical changes of cooking took place in the presence of light instead of heat?
   - What would society be like if all jobs involving the use of chemicals were eliminated?
   - What would the earth be like if all 91 naturally occurring elements were solids?

   Have students select one of the questions and prepare a response. Suggest that they present their ideas to the class as an oral report.

2. Ask students to imagine living without the many widely advertised household chemicals. Propose that students develop a project in which they trace how different household chemicals have been used throughout the years. Seniors in the community can serve as resource people. Have students explain what the improvements have been in the newer household cleaners. Students can then assemble the information in a booklet or video.

☀ LEP Students

1. Have students make posters or scrapbooks with examples of chemical and physical changes. They can use their own artwork or cut out magazine pictures. Have them write short labels for each poster or page describing what is taking place.

2. Have students report on chemical products from their home country. For example, food seasonings, cosmetics, household cleaners, and so on. Many countries have different laws regulating chemicals and pharmaceuticals, so students may be familiar with products that are not available in the United States.

3. At the beginning of each unit, give Spanish-speaking students a copy of the *Spanish Glossary* from the *Teacher's Resource Binder*. Also, let Spanish-speaking students listen to the *English/Spanish Audiocassettes*.

☀ At-Risk Students

This unit gives many opportunities for students to participate in making their own chemical changes. For example, *Exploration 2* presents many fun-to-do activities that demonstrate to students the clues that indicate that a chemical change has occurred. *Guess That Substance!* is a game using index cards that you can use to help students review the properties of different substances. For extra practice, have students indicate whether the properties listed are chemical or physical. Encourage your students to practice what they have learned in class by completing the at-home activities *Try This at Home,* in which students make and test their own baking powder, and *Activity 2* of *Exploration 5,* in which students make their own acid/base indicators using both red cabbage and violets.

☀ Cross-Disciplinary Focus

Creative Writing

In recent years, people from all over the world have become concerned over the effects of toxic chemicals in the environment. Toxic spills have caused the death of fish and wildlife, and some areas, such as the Love Canal, have become uninhabitable. As a result of these and other ecodisasters, some people have become frightened and have decided that all chemicals must be bad or toxic. Discuss these concerns with students. Ask them to think about what they would say to such a person. What would they tell them about chemicals? What examples and evidence could they use to support their position? Have students write a letter to a person who thinks that all chemicals are bad. Role-playing, along with a discussion of ecodisasters, will help students get started.

Art

Visual artists make use of their practical knowledge of chemicals when they create paintings, sculptures, and other art objects. Painters mix pigments to create an infinite variety of colors, and make use of the unique properties of different types of paints to create special effects such as transparency or impasto. Surfaces to be painted must often be prepared in advance with special coatings. Sculptors use a wide variety of materials including metal, stone, ceramics, and composite materials. All art materials have different physical and chemical properties that artists must manipulate in order to achieve the desired effect.

Artists must consider many questions when choosing materials. Can the material be manipulated to produce the desired image? What tools and other supplies are needed? What safety measures are necessary? Will the material last? Ask students to choose one or more subjects to depict artistically. Ask them what materials would lend themselves to the depiction of their subject and why. As an alternative, students could research how a well-known work of art was made.

Cross-Cultural Focus

Ancient Chemistry

Ancient people from all over the world learned how to manipulate a variety of chemical reactions to produce what they needed. The science of chemistry developed as technical knowledge of specific processes, such as metallurgy, began to accumulate. Artifacts from Africa indicate that iron smelting was going on in 1500 B.C. Sophisticated works in gold and silver date to an even earlier period. Meroë, the capital of the Kush culture (modern day Sudan), was a major iron-working center in 250 B.C. To smelt the iron, they built blast furnaces based on the same principles used today.

In addition to metallurgy, other complex chemistry is known to have been used by the ancient Africans. For example, a synthetic pigment known as Egyptian Blue was manufactured by a multistage chemical process around 5500 B.C. This and many other synthetic pigments have been found in prehistoric paintings.

Divide the class into groups to do group research projects on the practical chemistry used by different cultures in many parts of the ancient world. Each group could focus on a specific geographic region and topic, such as metallurgy, paints and pigments, pottery techniques, or medicine. Have each group present their findings to the class.

Chemists from Around the World

Chemistry, like all modern sciences, is an international affair. People in many countries around the world have made important contributions to modern chemistry.

Ask students to research the life and achievements of a prominent chemist. Encourage them to choose people from all parts of the world. To help them get started, you can refer them to local colleges and universities for a list of chemists and other scientists. Information gathered by students can be used to assemble a booklet or bulletin board of important chemists from around the world. If possible, invite a chemist to your classroom or take students to visit scientists' laboratories.

Resources

Bibliography for Teachers

Barber, Jacqueline. *Chemical Reactions*. Great Explorations in Math and Science (GEMS) Series, ed. by Lincoln Bergman and Kay Fairwell. Berkeley, CA: Lawrence Hall of Science, 1986.

Barber, Jacqueline. *Of Cabbages and Chemistry*. Great Explorations in Math and Science (GEMS) Series, ed. by Lincoln Bergman and Kay Fairwell. Berkeley, CA: Lawrence Hall of Science, 1990.

Chemical Education for Public Understanding Program (CEPUP), Lawrence Hall of Science. *Chemical Survey & Solutions and Pollution*. Menlo Park, CA: Addison Wesley, 1990. Includes optional kit.

Tocci, Salvatore. *Chemistry Around You: Experiments and Projects with Everyday Products*. Englewood Cliffs, NJ: Prentice Hall, 1987.

Bibliography for Students

Adair, Gene. *George Washington Carver*. New York, NY: Chelsea House, 1989.

Cobb, Vicki. *Chemically Active!: Experiments You Can Do at Home*. Philadelphia, PA: Lippincott, 1985.

Corrick, James A. *Recent Revolutions in Chemistry*. New York, NY: Watts, 1986.

Satler, Helen Roney. *Recipes for Arts and Crafts Materials*. New York, NY: Lothrop, 1987.

Woodburn, John H. *Opportunities in Chemistry Careers*. Lincolnwood, IL: VGM Career Horizons, 1987.

Films, Videotapes, Software, and Other Media

Acids, Bases, and Salts. Videotape. Coronet Film and Video 108 Wilmot Road Deerfield, IL 60015

Basic Lab Safety. Filmstrip. Encyclopedia Britannica 425 North Michigan Ave. Chicago, IL 60604

Chemistry at Work. Videodisk MECC 3490 Lexington Avenue North St. Paul, MN 55126

EasySearch: Chemical Hotline. Software. For Apple II family. MECC 3490 Lexington Avenue North St. Paul, MN 55126

Fire! Videotape. Coronet Film and Video 108 Wilmot Road Deerfield, IL 60015

Fun with Chemistry. Videotape. FocusMedia, Inc. P.O. Box 865 Garden City, NY 11530

Incredible Laboratory. Software. For Apple II family. Sunburst Comm. 39 Washington Ave. Pleasantville, NY 10570-9971

UNIT 5

Unit Focus

Begin the unit by asking students this question: What do you think of when you hear the word "chemical"? Accept all answers without comment. List the responses on the chalkboard.

Using a common classroom item such as a piece of chalk (composed of calcium carbonate), explain that all matter is made up of different chemical compounds. Other classroom examples include cellulose and lignin, which are the chemical compounds that form both wood and paper. Ink is composed of various colored chemical pigments dispersed in a chemical solvent. You may wish to include other examples.

Extend the discussion by asking students to consider how these various chemicals were formed. Explain that they will learn more about chemicals and chemical changes as they complete the activities in this unit.

About the Photograph

The photograph shows a variety of glassware used in chemical laboratory work. Volumetric flasks, an Erlenmeyer flask, a beaker, a test tube, and several reagent bottles are shown. In chemistry, special glassware is used to measure the volume of liquid samples.

For Your Journal

Write a paragraph summarizing your thoughts about each of the following:

1. What does the word "chemical" mean to you?
2. How do chemical changes affect you?
3. What happens when things burn?
4. How is burning related to processes like rusting?

✳ Using the Photograph

Have students study the photograph and compare the glassware shown. Ask: Why are there different shapes? Accept all reasonable answers. Have students study the markings visible on each piece of glassware. Explain that all laboratory glassware shown is calibrated to measure fluid volume in milliliters. Although all the glassware is calibrated, some types allow more precise measurement than do others. Generally, flasks (such as the Erlenmeyer flask shown on the right) give an approximate measure of fluid volume. However, volumetric flasks exist. A graduated cylinder can generally be used to measure fluid volumes to within ±0.5 mL. For small fluid volumes, graduated cylinders can be inaccurate. Ask students why they think this is so. (*Some fluid always sticks to the inside walls of the cylinder.*)

✳ About Your Journal

Students should answer the Journal questions to the best of their abilities.

These questions are designed to serve two functions: to help students recognize that they do indeed have prior knowledge about the topic, and to help them identify any misconceptions they may have. In the course of studying the unit, these misconceptions should be dispelled.

LESSON 1

✴ *Getting Started*

This introductory lesson encourages students to realize that chemicals play an important role in their daily lives. A series of open-ended questions and the opinion table *About Chemicals* are used to prepare the students for the activities that follow. In *Exploration 1*, students examine and observe the properties of water, salt, sugar, chalk, baking soda, and paper. Through these activities, they discover that substances are matter with predictable properties. The students are then encouraged to use what they have learned to make inferences about the chemical substances they encounter daily.

Main Ideas

1. Chemicals play an important role in the activities of daily living.
2. Chemicals are uniform substances with predictable properties.
3. Each chemical has certain properties that distinguish it from other chemicals.

✴ *Teaching Strategies*

Lesson 1 begins with a series of open-ended questions that are designed to initiate discussion of the students' prior knowledge about chemicals. The accompanying art can be used to introduce basic chemical apparatus (test tubes, flasks, mortar and pestle, Bunsen burner) and some chemical safety issues (the use of safety glasses, the washing of hands after using chemicals). The warning labels shown on the bottles of acids offer an opportunity to discuss the dangers of chemicals in the home.
(Continues on next page)

1 Chemicals in Our Lives

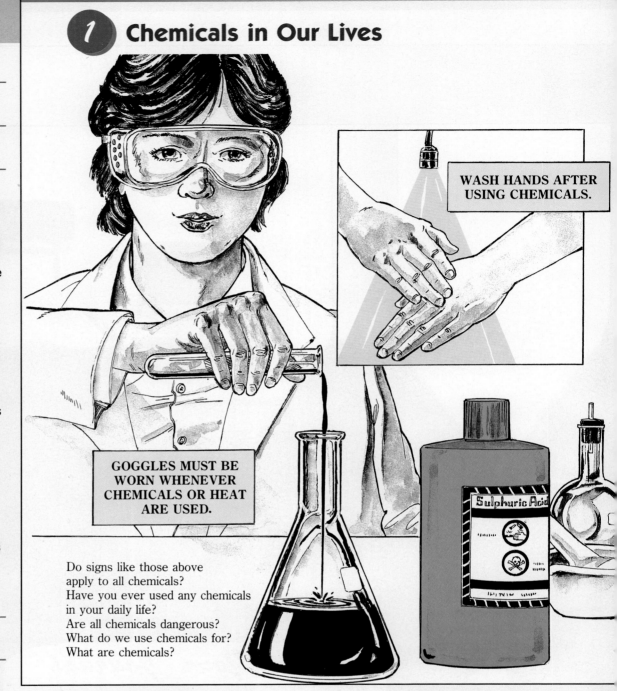

WASH HANDS AFTER USING CHEMICALS.

GOGGLES MUST BE WORN WHENEVER CHEMICALS OR HEAT ARE USED.

Sulphuric Acid

Do signs like those above apply to all chemicals?
Have you ever used any chemicals in your daily life?
Are all chemicals dangerous?
What do we use chemicals for?
What are chemicals?

LESSON 1 ORGANIZER

Objectives

By the end of the lesson, students should be able to:
1. Identify six chemicals by their specific properties.
2. Understand that they should not touch, taste, or smell chemicals unless instructed to do so by the teacher.

Process Skills

observing, inferring, hypothesizing, analyzing

New Terms

Chemical—a single substance with distinctive properties; all matter is in the form of chemicals, and a chemical always reacts the same way under any given conditions.

Are there any chemicals here?

(Teaching Strategies continued)
The opinion table offers an opportunity for students to communicate their feelings and possible misconceptions about chemicals. The table should be completed individually. Ask students to give reasons for their opinions. Then divide the class into small groups in order to encourage discussion and the sharing of ideas. The students' responses to the questions and the opinion table can be reexamined after they have completed *Exploration 1*.

These are only a few of the questions you will examine in this unit on chemical changes. But before going on, what do you and your classmates think? Some other students were asked what they thought about chemicals; you can read their opinions in the table below. Do you agree or disagree with them? Record your opinions in your Journal. If you are not sure about a statement, check the column "Uncertain." Don't write in this book.

About Chemicals	Agree	Disagree	Uncertain
"All chemicals are bad."			
"We can't live without chemicals."			
"Our house is insulated with fiberglass. Isn't that a chemical?"			
"Living things are made up of chemicals."			
"We need chemicals to keep insects under control."			
"I think chemicals are everywhere around us."			
"Chemicals cause cancer."			

Materials

Exploration 1
Activity 1: table salt, sugar, chalk, baking soda, different types of paper, distilled water, small containers
Activity 2: aluminum pie pan, vinegar, tin can lid, microscope slide, matches, clothespin, eyedropper, 25 mL of distilled water, hot plate, small containers, stirring rod, safety goggles, Journal

Teacher's Resource Binder
Resource Worksheets 5–1 and 5–2

Science Discovery Videodisc
Disc 2, Image and Activity Bank, 5–1

Time Required
three class periods

Exploration 1

In this activity, students explore the properties of various everyday chemicals.

Activity 1

Divide students into six groups of three or four students each, and provide each group with samples of the six chemicals. Put each one in a pie pan. Ask students if they can identify the chemicals from observation alone. *(probably not)* Tell them that the materials are all chemicals, and pose the question: What does examining these chemicals tell you about what the term *chemical* means? *(Each chemical has certain properties that distinguish it from other chemicals.)*

Activity 2

Set up six work stations (see guide below). Each group should complete the specified activity quickly and move to the next station. **CAUTION:** Review safety procedures regarding the use of hot plates, open flames, and matches, and remind students never to touch, taste, or smell chemicals unless instructed to do so.

Station 1—Water
* glass slide
* eyedropper
* hot plate
* distilled water

Station 2—Table Salt
* table salt
* small container
* 25 mL of distilled water
* stirring sticks

Station 3—Sugar
* sugar
* tin can lid
* clothespin (to hold the tin lid over the hot plate)
* hot plate

Station 4—Chalk
* chalk
* small container
* vinegar
* eyedropper

Station 5—Baking Soda
* baking soda
* small container
* vinegar
* eyedropper

Station 6—Cellulose
* samples of different types of paper
* matches
* aluminum pie pan

What are Chemicals?

Activity 1
You Will Need

* distilled water
* table salt
* sugar
* chalkboard chalk
* baking soda
* samples of different types of paper

What to Do

You probably recognize each of these common substances. They are all **chemicals.** Look at each chemical carefully. Feel each one. Taste each if it helps you identify it. Normally, you would not taste chemicals in the laboratory. You will do so in this Exploration only. Are you able to identify these chemicals from your observations? In Activity 2 you will investigate these same chemicals further.

> **CAUTION:** Some chemicals are dangerous to touch or taste. The ones mentioned here are not. Do not touch or taste any other laboratory materials.

Activity 2
You Will Need

* a glass slide
* a hot plate
* an eyedropper
* a tin can lid
* a clothespin
* an aluminum pie pan
* vinegar
* 25 mL of distilled water
* stirring sticks

What to Do

In the paragraphs that follow, each of the chemicals you examined in Activity 1 is described, and some activities are suggested. From your reading and your own observations, suggest at least one fact you have discovered about each chemical. In your Journal, record your results in a table like the one below.

Chemical	What I Have Discovered About This Chemical
water	
table salt	
sugar	
chalkboard chalk	
baking soda	
cellulose (paper)	

Water

This must be the most common chemical of all. You drink it for survival. You swim in it, sail on it, skate on it. It falls on the earth as rain, snow, and hail. It is one of our great natural resources.

Place a drop of distilled water on a glass slide and heat it over a hot plate. What remains on the glass slide after the water evaporates?

Table Salt

This chemical has been used by people for many thousands of years. At one time salt was so valuable in some areas that it was used for money! Throughout the world it is processed in many different ways. In some places, salt is mined. In others, salt is

Answers to

In-Text Questions

Water

If the students are using pure distilled water, there should be no residue left on the slide.

Table Salt

Pure salt is sodium chloride, NaCl, and it is the same everywhere. However, impurities may vary from place to place. When students stir the salt into the water, it dissolves. It can be recovered after the water evaporates.
(Answers continue on next page)

obtained through the evaporation of seawater. In still other parts of the world, such as northern Zambia, salt is produced from plants.

What do you think: Is the salt you use at home likely to be the same as the salt found in the home of a Zambian person?

Place a few crystals of salt in 25 mL of water and stir. What happens? Can the salt be recovered? How?

Sugar

Did you know that an average American consumes 29 kg of sugar a year? Sugar is found in all types of foods: in sweets, of course, but also in bread, fruits, and vegetables—even potatoes! Most of the sugar we use comes from sugar cane or sugar beets. It is purified by a chemical process called *refining*.

What do you think: Would the sugar obtained from sugar beets differ in any way from the sugar obtained from sugar cane?

Without tasting, how could you distinguish salt from sugar?

Place a bit of sugar on a tin can lid and heat it over a hot plate. What happens?

Chalk

"A classroom without chalk is like . . ." Finish this sentence yourself. Chalk contains limestone, which is found in many parts of the United States. Chalk is made from chemically produced calcium carbonate. This is the chemical name for limestone.

Break a piece of chalk into two pieces. Examine the powder on the surface of each piece where you broke it. Is there any difference between one piece of chalk and the other? How could you prove that chalk is chalk?

Add a dropperful of vinegar to a small piece of chalk. What happens?

Baking Soda

Without baking soda, cakes would be flat, refrigerators would be less sweet-smelling, and more stomachs would be upset. Baking soda is a very practical chemical!

Add a drop of vinegar to a small sample of baking soda. Compare your results with those of your classmates. Did everyone get the same reaction? What does this tell you about these chemicals?

Cellulose

You may not have heard of cellulose but you probably use it every day. What is it? Paper! As you know, there are many different types of paper. Some types are very light and flexible. Others are stiff and heavy by comparison.

Take three or four small (2 cm square) pieces of different types of paper—tissue paper, newspaper, and paper from a napkin, for example. One by one, place each piece in a pie tin and light it with a match. **Be Careful:** *Always use caution when handling burning materials.* How did each piece behave? Did they behave differently or more or less alike?

Answers to

Analysis Please!

1. Have one person from each group write their discoveries on the chalkboard. Ask students to compare and contrast the discoveries made by each group. Have students read the six discoveries on page 232 to see if they agree or disagree. Allow discussion to continue until a consensus is reached.

2. Students should think of several observations to support each inference. Here are a few possibilities:

Inference	Observation
(a)	Each particle of sugar turned black. Each experiment with baking soda fizzed.
(b)	Nothing remained on the slide after the water evaporated.
(c)	All baking soda is composed of the same substances and will always bubble when vinegar is added.

(Answers continue on next page)

Analysis Please!

By now you have made many observations and inferences about chemicals.

1. Compare your list of discoveries with that of another group of students. Do you agree with their statements?

2. Here are some inferences you may or may not have made. For each one of these inferences, state an observation from the experiments you just did that would support it:

   (a) One bit of a chemical is identical to any other bit of the same chemical.

   (b) Distilled water is a single chemical, not a mixture.

   (c) If my baking soda bubbles when vinegar is added to it, then everyone else's baking soda will do the same.

3. By now, you have discovered how scientists think of chemicals.

   First, a chemical is a single substance, while a mixture is made up of two or more substances. Salt water, for instance, is composed of salt and water. Each substance in the mixture can be recognized by its distinctive characteristics.

Our Discoveries

1. There is nothing else in pure water except more water.

2. Everyone's table sugar turned black when heated.

3. Table salt is table salt no matter what its source is.

4. Both chalk and baking soda fizzed with vinegar.

5. Paper always burns the same way, no matter what its color is.

6. None of the chemicals we used are mixtures.

Nothing to Sniff At!

Second, every part of a chemical or substance is like every other part. This is why you can recognize a piece of chalk whether you find it in your classroom or in the driveway.

Third, chemicals always behave or look the same under similar conditions. For instance, chalk can always be scratched with a fingernail; water always boils at 100 °C at sea level; baking soda and vinegar fizz when mixed together; and paper can always be burned. Properties or characteristics like these can help you identify a substance.

With a classmate, discuss all the ways you could distinguish the chemicals salt, sugar, chalk dust, and baking soda from one another. How many properties of each did you name?

4. Below is Jerome's description of one of the chemicals you examined. Which one is it? Has he named enough properties to positively identify the chemical?

"This chemical is a solid. It's white. If I add vinegar to it, it fizzes and bubbles. It does not dissolve in water."

Here are some of the chemicals that contribute to the aroma of coffee.

acetaldehyde	formic acid	methylamine
acetic acid	furan	methyl ethyl acetaldehyde
acetone	furfural	
acetyl methyl carbinol	furfuryl acetate	methyl ethyl acetic acid
acetyl propinonyl	furfuryl alcohol	methyl mercaptan
ammonia	furfuryl mercaptan	n-heptacosane
cresols	guaiacol	n-methylpyrrole
diacetyl	hexanoic acid	p-vinylguaiacol
diethyl ketone	hydrogen sulfide	phenol
dimethyl sulphide	hydroquinone	pyrazine
2,3-dioxyacetophenone	isovaleric acids	pyridine
esters	m-valeric acid	pyrrole
ethyl alcohol	methyl alcohol	resorcinol
eugenol		trimethylamine

There are actually many more chemicals in coffee. Imagine how many there must be in living things—in you! Just think how many chemicals you encounter each and every day!

Answers continued

3. Students were introduced to the concepts mentioned here in Unit 4, *Investigating Matter*. Some sample properties for salt, sugar, chalk dust, and baking soda are:
   Taste: salt—salty; sugar—sweet; chalk dust—no taste; baking soda—bitter.
   Smell: Answers will vary.
   State: All are solids.
   Solubility in water: salt—soluble; sugar—soluble; chalk dust—insoluble; baking soda—fairly soluble.
   Reaction with acid: salt—no reaction; sugar—no reaction; chalk dust—bubbles; baking soda—bubbles.
4. The solid could be white chalk or baking soda. Both bubble when vinegar is added. Baking soda is soluble in water; chalk is not. Therefore, the substance is baking soda. The feel of the solid or the rate of its reaction with vinegar could also be observed.

Nothing to Sniff At!

This list suggests to students the vast range of chemicals in an everyday beverage such as coffee. Students will probably be amazed at the strange-sounding names and the quantity of chemicals. The exercise on the following page develops this topic further.

Chemical Close Encounters

Have students read the stories of Sasha and Harold and, through discussion, identify some "everyday" chemicals. Sasha's chemicals include the oxygen she breathes, and the ingredients in: toothpaste with fluoride, soap and water, deodorant, eye shadow, lipstick, nylon tights, rayon-cotton blouse, wool skirt, orange juice, cereal, butter, and toast. Harold's chemicals include the ingredients in: contact lenses, cleaning solution, distilled water, mentholated shaving cream, after-shave lotion, polyester sweater and slacks, cereal with milk, and a blueberry muffin. Sasha and Harold are, of course, made of chemicals.

Chemical Close Encounters

Like most people, Sasha and Harold are not aware of the different chemicals they encounter each day. Even in the first two hours of their day, they use many chemicals or products containing chemicals.

Here is a description of their morning activities. Make a list of the chemicals or items that are made up of chemicals that they encounter.

Sasha

Taking a deep breath, Sasha gets up, goes into the bathroom, brushes her teeth with toothpaste containing fluoride, and washes her face with soap. She then applies deodorant, eyeshadow, and lipstick. She decides to wear nylon tights to work today, along with a rayon-cotton blouse and wool skirt. Finally comes a quick breakfast of orange juice, cereal, and buttered toast. Then off to work.

Harold

Harold throws back the sheet and struggles out of bed. The first thing he does is take his contact lenses from their cleaning solution. Then he washes them in distilled water and puts them in his eyes. Now he can see! Next, Harold shaves, using mentholated shaving cream, and then he splashes himself with after-shave lotion. He pulls on a polyester sweater and slacks.

For breakfast Harold has cereal with milk and a blueberry muffin. Finally he heads off for work.

Just like Sasha and Harold, we all eat, drink, breathe, and use chemicals all the time. Many chemicals occur naturally in the world—water and the gases in the air, for example. Other chemicals, such as nylon, plastics, and the dyes in lipstick, are made by industrial methods.

Tracking Down Chemicals

What kind of chemicals do you encounter in your day? One way to find out is to read the labels on the items you use. When you do this, you may be surprised to find more than corn in your cornflakes. Keep track of the chemicals you encounter in one day. Record them in your Journal. Afterward, make a collage of labels to display some of these chemicals.

Now write a brief story about your day. Include as many chemicals as you can. Try to think of chemicals not mentioned in the account of Sasha's and Harold's morning.

Tracking Down Chemicals

Have students make a list of the chemicals that they encounter in their day as suggested on page 235. Ask each student to bring in a label from an item they use and create a class collage of "Everyday Chemicals." Each student should write a brief story of his or her day. You may wish to have students read their stories to the class. Make a composite list on the chalkboard of all the chemicals that are mentioned.

✳ Follow Up

Assessment

1. Make a chart with two headings: "Chemicals" and "Uses." In the first column, list 10 chemicals you use in your everyday life. Next to each chemical, describe its uses. *(Answers will vary.)*
2. Cassie and Jeff were given four white substances to identify. They examined them carefully and performed three tests on them. Describe the tests they might have performed. Include the materials required, the necessary safety considerations, and the probable results of each test. *(Students should draw on techniques learned in this lesson.)*

Extension

1. Have students expand on the activity "Tracking Down Chemicals" by writing a mystery about tracking down a "villain" chemical. The story should contain clues about the properties of the chemical. Have students share their mysteries with the class so that all can participate in the solutions.
2. Invite a guest speaker who has a career related to chemistry to visit the classroom to discuss his or her job responsibilities.

LESSON 2

✳ Getting Started

This lesson helps students to develop a code of safety behavior in situations where chemicals are used.

Main Idea

When dealing with chemicals, safety is essential in the laboratory, the home, and the classroom.

✳ Teaching Strategies

Discuss the safety precautions illustrated in the pictures on pages 236 and 237. They include:
- Never inhaling chemicals directly
- Pouring carefully to avoid spilling
- Wearing gloves to wipe up spills
- Using care with an open flame
- Pulling long hair back
- Using a striker instead of matches
  Point out to students that all pictured are wearing safety glasses, a necessary precaution.

Safety Tips

This exercise helps students to formulate rules for the science laboratory. Display their posters around the classroom and have students add to them as more safety techniques are discussed in this unit.

② Safety First!

There is no need to put on your goggles when you add *sodium chloride* to popcorn, or when your teacher writes on the board with a piece of *calcium carbonate,* and certainly not when you read your *cellulose* newspaper or magazine. Washing your hands is not necessary after adding *sucrose* to your cereal or after taking some *sodium bicarbonate* for an upset stomach.

Can you replace these chemical names with common names? For instance, *sodium chloride* is salt.

However, safety is important when you are handling many substances in the home, the classroom, the lab, and at work. Each picture on these two pages illustrates one or more safety rules. Can you spot what each person is doing correctly?

Safety Tips

In groups of two or three, discuss the safety rules concerning chemicals and other materials that should apply to your classroom. Design a chemical-safety poster. Here are some suggestions for the poster:

- Draw cartoons.
- Make diagrams.
- Take photographs.
- Write poems.
- Describe humorous situations.
- List humorous statements.

LESSON ② ORGANIZER

Objectives

By the end of the lesson, students should be able to:
1. Identify and explain the warning symbols used on household chemicals.
2. State the chemical and common names for a number of substances.

Process Skills

observing, drawing a poster, classifying, applying knowledge

New Terms

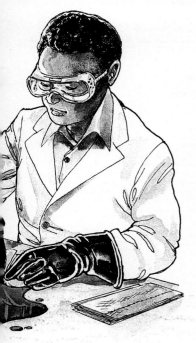

Here is a limerick that was part of one group's poster.

There once was a girl named Di
Who, in spite of the warnings, drank lye.
Her teacher said NEVER
to taste—not EVER!
She's now in that Great Lab in the sky.

Warnings!

Detergents are poisonous. Oven cleaners are corrosive (will burn your skin). Drain cleaners contain lye, which is also corrosive. Bleaches give off a poisonous, foul-smelling gas—chlorine. Where are these chemicals stored in your home? What kind of recommendations can you make about storing and using them? What other materials around your home are potentially dangerous?

Below are some of the warning signs used on dangerous household chemicals. They are also used throughout this book. Do you know what they mean? What warning signs are on the products in your home?

| WEAR GOGGLES | WEAR APRON | POISON | FLAMMABLE | CORROSIVE |

A Project

Many chemicals have both a chemical name and a common name. The introduction to this section used the chemical names for some of the chemicals you examined earlier in this unit. Can you replace the chemical names with the common names? As you proceed through the unit, you will encounter more common and chemical names for substances. Keep a list in your Journal of both names for all the substances you encounter. Also, list a use for each chemical. You can start with water.

Common Name	Chemical Name	Use
water	dihydrogen oxide	Plants and animals need water.
table salt		

Materials

Safety Tips: poster board, markers
A Project: Journal

Teacher's Resource Binder

Resource Worksheet 5–3

Science Discovery Videodisc

Disc 2, Image and Activity Bank, 5–2

Time Required

one class period

Warnings!

Have students read and discuss the questions on page 237. Chemicals in the home will probably be stored up high, out of the reach of small children. Some recommendations might be: to keep the chemicals in locked cabinets and to wash your hands after any contact with chemicals.

Ask students to make a list in their Journals of materials around their homes that are potentially dangerous. They should identify the warning signs that are found on these products.

Answers to

A Project

Common Name/Chemical Name/Use
1. water/dihydrogen oxide/plants and animals need water
2. table salt/sodium chloride/daily requirement of living things
3. chalk/calcium carbonate/writing utensil
4. paper/cellulose/all paper products
5. sugar/sucrose/in many foods as a sweetener
6. baking soda/sodium bicarbonate/antacid, cooking, cleaning

Assessment

Present students with the following situation: You have been appointed school safety officer. Outline six safety rules for the science laboratory. Explain why you included each rule.

Extension

Ask students to make a list of 10 everyday items. Then have them go to the library to research the chemical names for these items.

Answers to

Challenge Your Thinking

1. *sucrose—sugar; acetylsalicylic acid—aspirin; ammonium hydroxide—ammonia; polyhexanedioic acid diaminohexamide—nylon; polytetrafluoroethylene—Teflon*

2. *Carbon dioxide in the air dissolves in water to form a weak acid that reacts with the limestone by putting it into solution. Limestone caves are formed in this manner. In Exploration 1, the vinegar, a dilute solution of a weak acid, reacts with chalk to put the chalk into solution, and carbon dioxide is released.*

1. As you know, many common chemicals have a scientific name as well. Study the following table. Using the description and the scientific name, try to guess the common name of the chemical being described. Remember, don't write in this book.

Description	Scientific name	Common names
Colorless solid; used as a flavoring for food; rich in calories; extracted from plants.	sucrose	
White solid, easily powdered; common remedy for headaches.	acetylsalicylic acid	
Used as a cleaning agent, produces a strong-smelling gas, dissolves fats and oils.	ammonium hydroxide	
Light, flexible material; can be drawn into fibers; takes dyes well.	polyhexanedioic acid diaminohexamide	
Dark-colored material; forms a smooth surface; few materials stick to it.	polytetrafluoro-ethylene	

2. Limestone is found in many parts of the United States. Where you find limestone you also generally find caves. The limestone hills of Tennessee and Missouri are riddled with caves and sinkholes. This type of terrain is called a *karst landscape.* How do you think it was formed? (*Hint:* Review the experiment you performed on chalk in Exploration 1, Activity 2.)

3 Changes All Around

All Is Change

There is an old saying, "The more things change, the more things stay the same." Does this make sense to you? Does everything change, or are there things that do not change?

In small groups, examine some changes you may be familiar with. Choose one of the following topics, and list as many changes as you can.

- Kitchen changes
- Barbecue changes
- Backyard changes
- People changes

Here is a start to "kitchen changes":

1. water boiling   3. ....
2. plate breaking   4. ....

Now that you've finished, do you have things to add to your first thoughts about the saying that began this section?

L E S S O N **3**

✷ Getting Started

This lesson makes students aware of the number of chemical changes that occur around them and helps them to classify these changes as either chemical or physical. A list of clues is provided so that students will know how to recognize chemical changes.

Main Ideas

1. Changes are a natural part of our lives.
2. Changes can be classified as either chemical or physical.
3. Clues that suggest a chemical change are: color change, bubbles (gas) given off, heat or light given off, and difficulty in reversing the change.
4. Physical changes never cause the formation of a new substance. Chemical changes always form a new substance.

✷ Teaching Strategies

All Is Change

After students read page 239, refer them to the illustration. Ask them to name the changes that are shown. *(water boiling, eggs cooking, toast burning, and a plate breaking)* Divide the class into small groups and give each group a topic. Four topics are listed in the text. Other suggestions might be: weather changes and classroom changes. Gather groups back together to discuss their lists. During the discussion, challenge each group to explain why each of their examples is considered a change.

L E S S O N O R G A N I Z E R

Objectives

By the end of the lesson, students should be able to:
1. Distinguish between chemical and physical changes.
2. Identify situations in which a chemical change has occurred.

Process Skills

observing, comparing, interpreting data, classifying

New Terms

Chemical change—a change in which a new chemical is formed; burning is an example.

Physical change—a change in which no new chemical is formed; breaking, dissolving, boiling, evaporating, and freezing are examples.

(Organizer continues on next page)

Physical and Chemical Changes Revisited

Through discussion and analysis, this exercise helps students to classify changes as either physical or chemical.

Ask students to record the changes they observed in *Exploration 1* in a table in their Journals. Have students then read the conversation between Mr. Alexander and his students, and decide whether they agree with the decisions made by that class. Then divide students into small groups and have each group think of its own questions and answers to complete the table. Students should regroup and share their questions and answers.

Physical and Chemical Changes Revisited

In Unit 4, "Investigating Matter," you were introduced to chemical and physical changes. We will now explore these changes in more detail. In Exploration 1, you looked at six substances. You also observed a change involving each one. Review what you did in the Exploration, and record the change you saw for each substance in a data table in your Journal.

In the changes that you listed in your table, were new chemicals formed? How do you know whether a new chemical was formed during a change? These questions puzzled Mr. Calderon's class.

The Class's Table of Changes

	water evaporating	salt dissolving	sugar turning black when heated	baking soda fizzing when vinegar added	chalk breaking	paper burning when heated
1 Has a new chemical been formed?						
2						
3						
4						
5						
6						
7						

Mr. Calderon has just given them the table shown above, which lists the changes they noticed in Exploration 1. Copy the table into your Journal, and follow along with the class.

Mr. Calderon:
In row 1, I have written the question, "Is a new chemical formed?" Let's put a "√" under each change when you believe a new chemical is formed as a result of the change. An "X" will mean no new substance or chemical is formed. Jorge?

Jorge:
I saw black smoke when we burned the paper. I think a new chemical must have been formed.

(Organizer continued)

Materials

All Is Change: Journal
Physical and Chemical Changes Revisited: Journal
Physical and Chemical Words: Journal

Teacher's Resource Binder

Resource Worksheet 5–5
Graphic Organizer Transparency 5–1

Science Discovery Videodisc

Disc 2, Image and Activity Bank, 5–3

Time Required

two class periods

Sue:
We saw bubbles when the vinegar was added to baking soda. Would that mean we should put a check under baking soda?

Hal:
The burnt sugar smelled like bad cooking. Something new was certainly formed in that change.

Later, after much discussion about whether a new substance is formed when water evaporates, they agreed to finish the table in this way. Do you agree with their new table?

The Class's New Table of Changes

	water evaporating	salt dissolving	sugar turning black when heated	baking soda fizzing when vinegar added	chalk breaking	paper burning when heated
1 Has a new chemical been formed?	✗	✗	✓	✓	✗	✓
2						
3						
4						
5						
6						
7						

Mr. Calderon:
On lines 2–7 in your table, I would like you to write your own questions. Each question must have a yes or no answer. Each question can be used only once. Hal, what will your next question be?

Hal:
Was there a smell like bad cooking?

Mr. Calderon:
Fine. Now, working in your groups, decide on your questions and fill each square in the table with a "√" or an "X." We will examine the results in the next class.

Copy the table into your Journal and finish it yourself, using your own questions.

Finish the table you copied into your Journal earlier.

The Class's New Table of Changes

The new table correctly identifies chemical changes with a check and physical changes with a cross. Remind students to copy tables into their Journals and not to write in their books. Some sample questions are given in *Analysis Please!* on the following page.

Answers to

Analysis Please!

Discuss the questions in the text so that students can analyze the tables made in the previous exercise.

1. Students can compare their list to the list in the text.

2. From Joy's list the three most valuable questions are:
   - Was there a color change?
   - Were any bubbles formed?
   - Was the change easily reversible?

3. Answers may vary, but possible responses include:

   (a)
   - The smell of a new gas was detected.
   - If a chemical change did not occur, you can still detect the original substances.
   - New and different properties were observed.

   (b) Joy was right. The same clues cannot be used each time to identify chemical changes because the change depends on the properties of the chemicals involved.

   (c) Yes, heat can cause a physical change. When an ice cube is heated, it melts. This is a physical change.

   (d) Melting, freezing, and dissolving are examples of physical changes in which a substance seems to disappear or a new substance seems to appear.

   (e) No, not all physical changes are easily reversible. For example, sawdust cannot easily be changed back into lumber.

   (f) Answers will vary.

Analysis Please!

1. Mr. Calderon's class made a list of questions. Here are some of the questions Joy copied into her Journal. Add them to your table. Did you have different questions?

   - Was there a color change?
   - Was there any smell?
   - Was the change easily reversible?
   - Was heat given off?
   - Was light given off?
   - Was heat required for the change to happen?
   - Can the original chemical still be used?
   - Were any bubbles formed?

2. The answers to some of your questions may provide valuable clues as to whether a new chemical formed. What are the most important questions your class can ask?

3. Read this excerpt from Joy's Journal notes, then answer the questions that follow.

   Today we studied changes. We divided them into two types. In one type, a new chemical was formed. This type of change is called a **chemical change.** *Burning is an example of a chemical change.*

   If no new chemical is formed, then the change is a **physical change.** *Breaking, dissolving, boiling, evaporating, and freezing are all physical changes.*

   Our class concluded that there are some clues that show that a chemical change has occured:
   - *A new color appears.*
   - *Heat or light is given off.*
   - *Bubbles form.*
   - *The change is not easily reversible.*

   The only problem is that you can't use the same clues for each chemical change. Life certainly is complicated!

   (a) Have you and your classmates identified other ways of detecting chemical changes? What are they?

   (b) Was Joy right? Why can't you use the same clues each time to identify a chemical change?

   (c) Are some characteristics present in a chemical change that can also be present in a physical change? For example, heat often causes a chemical change. Can it also cause a physical change? If it can, give an example.

(d) In a chemical change, a chemical may "disappear" or a new one may form. Can you think of a physical change where a chemical seems to disappear, or where a new substance seems to form?

(e) Butter melts, but can become solid again. Water evaporates, but also condenses. These are both physical changes. Are all physical changes easily reversible?

(f) At the start of this lesson, you listed a number of changes. Now, underline all the changes you think are chemical changes.

Physical and Chemical Words

Kelly, who was also in Mr. Calderon's class, had a very good idea. She decided to make two vocabulary lists, one for each of the two types of changes, physical and chemical. Here are Kelly's lists. Copy them into your Journal, and give an example of a change associated with each word. But think hard—be sure you have the right type of change.

Can you add any words and examples to the two lists?

Physical Words

Word	Example
grinding	
breaking	
eroding	
evaporating	
melting	
....	
....	
....	
....	
....	

Chemical Words

Word	Example
burning	
rotting	
rusting	
....	
....	

Now look up the word *state* in the dictionary. It certainly has many meanings! The following sentence uses the word *state* in a scientific way.

"Water exists in three states: in the solid state, as ice; in the liquid state, as water; and in the gaseous state, as water vapor or steam."

What words in the "Physical Words" list do you associate with a change of state?

What physical and chemical changes are occurring in this photograph?

Assessment

1. Below is a list of statements about physical and chemical changes. Ask students to copy the list and write the letter "C" beside each chemical change and "P" beside each physical change. Students should then explain their answers.
   (a) Substance A, a solid, stretches when pulled gently. *(P)*
   (b) Substance B, a powder, dissolves in water. *(P)*
   (c) Substance C, a solid, burns when ignited. *(C)*
   (d) Substance D, a liquid, changes color when exposed to air for a long time. *(C)*
   (e) Substance E, a solid, shatters into small pieces when hit with a hammer. *(P)*
   (f) Substance F, a gas, pops when a burning match is brought near it. *(C)*
   (g) Substance G, a liquid, evaporates quickly in a warm location. *(P)*
   (h) Substance H, a liquid, freezes at −20°C. *(P)*
   (i) When substance I, a gas, passes through limewater, the limewater becomes cloudy. *(C)*

2. Have students write short descriptive paragraphs about some materials using the physical and chemical word lists they developed in the lesson. Ask them to be sure to describe what the materials were like before and after the changes.

Extension

1. Have students design a word-search game or crossword puzzle to review the terms that describe chemical and physical changes.

2. Have students research and compare chemical and physical changes in hair caused by the use of hair-styling products and techniques. Examples may include haircuts, permanent waves, hair straighteners, curling irons, and hair conditioners.

Answers to

Physical and Chemical Words

This is a summary activity for physical and chemical changes. An example of a completed table is given on page S169.

Words associated with a change of state: evaporating, melting, condensing, drying, freezing.

Answer to caption: The physical and chemical changes occurring in the photograph include wood rotting, leaves rotting, and a pail rusting (chemical); cut wood and evaporating water (physical).

Getting Started

This lesson focuses on the signs, or evidence, of chemical change. Laboratory chemicals, as well as household substances, are used so that students can observe chemical changes. The activities reinforce students' prior knowledge of physical and chemical changes. Having completed this lesson, students should be more aware of everyday examples of chemical changes.

Main Ideas

1. Color changes, release of gases, formation of new substances, and energy release are all signs of chemical change.
2. Identifying the presence of a new substance is the only true test for a chemical change; the signs listed above are only clues that a chemical change may have occurred.

Teaching Strategies

This series of activities gives students an opportunity to "discover" evidence of chemical change. Accept all reasonable answers to the questions posed in the introduction. Students will learn to use certain clues to determine whether a physical or chemical change has occurred.

Exploration 2

There are several variations for the set-up of this Exploration. Students can be divided into groups of three or four and assigned a specific change to investigate and report on. Or, the changes can be set up at different stations around the room, and students can move from station to station to complete each activity.
(Continues on next page)

---

4 Signs of Chemical Change

We know that there are two basic types of changes, chemical and physical, but how do you tell them apart? What are the signs of a chemical change? a physical change? The following Explorations will help you to learn to recognize the signs of chemical changes.

More Evidence of Chemical Changes

Let's examine more changes and look again for ways of recognizing whether a chemical change has occurred. You will also observe some new evidence of chemical changes here. But be careful—there are physical changes hidden among the rest. Construct a data table like the one below to record your findings. Decide whether each change is physical or chemical, and state your reasons.

You Will Need

- a tin can lid
- an iron nail
- an eyedropper
- an eggshell
- a clothespin
- a candle
- a drinking straw
- a test tube
- a graduated cylinder
- a sample of potato (or cereal or starch)
- 2 g of copper sulfate
- vinegar
- 25 mL of milk
- limewater
- cobalt chloride (a few crystals)
- lemon juice
- iodine solution
- baking powder
- toothpicks

The Change	Physical	Chemical	Reasons or Evidence
Limewater turns milky.		√	1. Color change occurs. 2. A new substance is formed. 3. Difficult to reverse change.

LESSON 4 ORGANIZER

Objectives

By the end of the lesson, students should be able to:
1. State the type of change (physical or chemical) when given an example, and explain the reason for their choice.
2. Explain the procedures used to test for water, carbon dioxide, copper, and starch.

Process Skills

observing, inferring, comparing, analyzing

New Terms

Precipitate—a solid formed as the result of a physical or chemical change.

What to Do

Be Careful: *Copper sulfate, cobalt chloride, and iodine are poisonous and can cause damage to skin. Do not allow them to contact your skin. Do not inhale their vapors.*

1. Add 1 g of copper sulfate to 10 mL of water and stir. Place an iron nail in the copper solution.
2. Add 3 droppersful of vinegar to 25 mL of milk.
3. Add a dropperful of vinegar to a piece of eggshell.

4. Heat a bit of candle wax on a tin can lid. (Use a clothespin to hold the lid.)

5. Using a drinking straw, blow slowly into a test tube one-quarter full of limewater. (Blow slowly, or you will splash limewater over yourself and others.)

6. Place a few crystals of cobalt chloride on a tin can lid and heat. Add a few drops of water to the substance remaining. Stir with a toothpick. If you don't notice a change, add a few more drops of water.

7. With a toothpick or a straw from a broom, write a word on a piece of paper using lemon juice. Heat the paper gently over a candle flame. Do not burn it.

8. Add a drop or two of iodine solution to a bit of starch. (A slice of potato, some cereal, corn, or a piece of bread may be used instead.)

(Exploration 2 continued)

Review the safety considerations regarding the use of an open flame and the use of chemicals (copper sulfate, iodine solution, limewater, cobalt chloride). The materials for each station are:

1. 1-g samples of copper sulfate, 10-mL samples of water, several small containers, stirring sticks, iron nails
2. small containers of milk (25 mL each), vinegar, eyedroppers
3. pieces of eggshell, vinegar, eyedroppers, small dishes
4. candle wax, tin can lids, candles, matches, clothespins
5. drinking straws, test tubes, limewater
6. crystals of cobalt chloride, tin can lids, candles, matches, clothespins, water, eyedropper, toothpicks for stirring
7. toothpicks or straws from a broom, paper, lemon juice, candles, matches
8. iodine solution, a starch sample, eyedroppers, dishes
9. water, eyedroppers, baking powder, small jars or containers

In the nine activities, there are only two physical changes. You may wish to add others such as diffusion, separation of iron from sulfur with a magnet, evaporation of alcohol, and dissolving sugar. The answers are given in a table on page S169.

Materials

Exploration 2: 2 tin can lids, iron nail, eyedropper, vinegar, eggshells, sample of potato (or other starch), 4 boxes of matches, 4 candles, drinking straw, 2 clothespins, lemon juice, iodine solution (10 drops to 25 mL water), baking powder, toothpicks or straws from a broom, 1 g of copper sulfate, cobalt chloride (a few crystals), limewater, 25 mL of milk, test tube, 2 graduated cylinders, water, 2 small bowls, stirring rods, paper

To prepare limewater: add 20 g of calcium hydroxide to 1 L of water, shake, and let settle. When needed, pour off some of the clear solution.
Chemical Tests: Journal
Exploration 3: seltzer tablet, carbonated drink (bottled), vinegar, baking soda, 10 mL of molasses, packet of yeast, hot plate, beakers, warm and cold water, tongs, safety goggles, graduated cylinder
Spotting a Chemical Change: Journal

Teacher's Resource Binder

Resource Worksheet 5–6
Graphic Organizer Transparency 5–2

Science Discovery Videodisc

Disc 2, Image and Activity Bank, 5–4

Time Required

three class periods

Answers to

Chemical Tests

- Copper will precipitate—reddish-brown color.
- Limewater turns milky.
- Cobalt chloride turns the solution pink or red.
- Starch changes to blue-black color.

9. Add a few drops of water to baking powder.

A New Word

Did you notice new evidence that a chemical change had occurred? In steps 2 and 5, you observed a *precipitate*—a solid formed as the result of a chemical change.

Chemical Tests

Chemical changes can be used to help identify substances. Here is a table of some common tests for chemical changes. Copy it into your Journal and complete it by recording the observation expected for each test. You have already seen these chemical changes in this unit.

Test For	Procedure	Result
copper in any substance	Place an iron nail in a solution of the substance.	
carbon dioxide	Pass the gas through limewater.	
water	Add the liquid to blue cobalt chloride.	
starch	Add iodine solution.	

Bubble Watch!

Formation of bubbles is often evidence of a chemical change—but not always. Try these changes, and decide which of the bubbles you see resulted from a chemical change.

You Will Need

- a beaker
- a seltzer tablet
- a carbonated drink
- vinegar
- baking soda
- 10 mL of molasses
- a packet of yeast

What to Do

1. Heat water in a beaker until it boils. Is this a chemical change? What are the bubbles made of? How could you prove your answer?

2. Examine a recently opened carbonated drink. Are you observing a chemical change?

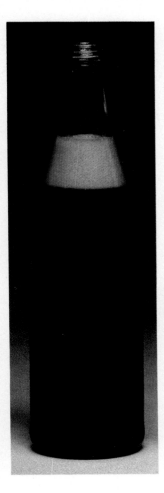

3. Drop one-quarter of a seltzer tablet into water. Is this a chemical change? What are the bubbles made of? Can you prove it?

Exploration 3

This Exploration is best done at several activity stations; although some activities could be performed as demonstrations. If you do some activities as demonstrations, it is best to do step 5 (fermentation) first. Bubbles should be seen at the end of 40 minutes. You will obtain the best results if the water is at 37°C. The students could then prove that the gas given off is carbon dioxide by doing the limewater test.

Fermentation involves the use of yeast to change sugar into alcohol. The gas given off is carbon dioxide. You can prove that the gas is carbon dioxide by using a set-up such as the one shown in the illustration below.

Although fermentation involves the use of living organisms, it still meets the criteria for chemical change.

Answers to

In-Text Questions

1. Boiling water is not undergoing a chemical change. The bubbles are water vapor. The vapor could be condensed on a glass beaker, and the drops that are formed could be tested for water by using the cobalt-chloride test.
2. The bubbles are not evidence of a chemical change. They are carbon dioxide dissolved under pressure in a liquid.
3. The bubbles are evidence of a chemical change. They are carbon dioxide. The limewater test will prove the identity of this gas.

(Answers continue on next page)

Fermentation

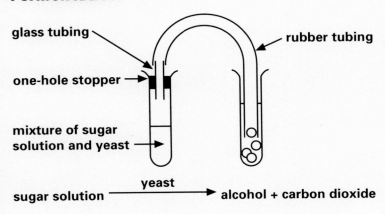

glass tubing

rubber tubing

one-hole stopper

mixture of sugar
solution and yeast

sugar solution → yeast → alcohol + carbon dioxide

Answers continued

4. The bubbles are not evidence of a chemical change.
5. Yes, this is a chemical change. A gas is given off by the yeast organisms and the mixture increases in size.
6. Yes, the bubbles are carbon dioxide. However, step 2 describes a physical change; step 6 describes a chemical change.

Answers to

Spotting a Chemical Change

Possible answers to the table include: color change, bubbles (gas formation), heat and/or light given off, precipitate forms, odor changes, new substance forms, change is not easily reversible. All of these clues are sometimes observed. Evidence that a new substance has formed is the best indication of a chemical change, but even this is not always directly observable.

Follow Up

Assessment

1. Ask students to explain how they would test for the presence of:
   (a) Carbon dioxide *(Pass the gas through limewater.)*
   (b) Water *(Add the liquid to blue cobalt chloride.)*
   (c) Starch *(Add iodine solution to the substance.)*
   (d) Copper *(Place an iron nail in a solution of the substance.)*
2. Have students write a paragraph in which they explain to someone else how to tell when a chemical change has taken place.

Extension

1. Have students research the chemical changes involved in a common household process such as baking a cake or mending a broken item with epoxy glue.
2. Students could plan a mini-science project to demonstrate how one of the following processes works:
   • Testing for starch
   • Fermentation
   • How antacids work

4. Let a cold glass of water reach room temperature. Do the bubbles indicate a chemical change?
5. To 50 mL of water, add 10 mL of molasses. The exact amounts you use are not critical. Make a yeast mixture by stirring half a packet of yeast into 25 mL of warm water. Add this to your molasses solution. Place the solution in a warm spot and record all changes over the next few days. Does a chemical change occur?
6. Add a few drops of vinegar to baking soda. Are these bubbles made of the same substance as the ones you encountered in step 2?

Spotting a Chemical Change

By now, you should be a champion "chemical change detective." Using a table similar to the one here, make a list of all the clues you would use to recognize a chemical change. Can evidence for a chemical change be observed in every chemical change or only in some? Write in your Journal only.

What to Look for in Chemical Changes

Evidence of a Chemical Change	Sometimes Observed	Always Observed
1.		
2.		
3.		
4.		
5.		
6.		

5 Classifying Changes

On the Menu: Changes

There are at least 10 physical and 7 chemical changes concealed in this story. Can you find them and list them in a table?

Ramón and Marta decided to make supper for their parents and grandmother. While Marta cut up the vegetables and cheese for the salad and boiled an egg to slice up, Ramón placed ice cubes into a glass of lemonade made from powdered concentrate.

They had also decided to make and cook some hamburger patties and to broil some frozen french fries. Earlier in the day, Marta made jello by mixing the powder in hot water and then allowing it to cool in the refrigerator until it set.

When the meat appeared to be completely cooked, so that it was no longer red, and the french fries were golden brown, they called their parents and grandmother. After the meal, it was time for dessert and coffee. Marta and Ramón boiled some water and poured it into mugs. Instant coffee powder and sugar were stirred in. Almost everything was ready. But where was the milk? They searched for it until they remembered that Ramón and Marta had left it outside earlier in the day. It smelled sour and had already started to curdle. So they had to serve the coffee black!

Later, the scraps were placed in the garbage. Papa washed the dishes in steaming hot water, and Ramón dried them. Marta finished an oil painting, while Mama read a book. The entire family agreed that they had enjoyed their supper thoroughly, though Abuelita did have some trouble with her stomach. However, a seltzer tablet soon helped soothe the problem. All in all, it was a successful venture for Marta and Ramón.

Write a story containing hidden physical and chemical changes. Then challenge a friend to find the changes.

✳ Getting Started

This lesson enables students to consolidate their knowledge of chemical and physical changes.

Main Idea

The knowledge of chemical and physical changes can be applied to everyday living.

✳ Teaching Strategies

Students are given the opportunity to use the terms and apply the concepts introduced so far. Ask a volunteer to read the story on page 249 to the rest of the class. Students should then work individually to complete their own stories. A list of the physical and chemical changes in the story follows.

Answers to

On the Menu: Changes

Physical Changes:	*Chemical Changes:*
cut up vegetables	boiled egg
cut up cheese	cooked hamburger
melted ice cubes	cooked french fries
made lemonade	milk soured and
made hamburger	curdled
patties	food was digested
defrosted potatoes	seltzer tablet was
dissolved jello	used
jello solidified	garbage decom-
boiled water	poses
dissolved coffee	
dissolved sugar	
cleaned dishes	

LESSON 5 ORGANIZER

Objectives

By the end of the lesson, students should be able to:
1. Identify changes in daily life as chemical or physical.
2. State five careers that require knowledge of chemicals and their changes.

Process Skills

analyzing, summarizing, interviewing, researching

New Terms

(Organizer continues on next page)

Answers to

More Changes to Classify

Have students copy and complete the table on this page in their Journals.

Change/Type/Reason

- Newspaper/chemical/
  The color change is an indication of a chemical change.
- Steel wool/physical/
  The steel wool scraped away the black, but did not change it into anything else.
- Lightning/physical/
  Static buildup of electricity within the clouds caused the lightning to flash.
- Limestone/chemical/
  Bubbles are evidence that a chemical change has occurred.
- Back steps/chemical/
  The wood is reacting with oxygen in the air to form carbon dioxide.
- Lemon/chemical/
  This is evidence of a precipitate and therefore evidence of a chemical change.
- Gasoline/physical/
  The gasoline evaporated. The smell of the gasoline molecules is still in the air.
- Gravy/physical/
  The liquid gravy solidified in the refrigerator. The change is easily reversible.
- Red meat/chemical/
  The color change is not reversible. The color change is a clue of a chemical change.
- Cavity/chemical/
  Acids, other chemicals, and bacteria caused the tooth to decay. The change is not reversible.
- Paint/chemical/
  The paint on the car is reacting with oxygen in the air and oxidizing. This is evidence of a chemical change. The color changed, and the change is not easily reversible.

Can You Be Fooled by the Clues?

This activity serves as a quick review of the material covered so far in the unit.

(Answers to In-Text Questions follow on next page)

More Changes to Classify

Now your knowledge of the two types of changes will be put to the test! Classify the changes listed below as either physical or chemical, and then give a reason for your decision. The first one has been done for you. Write in your Journal, not in your book.

Change	Type	Reason
A newspaper yellowed after a few weeks.	chemical	Color change indicates a chemical change.
The steel wool turned the black pot a shiny, silver color.		
Lightning flashed across the sky.		
Acid caused limestone to fizz.		
The back steps are rotting out.		
The piece of lemon turned the tea cloudy.		
Spilled gasoline dried, but left a bad odor in the room.		
The gravy in the refrigerator jelled.		
Red meat turned brown as it cooked.		
You got a cavity in a tooth.		
The paint on the car turned dull.		

Can You Be Fooled by the Clues?

In earlier lessons, you learned some words associated with physical and chemical changes. You also discovered several clues by which physical and chemical changes can be recognized. Here are the clues that show that a chemical change has occurred:

- There is a color change.
- A gas is given off.
- A solid is formed.
- Heat and/or light are given off.
- A new substance with new identifying properties is formed.

(Organizer continued)

Materials

More Changes to Classify: Journal

Teacher's Resource Binder

Resource Worksheet 5–7
Graphic Organizer Transparency 5–3

Science Discovery Videodisc

Disc 2, Image and Activity Bank, 5–5

Time Required

one to two class periods

But be careful! Can the clues fool you, as they fooled the students who made the statements below? You be the teacher, and explain (in writing) why each of the following conclusions is wrong.

"When I open a carbonated drink bottle, it fizzes. This shows that a chemical change has occurred."

"Salt is white. When it dissolves in water it becomes colorless and invisible. This color change is evidence that a chemical change has occurred."

"Heat and light are given off by a light bulb. Therefore, a chemical change is taking place in the light bulb."

"Ice is often a different color than liquid water. This is an example of a chemical change."

"The sawdust formed when wood is cut looks quite different from the original tree. A chemical change occurs during the cutting."

Who Uses Chemical Changes?

Who uses chemicals and chemical changes? Almost everyone! Cooks, nurses, parents, druggists, chemists, farmers, swimming pool managers, tropical fish owners, garage owners, joggers, and on and on.

Interview someone from your neighborhood. What chemicals does he or she use? What changes are involved in his or her line of work? But first, consider the following:

- Whom shall I interview?
- What shall I ask?
- How shall I record my information?
- What form will my report to the class take?

Who Uses Chemical Changes?

This activity builds on students' growing awareness of the impact of chemical changes in their lives. When this activity is completed, have students make presentations to the class. (These oral presentations could serve as an alternative method of assessment for this unit.)

✳ *Follow Up*

Assessment

1. Have students prepare a table like the one in *More Changes to Classify*. Give students the following list of changes. Have them classify the changes and explain their reasons.
   (a) The liquid gelatin solidified in the refrigerator. *(physical; the change is reversible)*
   (b) When the gas emissions from some industries mix with the water in the atmosphere, acids are formed. *(chemical; a new substance is formed)*
   (c) When Rick mixed the two clear liquids, a yellow precipitate was formed. *(chemical; a precipitate indicates a chemical change)*
   (d) The repeated freezing and unfreezing of water in the cracks in the rocks caused them to break up. *(physical; the rocks were broken apart, not changed into another substance)*
2. Have students write or make posters illustrating the "life story" of an object such as a candle, a nail, a piece of wood, a leaf, a rock, or an ice cube. Ask them to identify the chemical and physical changes involved at each stage.

Extension

Have students do some research and write a report about a career that requires knowledge of chemicals and chemical changes. They should include the educational background required and job responsibilities. They should mention two specific chemicals that the person encounters in this job. Some possible choices include: chemical engineer, chemist, laboratory technician, pharmacist, environmental ecologist, physician, and food scientist.

Answers to

In-Text Questions

- Not all bubbles are evidence of chemical change. These bubbles were dissolved in the soft drink. This is an example of a physical change.
- This time a color change does not indicate a chemical change. Dissolving is a physical change.
- Although heat and light are being given off by the light bulb, it is not a chemical change. Electricity that is produced elsewhere passes through the filament in the bulb to cause the bulb to give off light and heat. There is no other change taking place within the light bulb.
- Ice and water look different; however, one is just a different state of the other. Both are made of the same substance.
- The sawdust cannot be changed back into wood, but this is a physical change. Both the sawdust and the wood are the same material.

✴ *Getting Started*

This lesson examines the chemical and physical properties of a number of substances. The terms reactants, products, and word equations are introduced. Students learn how to write word equations to describe chemical changes.

Main Ideas

1. Properties can identify a substance.
2. Properties can be identified as either chemical or physical.
3. Properties determine the uses of substances.
4. Reactants are the starting materials in a chemical change; products are the materials formed as a result of the chemical change.

✴ *Teaching Strategies*

Mysterious Drops

Have students observe the changes occurring on the side of a cold, empty glass. Then students should read the six plans listed in the text and consider whether any of the tests could verify whether or not the drops are water. Remind students to consider the safety of each test. After they have considered the problem, have them use the cobalt-chloride test to confirm the identity of the water. Because cobalt chloride crystals must be used with extreme care, an alternative method would be to prepare cobalt chloride paper. Water droplets added to the cobalt chloride paper will turn the paper pink.
(Continues on next page)

Mysterious Drops

Annette's class had a problem. That is, Annette's teacher gave them a problem to solve.

A cold, empty glass was taken from a refrigerator. A few minutes later, droplets began to form on the outside of the glass.

"Water drops!" said one of Annette's classmates.

"Prove it," said the teacher.

How could Annette and her classmates prove that the drops were water? What would you do?

After some discussion, the class came up with a number of suggestions listed below. Working with another student, consider each one and decide whether it is a good plan of action.

Plan 1: Since it looks, feels, and smells like water, it must be water.

Plan 2: Collect enough of the drops to find their mass. If 1 mL of the sample has a mass of 1 g, then it must be water.

Plan 3: Collect a few drops and taste them. If they taste like water, then they are water.

Plan 4: Collect enough drops and find the boiling point of the sample. If it boils at 100 °C, then it's water.

Plan 5: Heat some cobalt chloride crystals until they turn blue. Add some drops of the sample to the blue cobalt chloride. If it turns pink, then the drops are water.

Plan 6: Try other chemical tests. For example, try to burn a sample, make it react with iron or aluminum, or get a chemical reaction with substances such as paper. If the drops do not burn or react with these substances, then they are probably water.

Which plan or plans seem most likely to work? Why? Are there some plans you should avoid? Using these tests could you prove that the droplets were water?

Substances are identified by their properties. You would make use of the **properties** of water to help you identify water. You would make use of the properties of salt to help you identify salt, and so on. How would you define property?

In Unit 4, "Investigating Matter," you learned that matter has two basic kinds of properties: chemical and physical. These are described for one chemical—water—on the right.

Physical Properties of Water . . .

. . . describe how water looks, feels, and behaves. Also describe what physical changes water can undergo.

Chemical Properties of Water . . .

. . . describe what chemical changes water can undergo. Also describe what chemical changes or reactions water cannot undergo.

LESSON ⑥ ORGANIZER

Objectives

By the end of the lesson, students should be able to:
1. Distinguish between physical and chemical change.
2. Explain the relationship between the properties and uses of a substance.
3. Define reactants and products, and explain the relationship between the two.

Process Skills

analyzing, investigating, summarizing, writing a report

New Terms

Properties—characteristics that distinguish one substance from another.
Alloys—a mixture of two or more metals.
Products—new substances formed in a chemical change.

Properties of One Chemical: Aluminum

How many uses of aluminum are you aware of? As with all substances, the uses of aluminum are determined by its properties. As you read the following description of this metal, list as many of its properties as you can. Even after reading about it, you may be able to think of other properties not mentioned here. Afterward, decide which of the properties are important for the purpose of each aluminum object shown here.

Although aluminum is one of the most common chemicals, it was not refined into metallic form until 1827, long after most other metals. This is because aluminum requires large amounts of electricity to extract it from ore. Until electricity became commonly available, aluminum cost as much as $500 a pound!

Aluminum is very versatile. Because it is much less dense than most metals, aluminum is used to form lightweight *alloys*. Alloys are a mixture of two or more metals. Aluminum and its alloys are used in canoes, boats, cars, bicycles, and space vehicles.

Aluminum is *ductile*—that is, it can be drawn into a wire. It is also *malleable*. This means it can easily be shaped into many useful products, from aluminum siding to aluminum cans. Because it does not corrode and is not poisonous, it can be used to wrap food.

Aluminum is used to make cooking utensils because it is a good conductor of heat. It is bonded to polyester fiber and used to make sleeping bags because, as a reflector of heat, aluminum reflects body heat inward to keep a person warm. Aluminum certainly is a "hot property." Can you suggest some new uses it might have in the future?

Properties of One Chemical: Aluminum

This reading examines the properties of aluminum and the uses that are dependent upon these properties. Through reading and discussion, students should be able to identify several properties of aluminum. The properties named in the text are *ductility, malleability,* and formation of lightweight *alloys.* Aluminum is a good conductor and can also be used in making permanent magnets. Discuss with students how the properties listed apply to the photographs. Aluminum could have many uses in the future, such as in building lighter and faster cars. Because a heavier car uses more fuel, a lighter car might be very important in the future.

Reactants—starting substances in a chemical change.
Word equation—a chemical equation that shows the reactants and products in a reaction with words and symbols.

Materials

Exploration 4: square of heavy aluminum foil (10 cm × 10 cm), stirring rod, 100 mL of water, beaker, 5 g of copper chloride, evaporating dish, metric ruler, safety goggles, graduated cylinder
Guess That Substance!: index cards

Teacher's Resource Binder

Resource Worksheet 5–8
Graphic Organizer Transparency 5–4

Science Discovery Videodisc

Disc 2, Image and Activity Bank, 5–6

Time Required

three class periods

Exploration 4

This activity examines a chemical change that is very dramatic. CAUTION: Copper chloride is toxic; make sure students wear safety goggles and wash their hands after the experiment. The chemical reaction that is taking place is:

Aluminum + copper chloride →
Aluminum chloride + copper

There is also a reaction between the aluminum and the solution that produces hydrogen gas. This accounts for the bubbles that are observed.

After the Exploration, examine the physical changes—the dissolving of copper chloride in water and the tearing of aluminum.

Answers to

Questions

1. Heat was given off, color changed, and a new substance was formed (a precipitate), which indicates a chemical change.
2. The copper chloride crystals dissolved in the water.
3. Aluminum reacts with a solution of copper chloride. This is a chemical property.
4. Some of the physical properties of copper chloride are: it is a green crystal, it is soluble in water, and it is denser than water.
5. Copper chloride is formed by copper and chlorine. When mixed with aluminum, copper chloride in solution yields copper plus aluminum chloride.
6. The red material is copper.

Answers to

Results

Students observed the disappearance of aluminum; the disappearance of the greenish-blue color; the appearance of reddish powder; and after the evaporation of water, the appearance of a white powder.

If you are interested in discovering what is now dissolved in the liquid, add enough foil to cause the solution to go from blue to clear and set aside a few milliliters of the solution to evaporate. A white solid will remain. It is aluminum chloride.

One Chemical Property of Aluminum

In this Exploration, you will use the chemical copper chloride to examine one of the chemical properties of aluminum. As you proceed, record all the chemical changes you observe.

Be Careful: *Make sure you do not handle the copper chloride with your bare hands. Wash your hands after the experiment.*

You Will Need

- 5 g of copper chloride crystals
- a square of heavy aluminum foil, 10 cm x 10 cm
- 100 mL of water in a beaker
- a stirring rod
- an evaporating dish

What to Do

1. Add the copper chloride to the beaker of water. Make all the observations you can, and then stir to dissolve the copper chloride.
2. Lightly crumple the aluminum foil and place it in the beaker. You can push it under the surface of the liquid with your stirring rod.

3. Make as many observations as you can, and then answer the questions.

Questions

1. What evidence do you have that a chemical change took place?
2. Name a physical change that took place.
3. What new properties of aluminum have you discovered? Are they physical or chemical properties?
4. What are some physical properties of copper chloride?
5. Name one chemical property of copper chloride.
6. Examine the red material that formed. What do you think it might be?

Results

Summarize the results of this Exploration.

Here's what you started with:
- silvery-gray aluminum
- greenish-blue copper chloride dissolved in water

What did you observe? Did the color of the liquid change? What happened to the aluminum? A new substance formed in the liquid. Describe its appearance. Do you think it could be copper? Pour the liquid into an evaporating dish and allow it to evaporate. Describe what is left. What do you think it could be?

Guess That Substance!

Each person in your class writes three properties of a substance on one side of an index card or piece of paper and the name of the substance on the other side. A classmate or your teacher reads the properties. The winner is the person who guesses the most substances.

Here is Ralph's index card:

• it's a metal
• its ductile
• it rusts

Answer: iron or steel

Guess That Substance!

This is a fun way of examining chemical and physical properties of a substance. You might want to assign a specific material to each student so that there are no duplications. Students may need to do a little research to fill out their cards.

Summarizing Chemical Changes

This page defines the terms *reactants* and *products.* It also introduces the phrase *word equations.* Be sure students realize that in a word equation, what is on one side of the arrow is equivalent to what is on the other side of the arrow in terms of mass, types of atoms, and so on. Have students copy the table into their Journals and add to it as they proceed through the unit. You may want to keep a running table on the chalkboard or on an overhead transparency.

If students have difficulty with the concept of reactants and products, discuss some everyday chemical changes that were described in previous lessons, such as burning, rusting, and digesting. For example, the burning of hydrocarbons (such as paraffin wax, gasoline, or oil) involves the combination of hydrocarbon with oxygen to produce carbon dioxide, water, and a release of energy. Have students describe what was present "before" and "after" these processes. Then have students identify the reactants and products in each situation.

Summarizing Chemical Changes

In every chemical change, new substances are formed. These new substances are called **products** of the chemical change. When you added vinegar to baking soda, carbon dioxide gas was formed. Carbon dioxide is a product of this chemical change. From observing the change, you would not realize that water and the chemical sodium acetate were also formed. These are products of this chemical change as well.

The starting substances are called the **reactants** of the chemical change. Baking soda and vinegar are the reactants.

The drawing below represents both the reactants and the products of a chemical change:

A **word equation** shows the reactants and products of a reaction like the one above in terms of words and symbols. For example, the word equation for the reaction between copper chloride and aluminum is as follows:

aluminum + copper chloride ⟶ copper + aluminum chloride
(metal)   (dissolved in)   (metal)   (dissolved in
                    water)   water)

Review the chemical changes you have observed so far in this unit. Try to identify some of the reactants and some of the products. (Don't worry if there are reactants and products you cannot identify. Often, doing so requires special chemical tests.) Record the ones you can identify in a table like the one below. Keep adding reactants and products to your Journal as you proceed through the remainder of this unit.

Some word equations

Reactants ⟶ Products	
baking soda + vinegar ⟶ sodium acetate + water + carbon dioxide	

Special Reactants and Products

You have seen that chemical changes are part of daily life. Some interesting examples are described below. For each chemical change, try to identify the reactants and products. Then write the word equation.

Kitchen Chemistry

Whenever you cook you are doing chemistry—mixing chemicals together to form delicious things to eat. A chemical that plays an important part in many recipes is sodium bicarbonate. It is found by itself in baking soda, or mixed with the acid, cream of tartar, in baking powder. During the cooking of a cake, the sodium bicarbonate in baking powder reacts with the cream of tartar to produce carbon dioxide. This reaction causes the cake to rise. Water and a chemical called sodium tartrate are also formed, but you don't notice them.

Try This at Home

Make your own baking powder by adding a few milliliters of cream of tartar to about 5 mL (1 tsp) of baking soda. Then add some water. Watch what happens!

Table Salt from an Acid and a Base

Concentrated hydrochloric acid can cause severe burns to the skin. Sodium hydroxide, a base found in many drain cleaners, is extremely corrosive and can also burn the skin. However, when these two chemicals are combined in the right amounts they react to form an essential part of our diet—sodium chloride, or table salt. Water is also formed in this chemical reaction. Does it seem strange that two potentially dangerous chemicals react to form chemicals that are not only harmless but essential for life?

You will learn more about acids and bases when you try Exploration 5 later in this unit.

Two corrosive, harmful chemicals react to form table salt, an essential part of your diet.

Answers continued

The Ingredients of Water

Electrolysis is not really a chemical reaction. Energy is used to separate water into its component parts, oxygen and hydrogen.

- When hydrogen is burned, water is produced.

Answer to caption: Electrolysis causes a chemical change in water.

Chemical Caverns

Reactants:
calcium carbonate, water, carbon dioxide
Products:
calcium bicarbonate
Equation:
calcium carbonate + water + carbon dioxide → calcium bicarbonate

Just for a Change

This exercise encourages students to summarize and apply what they have learned in this lesson. Be sure students' reports include the reactants and products. The corresponding word equations can be supplied by the class after the reports have been presented. Encourage students to find out the chemical names as well as the common names of the products and reactants.

✳ Follow Up

Assessment

1. Ask students to decide if the following statements are true or false.
   (a) New substances are formed during physical changes. *(False)*
   (b) The red material formed when copper chloride and aluminum are mixed is copper. *(True)*
   (c) Alloys are mixtures of two or more metals. *(True)*
   (d) Aluminum is a malleable element. *(True)*
   (e) Copper chloride is a green crystal. This is a chemical property. *(False; color is a physical property.)*
2. Ask students to choose a substance discussed in the lesson (other than water or aluminum). Have them design a plan by which they could prove its identity.

According to legend, James Watt experimented with his mother's kettle before inventing the steam engine. Steam engines cause a physical change in water to produce mechanical motion. What kind of change in water does electrolysis cause?

This cave was formed by a chemical reaction.

The Ingredients of Water

Water, as you know, is a liquid. Heating water to its boiling point can change liquid water into steam, a gas. But it is still the same chemical—water. However, passing an electric current through water breaks it apart into its two components: hydrogen and oxygen—both gases. This process, called *electrolysis*, is very useful because hydrogen gas is an excellent, clean source of energy. Can you guess what chemical is produced when hydrogen is burned? Who knows, in the future our homes may be heated and our cars powered by hydrogen produced by electrolysis.

Chemical Caverns

Have you ever visited a cave or a cavern? Did you wonder how it was formed? Most caves are found in limestone and are produced by a chemical reaction. Here's how.

Water from the surface seeps down into the limestone. This water contains dissolved carbon dioxide, the gas you exhale. The water-carbon dioxide mixture reacts with calcium carbonate (the main chemical in limestone) to form calcium bicarbonate. This chemical dissolves in the water and is carried away. Over time, more and more limestone is carried away. Eventually, a cave is formed.

Just for a Change . . .

Do research on a chemical change. In your research, try to determine the reactants and products of that change. Include in your write-up other interesting information you may find. Share your research with your classmates to see whether they can write a word equation for your chemical change.

Here are some possibilities:

- Aluminum is extracted from a mineral called bauxite. How is this done?
- What is the chemical change involved in obtaining iron from iron ore? If there is a steel mill nearby, you might ask somebody who works there for help with this question.
- Plaster of Paris is made from a mineral called gypsum. What chemical change is involved?
- What can you learn about the reactants and products in making cement?
- Car batteries use a chemical change to produce electricity. What are some reactants and products in this change?
- The process of photography uses many changes. Talk to a photographer to learn about the chemical changes involved in taking and developing photographs.

Extension

1. Students can investigate the process of aluminum-can recycling. Have them report on any chemical and physical changes, energy use or production, and any other aspects of the process. The report could include photographs or drawings, which could be included in a poster or bulletin-board display for the classroom.

2. Students could research and investigate a metal and its properties, both physical and chemical. A poster depicting the metal's uses could accompany the research. Examples include: silver, iron, magnesium, zinc, and so on.

1. A visitor from another solar system has landed in your classroom. On this visitor's home planet there is no such thing as water. Describe water to your guest so that he does not confuse it with other liquids such as antifreeze, oil, alcohol, vinegar, or any solutions that contain water.

2. Many common expressions refer to the properties of things. Read the expressions below. Compare the "scientific" meaning of each expression with its common meaning. Does each expression make sense from a scientific standpoint?

"She's as sharp as a tack."
"This baby is as good as gold."
"That idea went over like a lead balloon."
"She's as bright as a new penny."
"That person is as hard as nails."
"He's the salt of the earth."

What are some other expressions?
Try making your own!

Answers to

Challenge Your Thinking

1. At room temperature, pure water is a transparent, colorless, odorless, and tasteless liquid. Water freezes and melts at 0°C. Water has the unusual property of expanding when it freezes, so that the solid form is less dense then the liquid form. That is why ice floats in water. The boiling point of water is 100°C.

   Water can be distinguished from the other liquids by comparing physical properties such as color, feel, taste, boiling point, freezing point, and density. A chemical property of water that distinguishes it from other liquids: it does not burn.

2. "Sharp as a tack"—A person who is "sharp" has a good mind. A tack is sharp because it is pointed (physical property).

   "Good as gold"—Gold is the standard of most money systems. It represents good value because gold does not easily react with other substances (chemical property), and therefore does not deteriorate easily.

   "Like a lead balloon"—This refers to the high density of lead as compared to most elements (physical property). A lead balloon wouldn't float very high.

   "Bright as a new penny"—This refers to the the shiny quality (physical property) of a new copper penny. A person with this quality would be lively and enthusiastic.

   "Hard as nails"—This refers to someone being thick-skinned and tough. The metals used in nails have the physical property of hardness.

   "Salt of the earth"—This probably originated because salt is essential in the diets of many organisms (chemical property) and is very valuable. A person described in this way would also be very valuable.

   Some other expressions:
   "Oil and water don't mix"—This refers to the fact that these two liquids are not soluble in each other (physical properties).

   "Slower than molasses in January"—This refers to the physical property of molasses becoming more viscous upon cooling.

LESSON 7

✳ *Getting Started*

This lesson introduces elements and compounds. Students realize that they can use these terms to identify the substances that they have been observing in their study of chemical changes. Then students explore the variety of elements as they examine and interpret the periodic table.

Main Ideas

1. All chemicals can be classified as either elements or compounds.
2. A compound can be broken apart by chemical changes into the elements it is composed of.
3. Elements cannot be changed into other elements by means of chemical changes.
4. Ninety-one elements exist naturally on earth.
5. The periodic table arranges elements with similar chemical properties into chemical families.

✳ *Teaching Strategies*

The tasks on pages 260 and 261 relate the new terms *element* and *compound* to the student's previous observations of chemical changes.

Explain to students that all matter on earth is made of one or more elements. Different substances are formed from different combinations of elements. Aluminum is an example of a substance made of a single element. Salt is a substance made of two elements, sodium and chloride. Answers to the tasks posed in *Elements and Compounds* follow on page 261.

7 The Nature of Chemicals

Elements and Compounds

You have probably heard the legend of King Midas, who turned everything he touched into gold. For centuries, people dreamed of finding ways to make this legend a reality by turning common substances into gold. Alchemists—the earliest chemists—believed that it was possible to turn lead and other "base metals" into gold. In the course of their work, they discovered many chemical changes, but never the one that they really wanted—a way to convert other metals into gold.

We now know that theirs was an impossible task. All chemicals can be classified either as **elements** or as **compounds**. Gold and lead are both elements. So are iron and aluminum. These are just a few of the over 100 basic materials out of which more complex substances are formed. Elements can combine with other elements in chemical reactions to form compounds. Compounds can be broken apart by chemical changes into the elements that make them up. However, no element can be changed into a different element by means of chemical changes.

By analyzing the light received from distant stars, scientists have determined that the same elements found on earth are found throughout the rest of the universe.

Here are two tasks you can try. Each one makes use of your understanding of elements and compounds. The periodic table of the elements, on pages 262–263, may help you.

Task 1

In your Journal, fill in the blank with the word *element* or *compound.*

Many of the ___?___ of copper are blue or green. Copper chloride is a green ___?___. It contains two ___?___, copper and chlorine. The Statue of Liberty, which is made of copper, has a green coloring. This green coloring is the ___?___ copper carbonate. Two ___?___ found in the air, carbon dioxide and water, react with the ___?___ copper to form this green coating.

During chemical changes, elements react with other elements to form ___?___. As well, ___?___ can decompose into ___?___, or compounds can react with compounds to form still other ___?___. You have already seen examples of all of these types of chemical changes.

How did this lady get her color?

LESSON 7 ORGANIZER

Objectives

By the end of the lesson, students should be able to:
1. Distinguish between elements and compounds.
2. Identify examples of elements.
3. Identify examples of compounds.
4. Recognize the chemical symbols for common elements and understand the organization of the periodic table.

Process Skills

analyzing, identifying, comparing, researching

New Terms

Elements—substances that cannot be broken down during a chemical reaction.

Task 2

The following chemical changes all involve elements. Identify the elements, and state whether each is a reactant or a product of the chemical change.

(a) A flashlight battery uses a chemical change between zinc and ammonium chloride to produce electricity.

(b) Gunpowder, an early Chinese discovery, is made up of sulfur, carbon, and potassium nitrate. Ignition causes a flash or an explosion.

(c) Passing an electric current through water produces hydrogen gas and oxygen gas.

(d) Skiers sometimes use chemical hand warmers. Each package contains iron filings, carbon, water, and sodium chloride. When these substances are exposed to oxygen in the air, a chemical change occurs, producing heat.

Task 3

Here are some chemical changes you can try. In each case, both elements and compounds are involved. List the elements, as you did in Task 2.

(a) Take a deep breath. The oxygen you are breathing is taking part in a chemical change inside your body to form carbon dioxide.

(b) Wet a piece of steel wool. The rust that forms in a couple of days is a compound made up of iron and oxygen, called iron oxide.

(c) Place a piece of zinc or magnesium ribbon in dilute hydrochloric acid. The bubbles formed are hydrogen gas. Do this only with an adult present.

Chemical Science Today

Today's scientists know far more about the nature of chemicals and chemical changes than did the scientists of yesteryear. Today's scientists have even done what alchemists only dreamed of—they have made gold, though only in tiny amounts. They achieved this not by means of chemical changes, but rather by using powerful machines to alter the fundamental particles that make up matter.

Ninety-one elements exist naturally on earth. Scientists have created a few more to bring the number to over 100. But it is the 91 naturally occurring elements that make up everything in this world. That's incredible!

A modern chemist in a laboratory

Compounds—formed when elements combine with other elements in chemical changes; can be broken down into elements during a chemical reaction.

Periodic table—a chart in which all known elements are organized according to their chemical properties.

Materials

Task 3: steel wool, water, zinc or magnesium ribbon, dilute hydrochloric acid (0.1 *M*), dish, safety goggles, gloves, apron
Getting to Know the Elements: glue, poster board, index cards

Teacher's Resource Binder

Research Worksheet 5–9
Resource Transparency 5–5
Graphic Organizer Transparency 5–6

Science Discovery Videodisc

Disc 2, Image and Activity Bank, 5–7

Time Required

two class periods

Getting to Know the Elements

As you introduce the periodic table to students, emphasize that everything they see around them is composed of some combination of these elements. For example, all living things are composed of six elements: hydrogen, oxygen, carbon, nitrogen, phosphorus, and sulfur. Traces of nine other elements (sodium, magnesium, chlorine, potassium, calcium, manganese, iron, copper, and iodine) are also found in living things. The following table gives the approximate percentages for each major element in the human body.

Element	Percentage
Hydrogen	65.4%
Oxygen	25.6%
Carbon	7.5%
Nitrogen	1.25%
Phosphorus	0.24%
Sulfur	0.06%
Trace elements	0.0001%

Write this information on the chalkboard or overhead transparency, and discuss properties of each of the six elements with the class. Ask: Why are the properties of these separate elements nothing like the properties of a human body? *(The elements are combined into complex compounds that form bone, skin, muscle, and so on.)* Ask students why they think hydrogen and oxygen are the most abundant elements in our bodies. *(Oxygen and hydrogen combine to form water, and water accounts for about 70% of our body mass.)* Explain to students that the elements in the periodic table can be combined in different ways to form everything in the known universe. Ask students to name any other elements that they are familiar with and to name some of their uses.

(Continues on next page)

Getting to Know the Elements

On these two pages is the **periodic table** of the elements. The large letters are the symbols for each element, a kind of shorthand. The periodic table is arranged by *families* (elements in the same column) and *periods* (elements in the same row). Elements in the same family have similar chemical properties. Elements close together in the same period are also similar. Only 91 of these elements occur naturally. The rest are created artificially in the laboratory. Do you recognize some of these elements? What are they used for?

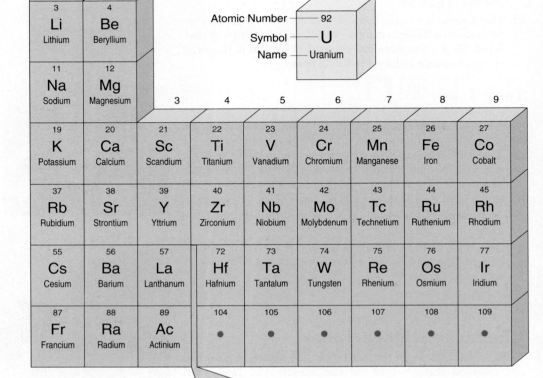

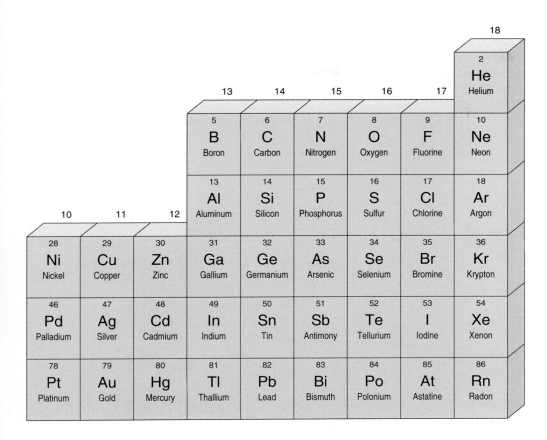

● Elements synthesized, but not officially named

(Getting to Know the Elements continued)

To help students start interpreting the periodic table, have each student choose a box representing a familiar element. Discuss the meaning of each item in the box. The following information is provided to help you explain the items in the table. Atomic structure is not discussed in the text, so including this material at this point is up to you. However, atomic structure is discussed in Units 4 and 5 of the *SourceBook*.

- *Atomic Number*—**the number of protons in the atom's nucleus.** Protons are positively charged particles in an atom. Have students note that the periodic table is arranged in order of increasing atomic number. Each succeeding atom has one more proton in its nucleus. **All atoms of the same element have the same number of protons.**
- *Symbol*—**the internationally agreed upon symbol for a particular element.** Have students discuss the symbols. Many were adapted from the Latin name for an element. (Names derived from Latin: gold, silver, lead, tin, mercury, iron, tungsten, potassium, and sodium.) Elements have also been named after places and people. (Named after places and people: Mendelevium, Fermium, Einsteinium, Californium, Berkelium, Curium, Americium, Plutonium, Neptunium, Nobilium, Lawrencium, Francium.) Have students look for examples of each.
- *Name*—**the names of the chemicals are usually derived from the Latin or Greek name for the element or from the name of a person or place.**

Have students look for elements with similar properties and compare their locations in the table. For example, have them locate the precious metals, silver (Ag), gold (Au) and platinum (Pt). Ask them to think about what properties these metals have in common. Students may begin to see the relationship between the properties of a substance and its underlying structure.

(Continues on next page)

(Getting to Know the Elements continued)

The index-card activity encourages students to practice their research skills as they get to know the elements better. You can adapt this activity to cooperative-learning groups by having groups of students investigate the elements in a particular chemical family; for example, halogens, alkali metals, noble gases, and so on. After they have done their research, have each group present a "Family History" of a group of elements to the class as an oral report.

Follow Up

Assessment

1. Give students the following list of items. Ask them to state whether each is an element or a compound. If the item is an element, ask them to write the chemical symbol. They may use their periodic tables for reference.
   (a) sodium chloride *(compound)*
   (b) carbon dioxide *(compound)*
   (c) water (dihydrogen oxide) *(compound)*
   (d) tungsten *(element, W)*
   (e) potassium nitrate *(compound)*
   (f) nitrous oxide *(compound)*
   (g) molybdenum *(element, Mo)*
   (h) cesium *(element, Cs)*
   (i) iron oxide *(compound)*
2. Divide the class into two teams. Have Team A ask the members of Team B what the symbols are for the common elements. Let each member of Team A have a turn. Then reverse roles, with Team B asking the questions and Team A supplying the symbols. The first team to answer 20 symbols correctly wins.

Extension

Students can build atomic models of various elements for a class display. Some students may want to try making a model of a simple compound. Marshmallows, gum drops, and toothpicks can be used for this task.

Now select an element from the periodic table and investigate it. What is the origin of its English name? Is its symbol very different from its English name? If so, why? What are its physical and chemical properties? What is its most interesting property? What are some of its uses?

Record your information on index cards, and form a class display about the elements by gluing the cards to a sheet of poster board.

Here is what Weldon and Lawanda found out about the elements silver and mercury.

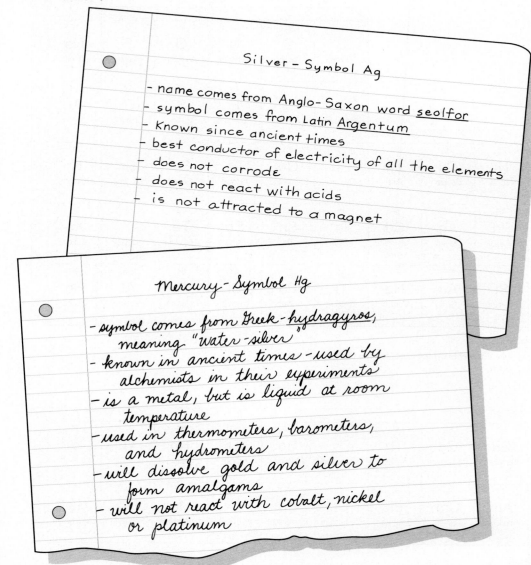

8 Acids and Bases

If you were asked to talk about **acids,** what would you say? Would you be surprised to learn the following facts?

• Vinegar is an acid.

• Milk contains an acid.

• Apples contain an acid, and so does lemon juice.

• Your stomach produces hydrochloric acid to digest food.

As you can see, there are many acids that are already familiar to you. Acids form a class of substances with similar properties. All acids have a sour taste. They react with metals, as well as with another class of compounds called **bases.**

In your home, you can find bases in drain cleaners, in household ammonia for cleaning floors, and in the bottle of milk of magnesia that you may have in your medicine cabinet. Bases feel slippery and have a bitter taste. They react with acids.

Acids and bases can be detected by chemical changes. There are some natural dyes that have one color in acids and another color in bases. These dyes are called **indicators.** The table below gives the expected color of three different indicators in acids and in bases.

Three Acid/Base Indicators	Color	
	In Acids	In Bases
litmus	red	blue
bromthymol blue	yellow	blue
phenolphthalein	clear	pink

Never touch or taste any acid or base unless you are instructed to do so. Some strong acids and bases can destroy skin on contact. Use acids and bases with extreme caution and only in the presence of an adult.

In Activity 1 of Exploration 5, you will use these three indicators to answer three questions:

(a) What materials are acids or bases?

(b) Can carbon dioxide dissolve in water to form an acid?

(c) What happens when you mix an acid and a base?

In Activity 2, you will make your own acid/base indicator out of a red cabbage!

LESSON 8 ORGANIZER

Objectives

By the end of the lesson, students should be able to:

1. State two properties of acids and bases.
2. List the properties of an acid-base indicator.
3. Safely perform acid-base indicator tests on a variety of household substances.
4. Identify substances as acidic or basic.

Process Skills

observing, comparing, classifying, researching

New Terms

Acids—compounds that react with metals and bases; they have a sour taste.

Bases—compounds that react with acids; they feel slippery and have a bitter taste.

(Organizer continues on next page)

✳ Getting Started

This lesson helps students identify **acids and bases that are common in everyday life.** It provides activities that demonstrate a variety of acid/base indicators and a neutralization reaction.

Main Ideas

1. Acids are a class of compounds that have a sour taste and react with bases and metals.
2. Bases are a class of compounds that have a bitter taste and react with acids.
3. Acids and bases can be detected by natural dyes called indicators.
4. Acids react with bases in a neutralization reaction to form a class of compounds called salts. Water is also produced in this reaction.

✳ Teaching Strategies

The investigations in this lesson familiarize students with common acids and bases found in the classroom and at home.

Have students read the introduction on page 265. Start a list on the chalkboard of the acids and bases mentioned in the text, and add any others that the students may be aware of. Tell students that in the next Exploration, they will be testing some substances to see if they are acids or bases. At this point, you can demonstrate the color changes in the three indicators mentioned in the table so that students will know what to expect.

Answers to

Exploration 5

Activity 1

1. To answer this question, supply each student with 10–15 pieces of litmus paper. Cut each regular-sized piece into four smaller pieces.

   Set up a number of activity stations in the classroom. Students can record their observations in a table in their Journals.

2. To answer this question, prepare a bromothymol blue solution: add a few drops of bromothymol blue to a beaker of water. The solution should be bluish. If it is not, add a drop or two of household ammonia until the solution turns blue. (Adding ammonia makes the water basic enough to turn the indicator blue.)

   Provide each group of students with a beaker of the dilute bromothymol blue solution. (This solution will turn yellow when students blow into it with a straw because carbon dioxide in their breath combines with the water molecules to form a weak acid, carbonic acid.) **Caution:** Make sure that students only *blow* through the straw; they should *not* drink the solution. This reaction also takes place in the atmosphere, making normal rain slightly acidic. Acid rain forms when exhaust gases from cars and emissions from factories mix with water in the air in reactions similar to that which formed carbonic acid.

   Students can change each beaker back to blue by adding a drop of household ammonia. This shows that indicator changes are reversible.

(Answers continue on next page)

Investigating Acids and Bases

Activity 1

For the Classroom

You Will Need

- litmus paper
- bromothymol blue
- phenolphthalein
- a variety of substances to test
- a beaker of water
- a plastic straw
- household ammonia
- dilute hydrochloric acid
- dilute sodium hydroxide
- an evaporating dish or other glass container
- an eyedropper
- a microscope

What to Do

Be Careful: *These experiments involve certain hazardous chemicals. Do not allow them to contact your skin or eyes. Avoid inhaling ammonia fumes. Wear safety goggles.*

1. Which materials are acidic? Which are basic? Use the *litmus* test to find out. Cut each piece of litmus paper into four parts and use them to test different materials. Try lemon juice, apple juice, a tomato, coffee, milk, water, baking soda, milk of magnesia, antacid tablets, aspirin, household ammonia, soap, and anything else that you may have around. Any solid material must be mixed with a few milliliters of water before being tested.

2. Could carbon dioxide be a contributor to the acid rain problem? Obtain a beaker of water and add a few drops of *bromothymol blue*. If your solution is a slight yellow color, add a drop or two of household ammonia until a blue color results. Using a plastic straw, blow gently into the solution for a minute or two. What happens? Has your breath affected the acidity of the water? What component of the air you exhale could cause this effect? How might this be related to the acid rain problem?

3. Do you know how to make table salt? To do so, you need a dilute solution of both hydrochloric acid and sodium hydroxide. Place 5 mL, or 25 drops, of dilute hydrochloric acid in an evaporating dish or other glass container. Add one drop of *phenolphthalein* indicator. Next, add sodium hydroxide drop by drop, until the solution turns a very faint pink color. If the pink color seems too intense, add a drop of hydrochloric acid. Place the dish in a quiet spot to allow the liquid to evaporate. Observe what remains. Examine the crystals under a microscope. This is an example of a **neutralization reaction.** The acid *neutralizes* (reacts with) the base to form *salt.* Water is formed as well.

acid + base → salt + water

hydrochloric acid + sodium hydroxide solution → sodium chloride solution + water

---

(Organizer continued)

Indicators—natural dyes that have one color in acids and another color in bases.

Neutralization reaction—a reaction in which the acid neutralizes (reacts with) the base to form a salt.

Materials

Exploration 5
Activity 1: variety of substances to test including: lemon juice, aspirin, hand soap, apple juice, tomato, coffee, milk, water, baking soda, milk of magnesia, seltzer tablet; household ammonia; litmus paper; dilute sodium hydroxide (0.1 *M*); bromothymol blue; phenolphthalein; dilute hydrochloric acid (0.1 *M*); evaporating dish; eyedroppers; beaker of water; plastic drinking straws; microscope, scissors, safety goggles
Activity 2: raw red cabbage, vinegar, household ammonia, hot water, eyedropper, drinking glass, knife, test tubes, watch or clock

Teacher's Resource Binder

Resource Transparency 5–7

Science Discovery Videodisc

Disc 2, Image and Activity Bank, 5–8

Time Required

two class periods

Activity 2

Make Your Own Acid/Base Indicator at Home

You have already used three prepared acid/base indicators. Now you will make your own indicator using a red cabbage.

You Will Need

- red cabbage leaves
- vinegar
- household ammonia
- hot water
- an eyedropper
- a glass
- test tubes
- a knife

What to Do

1. Cut a red cabbage leaf into small pieces.
2. Fill a glass one-quarter full with the cabbage pieces.
3. Add enough hot water to fill the glass halfway.
4. Allow the cabbage to soak for 20 minutes.
5. Save the colored liquid and throw out the cabbage pieces. The purple cabbage juice is your indicator.

Questions

1. What color does the cabbage juice indicator turn in acids? Fill a test tube one-quarter full of cabbage juice. Add a dropperful of vinegar.
2. What color does the cabbage juice indicator become in bases? Again fill a test tube one-quarter full of cabbage juice. This time, add a drop of household ammonia. What happens? Continue to add ammonia, one drop at a time. Do you get another color change?
3. Can you neutralize the basic solution? Try by adding more vinegar. What happens?

> **Violets are . . . red(?)**
> Violets are another natural indicator. Put a bluish-purple violet into a glass and pour some vinegar on it. Wait 10 minutes. The violet will turn red!

Activity 3

Research

In Activity 1, you learned an important fact about acid rain. Now find out some more. What causes acid rain? Why is it harmful to the environment? Do research on this important problem. Take your findings and make a classroom display of headlines, articles, and letters to the editor on this issue.

Answers to

Questions

1. In acids, indicator turns pink.
2. In bases, indicator turns blue; another color change is not possible if only basic substances are added.
3. Yes, the basic solution can be neutralized by adding vinegar. The indicator will turn pink again.

Activity 3

Give students a certain amount of time to complete their research projects on acid rain. Information is available from several environmental agencies.

✳ Follow Up

Assessment

1. Ask students to explain what happens to three different indicators when an acid or a base is added.
2. Ask students to write a summary of the content of this lesson using the following words: acids, bases, bitter, sour, reactants, indicators, salts, product, neutralization.

Extension

1. Students could research how the pH scale relates to acid/base indicators, and then compare the pH of common substances. Have them make a large poster depicting the pH scale. Alongside the scale at appropriate points, they could place drawings or magazine pictures representing the substances they have researched.
2. Stage a debate about acid rain. One group could represent industrial concerns, the other group could represent environmental concerns. The presentation should include background information about the different viewpoints and the origins of the acid-rain problem. The debate format should include initial arguments, rebuttals, and audience participation in the form of questions and answers.

Answers continued

3. Students will find it interesting to change the solution to pink (base) and then to clear (acid) by first adding the base, and then more acid. Encourage them to finish up with a solution that is just slightly pink. The crystals formed after evaporation of the liquid will be three-dimensional (cubic) in shape. Have students examine these crystals with a microscope. The reaction equation is: sodium hydroxide + hydrochloric acid → sodium chloride + water.

Activity 2

This can be done at home, as the title suggests, or as a classroom activity.

To make a purple cabbage indicator for the whole class, add a couple of cut-up cabbage leaves to 500-1000 mL of boiling water. When the water is deep purple, cool it and bottle it. Store it in the refrigerator until needed.

Getting Started

Students work through the development of a theory and learn how a theory can change over time. Students follow the thoughts of Empedocles, Stahl, and Lavoisier as each ponders the question—What causes burning? In *Explorations 7* and *8*, students will perform a variety of activities that support Lavoisier's theory of burning.

Main Ideas

1. Burning (combustion) is a chemical change that involves a rapid reaction with oxygen.
2. Corrosion is a chemical change that involves a slow reaction with oxygen.
3. Theories can change as new observations are made.

Teaching Strategies

After students read the theories, they will notice that all the theories *seem* to work. Divide the class into small groups, distribute the materials, and have them proceed through the three Explorations. This should help students formulate their own ideas about the true nature of burning.

Flashback! Greece, 460 B.C.

According to Empedocles, all things were made up of one or more of the four elements: earth, air, fire, and water. The properties of a substance depended on the mixture and amount of each of these elements.
(Continues on next page)

9 The Nature of Burning— A Chemical Change

The role of elements and compounds in chemical changes was not always known. Even a very familiar change like burning mystified observers for thousands of years. Let's listen in on three scientists as they discuss what they think burning is all about.

Flashback! Greece, 460 B.C.

Empedocles is eating a simple meal of bread and cheese by the light of an oil lamp. He studies the flame and wonders, "What causes burning?"

Empedocles' Theory and Conclusion

All matter is composed of four elements—earth, air, fire, and water. If a piece of matter contains the element fire, then it will burn.
Wood contains fire—wood burns!
Oil contains fire—oil burns!
Rock does not contain fire—rock does not burn!

Good theory. It works. Or does it? What can you do to support his theory—or prove it wrong? According to Empedocles' theory, salt is made up of earth and water. What might have been the reasoning behind this conclusion?

Invent a good caption for this cartoon.

Flashback! Germany, 1710

George Stahl is having dinner by candlelight. He and his wife are discussing a question that has often come up before: "What causes burning?"

Stahl's Theory and Conclusion

Phlogiston! That's right. All objects that burn contain phlogiston. And when the phlogiston is all gone or when the air becomes saturated with the released phlogiston, then burning stops.
Wood contains phlogiston—wood burns!
Coal contains phlogiston—coal burns!
Rock does not contain phlogiston—rock does not burn!

Good theory. It explains many observations. Or does it? Can you suggest any ideas that would support or disprove this theory of burning?

Invent a good caption for this cartoon.

LESSON 9 ORGANIZER

Objectives

By the end of the lesson, students should be able to:
1. Compare the theories of burning developed by Empedocles, Stahl, and Lavoisier.
2. Discuss the components of each theory that made it seem reasonable at that time in history.

Process Skills

inferring, analyzing, comparing, investigating

New Terms

Combustion—the process of chemically combining a substance with oxygen so rapidly that heat and light are produced.
Corrosion—a slow, destructive chemical change, often involving metals that combine with oxygen to form a new compound.

Testing Stahl's Theory

You Will Need

- a candle
- a metal lid
- a gram scale
- a bottle with a wide opening

What to Do

1. Observe a burning candle. Does anything seem to enter or leave the candle as it burns?
2. Attach the candle to a metal lid. Find the mass of the candle and the lid. Light the candle, and after 10 minutes, blow it out. Find its mass again. Using Stahl's theory, explain why its mass is different.
3. Light the candle, and place a bottle over it. What happens? How would Stahl explain this?

Flashback! France, 1775

Antoine Lavoisier is eating a dinner of onion soup and frogs' legs. A candle is burning. Lavoisier is celebrating. He has devised a new theory of burning.

Oxygen causes burning!
The best theory!
Explains all observations!

(Flashback! Greece continued)

Encourage students to think of other substances that could support or disprove this theory. Have them explain their reasoning. For example, salt was probably thought to be made up of earth and water because it is a solid, and because when it dissolves in water, it looks just like the water it is dissolved in. You might also point out to students the similarities this theory has with the way in which elements and compounds make up all matter, and how the combination of the elements determines their properties. Explain to students that although a theory may be incorrect, valuable information is often gained from the thought that went into the development of the theory.

Flashback! Germany, 1710

This theory is different from Empedocles' in that a substance (phlogiston) is released from a burning object. However, the connection had not yet been made between oxygen in the air and burning. Again, have students think of substances that help to prove and disprove this theory.

Answers to

Exploration 6

1. Something does seem to leave the candle, since it gets smaller.
2. The candle's mass is decreasing as it burns. Stahl would say it is losing its phlogiston.
3. When a jar is placed over the candle, the candle goes out. Stahl would say that the air has become saturated with the released phlogiston, extinguishing the candle.

Flashback! France, 1775

Even though students will probably be aware of Lavoisier's theory, treat it as a theory that can be either supported or disproved by observation and experiment. *Explorations 7* and *8* provide observations to support the oxygen theory of burning.

Materials

Exploration 6: metal lid, candle, matches, gram scale, bottle with a wide opening, watch or clock, safety goggles
Exploration 7: small can (such as a tuna fish can), steel wool, matches, balance, clothespin, safety goggles
Exploration 8: candle, jar with cover, matches, 25 mL limewater (See page 245 for limewater preparation), graduated cylinder, safety goggles

Teacher's Resource Binder

Activity Worksheets 5–10 and 5–11
Graphic Organizer Transparencies 5–8 and 5–9

Science Discovery Videodisc

Disc 2, Image and Activity Bank, 5–9

Time Required

two to three class periods

Exploration 7

Impress upon students the importance of accurate measurements in this activity.

Answers to

In-Text Questions

3. Students will observe a mass increase of 0.1 g or more depending on how many times the steel wool is touched with the match. Stahl would have predicted a mass decrease because of the loss of phlogiston. This evidence contradicts his theory. Lavoisier would have suggested that the steel wool was combining with oxygen from the air, thus increasing its mass. This experiment supports his theory.

4. When a candle burns, it loses mass. The wax combines with oxygen from the air to form a gas, which is now known as carbon dioxide. Lavoisier would also have said that a candle goes out when a jar is placed over it because all the oxygen from inside the jar was used up.

5. The word equation for the reaction is:
   iron (steel wool) + oxygen →
   iron oxide

Testing Lavoisier's Theory

You Will Need

- steel wool
- a balance
- a clothespin
- matches
- a small can, such as one used for tuna fish

What to Do

Be Careful: *Always use caution when handling burning materials.*

1. Place about 1 g of loosely packed steel wool into a small can. Very carefully find the mass of the steel wool and the can.

2. Now touch a burning match to the steel wool. The steel wool burns! Repeat this three or four times.

3. Find the mass of the can and the steel wool again. Was there a mass change? Could Stahl explain this observation with his theory? How would Lavoisier explain it?

4. According to Lavoisier, why would a candle go out after a jar is placed over it? Why does a candle have less mass after burning?

5. Complete this word equation in your Journal:
   iron   + ? → iron-
   (steel wool)   oxide

Learning About Burning

The students in the illustrations are performing simple experiments. Try the experiments yourself in the next Exploration to find out what observations the students are making.

EXPLORATION 8

Student Conclusions

You Will Need

- a candle
- 1 jar
- 25 mL of limewater

What to Do

1. Hold the jar very close to a candle flame. What is being deposited on the jar? Where is the substance coming from?

2. Place the jar over the candle. What is being deposited inside the jar? Where is this substance coming from? How could you prove what it is?

3. After the candle has gone out, add 25 mL of limewater to the jar and cover it quickly. Shake. What happens? What does this prove?

4. What evidence did you see that a burning candle produces water when it burns? carbon dioxide?

5. Complete this word equation in your Journal. Candle + oxygen → ? + ___.

Attaboy Antoine!

"Dear Lavoisier . . . " Write a letter to Lavoisier congratulating him on his new theory. Tell him how your own candle experiments support his theory of burning.

Shedding Some Light on Candles

- The word *candle* originally comes from a Latin word meaning "to shine."
- Candles have been made from fish oil, whale oil, beeswax, tallow, tree bark, cinnamon, bayberry, and paraffin.
- Native peoples of the Pacific Northwest used the oily "candle fish" in an interesting way. After drying it, they would place it in the fork of a tree and light it—creating a strange-looking candle!
- North Americans use more than 90 million kilograms of paraffin each year to make candles.
- When a lighted candle casts a shadow, the darkest part of the shadow is the brightest part of the flame.

Slow, Slow Burning

A candle may burn for hours. During burning, or **combustion**, carbon and hydrogen, the two main elements making up a candle, combine with oxygen to form carbon dioxide and water. Noticeable heat and light are also produced.

In Exploration 7, you saw that steel wool can burn. Iron (steel wool) combines with oxygen to produce iron oxide. This explains why steel wool gained mass in this chemical change.

When iron is exposed to air, it reacts slowly with the oxygen in the air. Again, iron oxide is formed. This process, called rusting, is an example of **corrosion**, which can be seen all around you. How many examples of corrosion can you think of? Why do some things corrode and others burst into flame? How can material be made resistant to corrosion? The process of corrosion can be used to investigate a variety of questions:

1. What percentage of the air is oxygen?

2. Does the air you exhale contain oxygen? If so, how much?

3. What treatments can speed up or slow down corrosion?

4. Do different brands of steel wool rust at the same rate?

Do you think you could design experiments for answering these questions?

compound containing the elements hydrogen and carbon.

5. Candle + oxygen → water + carbon dioxide.

Attaboy, Antoine!

Students need to summarize all the information they have learned in this lesson and then make a list of the major points. They can then use this list to write a letter to Lavoisier in support of his theory.

Slow, Slow Burning

After students have read this material, ask them to compare and contrast the processes of combustion and corrosion. Encourage them to name examples of both. Assign the questions at the bottom of the page as research activities. Students can also design experiments to find the answers.

Assessment

1. Have students write an essay comparing and contrasting the viewpoints of Empedocles, Stahl, and Lavoisier.

2. Ask students to summarize what they have learned about how a theory develops and changes. Students can use examples from this unit.

Extension

1. Have students investigate the phenomenon of "spontaneous combustion." Ask them to explore the causes and the materials involved. Have them relate what they find out to possible fire hazards in the home and the workplace.

2. Have students investigate how chemical hot packs work. Ask them to examine the chemical reaction that causes the product to release heat.

Answers to

Exploration 8

1. When a jar is held very close to a candle flame, a black deposit is formed on the outside. This is unburned carbon. The substance is coming from the candle. The candle wax must be made up of a compound containing carbon.

2. When a jar is placed over the candle, moisture can be seen condensing on the inside of the jar. The candle wax must be made up of a compound containing hydrogen.

The hydrogen combines with the oxygen from the air during the burning process to form water. This can be proved by the cobalt chloride test. (See "Mysterious Drops," Lesson 6.)

3. If 25 mL of limewater is added to the jar from step 2, the limewater will turn milky. This proves that upon burning, the carbon in the candle combined with the oxygen to form carbon dioxide.

4. The cobalt-chloride test confirmed the presence of water; the limewater test confirmed the presence of carbon dioxide. We can deduce that wax is made up of a

Did you have fun learning about chemical changes? All living things depend on chemical changes—from the smallest bacteria to blue whales and giant redwoods. Chemical changes are all around us— they power cars and trucks, feed and clothe us, settle our upset stomachs, and even make life itself possible. Wherever you go, whatever you do, you use chemicals and chemical changes.

Opinions Please

This unit started by asking your opinion about chemicals. It will close by examining your opinion about chemical changes.

In groups of three, choose one of the statements below. These are direct quotes from this unit. In your group, form an argument in support of the statement. Your argument can consist of observations, findings, examples from the unit, or observations and examples from your everyday experiences. Later, you will share your argument with the class.

"I think chemicals are everywhere around us."

"If my baking soda reacts with vinegar, then everyone else's will do the same."

"Our class concluded that there are some clues that show when a chemical change occurs:

- A new color appears.
- Heat or light is given off.
- Bubbles form.
- The change is not easily reversible."

"The only problem is that you can't use the same clues for each chemical change. Life certainly is complicated!"

"Who uses chemicals and chemical changes? Almost everyone!"

"In every chemical change, new substances are formed. These new substances are called the products of the chemical change."

"All chemicals or substances can be classified as either elements or compounds."

✴ Getting Started

This lesson helps students review the concepts and terms introduced in this unit.

Main Idea

Chemical changes are all around us and are essential to everyday life.

✴ Teaching Strategies

Opinions Please

This activity encourages students to summarize many of the concepts discussed in the unit. Each group should choose one statement to discuss. Students should provide examples to illustrate their statements and locate text pages where the pertinent ideas are discussed.

✴ Follow Up

Assessment

Ask students to summarize, using specific examples, how their thinking about chemicals has changed since the beginning of the unit.

Extension

1. Students can apply what they have learned about chemical changes to explore an earth- or life-science topic of their choice. Some possibilities include: formation of gems and minerals, composition of stars, hydroponics, and the chemistry of tears.

2. Ask students to prepare a lesson on chemicals for children in the primary grades. Ask them to describe how and what they would teach.

LESSON 10 ORGANIZER

Objective

By the end of the lesson, students should be able to use their scientific knowledge to discuss a variety of statements about chemical changes.

Process Skills

analyzing, communicating, summarizing, writing

New Terms

1. Sandra has been given five bottles labelled P, Q, R, S, and T, with a colorless liquid in each. She is told that two of the liquids are dilute acids, one is a base, and the other two are water. She is also given the liquid acid/base indicator, phenolphthalein.
   Write down some instructions for Sandra to help her find out whether each liquid is an acid, a base, or water. She can use test tubes, droppers, etc.

2. Instructions for a coffee maker: "Every month or so, run vinegar through your coffeemaker."
   Why do you think this is suggested?

3. A scientist performed an experiment involving a chemical reaction. She recorded data every five minutes for 35 minutes. Here is a table showing the results. Unfortunately, some of the data was ruined, so the table is incomplete.

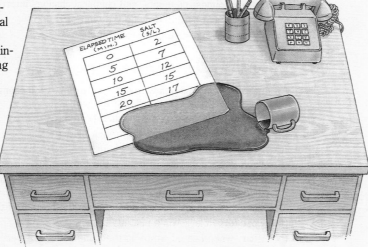

ELAPSED TIME (MIN.)	SALT (S/L)
0	2
5	7
10	15
15	17
20	

   (a) Copy the table into your Journal. Graph the data.
   (b) What kind of a chemical reaction do you think took place? Why do you think this?
   (c) Complete the table and graph based on your estimate of the outcome.
   (d) Justify your reasoning.

4. Which of the chemicals listed below belong to the same chemical families? Which ones belong to the same periods? Refer to the periodic table on pages 262–263.

   Boron, oxygen, helium, fluorine, neon, arsenic, krypton, bromine, nitrogen, iodine, and chlorine.

Answers to

Challenge Your Thinking

1. **(a)** Place samples of all five liquids into separate test tubes.
   (b) Add phenophthalein. The basic solution will turn pink.
   (c) Now add two drops of the base to each of the other liquids. The water samples should now be basic and will turn pink with phenophthalein. The acid solution will still be acidic.

2. The vinegar reacts with the build-up of lime or scale deposits from water and eliminates these deposits.

3. **(a)** See graph on page S170.
   (b) A neutralization reaction took place between an acid and a base, forming a salt.
   (c) See table on page S170.
   (d) The salt will continue to form until either the base or the acid is depleted.

4. • Boron, nitrogen, oxygen, fluorine, and neon are in the same period.
   • Arsenic, bromine, and krypton are in the same period.
   • Nitrogen and arsenic are in the same family.
   • Fluorine, chlorine, bromine, and iodine are in the same family.
   • Helium, neon, and krypton are in the same family.

Materials

Teacher's Resource Binder

Activity Worksheet 5–12

Time Required

one class period

Summary for

The Big Ideas

Student answers will vary. The following is an ideal summary.

Chemicals are found in all matter that surrounds us. Air, water, food, soil, our homes, our clothes, and all living things are made of chemicals. A chemical change takes place when one or more substances are converted into different substances with different properties. Some examples of chemical changes include the formation of a salt, rusting, combustion (burning), decomposition, respiration, and corrosion. Some signs that a chemical change has occurred include the following: formation of a precipitate, production of a gas (bubbling), release of heat and/or light, change in color, change in odor, formation of a new substance, and difficulty in reversing the change.

A physical property of matter is one that can be observed without producing a new kind of matter. Color, size, shape, boiling point, and melting point are examples of physical properties. Chemical properties can only be observed when there is a chemical change involved. Chemical properties determine how a substance will react in a given situation. The ability to rust in the presence of oxygen is an example of a chemical property.

Elements are composed of only one type of matter. Elements combine with other elements in chemical reactions to form compounds. The formation of compounds in reactions is an example of a chemical change.

Acids are compounds that react with metals and bases; they have a sour taste. Bases are compounds that react with acids; they feel slippery and have a bitter taste. Burning (combustion) is a fast reaction in which a substance combines with oxygen to form carbon dioxide and water; noticeable heat and light are produced. Rusting is a much slower chemical change in which metal combines with oxygen to form a new compound, rust.

The Big Ideas

In your Journal, write a summary of this unit, using the following questions as a guide.

- What are chemicals?
- How do we use chemicals in our daily lives?
- What happens during chemical changes?
- What are some examples of chemical changes?
- What are some signs of chemical changes?
- How do physical and chemical properties differ?
- How are compounds, elements, and chemical changes interrelated?
- What are acids and bases? How do they interact?
- How are burning and rusting similar? different?

Checking Your Understanding

1. From the descriptions below, would you expect each change to be chemical or physical? If you can't tell, explain why.
   (a) A colorless liquid disappears when heated.
   (b) A colorless liquid turns yellow when heated.
   (c) A flash of light occurs.
   (d) When two chemicals are mixed, the temperature rises 20 °C.
   (e) When two clear liquids are mixed together, the resulting mixture is cloudy.
   (f) A liquid is cooled, and a solid forms on the bottom of the beaker.
   (g) A bar turns black when heated.
   (h) A bar, when heated, remains the same color, but becomes 2 mm longer.
   (i) A yellow solid is heated, and the room is filled with choking fumes.
   (j) A blue solid is dropped into water, and the water turns blue in color.

2. How might you prove or disprove the following statements?
   (a) A burning match produces carbon dioxide.
   (b) Water is given off when blue copper sulfate is heated.
   (c) The upper surface of a plant leaf gives off water.
   (d) The bubbles given off by soda water and the bubbles found in ordinary water are made up of different substances.

Answers to

Checking Your Understanding

1. (a) physical—evaporation, change of state.
   (b) chemical—color change
   (c) physical or chemical—if lightning occurs and there is no new material produced, the change is physical. If the flash was caused by something burning or exploding, then the change was chemical.
   (d) physical or chemical—a change in temperature can be caused by both physical and chemical changes.
   (e) chemical—color change; a precipitate forms.
   (f) physical—crystallization is occurring.
   (g) chemical—probably a coating formed when oxygen combines with a metal. However, if it is soot from a candle, it is a physical change.
   (h) physical—the bar has expanded when heated.
   (i) physical or chemical—the material could have either vaporized or a new gas was formed.

(Answers continue on next page)

3. Your friend Marcus has a theory: All the caves in the world have formed in the last few hundred years. Marcus bases his theory on the following points:
   - Caves form through the action of groundwater on limestone.
   - The groundwater has to be acidic to dissolve the limestone.
   - Groundwater begins as rainfall, therefore rain must be acidic.
   - Acid rainfall is caused by people burning fossil fuels.
   - People have only used fossil fuels for the last few hundred years. Therefore, all the caves in the world have formed in the last few hundred years!
   Is Marcus right? If not, then where did he go wrong?
   Do a little research to answer this question, if necessary.

4. In this unit you have used the kitchen chemicals: sugar, salt, baking soda, baking powder, and starch. Develop a system for identifying these chemicals without tasting them. Base your system on your knowledge of the changes that occur when using the reactants iodine, water, and vinegar.

5. Make a concept map using the following words and phrases: *chemicals, elements, compounds,* and *broken down.* You will use one word or phrase twice.

Reading *Plus*

Now that your have been introduced to chemical changes, let's find out more about what causes chemical changes. By reading pages S73–S98 in the *SourceBook,* you will learn about the particles that make up chemicals, the structure of these fundamental particles, the ways in which these particles interact, and the history of the discovery of these particles.

Updating Your Journal

Reread the paragraphs you wrote for this unit's "For Your Journal" questions. Then rewrite them to reflect what you have learned in studying this unit.

About Updating Your Journal

The following are sample ideal answers.
1. Chemicals are substances that make up all kinds of matter. *(Thus, Scale and Structure of all matter can be viewed at the chemical level.)*
2. Chemical changes affect us in almost everything that we do: they produce the clothes we wear and the materials that make up our environment; they help us gain energy from the food we eat; and they produce medicines, household products, and foods—chemical changes are everywhere.
3. When a substance burns, it combines with oxygen to produce carbon dioxide and water, and noticeable heat and light are produced.
4. Burning is similar to rusting in that oxygen combines with a substance to form a new substance.

(j) physical—the blue solid has dissolved and can be recovered by evaporating the liquid.

2. **(a)** Drop a match in a bottle and let it burn. Then add limewater and shake. If the limewater turns milky, carbon dioxide was produced.

   (b) Heat copper sulfate in a test tube. Test the condensate with cobalt chloride paper. It will turn pink. The copper sulfate should now be white. Add water to the white material. If it turns back to blue, you can infer that water was given off during heating.

   (c) Put blue cobalt chloride paper on each side of a leaf. Hold it with a paper clip. Wrap it tightly with plastic wrap. After half an hour, the piece on the bottom will be pink, indicating that water was released from the bottom of the leaf.

   (d) Pass bubbles from both sources through limewater and see if a precipitate forms. The carbon dioxide in the soda water turns the limewater cloudy.

3. Marcus was correct up until his fourth point. Rainfall becomes acidic not only from man-made pollutants but also from naturally occurring oxides in the atmosphere and in the thermal groundwater. Therefore, it would not be possible to determine when the limestone was dissolved.

4. **sugar**—dissolves in water, but the sugar crystals can be recovered by evaporation.
   salt—the same system can be used as for sugar.
   baking soda—reacts with vinegar to produce carbon dioxide gas.
   baking powder—reacts with vinegar to form carbon dioxide gas.
   starch—reacts with iodine to produce a purple-black substance.

5.

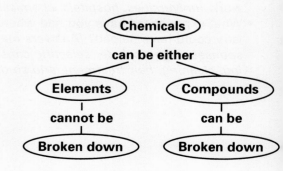

Chemicals
can be either
Elements — Compounds
cannot be — can be
Broken down — Broken down

Science in Action

Background

Chemical technologists are responsible for performing hands-on laboratory work in medical, industrial, and academic settings. They perform "wet" chemistry (involved with chemical solvents and solutions) and use a variety of scientific equipment ranging from simple centrifuges to specialized computer-linked chromatographs and other analytical devices.

Chemical technologists in hospitals and industrial, quality-control laboratories perform routine sample analyses. Specialized training after high school in a junior college or trade school is adequate for these careers.

However, chemical technology careers in research, such as the one described here, often involve developing new laboratory procedures and interpreting data. These careers require a minimum of a Bachelor's degree in chemistry or biochemistry.

Science in Action

Spotlight on Chemical Technology

Gloria Hidalgo is a chemical technologist. Technologists assist with research work and testing in industry, and with teaching in schools and universities. Some technologists obtain their basic qualifications by completing two or three years of specialized training after high school. Others are university science graduates. Gloria has a Bachelor of Science degree with a specialization in chemistry, and now she works at a university.

Q: What do you do as as chemical technologist?

Gloria: I do a lot of things. I do research projects and teach in the labs here at the University. I do consultant work and chemical testing for outside companies. My job offers me a lot of variety and I like that. Every day is different.

Q: How did you become interested in chemistry?

Gloria: There's no single starting point to this. As a child, I had a smoldering interest in chemistry—chemistry sets, Mister Wizard and so on. Then, when I got to high school my interest in the subject really caught fire, thanks to a terrific teacher who gave me the opportunity to do real chemistry.

Q: Have you had any memorable experiences in your work?

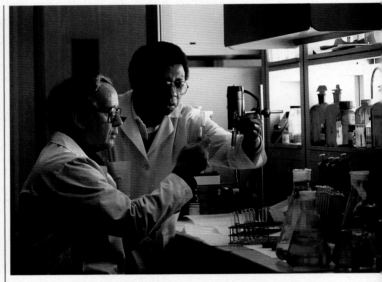

Gloria: One incident in particular comes to mind. Now this had nothing directly to do with my work, but it was memorable and did involve chemistry. A student had spilled something that left a bad stain on the floor, I forget exactly what. This student decided that he needed a really potent cleaning agent to get out the stain. So he mixed ammonia and chlorine bleach in a bucket, figuring that if one didn't do the job, the other would. Well, when you do this, you get an instant chemical reaction, the most noticeable by-product of which is chlorine gas. If you've ever swum in a chlorinated pool, you know that chlorine in even tiny amounts is intensely irritating. Imagine a cloud of chlorine gas filling the room. That's what happened. Everybody scattered, coughing and choking. It's ironic, but my students probably learned more from that bit of unintentional chemistry than from the chemistry course itself.

Q: It seems, then, that chemistry can be dangerous.

Gloria: Obviously, there is some danger, but then so is there whenever you use a power tool or an electrical appliance, or for that matter, whenever you

Using the Interview

Have students read the interview silently or choose volunteers to read it aloud to the class. To assess student understanding, ask questions similar to the following:
- Suggest some places where chemical technologists might work. *(universities, hospitals, chemical factories)*
- What experiences have you had where a knowledge of chemistry could have helped? *(Answers may vary, but possible responses might include: selecting consumer products, cooking, cleaning, hair treatment, and so on.)*

- Why are people not allowed to wear contact lenses in the laboratory where Gloria Hidalgo works? *(Vapors from chemicals can get underneath the lenses, causing serious eye damage.)*
- Suggest some other common-sense safety precautions in the laboratory. *(Answers may vary; possible responses might include: tying back long hair, wearing closed shoes instead of sandals, working in a well-ventilated area, avoiding horseplay, and so on.)*

walk out your front door. The key to a long and healthy career in chemistry is to be cautious but not fearful, to use common sense, to treat chemicals with respect, but to be prepared for emergencies. Students can protect themselves from possible harm by always following instructions and by wearing proper safety equipment—particularly aprons and goggles.

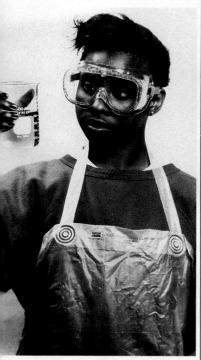

Proper safety equipment should be worn at all times in the lab.

Some Project Ideas

Practical chemistry is something almost everybody does at one time or another. Baking is a good example. Many worthwhile experiments can be done in the kitchen. Start with a standard recipe. Vary the proportions of the ingredients, and compare the results. For example, what is the effect of varying the amount of salt, baking powder, yeast, or liquid ingredients when following a particular recipe for bread? What is the effect of varying the oven temperature?

Another project is to test for starch, calcium, alkalinity or acidity in a variety of household materials. You have already performed each of these tests. Another project is to identify any harmful chemical changes that take place around your home or school, and then designing ways to counteract them. Corrosion, for example, is probably a problem in your area. How could you overcome this problem?

First, you would have to clearly identify the problem. Second, identify whether the cause of the problem is chemical or physical. Third, identify the chemical responsible. Finally, devise a method of preventing or counteracting the problem.

For Assistance

Begin by discussing the subject with your teacher. He or she can help you get started. You could also consult a chemist.

Chemists work in schools, universities, industry, medicine, agriculture, and many other fields.

Be sure to consult with your teacher or a chemist about safety concerns before starting on your project.

◆ Using the Project Ideas

1. Remind students that for a fair test, they must change only one variable at a time. To test the effect of temperature, for example, they must use the same dough recipe for each batch, but may bake the dough at different temperatures. Have them describe in writing how they would proceed to test the effect of varying the amount of each ingredient in the bread recipe.

2. Have students brainstorm a list of possible chemical changes to investigate. Possibilities might include: chemical changes involving food spoilage, such as souring of milk, which may be measured by decreased pH; oil turning rancid; and paint drying. Various chemical testing kits to help students are available from scientific supply houses.

◆ Going Further

One of the greatest threats to our environment involves the disposal of hazardous chemical wastes. One of the safest ways known to eliminate these chemical wastes is to burn them. Ask students to do some research to find out more about hazardous waste disposal.
• What are the advantages and disadvantages of burning these wastes?
• Would you want an incinerator in your neighborhood?

Science and the Arts

Science and the *Arts*

Background

Film is composed of tiny crystals of a compound of silver salts (usually silver bromide, AgBr). These crystals are embedded in a thin, gelatin layer called the *emulsion.* This emulsion of silver salt crystals rests on a transparent plastic backing. The emulsion and the backing constitute the familiar photographic film. The process of converting the unexposed film to a finished black and white photograph takes several steps. First, the camera shutter is opened, and light that is reflected from the object being photographed strikes the emulsion. In the areas where the light hits, the AgBr crystals are sensitized and an image, sometimes called the *latent image,* is produced. The degree of change in the AgBr crystals depends on the amount of light that reaches them. A large amount of light results in a greater change than a small amount. At this point the image cannot be seen. The film, with its latent image, is then placed in a developing solution.

The developing process is carefully timed so that the latent image will produce shades of black, white, and gray. Chemical developers convert the AgBr crystals into particles of silver metal, which then form the desired image. Any leftover AgBr crystals must then be removed from the emulsion. The film, now called a *negative,* is washed with water and allowed to dry.

Drawing with Light— With the Aid of Chemicals

The word *photography* was coined from Greek words meaning "drawing with light." Artists of the nineteenth century knew how to project images on a wall or a piece of ground glass by using a lens or a pinhole. They would trace the images to make accurate drawings of scenes or objects. But by using chemical reactions, the light itself could be made to leave its imprint on a specially prepared surface.

How Does It Work?

The underlying chemical principles of photography go back to a single discovery: certain silver-containing substances known as *silver salts* are extremely sensitive to light. Even very small amounts of light cause changes in the silver salts. These changes may not be visible at first, but when an exposed film containing silver salts is bathed with a chemical *developer*, the places that were exposed to light turn gray or black.

Adding Color

Color photography also makes use of the chemical principles described above. Color film has three layers, each sensitive to a different color of light. In the developing process, magenta, yellow, and cyan dyes are attached to the black silver particles in the different layers. Then the silver particles are dissolved, leaving just the colored dyes. Different combinations of the three colors produce all the visible colors.

Promoting Observational Skills

Ask the students to identify aspects of the photographs in this feature that reveal the artistic side of photography. Some questions for discussion might include the following:

- The picture of the workman is a famous photograph by Lewis Hine. Do you think it conveys an attitude of the photographer for his subject matter?
- In the still life, how has the photographer chosen and controlled the subject matter for artistic impact?
- How does the photograph showing the girl's hands illustrate the selectivity of the photographer's vision?

Discussion

Promote discussion in the classroom by posing the following questions.
1. Do you own a camera? If you do, what kind is it?
2. Do you enjoy taking pictures?
3. What have been some of your most exciting photographic experiences?
4. Have you ever had any photographs turn out badly or not at all? Explain why.
5. What makes a photograph artistically interesting?

Photography as Art

Photography opens up creative possibilities to the visual artist. For instance, photographers can capture their subjects in unposed or "candid" shots that may be very revealing—perhaps humorous. Cameras can be made to "see" things that people cannot. With the addition of a microscope or telescope, for example, they can record beautiful images we would otherwise never see. High-speed photography lets us look at things that are moving too fast to be seen with the unaided eye. Also, images can be treated or enhanced in many ways in the photographer's darkroom.

Much of the creative work of photography is in the selection of what is actually shot. Photography is an expression of an individual's way of seeing things, of his or her particular *vision* of the

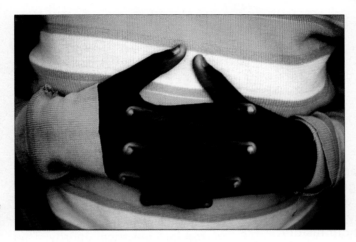

world. The subjects chosen, or the details of a scene that are emphasized, show us what the photographer finds beautiful, important, or interesting. The photographer can also convey a personal feeling toward his or her subjects, such as compassion or hostility. In studying a photographer's work, we may learn a great deal about the person who created it.

Think About It

Early critics thought that photography should not be called art because it was produced by mechanical means. What do you think about their reasoning?

What are some artistic skills that go into the making of a fine photograph?

Find Out for Yourself

To learn more about photographic techniques and the history of photography and photographers, the following readings are suggested:

Pollack, Peter. *The Picture History of Photography.* New York: Harry N Abrams, Inc., 1969.

Macaulay, David. *The Way Things Work.* Boston, MA: Houghton Mifflin Company, 1988.

Adams, A. *Ansel Adams, An Autobiography.* Boston, MA: Little, Brown and Company, 1985.

Find out what chemical reactions are involved in black-and-white photography. How are color slides made? Write a report about the life and work of a photographer whose work you enjoy.

Answers to

Think About It

- To answer this question, students could organize a class debate. Those who express specific opinions about one side or the other could write arguments in support of their viewpoints. Then both sides could deliver their statements. The rest of the class could listen to the arguments and then ask questions. Each side could have the opportunity for a rebuttal and final closing statement. Then the class could vote for the team that had presented the most convincing argument.
- To answer this question, students could interview local artists or art students, or analyze art photographs from a catalog or local museum exhibit. Answers may vary, possible responses might include: composition, layout, perspective, color, depth of field, and spatial relationships.

✦ *Going Further*

- Have students research the early days of photography from a technical and an artistic point of view. They could focus on a single photographer or historical period.
- Suggest that students investigate other uses of photographic processes, such as autoradiography, medical X rays, and infrared photography.
- Have students research how photographs can be modified and retouched. They could include an investigation of how photographs can be digitized and transmitted across long distances.
- Suggest that interested students organize a photography club or build a home darkroom.

✳ Teaching the Unit

 Unit Overview

In this unit, students explore the concept of energy. In the section *All About Energy,* students gain concrete experience with energy by experimenting with six energy-containing systems. Students study electricity and explore energy-related events throughout history. In the section *The Many Faces of Energy,* students explore the different forms of energy, and how one form of energy can be converted into another. In the section *Getting the Most From Energy,* students first learn how electrical energy is measured. They then explore the power requirements and costs of different appliances. In the final section, *Energy Today and Tomorrow,* students research the future of renewable and nonrenewable resources.

 Using the Themes

The unifying themes emphasized in this unit are **Energy, Systems and Interactions,** and **Patterns of Change.** The following information will help you weave these themes into your teaching plan. A focus question is provided with each theme as a discussion tool to help you tie the information in the unit together.

Energy ties all of the sciences together. Whether you are discussing physics, chemistry, biology, geology, or ecology, energy is the underlying "force" that keeps these systems running.

Focus question: *Using the words sun, plants, animals, microscopic organisms, soil, water, and atmosphere, trace the flow of energy and energy conversions through a biological system.*

Encourage students to set up a flow chart, using arrows to indicate the path of energy. The type of energy conversion that occurs and waste energy given off should be indicated. Answers will vary, but make sure that students understand that energy is never lost, it is merely converted into another form.

Systems and Interactions is evident in the energy that underlies any system of interactions. For example, energy causes reactions to occur between different chemical substances, causes matter to move and change its form, and causes living things to grow and interact with the environment.

Focus question: *How are electricity and magnetism related?*

Students should refer to *Lesson 6*, which describes

how a generator works. The movement of the wire inside the magnet generates an electric current in the wire. Thus, mechanical energy is converted into electrical energy. This electrical energy can then be converted into some other useful form of energy.

Patterns of Change can be discussed in relation with the conversion of one form of energy to another. It is only when energy is converted that changes occur. For example, when fuel in a car is burned, a chemical change occurs, producing mechanical energy and heat.

Focus question: *How do energy changes affect our environment?*

Approach this question in terms of the positive and negative effects of energy change. For example, the flow of energy from the sun through living systems is what allows life to exist on our planet. On the negative side, some attempts by humans to harness energy have resulted in unwanted side effects such as excess heat loss and pollution.

 Using the *Science Discovery* Videodiscs

Disc 1 *Science Sleuths, The Energy Mystery House* Potential home buyers discover that the utility bills for the home of their choice are three times the normal amount for a house that size. The Science Sleuths must analyze the information for themselves to find out why the bills are so high.

Disc 2 *Image and Activity Bank* A variety of still images, short videos, and activities are available for you to use as you teach this unit. See the *Videodisc Resources* section of the **Teacher's Resource Binder** for detailed instruction.

Using the *SciencePlus SourceBook*

Unit 6 focuses on energy and the many forms in which it is manifest. Energy transformations from one form to another are viewed in light of the law of conservation of energy. Students also learn that useful energy decreases with each transformation. Finally, the historical role of energy in society is discussed, and the possibilities of future sources of energy are explored.

PLANNING CHART

SECTION AND LESSON	PG.	TIME*	PROCESS SKILLS	EXPLORATION AND ASSESSMENT	PG.	RESOURCES AND FEATURES
Unit Opener	280		observing, discussing	For Your Journal	281	Science Sleuths: *The Energy Mystery House* Videodisc Activity Sheets TRB: Home Connection
ALL ABOUT ENERGY	282			Challenge Your Thinking	295	Graphic Organizer Transparency 6–3
1 Energy Is . . .?	282	1	observing, describing, inferring, writing			Image and Activity Bank 6–1 Resource Transparency 6–1
2 Energy in Action	284	2 to 3	classifying, hypothesizing, inferring, experimenting	Exploration 1	284	Image and Activity Bank 6–2 TRB: Resource Worksheet 6–1
3 One Form of Energy: Electricity	288	2	experimenting observing, inferring, predicting	Exploration 2	288	Image and Activity Bank 6–3
4 Energy Then and Now	290	1	comparing, sequencing, analyzing, drawing conclusions	Exploration 3	291	Image and Activity Bank 6–4 Graphic Organizer Transparency 6–2
THE MANY FACES OF ENERGY	296			Challenge Your Thinking	310	
5 The Energy Picture	296	1	observing, analyzing, classifying, inferring			Image and Activity Bank 6–5
6 Making Electricity from Scratch	300	2 to 3	observing, analyzing, sequencing, interpreting data			Image and Activity Bank 6–6 TRB: Resource Worksheet 6–2
7 More About Energy Conversion	304	1 to 2	observing, analyzing, inferring, describing			Image and Activity Bank 6–7 TRB: Resource Worksheet 6–3
GETTING THE MOST FROM ENERGY	311			Challenge Your Thinking	331	
8 Measuring Energy	311	1	calculating, predicting, comparing, sequencing	Exploration 4	313	Image and Activity Bank 6–8 TRB: Resource Worksheets 6–4, 6–5, and 6–6 Graphic Organizer Transparency 6–4
9 The Energy Bottom Line	314	2	calculating, comparing, estimating, drawing conclusions	Exploration 5 Exploration 6	316 322	Image and Activity Bank 6–9 TRB: Resource Worksheet 6–7 Graphic Organizer Transparencies 6–5 and 6–6
10 A Plan for Saving Energy	323	1	calculating, problem solving, evaluating, drawing conclusions			Image and Activity Bank 6–10
11 Keeping in the Heat	325	2 to 3	predicting, controlling variables, calculating, comparing	Exploration 7 Exploration 8 Exploration 9 Exploration 10	325 329 330 330	Image and Activity Bank 6–11 TRB: Resource Worksheets 6–8 and 6–9 Graphic Organizer Transparency 6–7
ENERGY TODAY AND TOMORROW	332			Challenge Your Thinking	343	
12 Bye-Bye Black Gold	332	1	classifying, problem solving, evaluating, summarizing			Image and Activity Bank 6–12 Resource Transparencies 6–8 and 6–9 Graphic Organizer Transparency 6–10
13 Energy for the Future	334	2 to 3	researching, comparing, drawing conclusions, decision making	Exploration 11	334	Image and Activity Bank 6–13
14 What Does the Future Hold?	339	1	predicting, analyzing, evaluating, decision making, writing			TRB: Activity Worksheet 6–10
End of Unit	344		applying, analyzing, evaluating, summarizing	Making Connections TRB: Sample Assessment Items	344	Science in Action, p. 346 Science and Technology, p. 348 *SourceBook*, pp. S99–S116

*Time given in number of class periods.

Meeting Individual Needs

Gifted Students

1. Challenge students to do experiments with solar heaters. Have them build solar collectors, such as the one shown on page 336. Have them find out the most efficient placement of the collectors in reference to the sun's angle. To do this, they should prepare three identical solar collectors and vary the tilt in reference to the surface of the earth.
2. Recreational activities in the United States, such as night baseball games, consume tremendous amounts of energy. Organize students into two groups to simulate a Senate subcommittee meeting. One group will be the subcommittee doing the investigating, and the other group will be the witnesses who testify in front of the subcommittee. Tell the first group that they have been instructed to investigate the desirability of outlawing or drastically reducing the high energy use of recreational activities. Have the second group prepare and read short statements in support of or in opposition to the idea under investigation. After hearing all of the testimony, the subcommittee should prepare its recommendations to submit to the Senate (the entire class). The report should include the major considerations that shaped the subcommittee's judgment. After a review of the report, the Senate should vote to accept or reject the subcommittee's judgment.

LEP Students

1. Have students play a game of Energy Bingo. Each student will need a card divided into 16 squares. Words, as well as drawings, that represent certain energy-related terms can be drawn on each square in any order. The role of the caller is to give clues that describe one of the energy terms. When students hear the clue being given, they cross off that term or picture on their card. The first student to get four squares in a row says "Bingo."
2. Bring in old magazines and catalogs. Have students cut out pictures of things that use energy, such as electrical appliances, cars, and motor boats. Then have them place the pictures into two groups: those that their family needs and those that are "extras."
3. At the beginning of each unit, give Spanish-speaking students a copy of the *Spanish Glossary* from the *Teacher's Resource Binder.* Also, let Spanish-speaking students listen to the *English/Spanish Audiocassettes.*

At-Risk Students

As many students may have trouble understanding the concept of energy, this unit has several helpful hands-on projects that illustrate what energy is all about. In the first Exploration, students demonstrate for themselves several different types of energy and energy conversions. After students have completed reading *A Science Fair Project,* challenge them to make their own windmills, following the design in the book or their own designs.

Exploration 11, Here Comes the Sun, presents a fun project that allows students to directly observe energy conversion by making their own solar heaters. Students may need to do a little outside research to complete their solar heaters, but the illustration in the text should help them get started. This project also gives students a chance to learn more about alternative energy sources.

Cross-Disciplinary Focus

Mathematics

Have students calculate the amount of energy required to transport students to school in school buses. First, they should call the school bus garage to find out the number of buses operating and the number of kilometers driven by the buses each day. They need to find out the average number of kilometers per liter of gasoline that the buses get. Then they can calculate the amount of gasoline used by the buses per year.

Agriculture

Since 1930, the yield of most major crops grown on farms in the United States has increased from 200 to 400 percent. The factors responsible for these increases include: increased use of machinery, greater use of nitrogen and other fertilizers, better seeds, use of herbicides and insecticides, and improved transportation. Ask each student to select one of these factors and research how it is related to energy. After the research is completed, engage the class in a discussion of the dependency of agriculture on energy sources. Ask: Is it likely that our farming methods will change as oil and gas supplies are depleted? What types of changes are possible?

Cross-Cultural Focus

Lifestyles and the Price of Gasoline

Point out that gasoline is cheaper in the United States than in any other industrialized country. Divide the class into groups of four students. Ask each group to develop a list of ways in which lifestyles in countries with high gasoline costs are likely to be different from lifestyles in America. For example, in America, there are larger cars and more super-highways. Americans are not as likely to use public transportation, such as trains and buses. They are more likely to travel long distances on vacations and use recreational vehicles. (These conditions are just the opposite with countries where gasoline prices are higher.) After sharing their lists with the class, ask each group to decide which lifestyle they prefer. Students should explain their choices.

Packaging Practices

Point out to students that in the world, food is packaged in many different ways. In the United States, food is wrapped in polyethylene or placed on plastic foam trays and then wrapped. In other countries like Indonesia, China, and Tunisia, shoppers bring their own shopping bags to market. They place the unwrapped and unbagged produce and meat wrapped only in butcher paper directly in their shopping bags. Thus, much of the energy used to produce our packaging containers is saved in other countries. Ask students to interview their parents about their willingness to use the simpler system found in other countries. What problems do they foresee? Do they think the present system should be kept? Are they concerned about the amount of packaging materials they throw away? Have students report their findings. What was the consensus? If they believe overpackaging is a problem, have students write letters to supermarket managers.

# Resources

Bibliography for Teachers

Lawrence Hall of Science. *Hot Water and Warm Homes from Sunlight.* Great Explorations in Math and Science. Berkeley, CA: Lawrence Hall of Science, 1986.

Lawrence Hall of Science. *Environmental Energy.* Berkeley, CA: Lawrence Hall of Science, 1983.

Lawrence Hall of Science. Center for Multisensory Learning. *Magnetism and Electricity: Science Activities for the Visually Impaired/Science Enrichment for Learners with Physical Handicaps.* Berkeley, CA: Lawrence Hall of Science,1979.

Bibliography for Students

Hansen, Michael C. *Coal: How It Is Found and Used.* Hillside, NJ: Enslow, 1990.

National Research Council. *Fuels to Drive Our Future.* Washington, DC: National Academy Press, 1990.

Pringle, L. *Global Warming.* New York, NY: Arcade, 1990.

Pringle, L. *Nuclear Energy: Troubled Past, Uncertain Future.* New York, NY: MacMillan, 1989.

Films, Videotapes, Software, and Other Media

The Big Spill.
  Videotape. NOVA.
  Coronet Film
  and Video
  108 Wilmot Road
  Deerfield, IL 60015

Electric Bill.
  Software.
  For Apple II family.
  Queue, Inc.
  562 Boston Avenue
  Bridgeport, CT 06610

Electromagnetism.
  Software.
  For Apple II family.
  Prentice-Hall Allyn
  Bacon
  Sylvan Avenue
  Englewood Cliffs, NJ
  07632

Energy Seekers.
  Film and Video.
  Coronet Film and Video
  108 Wilmot Road
  Deerfield, IL 60015

Hot Enough for You?
  NOVA. Film.
  Coronet Film and Video
  108 Wilmot Road
  Deerfield, IL 60015

Introducing Atoms and Nuclear Energy.
  Film and Video.
  Coronet Film and Video
  108 Wilmot Road
  Deerfield, IL 60015

Unit

6

Energy and You

✳ Unit Focus

Ask students to write a sentence using the word *energy.* Then have them read their sentences and discuss the many different meanings the word *energy* has.

Have students begin thinking about the scientific meaning of the term energy. Ask: Where does your energy come from? *(from the food you eat)* Where does the energy in food come from? *(the sun)* What happens to the energy in food after your body burns it? *(It is changed into the energy of motion and body heat, and it is used by body cells to build and repair themselves.)*

Students should understand that energy can be quantified, and that it can change from one form into another.

✳ About the Photograph

Lightning is an electrical phenomenon. For lightning to occur, the clouds must have areas with distinct electrical charges. The upper part of the cloud usually carries a positive charge, while the lower part carries both positive and negative charges. Lightning occurs as a huge spark that travels between the two parts of the cloud, or the cloud and the ground, when the difference in their electrical charges becomes great.

Ask students:

- Have you seen sparks fly from clothes when they come out of a clothes dryer?
- Have you ever gotten an electric shock when touching a metal doorknob?

Explain that these phenomena, as well as lightning, are caused by the movement of negatively-charged particles to a positively-charged area. Explain that this movement is a form of energy. All forms of energy can change from one form of energy into another.

Have students look at the photograph, and ask:

- Where is electrical energy changing to light energy? to sound energy? to heat energy? *(Light energy is seen as bright bolts of lightning; sound energy is heard as thunder; heat energy heats the air around the lightning.)*

For Your Journal

Write a paragraph summarizing your thoughts about each of the following:

1. What is energy? How important is it to you?
2. Where does energy come from?
3. Can energy take different forms? If so, what are some of them?
4. How is energy being transmitted in this photograph?

✴ About Your Journal

Students should answer the Journal questions to the best of their abilities.

These questions are designed to serve two functions: to help students recognize that they do indeed have prior knowledge about the topic, and to help them identify any misconceptions they may have. In the course of studying the unit, these misconceptions should be dispelled.

LESSON 1

 Energy Is . . . ?

Energy! You can't see it! You can't smell it! Energy is invisible, but it's certainly there. All kinds of people talk about it every day. What do they say about it?

✳ *Getting Started*

To begin the lesson, students are asked to think about what energy is. After observing several photos of different types of energy use, students are asked to describe in writing how energy is involved in each one. Finally, they develop a working definition of energy.

Main Ideas

1. Energy is an abstract concept that is difficult to define.
2. The term energy is used in many different ways.

✳ *Teaching Strategies*

Before the lesson begins, ask students to write a definition of energy in their Journals. After students have completed writing in their Journals, ask them to share their definitions of energy with the class. Then ask a student to look up the word energy in the dictionary. Discuss the different ways that the word energy can be used. Point out to students that in this unit, they will learn how the word energy is used in science.

LESSON ORGANIZER

Objectives

By the end of the lesson, students should be able to:
1. Observe and describe photographs in terms of what energy changes are taking place.
2. Write a working definition of energy.

Process Skills

observing, describing, inferring, writing

New Terms

Getting a Picture of Energy

Just what *is* energy? Can you put your ideas about energy into words? The photos here might give you some hints about what energy is. Look at them, and then write a sentence or two in your Journal about each one. Use the word *energy* in your description of what is happening in each picture.

Now compare your descriptions with those written by a classmate. Using your combined ideas, compose a single statement starting with the words "Energy is . . ." When you come to the end of this unit, you will be able to check whether your definition can be improved.

Getting a Picture of Energy

Have students work individually to describe, in terms of energy, what is happening in the photographs. Tell them that their sentences should include descriptions of what energy does *(it makes things happen)* and what forms it takes *(wind, fuel, and so on)*. Then divide the class into groups of two to four to compare their descriptions. Students should read their statements, and ask the other students in the group whether they agree or disagree. After completing this discussion, each group should update their definitions of energy. Then groups can share their definitions with the rest of the class.

✳ *Follow Up*

Assessment

1. Take students on a 15 to 20 minute walk around the school. Ask them to list all the things they observe where energy is making something happen. Also, have them identify the energy sources.
2. Ask students to keep an energy "diary" for a week. Have them record how they use energy each day.

Extension

Have students bring in magazine pictures showing energy at work. Have them make a collage with these pictures, and as a class, have students describe the part played by energy in each picture.

Materials

Getting a Picture of Energy: Journal

Teacher's Resource Binder

Resource Transparency 6–1

Science Discovery Videodisc

Disc 2, Image and Activity Bank, 6–1

Time Required

one class period

LESSON 2

✳ Getting Started

In this lesson, students are given the opportunity to experiment with mechanical, solar, heat, chemical, and electrical energy.

Main Ideas

1. Energy is stored in many forms.
2. Once it is released, energy makes many things happen.

✳ Teaching Strategies

After students have read the page, ask: Is energy visible? *(no)* If energy is invisible, how do you know it is there? *(You can see energy making things happen.)* Have students look at the picture and ask: Does the load of bricks contain energy? What would happen if the man let go of the rope? *(The bricks do contain energy, since they would fall if they were released.)*

Answer to caption: the energy stored in the raised load of bricks will be released when the worker releases the rope.

Exploration 1

These activities introduce students to mechanical, electric, solar, elastic, and chemical energy. This Exploration works well set up as six stations around the classroom. Two sets of apparatus at each station are adequate.

The Swinging Pendulum

When the pendulum is pulled to the side and held, it has stored energy. When it is released, the stored energy is released. The name for stored energy is *potential energy.* To prove that a pendulum has energy when it is vertical, the students can place an object, such as a paper tube, in its path. The object will move when it is hit by the pendulum.

---

② Energy in Action

You probably realize now that energy comes in many different forms. You probably also realize that energy is necessary to us—just think of trying to get along without energy! Although energy itself is invisible, you can see what it does. Energy makes things happen.

Where is energy found? In many places. One place is in a battery. You can't see the energy in the battery, but you can see what it does, so you know it must be there. The energy is *stored* in the chemicals inside the battery until it is needed; when it is used, it is *released.* How is the energy stored in the battery put into action?

Energy is stored in many places besides batteries. Look at the picture below. Does the load of bricks contain stored energy? How could you tell? What would happen if the man let go of the rope?

Is energy about to be released?

In Exploration 1, you will encounter six simple energy-containing systems. Ask yourself two questions about each:

1. Is energy causing something to happen? (This is your clue that energy really is there.)
2. Where was the energy stored before you made use of it? (You might have to make some guesses.)

Simple Energy Systems

1. The Swinging Pendulum

You Will Need

- an angled stand
- a 20-cm length of string
- a weight or bob

What to Do

Make your pendulum by attaching the weight to the stand with the string. Pull the pendulum to one side and hold it. Do you think it has any energy now? How could you show that it has energy? How is the energy stored? Give this type of energy a name.

Now let the pendulum go. Watch it a number of times as it swings. Do you think the pendulum has any energy when the string is vertical? How could you prove whether or not it does?

LESSON ② ORGANIZER

Objectives

By the end of the lesson, students should be able to:
1. Classify different forms of stored energy.
2. Infer the relationship between the release of stored energy and its effects on an object.

Process Skills

classifying, hypothesizing, inferring, experimenting

New Terms

---

2. A Light Touch

You Will Need

- a magnifying glass
- a small piece of newspaper, a dry leaf, or a small chip of wood
- a lid from a jar or can
- a bottle of water

What to Do

Put a tiny piece of newspaper, wood, or dead leaf on the lid. For safety, have a bottle of water close by. With a magnifying glass, focus the rays of the sun onto a tiny piece of newspaper, a dead leaf, or a piece of wood. What happens? Where does the energy come from? Can you give the energy source a name?

lid

3. The Spinning Spool

You Will Need

- an empty spool of thread
- a small nail
- a rubber band
- a slice of candle or piece of plastic
- a match stick

What to Do

Make a spool toy like the one shown. Give the rubber band 5 turns. Does the toy move? Try 10 and then 15 turns—what happens? Where does the energy come from? How does the toy store energy?

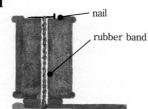

nail

rubber band

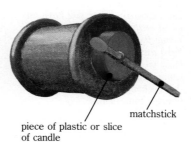

piece of plastic or slice of candle

matchstick

A Light Touch

The newspaper, wood, or dead leaf should ignite when the magnifying glass is used to focus the sun's rays. The energy comes from the sun; it is called *solar* energy. CAUTION: Students should use care whenever burning something.

The Spinning Spool

Explain that the wax or plastic washer is needed to reduce the friction so that the match stick can turn without getting stuck against the spool. It can be made by cutting a 0.5-cm thick slab of wax from the end of a candle. Bore a hole in the center of the washer and notch one side. The match stick fits in the notch.

When the match stick is given 10–20 turns, the spool moves forward at a slow, steady pace. The energy that causes this movement is stored in the twisted rubber band. It is called *elastic* energy.

Materials

Exploration 1
The Swinging Pendulum: angled stand, 20-cm length of string, weight or bob, object such as paper tube, scissors
A Light Touch: magnifying glass; piece of newspaper, dry leaf, or wood chip; jar or can lid; bottle of water
The Spinning Spool: empty spool of thread, small nail, rubber band, slice of candle or piece of plastic, match stick, scissors

Hot Stuff: candle or Bunsen burner; metal bottle cap; variety of materials to be heated, including copper sulfate crystals or a chip of plastic; tongs or pliers; empty can; safety goggles; matches
Chemical Magic: white vinegar, small piece of chalk, fine steel wool, test tube, test-tube clamp, water
Paper Clip Magic: bolt or spike, 20-cm length of fine insulated wire, masking tape, paper clips or iron filings, D-cell battery, wire cutters, wire strippers
Making Sense of Your Observations: Journal

Teacher's Resource Binder

Resource Worksheet 6–1

Science Discovery Videodisc

Disc 2, Image and Activity Bank, 6–2

Time Required

two to three class periods

Hot Stuff

CAUTION: Tell students to be very careful when heating each substance. Insist that they always use the tongs to pick up the bottle cap, and that they put the cap inside the empty can when they are finished heating it. Tell students to use very small quantities of the copper sulfate and plastic.

As these substances are heated, have students watch for any changes. The water should boil; the copper sulfate should change from blue to white; the plastic should either burn or melt. The energy source is the burning gas in the Bunsen burner or candle.

Chemical Magic!

When the vinegar reacts with the chalk, bubbles are given off—signaling that a chemical change has taken place. The bubbles are carbon dioxide. Steel wool is made of iron. When vinegar is added, bubbles are given off. The bubbles are hydrogen gas. The energy source is chemical energy.

4. Hot Stuff

You Will Need

- a candle or Bunsen burner
- a metal bottle cap
- a variety of substances to be heated
- tongs or pliers
- an empty can

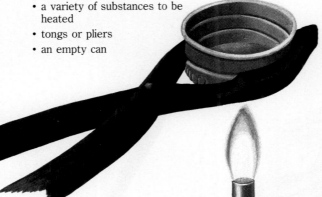

What to Do

Grip the bottle cap with tongs or pliers. Use the flame from a candle or Bunsen burner to heat the bottle cap. Try heating:

(a) A drop of water

(b) A copper sulfate crystal

(c) A small chip of plastic

Carefully record how the substances change.

Be Careful: *When you have finished heating the bottle cap, put it inside the empty can where it can't burn anything.*

How would you explain to your friends that energy is involved in these changes? Where does the energy come from?

5. Chemical Magic!

You Will Need

- white vinegar
- a small piece of chalkboard chalk
- fine steel wool
- a test tube
- a test tube clamp

What to Do

Put a small amount of white vinegar in a test tube. Add a small piece of chalk. Does anything happen? Where do you think the energy comes from?

Wash your test tube. Again put in a little vinegar. This time, add a few strands of steel wool. Explain what happens.

vinegar

chalk

6. Paper Clip Magic

You Will Need

- a bolt or spike
- a 20-cm length of fine insulated wire
- masking tape
- paper clips or iron filings
- a D-cell battery

What to Do

Wind about 20 turns of insulated wire around a bolt or spike. Scrape the insulation from the ends of the wire and connect them to a dry cell with masking tape. What happens when you move the end of the bolt near some paper clips or some iron filings? Why do you think this happens? Where does the energy come from?

Now disconnect the cell. What happens? How do you explain what happens?

Making Sense of Your Observations

In each situation in Exploration 1, energy was involved. How do you know? Energy must have been involved because *something happened* in each case. Give a name to each type of energy you encountered.

Now make up a table like the one below. The table has been completed for one situation—the Spinning Spool—as an example.

Title of Situation	What happened? (What evidence is there that energy was used?)	Where did the energy come from? (Where was it stored?)	My name for this type of stored energy.
The Spinning Spool	The Spool moved.	In the rubber band	Elastic energy
Hot stuff			

Assessment

Perform the following demonstrations. For each demonstration, ask students to name the energy used, where the energy is stored, and what happens when it is released.

(a) Blow up a balloon and release it. *(Energy name: elastic energy; where stored: in the stretched-out balloon; what happens: balloon moves all around when released.)*

(b) Lift a marble above a pan of smooth sand and release it. *(Energy name: mechanical energy; where stored: in the marble; what happens: marble dents the sand when it is dropped.)*

(c) Do jumping jacks. *(Energy name: chemical energy; where stored: in food; what happens: muscle cells are able to move because of the chemical energy from the food.)*

(d) Push the coils of a spring together and place it next to a marble. Then let the coil extend. *(Energy name: elastic energy; where stored: in compressed coils; what happens: the marble rolls when the coil is released.)*

(e) Light a candle. *(Energy name: chemical energy; where stored: in candle wax; what happens: heat and light energy are given off when candle burns.)*

Extension

Ask students to bring in toys that convert one form of energy into another. Have them demonstrate the toys and explain the energy changes.

Paper Clip Magic

Students discover that when electricity flows through a wire wrapped around an iron bolt, it sets up a magnetic field around the bolt and wire. This set-up is called an *electromagnet*. The electromagnet picks up things made of iron, including paper clips and iron filings. The magnetic field lasts as long as the current flows. Once the current stops, the field collapses. This shows that the energy source is in the D-cell battery.

Making Sense of Your Observations

To summarize the six activities, have students duplicate and complete the chart on page 287 in their Journals. Students should share their completed charts.

LESSON 3

✳ *Getting Started*

In this lesson, students build two devices to detect the presence of electricity. They then try to generate electricity in three different ways, and use electricity testers to find out if they have been successful.

Main Ideas

1. A galvanometer or an electric bulb connected in a circuit can be used as an electricity tester.
2. Electricity can be generated in many ways.

✳ *Teaching Strategies*

Exploration 2

The Exploration works well with five stations set up around the classroom. Two sets of apparatus are adequate at each station.

Activity 1
A. A Flashlight-Bulb Tester

Explain that there must be a complete circuit before electricity will flow. Draw a diagram of each circuit, and have students trace the path of electricity.

B. A Homemade Galvanometer

Explain that a galvanometer can be used as an electricity tester because when electricity flows through a wire, it creates a magnetic field. The needle reacts to this magnetic field by being deflected. The amount of deflection indicates the amount of electric energy present.

---

3 One Form of Energy: Electricity

There are many ways of producing electricity. In the following Exploration, you will try three methods. For each method, test whether you were successful by using a flashlight bulb or a homemade galvanometer. The galvanometer is much more sensitive and can measure very small currents.

Making and Testing for Electricity

Activity 1
Making Electricity Testers

In this Activity you will make two simple electricity testers. After making your testers, check their operation with a dry cell.

A. A Flashlight-Bulb Tester

You Will Need
- a flashlight bulb
- 2 pieces of fine insulated wire, 1-m long, with 2 alligator clips attached
- a D-cell battery

What to Do

Use the masking tape to attach the ends of the wires to the light bulb (as shown below). Touch a clip to each pole of a dry cell to see if the tester detects electricity.

B. A Homemade Galvanometer

You Will Need
- a 1-m length of fine insulated wire with 2 alligator clips attached
- a compass
- a D-cell battery

What to Do

Wind about 20 turns of fine insulated wire right over the north-south axis of a compass. Line up your needle in a north-south direction, then touch the clips to the dry cell to test your galvanometer. The needle will move if a current flows—the larger the current, the larger the movement.

LESSON ORGANIZER

Objectives

By the end of the lesson, students should be able to:
1. Construct two different devices that can test for the presence of electricity.
2. Experiment with three different devices that generate electricity.

Process Skills

experimenting, observing, inferring, predicting

New Terms

Activity 2
Making Electricity
A. A Liquid Cell
You Will Need

- a jar or beaker
- a strip of copper metal
- a strip of zinc metal
- dilute sulfuric acid
- your electricity testers

What to Do

Set up the cell as in the diagram. Do not allow the metal strips to touch. Connect the light bulb tester as shown. Does the bulb light up? How long did it stay lit? Did you see anything happening to the copper or the zinc? Where do you think the electricity is coming from? Do you think it will go on forever? Rinse off the metal strips with water. Then place them back in the acid. Attach the galvanometer to the zinc and copper strips. What happens?

B. A Solar Cell

Solar cells are usually made from thin layers of very pure silicon. They are used to provide electricity for a variety of things, from calculators to satellites. Do you know of any other uses of solar cells?

You Will Need

- a solar cell
- a light source
- your homemade galvanometer

What to Do

Attach your galvanometer to the solar cell. Line up the needle with the north-south axis of the compass. Put the solar cell under the light. Does the needle move? Move the light closer, then farther away. Did you see anything happen? Move the light over the cell, from side to side. Test your apparatus in sunlight. Where do you think the electricity is coming from?

solar cell

C. A Simple Generator

A generator is a device used for making electricity. You will learn more about generators in the next lesson.

You Will Need

- a 2-m length of fine insulated wire
- a cardboard bathroom-tissue tube
- a strong magnet
- your electricity testers

What to Do

Wind about 50 turns of insulated wire around the outside of a cardboard bathroom-tissue tube. Scrape the insulation from the ends of the wire, and connect them to your light bulb tester. Quickly thrust one end of a strong magnet into the coil. Did the bulb light up?

Now test the apparatus with your galvanometer. (Keep the compass needle away from the magnet!) Did the needle move? How could you make the galvanometer needle move even farther?

Where do you think the electricity is coming from? What do you think you would find inside a factory-made generator?

Activity 2
A. A Liquid Cell

Caution students to be careful of the sulfuric acid. In your class preparation, scour the copper and zinc strips with steel wool between use of the cell.

The electricity is a result of the chemical reaction between zinc, copper, and sulfuric acid. Electricity should be generated until the zinc is corroded away. This can be detected by both testers.

B. A Solar Cell

The solar cell uses light to generate electricity. This can be detected by the deflection of the compass needle.

C. A Simple Generator

When either pole of the magnet is inserted into the center of the coil, a current is generated. The faster the magnet moves, the more electricity gets generated. This can be detected by both testers.

Follow Up

Assessment

Ask students to draw pictures of three ways to generate electricity.

Extension

To demonstrate that an electric current produces a magnetic field, make a hole in the center of a small index card. Put a copper wire, about 25-cm long, through the hole and connect the ends to a D-cell battery. Hold the card horizontally. Sprinkle iron filings on the card, and tap gently with a pencil. Watch the pattern develop.

Materials

Exploration 2
Activity 1 A: flashlight bulb, 2 pieces of a 1-m length of fine insulated wire with 2 alligator clips attached, piece of masking tape, D-cell battery, wire cutters, wire strippers
Activity 1 B: 1-m length of fine insulated wire with 2 alligator clips attached, compass, D-cell battery

Activity 2 A: jar or beaker, strip of copper metal, strip of zinc metal, 80 mL of 0.05 *M* sulfuric acid, electricity testers, safety goggles, water, steel wool
Activity 2 B: solar cell, light source (flashlight), homemade galvanometer
Activity 2 C: 2-m length of fine insulated wire, cardboard bathroom-tissue tube, strong magnet, wire cutters, wire strippers, electricity tester, galvanometer

Science Discovery Videodisc

Disc 2, Image and Activity Bank, 6–3

Time Required

two class periods

 Getting Started

This lesson begins with a short story depicting life in 1893. Students are asked to compare their lives to that of the young man in the story. In *Exploration 3*, students read an abbreviated history of energy-related events, and they are asked to reflect on how these events have changed people's lifestyles.

Main Ideas

1. Sources and use of energy today are very different from those of our ancestors.
2. In the last 100 years, energy use has increased dramatically.

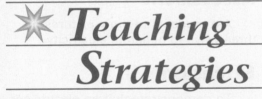 Teaching Strategies

Luke Booker's Diary— January 18, 1893

Begin by having students read the diary. Then have students list some of the differences between Luke's lifestyle and their own in their Journals. Make a composite list of these differences on the chalkboard. Ask: Which of these have something to do with energy? Have students rate the list of differences. You could use a three-point scale:

0 = nothing to do with energy
1 = somewhat connected with energy
2 = strongly connected

4 Energy Then and Now

Imagine going back in time 100 years. What do you see? You walk to the nearest house. How does it differ from your home? You knock and are invited in. Is it like your home inside? What are the people doing? If it's early in the morning, what you see might be very much like what follows.

Luke Booker's Diary—January 18, 1893

"Luke! Time to get up." My mother's voice roused me from a sound sleep. Must be six o'clock. I stretched, got out of bed, and felt my way toward the window. The wooden floor was cold under my feet. I scraped the ice off the pane and peered out, but it was still dark outside.

"Hurry up, Luke!" I went into the kitchen. The kerosene lamp shone warmly on the table. Already my mother had breathed some life into the dying embers in the range. The kindling crackled.

"Luke, I need some wood." I wiped the sleep from my eyes and found my heavy woolen shirt and corduroy pants, which had been hung to dry. I staggered outside to the woodpile.

When I returned, the fire was well lit. It beckoned to me. I went across and ladled some warm water from the cistern which was attached to the range. It never ceased to amaze me that it was still warm. I remembered the old days. There's nothing worse than washing in cold water!

"Here's your breakfast, Luke." I really quite liked hot porridge but pretended I didn't. Mother said it kept the cold out.

"Time for school, Luke." I put on my coat, said goodbye, and ran outside. It was light now. A horse and buggy clattered down the road. I'd rather walk anyway!

List some of the main ways in which your life is different from Luke Booker's. Do you think lifestyle has any connection with energy?

As far back as we have evidence of their existence, human beings have harnessed the energy around them. Exploration 3 examines the ways in which our use of energy has changed over time.

LESSON ORGANIZER

Objectives

By the end of the lesson, students should be able to:
1. Compare modern and historical energy sources.
2. Describe how energy-related events in history have affected people's lives.

Process Skills

comparing, sequencing, analyzing, drawing conclusions

New Terms

Energy Through the Ages

This exploration shows a few of the energy-related events that have occurred throughout history. As you read the time line, think about how energy affects lifestyle. Then discuss the questions that follow.

Timeline

500,000 B.C.
Early humans use fire. Using the energy released when wood burns, humans warm themselves and cook food.

8000 B.C.
The first oil lamps are used by cave dwellers in Western Europe.

2400 B.C.
The sail is invented in Egypt. Sails use the wind, rather than human muscles, to move boats.

1000 A.D.
The Pueblo peoples of North America learn to use "passive solar heat" by building homes that take the greatest advantage of the winter sun.

1712
Thomas Newcomen invents the first practical steam engine. His design is later improved by James Watt. The steam engine revolutionizes industry by allowing the construction of machines requiring large amounts of power.

1800
Alessandro Volta invents the first chemical cell to produce electricity. It becomes known as the "voltaic pile."

1831
Michael Faraday constructs the first true electrical generator. It consists of a copper disk rotating between the poles of a permanent magnet.

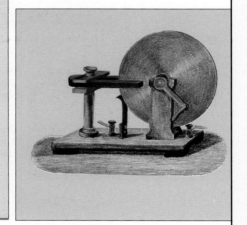

Exploration 3

Have students work in groups of three or four to read the *Timeline* and answer the questions on page 294.

You may wish to have students do reports on the contributions of some of the inventors and scientists mentioned in the *Timeline,* for example, Newcomen, Watt, Volta, Faraday, Edison, Daimler and Benz, Ford, and Fermi.

With two coins, you can demonstrate a simple voltaic pile like the one referred to under *1800* in the *Timeline.* Take two coins made of different metals. Clean them well with steel wool. Fold a paper towel into a pad so that it is slightly larger than the coins. Soak the paper in salt water. Place one coin on top of the pad and the other coin underneath. Hold the pile between your thumb and index finger. Connect both leads of a galvanometer to the coins and watch the deflection.
(Continues on next page)

Materials

Teacher's Resource Binder

Graphic Organizer Transparency 6–2

Science Discovery Videodisc

Disc 2, Image and Activity Bank, 6–4

Time Required

one class period

(Exploration 3 continued)

You may wish to have students find out more about how food, clothing, and shelter were provided during pioneer days. Point out that the energy sources used to do most of the work at that time were human muscle, animal muscle, and wood. Divide the class into three groups: food, clothing, and shelter. Ask each group to research, through reading and interviews, how basic necessities were provided for in earlier generations. Also ask them to research how those same three necessities are provided for today. Have each group summarize their findings in writing so that they can be presented to the class.

Have students compare toys and games commonly used in colonial times to those used today. Which cost more and why? Which type requires more action from the person playing with it? Which type requires more thinking? Which type requires electricity to work? Ask students to name some toys developed within recent years that might be a waste of energy.

Ask students to read about the energy events since 1950. Ask: Why do you think energy usage has increased so dramatically since 1950? *(Consumers have purchased and used more and more energy-consuming goods, such as cars and electrical appliances.)* What has spurred the increased interest in energy conservation in the 1980s? *(rising fossil-fuel prices and the new awareness of the damage caused to the environment)* What energy trends do you foresee in the future? *(Answers may vary, but possible responses include: more interest in conservation of energy; more interest in recycling; people using fewer energy-consuming goods; the development of alternative, non-polluting energy sources.)*

(Continues on next page)

1859
Col. Edwin Drake drills the first oil well near Titusville, Pennsylvania. He strikes oil at a depth of 21 m.

1879
Thomas Edison invents the light bulb.

The California Electric Light Company begins operating the first commercial power plant, selling electricity to private customers.

1885
Gottfried Daimler and Karl Benz, working independently, develop an improved internal combustion engine that uses gasoline as fuel.

1900
Over 3600 electric utility companies are in operation across America.

1908
The automobile age begins when Henry Ford introduces the Ford Model T. The demand for petroleum soars as automobiles come into widespread use. More than 15,000,000 Model T's will eventually be manufactured.

1941
The first commercial wind-powered electric generator begins operating in Vermont.

1942
The world's first nuclear reactor, designed by Dr. Enrico Fermi, is activated at Stagg Field, on the campus of the University of Chicago.

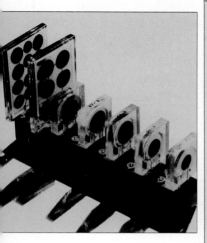

1954

Bell Laboratories develops the solar cell, which converts sunlight directly into electricity.

1950–1970

The population of the United States increases by about 20 percent, while at the same time, energy usage increases by 90 percent.

1973

The Arab Oil Embargo disrupts American oil supplies, causing fuel shortages all over the United States. This motivates the government to enact the first peacetime energy-conservation measures. The embargo also signals the dawn of an era of rising fuel prices.

1977

The Trans-Alaska Pipeline begins transporting oil. A major engineering feat, the pipeline is built to lessen America's dependence on foreign oil by tapping the rich oil fields of Alaska's North Slope. The pipeline is strongly opposed by many people, who fear it will damage Alaska's delicate environment.

1980s

Rising fossil-fuel prices spur increased interest in energy conservation. Fossil fuels—oil, coal, and natural gas— are shown to be a major source of greenhouse gases, adding urgency to the search for alternative sources of energy.

2000 and Beyond
???

(Exploration 3 continued)

Point out that tools and machines have evolved from simple stone tools made by primitive humans to the complex machines of today, such as computers and jet airplanes.

List these energy sources on the chalkboard: human muscle power, animal muscle power, wind, water, wood, coal, petroleum, natural gas, solar, and nuclear energy. Divide the class into groups of four or five and ask each group to list several machines that are powered by each of the listed energy sources. Ask: What type of energy seem to be associated with very big or very complicated machines? *(electrical)* When did people start making big or complicated machines? *(after electricity was invented)* Why were they not developed before that time? *(There was no electricity to power them.)*

All About Energy   293

Answers to

For Discussion

1. Have students assume a generation time of 25 years. Therefore, grandparents used energy 50 years ago, great-grandparents, 75 years ago. Using the energy Timeline, ask them to speculate on how the lives of earlier generations would have been different. As an extension, have students interview their older relatives to find out how energy use has changed.

2. Fifty years ago, coal was the major source of energy. Today, it is petroleum. Coal use has diminished while natural gas use has increased. Nuclear energy is now available.

3. We use almost twice as much energy today as we did 30 years ago.

4. Answers will vary. Encourage students to think of the many types of energy they use so they can justify their answers.

5. Oil, coal, and natural gas are called "fossil fuels" because they were formed from the remains of ancient plant and animal life.

6. Answers may vary, possible responses might include:
   (a) Light bulbs greatly increased people's night-time activities. Cars made transportation easier and faster, thus people began traveling more often and farther from home.
   (b) It is unlikely that they would have been invented since they would not have worked without electricity or gasoline.
   (c) Energy consumption has greatly increased since the invention of light bulbs and cars.

7. There are many connections between lifestyle and the way energy is used. For example, many electrical appliances in homes make life easier but require electricity, so our society produces and uses a great deal of electricity. Also, many people work long distances from their homes. They are able to do this because of the automobile.

8. Students will probably suggest alternative energy sources, such as wind, solar, or nuclear fusion.

For Discussion

1. How might the way you use energy differ from the way your grandparents did when they were your age? How about when your great-grandparents were your age?

2. How is the nation's energy consumption of today different from that of 50 years ago?

3. How many times more energy do we use now than 30 years ago?

4. Which form of energy is most important to you?

5. Why do you think oil, coal, and natural gas are called "fossil fuels"?

6. (a) How have light bulbs and cars influenced our lives?
   (b) Do you think light bulbs or cars would have been invented if electricity or gasoline had not already been discovered? Explain.
   (c) What kind of effect do you think light bulbs and cars had on energy consumption?

7. What do you think is the connection between our lifestyle and the way we use energy?

8. By the middle part of the twenty-first century, much of the oil will be gone. Where do you think our energy will come from in the future? Write your own timeline entries for the future.

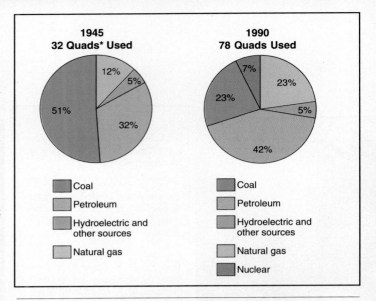

Short for quadrillion BTUs *(British Thermal Units), a measure of energy usage.*

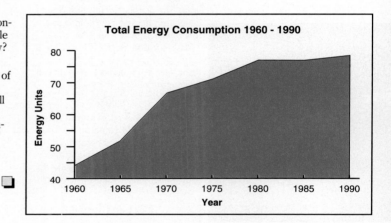

✴ *Follow Up*

Assessment

1. Ask students to chose one invention from the *Timeline* and describe how it has influenced their lifestyle.

2. Have students pick a time along the *Timeline* and describe what forms of energy would have been used to provide the basic needs of food, clothing, and shelter.

Extension

Have students interview senior citizens about what life was like when they were growing up and how their lifestyles have changed since the advent of the automobile and electricity. Students should share their interviews with the class.

Where is the energy now? Below are three picture sequences, in random order. In your Journal:

1. Put the pictures in the correct order.

2. Explain what is happening in each sequence.

3. Identify where the energy is in each picture.

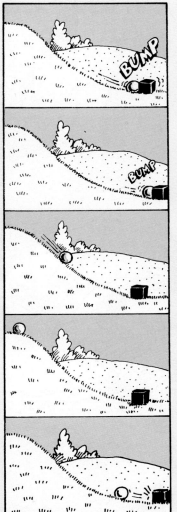 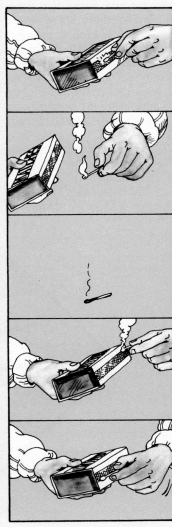 

Answers to

Challenge Your Thinking

1. For the correct order of figures, see illustration below.

2. In the first sequence, a ball rolls down a hill and bumps into a box. After this initial contact, the ball rolls back slightly. It then rolls back down against the box with a weaker impact.

   In the second sequence, a girl strikes a match against the outside of a match box. The match lights and then burns out.

   The third sequence covers a long period of time. The first picture simply shows the sun over an empty hill. The second picture shows seedlings beginning to grow. The third picture shows a mature group of trees. The fourth picture shows stacked firewood left from cutting down the trees. The final picture shows a house built by the logs in the previous picture.

3. In the first sequence, the ball has energy as it rolls down the hill, rolls backward, and then rolls downward again. Energy is transferred from the ball to the box when the ball crashes into it.

   In the second sequence, the hands use energy to strike the match. The match head has energy, which is converted into a flame. The flame and the matchstick have heat and light energy.

   In the third sequence, the sun has energy in every picture. The seedlings use energy from the sun to grow. The trees use energy for life processes. The stacked wood represents the energy used to chop down the trees and the energy stored within the logs. Energy was used to build the house. Energy is indicated by the smoke coming from a fireplace inside the house.

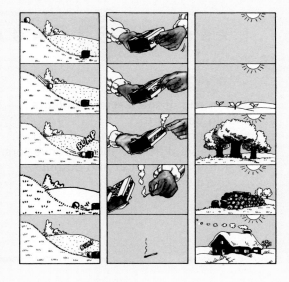

Getting Started

In this lesson, students identify different forms of energy. Then they are asked to infer the input and output energies associated with different energy converters.

Main Ideas

1. Energy comes in many forms, including light, heat, sound, electrical, nuclear, and chemical energy.
2. Potential energy is stored energy; kinetic energy is energy of motion.
3. Energy makes things happen when it is converted from one form to another.

Teaching Strategies

Ask students to read page 296. Then ask: What forms of energy can you observe in the pictures on pages 296 and 297? *(light and heat energy from the sun and from the campfire; electrical energy from the power lines and the lightning; sound energy from thunder and everything else that makes noise; nuclear energy in the nuclear power plant; and chemical energy from the gasoline, battery, and skier.)* **(Continues on next page)**

5 The Energy Picture

The collage on these pages illustrates many forms of energy: light energy, heat energy, sound energy, electrical energy, nuclear energy, and chemical energy. Look at the collage and find examples of each form of energy.

As you find each form of energy, you may notice that some examples show energy in motion, while others show stored energy. Another name for energy in motion is *kinetic* energy. Stored energy is called *potential* energy, because it has the potential to make something happen. Think back to the picture of the construction site on page 284. The bricks on top of the building have potential energy. If the worker were to drop the bricks, they would have kinetic energy. A coiled spring has potential energy, as does the air inside a balloon. A turning wheel has kinetic energy, as does the wind. Now do you get the idea?

Look closely at these pictures. In every one of them, the conversion of energy from one form to another is either shown or suggested. Can you describe these conversions?

After analyzing the collage, look back at Exploration 1, "Simple Energy Systems." What forms of energy did you see there?

LESSON 5 ORGANIZER

Objectives

By the end of the lesson, students should be able to:

1. Classify different forms of energy.
2. Observe different energy converters, and infer the input and output energies.

Process Skills

observing, analyzing, classifying, inferring

New Terms

Kinetic energy—the energy of motion.
Potential energy—the energy stored by an object.

This model will give you an acceptable level of gasoline conversion.

The Energy Converters are here

(Teaching Strategies continued)
Make sure that students understand the difference between potential and kinetic energy. Ask them to demonstrate potential and kinetic energy using a marble that is about to be dropped, a coiled spring, and an air-filled balloon. (The potential energy is in the lifted marble, the compressed spring, and the air-filled balloon. When these objects are released, the potential energy is released and becomes kinetic energy.)

Answer to

In-Text Question

In *Exploration 1*, the forms of energy that could be seen were: mechanical energy (potential and kinetic) in the pendulum; solar energy from the sun; elastic energy (potential and kinetic) in the spinning spool; heat and light energy in the Bunsen burner; chemical energy in the white vinegar reacting with the chalk and steel wool; chemical energy in the heating of the copper sulfate crystal and the plastic; and electrical energy in the electromagnet.

Materials

Science Discovery Videodisc

Disc 2, Image and Activity Bank, 6–5

Time Required

one class period

Following the Energy Conversion Trail

Have students read page 298. Discuss the terms *energy converter, input,* and *output.* Ask students to think of examples in which they can use these words to describe energy changes. Then have them look at the table in the middle of the page. *(Other forms of output: for humans, sound and heat energy; for the woodstove, light energy.)*

Answers to

Problems to Ponder

1. ***Giant redwoods***
   energy input: solar energy
   energy output: chemical energy (plants make food)
   Jet plane
   energy input: chemical energy (fuel)
   energy outputs: mechanical energy (potential energy due to height and kinetic energy due to motion), sound energy, electrical energy (cabin lights), and heat energy (the exhausts)
   Roller coaster
   energy input: electrical energy
   energy outputs: mechanical energy (potential energy due to height and kinetic energy due to motion), heat energy, and sound energy
   Windmill
   energy input: wind energy
   energy outputs: mechanical energy (kinetic energy due to motion) and heat energy (due to friction)
   Telephone
   energy input: electrical energy
   energy outputs: sound energy and heat energy
2. When you stop pedaling, the kinetic energy of the moving bicycle is converted into heat energy due to friction.
3. The kinetic energy of the ball is converted into heat energy due to friction.
4. **(a)** chemical energy into mechanical energy: cars, trains, boats, people, airplanes
   (b) electrical energy into heat energy: heaters, electric blankets, toasters, stoves, light bulbs
5. Students should begin to realize that energy does not disappear, but changes from one form into another.

Following the Energy Conversion Trail

Think about the energy that you use. Does the energy originate in the form in which you use it, or might it have started out as another form of energy? The fact is, energy only makes things happen when it is converted from one form into another. For example, chemical energy in the food you eat enables you to run or walk. *You* are an energy converter. As you move, the chemical energy in the food is changed into the energy of motion. A woodstove is another example of an energy converter. It works by changing the chemical energy in wood into heat energy. Food and wood are both examples of energy inputs.

Now think a bit more about yourself and the woodstove. Is the food or the wood converted in some way to make it useful?

Energy Input	Energy Converter	Energy Output
Chemical energy (food)		Kinetic energy (running, breathing, etc.) Other forms?
Chemical energy (wood)		Heat energy Other forms?

Problems to Ponder

1. Look at the five energy converters shown in the photographs on this page and on the next page. What is the energy input for each? How many different types of energy output can you think of? Give yourself 1 point for each energy output you identified. Now total your score. Here is the rating system: 15 points—Energy hot shot!!! 10 points—Energy-wise!! 5 points—More energy required!

6. Discuss with students the term *work.* Point out to students that in the scientific sense, work is the product of a force that is exerted on matter, causing it to move a distance. Energy is required to do work, so energy could be defined as "the ability to do work." For example, a moving marble, spring, or rubber band has the ability to do work—to push another object that is placed in its path.

   Have students compare this definition with the one they wrote at the beginning of the unit, and write a new definition based on what they have learned so far.

2. You're riding your bicycle and you stop pedaling. Where does all the energy go?

3. A bouncing ball comes to rest sooner or later. Where does all the energy go?

4. How many energy converters can you suggest for each of the following energy changes?
   (a) chemical energy → mechanical energy
   (b) electrical energy → heat energy

5. Do you agree with Alicia (pictured right)? If yes, why? If no, why not?

6. Energy is sometimes defined as "the ability to do work." Do you feel this is a good definition? Why or why not? How does this definition compare with the one you wrote at the beginning of this unit?

You can't create energy. You can't destroy energy...but you can change energy from one form to another.

✷ Follow Up

Assessment

1. Bring in pictures of energy conversions taking place. For each picture, ask students to identify the energy converter, energy input, and energy output.

2. Divide the class into two teams. Have Team A name an energy converter and Team B name the energy input and energy output. Be sure that all members on each team have a chance to suggest and to respond. The first team with 10 correct answers wins.

Extension

Have a pizza party. During the party, ask students to identify the ingredients they see or taste in the pizza, and list them on the chalkboard. For each ingredient, ask students to find out the energy required to make it available for the pizza and the energy conversions that occurred to make that food. For example, some of the energy required could include: energy from the sun for plant growth, energy to cultivate and harvest the crops, energy to preserve and transport the foods, and energy to cook the food.

The Many Faces of Energy   299

In this lesson, students learn how an electrical generator and a motor work, and how electricity is made commercially.

Main Ideas

1. In an electrical generator, the wire coil moves within a magnetic field.
2. Steam and moving water are used to turn coils in commercial generators.

Teaching Strategies

Be sure that students understand that moving the wire coil inside a magnet has the same effect as moving the magnet inside the wire coil.

Answers to

In-Text Questions

- Magnetic energy is changed into electrical energy in a generator.
- By moving the coil of wire rapidly through the magnet, a generator will produce a large amount of energy.

---

6 Making Electricity From Scratch

In Exploration 2, you made your own electricity generator. It was simple but not very practical since you had to be there to push the magnet into the coil. Think how much more practical your generator would be if you could find a way of keeping the magnet moving continuously with respect to the coil. How might you do this?

The people who invented the type of generator used for producing electricity today had a really clever idea: move the coil instead of the magnet. Can you figure out how this type of generator works? Do you see how the electrical current flows from the coil (ABCD) and into the wires attached to the light bulb?

Do you see now that an electricity generator is really just a special type of energy converter? What change takes place? How do you think you could get a generator to produce a really large amount of electricity?

The Principle of a Modern Generator

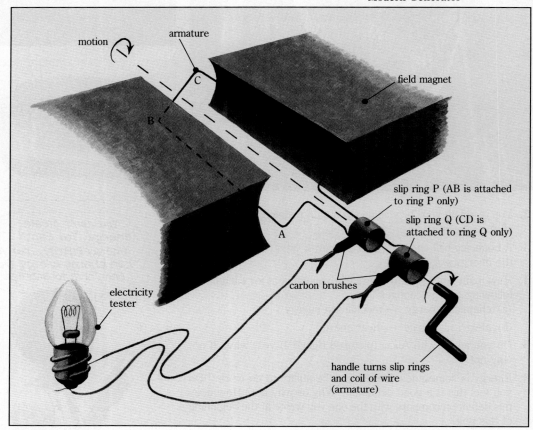

LESSON 6 ORGANIZER

Objectives

By the end of the lesson, students should be able to:

1. Describe the structure of an electrical generator and explain how it works.
2. Sequence the energy changes that take place from the generation of electricity in a power plant to its use in a home.
3. Analyze the set-up and results of an experiment.

Process Skills

observing, analyzing, sequencing, interpreting data

New Terms

Turning Motion Into Electricity

The simplified generator on the previous page was turned by hand. Obviously there are better ways to drive a generator. What are some of them? Examine the methods of driving a generator shown below. Explain what is happening in each case.

Many of the little electric motors found in battery powered devices are also generators. You can either send an electrical current through the motor and cause the spindle to turn, or you can turn the spindle of the motor and cause electricity to be generated. Imagine using each of the devices below to drive a generator. Which do you think would be the best at generating electricity?

(a) (b) (c) pulley motor from model shop (d)

Turning Motion Into Electricity

After students have studied the pictures, ask them what is happening in each one. Make sure students understand that the spindles that are being turned in the pictures could each be attached to the wire coil in a generator. Thus, when the spindle turns, the wire coil turns also.

Answers to

In-Text Questions

The spindles are being turned in picture (a) by heat (steam), in picture (b) by running water, in picture (c) by gravity, and in picture (d) by wind. The device that succeeds in generating and transferring the greatest amount of energy, in the most efficient manner, would be the best at generating electricity.

Try to obtain a small motor, such as one found in a battery-powered toy, to demonstrate how it can be used as a motor or a generator. First, connect the wires from the motor to a battery to get the spindle to turn. Then connect the wires to a flashlight bulb and turn the spindle as quickly as possible to generate electricity. The bulb will light. (You may need a starter cord to get the spindle to turn fast enough.)

Be sure that students understand that the same device can be used as a generator or as a motor. To use it as a generator, you turn the coil, and a current is produced in the coil. To use it as a motor, you send current through the coil, and the coil then turns. Remind students that electricity flowing through a wire coil sets up a magnetic field around the coil. The magnetic field around the wire coil reacts with the magnet, causing the coil to turn.

Materials

Teacher's Resource Binder

Resource Worksheet 6–2

Science Discovery Videodisc

Disc 2, Image and Activity Bank, 6–6

Time Required

two to three class periods

Industrial-Strength Generators

Have students individually read the page, study the diagram, and fill in the blanks in the story at the bottom of the page. Then call on volunteers to read and fill in the answers in the story. Be sure that all members in the class agree.

Answers to

The Story of a Steam-Powered Generator

The answers are listed in order of appearance in the paragraph: *chemical, heat, mechanical, electrical, electrical, light, heat.*

Build a model turbine in the classroom. Use a flask fitted with a one-hole stopper. Partly fill the flask with water and heat the water with a Bunsen burner to create steam. Fit a 50-cm length of tubing into the stopper. The steam coming from the tube can be aimed at model turbine blades made from a tinkertoy or erector set. (This could be similar to the design of the windmill on page 304. Add more blades for the model turbine.)

Industrial-Strength Generators

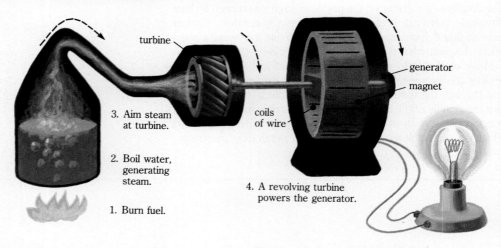

3. Aim steam at turbine.

2. Boil water, generating steam.

1. Burn fuel.

turbine

coils of wire

generator

magnet

4. A revolving turbine powers the generator.

Steam power can be used to generate electricity.

Engineers have designed some very sophisticated systems for driving generators. The turbine is one way of converting the energy contained in steam into the kinetic or mechanical spinning energy of a generator. The turbine fits snugly into a pipe along which water or steam flows. The only way the water or steam can get through the pipe is to turn the turbine. The motion of the turbine drives the generators, producing electricity.

In the diagram above, you see how steam causes the turbine to turn the coil of wire in the generator. In large generating stations, the fuel used to produce the steam is oil, gas, coal, or the uranium in a nuclear reactor. Examine the diagram closely, following all the steps.

Did you trace the steps from the making of the steam to the lighting of the lamp? If so, you will have no trouble in filling in the blanks in the following story. Write the completed story in your Journal. Do not write in this book.

The Story of a Steam-Powered Generator

_____?_____ energy from gas, oil, or coal provides _____?_____ energy to water to produce steam. A turbine changes the energy of the steam into the _____?_____ energy of the rotating turbine and generator. The generator converts this energy into _____?_____ energy. The lamp is an energy converter, changing _____?_____ energy to _____?_____ energy and _____?_____ energy.

Here are the forms of energy that fit into the blanks, in random order: *chemical, electrical, heat, light,* and *mechanical.*

The Hydroelectricity Story

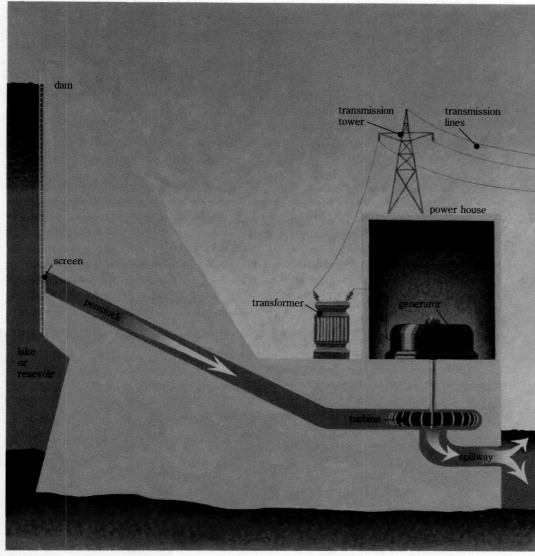

A hydroelectric power plant

Here is a diagram of a hydroelectric power plant. Can you see how it works? What do you think the transformer does? If you don't know, find out. With another person, write a story about a hydroelectric power plant. What kind of energy conversions take place there? Extend the story to talk about the energy conversions that happen when the electricity leaves the plant, travels through the wires, enters your home, and finally reaches an electric stove that is boiling water.

Follow Up

Assessment

Ask students why an electric motor can also be a generator. Have them demonstrate how to make a generator from a small electric motor and how to test whether or not it works.

Extension

Have students research and write a report on the use of geothermal power to create electrical energy. In their reports, they should include information about areas on earth where geothermal power has been tried, the mechanics of trapping and converting the steam into electricity, and the relative cost of the electrical energy produced.

The Hydroelectricity Story

Have students read page 303 and study the diagram. Ask students to work in pairs to write their hydroelectric stories. Suggest that they research to find out how transformers work and how electricity is carried from a hydroelectric plant to individual homes.

Here is one example of a student's story about hydroelectricity.

Hydroelectricity is produced from moving water. In the picture, water behind the dam travels downward through a tube to a turbine. The falling water turns the turbine, which is connected to the spindle of a generator. The spindle turns the wire coil inside the magnet to produce electricity. The transformer steps up the voltage of the electricity. (Voltage can be thought of as the pressure of the electricity in the electric wires.) Electricity is carried over the electric lines at a very high voltage. Less electrical energy is lost to the heat of friction when the voltage of the electricity is high during transmission. Thus, increasing the voltage is the most efficient and economical way to distribute the electricity. Once the electricity reaches individual homes, the voltage has been decreased by transformers that step down the voltage. When the electricity enters the home, it is converted by various electrical appliances into useful forms of energy.

You have seen that energy is able to change forms. In fact, you have learned that energy makes things happen only when it is converted from one form into another. But what happens when energy is not in the form that we want to use? You can't plug your car into an outlet when you want to go for a drive! You can't power a flashlight with wind! To solve these problems, engineers have designed special energy converters. A few examples are shown on these pages.

* Getting Started

In this lesson, students learn more about devices that convert one form of energy into another. They are asked to match different energy converters with their appropriate energy changes, and then to solve some energy conversion problems. The idea of energy efficiency is introduced, and the flaws in a perpetual motion machine are discussed. Then students analyze a science fair project about wind energy.

Main Ideas

1. Many different devices have been designed to convert one form of energy into another.
2. Energy converters cannot be 100% efficient because they lose useful energy to friction when they are operating.
3. Good experimental designs take into account all possible variables and test them one at a time.

* Teaching Strategies

After students have read the introductory paragraph, ask them to observe the pictures on pages 304 and 305. Ask: What energy conversion is taking place in each picture? *(The cars convert chemical energy in gasoline into mechanical energy; the windmills convert kinetic energy in wind into mechanical energy; the steam locomotive converts chemical energy in fuel into heat energy that causes steam, producing mechanical energy; the eggbeater converts electrical energy into mechanical energy.)*

LESSON 7 ORGANIZER

Objectives

By the end of the lesson, students should be able to:
1. Infer the energy conversions associated with different energy converters.
2. Observe and describe where energy converters lose useful energy to friction.

Process Skills

observing, analyzing, inferring, describing

New Terms

Look at the lists below, and try to match each energy-converting device with the appropriate energy change.

Energy Converter	Energy Change
1. Car engine	**A.** Electrical energy → mechanical energy
2. Electric motor	**B.** Light (radiant) energy → heat energy
3. Home gas or oil furnace	**C.** Electrical energy → light (radiant) energy
4. Electric generator	**D.** Chemical energy → mechanical energy
5. Incandescent lamp	**E.** Light (radiant) energy → electrical energy
6. Solar cell	**F.** Chemical energy → heat energy
7. Tree	**G.** Light (radiant) energy → chemical energy
8. Greenhouse	**H.** Mechanical energy → electrical energy

Some Problems for You

1. How can you turn mechanical energy into heat energy?
2. Pick any two types of energy. Is it possible to convert each type directly into the other, or are several steps needed? How many ways are there of making these changes? (For hints, look at the lists above.)
3. Imagine that you are a pioneer. You have an ample supply of wood. To reduce your workload, you design a simple device to change the energy in wood into mechanical energy. What would your device look like? How would it work?
4. Imagine you are a "wave-energy engineer." Design a device to convert the up-and-down movement of ocean waves into electrical energy.

Materials

Teacher's Resource Binder

Resource Worksheet 6–3

Science Discovery Videodisc

Disc 2, Image and Activity Bank, 6–7

Time Required

one to two class periods

Answers to

In-Text Questions

Have students complete the matching exercise either individually or in groups. They can record the exercise in their Journals.
1. D **2.** A **3.** F **4.** H
5. C **6.** E **7.** G **8.** B

Answers to

Some Problems for You

1. Mechanical energy is turned into heat energy when heat is produced by the friction of the moving parts.
2. Answers may vary. For a car, one possible response is the conversion of chemical energy into electrical energy and vice-versa.
3. One possible response might be a steam engine. Steam engines are devices that can change the chemical energy in wood into mechanical energy.
4. Encourage creative and imaginative ideas. Each student should produce a sketch, which then could be posted on a bulletin board in the room.

Efficiency

After students have read page 306, make sure that they understand that the energy changed into heat energy is not really "lost." Energy cannot be created or destroyed. The "lost" energy becomes heat energy.

Explain that an incandescent light would not work if some of the electrical energy were not converted into heat energy. When electricity flows through the tungsten filament in a light bulb, heat from friction is produced. When enough heat is produced, the tungsten filament begins to glow.

After students have drawn pictures or written passages to show why different devices are not 100 percent efficient, discuss why this is so, and where the "lost" energy goes.

Perpetual Motion

Students should understand that if a generator were linked to a motor and the motor to the generator, the motor would not run forever because much of the energy involved is converted to heat due to friction.

Use small groups to brainstorm the flaws in the perpetual motion machine pictured in the text. *(The most serious flaw is that it does not take into account the friction in the axle of the large wheel, which will slowly bring the wheel to a halt.)*

Efficiency

Every time you change energy from one form into another, some energy is "lost." No machine is 100 percent *efficient*. Look at the table on the right, which shows the efficiency of some common devices.

Where do you think the "lost" energy goes? Is it truly lost—that is, does it no longer exist—or does it just change form?

Consider the following situation. If you place your hand close to a glowing light bulb, you feel heat. Thus, a light bulb produces both light *and* heat. Since the purpose of a light bulb is to produce light, any heat produced is wasted energy.

Device	Efficiency
Windmill	35%
Hydroelectric plant	95%
Solar collector	62%
Nuclear reactor	30%
Photocell	20%
Steam locomotive	9%
Electric motor (large)	93%
Electric motor (small)	62%
Furnace (oil)	66%
Furnace (gas)	85%
Incandescent lamp	5%
Fluorescent lamp	25%

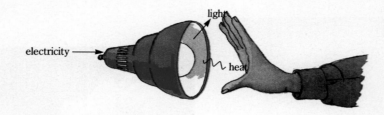

You can see from the table above that an incandescent lamp (a light bulb) is only 5 percent efficient; 95 percent of the energy is "lost" as heat.

Select another device and draw a picture or write a passage to show why it isn't 100 percent efficient.

Perpetual Motion

What would happen if you linked an electric generator and a motor so that the generator powered the motor and the motor drove the generator. Would the motor run forever? Why or why not?

Many ingenious inventors have tried to develop *perpetual motion machines,* machines that would run forever once started, without any additional input of energy. No one has ever succeeded. The reason is that no machine is 100 percent efficient—some energy always escapes. Also, energy cannot be created by a machine. Energy can only be changed from one form into another.

See if you can spot the flaws in the machine illustrated at the right.

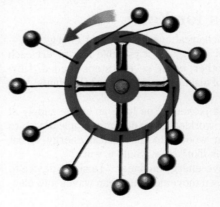

The wheel is designed to turn counterclockwise.

Just after an arm and its weight reaches the top, it flips out straight.

A weight that sticks out has more downward pull than one that dangles. The resulting imbalance keeps the wheel spinning.

Energy From Thin Air

Melanie and Theresa were interested in generating electricity from wind. They decided they wanted to design the most efficient windmill possible and make it their Science Fair project. After reading about their project, put yourself in Melanie's and Theresa's shoes as they face the judges at the Science Fair!

A Science Fair Project

ENERGY from WIND

INTRODUCTION

* Wind is a free source of energy

* Which is the best design for a windmill

* We decided to investigate this systematically

  (a) Does the angle of the blades make a difference?

  (b) Does the length of the blades make a difference?

APPARATUS

We found a design for a windmill in the book "Renewable Sources of Energy"

The windmill was made from Tinkertoy

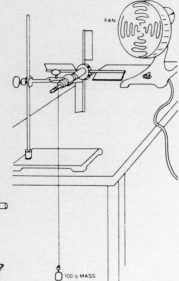

FAN

100 g MASS

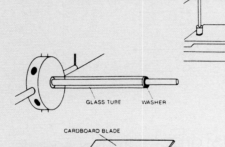

GLASS TUBE   WASHER

CARDBOARD BLADE

Energy From Thin Air

Have students work in groups of three or four to analyze Melanie and Theresa's Science Fair Project. Tell students that you will play the part of the science fair judge and that they will play the parts of Melanie and Theresa. They should analyze the science fair project carefully so that they are able to answer your questions. Tell students that as the judge, you will ask the following questions:

- What was the purpose of each experiment?
- Why were they set up the way they were?
- What were the controlled and experimental variables?
- What were the results of the experiments?
- What conclusions were drawn?

After students have analyzed and discussed the experiments, interview each group separately.

(Continues on next page)

(Energy From Thin Air continued)

The following questions will help you act as the Science Fair judge. Possible answers to the questions are also given.

1. Why did you choose this design for your first experiment? *(This design allowed us to do an experiment without using expensive equipment.)*

2. What were you trying to find out in *Experiment One*? *(the effect of the blade angle on the speed of the windmill)*

3. In *Experiment One*, what were the controlled variables and what was the experimental variable? *(The controlled variables were the distance of the windmill from the fan, the size of the blades, and the fan setting. The experimental variable was the angle of the blades to the wind.)*

4. How did you measure the speed of the blades? *(We counted the number of times the blades turned per minute.)*

5. What made you conclude that 45° was the best angle for the blades? *(When the blade angle was 45° the windmill turned at the highest speed—49 turns per minute.)*

6. Do you think 45° would be the best angle at higher wind speeds? *(A 45° angle would probably also be the best angle at higher wind speeds, but this cannot be concluded without first carrying out further experiments with higher wind speeds.)*

7. What were you testing in *Experiment Two*? *(the effect of the blade length on the average time taken for the windmill to raise a 100-g mass through 1 m)*

8. What were the controlled variables and the experimental variable in *Experiment Two*? *(The controlled variables were the distance of the windmill from the fan, the fan setting, the width of the blades, and the blade angle. The experimental variable was the length of the blades.)*

9. Why do both graphs have a curved line connecting their points? *(Drawing a curved, continuous line between the readings on each graph results in the best estimate of the location of the points between the readings.)*

Experiment One:

THE EFFECT OF BLADE ANGLE

* The number of times the windmill turned per minute was counted (one blade was colored red).

* The angle of the blade to the wind was varied: 0° to 90° (nothing else was changed).

* Experimental Conditions:
  Distance of windmill from fan = 1 meter.
  Size of blades = 3 cm × 10 cm.
  Fan setting - medium.
  Counting started when windmill speed was steady.

RESULTS

Angle in degrees	Revs per min
0	0
15	21
30	40
45	49
60	43
75	24
70	0

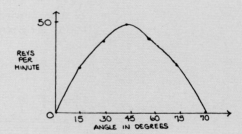

* **Conclusions:** The best angle for windmill blades is 45° (at low speeds)

Experiment Two:

THE EFFECT OF BLADE LENGTH

* The average time taken for the windmill to raise 100 g. mass through 1 meter was measured.

* The blade length was varied: 5 cm, 7.5 cm, 10 cm, 12.5 cm, 15 cm (nothing else was changed).

* Experimental Conditions:
  Distance of windmill from fan = 1 meter
  Fan setting - maximum
  Width of blade = 3 cm
  Blade angle = 45°

Results:

Length of blade, cm	5	7.5	10	12.5	15
Time 1, sec	195	147	95	85	73
Time 2, sec	210	151	97	83	75
Time 3, sec	202	154	104	87	72
Average time, sec	202	152	99	85	73

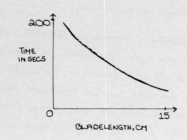

Conclusions: The longer the blade the more powerful the windmill. But long blades bend a lot.

Assessment

1. Ask students to draw pictures to illustrate why a lamp, a radio, a television, and an electric stove are not 100 percent efficient.
2. Ask students to name at least five energy converters that they use each day, and to describe the energy changes.

Extension

1. Invite students to research different perpetual motion machines developed by inventors throughout history. Have them present a report on the designs of the machines and their flaws.
2. Have students do research on the efficiency of different appliances in their homes. Ask them to identify the appliances that waste the most energy and to think of substitutes.

Answers to
Challenge Your Thinking

1. **(a)** The distance between the fan and the windmill must be carefully controlled (held constant) because distance is a variable that could influence the number of revolutions. The fan-setting had to be constant for the same reason.
   (b) Wind speed could have been measured by placing a wind speed meter (anemometer) 1 meter from the fan.
   (c) When the blade angle was 45°, the blades of the windmill made the greatest number of revolutions.
   (d) Answers will vary, but possible responses might include that applying the weight caused the greatest measurable difference in performance level among the different blade lengths.
   (e) Because the blades are made from cardboard, the gain in mass is very small. One way to test the difference would be to compare the number of revolutions of the different blade lengths.
   (f) One reading is insufficient because if it is made incorrectly, the conclusion will most likely be incorrect also. Increasing the number of trials and taking the average of the answer would give the most accurate results. However, 10 trials might take too long.
   (g) Other experiments could test a change in blade shape, wind speed, or the number of blades.
2. Tania made several errors in her diary. The following are the correct answers.
   light—electrical to heat to light
   TV—electrical to heat, sound, and light
   radio—electrical to sound and heat
   cooking on stove—electrical to heat to chemical
   light—electrical to heat to light
   springy toy—could be mechanical (potential) to mechanical (kinetic)

1. In the Hot Seat!
   Here are some of the questions that the judges asked Melanie and Teresa at the Science Fair. How would you have answered them?
   (a) Why did you specify the distance between the windmill and the fan, as well as the fan setting?
   (b) How could you have measured wind speed?
   (c) What made you conclude that 45° is the best angle for the blades?
   (d) Why did you use a 100 g mass in the second experiment but not in the first?
   (e) As you increase the length of the blade, doesn't the mass of the blade increase, offsetting any gain in performance?
   (f) Why did you take the average of three readings —why not one reading, or ten?
   (g) What other experiments could you have done to learn more about windmill design?

2. Tania's Energy Diary
   Tania's teacher asked her class to write an energy diary. "Any time energy changes form, put the kind of change that takes place in parentheses," the teacher said. Check Tania's answers for her.

> When I got home, I turned on the light (electrical to light) and went into the living room. The television (sound to electrical) was on, but I switched it off and turned on the radio (electrical to sound). I got up and went into the kitchen and saw my mom cooking on the stove (heat to electrical). We were going to have tuna casserole.
> After this I went up to my bedroom and turned on the light (electrical to light). My eye caught Zebedee, my springy fluffy toy (potential to movement). I sat down on the bed and did my homework (very hard work to movement). Then I remembered that I had left the radio on (sound to electrical) and went downstairs to turn it off.
> I heard a car pull up (movement to chemical). It was my dad coming home from work. He was late getting home and he looked at the clock (potential to movement). We ate our dinner in silence. After dinner I excused myself from the table and went to the store to get some machine oil (chemical to movement) for my sewing machine.

doing homework—chemical to mechanical
radio—electrical to sound and heat
car—chemical to mechanical, heat, and sound
clock—mechanical (potential) to mechanical (kinetic) or electrical to mechanical
went to store—chemical to mechanical and heat
machine oil—chemical to mechanical

Measuring Energy

Electrical Energy

Have you ever looked at the metal tags on such electrical appliances as a motor, refrigerator, electric kettle, or curling iron? On all of them—unless they are quite old—you would have seen a number followed by the letter *W*. These show the *power* of the appliance. Power is measured in watts (W), a unit named after the scientist and engineer James Watt. The power *(wattage)* of an electrical appliance tells you how fast it uses electrical energy.

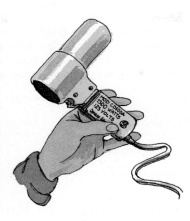

If you multiply the power by the amount of time the appliance is used, you will find the total amount of energy consumed by the appliance, measured in a unit called a **watt-hour (Wh)**. The most commonly used unit of energy, the *kilowatt-hour*, is 1000 Wh. A *megawatt-hour* (MWh) is 1,000,000 Wh. It's time to check your understanding of measuring electrical energy. Complete the following table; the first example has been done for you.

Appliance	Power		Hours Used	Electrical Energy Used or Produced
100 W desk lamp	100 W		Kiyoshi forgets and leaves it on for 20 hours.	2000 Wh *or* $\frac{2000}{1000} = 2$ kWh
Electric kettle	1500 W		Ben uses the electric kettle for 10 minutes, 3 times a day.	___?___ Wh each day ___?___ kWh each day
Curling iron	800 W		Anna uses it for 15 minutes, 6 days a week.	___?___ Wh in a day ___?___ Wh in a week ___?___ kWh in a week
Generator (electricity producer)	1000 kW		John's generator runs steadily for 1 month.	___?___ Wh per month ___?___ kWh per month ___?___ MWh per month

LESSON 8 ORGANIZER

Objectives

By the end of the lesson, students should be able to:
1. Calculate and compare the amount of electricity used by different electrical appliances.
2. Compare the cost of heating water using different forms of energy.

Process Skills

calculating, predicting, comparing, sequencing

New Terms

Watt—a measure of how much power an appliance will consume.

Watt-hour—the total amount of electric energy consumed by an appliance in one hour.

(Organizer continues on next page)

✳ *Getting Started*

In this lesson, students are introduced to the concepts of watts (W), watt-hour (Wh), kilowatt-hour (1000 Wh), and megawatt-hour (1,000,000 Wh). They investigate how many kilowatt-hours of electricity are used by different appliances in their homes.

Main Ideas

1. The total energy consumed by an appliance is measured in watt-hours.
2. Electrical appliances use different amounts of electricity.

Answers to

Electrical Energy

Electric kettle
1500 W × 0.5 hr (30 min.)
= 750 Wh/day *or*
$\frac{750}{1000} = 0.75$ kWh/day

Curling iron
800 W × 0.25 hr (15 min.)
= 200 Wh/day
200 Wh × 6 days
= 1200 Wh/week
$\frac{1200}{1000} = 1.2$ kWh/week

Generator
1000 kW × 720 hr/mo = 720,000 kWh/mo
720,000 kWh/mo × 1000 Wh/kWh = 720,000,000 Wh/mo
720,000,000 Wh/mo × MWh/1,000,000 Wh = 720 MWh/mo

Teaching Strategies

Lead a class discussion to clarify measuring electricity.

Ask students to read the top of page 312. After they have made their predictions and checked the appliance tags at home, they can complete the table in their Journals.

Answers to

In-Text Questions

The power ratings should be within these ranges:
stereo: 30–130 W
washing machine: 70–80 W
television: 50–200 W
refrigerator: 200–300 W
bright light bulb: 200 W
drill: 200–300 W
vacuum: 500–900 W
toaster: 800–1200 W
iron: 1100 W
kettle: 1200–1500 W
hair dryer: 1500 W
clothes dryer: 2500–3000 W

The table answers will vary with students according to differences in wattages among appliances.

Answers to

Other Forms of Energy

According to the table at the end of *Exploration 4,* 1 cubic meter of gas, 1 L of oil, 1 kg of propane, and 1 L of gasoline all provide the same amount of heat. One kWh of electricity would provide one-tenth as much heat, and a log weighing 1 kg would provide only one-twentieth as much heat.

Now—which appliance do you think consumes the most electrical energy in 1 hour? Place the appliances listed below in order, from the greatest amount of electricity used to the least.

- an electric kettle
- a toaster
- a bright light bulb
- an iron
- a stereo
- a hair dryer
- an electric drill
- a clothes dryer
- a washing machine
- a refrigerator
- a television set
- a vacuum cleaner

Check your predictions at home by looking at the tags on the appliances. Then calculate how many kilowatt-hours each appliance would consume in an hour, and enter your findings in a table like the following. Do not write in the book.

Appliance	Power in Watts (W)	Power in Kilowatts (kW)	Energy Used in 1 Hour (kWh)

Other Forms of Energy

In most countries, electricity is measured and sold by the kilowatt-hour, oil and gasoline by the liter, natural gas by the cubic meter, and propane by the kilogram. Which energy source would warm you up the most: a liter of oil, a liter of gasoline, a cubic meter of gas, a log of hardwood weighing 1 kilogram, a kilogram of propane, or a kilowatt-hour of electricity? You can check your prediction by studying the table at the end of Exploration 4, which shows the approximate amount of energy you would need to heat water for your bathtub.

> In the United States, fuels such as gasoline, propane, and heating oil are usually sold by the gallon. Natural gas is sold by cubic feet or thousand cubic feet (mcf).

(Organizer continued)

Materials

Exploration 4: electric kettle, 1-L measuring container, propane burner, 1-L pan with lid, water, oven mitt, matches, watch or clock, kilogram scale, safety goggles

Teacher's Resource Binder

Resource Worksheets 6–4, 6–5, 6–6
Graphic Organizer Transparency 6–4

Science Discovery Videodisc

Disc 2, Image and Activity Bank, 6–8

Time Required

one class period

The Energy Economy Contest

You Will Need

- an electric kettle
- a 1-L measuring container
- a propane burner
- a 1-L pan

What to Do

Plan an experiment to determine which is the most cost-effective way to boil water.

1. Which do you think will win the competition to boil a liter of water more cheaply, the electric kettle or the propane stove? Predict how long it will take to boil water with a kettle, and then try it.

2. Calculate the number of kilowatt-hours used by the electric kettle.

3. How much propane is used to boil the water? How will you find out?

4. Find out the cost of electricity and the cost of propane. Use these figures to calculate how much it costs to boil water using each method.

5. Write a report in which you pick the better energy source. Imagine that your report will air on "Market Place," a consumer-interest TV program.

6. Find out the cost of oil and natural gas. Calculate the approximate cost of heating water for your bathtub with each of the energy sources listed in the table. Write in your Journal, not in this book.

Approximate Amount of Energy Required to Heat Bathtub Water	Approximate Cost
1 m³ (cubic meter) of natural gas	
20.5 kg of wood logs	
1 L of oil	
10 kWh of electricity	
1 kg of propane	
1 L of gasoline	

Exploration 4

To make this a fair test, ask students to remember to control the amount of water heated in each container. (Suggest 1 L.) To calculate the amount of energy in kilowatt-hours, use the power rating on the kettle and the time required to boil the water. To calculate how much propane was burned, weigh the propane tank in kilograms before and after the water is boiled. Have students find out the cost of electricity and propane in their community. With this information, they can calculate the cost of heating the water with electricity versus heating it with propane.

In order to fill in the chart, students will also need to investigate the costs of oil, gasoline, and natural gas in their community.

Assessment

1. Ask students to determine how much electrical energy is needed to operate a 12-watt computer and its 200-watt monitor for 8 hours. *(1696 Wh)*

2. Bring in some energy information tags from different appliances and ask students to interpret the information. Students can find out how many kilowatts per hour are required to run the appliance.

Extension

Have students draw a bar graph to illustrate the amount of electrical energy used by different home appliances. The appliances could be placed on the graph in order from most to least energy-consuming.

LESSON 9

✳ Getting Started

In this lesson, students calculate the cost of running various home appliances. First they read about how other students have carried out their investigations. Then they conduct their own investigations in their homes.

Main Ideas

1. There are many ways to save energy in the home.
2. It is possible to calculate how much energy it takes to run an appliance by multiplying the estimated number of hours it is used by its power rating.

✴ Teaching Strategies

Have students read the cartoon on pages 314 and 315. It sets the stage for *Exploration 5.* Tell students that they will be conducting an investigation similar to the one conducted by the Kilowatt Kids.

After students have read the cartoon, ask: What information do you need to know to calculate the energy used by an appliance in a month? *(You need to know the power rating of the appliance, the amount of time the appliance is used, and how many times it is used in a month.)*

Students should begin to realize how energy can be saved, for example, by turning off appliances and lights when they are not being used. Students may be surprised to learn how much electricity a clothes dryer uses.
(Continues on next page)

---

9 The Energy Bottom Line

If I can save you $10.⁰⁰ a week on your energy bills, will you increase my allowance by $1.⁰⁰?

Here's your chance to help your family save energy—and money. Even if your parents don't increase your allowance, they will be delighted to have you help them save on their utility bill!

THE KILOWATT KIDS INVESTIGATE…
Here's how some other students went about it. Kelly, Kristi, Karl and Kevin (the Kilowatt Kids) decide to work together as a team. They all have different ideas about which appliances use the most electricity in a certain time period…

I bet the t.v. uses the most energy.

No, I bet the lights use more.

I think the dryer does…

③ KELLY INVESTIGATES HOW MUCH IT COSTS TO MAKE A CUP OF HOT CHOCOLATE…

KETTLE KILOWATT HOUR
• Power Rating = 1.5 kw
• Time to Boil = 3 min. or 3/60 hour
• Energy Used To Boil = .075
• Times used per day = 10
• Times used per month = 3
  Energy Used per Month 22.5 Kw

④

⑥ KRISTI IS GOING CRAZY. LIGHTS ARE GOING ON AND OFF EVERYWHERE IN THE HOUSE. SHE CAN'T BE IN TWO PLACES AT ONE TIME…

Bedroom light! Good. I'm pooped. I'll never find out how much these lights cost us each month.

BATHROOM LIGHT!!

KITCHEN LIGHT!

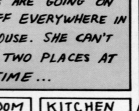

Time	Number of Lights	Wattage Being Used	Total Wattage
6:00	4	60,60 100, 40	260
7:00 8:00 9:00			

⑦

LESSON 9 ORGANIZER

Objectives

By the end of the lesson, students should be able to:
1. Calculate the average amount of energy an appliance uses in one month.
2. Compare the amount of energy used by different appliances in one month.

Process Skills

calculating, comparing, estimating, drawing conclusions

New Terms

(Teaching Strategies continued)

Ask: How could you cut the cost of drying clothes? *(Hang your clothes to dry when possible; do not run the dryer when it is not full.)*

The cartoon points out some of the problems involved in trying to estimate the amount of energy used by some appliances. Tell students that when they carry out their own investigations, it may be necessary to estimate how often and for how long some appliances use energy. For example, they could time how long a refrigerator runs during a half-hour period, and multiply that number by 48 to estimate how long it runs during the course of a day. However, they should take into account that it will run much more often when it is opened and closed frequently.

Materials

Teacher's Resource Binder

Resource Worksheet 6–7
Graphic Organizer Transparencies 6–5
   and 6–6

Science Discovery Videodisc

Disc 2, Image and Activity Bank, 6–9

Time Required

two class periods

Exploration 5

Have students work in groups of four or five to complete this Exploration. Each team should choose several appliances—ones that are different from those chosen by the other groups. Appliances not listed in the text may be added to the list. Be sure that students understand that for each appliance, they should record its power rating and estimate the time it is used each day (how long it is used each time and how many times it is used each day). Then they should estimate how many times it is used each month.

Besides making observations, students may need to interview family members to get a good estimate of how often and for how long different appliances are used each month. Allow time for team members to meet and discuss any problems they may be having. Each team should report back to class so that the class as a whole can complete the data chart. Discuss with students how their results compare with to those of Mr. Catalano's class, given on page 317. Ask: How are the sets of data the same? How are they different? Finally, have students find out the cost of electricity in their area and calculate the cost of operating each appliance for one month.

How Much Energy Do Appliances Use?

So, do you think you could save your family $10.00 per month on the utility bill? You have seen how the 4K's Consultants went about the job and how they made their calculations. Now plan your own survey of the electrical energy use in your home. Here are some guidelines.

1. Team up with three or four classmates. There are numerous appliances to investigate, enough for each team to have several.

2. Each team should select four or five appliances from the chart on the right. Can you add any others?

3. Check that the different teams have covered all appliances among them.

4. Each team should now be ready to plan the investigation. Choose one appliance each, and prepare job sheets, just as Karl, Kelly, Kevin, and Kristi did. Discuss any problems that may arise.

5. Bring your findings back to class, and fill in a table like this one. Work out the average energy (kWh) used by each appliance.

6. How much does a kilowatt-hour cost? Work out the cost per month of each appliance.

Appliance	Team 1	Team 2	Team 3	Team 4	Team 5	Team 6	Average kWh (used per month)
Air conditioner							
Blender							
Clock							
Clothes dryer							
Curling iron							
Dehumidifier							
Dishwasher							
Freezer							
Electric blanket							
Electric frying pan							
Hair dryer							
Humidifier							
Iron							
Kettle							
Lights							
Microwave oven							
Mixer							
Radio							
Range							
Refrigerator							
Television							
Toaster							
Vacuum cleaner							
Washing machine							
Others							

Mr. Catalano's Class Investigates

Here are the results that Mr. Catalano's class obtained. Are they similar to yours?

Appliance	Average kWh (used per month)	Appliance	Average kWh (used per month)
Air conditioner	200.2	Iron	9.8
Blender	1.0	Electric kettle	23.1
Clock	1.5	Lights	96.4
Clothes dryer	80.3	Microwave oven	25.6
Curling iron	0.4	Mixer	0.9
Dehumidifier	33.3	Range	100.7
Dishwasher	30.0	Radio	8.2
Freezer	107.5	Refrigerator	117.5
Electric blanket	10.4	Television	39.8
Electric frying pan	15.0	Toaster	3.2
Hair dryer	2.0	Vacuum cleaner	3.8
Humidifier	14.9	Washing machine	5.0

For Discussion

1. Which appliances use the most electricity?
2. How could you save on the amount of electricity your family uses?
3. Would your family support your plan? Prepare a report on all the findings, with recommendations for your family.

Answers to

For Discussion

1. It is likely that refrigerators, freezers, stoves, clothes dryers, and lights use the most energy (electrical) in a home.
2. Answers may vary, but possible responses include: turning up the refrigerator thermostat, keeping the refrigerator door closed as much as possible, turning off unused lights, using light bulbs with lower wattage, baking several items in the oven at one time when the oven is already hot, and raising the thermostat on the air conditioner.
3. Answers may vary, but hopefully students will be able to encourage all their family members to cooperate by using less energy. Ask volunteers to share their reports with the class.

Answers to

The Energy Efficiency Challenge

Have students work in groups of four or five to brainstorm answers to the questions.

The cyclist would go farther than the walker; the airplane would go farther than the helicopter; the seagull would go farther than the bee; the salmon would go farther than the car and the hummingbird. The cyclist would come in first, and the salmon second.

These predictions are based on the fact that cold-blooded creatures waste the least amount of energy, since they do not need to expend energy to keep their bodies warm. Also, the most energy efficient machines would be those that do not lose a lot of heat in exhaust and that do not have a lot of fast moving parts, which lose energy to the heat of friction.

The Energy Efficiency Challenge

Who or what is the most efficient energy user? Who gets the most bang for their energy buck? Let's hold a contest to find out. The winner of the competition is the one who goes the farthest on a certain amount of energy. To make the competition fair, all participants will be given the equivalent of one kilowatt-hour for each kilogram of body mass.

Think about the ways in which each contestant might waste energy. The runner and the cyclist will get hot because not all the energy they use will be converted into motion; some of it will be converted into heat. Much of the energy given to the machines also gets wasted as heat energy.

Who do you think will go farther, the walker or the cyclist? the helicopter or the plane? the seagull or the bee? the salmon, hummingbird, or car? How does each contestant waste energy? Who wastes the most energy? the least? Try to predict the order in which the contestants will finish. How did you arrive at your prediction?

The Cost of Comfort

The next time an energy bill arrives in the mail, watch what happens! Is there a rush to open it as if it were a letter from a dear friend, or is it greeted with a lot of grumbling, as though it isn't particularly welcome?

Energy bills are not good news. They hit us where it hurts—our wallets. Energy bills account not only for the electricity that runs our appliances, but also for the energy we use to warm or cool our homes. Unless the weather is very mild, the largest part of a utility bill is usually the cost of heating or cooling. How much do you think it costs to keep warm—to heat the water and the air in your home—or to keep cool? Here's how to find out.

Some homes are heated with gas, some with oil, and some with electricity. Air conditioners use electricity. If your home is heated with gas, just read the gas meter. If your home is heated with oil, simply find out how much oil you use. If your home is heated with electricity, you can find the cost of keeping warm by subtracting the amount used to run the appliances from the total amount used. Follow the same procedure to calculate how much it costs to keep your house cool.

The "A Team" Investigates

Antonio, Aldo, and Anila decided to investigate how much their families spent on energy.

The Cost of Comfort

Tell students to read page 319 to find out how to calculate the amount of fuel or electricity used to heat their homes. Ask for a show of hands to determine how many students use gas, oil, electricity, or a combination of these to heat their homes. Tell students who don't know what type of fuel they use to find out when they go home. Then have a volunteer recite the instructions that explain how to determine how much of each kind of fuel is used in the home.

Antonio in Action

Explain to students how to read the electricity meter shown on page 320. The first dial is read counterclockwise, the second is read clockwise, the third counterclockwise, and the fourth clockwise. Each dial represents a digit in a 4-digit number. Therefore, Antonio's electricity meter reads 6718 kW × 10 = 67,180 kW. According to his notes, 10 days ago (Nov. 4), the corrected reading was 66,830 kW. Therefore, 350 kW were used over 10 days, or 1050 kW (350 kW × 3) during a month. His calculations were correct.

Ask: How could Antonio calculate what part of the total electricity had been used to heat his house? *(He could subtract the amount of electricity used for appliances from the total. Or, he could read the meter on warm days, when the heater is not being used.)*

Antonio in Action

Antonio's home uses only electricity, so all he had to do was read the meter. He read it at five o'clock one day and again at five o'clock 10 days later.

The meter wasn't easy to read because some pointers turned clockwise and some counter clockwise. He wished someone could have helped him. Can you?

Meters with four dials, like Antonio's, often have "Multiply by 10" written on them. When meters have five dials, it is not necessary to multiply.

Antonio calculated how much energy his family used in a month: 1050 kWh. Wow! He found that hard to believe, so he asked to see the latest electric bill. Was Antonio's calculation right?

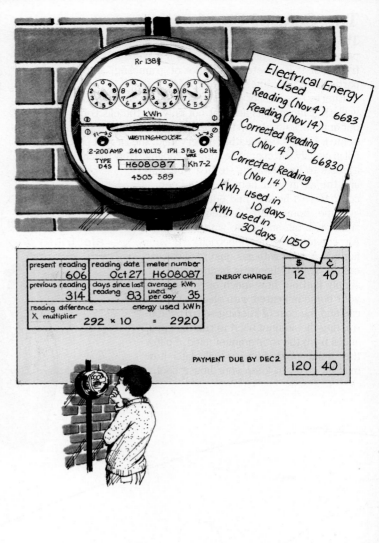

Aldo in Action

Aldo's home uses both electricity and gas. The furnace and water heater use natural gas. The gas meter looks very much like an electric meter. But as you know, gas is measured in cubic meters or feet, not kilowatt-hours. Aldo decided that he should measure how much gas his family used in a day, as well as their electricity consumption.

Anila in Action

Anila's home uses oil for heating and hot water, and electricity for everything else. She tried to find out how many liters of oil were used in 24 hours. She decided the only way to be sure was to check the oil bills. Like Antonio and Aldo, Anila also looked at the electric meter.

Anila got some excellent data. Her dad showed her the oil bills for the whole year. She started by plotting the amount they used during the year on a bar graph, and then tried to explain why it went up and down so much.

This meter is not accurate enough!

Anila Afshar Energy Consumption

HOT AIR AND WATER AVERAGE FOR NOV.	APPLIANCES (NOV. 10th)
14.2 LITERS OF OIL	27 kWh OF ELECTRICITY

FILL-UP DATE	LITERS OF OIL DELIVERED
APR. 21	498
JULY 4	481
OCT. 29	661
DEC. 9	584
JAN. 8	490
FEB. 6	575
FEB. 28	450
MAR. 24	462
MAY 1	526

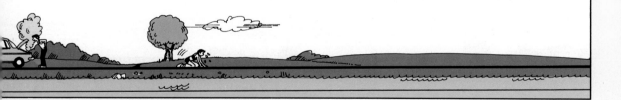

Aldo in Action

Have students read Aldo's plans for figuring out the amount of electricity and gas used in his home and determine if they agree with him or not. *(To find the amount of gas used, he read the gas meter. To find the amount of electricity used, he read the electric meter.)* Remind students that 1 m^3 = 10 kWh of electricity, according to the table on page 313.

Anila in Action

Have students study the chart showing the number of liters of oil delivered on the different dates. Ask students to notice when the deliveries were most frequent. *(during the winter months)* For practice, ask students to plot Anila's data in a bar graph in their Journals.

To get an accurate picture of how oil consumption changed over the year, have students do what Anila did, and make a bar graph of their own data. The x-axis could be labeled "Weeks" and the y-axis labeled "Liters of Oil Delivered." Then have students hypothesize about why the amount of oil used varied so much.

Ask students to speculate why Anila said in the comic: "This meter is not accurate enough." *(It does not show the amount of oil used on a daily basis.)*

Exploration 6
Activities 1 and 2

Have students complete *Activity 1* or *2*, depending on the season. Since they need to read their meters, it will take 10 days to collect their data.

You may wish to have students draw class graphs of energy consumption and costs over a one-month period. Each student could draw one bar on a graph to represent the amount of energy consumed in their home and another bar to represent the cost. Then the costs of heating using different kinds of energy could be compared.

If the weather is warm, you could bring in some heating bills from winter months so students can calculate heating costs per month. If the weather is cool, bring in electric bills from summer months so that students can calculate air-conditioning costs per month. For students who live in apartment complexes, the exercise that follows allows them to participate in calculating energy use.

How Much Energy Does Your School Use?

To find out how much energy their school uses, the "B Team" needed to ask some questions and set up some procedures. For example:

- What forms of energy are used in the school?
- How much of each form is used per month?
- Who should you ask for permission to read the meters?
- How might energy be conserved?
  Students can find out how much energy is consumed by:
- Reading each meter (at the same time each day) during a 10-day period
- Multiplying each number by 3 (based on 30 days in a month)

✳ *Follow Up*

Assessment

1. Ask students to list five things that their family could do to save electricity. *(Answers could include lowering the thermostat, taking cooler and shorter showers, turning off lights, running dishwasher only when full, buying appliances with a greater efficiency rating.)*

Activity 1
Keeping Warm

1. Find out what type of energy is used to heat your home.
2. Wait for a cold snap. Whatever form of energy you use to heat your house, find out how much of it you use over a ten-day period. Be sure to start and stop measuring at the same time of day. Multiply by 3 to estimate how much energy you would use in a month.
3. If your home is heated by gas or oil, the figure you found in step 2 is the amount of energy you use to heat your home.
4. If your home is heated electrically, you need to subtract the energy used to operate appliances from your energy total. One way to do this is by looking at an energy bill from a month in which little or no heating or air conditioning was used. This should show you about how many kilowatt-hours are used by appliances alone. Subtract this number from the number you found in step 2 to find out how many kilowatt-hours you use for heating.
5. Find out the cost per unit of whatever form of energy you use to heat your house. Multiply the amount of energy you used by the cost of the energy per unit. This gives you your total heating cost. Compare your results to your classmate's. Compile a class average.

Activity 2
Keeping Cool

1. Wait for warm weather to do this. Follow the procedure outlined in Activity 1. Find out how many kilowatt-hours you use in ten days. Multiply by 3 to estimate how many kilowatt-hours you use in a month.
2. Subtract the energy used by appliances from this total by following the procedure outlined in step 4 of Activity 1. This gives you the amount of energy used by the air conditioning system.
3. Multiply this amount by the cost per unit of electricity to figure out how much the air conditioner costs to run for a month.

◻

Finding the Cost of Heating or Cooling

Wait for warm or cold spell

↓

Find the amount of electricity used in 10 days

↓

Multiply by 3 to find energy used in 1 month

↓

Subtract energy used by appliances

↓

Multiply by cost per unit of energy

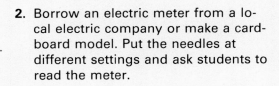

How Much Energy Does Your School Use?

The members of "B Team" (Brett, Barb, and Beth) all lived in apartments where the energy bills were included in the rent. They decided to survey their school instead. Quite a task! How did they go about it? They began by making a list of questions. What questions would you add to theirs?

---

2. Borrow an electric meter from a local electric company or make a cardboard model. Put the needles at different settings and ask students to read the meter.

Extension

1. Have students make a chart in which they list all the electrical appliances used in the classroom. Ask them to estimate, on a weekly basis, the following things for each appliance: the hours used, the average kilowatt-hours, and the cost.

2. Have students interview their parents to find out which appliances they may have purchased during the last 10 years. Students should find out the brand name, size, and the amount of electricity required to operate the appliance. They should also ask if the amount of electricity required to operate the appliance was considered. Finally, students should inquire if their parents would make the same choice again after being made aware of these new energy-saving considerations.

10 A Plan for Saving Energy

Could you imagine yourself throwing away money? Of course not. Wasting energy is just like throwing away money. How difficult is it to avoid wasting energy? It depends. It takes very little effort to turn off the lights when you leave a room. It doesn't require much effort to turn off the TV when you've finished watching it. On the other hand, saving large amounts of energy requires some effort. Saving energy whenever possible makes good sense—but are you prepared to make sacrifices? Is your family?

Personal Sacrifices

- You can save about 0.1 kWh every hour by watching black-and-white TV rather than color. The personal cost is minimal! Do you think it's worth the savings? Find out the cost of 1 kWh. How much would the savings be in one month?

- If you wash the dishes by hand you need about 20 L of hot water. An automatic dishwasher uses 40 L to 60 L. You could save between 1 kWh and 2 kWh on heating water every time the dishes needed washing. The personal cost is time and effort! Is it worth the savings? How much would the savings be in one month if you made the effort? How might you use a dishwasher in a way that would actually save energy?

- A shower typically uses 30 L to 50 L of water; a bath, 40 L to 60 L. You could easily save 10 L of hot water, or half a kilowatt-hour. But what would be the savings in money? in cleanliness? in relaxation? Is it worth it? How much could you save in one month by showering instead of bathing?

✴ Getting Started

This lesson focuses on the personal and family sacrifices that may be required in order to conserve energy.

Main Idea

By analyzing how energy is used in the home and where energy use can be reduced, an energy-savings plan can be developed.

✴ Teaching Strategies

Personal Sacrifices

Find out the cost, in cents per kWh, of electricity in your area. Then discuss the three scenarios.

- Watching black and white television saves 0.1 kWh for each hour of viewing. If the television is on 6 hours a day, or 180 hours a month, a family could save (180 kWh/month × 0.1 kWh/h =) 18 kWh per month. Multiply 18 kWh per month times the cost of electricity per kWh to find the total savings.

- Washing dishes twice a day by hand saves 2 kWh per day or 60 kWh per month. A dishwasher can be used more efficiently if it is only turned on after it is completely filled.

- A shower saves 0.5 kWh each day, or 15 kWh per month.

LESSON 10 ORGANIZER

Objectives

By the end of the lesson, students should be able to:

1. Calculate the energy savings that can be made by changing some activities in a family's lifestyle.
2. Develop a list of recommendations to reduce a family's total energy consumption by 25 percent.

Process Skills

calculating, problem solving, evaluating, drawing conclusions

New Terms

(Organizer continues on next page)

Answers to

Family Sacrifices

Divide the class into six groups. Assign one situation to each group for discussion.
- Keeping the lights or radio on for 24 hours each day for two weeks uses from 33.6 to 67.2 kWh of energy.
- A non-frost-free refrigerator saves 50 kWh of energy per month.
- If the washing machine is used twice a week, rinsing with cold water saves 8 kWh per month.
- Fluorescent lights also have a much longer life. However, some types require special fittings.
- Turning down the thermostat 1 degree saves 200 L of oil, 200 m³ of gas, or 2000 kWh of electricity.
- If you turn down the thermostat by 4 °C, the amount of savings depends upon the cost of gas or electricity in your area.

Answers to

A Call to Action

Possible responses: install timers on lights, purchase a smaller television set, only use the dishwasher when it is full, take showers instead of baths, and use cold water in the washing machine.

Follow Up

Assessment

Have students list all the electrical appliances in their homes. Ask them to decide which are luxuries and which are necessities. Ask them to estimate the savings if they eliminate using the luxuries.

Extension

Ask students to list different ways electricity is wasted in their homes. Then for a week, have them grade themselves on how they saved or wasted energy.

Family Sacrifices

Here are some more situations. Ask yourself what the cost of each would be. Do your friends and family agree? Would you make the sacrifice? Would they?

- Should you leave the house lights or a radio on (0.1 kWh–0.2 kWh per hour) to discourage break-ins? If you were away on a two-week vacation, how much would this warning system cost you? Would it be worth it?
- The energy consumed by a frost-free refrigerator is about 140 kWh per month; by a nonfrost-free, about 90 kWh per month. Which would you recommend buying? Why do people buy frost-free refrigerators?
- Washing machines generally use about 120 L of hot water per load. Rinsing in cold water saves about 40 L of hot water (about 2 kWh). How much could you save per month by making use of this information? Is rinsing in cold water worth it?
- Fluorescent lights are about five times as efficient as regular incandescent lights. Would you install them in your home?
- If you turned down the thermostat in your house by 1 °C (from 20 °C to 19 °C), you would reduce your heating bill by about 5 percent. How much would this be in dollars per year? Would you do it?
- If you turned down the thermostat at night by 4 °C (from 20 °C to 16 °C), you would reduce your heating bill by about 10 percent. It would be possible to save as much as 400 L of oil or 400 m³ of gas or 4000 kWh of electricity per year. How much of a savings would this be? Would you turn down the thermostat at night?

A Call to Action

Crisis!

- Your family is having financial difficulties.
- An energy crisis is looming.

Your Response

You decide to reduce your total family energy consumption by 25 percent. How will you achieve this goal? Prepare a list of recommendations. Then look back over this and the previous lesson to get help in estimating the savings—in both money and energy—that each recommendation will bring. Report to your family—they may want to try it!

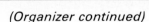

(Organizer continued)

Materials	Time Required
none	one class period

Science Discovery Videodisc

Disc 2, Image and Activity Bank, 6–10

---

11 Keeping in the Heat

People who live in a cold climate spend a great deal of money heating their homes. On a cold day, heat from inside our houses travels through the walls and escapes to the outside. How does heat escape from your home? Can we slow down its escape? First, consider what materials your home is made of. Does the material make a difference when it comes to saving heat? Is your home well-insulated? Does the type of insulation your home has matter? The following Exploration will help you answer these questions.

A Heat-Saving Competition

In this Exploration, you will construct an experimental "house" out of two cans. You will then test your house to see how quickly it loses heat. You will compare your results with those of your classmates to find out who had the best design.

You Will Need

- 2 cans—one should fit easily into the other
- a variety of insulating materials
- a thermometer

LESSON 11 ORGANIZER

Objectives

By the end of the lesson, students should be able to:

1. Control variables in an experiment to make a fair test.
2. Observe the areas in a home through which heat energy escapes.
3. Compare the insulation in a home to the recommended insulation levels.

Process Skills

predicting, controlling variables, calculating, comparing

New Terms

Thermal resistance or R-value—a measure of how well materials can prevent heat from getting through them.

(Organizer continues on next page)

LESSON 11

✴ Getting Started

This lesson helps students understand the problem of insulating homes to keep heat energy inside. Students conduct a controlled experiment to test the insulation properties of different materials. Then they do an at-home experiment to find out where heat is escaping. Finally, they research different types of insulation materials, and evaluate the adequacy of insulation in their homes.

Main Ideas

1. Heat energy can escape from homes in many ways.
2. Insulation reduces heat loss from homes.

✴ Teaching Strategies

Exploration 7

After students have read the introductory paragraph, divide the class into small groups of four or five to complete the Exploration. Call on a volunteer to define the word *insulation* so that everyone is familiar with the term. Invite students to predict which material will slow down the escape of heat the most. Ask one group to perform the experiment with no insulation (the control) and the other groups to choose one insulating material each (the variable that changes).

(Continues on next page)

(Exploration 7 continued)

Be sure that students understand that all factors, other than the changed variable, must be the same if the experiment is to be a fair test. Ask: Why is it unfair to compare the temperatures of the water in the cans shown in the pictures? *(They are not the same size, so one might lose more heat due to greater surface area.)* Ask: What procedures must each experimental group be certain to follow? *(The group must be sure to change only one variable: The size of the cans, as well as the amount of hot water, must be the same. One group cannot stir its hot water if the other groups do not. The temperature must be taken the same way in every group. All groups must take readings during the same 10-minute interval, and all groups should start with the same temperature of hot water.)*

Appoint one student in each group to be the timer. Readings should be taken at 1-minute intervals, and the results charted and graphed on the chalkboard. Refer students to the graph on page 326. Have them duplicate the graph by labeling "Time" on the x-axis and "Temperature" on the y-axis. Then ask them to graph their results. Have groups discuss their results, comparing each type of insulation. Remember, the "house" with the smallest change in temperature has the best insulation.

What to Do

To ensure fairness, all the competitors should follow the same procedure. How can you make the competition a fair one? Look at these pictures of two experimental set-ups. Would they show the same results? What procedure must each competitor be certain to follow?

Place the small can inside the large can. Fill the space between the cans with any type of insulation that occurs to you—sand, tissue paper, dried grass, cotton batting, wool, water, sawdust, Styrofoam, or air. Fashion a snug-fitting cover with a hole for the thermometer. Put 100 mL of water at 60 °C in each can. Competitors must all have the same starting temperature. Why do you think this is so?

Take the temperature every minute for 10 minutes. Plot your results on a graph like the one shown here. Compare your results with those of a classmate by plotting your classmate's results on the same graph. The winner of the heat-saving competition is the person whose "house" has the warmest water after 10 minutes.

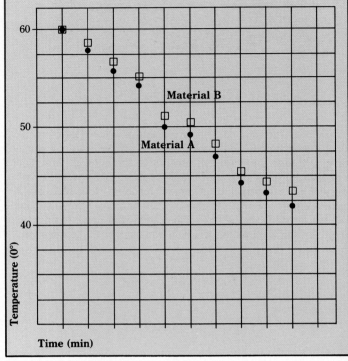

Where does the heat go?

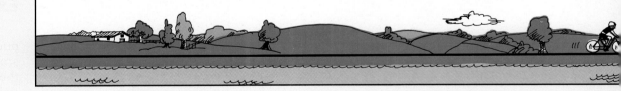

(Organizer continued)

Materials

Exploration 7: 2 cans—one should fit easily into the other, various insulating materials (sand, tissue paper, dried grass, cotton batting, wool, water, plastic foam, sawdust), thermometer, 100 mL water, watch or clock, graduated cylinder
Exploration 8: plastic wrap, wire hanger
Exploration 9: Journal

Teacher's Resource Binder

Resource Worksheets 6–8 and 6–9
Graphic Organizer Transparency 6–7

Science Discovery Videodisc

Disc 2, Image and Activity Bank, 6–11

Time Required

two to three class periods

Where Does the Heat Go?

You have seen that insulation can help to keep heat from escaping from a building. Still, some heat energy will always be lost. This section will help you find out how this happens and will help you prepare a home energy report for your family.

How does the heat escape from your home? Much of it is lost by *air exchange,* the movement of warm air from the inside to the outside. Air exchange occurs when air leaks through gaps around doors, windows, attic entrances, and electrical outlets, as well as through cracks in ceilings and walls.

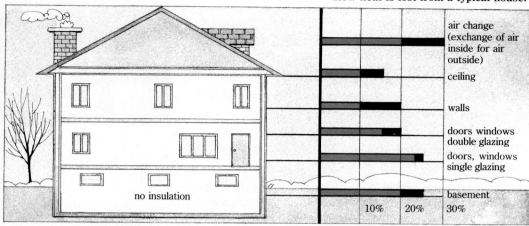

How heat is lost from a typical house.

Even if the gaps around the openings in your home are sealed and the ceilings and walls have no cracks, heat can still get through. It escapes when the warm air inside comes in contact with the cold walls, ceilings, windows, and doors. Why are they cold? At the same time that the inside air warms them, the outside air cools them down. The result is heat loss.

How much heat escapes through air exchange? How much is lost to the cold surfaces of the building? The bar graph will give you some idea. The exact amounts vary from home to home, of course, because not all buildings are constructed the same. The amount by which most buildings vary is shown by the shaded areas of the bars. After studying the bar graph, answer the questions on the next page.

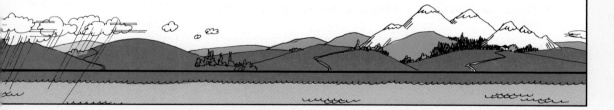

Where Does the Heat Go?

Have students read page 327 to get an idea of how heat is lost from homes through air exchange. Pause to allow students time to look at the bar graph. Ask some appropriate questions so that you can tell by student answers that all understand the graph. Emphasize to students that the black areas of the bars indicate the average range of heat loss for many homes. Heat loss will vary from home to home. Then have students read pages 328 and 329 and answer the questions.

Answers to

In-Text Questions

- The most heat is lost through air exchange.
- Double-glazed windows and doors lose less heat because there is an insulating, sealed layer of air between the two glass panes.
- Basements lose a lot of heat because they are seldom insulated and their walls are made from cement blocks, which do not retain heat.
- The percentages do not add up to 100 percent because they represent average values for many homes, and because it is impossible to measure and categorize all the heat loss from a home. Some heat loss is probably unaccounted for.

  Suggested answers for the questions about the thermal photograph are:

- The basement is so bright because it shows the greatest heat loss.
- The outside steps are black because they are not heated and are not hot. They are at the same temperature as the outside air.
- The windows without heavy blinds are bright because they allow a lot of heat to escape through them. Therefore, they are warmer than the walls around them.
- The upstairs window appears dark because it is probably covered with heavy curtains or blinds, which help to insulate it.
- The curtains appear to be closed in the room on the left side of the house on the first floor. The window appears slightly darker because less heat is escaping through it.
- The front door appears to be quite dark which would mean that little heat is escaping. Therefore, it probably has a storm door.
- Heat that has already escaped into the attic will complete its exchange with the outside air in the easiest way possible, along the edge of the roof. Therefore, the escaping heat appears bright along the line of the roof in the photograph.
- The heat escapes between overlapping shingles rather than through them, making the shingle lines visible.

- Where is the most heat lost?
- Why do you think double-glazed windows and doors are better than single-glazed?
- Why is so much heat lost from the basement?
- Why don't the percentages add up to exactly 100?

This thermal photograph of a house is similar to a normal photo—except that it shows heat instead of light. Indeed, thermal photographs are often taken at night! See if you can interpret this one.

- Why do you think the basement is so bright?
- Why are the steps leading to the house black?
- Why are some of the windows bright?
- Why is the upstairs window dark?
- Are the curtains drawn in any of the rooms?
- Do you think the house has a storm door? Why or why not?
- Why is the line of the roof so bright?
- Why do you think the house appears to be striped?
- Do the bar graph and the thermal photograph both tell the same story?

How is it possible to slow down the escape of heat from a building? You found the answer in Exploration 7: use insulation. For insulating buildings, foamy or fluffy materials such as Styrofoam (foamed plastic), fiberglass batts (fluffy, thick sheets), or vermiculite (loose particles) are used. Do you know of any other types of insulation?

The **thermal resistance** of insulating materials is called the **R-value.** It measures just how good materials are at preventing heat from getting through them. Most common insulating materials have an R-value of about 1.25 for every centimeter of thickness. Some plastic foams have higher R-values. The lower the thermal resistance of a material, the more easily heat travels through it. For instance, twice as much heat escapes through a wall whose R-value is 1.5 than through a wall whose R-value is 3.0. If you visit a building supplier, you will see the R-value of insulation products stamped on the packages.

- What is the R-value of a wall filled with 10 cm of fiberglass batting?
- What is the R-value of a ceiling insulated with 15 cm of fiberglass?

Thermal photograph showing heat loss from a house.

Thermal Resistance of Some Common Building Materials

Material	R Value (per cm)
Brick or concrete	0.06
Gypsum board	0.24
Wood	0.48
Glass fiber or rockwool	1.25
Cellulose fiber	1.49
Expanded polystyrene ("Beadboard")	1.6
Extruded polystyrene ("Styrofoam")	1.9

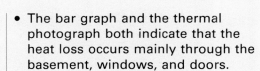

- The bar graph and the thermal photograph both indicate that the heat loss occurs mainly through the basement, windows, and doors.
- Other types of insulation: old newspapers, ground up and treated with fire retardant, can be blown into attics to serve as insulation. Strips of foam rubber can be used to insulate around windows and doors.
- A wall filled with 10 cm of fiberglass batting has an R-value of 10 cm × 1.25/cm = 12.5
- A ceiling insulated with 15 cm of fiberglass has an R-value of 15 cm × 1.25/cm = 18.75

How much insulation should you have in your ceilings and walls? Too little and you will waste heat. Too much and you will spend a fortune on insulation! Architects have been trying to find the best balance. Here are their recommendations:

Recommended Insulation Levels

Parts of a House	Recommended R-Values	
	warmer climates	colder climates
Ceiling or roof	33	38
Walls	18	21
Basement	12	12

- How many centimeters of fiberglass would you hope to find in the roof of your home? in the walls? the basement?

In Exploration 9, you can check out your own home to see whether it meets these recommendations.

If you live in a warm or hot climate you may be more concerned with keeping your house comfortably cool, rather than keeping it warm. Insulation works just as well to keep heat *out* as to keep it *in*. A well-insulated house will have lower heating bills but also lower cooling bills. So you see that it makes good sense to have a well-insulated, energy-efficient house no matter where you live.

Many homes, especially older ones, are not well insulated. But your family may be able to do something about adding insulation to your home. In Exploration 10, you can check out the best buys. Perhaps you will have some important suggestions about insulation to make to your family.

EXPLORATION 8

Find Those Gaps!

Warm air can find every gap in your home, even small cracks that you didn't know existed! About a quarter of the total heat loss in your home is from air exchange, and a quarter of that is from gaps around doors and windows.

Suppose that your family's heating bill for the winter is $400. You could save $25 just by sealing these gaps.

You Will Need

- plastic sandwich wrap
- a clothes hanger

What to Do

Make a simple draft gauge from some sandwich wrap and a clothes hanger. Choose a cold day and look for those gaps! Any gaps you find can easily be fixed with weatherstripping (between moving parts) or with caulking. Before you prepare your report, check the cost of weatherstripping and caulking.

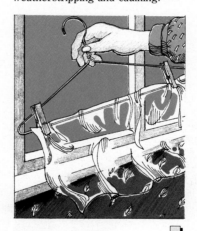

Answers to

Recommended Insulation Levels

- A home insulated to the recommended levels should have the following amounts of fiberglass
  in the ceiling:
    33 ÷ 1.25 = 26.4 cm (warmer climate)
    38 ÷ 1.25 = 30.4 cm (colder climate)
  in walls:
    18 ÷ 1.25 = 14.4 cm (warmer)
    21 ÷ 1.25 = 16.8 cm (colder)
  in basement:
    12 ÷ 1.25 = 9.6 cm (both warmer and colder climates)

Exploration 8

Assign this Exploration as an at-home activity. It works best when the weather is cold. Drafts are less noticeable on a warm day. Ask students to prepare a brief report by listing the places they found drafts, explaining the procedures they used to fix them, and calculating the total cost of their work. Caution students to ask their parents for permission before making any repairs.

Exploration 9

This activity will give students an opportunity to evaluate the kind and thickness of insulation in the attics, walls, and basements of their homes. Stress to students that they should do the activity with the help of an adult; some older buildings may still have asbestos insulation, which is potentially harmful. Afterward, they can share their findings with the entire family.

The activity could be optional, since many students may not be able to get this information. If the activity is done, results could be recorded in a data table like the one shown. Students could duplicate and complete the table in their Journals.

Exploration 10

This Exploration could be assigned to students who were not able to do *Exploration 9*. Display the collection of insulation samples in the classroom for all to see.

☀ *Follow Up*

Assessment

1. Provide students with samples of different kinds of insulation materials and their R-values. Or, using the chart on page 328 in their texts, ask students to figure out how thick each material would need to be to insulate the walls and ceiling of their classroom. *(Thicknesses will of course depend upon the material used. Calculations should be based on an R-value of 18–21 for the walls and 33–38 for the ceiling.)*
2. Ask students to design and perform an experiment to test the insulating capability of cotton, wool, polyester, paper, and mylar.

Extension

1. Have students send for consumer information on energy conservation in the home, either from a local utility company or from a county cooperative extension agency. Have them draw posters and set up an exhibit on energy conservation based on this information. If possible, have their posters and exhibit displayed in a public place, so that many people can benefit from the information.

Is Your Home Well Insulated?

Ask an adult member of your family to help you with this survey. You will need to look:

- In the attic. (Don't put your foot through the ceiling!)
- In the walls. You can often see inside if you unscrew the covers to electrical fittings. **Do this with an adult—you could get a nasty shock.**
- In the basement.

Make a note of the type and thickness of the insulation in each place (in centimeters). Use a table like the one shown to record your results.

Don't let this happen to you!

Place	Type of Insulation	Thickness of Insulation	R-Value of Insulation	Recommended R-Value
Ceilings				
Walls				
Basement				

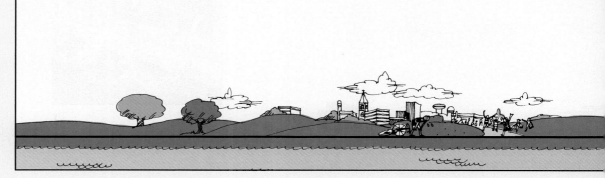

2. Students should work with teachers, the principal, or the custodian at the school to determine the amount and type of insulation in key areas of the school. Then they should report to the class.

Best Buys in Insulation

Get together with some of your classmates and make a display of common insulation materials. Go to a building supply store and find out all you can about different insulation materials. Find out the R-values of each material and how much each material costs. Try to obtain small samples of different types of insulation to display. If you can't get samples, draw an illustration of each material and provide the information you found. Which is the best buy?

1. Kilowatt-Hour Quiz

a. Which appliance uses the most energy during the same period: an iron, a light bulb, a television set, or a clothes dryer? Put them in order from most energy to least energy used.

b. Match each device (left-hand column) with the approximate amount of energy needed to run it (right-hand column).

   (a) 100-W light bulb burning for 6 hours   A. 0.60 kWh

   (b) television set operating for 4 hours   B. 0.20 kWh

   (c) microwave operating for 10 minutes   C. 0.25 kWh

   (d) washing machine operating for 1 hour   D. 0.30 kWh

   (e) radio operating for 4 hours   E. 1.20 kWh

2. The hot water tap in the bathroom drips about one drop every second. The family argues about how much energy it wastes. Can you design an investigation to find the answer?

1. (a) Although different models of appliances will have different energy requirements, in general, the answers are as follows, from most to least: *clothes dryer, iron, television set, light bulb.*

  (b) Because different models of appliances need different amounts of energy, supply students with the following wattage amounts for the items listed:

      100-W light bulb
      300-W television
      1200-W microwave
      300-W washing machine
      70-W radio

     (a) A 0.60 kWh
     (b) E 1.20 kWh
     (c) C 0.25 kWh
     (d) D 0.30 kWh
     (e) B 0.20 kWh

2. Encourage students to be creative in their solutions to this problem. There is more than one correct answer. One possible response is to measure how long it takes to collect 1 L of water from the tap (about 30 minutes). Next, compare the temperature from the hot water tap with that from the cold water tap. Find out how much energy it takes to raise the temperature by this amount. Then multiply this figure by the amount of liters lost in a day to determine how many kWh are wasted.

LESSON 12

✴ Getting Started

This lesson introduces students to the concept that some energy sources are being exhausted and will not be available for much longer. To illustrate this point, production and consumption of oil in the United States in the 1970s and 1990s are compared.

Main Ideas

1. Energy sources that can be replaced are called renewable; those that cannot are called nonrenewable.
2. The supply of oil and other nonrenewable energy sources is running out.

✴ Teaching Strategies

Ask students to read page 332. Call on a volunteer to summarize the story of how crude oil was formed. Ask if any students have ever heard the word *petrochemicals* before. If they have, ask them to define the word and name some examples. *(Petrochemicals are chemicals made from petroleum or natural gas; examples include: plastics, synthetic fibers, paints, and medicines.)*

Answers to

Renewable and Nonrenewable Resources

The graph at the bottom of page 332 is based on percentages, so it could indicate either a switch from oil to other sources of energy by all areas except transportation, or an increased dependence on oil by transportation, or both.
(Answers continue on the next page)

12 Bye-Bye Black Gold

What is this stuff we call "black gold"? Where does it come from? How did it form? Here is the story. Imagine a time, millions of years ago, long, long before humans arrived on the scene. Most of the earth is covered by warm seas teeming with tiny plants and animals. When these tiny organisms die, their remains fall to the ocean floor, where they accumulate century after century. As time passes, sediments cover the layers of dead organisms. Over long periods of time, the sediments continue to pile up, higher and higher, until eventually they may be several thousand meters thick. Crushed by the heavy load of sediments and warmed by the heat of the earth, the tiny plants and animals are "cooked"; the chemicals that made up their bodies are slowly changed into crude oil. Presto: black gold!

Without oil, our civilization would collapse. Oil makes our industrial world go 'round. It provides energy for our factories, heat for our homes, and gasoline for our cars. It is no wonder that crude oil is called "black gold." Oil also supplies us with *petrochemicals*, which are used to make plastics, paints, fibers, medicines . . . the list is almost endless. Look around you. Most likely you are surrounded by things made from petrochemicals.

Our appetite for oil is increasing, but the supply is running out—not just in the United States, but all around the world. Once it's gone, it's gone for good. Why do you think this is so?

Renewable and Nonrenewable Resources

The figure on the right compares the use of oil in the United States in 1970 with its use in 1990. How has our use of oil changed? Compare the figures for transportation. What would you conclude? Less oil is used on a percentage basis in every category other than transportation. Would you conclude that less power is being generated, fewer manufacturing facilities are operational, and fewer homes are being heated? Explain.

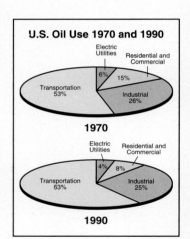

U.S. Oil Use 1970 and 1990

1970:
Electric Utilities 6%
Residential and Commercial 15%
Transportation 53%
Industrial 26%

1990:
Electric Utilities 4%
Residential and Commercial 8%
Transportation 63%
Industrial 25%

LESSON 12 ORGANIZER

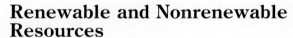

Objectives

By the end of the lesson, students should be able to:
1. Classify energy sources as renewable or nonrenewable.
2. Make predictions about future sources of energy.

Process Skills

classifying, problem solving, evaluating, summarizing

New Terms

Renewable resources—energy sources that can be replaced naturally, such as wood, hydroelectricity, and solar energy.
Nonrenewable resources—energy sources that cannot be replaced once they are used up, such as oil, natural gas, and coal.
Petrochemicals—chemicals derived from petroleum; used to make plastics, paints, fibers, and medicines.

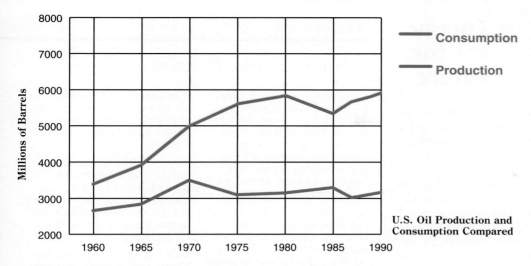

Millions of Barrels (y-axis): 2000, 3000, 4000, 5000, 6000, 7000, 8000

— Consumption
— Production

U.S. Oil Production and Consumption Compared

x-axis: 1960, 1965, 1970, 1975, 1980, 1985, 1990

Now look at the figure comparing oil production and consumption. What would you conclude from this? How might these comparisons look 10 years from now? 50 years from now? Explain.

Fortunately, oil is not our only source of energy. There are others: coal, hydroelectricity, wood, and natural gas, to name a few. Like oil, some of these cannot be replaced once they have been used up. Such energy sources are known as **nonrenewable resources.** Energy sources that are replaced naturally, if wisely used, are called **renewable resources.** Make a two-column list of nonrenewable and renewable sources of energy.

Even though the United States is one of the world's leading producers of oil, it must import much of its oil to meet its energy needs. So far, the U.S. has had no trouble finding enough oil to keep things going, but oil is running out throughout the world, and its price, although fluctuating, is heading generally upward. What about the future? How should we respond?

- Not worry, something will happen.
- Cut back on energy consumption.
- Search harder for more nonrenewable resources—oil, coal, and natural gas.
- Develop more renewable resources—hydroelectricity, solar energy, tidal power, geothermal, and wind energy.
- Increase the number of nuclear power stations.
- Try to find new energy resources.
- Other (specify)

Take a few minutes and discuss each of these options. With the knowledge you currently have, which option(s) would you favor? Why?

Oil shale

Squeezing Oil from Stone

Geologists have long known of vast deposits of oil-bearing rocks called oil shales. The United States alone has billions of barrels of oil in the form of oil shales. What's the catch? Extracting oil from oil shales is difficult and costly. The rock must be mined (usually strip mined), crushed, and heated to separate the oil from the rock. Then the waste rock must be disposed of. The cost of oil would have to be much higher to make extracting oil from oil shales a realistic option.

✳ *Follow Up*

Assessment

The characteristics of good energy resources are high energy potential, abundant supply, easy to obtain, easy to convert into useful forms of energy, no negative effects on the environment, and no threat to human health. Have students rate different energy sources with a plus or a minus, based on these characteristics. The energy sources should include petroleum, coal, natural gas, wood, wind, solar, hydroelectricity, and geothermal.

Extension

Have students research the known locations of energy resources. On a map of the world, have students locate these energy resources using different colored pins for each fuel. Then have students determine which countries have the most fuel reserves and which have the greatest demands.

Materials

Teacher's Resource Binder

Resource Transparencies 6–8 and 6–9
Graphic Organizer Transparency 6–10

Science Discovery Videodisc

Disc 2, Image and Activity Bank, 6–12

Time Required

one class period

LESSON 13

Getting Started

In this lesson, students research the energy options for the future. They compare eight sources of energy, and learn about the social and/or environmental problems associated with each one.

Main Idea

Each energy source has advantages and disadvantages that must be evaluated.

Teaching Strategies

Students should use the Exploration that follows as a starting point for their investigations. Encourage students to use as many resources as they can in addition to the library.

Exploration 11

This Exploration is a research project that requires students to use the library as well as other sources of information. The questions posed after each article are designed to start students thinking about the advantages and disadvantages of each type of energy. Each group of three students should choose a different energy source to research and then display their findings.

Prepare an Energy Open House so that students can share and discuss their projects. This could be scheduled during class hours, after school, or in the evening to include parents.

13 Energy for the Future

What is the future of our energy resources—oil, hydro-electricity, coal, natural gas, solar, geothermal, wind, and nuclear?

This is a big question, because our whole way of life is dependent on having enough energy. It is also a big question in that answering it is quite a challenge. There is a huge amount of information available on this topic, and you may find yourself having to make some difficult decisions about what to investigate.

A Big Question to Answer

Get together with about three friends and select one energy source that you would like to research. Then list some of the questions about this energy source that you think will help you answer the big question, "What is the future of this energy source?"

In the pages that follow, you will find some information and a few important questions about each energy source. Treat these as starting points for your investigation, using the questions to supplement your own list.

The government publishes many papers and pamphlets on the subject of energy. Write or call the U.S. Department of Energy for more information.

Many government agencies such as the Department of Energy, the Nuclear Regulatory Commission, and energy-related businesses are pleased to provide information.

Which agencies or companies are involved with your chosen source of energy? You might like to write a letter to ask them for information.

When you have completed your project, create a display on poster board to let your classmates know what you have found out. Do they feel that the future of your energy source is cause for optimism?

Once you have heard about the future of other energy resources from the other groups, you should be able to discuss more fully what course our country should take.

As you read about these energy sources, think about the advantages and disadvantages of each. Is any single energy source the answer to all our energy needs?

> 345 Sixth St.
> Anytown, USA 10010
>
> Department of Energy,
> 1000 Independence Dr.
> Washington, DC 20585
>
> Dear Sir or Madam:
>
> I am collecting information on energy from coal for a school project.
>
> I would really appreciate your sending me any pamphlets etc., which you think might be useful.
>
> Yours Sincerely
> Joe Cool

LESSON 13 ORGANIZER

Objectives

By the end of the lesson, students should be able to:
1. List the eight different sources of energy that are available.
2. List the advantages and disadvantages of eight different energy sources.

Process Skills

researching, comparing, drawing conclusions, decision making

New Terms

Drilling rig in the Arctic

Natural Gas—A Clean, but Limited Alternative

Natural gas is found on every continent. It is abundant, cheap, and produces no harmful emissions when it burns. Natural gas is tapped by drilling wells, just as is oil. Because it is such a clean fuel, natural gas is growing in importance. Like oil, though, natural gas is a fossil fuel. Current supplies will not last forever.

Natural gas pipeline (under construction)

Oil—Old Reliable in Decline

Even though our country is one of the world's leading oil producers, the United States must import about 35 percent of the oil it uses. Because of the great demand for petroleum products, researchers are developing oil production methods for very harsh climates such as the Arctic and for very deep water.

Questions

1. How much oil is left in the United States?
2. What are the problems of getting it out from under the sea? Is there any risk of pollution?
3. What are oil shales and how is oil extracted from them? What's stopping us from extracting as much oil as possible from them?
4. Where else are we looking for oil?

Questions

1. Are there untapped supplies of natural gas in the United States? If so, where?
2. How much gas is there left to recover in the world?
3. What is one major drawback of natural gas?
4. It's possible to condense natural gas into liquid form. How will this help relieve gas transport and distribution problems? What are some drawbacks of this approach?

Materials

Exploration 11: poster board, markers

Science Discovery Videodisc

Disc 2, Image and Activity Bank, 6–13

Time Required

two to three class periods

Answers to

Here Comes the Sun

1. Solar collectors are insulated boxes with glass covers. The interiors of the boxes are painted black to absorb the most energy. A heat-transferring fluid is heated as it circulates through pipes in the collector.
2. For an average size solar collector (74 square meters) including collectors, storage tank, pumps, heat exchangers, plumbing, controls, insulation, and labor, the cost might be $20,000.
3. The amount of heat produced by a collector depends on its area and efficiency. In a sunny location, a 20-m solar collector could capture millions of kilowatts of energy in an average year.
4. They are expensive to install. Solar collectors cannot be used in all locations—they need a lot of sunlight to be effective.
5. Every family should have the choice. But if locations do not get enough sun, they are not suitable for solar collectors.

Answers to

Current Technology

1. Not very many rivers are available. Furthermore, most that could be used are in remote locations.
2. Reservoirs often destroy wildlife habitats as well as the scenic beauty of an area.
3. A large dam can cost millions of dollars to build, whereas a small dam, for local use, may only cost a few thousand dollars. Also, the storage of water may damage the environment by flooding areas and changing the flow of rivers.
4. Many sites that are suitable for building a dam for hydroelectric power are not near populated areas. Transporting electricity to where it is needed is expensive.
5. Since most of the hydroelectric resources have already been tapped, this is a very limited resource. It cannot fully meet our energy needs.

Here Comes the Sun

Solar energy is the ultimate renewable resource. It isn't difficult to make your own solar heater. In many ways it's similar to a greenhouse. Why not try to make one and test it? The illustration can give you some ideas.

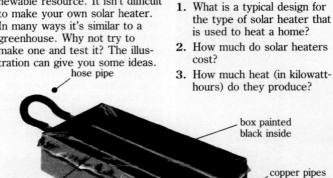

hose pipe

box painted black inside

top of box covered with glass or plastic wrap

copper pipes

hot water out

cold water in

A hydroelectric dam

Questions

1. What is a typical design for the type of solar heater that is used to heat a home?
2. How much do solar heaters cost?
3. How much heat (in kilowatt-hours) do they produce?
4. What are the drawbacks of solar-powered systems?
5. Should every family that can afford to install a solar heater do so?

A solar heated house

Current Technology

The source from which hydroelectric power comes never runs out: rain falls, rivers flow, and dams fill up. Hydroelectricity seems ideal, but is it?

Questions

1. How many rivers are still available that have hydroelectric possibilities?
2. Does the building of a hydroelectric dam have any negative effects on the environment?
3. How much does it cost to build a dam?
4. Are there any problems in getting electricity from the generating station to where it is needed?
5. How fully can our energy needs be met by hydroelectricity?

A New Look at an Old Fuel: Wood

The U.S. currently meets only a tiny fraction of its energy needs with wood. But at least one country—Sweden—has big plans for this renewable resource. The people of Sweden were concerned enough about the risks of nuclear power to do something about it; they are changing over to wood as one of their main energy sources. The Swedes look after their forests very carefully. They cut trees selectively instead of clear-cutting whole areas. They also replant immediately wherever they cut. This practice turns forests into a valuable, endlessly renewable energy source.

The Swedes use every part of the tree. Top grade wood is used for lumber, and medium grade for pulp and paper. Wood trash is burned to supply electricity.

Wood can also be turned into a synthetic fuel—methyl alcohol, or methanol—which can be used in cars and trucks in place of gasoline.

Questions

1. How much of the United States is covered with forests?

2. How does forestry as practiced in the United States compare with forestry in Sweden?

3. How would a power plant using wood work?

4. How else may wood be used as a source of heat for homes? How many homes in the United States use wood for heating?

5. What is the process by which wood is converted to methanol?

6. How much oil would be saved by using wood for electricity, cooking, and for making synthetic fuel for cars?

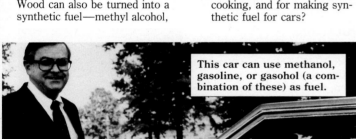

This car can use methanol, gasoline, or gasohol (a combination of these) as fuel.

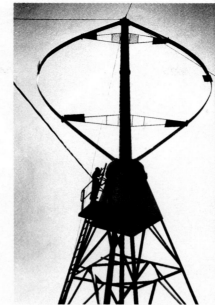

An experimental, high efficiency windmill for electrical generation.

Energy from Wind

Electricity was first generated using the wind in 1880. The first wind-operated power plant went on line in 1941, but even today, relatively few such power plants are in operation. This may change in the future, though, as the cost of energy continues to rise.

Questions

1. Would wind-powered generators be feasible in your part of the country?

2. What drawbacks does this energy source have?

3. What is the best design for a windmill and its generating system?

4. Should more power be generated using the wind?

Answers to

Unlocking the Power of the Atom

1. Nuclear reactors contain uranium-235. Uranium-235 can split and give off neutrons and energy. These neutrons hit other uranium-235 atoms, setting up a chain reaction. Uncontrolled chain reactions result in an explosion. However, in a nuclear reactor, the chain reaction is controlled by boron steel control rods.

   The energy that is released in the chain reaction is used to make steam to generate electricity.

   There are just over 100 nuclear reactors in the United States.

2. In 1987, nuclear power plants in the United States reported nearly 3000 mishaps, at least 430 emergency shutdowns, and 104,000 incidents in which workers were exposed to radiation.

3. In the Three-Mile-Island accident, a malfunctioning pump and valve combined with a series of operator errors to drain water from the reactor's core. This caused a partial melt-down. The containment system held an estimated 18 billion curies of radioactivity. (The curie is the unit of measurement for radioactivity.)

   Operators at the Chernobyl plant made a mistake when they were carrying out a test on one of the reactors. Attempting to correct it, they deliberately overrode a series of safety systems designed to prevent an accident. The reactor's power surged several hundredfold in a second. Two huge explosions blasted the 1000-metric-ton lid off the reactor and ignited a fire that blazed for 10 days.

   When humans are involved, there is always the possibility of error.

4. At present, it is being stored and cooled while industries try to figure out what to do with it.

5. Normal operation of nuclear power plants causes little environmental damage. However, accidents pose infinitely greater dangers than those at conventional power plants. Also, the disposal of nuclear waste is still an unsolved problem.

Unlocking the Power of the Atom

Radioactive substances such as uranium break down naturally all the time, one atom at a time. When they do, they give off heat, as well as other forms of energy. We don't notice this process because it occurs slowly, and because these substances are spread thinly throughout the earth's crust. But when radioactive substances are concentrated, the breakdown speeds up dramatically. The breakdown of one atom can trigger the breakdown of another, and so on—much like one match setting fire to another. Nuclear reactors harness this natural breakdown by keeping the process going at a controlled rate while at the same time using the enormous amount of heat that is released to boil water. The steam generated in this way is used to drive a turbine, which in turn drives a generator.

Questions

1. How do nuclear reactors work? How much power can they generate? How many are there in the United States? Are there plans for more?

2. How risky is nuclear power, really?

3. What happened at Three Mile Island? Chernobyl? How did these accidents happen? Could what happened at Chernobyl happen here?

4. How is nuclear waste disposed of?

5. What are the pros and cons of using nuclear energy?

Coal—The Rock that Burns

Coal is formed from the remains of plants that died millions of years ago. Sometimes it's found close to the earth's surface and is strip mined; sometimes it's found far below the ground and must be mined conventionally. Strip mining can often leave ugly scars on the landscape. The United States has huge amounts of coal. Most is used for electricity; much of the rest is exported. Unfortunately, most coal produces harmful gases when it is burned. Coal is a major cause of acid rain.

Questions

1. Where in the United States is coal found? How much is there?

2. What is coal used for? How is electricity made from coal?

3. Can the problems caused by strip mining and acid rain be overcome?

Answers to

Coal—The Rock that Burns

1. Twenty-eight percent of the known coal deposits are found in the United States. Most reserves lie in Kentucky, Wyoming, West Virginia, and the eastern United States.

2. Coal is burned to produce steam, which runs an electric generator.

3. Efforts could be made to restore a mined area to its original condition following strip mining. Stack scrubbers could be installed to clean impurities from the smoke.

✳ Follow Up

Assessment

Have students make a chart listing the different energy sources and the advantages and disadvantages of each.

Extension

Plan a field trip to a solar-heated home so that students can learn how solar heating works.

14 What Does the Future Hold?

No one knows for sure what the future holds. The two essays that follow portray very different futures. Which do you think is more realistic?

The first article, written by scientist Glenn Seaborg, has an optimistic tone. As you read it, keep the following questions in mind:

1. Why does Seaborg think people will need even more energy?

2. What is his solution to the energy problem?

3. Pick out the two most important statements in his article.

4. Do you see any difficulties with Seaborg's ideas about energy production and use in the future?

5. Why do you think Seaborg wrote this article?

There are those who see energy problems in the future that can't be solved. In the second essay, Ron Scammell presents a different picture of what the world may be like for your children and grandchildren. As you read the essay, think about the following questions:

1. Which of the problems outlined in the story would not have occurred had alternative sources of energy been found?

2. What do you think might have happened to cause the energy crisis described in this article? How might it have been avoided?

3. Do you think the scenario Scammell describes is possible? Would you change his story in any way to make it more realistic?

4. Why do you think Scammel wrote this article?

Two Views

Nuclear Energy and Our Future
by Glenn T. Seaborg, Nobel Prize winner

Humans live by energy. The more energy we can put to work, the better we live. By harnessing energy, we can flick a switch to pump water, start a train, heat a home, or light a city. In the twenty-first century, most of this energy will come from the nucleus of the atom, and by using it wisely people can improve the way they produce food, use water and raw materials, handle waste, and build cities.

The need for improvement is evident. In the decades ahead, the earth's population will double and double again. But the earth itself

 # LESSON 14 ORGANIZER

Objectives

By the end of the lesson, students should be able to:
1. Analyze articles about future sources of energy.
2. Describe how future energy supplies will affect lifestyles.

Process Skills

predicting, analyzing, evaluating, decision making, writing

New Terms

(Organizer continues on next page)

Answers to

Nuclear Energy and Our Future

Possible responses to Seaborg's article might include:

1. Seaborg thinks that the earth's population will double by the year 2000, thereby creating a great need for more energy.
2. Seaborg's solution is to couple large, dual-purpose nuclear power plants located in coastal desert areas with highly scientific farms or "food factories."
3. Answers will vary, but two very important statements are: "One must emphasize that having a large amount of cheap energy is not a panacea in itself" and "Whenever and wherever man can benefit from heat and electricity, nuclear energy in its many forms can help bring about a better world."
4. Seaborg's ideas do not take into account the potential danger of nuclear accidents, the problem of nuclear-waste disposal, or the amount of land required to create these huge "Nuplexes."
5. Seaborg probably wrote this article to share his vision of the future. He supports nuclear energy and wants it to be the major source of energy in the future.

Primary Source
Description of change: excerpted
Rationale: excerpted from *Union Courier* to reduce length. Minor changes made to update and to eliminate gender-specific references.

will not grow, and to support these extra billions we must learn to use and reuse our resources with an efficiency we rarely even approach today.

By far the most important contribution the atom will make to the world of tomorrow will be cheap electricity and huge amounts of heat for use in manufacturing processes. We should proceed with deliberate speed in the full development of breeder reactors, which create more nuclear fuel than they burn.

One must emphasize that having a large amount of cheap energy is not a panacea in itself. We must develop the technology to take advantage of this energy; it must be applied skillfully, productively and wisely by people who have the tools and training to use it.

Some scientists have considered the concept of using these huge amounts of energy in giant nuclear powered industrial complexes, which we have called "Nuplexes," the energy heart of which would be breeder reactors, with a generating capacity in the multi-million kilowatt range.

A report by the Oak Ridge National Laboratory indicates some exciting prospects for coupling large dual-purpose plants located in coastal desert areas with highly scientific farms or "food factories."

One study in this report considers the energy heart as a huge breeder reactor which could generate 1,000,000 kW of electricity and desalt 400 million gallons (1,800,000,000 L) of water a day. At the same time, power from the plant could be used to make ammonia fertilizer and phosphorus-bearing fertilizer. It could be that many other by-products from the seawater brine could be produced and used locally or exported.

Electricity from the plant would be used for highly mechanized farming and food processing, as well as to supply light, air-conditioning, and power for transport and communications for the personnel operating the complex.

On 200,000 acres (80,000 ha) irrigated with the desalted water and fertilized with locally manufactured products, crops would be grown which were specifically bred for the area. Hardly anything would be left to chance or the whims of nature.

Such a food factory could produce half a billion kilograms of grain each year, enough to feed almost 2,500,000 people at a level of 2,400 calories (10,050 kJ) a day. In addition, it could export enough fertilizer to other agricultural areas to cultivate another 10,000,000 acres (4,000,000 ha) of land.

Whenever and wherever people can benefit from heat and electricity, nuclear energy in its many forms can help bring about a better world.

(Organizer continued)

Materials

Teacher's Resource Binder

Activity Worksheet 6–10

Time Required

one class period

Energy and Our Way of Life

by Ron Scammell

You are living in the year 2070. In the aftermath of a worldwide energy crisis your government has banned all energy consumption, except for the bare necessities.

Electric lighting has been limited to one 50-watt outlet per house, electrical appliances have been banned completely, and coal for heating has been carefully rationed since the exhaustion of oil and gas supplies. A typical day in such an environment begins rather uninvitingly. The house is dark and cold when you wake up in the morning. In the flickering candlelight, you search for an extra sweater to put on. The weekly ration of coal ran out and a cold winter chill snuck up on you during the night, leaving you shivering in the darkness. Performing the morning chores is no easy task. There is no toaster, microwave, stove, or running water. It takes time to run out to the community water supply, fill the bucket, stoke up the wood fire, and cook breakfast. The trip to school during the winter is a real downer; long waits on windswept corners for the rickety old community bus, and then the long walk the rest of the way. Spring and fall are much better, when you can ride your bicycle, as most people do. Private automobiles were outlawed long ago. You have heard your father talk about the days when people jumped in their own cars every morning and drove right from home to school or work. No one can forget the automobile. Its mark is everywhere; miles and miles of deserted freeways, roads, and parking lots. Some communities have tried to convert them into parks and recreational areas but it is a difficult and expensive task.

The school for your district is overcrowded to the point of bursting. But it can't be avoided. The more people who can fit into one building, the less fuel consumed for heating and the less electricity for lighting.

There's not much enjoyment to be found after school either. First the lineup for two hours at the local shopping center for the day's allotment of food—that's because of the food shortage across the country caused by the breakdown in transportation. Farmers and food producers cannot guarantee delivery of their products. After that, the weekly ration of coal must be stored. Then there is the washing. It must be done by hand. Washing machines and dryers are luxuries of an earlier day. Finally, the day comes to an end, and it's time to relax. But there is not much to do. No TV. No radio. No stereo. Saturday night dances and discotheques went the way of the dinosaur long ago. Rock bands with their electric guitars, pianos, organs, synthesizers, and sound systems consume a fantastic amount of electricity. A definite impossibility in this day and age. There is a community entertainment hall a few miles away, but you don't feel like making the long trek at the end of the day.

Answers to

Energy and Our Way of Life

Answers may vary, but possible responses to Scammell's article might include:

1. If alternative sources of energy had been found, there might not have been an energy crisis. The reduction of business and industry, as well as goods and services, would not have occurred. For example, there would not have been a lack of transportation, food, electricity, heat, and appliances such as electric lights, TVs, stereos, washers, or dryers.

2. Several things might have happened to cause the energy crisis illustrated in Scammell's article. Perhaps Americans simply ran out of petroleum products and had no alternative energy sources available. Perhaps Americans ran out of nuclear reactor fuel or reactors became too dangerous or too expensive to build. Or, the increased population of the earth placed enormous demands on the energy supply, depleting it very quickly. This might have been avoided if renewable energy resources had been developed and the reliance on non-renewable resources had been lessened.

3. Students may believe that alternative sources of energy would be developed before such a catastrophe would be allowed to occur.

4. Scammell probably intended this article to be a warning to the world. He wanted others to see what might happen in the future if alternative energy sources are not developed. Perhaps he thought this article might scare some people into taking steps to prevent his bleak vision from happening.

Primary Source
Description of change: excerpted
Rationale: excerpted from the pamphlet *Energy and Our Way of Life* to reduce length and to update.

Crystal Ball Gazing

Have students read the headlines. Students may disagree on the meaning of some of the headlines. Encourage an open discussion. Remember, there are no "right" answers.

For homework, ask students to choose one of the headlines and write a letter to the newspaper editor about it.

Follow Up

Assessment

1. Ask students to draw a poster that carries an energy message of their own choice. Students could illustrate an actual poster or design one in pencil on construction paper. The posters should express the students' attitudes about energy.
2. Tell students it is possible that in the future their community might find its energy supply curtailed significantly. Ask students to identify the major energy users in the community, such as homes, schools, industries, hospitals, power plants, police, firefighters, and so on. Then ask them to develop a list of criteria that could be used in a crisis situation to assign priority status. Finally, have them apply their criteria to their identified energy users and designate priorities.

Extension

Have students interview people in the community to find out their reaction to the energy situation. Questions might include:
- In your judgment, is there really an energy problem?
- If there is a problem, who is at fault?
- If there is a problem, what can you do about it?
- What, if anything, are you doing about it now?

Have students tape-record the interviews and share them.

Fuel for transportation is so scarce that only the privileged few are able to travel. Major air, rail, and sea passenger services were phased out long ago.

Because of the energy rationing, business and industry have been severely cut back. Jobs are few. The economy never really recovered after the car industry crumbled. After that it was like a house of cards collapsing, as other industries and businesses went bankrupt. There is no use dwelling on dismal thoughts of the future, or fanciful dreams of the past. You decide to stay at home at the end of the day and read a good book. But soon your eyes are tired from reading by candlelight and, anyway, the day's activities have left you exhausted.

Crystal Ball Gazing

No one can predict what the future holds, but much depends on what happens in the world, what the governments of the world do, and whether the people of the world make wise, well-informed decisions. The future depends on *you*.

Here are some imaginary newspaper headlines from the future. Would you be pleased to read them? Which do you connect with an improving energy picture? Which do you connect with wise decision-making? Explain your choices.

Sound Off

Choose one of the headlines. Write a letter to the editor, commenting thoughtfully on the event or situation.

Environment Lobby Shuts Down Open Pit Mine

Speed Limit of 80 km/h Imposed—Conservation Measure

Improved Technology Makes Nuclear Power Safer

Another Oil Crisis? Middle East Conflict Threatens Supply

SHIP (Solar Heating Incentive Program) Launched

NUCLEAR FUSION RESEARCH RAISES HOPE FOR CHEAP ENERGY

Acid Rain Fear Halts Opening of Coal Power Plant

Not in Our Backyard! People Reject Plans for Nuclear Waste Disposal

1. Are They Exaggerating?
The glossy brochure describing Millstone Nuclear Power Station (New England) says this:

> *The first unit of the new plant went into full power operation in January 1971 at a power output of 650,000 kW, producing more than enough electricity to cook Sunday morning breakfast for half a million people.*

Half a million people! Are they exaggerating? How much energy does your family use to cook breakfast? How could you find out?

2. What's the Scoop?
Do some investigative reporting. (Don't be shy!) Find out as much as you can about the electrical energy you use. Try to find the answers to questions like the following:

- What is the primary source of your electricity?
- What energy conversions take place in producing the electricity?
- Is there more than one power plant in your community?
- How much power do they produce?
- How many families do they serve?
- How much electricity does an average family use?
- Is the primary source of the electricity renewable or non-renewable?
- Are the plants operating at full capacity?

What recommendations can you make about the energy production in the future for your community?

Summary for

The Big Ideas

Student responses will vary. The following is an ideal summary.

Energy is the force that makes things happen. Energy comes in many forms. These include heat (thermal), electrical, chemical, mechanical, and light (radiant) energy.

Energy can be stored as chemical energy in the cells of living tissue and in the chemicals in a battery. Potential energy is the stored mechanical energy of a coiled spring, a taut rubber band, or an apple dangling from a tree branch.

Energy makes things happen when it is converted from one form into another. An energy converter changes the form of energy. Converters include steam engines, generators, automobiles, and the human body.

A generator converts mechanical energy into electrical energy. A current flows when a magnetic field is changed, either by moving the magnet or by moving coils of wire within the magnetic field. Simple generators can be powered by hand. More complicated generators can be run by steam-powered, revolving turbines, which in turn, drive the generator and produce electricity. In addition to steam-powered generators, energy from running water can turn the turbines of a generator.

Using steam-powered or water-powered generators allows electricity to be made on a large scale.

No machine is 100 percent efficient. Some of the energy is always turned into forms that the machine cannot use. Machines cannot create energy; they can only convert energy from one form to another.

The energy a particular appliance requires in order to function is indicated by its power rating, measured in units called *watts*. The number of watts required multiplied by the num-

The Big Ideas

In your Journal, write a summary of this unit, using the following questions as a guide.
- What is energy? What are some of its forms?
- What are some ways that energy is stored?
- How does energy makes things happen? What is an energy converter?
- How does a generator work? What are some ways that a generator can be powered?
- How is electricity made on a large scale?
- Why is a perpetual motion machine impossible?
- How might you determine the amount of energy an appliance uses over a period of time?
- Where is heat lost from a house on a cold day? How can this heat loss be reduced?
- Explain the difference between renewable and non-renewable resources. Of the energy sources we use, which are renewable and which are nonrenewable?
- What can we do to improve our energy future?

Checking Your Understanding

1. What is the source of energy in each of the following situations?
   (a) A girl pedals her bicycle down the street.
   (b) A race car hurtles down the track.
   (c) A candle bathes the room in flickering light.
   (d) A redwood tree grows to a height of 100 meters.
2. What happens when you blow up a balloon and release it? Describe what you would see in terms of energy.
3. Each machine listed below wastes some of its energy when it operates. Complete the chart, naming the desired form of energy and the forms of waste energy the machine produces.

Machine	Efficiency	Desired Energy Form	Waste Energy Forms
Toaster	90%	Heat	Light, excess heat
Steam boat	10%		
Hair dryer	85%		
Car engine	30%		

ber of hours used tells you how much energy an appliance uses over time.

Heat is lost from buildings primarily through air exchange. Inside-air is exchanged for outside-air through cracks in the walls and gaps around doors and windows. Heat is also lost when warm air comes into contact with cold surfaces. Heat loss can be reduced by sealing cracks and by providing adequate insulation.

Renewable energy sources can be replaced. These include solar energy, tidal power, wood, and wind energy.

Nonrenewable energy resources are those that cannot be replaced once they have been used up. These include coal, oil, and natural gas.

Because we depend so much on nonrenewable energy sources, and these sources are running out, we need to do two things. First, we need to use less energy by practicing conservation methods and developing more efficient machines. Second, we need to develop other resources of renewable energy that are safe and inexpensive to use.

4. Make a concept map using the following words and phrases: *energy of motion, energy, potential energy, stored energy,* and *kinetic energy.*

5. Tony left a 100-W light bulb on in the attic for a month by mistake. How much energy did he waste?
   (a) 64,000 kWh
   (b) 72 kWh
   (c) 36 kWh
   (d) 30,000 kWh

6. A refrigerator has a power rating of 400 watts. It runs about half the time. How much electricity does it consume in a day?

7. Classify the following energy sources as Renewable (R) or Nonrenewable (N).

natural gas	_____	wood	_____
kerosene	_____	hydroelectricity	_____
uranium fuel	_____	petroleum	_____
wind	_____	sunlight	_____
coal	_____	gasoline	_____

8. Design a poster that carries the energy message of your choice.

Reading *Plus*

Now that you have been introduced to energy, let's take a closer look at it. By reading pages S99–S116 in the *SourceBook*, you will learn more about the different forms of energy and how they are transmitted. You will learn how energy is converted from one form to another, and about the Law of Conservation of Energy. You will also learn about the various energy sources tapped by humans to meet their needs today and in the past, as well as promising new sources of energy that will power the society of tomorrow.

Updating Your Journal

Reread the paragraphs you wrote for this unit's "For Your Journal" questions. Then rewrite them to reflect what you have learned in studying this unit.

About Updating Your Journal

The following are sample ideal answers.
1. Energy makes things happen; it is the ability to make a change. Everything that happens requires energy to make it happen.
2. Energy appears in many different forms: in chemical reactions, in moving objects, in objects that have the potential for movement, and in light. Energy is never lost, it merely changes forms. *(The theme of **Patterns of Change** is related to the way energy changes form in predictable ways.)*
3. Energy can take many different forms, including heat (thermal), light (radiant), chemical, electrical, and mechanical. Humans can harness energy in different forms in order to produce work.
4. The photograph of lightning is an illustration of electrical energy converted into heat and light.

1. **(a)** Chemical energy from food is turned into mechanical energy and heat (caused by friction).
   (b) Chemical energy from burning fuel is turned into mechanical energy and heat.
   (c) Chemical energy stored in the candle is released as heat and light energy.
   (d) The tree absorbs light energy, which it converts into chemical energy.

2. Chemical energy from the food you eat allows you to blow air into the balloon. The air causes the balloon to expand, and mechanical energy is stored as potential energy in the stretched material of the balloon. When the balloon is released, the potential energy becomes kinetic, and pushes the air out of the balloon.

3. See table on page S170.

4.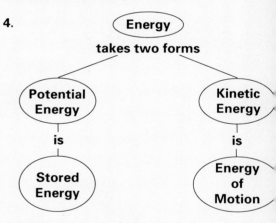

5. **(b)** Tony wasted 100 W × 24 hours × 30 days = 72,000 Wh/1000 = 72 kWh

6. The refrigerator consumes 400 W × 12 hours/1000 = 4.8 kWh

7. natural gas—N; kerosene—N; uranium fuel—N; wind—R; coal—N; wood—R; hydroelectricity—R; petroleum—N; sunlight—R; gasoline—N

8. Encourage students to be creative and include illustrations and photographs. Topics could include environmental issues, energy sources, and energy conservation.

Science in Action

Science in Action

✦ Background

Mechanical engineers are concerned with the production, transmission, and use of mechanical power. They design and develop power-producing machines such as internal combustion engines, steam and gas turbines, and jet and rocket engines. They also design and develop power-using machines such as refrigeration and air-conditioning equipment, robots, machine tools, and industrial production equipment.

Spotlight on Mechanical Engineering

Mechanical engineering involves machines and equipment of all sorts. Engineers like Bill Kane apply both scientific and practical knowledge to the tasks of designing, selecting, building, or repairing machinery. The learning process formally begins in high school and continues in college. After college, practical experience and continuing study of new technology expand the engineer's horizons even further.

Q: How did you become interested in mechanical engineering?

Bill: I guess it started when I was a young boy. I was really rough on toys, bikes, and cars as a youngster. I was so talented at breaking things that I just had to learn how to repair them as well. I developed a mechanical bent and also an electrical one, since many of the toys were electric, or had electric motors.

My parents bought me construction sets, where you connect parts together to make model cranes, ships, and things like that. You could even make little cars and boats that moved under their own power. It was great! Also, I was very keen on model planes. I spent a lot of time trying to get these things to fly right. I have to admit, though, that this is something that I never really mastered completely. There are bits and pieces of smashed-up model planes all over

the field next to my boyhood home.

Q: What kind of education does a mechanical engineer need?

Bill: He or she needs a good grounding in math and physics. Chemistry can be pretty important too. You need to know about the properties of materials. Obviously, you also have to be well-versed in mechanics, that is, how mechanical components—gears, levers, wheels, chains, bearings pulleys, and so on—work together.

Education should be an eye-opener, though. It's a mistake to study only those things you think you're going to need in your career. You need exposure to the arts as well as the sciences. People should be as well-rounded as their time and talents permit them to be.

Q: What main idea is most important to engineering?

Bill: That energy and matter are neither created nor destroyed. Take heat energy, for example. You can turn it into

✦ Using the Interview

You may wish to have students read the interview aloud, with one student playing the part of the interviewer and another playing the part of Bill.

After reading the interview, ask students to take out a pencil and paper. Ask them to answer *yes* or *no* to the following questions:
1. Did you ever repair a broken toy?
2. Do you like building models of motor-driven vehicles?
3. Do you like physics and chemistry?

4. Would you be interested in taking a class in automotive repair?
5. Do you like to take things apart and figure out how they work?

Tell students that those who answered yes to all these questions have a natural interest in mechanics. Give students an opportunity to discuss their own hobbies and interests that are related to mechanics. Ask them if mechanical engineering is a career they have ever thought of pursuing.

mechanical energy—to drive a car for example—or some other form of energy. But you have not created energy. All you have done is taken energy in one form and turned it into another. No matter what happens, the total energy in the world never changes.

Q: What skills and abilities are particularly important in engineering?

Bill: It is important to be able to reduce problems to fundamentals. A complicated problem can always be broken down into separate, simpler problems. Common sense also plays a very important part in what engineers do. I really can't emphasize that enough. You just have to learn to use your head. A broad background of knowledge is also indispensable.

Q: Is there an important social issue connected with your work that you would single out?

Bill: Yes. Designing systems that best serve the needs of people. Suppose you are building a hydroelectric facility. People depend on this system. It needs to be as efficient and reliable as possible. Engineers need to remember that they don't work in a vacuum; people's lives are disrupted whenever a system or structure they designed fails.

Some Project Ideas

1. Design a labor-saving device. Start by identifying a problem. Then devise a solution. Watch people as they work at various tasks around your home or school. Which tasks might be done more easily or better if an appropriate device or piece of equipment were created? You have now defined a problem. Design a solution and, if feasible, construct it.

2. Can you think of something that you or others would enjoy doing if only a device existed to allow you to do it? Begin by identifying such an activity. This defines a problem requiring a solution. Can you come up with a practical solution? If so, design it. If possible, construct it, and if it is safe, try it out.

3. Compare the energy value of different materials. Find out which materials give the most heat at the least cost. For example, how does wood compare with coal, or coal with oil? How do different grades of the same fuels compare? What conditions are required for good combustion? Can a clean-burning, low-maintenance, wood-burning system be designed? Can waste products be burned to provide energy? Before you proceed, be sure that the project you propose is safe to do.

For Assistance

Mechanical engineers can be found in engineering consulting firms and most larger industrial plants and companies. You might also try the Mechanical Engineering Department at a university. Other assistance can be obtained from industrial arts teachers, science teachers, and mechanics (automobile, airplane, and various specialties).

◆ Using the Project Ideas

For projects 1 and 2, give students some pointers on how to go about working on an invention. Tell them to think of as many ideas as possible for solving the problem or fulfilling the need. They should let their imaginations run wild. Tell them to be sure to learn everything they can about their problem or need. This will help them to select one of their ideas to work on. After they choose an idea, they should decide if the idea is original and practical. Finally, they should test the invention to see if it solves the problem or fills the need. Then invite potential users to try it out, and ask them for their opinions.

For project 3, suggest to students that they find a mentor, such as a practicing mechanical engineer or a science teacher, to help them with this project. One simpler project they may wish to try is to watch several substances burn, such as a wooden splint, a sliver of very soft coal, alcohol, kerosene, or natural gas. As each substance is burned separately, students should try to answer questions such as the following:
- Does it burn easily?
- Does it smoke a lot as it burns?
- Does it give off odors?
- Does the flame seem to be very hot?

The superiority of natural gas over the other substances will be easily apparent. The problems associated with coal, especially the amount of smoke it gives off, will also become apparent.

◆ Going Further

Nuclear power plants can provide a tremendous energy supply. However, controversy surrounds the use of nuclear reactors as a safe energy source. Are the risks of nuclear power worth the energy gained? Have students do research to discover the advantages and disadvantages of nuclear power. They should decide if they believe nuclear power is worth the risk. Then design a poster that explains their position on this issue.

Have interested students write for additional information:

The American Society of Mechanical Engineers
345 E. 47th Street
New York, NY 10017

American Society of Heating, Refrigerating, and
Air-Conditioning Engineers, Inc.
1791 Tullie Circle NE
Atlanta, GA 30329

Background

Superconductivity is a phenomenon in which certain materials conduct electricity without resistance. The current theory of superconductivity was developed by three American physicists—John Bardeen, Leon Cooper, and John Schrieffer. According to this theory, a superconductor has no electrical resistance because of an attractive interaction between electrons that results in the formation of pairs of electrons. The electron pairs are bound to one another and flow without resistance around imperfections. In an ordinary conductor, resistance occurs because unbound electrons collide with imperfections and scatter. Scientists hope that a fuller understanding of superconductivity will enable them to develop materials that will superconduct at room temperature.

Science and Technology

Superconductivity

When electricity flows through a wire or other **conductor,** there is ordinarily a certain amount of **resistance** to its flow. Because of this resistance, you have to keep "pushing" the electricity with a battery or a generator, or else it will stop flowing. What do you think would happen if electricity could flow through a conductor with *no electrical resistance at all*—like something sliding on ice, only *much more* "slippery"?

Magnet levitating over a superconducting material

A Strange Discovery

In 1911 a Dutch scientist named Heike Onnes was experimenting to find out about the electrical resistance of frozen mercury. Then he discovered something very strange: if you cool certain materials down to extremely low temperatures—close to *absolute zero* (or −273 °C)—they lose *all* their electrical resistance. Onnes started a current flowing in a circular conductor that he kept cooled to near absolute zero. Surprisingly, the current kept on flowing without any electrical force pushing it. A year later, in fact, the current was still flowing, just as strong as ever! Onnes had discovered **superconductivity.**

Manufacturing superconducting materials

Great Idea, But . . .

You would think that scientists would have made use of Onnes' discovery immediately. After all, a lot of energy could be saved by using superconducting electrical lines instead of ordinary power lines. There is, however, one major problem with superconductors. It is expensive to maintain the incredibly low temperatures needed for superconductivity.

The need for refrigeration near absolute zero makes it impractical to use superconductors for common purposes such as carrying electricity to people's houses.

Coming in from the Cold

In 1986 two Swiss scientists, Alex Muller and Georg Bednorz, made a breakthrough in superconductivity that earned them the Nobel Prize for physics. They found a material that would superconduct at a much higher temperature than the metals that had been tested before. It was a ceramic compound made of lanthanum, barium, and copper, and it lost all resistance at 30° above absolute zero.

Discussion

When students have finished reading the feature, involve them in a discussion. You may wish to use questions similar to the following:

1. What practical problems have to be solved before superconductivity can be used to build energy-efficient power lines? *(The materials will need to superconduct at higher temperatures and must be capable of being made into flexible wire.)*

2. Find out the distance between New York City and San Francisco. Calculate how long would it take to travel this far in an automobile at the speed limit of 90 km/h. How long would it take to travel this far in an elevated train? *(It would take about 55 hours by automobile and 10 hours by elevated train.)*

The race was on! Scientists worked feverishly to find other ceramic materials that would act as superconductors at higher and higher temperatures. Their goal was to reach superconductivity at the temperature of liquid nitrogen. If they could reach this temperature, then liquid nitrogen—a relatively inexpensive coolant—could be used to refrigerate the new superconductors. Researchers at the University of Houston, led by Dr. Paul Chu, finally broke the liquid nitrogen barrier when they reached superconductivity at 94° above absolute zero, or −179 °C. By superconductor standards, this is quite *warm!*

Another problem is to find materials that not only superconduct, but that can also be made into flexible wire. Unfortunately, ceramic materials tend to be too brittle.

Perhaps scientists will soon find a flexible material that superconducts electricity at room temperature. It's a long shot, but if they succeed, it will be good news for all of us. Superconductors could help us to get the maximum benefit from the electricity we generate.

Into the Future

Building energy-efficient power lines isn't the only potential application of superconductors. Scientists hope to build computers with superconductor circuits that are ten times faster and ten times smaller than today's models. Already, Japanese engineers have built an experimental train using superconducting magnets that cause the train to rise above the tracks and travel friction-free at close to 500 kilometers per hour.

Check Out the State of the Art

Find out how close scientists are to realizing the dream of perfecting a practical superconducting material. What materials are scientists experimenting with now? At what temperatures will these materials act as superconductors? What new ways have scientists found to use superconductors?

✦ Going Further

1. Ask students to find out what ceramics are, how they are made, and their practical applications.
2. Have interested students research current theories that explain why ceramic materials become superconductors at relatively high temperatures.

Temperature and Heat

✳ *Teaching the Unit*

 Unit Overview

In this unit the concepts of heat and temperature are examined through numerous activities and investigations. In the section *Temperature,* students investigate what temperature is, how it is measured, and how it changes. Students then make their own thermometers. In the section *Heat,* students explore the difference between heat and temperature. They examine what happens when hot and cold substances are mixed and look for patterns that can be used to make predictions. Students then look at heat as a form of energy and learn how the joule became the standard unit of measurement. Students also examine heat energy in food and learn to calculate their daily energy intakes. In the final section, *Heat on the Move,* students investigate the ways heat is transferred from one place to another through conduction, convection, and radiation. They learn about the properties of insulators and conductors, and examine how heat can be focused, reflected, and radiated.

 Using the Themes

The unifying themes emphasized in this unit are **Systems and Interactions, Scale and Structure,** and **Energy.** The following information will help you weave these themes into your teaching plan. A focus question is provided with each theme as a discussion tool to help you tie the information in the unit together.

Systems and Interactions is an integral part of each section because heat and temperature are changing phenomena within closed systems.

Focus question: *How do insulators slow the flow of heat energy?*

First, insulators are usually made of substances that are poor conductors of heat energy. Second, insulation prevents heat loss from air movement caused by convection currents.

Energy is developed through discussions of what heat is and how it is transferred from one object or place to another. Students learn that these changes result from the transfer of energy from one form into another and from one place to another.

Focus question: *How is heat energy used?*

Radiant energy from the sun warms our planet and drives climatic cycles. Plants convert sunlight into food, both for themselves and for the animals that eat the plants. Humans produce heat energy by metabolizing food and by burning fuel for heating our homes and doing mechanical work.

Scale and Structure can be discussed by comparing the underlying structure of matter and the different methods of heat transfer presented in section 3.

Focus question: *How is the structure of matter related to heat transfer?*

The particles that make up a solid are tightly packed together. Therefore, heat energy in a solid is easily transferred from one particle to the next by collisions as the particles take on heat energy. In liquids and gases, particles are less tightly packed together and expand when they are heated. Because groups of heated particles are farther apart, they become lighter and move upward, distributing the heated particles.

 Using the *Science Discovery* Videodiscs

Disc 1 *Science Sleuths, Burning Barns and Exploding Silos* The Sutfins and the Zencks have been feuding for years. When Mr. Sutfin's silo explodes and Mrs. Zenck's barn burns down, the two farmers accuse one another of arson. The Science Sleuths must analyze the evidence for themselves to determine the true cause of the damage.

Disc 2 *Image and Activity Bank* A variety of still images, short videos, and activities are available for you to use as you teach this unit. See the *Videodisc Resources* section of the **Teacher's Resource Binder** for detailed instructions.

Using the *SciencePlus SourceBook*

Unit 7 focuses on thermal energy and heat and their relation to work. Students learn about the three methods of heat transfer—conduction, convection, and radiation—and how this affects climates on earth. Finally, the unit compares the measurement of temperature and heat and introduces specific heat.

PLANNING CHART

SECTION AND LESSON	PG.	TIME*	PROCESS SKILLS	EXPLORATION AND ASSESSMENT	PG.	RESOURCES AND FEATURES
Unit Opener	350		observing, discussing	For Your Journal	351	Science Sleuths: *Burning Barns and Exploding Silos* Videodisc Activity Sheets TRB: Home Connection
TEMPERATURE	352			Challenge Your Thinking	367	TRB: Resource Worksheet 7–2
1 How Hot Is Hot?	352	3	predicting, observing, investigating, hypothesizing	Exploration 1 Exploration 2	354 356	Image and Activity Bank 7–1 TRB: Resource Worksheet 7–1
2 The Thermometer	358	3	observing, measuring, investigating, analyzing, comparing	Exploration 3	358	Image and Activity Bank 7–2 Resource Transparency 7–1
3 Signs of Temperature Change	363	2	observing, analyzing, inferring, calculating	Exploration 4	365	Image and Activity Bank 7–3
HEAT	368			Challenge Your Thinking	380	
4 Heat Versus Temperature	368	2	observing, measuring, analyzing, evaluating	Exploration 5	368	Image and Activity Bank 7–4
5 Hot + Cold = . . .?	372	1	observing, measuring, predicting	Exploration 6	372	Image and Activity Bank 7–5 TRB: Resource Worksheet 7–3 Graphic Organizer Transparency 7–2
6 Heat Is Energy	374	3	observing, measuring, investigating, collecting data	Exploration 7 Exploration 8	374 376	Image and Activity Bank 7–6 TRB: Activity Worksheet 7–4 Resource Transparency 7–3 Graphic Organizer Transparency 7–4
HEAT ON THE MOVE	381			Challenge Your Thinking	403	
7 How Heat Gets Around	381	1	observing, measuring, investigating, comparing	Exploration 9	383	Image and Activity Bank 7–7
8 Conduction—Heat Travel Through Solids	385	4	observing, measuring, predicting, investigating	Exploration 10	386	Image and Activity Bank 7–8 TRB: Activity Worksheets 7–5 and 7–7 Resource Worksheet 7–6
9 Convection—Heat Travel by Currents	392	2	observing, predicting, investigating, illustrating	Exploration 11	392	Image and Activity Bank 7–9 Graphic Organizer Transparencies 7–5 and 7–6
10 Radiation—Heat in a Hurry	398	3	observing, measuring, investigating, interpreting data	Exploration 12	400	Image and Activity Bank 7–10 TRB: Resource Worksheet 7–8 Activity Worksheets 7–9 and 7–10 Graphic Organizer Transparencies 7–7 and 7–8
End of Unit	404		applying, analyzing, evaluating, summarizing	Making Connections TRB: Sample Assessment Items	404	Science in Action, p. 406 Science and Technology, p. 408 *SourceBook,* pp. S117–S132

*Time given in number of class periods.

349B

✳ *Meeting Individual Needs*

Gifted Students

1. Explain to students that all things are made up of atoms or molecules that are always in motion. This motion gives every object internal energy. The amount of energy an object has depends on how rapidly its atoms and molecules move. If they move quickly, the object feels hot. If they move slowly, the object feels cold. Challenge students to do some research on the molecular basis of heat. Encourage them to share what they learn by making diagrams or models to use in an oral report to the class.

2. Suggest that students make a solar still. A solar still is a device that uses heat from the sun to separate impurities, like salt, from water. Point out to students that they may have to do some research to discover how to make their still. Students should set up a display in the classroom, similar to the type they would use for a science fair, for their classmates to observe. Suggest that they be prepared to answer any questions their classmates may have. In their display, encourage students to explain some practical uses for their solar stills.

✳ LEP Students

1. Point out to students that in this unit they learned about many terms that relate to heat and temperature. Suggest that they make a list of the terms and use them to create a bilingual dictionary. Some of the terms they may wish to include are: heat, temperature, thermostat, thermometer, conductor, insulator, conduction, convection, radiation, expansion, and contraction. Suggest that students add illustrations to help clarify their definitions. Remind students to make a cover for their bilingual dictionary and to think of a title. When students finish, review their work for science content, with only minimal emphasis on language proficiency.

2. Remind students that in this unit they learned about the three ways in which heat flows from one object or place to another object or place—conduction, convection, and radiation. Suggest that they make bilingual posters to illustrate each of these phenomena.

   Invite volunteers to share their finished posters with the class by reading their information in both English and their native language.

3. At the beginning of each unit, give Spanish-speaking students a copy of the *Spanish Glossary* from the *Teacher's Resource Binder.* Also, let Spanish-speaking students listen to the *English/Spanish Audiocassettes.*

At-Risk Students

To help students better understand the effect of heat energy on matter and how this effect can be used to measure temperature, challenge your students to make a thermometer using a bimetallic strip as suggested on page 359. The endpoints of the thermometer's scale can be determined by attaching a pointer to the strip and immersing it first in ice water and then in boiling water. Point out to students that the properties of the two metals cause the strip to bend. One of the metals is a better conductor of heat, and it expands more rapidly, thus bending the strip.

Some students may have difficulty understanding the difference between temperature and heat. A good experiment illustrating the two concepts can be carried out using a bundle of nails, two thermometers, two plastic-foam cups, a measuring cup, a pan of water, a heat source, tongs, and pot holders. Heat the nails in boiling water. Point out to students that the temperature of the nails in boiling water is 100 °C. Add the same amount of tap water to each of the cups. Using the pot holders and tongs, transfer one nail to one cup, and the remaining nails to the other cup. Have students note the temperature change in each cup. Ask students: Why is there a temperature difference between the cups, even though all the nails had the same temperature when they were taken from the boiling water? *(The larger number of nails in the second cup caused a greater amount of heat energy to be transferred to the water.)*

Cross-Disciplinary Focus

Creative Writing

Students might enjoy working together to develop a cartoon strip to illustrate one of the following topics from the lesson:

- The difference between heat and temperature
- The difference between an insulator and a conductor
- The difference between conduction, convection, and radiation

Suggest to students that they create a central cartoon character for their strips. You may wish to display several cartoon strips from a newspaper so that students can observe different styles. Have students share their finished cartoon strips by using them in a bulletin-board display.

Health

Remind students that in this unit, they read about normal body temperature. Point out that sometimes a person's body temperature goes up. In some cases, it may even go down. Suggest that students do some research to find out why and when body temperature fluctuates above or below normal. They should find out the number at which high temperatures and low temperatures become dangerous. Invite them to share their information with the class.

Mathematics

Remind students that water freezes at 0°C and boils at 100°C. Suggest that they make a graph to show how the temperature of water changes as it goes from ice to steam. Point out that it might not be as simple as they think. Suggest that they do some research to discover what their graphs should look like. Have students share and explain their graphs to the class.

Art

Students that have access to cameras might enjoy taking photos and making photo essays on heat and temperature. Allow students latitude on how they interpret the concepts. Arrange the finished essays around the classroom in a manner that suggests an art gallery.

 Cross-Cultural Focus

Temperatures Around the World

Point out to students that the average air temperature may vary greatly in different parts of the world. Suggest they make a world map and use it to show what the average summer and winter temperatures are in different continents and countries. Display their maps around the classroom. Let the students research different countries to determine how the temperature affects the culture of the people, the food they grow and eat, and the clothes they wear.

What Do You Use for Heat?

Point out that in different parts of the world, different energy sources are used to heat people's homes. Many countries in Europe rely on nuclear energy to produce electricity for heat. Much of China relies on coal. Many Scandinavian countries use solar energy to generate heat; some use wood. Some countries in Africa burn wood or grass for heat. Discuss the sources of heat used in the United States and then assign a different country to students to research sources of heat in different parts of the world. Organize the information into a chart to display in the classroom.

 **Resources**

Bibliography for Teachers

Bacon, D.H. *Basic Heat Transfer*. Stoneham, MA: Butterworth Publications, 1990.

Chapman, Alan J. *Fundamentals of Heat Transfer*. New York, NY: Macmillan Publishing Company, Inc., 1987.

Global Warming, The Greenpeace Report. Jeremy Leggett, Ed. New York, NY: Oxford University Press, 1990.

Mach, Ernst. *Principles of the Theory of Heat*. Hingham, MA: Reidel NE, 1987.

Oppenheimer, Michael, and Robert H. Boyle. *Dead Heat: The Race Against the Greenhouse Effect*. New York, NY: Basic, 1990.

Zemansky, Mark W. *Temperatures Very Low and Very High*. New York, NY: Dover Publications, 1981.

Bibliography for Students

Johnson, Rebecca L. *The Greenhouse Effect: Life on a Warmer Planet*. Minneapolis, MN: Lerner Publications Co., 1990.

Maury, Jean-Pierre. *Heat & Cold*. Hauppauge, New York, NY: Barron's Educational Series Inc.,1989.

Pringle, Laurence. *Global Warming*. New York, NY: Arcade, 1990.

Santrey, Laurence. *Heat*. Mahwah, NJ: Troll, 1985.

Wood, Robert W. *Physics for Kids—Forty-Nine Easy Experiments with Heat*. Blue Ridge Summit, PA: TAB Books Inc., 1989.

Films, Videotapes, Software, and Other Media

Exploring Science: Temperature. Software. For Apple II Family. Sunburst Comm. 101 Castleton Street Pleasantville, NY 10570

The Flow of Heat Energy. Videotape. Focus Media, Inc. P.O. Box 865 Garden City, NY 11530

Heat and Energy Transfer. Film and Videotape. Coronet Film & Video 108 Wilmot Road Deerfield, IL 60015

Heat, Temperature, and the Properties of Matter. Film and Videotape. Coronet Film & Video 108 Wilmot Road Deerfield, IL 60015

Hot and Cold. Filmstrip.

Learning About Heat. Film and Videotape. Encyclopedia Britannica 425 North Michigan Ave. Chicago, IL 60611

7

✳ Unit Focus

Call on several different students to guess what the outside temperature is. Write their guesses on the chalkboard. Hold up a weather thermometer and have students describe what it is used for. *(to measure temperature)* Then place the thermometer on the outside windowsill, or ask a student to take it outside and determine what the temperature really is. In the meantime, ask students why it is better to use a thermometer to find out the temperature rather than to make a guess. *(A thermometer is more accurate.)* Compare the outside temperature to the guesses listed on the chalkboard and point out the differences. Use the information to make the point that people can have very different ideas about temperature.

✳ About the Photograph

The men pictured in the photograph are involved in the process of making steel. Steel is made from a mixture of iron and other elements. Heat from a furnace causes a chemical reaction that refines the iron by removing its impurities. Other elements are then added in specific amounts to produce steel with the desired characteristics. The workers here are testing a sample from the furnace.

For Your Journal

Write a paragraph summarizing your thoughts about each of the following:

1. What is heat? What is temperature? How do they differ?
2. How do we measure temperature?
3. How does heat travel from place to place?
4. Would you describe the scene in the photograph as "warm," "cold," "hot," or "can't tell"? How did you reach this conclusion?

LESSON 1

"It's pretty hot today," sighed Eddie.

"Aw, it's not so bad," replied Sonia. "Do you want to go sit in the shade?"

"That sun is blazing . . . I wonder how hot it is," said Eddie as they moved over to the shade by the school.

"The radio said it was going to reach 36 °C. Hey Eddie, let's try that trivia quiz the teacher gave us this morning. Let's see who can come closest to guessing the temperature of things."

A Guessing Game

Let's join Sonia and Eddie in their guessing game. Try to come up with some "educated guesses" to the questions on the next page. For example, you probably already know that water boils at 100 °C and freezes at 0 °C. In some cases, the answer to one question will help you to answer other questions. Of course, most of your answers will be approximate.

All the temperatures (exact or approximate) you need to answer these questions are given in the illustration. They are ranked from coldest to hottest. You can use the same answer for more than one question.

All temperatures are in Celsius (°C). Of course, a thermometer like the one in the drawing does not actually exist. Why do you think that this is so?

✳ Getting Started

This lesson introduces students to the concept of temperature and demonstrates why it is important to be able to measure temperature accurately. As the lesson continues, students complete several activities in which they are required to estimate temperature. The lesson concludes by having students perform several activities that demonstrate how thermometers work.

Main Ideas

1. A wide range of temperatures can exist, depending upon the location and the time.
2. Our sense of temperature is not always accurate.
3. Thermometers increase the accuracy with which temperature is determined.
4. As the temperature of a substance changes, its physical characteristics may change as well. These changes can also be used to measure temperature.

✳ Teaching Strategies

A Guessing Game

Have students read the introduction to the game silently. Then involve them in a discussion of the questions. Help students recognize that the thermometer in the illustration could not really exist because the temperature range is too great. Also, the scale on the thermometer shows irregular intervals.

LESSON 1 ORGANIZER

Objectives

By the end of the lesson, students should be able to:
1. Predict with reasonable accuracy the temperatures that exist in nature and in their daily lives.
2. Explain the reason for using a thermometer to measure temperature.
3. Explain the principles by which a thermometer works.

Process Skills

predicting, observing, investigating, hypothesizing

New Terms

1. What is the temperature in your classroom when the room feels comfortable?

2. Guess the highest temperature or hottest day on record for (a) Gann-Valley, South Dakota; (b) Phoenix, Arizona; (c) Reykjavik, Iceland; (d) the world.

3. What is the maximum temperature on the moon?

4. Guess the lowest temperature or coldest day on record for (a) Rogers Pass, Montana;

(b) Shanghai, China; (c) the state of Florida; (d) Vostok, Antarctica; (e) the world.

5. What is the minimum temperature reached on the moon?

6. What is the temperature of your blood?

7. How hot is the surface of the sun?

8. At what temperature does iron melt?

9. At what temperature does seawater freeze?

10. Scalding water is not as hot as boiling water, but it can cause very bad burns. How hot is "scalding hot"?

11. What is the temperature of a burning match? You can't use an ordinary

thermometer to measure the flame's temperature because it will break. Why?

12. Have you heard of dry ice? Dry ice is frozen carbon dioxide. It is often used by ice cream vendors to keep their wares cold. How cold do you think dry ice is?

13. When ironing a cotton shirt or blouse, you set the iron to "cotton." What temperature does the iron reach at this setting?

14. A recipe calls for a very hot oven. On what temperature should the oven be set?

15. How hot does the filament of a light bulb get?

16. What is the lowest temperature possible, according to scientists?

17. How hot is it at the center of the earth?

18. An atomic explosion is so hot (hotter than the center of the sun) that the strongest materials known are instantly vaporized. How hot does it get?

Answers to
In-Text Questions

1. About 20°C
2. Highest recorded temperature:
   (a) 49°C
   (b) 47°C
   (c) 23°C
   (d) el Aziza, Libya, 58°C
3. 117°C
4. Lowest recorded temperature:
   (a) −56°C
   (b) −12°C
   (c) −19°C
   (d) −88°C
   (e) −88°C
5. −163°C
6. 37°C
7. about 6,000°C
8. 1,530°C
9. −2°C
10. 55°C
11. about 400°C; this temperature causes the fluid inside an ordinary thermometer to expand and break the glass of the thermometer.
12. about −78°C
13. about 200°C
14. about 250°C
15. about 3,000°C
16. about −273°C
17. 2,000 to 10,000°C
18. 300,000,000 to 400,000,000°C

Materials

Exploration 1: thermometer; 3 pails or buckets—one filled with cold water, one with warm water, and one with hot water; kettle; hot plate; oven mitt; ice cubes, safety goggles

Exploration 2
Activity 1: thermometer, hot water, jar or beaker, kettle, hot plate, oven mitt, safety goggles

Activity 2: bottle, balloon, bucket of hot water
Activity 3: bimetallic strip, candle or alcohol lamp, matches, tongs or a clothespin, clock or watch with a second hand, safety goggles

Teacher's Resource Binder

Resource Worksheet 7–1

Science Discovery Videodisc

Disc 2, Image and Activity Bank, 7–1

Time Required

three class periods

Exploration 1

Be sure the buckets are not so full that they overflow when a finger is submerged in the water. A kettle can be used to heat the water, but make certain that the water is not so hot that it can scald. Suggest that students label all three buckets as shown on page 354.

If it is more convenient to complete the activity as a classroom demonstration, you may wish to follow a procedure similar to the following:

- Place the three buckets of water on a table or desk in front of the class.
- Invite two students to use a thermometer to measure the temperatures of the hot and cold water. Have them record their results on the chalkboard.
- Invite six or more students to estimate the temperature of the warm water by dipping their fingers into it. Keep track of their estimates on the chalkboard.
- Now invite a student to measure the temperature of the warm water with a thermometer and record the results on the chalkboard.
- Discuss the discrepancies between the measurement and the estimates. Entertain any ideas for improving the estimates. Help students draw the conclusion that the only sure way of obtaining the accurate temperature is by using a thermometer.

How did you fare in the temperature quiz? In the next two Explorations, you will refine your method of estimating temperature.

Estimating Temperature

You Will Need

- 3 pails or buckets: one filled with cold water, one with warm water, and one with hot water (Make sure the hot water isn't so hot it scalds your hand!)
- a thermometer

What to Do

1. Measure the temperature of the hot water and the temperature of the cold water with a thermometer.
2. Estimate the temperature of the warm water by dipping a finger into each bucket in turn.
3. Write down your answer.
4. Your classmates will be doing the same thing. Compare your estimate with theirs.
5. Finally, use a thermometer to check whose answer is closest to the actual temperature.

The Difficulty of Estimating Temperature

Here is a puzzle for you to solve. Try it on as many people as you wish, both at school and at home.

Put one hand into a bucket of hot (but not scalding) water, and the other hand into a bucket of cold water. Leave them in for about a minute.

Now put both hands into a bucket of warm water at the same time. How do they feel? Do they feel the same? If not, what is the difference?

Does everyone have the same experience? After this experience, would you trust your ability to estimate temperature?

The Difficulty of Estimating Temperature

If the hot water is still hot enough and the cold water is still cold enough, you may wish to move directly into this activity from the previous one. However, it is likely that the water has approached room temperature, and you may need to change it. Keep in mind that the greater the difference in temperature between the hot and cold water, the more dramatic the results will be. Therefore, add some ice cubes to the cold-water bucket to make the temperatures more extreme.

Invite two or more students to perform the activity in front of the class and relate what they experience. As a follow up, involve the class in a discussion of what happened, and encourage students to explain the results.

Answers to

In-Text Questions

Students should expect to experience that the hand held in the hot water will feel cooler when placed in the warm water, while the hand held in the cold water will feel hotter. The difference can be explained by the extremes in temperature experienced by the two hands. Students should conclude that the temperature of a person's hand would greatly affect his or her ability to estimate the temperature of the water.

Students might also report a variation in temperature extremes based on their own personal sensitivities. Therefore, not everyone will have exactly the same experience.

Improving Your Accuracy

Have students silently read the first paragraph or call on a volunteer to read it aloud. Then suggest that students pair off to role-play the situation between the man and the thermometer-seller. Provide time for them to prepare a dialogue. Then invite pairs of students to role-play their scenarios for the class. Involve the class in a discussion of the merits of the arguments presented in each of the scenarios.

Have students read the rest of the page, pausing at the Exploration. Invite them to offer other examples of changes that take place when substances are heated.

Exploration 2

To organize this Exploration, you may wish to invite small groups of students to prepare and demonstrate each of the activities for the class. By the end of the Exploration, students should be able to discuss observations, explain the phenomena they observe, and use their observations to explain how a thermometer works.

Activity 1

Observation: The mercury rises very quickly when the thermometer is placed in hot water.

Conclusion: This observation can be explained by the rapid expansion rate of the mercury trapped inside the thermometer itself. Students may also recognize that as the mercury expands, the only place it has to go is up the thin tube of the thermometer.

To extend the activity, have students observe what happens when the thermometer is removed from the hot water. Help them to recognize that as the mercury cools, it contracts and moves down the tube in the thermometer.

Improving Your Accuracy

A man down the street tests the air temperature every morning by holding up a finger in the air. Imagine that you are selling thermometers. What would you say to him to convince him to buy one?

Estimating temperature is useful when you only need an approximation; for example, when deciding what to wear outside. But if you need the exact temperature, estimates are not reliable—you must use a thermometer.

How do thermometers work?

Think about what happens to iron or maple syrup as the temperature rises? Iron changes color: first it turns "red hot," then "white hot." Maple syrup expands, taking up more space. It also becomes thinner and runnier. Finally, it starts to boil away. Changes in temperature can bring about changes in a substance. Thermometers make use of these changes to measure temperature.

Each of the following activities shows how to use changes to measure temperature. Answer the questions for each activity in your Journal.

How could the changes you observe in Activities 2, 3, and 4 be used to make a thermometer? In each case, how would you change the apparatus?

Be Careful: *In this unit there are many activities that require the use of open flames or other heat sources.*

- **Never work with heat sources unless your teacher gives you permission to do so.**
- **Do the activities only as instructed by your teacher. Make sure that hair and clothing are kept well away from heat sources.**

Temperature Changes

You Will Need

- a thermometer
- hot water
- a jar or beaker
- a bottle
- a balloon
- a bimetallic strip
- a candle or alcohol lamp
- tongs or a clothespin

Activity 1

How quickly does the liquid mercury rise when you put the thermometer in hot water? Why do you think the mercury rises?

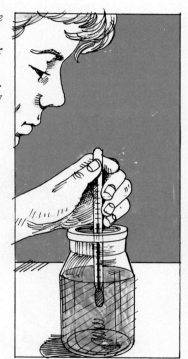

Activity 2

Fasten an empty balloon over the neck of a bottle. Put the bottle in hot water. Explain what happens.

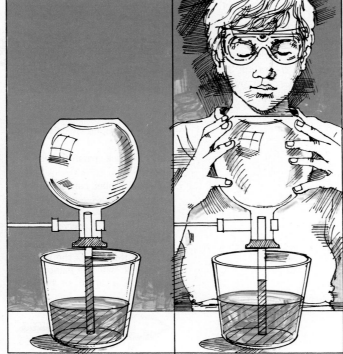

Activity 3

Use tongs or a clothespin to hold a bimetallic strip in a flame for 30 seconds. Explain what happens.

Activity 4

Observe the difference between the colored water levels in the illustrations above. How is the student in the illustration causing this to happen? How could you get the colored water into the tube in the first place?

✳ *Follow Up*

Assessment

1. Students may enjoy making "thermometer mobiles." Each part of the mobile should resemble a small thermometer with the temperature of a particular phenomenon, such as the temperature at which water boils or normal body temperature. Hang several of the mobiles around the classroom.
2. Tell students to imagine a hot, bright light shining on a balloon filled with air. They should write a brief paragraph in which they use the words *heat, temperature, expand* and *contract* to describe what happens to the balloon.

Extension

1. Have students keep track of the high and low temperatures in your area for a week. Then have them use the information to make line graphs showing how the temperature varied from day to day. Display the finished graphs for others to see.
2. Have students research the development of the thermometer. Suggest that they share what they discover by making posters or a timeline.

Activity 2

Be sure that all of the air is out of the balloon before it is fastened over the top of the bottle. Set the bottle into a beaker or pan of hot water.

Observation: As the air in the bottle cools, it contracts. (Have students remove the bottle from the hot water and observe the balloon deflate.)

Conclusion: The balloon inflates as the air inside the bottle expands.

Activity 3

Observation: As the bimetallic strip is heated, it curls. When the strip is taken out of the flame, it cools and returns to its original shape.

Conclusion: One part of the bimetallic strip expands more rapidly than the other when it is heated. Conversely, it contracts more rapidly when it is cooled.

Activity 4

Observation: As heat from a person's hands warms the air in the flask, the air expands, forcing the liquid down the tube. When the person's hands are removed from the flask, the air inside it cools and contracts, thereby pulling the liquid up the tube. To get the water into the tube in the first place, heat the flask well with your hands, and then immerse the tube in the water.

Getting Started

In this lesson, students construct their own thermometers and discover how to calibrate them using fixed points. Students then examine many different kinds of thermometers for use at home, in the hospital, and at the weather station. Design differences of various thermometers are also discussed.

Main Ideas

1. Thermometers may be calibrated with respect to known temperatures.
2. Most thermometers measure temperature by gauging the expansion of a gas or a liquid or by the extent to which a bimetallic strip bends.
3. There are many different kinds of thermometers, each designed for use in a specific setting.

Teaching Strategies

Before students begin reading the lesson, ask them to describe some of the thermometers they have seen and used. How do thermometers differ? Point out that in this lesson they will have an opportunity to make their own thermometer. They will also learn about different types of thermometers and examine how these different thermometers work.

Exploration 3

Demonstrate how to make an air thermometer before students make their own. Invite discussion about what is happening to the air inside the pipette.

To calibrate the thermometer, divide the distance between the hot and cold temperatures into millimeters.

---

2 The Thermometer

The thermometers you have been using until now have been commercially manufactured. In Exploration 3 you will construct your own working thermometer!

The Air Thermometer

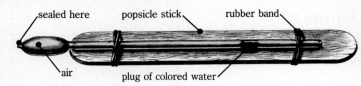

sealed here   popsicle stick   rubber band
air   plug of colored water

You Will Need

- a pasteur pipette (sealed at one end)
- a craft stick, painted white if possible
- 2 small rubber bands
- red food coloring
- water

What to Do

1. Heat the bulb of the sealed pipette with the flame of a match, a candle, or an alcohol lamp.

2. When the pipette is hot, dip its open end into a drop of water colored with red food coloring. Draw up about 5 mm of the colored water. It will act as a marker.

3. Test your thermometer by first putting it in hot water, and then in cold. Does it seem to work? Could you improve it? It might be necessary to change the position of the marker (the plug of colored water).

4. Make a scale on the craft stick by marking it at intervals of 1 mm. Mount your thermometer using the rubber bands.

5. Now you'll *calibrate* your thermometer. Put it into cold water. Mark the position of the bottom of the colored water on the craft stick. Use a commercial thermometer to find out the temperature of the same sample of water. Repeat this procedure using hot water. What change in temperature makes the colored water marker of your thermometer move 1 mm?

LESSON 2 ORGANIZER

Objectives

By the end of the lesson, students should be able to:
1. Describe how to construct a simple thermometer, calibrate it, and use it to make measurements.
2. Explain some of the problems inherent in an air thermometer and provide suggestions for minimizing them.
3. Describe three different kinds of thermometers.
4. Explain how a thermostat responds to temperature change.

Process Skills

observing, measuring, investigating, analyzing, comparing

New Terms

Calibrate—to mark an instrument with a series of degrees for measuring.
Thermostat—a thermometer that regulates temperature by controlling a heating or cooling unit.

How Good Is Your Thermometer?

Trying Out Your Thermometer

Using your thermometer, find out the temperatures of the following:

(a) the air in the room you are in
(b) an area near a radiator or hot air vent
(c) your sock
(d) your hand
(e) the area near an incandescent light bulb
(f) the area near a fluorescent light
(g) warm water
(h) a cold drink and a hot drink
(i) the air outdoors (in the sun and in the shade)

Compare your values with those obtained by your classmates.

Were you satisfied with how your thermometer worked? Did the marker move up and down as much as you would have liked? Would it help if you increased the amount of air in the thermometer? When you measured the temperature of the liquid, did it make a difference how deep you dipped your thermometer? Did it take a long time for the marker to stop moving? Would you be worried if some of the water from the marker evaporated? Have you some suggestions for improving the design?

To help get your ideas and answers straight, write a letter to one of your fellow students. In it, suggest ways in which he or she might improve the thermometer.

Building a Better Thermometer

One major problem with your air thermometer is that you need to calibrate it every time you use it. Blow into your thermometer. What happens? Why? When the pressure of the atmosphere changes, the volume of the air inside the thermometer changes. On *high pressure* days, when the weather is fine, the air in your thermometer will occupy less space than on *low pressure* days, when the weather is stormy. For this reason, ordinary thermometers often use liquids instead of air.

Rather than filling your thermometer with air, fill it with a liquid. The size of the bulb you use makes a big difference, as you will discover.

Hold a thermometer competition. Each group is to design and build the best possible thermometer. Decide what rules for the competition should be laid down. On what basis should the thermometers be judged?

You can calibrate your simple thermometer using one that has already been calibrated. Or, you can start from scratch. Most temperature scales are based upon two fixed points—the freezing point of water (0 °C) and the boiling point of water (100 °C). You can use these fixed points to calibrate your thermometer.

There is yet another way to make a better thermometer. It involves using a *bimetallic strip*. Can you devise a way to do this?

Trying Out Your Thermometer

After students have used their thermometers to find out the temperature of the 11 items, ask them to compare their answers with those of their classmates. Discuss the reasons for any differences in their answers.

How Good Is Your Thermometer?

You might want to have students read this section prior to testing their thermometers, or they can test their thermometers again with these questions in mind. Involve students in a discussion of the evaluation questions posed in the first paragraph. Students should use the points raised in the discussion in writing their letters. After students have finished writing, have them exchange their letters with a classmate. Provide time for them to read and discuss the letters.

Building a Better Thermometer

Have students read the first two paragraphs to see if any of the suggestions they made in their letters were similar to those made here. Then introduce the idea of a thermometer competition. Invite students to think of some rules and judging criteria.

To make a thermometer using a bimetallic strip, first attach a pointer to one end of the strip; the other end should be attached to a support. The strip should then be subjected to temperature extremes and calibrated in a manner similar to that used in making the air thermometer.

Encourage students to make a thermometer using this method or a method of their own. You can then hold a thermometer contest.

Materials

Exploration 3: pasteur pipette (sealed at one end), craft stick (painted white), 2 small rubber bands, red food coloring, water, Petri dish or saucer, candle or alcohol lamp, matches, metric ruler, thermometer, safety goggles

Teacher's Resource Binder

Resource Transparency 7–1

Science Discovery Videodisc

Disc 2, Image and Activity Bank, 7–2

Time Required

three class periods

Thermometers at Work

In the Home

Ask students to respond by a show of hands if they have a thermostat in their home to control a furnace. Call on a volunteer to describe how it is set. *(by turning it to the desired temperature)* What controls it? *(the temperature of the air)* Why is it convenient to have? *(It turns the furnace on and off automatically, which keeps the house at an almost constant temperature.)* What might the coil be made of? *(a bimetallic strip)* Have two volunteers take the roles of the cartoon characters and read the story aloud to the class. Involve students in a discussion of how the thermostat shown in the cartoon works. You may wish to remind students that as a material cools, it contracts, and as it warms, it expands. (An exception to this is water, which expands when it freezes.) As the air in the house cools, the bimetallic strip contracts and coils up. If it coils up enough, the bead of mercury will flow to the other side of its container. When this happens, the mercury closes the circuit, causing electricity to flow. The furnace is then turned on.

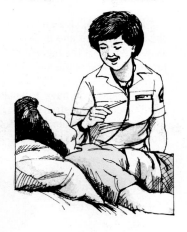

. . . In the Hospital

You have probably had your temperature taken when you were not feeling very well. In a hospital, taking temperatures is a regular practice. Sandra is a student nurse who has been looking after a patient suffering with a high fever. Imagine Sandra trying to take the patient's temperature with an ordinary mercury thermometer. As soon as the thermometer was taken out of the patient's mouth, the mercury thread would begin to shrink. Therefore, Sandra uses a *clinical* thermometer instead. It has a constriction, a kink in the fine tube, just above the bulb of mercury.

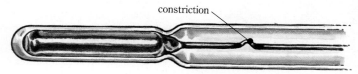

constriction

When a clinical thermometer is removed from the mouth, the mercury thread breaks at the constriction. Above the break, the mercury stays at the same place. After recording the patient's temperature on the chart, Sandra shakes the thermometer to return the mercury to the bulb, and places it in sterilizing fluid.

. . . At the Weather Station

". . . cloudy with some sunny periods. Winds northwest at 10 to 15 kilometers per hour. Low this morning 8 °C. High late afternoon 14 °C . . ."

Ched and Elena visited the weather station to find out exactly how the weather station collected its data.

Sun Ling, a meteorologist, showed the students the thermometer shelter shown on the right (*a*). She then began to explain how the shelter worked.

"See the two thermometers that are mounted almost horizontally? The one on top (*b*) gives the minimum temperature of the day. The bottom one (*c*) gives the maximum temperature."

Elena looked closely at the maximum-temperature thermometer. "It's like a big clinical thermometer."

"Yes, it has a kink (*d*) just above the bulb," Ched observed.

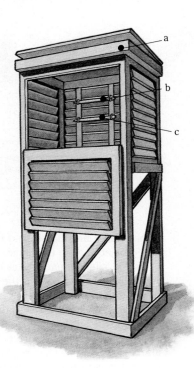

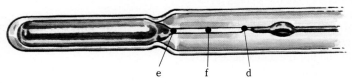

e f d

In the Hospital

Have students silently read the selection and study the diagram. Be sure that they understand that the constriction is in the tiny tube inside the thermometer—not the constriction at the end of the thermometer bulb. If possible, bring a clinical thermometer to class for students to examine. Demonstrate how to hold the thermometer in order to read it correctly. If students wish to take their temperature, be sure the thermometer is sterilized properly in rubbing alcohol after each use.

To extend the information presented here, you may wish to invite the school nurse to class to demonstrate how to use a clinical thermometer and to discuss body temperature and what it means if it is too high.

At the Weather Station

Have students read the selection silently, pausing at the illustration on page 361. Then direct their attention to the diagram of the maximum-temperature thermometer. Explain to students that the maximum temperature thermometer is much larger than the clinical thermometer. Ask: Why do you think this is so? *(The maximum thermometer must include a much larger temperature range than the clinical thermometer.)* If possible, bring a clinical and maximum-temperature thermometer to class for students to examine and compare.

Have students read the rest of the selection. Then direct their attention to the diagram of the minimum thermometer. Help students review each of the steps detailing how it works. Make certain students understand that when the thermometer is reset, the top of the index lines up with the top of the column of alcohol. As the alcohol falls in the column, the index falls with it. But when the alcohol rises in the column, the index stays at the lowest point reached, indicating the lowest temperature reached.

1. A thermometer measures the expansion due to an increase in heat of the liquid or gas inside it.
2. Thermometer means *heat + measure;* a thermometer measures average kinetic energy from heat. Thermostat means *heat + the same.* A thermostat is an instrument that keeps the temperature stationary by controlling a heating unit.
3. Answers will vary, but the sentence could conclude "because it regulates itself."
4. The shelters are set at a standard height so that temperature readings will be uniform. (The height of a standing person is approximately 1.6 m.) Also, varying the distance from the ground could influence the results. The thermometers are enclosed to keep the sun off, yet ventilated to allow air to circulate.
5. Encourage your students to be creative. For extra credit, they can actually build their designs.

✳ *Follow Up*

Assessment

1. Have students make posters to illustrate the step-by-step procedure for making an air thermometer.
2. Have students make posters to illustrate the differences between a clinical thermometer, a maximum-temperature thermometer, and a minimum-temperature thermometer. Ask students to include a brief explanation of how each one works.

Extension

1. Have students do some research to find out how digital and electrical thermometers work.
2. Point out to students that there are several different temperature scales—Fahrenheit, Celsius, and Kelvin. Suggest that they make posters to illustrate how these scales differ.

"That's right," Ling answered. "When the temperature rises to the highest point and then cools off, the mercury beyond the kink stays there—at the highest temperature. Notice that the mercury on the bulb end of the kink (*e*) moves back toward the bulb, leaving a space (*f*)."

"I suppose you have to shake the mercury down for the next day," Elena suggested.

"You're right again! Let's look at the minimum thermometer. Do you see anything different about it? Look at it very closely."

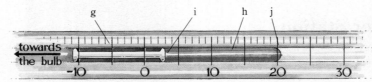

Ched and Elena did so, and Ched pointed to an odd dumbbell-shaped object (*g*) in the liquid of the thermometer.

"That's called an *index.* This thermometer contains alcohol (*h*). The alcohol shrinks toward the bulb as the temperature falls. At the same time, the surface of the alcohol draws the index with it. When the temperature rises, the index stays where it is and the alcohol moves away from it."

"The end of the index farthest from the bulb (*i*) gives the minimum temperature. The curved surface (*j*) of the alcohol gives the present temperature. Can you read the two temperatures?" Ched and Elena nodded that they could. Then they asked her how she reset the index to take tomorrow's reading.

"Easy! All you do is tilt the bulb end up; the index glides slowly through the alcohol back to the curved surface."

Using What You Learned

1. What is a thermometer really measuring when it shows the temperature?
2. Break the words *thermometer* and *thermostat* down into root words. What do they mean? How are their meanings reflected in what they do?
3. Using your own words, complete the following sentence. "The thermostat is a special kind of thermometer because. . . ."
4. Look at the thermometer shelter on page 361. Official meteorological thermometers are always enclosed in such shelters, and the shelters are always set the same distance from the ground (about 1.6 meters). Why do you think these procedures are followed?
5. Design your own thermostat or maximum/minimum thermometer system. Your invention could be an improved version of the old, or it could be an entirely new design.

3 Signs of Temperature Change

Which Expands Most?

Three friends were interested in improving the thermometers they had made. They wanted to know whether water expands more than cooking oil or other liquids. They also wanted to find out whether water expands more than a gas such as air, or a solid such as copper. They tried the following three experiments.

Read through the experiments carefully. As you read, ask yourself whether or not the experiments were satisfactory. Can you detect any problems? How would you improve the experiments?

Experiment 1

How much do water, cooking oil, and a mixture of water and antifreeze expand?

This was a simple experiment to carry out. The three took a 500 mL bottle, filled it to the brim with water, and placed it in a pan of boiling water. The first thing they noticed was a bulge of water at the mouth of the bottle. Some water then spilled into the pan. When no more water spilled out, they took the bottle out of the pan and let it cool to 20 °C. Finally, they measured how much water was needed to fill the bottle back to the brim.

| they filled the bottle to the brim | the liquid began to bulge | it spilled into the pan | they let the bottle cool, and then they refilled it |

They repeated the experiment for cooking oil and for the mixture of water and antifreeze.

The amount of expansion for each was as follows:
14 mL for the water
21 mL for the cooking oil
14 mL for the water-antifreeze mixture

LESSON 3 ORGANIZER

Objectives

By the end of the lesson, students should be able to:
1. Compare the expansion rates of liquids, gases, and solids.
2. Explain the expansion properties of a bimetallic strip.
3. Describe ways to demonstrate that liquids, gases, and solids expand when heated.

Process Skills

observing, analyzing, inferring, calculating

New Terms

(Organizer continues on next page)

✳ Getting Started

In this lesson, students compare the expansion rates of liquids, gases, and solids. The lesson begins by having students analyze and evaluate three expansion experiments. Next, students are presented with several demonstrations that are extensions of the experiments they studied earlier. The lesson concludes with students using a Celsius thermometer to identify temperatures at which specific events occur.

Main Ideas

1. When heated, gases expand more than liquids, and liquids expand more than solids.
2. Different liquids, gases, and solids expand at different rates.

✳ Teaching Strategies

Which Expands Most?

Have students read the introductory paragraphs silently. Then divide the class into groups of three or four students, and assign one of the experiments to each group to discuss. Then, have one member from each group report their ideas about the experiment.

Experiment 1

As discussion starters, ask students: Is the size of the pan important? If so, why? *(The deeper the pan, the more evenly the liquid in the bottle will be heated. Each substance should be heated in the same pan with the same amount of boiling water.)* Is the temperature of the water at the neck of the bottle the same as that at the bottom of the bottle? Why or why not? *(The temperature is cooler at the neck because it is farther from the heat source.)*
(Continues on next page)

(Experiment 1 continued)

The main design flaw in the experiment is that the bottle also expands when it is heated, and this expansion varies with the materials contained in the bottle. Therefore, the expansion of the bottle would have to be measured for each liquid, and then this amount would be added to the results from the experiment. For example, if the bottle expanded by 5 mL, an additional 5 mL should be added to the total measured. Another flaw of the experiment is that the liquid might spill out of the bottle by sudden bubbling, rather than by expansion.

Experiment 2

One important source of error is that the volume of the air in the balloon will shrink when it cools if it is not measured fast enough. Submerging the balloon in water will most likely cool the air inside the balloon, causing it to contract. The best way to avoid this problem would be to construct a device for measuring the expansion of the balloon while it is still attached to the bottle. For example, if the balloon was encased in a container, the air forced out of the container could be measured as the balloon expanded.

Experiment 3

The design problem is to find a way of measuring very small changes in length. A better approach might have been to measure the length of the copper pipe when it was cold, and again after steam had been passed through it. The ruler should not have been heated along with the copper pipe.

Experiment 2

How much does air expand when it is heated?

The friends tied an empty balloon to the neck of the same 500 mL bottle, and then placed the bottle in a pan of boiling water. The balloon gradually got bigger and bigger; finally, it stopped expanding. They tied off the balloon just above the neck of the bottle. To measure the volume of air in the balloon, they immersed it in a can of water. They found that the balloon contained 105 mL of air. Because the three could not agree that the experiment was a good one, they decided to look for other ways of measuring the expansion of air.

they tied an empty balloon to the neck

the balloon got bigger

they tied off the balloon

and immersed it in a can of water

Experiment 3

How much does copper expand when heated?

The three friends started by taking a piece of copper pipe 25 cm long. They strapped a wooden ruler to it and placed the copper pipe into a beaker of boiling water. Nothing much seemed to happen! One of the friends thought that the copper had expanded about 1 mm, but the others felt that the whole experiment didn't work because the ruler probably expanded along with the copper. What were they going to do now?

(Organizer continued)

Materials

Exploration 4
Demonstration 1: a 500-mL flask, food coloring, hot plate, water, one-holed stopper, glass tubing, marker, safety goggles
Demonstration 2: balloon, 2 books, metric ruler, cold water, paper towels

Demonstration 3: 2 cans, weight, metal rod, candle, matches, 2 blocks of wood, plastic drinking straw, pin, marker, safety goggles

Science Discovery Videodisc

Disc 2, Image and Activity Bank, 7–3

Time Required

two class periods

Thinking About the Results

1. How do different liquids compare in their expansion?
2. By comparison, how much more does air expand than water?
3. How much does l L of water expand when you heat it by 1 °C?
4. One of the friends looked up the expansion of copper in a handbook and found that when a 1-meter copper bar is heated from 20 °C to 100 °C, it lengthens by 1.4 mm.
   (a) How much longer should the copper pipe have gotten in their experiment?
   (b) The handbook also indicated that a 1-m iron bar would become 0.88 mm longer when heated from 20 °C to 100 °C. How much would a 25-cm iron bar lengthen?

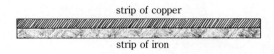
strip of copper

strip of iron

5. Now you can understand why a bimetallic strip works as it does when there is an increase in temperature. Write a brief explanation in the form of a note to a friend.
6. Suppose that the bimetallic strip in Sarah's furnace thermostat (on page 360) was made of copper and iron cemented together. On which side of the coil is the copper, the inside or the outside? Why?

EXPLORATION 4

Try One of These Demonstrations Yourself 🔥 🥽

Demonstration 1

Answers to

Thinking About the Results

1. All liquids expand when they are heated, but they may expand by different amounts.
2. Even though there is some experimental error in *Experiments 1* and *2,* students should see that when heated from 20°C to 100°C, air expands much more than does water: 500 mL of water expands 14 mL; 500 mL of air expands 105 mL (7.5 times more than water).
3. If 500 mL of water expands 14 mL when heated from 20°C to 100°C, then 1 L of water expands 28 mL when heated to the same temperature. Therefore, 1 L of water expands 28 mL ÷ 80°C, or 0.35 mL for every 1°C rise in temperature.
4. (a) If 1 m of copper expands 1.4 mm when heated from 20°C to 100°C, then a copper pipe 25 cm long (¼ of a meter) should expand 1.4 mm ÷ 4, or 0.35 mm.
   (b) 0.88 ÷ 4 = 0.22 mm longer
5. In a bimetallic strip, the different expansion rates of the metals cause the strip to curve when it is heated. If the strip is coiled, it gets tighter when it cools and looser when it warms.
6. The iron would be on the outside and the copper on the inside because the copper expands and contracts more than the iron does.

Exploration 4

Divide the class into three groups and have each group prepare and present what they learned.

Demonstration 1

This activity demonstrates that a liquid expands when it is heated. Caution students to be *careful* not to break the glass tubing when they insert it into the stoppers. To avoid injury, you might want to do this ahead of time for your students. Suggest that they use a 500-mL flask, as it will make any follow-up calculations easier. Instruct students to mark the level of the water in the tube before heating begins, and again just as the water begins to boil. When the tube cools and the water has receded back into the flask, ask students to carefully measure how much water it takes to fill up the tube to the high-level mark. This procedure should give a good approximation of how much the water expanded.

Demonstration 2

This demonstration shows that a gas contracts when cooled. The following may be used as a guide:

1. Blow up the balloon and tie off the end so that no air can escape.
2. Place the balloon between two books. Be sure the books do not squeeze the balloon out of shape.
3. Measure the distance between the books to determine the balloon's diameter.
4. Now run cold water on the balloon or place it in a pan of ice water for a couple of minutes. Dry the balloon off quickly.
5. Repeat steps 2 and 3 and compare the results with the first measurement of the balloon.

Demonstration 3

This demonstration shows that a solid expands when it is heated. Have students set up the equipment as shown in the illustration. Insert a thumbtack through one end of the straw to attach it to the wooden block. The end of the metal rod should touch the straw. As the metal is heated by the candle, it will expand, causing the straw to move. Make sure students mark the starting and ending positions of the straw. Caution students not to touch the rod until it has cooled.

 Follow Up

Assessment

1. Challenge students to design three simple demonstrations to show what happens to liquids, gases, and solids when they are heated. Have students record their ideas.
2. Suggest that students write poems about what happens to liquids, gases, and solids when they are heated and cooled. Their poems may be serious or humorous.

Extension

1. Challenge students to do some research to find out why heat causes things to expand and why cooling causes things to contract. Suggest that they make poster-sized diagrams to share what they discover.

Demonstration 2

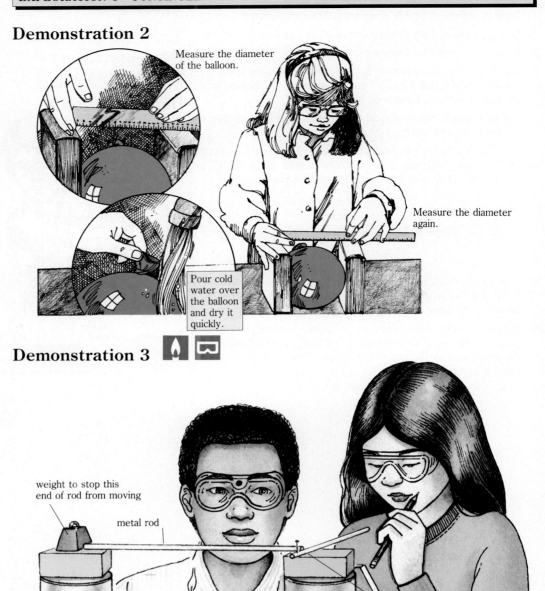

Measure the diameter of the balloon.

Measure the diameter again.

Pour cold water over the balloon and dry it quickly.

Demonstration 3

weight to stop this end of rod from moving

metal rod

pin through straw and into block

2. Suggest that students do some research to find out about different kinds of thermostats. For example, some thermostats use the expansion and contraction of a gas or liquid, some use infrared detectors, and some use bimetallic strips. Have students share what they have learned.

1. Test your knowledge of the Celsius scale. Match the descriptions below with the corresponding numbered positions on the thermometer. Do not write in this book.

   (a) "It's hotter'n a firecracker!"
   (b) "Come on in, the water's great."
   (c) butter melts

   (d) sweater weather
   (e) a rolling boil at sea level

   (f) a rolling boil on a mountaintop
   (g) "Dadgum water pipes froze up."

   (h) ice cream stays hard
   (i) "Ouch—that water's hot!"
   (j) dead battery weather

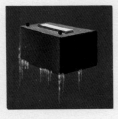

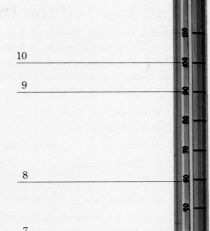

2. Honey becomes runnier as it warms up. Design a thermometer that uses this property.

LESSON 4

✳ *Getting Started*

In this lesson, students investigate the difference between heat and temperature. To begin, students discuss their ideas about heat and temperature by examining how they use the terms. Then, through a series of experiments, students observe the relationship between the temperature of a substance and the amount of heat applied to it. The lesson concludes with students designing experiments to show what happens to the temperature of a substance in the presence of heat.

Main Ideas

1. The temperature of a substance is a measure of how hot or cold it is.
2. The amount by which the temperature of a substance increases depends on the mass of the substance and the amount of heat applied to it.

Answers to

Can You Tell the Difference?

When students have completed the four questions, have them share and discuss their responses. Then have them write brief descriptions of heat and temperature in their Journals. Ask them to save their descriptions to review and revise later.
1. *heat*
2. *temperature*
3. *heat*
4. *temperature*

---

4 Heat Versus Temperature

Can You Tell the Difference?

Up until now you have been looking at temperature—how cold, warm, or hot something is. Is heat the same thing as temperature? What is the difference between heat and temperature? Test yourself! Using a separate piece of paper, fill in the blanks in the following sentences with the right term: heat or temperature.

1. Would you get more ____?____ in your home by burning wood or by burning oil?
2. At what ____?____ should you set the house thermostat?
3. Is there enough ____?____ from a burning match to boil water?
4. At what ____?____ does water boil?

Now write what you think about heat and temperature. Compare your descriptions with those of a classmate.

In Exploration 5 you will conduct a number of experiments. These experiments are designed to help you to clear up any uncertainties that you may have about the difference between heat and temperature.

A Circus of Experiments

Experiment 1

Heat From a Match

Stick a pin into a match taken from a book of matches. Light the match and hold it under a test tube containing 5 mL of water. Measure the rise in temperature with a thermometer. Repeat with 10 mL and 15 mL of water. Record your results. Do your results make sense? How do you explain them?

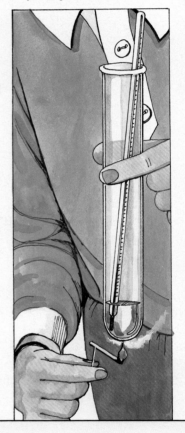

LESSON 4 ORGANIZER

Objectives

By the end of the lesson, students should be able to:
1. Describe the difference between heat and temperature.
2. Explain the relationship between the heat content of a substance and the temperature and mass of the substance.

Process Skills

observing, measuring, analyzing, evaluating

New Terms

Experiment 2
Heat From Dissolving

Record the temperature of 10 mL of water. Add 5 mL of soda ash to the water. Very carefully stir the mixture with a thermometer. Now measure and record the water's temperature again. Repeat the procedure using 15 mL and then 20 mL of water. Record your results. Do they make sense?

Experiment 3
Heat From Friction

Put 25 mL of water into a metal soup can. Measure its temperature. Loop a 1-meter length of cord around the outside of the can. Pull the cord back and forth a number of times and measure the temperature again.

Repeat the procedure using 50 mL and 100 mL of water. Record the changes in temperature. Are they what you expected? Why or why not?

Experiment 4
Heat From Electricity

Put 500 mL of water into an electric coffee pot. Measure its temperature. Now plug it in for 30 seconds and measure the rise in temperature. Repeat this procedure using 1000 mL of water. Record your results. Are they what you expected?

Materials

Exploration 5
Experiment 1: book of matches, straight pin, test tube, 30 mL water, thermometer, graduated cylinder, safety goggles
Experiment 2: 3 test tubes, test-tube rack, 40 mL water, 15 mL soda ash, thermometer, graduated cylinder

Experiment 3: metal soup can, 175 mL water, 1-m length of cord, thermometer, graduated cylinder
Experiment 4: 1500 mL water, electric coffee pot, thermometer, watch or clock with second hand, graduated cylinder
Experiment 5: Materials have already been gathered.
Making Sense of Your Results: Journal

(Organizer continues on next page)

Teaching Strategies

Exploration 5

Set up five work stations, one station for each experiment. Two sets of apparatus are adequate at each station. Then divide the class into groups of three or four students. Provide each group with about 10 minutes to complete each experiment.

Experiment 1

Caution students to close the book of matches before striking the match. For more accurate results, suggest that one student hold the match under the test tube while another holds the thermometer in the water, keeping the thermometer bulb from resting on the bottom of the test tube. The entire match should be allowed to burn each time. Students should observe that as the amount of water increases, the rise in temperature is less. The reason for this is that the same amount of energy is added to an increasingly larger system.

Experiment 2

To prevent accidents, caution students to use a test-tube rack. Be sure that they understand they are to add the same amount of soda ash (5 mL) to each amount of water. Students should observe that as the amount of water increases, the rise in temperature decreases. As in *Experiment 1,* the same amount of chemical energy is released; the size of the system into which the energy is released is increasing.

Experiment 3

Point out to students that one person should hold the can while another pulls the cord. Again, students should observe that as the amount of water increases, the rise in temperature decreases.

Experiment 4

Caution: Students should be careful using electrical appliances around water. Suggest that one student hold the thermometer so that the bulb does not rest on the bottom of the coffee pot. Students should observe that as the amount of water is increased, the rise in temperature decreases.

Experiment 5

You may wish to provide students an opportunity to complete each of the experiments again, or have students choose one and report their results to the class. Students should observe that doubling the heat causes the temperature to rise to about double.

Answers to

Making Sense of Your Results

1. You would expect that doubling the amount of water would cause the temperature to rise half as much. However, because of experimental error, this exact result seldom occurs. An acceptable conclusion would be: The more water there is, the less the temperature rises with the same amount of heat.

2. You would expect that doubling the heat doubles the temperature increase.

3. There should be no change in temperature.

4. Both fingers would experience the same sensation. The water in the bathtub and the glass are equally hot (i.e., at the same temperature). However, the tub contains more *heat* because there is more water.

5. Because the temperature is raised by the same amount in both cases —10°C—students will probably infer that the same amount of heat is required. This is not what actually happens, though. Raising 1L of water from 20°C to 30°C requires more heat than raising it from 30°C to 40°C. This occurs because the average specific heat of water is higher from 20°C to 30°C than it is from 30°C to 40°C. The magnitude of that difference is so small, however, that students would probably not notice any difference at all.

6. In each case, the temperature of the water falls to 0°C as it melts the ice.
   - 15 mL of water at 80°C melts the most ice.
   - 20 mL at 50°C and 10 mL at 100°C melt the same amount of ice.
   - 10 mL at 50°C melts the least amount of ice.

(Answers continue on next page)

In each of the previous four Experiments, the same amount of heat was added to different amounts of water. In Experiment 5, the amount of heat changes, while the amount of water stays the same.

Experiment 5

Doubling the Heat

Repeat one of Experiments 1 through 4, but vary the amount of heat while you keep the amount of water the same. For example, try: burning two matches under 10 mL of water; dissolving 10 mL of soda ash in 20 mL of water; pulling the cord twice the number of times with 50 mL of water; plugging in the coffee pot for 1 minute with 1000 mL of water. Keep track of your results.

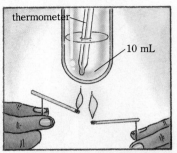

Making Sense of Your Results

First, compare your results with those of other students. Afterwards, work through the questions below. You should now be able to make sense of your results.

1. In each of the first four experiments, the amount of water in each container was changed. Was the temperature rise the same in each? Why or why not?

2. Compare Experiment 5 with its earlier counterparts. How does doubling the heat affect the temperature increase?

3. What would happen to the temperature increase if you doubled the amount of heat and also doubled the amount of water?

4. If, for 2 seconds, you put one finger in a glass of water at 50 °C and another in a bathtub of water at 50 °C, would both fingers have the same sensation? Is the water in each equally hot? Do the glass and the tub contain the same amount of heat? Explain your reasoning.

5. A tricky question. Which do you think would require more heat: raising 1 L of water from 20 °C to 30 °C, or raising 1 L of water from 30 °C to 40 °C? How could you find out?

6. Another tricky question. Which do you think would melt more ice:
   10 mL of water at 50 °C?
   20 mL of water at 50 °C?
   10 mL of water at 100 °C?
   or 15 mL of water at 80 °C?

(Organizer continued)

Science Discovery Videodisc

Disc 2, Image and Activity Bank, 7–4

Time Required

two class periods

7. Describe again in your own words the difference between heat and temperature. Compare your answers with those you wrote at the start of this section.

8. Can you help set Dave's thinking straight? In your Journal, rewrite this report for him.

Dave's Report

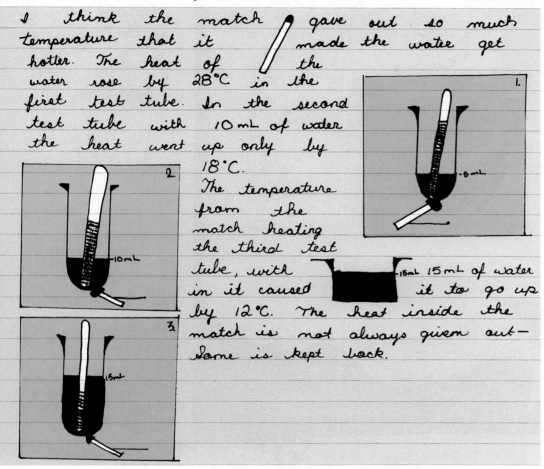

I think the match gave out so much temperature that it made the water get hotter. The heat of the water rose by 28°C in the first test tube. In the second test tube with 10 mL of water the heat went up only by 18°C. The temperature from the match heating the third test tube, with 15 mL of water in it caused it to go up by 12°C. The heat inside the match is not always given out — Some is kept back.

Sense or Nonsense?

Chuck did two more experiments.

1. He used one match to heat 10 mL of water. He used another match to heat 10 mL of cooking oil. To his surprise, the temperature of the cooking oil rose more than the temperature of the water.

2. He then used a match to heat 10 mL of water with a small lump of ice in it. The temperature started at 0 °C and stayed at 0 °C, even after heating.

Strange? Can you design some better experiments to sort out these problems?

LESSON 5

✳ Getting Started

In this lesson, students consider what happens when heat is transferred from one substance to another. By completing the Exploration, students observe how mixing hot and cold water in specific ratios affects the temperature of the combined water. The lesson concludes with an application activity.

Main Ideas

1. Hot and cold water mixed in equal volumes results in water with a temperature halfway between the two.
2. Mixing unequal volumes of hot and cold water produces water whose temperature is closer to that of the greater amount of water.

✳ Teaching Strategies

Have a volunteer read the introductory paragraph aloud. Then engage students in a discussion of how they adjust their bath or shower to the right temperature. Most students will agree that they mix hot and cold water by trial and error. Point out that in the following Exploration, they will observe how temperature changes when hot and cold water are mixed.

Exploration 6

Divide the class into groups of three, and instruct each group to complete the Exploration. Emphasize that accurate recording of data is very important. Involve the class in a discussion of their results and procedures.

5 Hot + Cold = . . . ?

Have you ever wished you could find a formula for getting the temperature of your bath or shower just right? There is a formula, to be sure! The best way to discover it is to experiment. Try mixing different amounts of hot and cold water.

Mixing Hot and Cold

You Will Need

- 3 plastic-foam cups: one containing hot (but not scalding) water, one containing cold water, and one empty
- a measuring cup
- a thermometer

What to Do

1. Tip one measure of hot water into the empty cup.
2. Record the temperature of the hot water in the cup.
3. Record the temperature of the cold water.
4. Now add one measure of the cold water to the hot water. Mix, and then record the temperature.
5. Try adding one measure of cold water to two measures of hot water. Record the temperature. Continue experimenting, using different ratios of hot and cold water. In each case, record the temperature.
6. Record your results in a table like the one at the top of page 373.

LESSON 5 ORGANIZER

Objectives

By the end of the lesson, students should be able to:

1. Describe what happens to temperature when heat is transferred from one substance to another.
2. Modify an experiment in order to solve a specific problem.

Process Skills

observing, measuring, predicting

New Terms

Number of Measures of Hot Water	Temperature of Hot Water	Number of Measures of Cold Water	Temperature of Cold Water	Temperature of Mixture

Searching for a Pattern

Look at the final temperature of each mixture, and at the proportion of hot water added. Does any pattern emerge? Now is the time to try to write your bathwater formula.

Decide which measurements you should make to test your formula (or hypothesis).

Dear Juanita:
I hear you have been studying what happens when you mix hot and cold liquids. Can you help me?

My problem is this. I always get up late and have to rush my morning coffee. How much milk should I add to bring it to the right temperature? I always seem to add too much or too little!

Many thanks,
Elinor

How could Juanita solve Elinor's problem? What does this activity tell you about the difference between hot and cold things?

Answers to

Searching for a Pattern

Students should recognize that a pattern does emerge—one that is dependent upon the ratios of hot and cold water that are mixed together. Assuming that all measures were the same mass, the resulting temperature would be an average of the temperatures of the measures mixed. For example, 2 measures at 10°C and 1 at 40°C would be $(10 + 10 + 40) \div 3 = 20$°C.

Involve the class in a discussion of how Juanita can solve Elinor's problem. If students do the activity, they should decide on one set of data on which to work. For example, the volume of the coffee cup might be 200 mL, the temperature of the coffee 65°C.

✳ Follow Up

Assessment

Have students make a list of times during the day when they mix hot and cold substances together. Next to each item, ask them to suggest the ratios they think should be used to arrive at the desired temperatures.

Extension

Suggest that students make a graph to show the change in temperature as specific amounts of hot water are added to a container of cold water. Invite a volunteer to explain the graph and procedure to the class.

Materials

Exploration 6: 3 plastic-foam cups—one containing hot (not scalding) water, one containing cold water, and one empty; measuring cup; thermometer; kettle; hot plate; oven mitt, safety goggles

Teacher's Resource Binder

Resource Worksheet 7–3
Graphic Organizer Transparency 7–2

Time Required

one class period

Getting Started

This lesson reinforces the idea that heat is energy. In *Exploration 7,* students perform two experiments that demonstrate the conversion of mechanical energy into heat energy. Then they examine the relationship between food energy and heat. The lesson concludes with students examining their daily energy intake.

Main Ideas

1. Heat is a form of energy.
2. The joule is the metric unit used to measure energy. It is roughly equal to the amount of energy required to raise a 100-g mass 1 m.
3. The human body requires a certain number of kilojoules of energy daily in order to function.

Teaching Strategies

Before students begin the Exploration, ask them to rub their hands together. Call on several volunteers to describe what they feel. *(some warmth or heat)* Point out that by rubbing their hands together, they are converting mechanical energy into heat energy.

Exploration 7

Conduct this activity as a competition. Be sure students record the temperature of the water before they begin each activity. Point out to students that some heat will be lost to the environment surrounding the piece of lead before it is transferred to the water. So, the amount of energy added to the lead will not all transfer to a rise in temperature.

Changing Your Energy into Heat Energy

1. Completely wrap a small jar containing 50 mL of water at room temperature in about eight thicknesses of newspaper. Shake it for about four minutes. Get some friends to help with the shaking. Did the temperature rise? How much heat did you add?

2. Hit a small (thimble-sized) piece of lead about 30 times with a hammer, then drop it into 25 mL of water at room temperature. How much heat does the lead add to the water? How much heat did you add to the lead?

LESSON 6 ORGANIZER

Objectives

By the end of the lesson, students should be able to:
1. Identify heat as a form of energy.
2. Describe what a joule is.
3. Explain the role of food in meeting the energy needs of the body.
4. Recognize that different foods contain different amounts of energy.
5. Determine the energy obtained from a given meal.

Process Skills

observing, measuring, investigating, collecting data

New Terms

Calorie—a unit that is used to record energy content. Multiply by 4.2 to convert calories to joules.

Calorimeter—a device that measures the amount of heat in a substance.

Meet Mr. Heat

James Prescott Joule, a famous British scientist who lived in the 19th century, was fascinated by the idea of changing mechanical energy into heat, just as you did in Exploration 7. He wasn't satisfied with merely showing that it could be done. He also wanted to know exactly how much heat could be made from a definite amount of mechanical energy. His research took 35 years!

Before Joule came along, people thought that heat was a weightless fluid called "caloric." But Joule was able to show that the same amount of heat was always obtained from a given amount of mechanical energy. His work and that of other scientists showed that heat is a form of energy.

One of Joule's devices, shown on the right, was used to change mechanical energy into heat energy. Can you gather how it works from the diagram?

As a tribute to his work, the unit in which energy is measured is called the joule (J). A joule is the amount of energy required to raise a 100-g mass 1 m. Or to put it another way, a 100-g mass that has been raised to the height of 1 m has been given 1 J of energy.

In the paddle-wheel apparatus, when the crank is turned, masses are raised. When the crank is released, the masses fall down, the paddle wheels spin, and the temperature rises. The mechanical energy of the falling masses is transferred to the water as heat energy. It takes 4.2 J of heat to raise the temperature of 1 g of water by 1 °C. A device that measures the amount of heat is called a *calorimeter*.

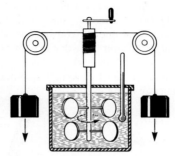

Joule's Apparatus

Something to Think About

1. Explain how Joule's apparatus works. Why did he use this particular apparatus?

2. If you converted the energy required to raise 10 kg through 4 m into heat, by how much would the temperature of 100 g of water in the calorimeter of his apparatus rise?

3. How many joules are needed to raise the temperature of 200 g of water (enough to make a cup of tea) by 50 °C?

4. Suppose you added a pot full of boiling water (2000 g) to a bath of cool water, bringing the temperature of the bath water up to 40 °C. How much heat did the hot water give to the bath water?

5. What is the rule for finding the number of joules of heat energy added to or given off by water?

Meet Mr. Heat

Have students read about the work of James Joule. Involve them in a discussion of how the paddlewheel apparatus works. Point out to students that the device holding the water is insulated so that heat cannot escape, which will make the measure of the amount of heat added to the water more accurate.

Remind students that the potential energy of the raised weights becomes kinetic energy as the weights are released.

Answers to

Something to Think About

1. When the crank is turned, the weights are raised. When the weights are released, the paddles turn and the temperature of the water is increased. Joule probably chose this apparatus because it is easy to put a quantifiable amount of work into the system.

2. Heat produced when a 100-g mass is raised 1 m ≅ 1 J. Heat produced when 10 kg is raised 1 m ≅ 100 J. Heat produced when 10 kg is raised 4 m ≅ 400 J. To raise the temperature of 1 g of water by 1 °C requires 4.2 J. Therefore, 400 J will raise the temperature of 1 g of water by approximately 100 °C, and 400 J will raise the temperature of 100 g of water by approximately 1 °C.

3. To raise the temperature of 1 g of water by 1 °C requires 4.2 J. Therefore, 4.2 J × 200 g × 50 °C = 42,000 J.

4. Heat given to the bath = heat lost by the kettle of water. Heat lost by the kettle of water = 2000 g × (100 °C − 40 °C) × 4.2 J = 504,000 J.

5. The formula is: 4.2 × mass of water (in grams) × temperature rise (in °C) = number of joules.

Food Energy

Have students silently read the two paragraphs. You may wish to point out that the chemical process by which the body produces energy is called *metabolism.* Food provides the raw materials for metabolism to take place. During this process, cells break down complicated substances into simpler ones, releasing chemical and heat energy. The energy needed to keep the body functioning at rest (to maintain breathing, heart beat, body temperature, and other basic functions) is called the *basal metabolic rate.* The energy produced and used by the body is measured in calories or joules.

You might want to work through the answer to the question in the second paragraph along with your students. If necessary, review the definition of a joule as discussed earlier in the lesson. Point out to students that a kilojoule is the same as 1000 joules.

The rationale for finding the amount of energy (400,000 J) required to climb a mountain 1000 m high if you weigh 40 kg is as follows:
If it takes 1 J of energy to raise 100 g 1 m, then it will take 400 J of energy to raise 40 kg (40,000 g) 1 m. And it will take 400,000 J (400 g × 1000 m) to raise 40 kg 1000 m.

Exploration 8

This Exploration may be done by small groups of students. Instruct them to set up the apparatus as it is shown in the diagram. Check to be sure that they have set it up correctly and safely before they begin the activity. Caution students to be particularly careful when they burn the peanut. It may be wise to have the apparatus set up near an open window or an exhaust hood to allow any smoke or fumes from the peanut to escape.

When students calculate the number of joules of heat energy produced, be sure that they use the number of degrees the temperature rises and not the final temperature. You may find it necessary to demonstrate to students how to make the calculation. When students have completed the Exploration, involve them in a discussion of their results. Encourage students to speculate on how to change the activity to make the results more accurate.

Food Energy

The energy you need to walk, dance, ride a bike—even study—comes from the food you eat. In many ways, your body is like a very efficient car. When you exercise hard, it's as though your body is operating at full throttle. Air goes quickly into your lungs. Oxygen from the air is carried through your bloodstream to your muscles. It "burns" the food stored there and releases the energy you need. You get hot because some of the energy escapes as heat; your body is not 100 percent efficient!

How many peanuts would you have to eat to have enough energy to climb a mountain 1000 m high? If your mass is 40 kg, the amount of energy you would use climbing the mountain would be 400,000 J—that is, 400 kJ (kilojoules). (Remember, a joule is the amount of energy you have to use to raise a 100-g mass 1 m.) Although your body doesn't "burn" a peanut in quite the same way that a flame does, the amount of energy the peanut gives off is the same. In the following Exploration, you can find out how much energy is involved.

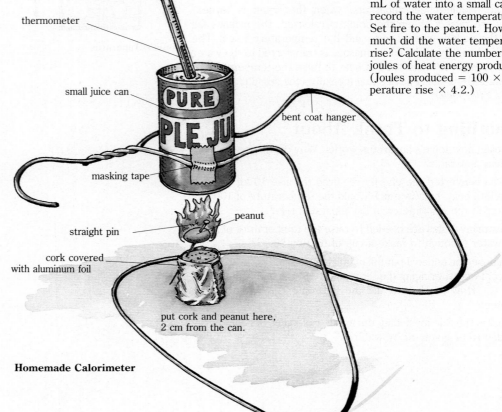

Homemade Calorimeter

How Much Energy Is in a Peanut?

You Will Need

- a thermometer
- a bent coat hanger
- a small juice can
- masking tape
- a peanut
- a straight pin
- a cork covered with aluminum foil

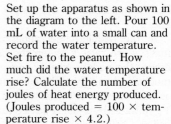

What to Do

Set up the apparatus as shown in the diagram to the left. Pour 100 mL of water into a small can and record the water temperature. Set fire to the peanut. How much did the water temperature rise? Calculate the number of joules of heat energy produced. (Joules produced = 100 × temperature rise × 4.2.)

Tallying the Energy in Food

You could use the same apparatus to measure how much energy you get from other types of food—cornflakes or potato chips to name just two. You would have to dry out moist foods such as fruits or vegetables before you could test them.

Food scientists use an elaborate apparatus called a *bomb calorimeter* to measure the amount of energy in food. ("Bomb" refers to the closed chamber in which the food is burned.) With this device, researchers can get very accurate results.

The food sample is put inside the bomb. Pure oxygen is fed in under pressure. The bomb is then lowered into a water bath and is ignited by passing a burst of electricity through a coil surrounding the sample. The temperature increase is measured to a hundredth of a degree Celsius. Many corrections are made to ensure accuracy. The experiment is repeated many times, and the average result is taken.

Bomb Calorimeter

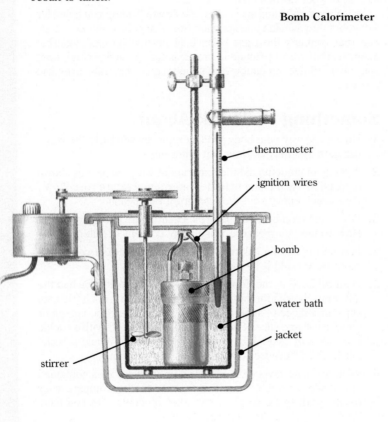

thermometer

ignition wires

bomb

water bath

jacket

stirrer

Tallying the Energy in Food

Have students read the material silently. Ask them why moist foods must be dried before they can be tested in the calorimeter. *(They must be dry in order to burn.)*

Involve students in a discussion of the diagram of the bomb calorimeter. Encourage them to offer ideas about why the bomb calorimeter is more accurate than the simple apparatus they used in *Exploration 8. (Responses may include: the temperature is measured much more precisely; the heat given off by the food is confined to a small, enclosed area and is not dissipated; the electrical charge adds less heat than a burning match; the experiment is repeated several times.)*

What's Your Daily Energy Intake?

Answers to
Something to Think About

1. Possible responses include:
   Car:
   - uses gasoline as fuel
   - uses more fuel when it goes fast
   - emits carbon dioxide from exhaust
   - burning is noisy

   Body:
   - uses food as fuel
   - uses more fuel when it goes faster and works harder
   - lungs exhale carbon dioxide
   - burning is quiet

2. To raise the temperature of 1 g (1 mL) of water by 1°C requires 4.2 J. Therefore, 420 J raises the temperature of 100 mL of water by 1°C. And 10,500 J raises the temperature of 100 mL of water by 25°C (420 × 25). Therefore, about 10,000 J, or 10 kJ, is released when a peanut burns.

3. If food is not dried before measuring the energy it contains, then the energy is used to heat up the water

---

What's Your Daily Energy Intake?

You can sometimes discover the energy content of the foods you eat by reading the package. Have a look at the side of a cereal box, for instance.

Nutritionists often use a unit known as the **calorie** to measure the energy content in food. Calories are not **SI** units, but converting calories to joules is easy. Simply multiply by 4.2. To convert calories to kilojoules, multiply by 0.0042.

What was your energy intake yesterday? Use the Food Energy Table on the facing page to find out. Young teenagers normally require 8,000 to 10,000 kJ per day. About half of this is used to keep your body's basic systems running; your heart beating, your lungs breathing, your brain thinking. The rest is used for movement. Eat too little and you won't have enough energy. Eat too much and you will put on mass—about 1 kg for every 35,000 kJ in excess of your normal intake.

Six slices of cake and six bottles of cola would keep you going for a day, but they wouldn't be good for you. You need a *balanced* diet, one that contains the right balance of protein (primary source: meat), carbohydrates (found in bread, potatoes, and grains), fats, and fiber. Small amounts of vitamins and minerals are also needed.

Something to Think About

1. How is the way your body produces energy similar to the way a car gets its energy? How is it different?

2. A group of students did the experiment with the peanut shown on page 376 and found that the water temperature rose 25 °C. How much energy did they get from this peanut?

3. Why must food be dried before measuring its energy content? How would you measure the energy content of milk?

4. In what ways is our calorie-measuring apparatus not very accurate? How could it be improved?

5. Dieters! Look at the Food Energy Table. Suppose you had the following choices for dinner: A boiled potato or french fries, an apple or a piece of apple pie, green salad or carrots, an egg or meat, a roll or a slice of bread. You could top it off with a cookie or a piece of cake. Which would you choose? Would it make much of a difference to the balance of your diet?

6. What are your favorite foods? Add up the kilojoules contained in a single serving of your five favorite foods. Compare your results with those obtained by other students. Do you have "high energy" or "low energy" tastes?

---

in the food, and the substance does not have enough energy to combust. To measure the energy content of milk, you would first need to turn it into dry powder.

4. Possible responses may include: Some heat escapes from the flame. Some of the heat from the flame itself, rather than from the burning peanut, may be causing the temperature to rise. Some heat escapes from the can and the water. It takes some heat to warm up the can. The water in the can may be hotter in some places than in others. The accuracy of the apparatus could be improved by stirring the water con-

stantly and placing a lid on the can.

5. Students' answers may vary but should indicate an understanding of the importance of a balanced diet and demonstrate an ability to calculate the energy content of food. The choices here might not change the balance of the diet, but certain choices have a much higher energy content, possibly well over a person's energy needs.

6. Answers will vary depending on the foods each student chooses to evaluate. You may wish to use the questions and student responses as a springboard for a discussion of good nutritional practices.

The Food Energy Table

Food (Single Serving)	Mass in Grams	Energy in Kilojoules
Apple (1 medium-size)	100	380
Bacon (3 crisp strips)	25	650
Banana (1 medium-size)	125	440
Beans, canned	130	670
Bread (1 slice)	23	250
Bread roll	38	400
Butter (1 pat)	10	300
Cake, plain, iced	100	1550
Candy bar	30	550
Carrots, cooked	100	130
Cereal, cornflakes, etc.	25	400
Cereal, puffed	13	220
Cheese	30	460
Cookies (3 small or 1 large)	25	500
Corn (1 small ear)	100	380
Egg (1 large)	50	340
Fish	100	800
Fruit juice	180	380
Hot dog	50	630
Ice cream	100	890
Jam	20	230
Meat	100	800-1000
Milk	250	670
Orange (1 medium-size)	150	320
Peanut butter	16	380
Pie	160	1700
Potatoes, boiled	100	270
Potatoes, fried	100	1160
Potato chips	20	480
Salad dressing	15	260
Salad, green	70	40
Soft drink	240	450
Soup, canned	185	100-540
Spaghetti	100	320
Sugar	12	190
Tomato (1 medium)	150	150
Vegetables, green	100	100
Waffle	75	860

Which food is the best "energy bargain"? the worst?

Assessment

1. Suggest that students make posters to illustrate what a joule is, and how many joules are needed to raise 1 g of water 1°C. Encourage students to be creative. Their posters can be either serious or humorous. They may wish to draw cartoons. *(A joule is the amount of energy used to raise a 100-g mass 1 m. It takes 4.2 J to raise the temperature of 1 g of water 1°C.)*

2. Suggest to students that they might enjoy working in small groups to prepare a TV commercial that focuses on the energy content of various foods. Calculations of the energy content should be part of the presentation. Provide time for students to present their commercials to the class.

Extension

1. For two weeks, have students keep track of the foods they eat on a daily basis. Ask them to show, in chart form, the food groups that these foods represent. Invite them to analyze their charts and make some suggestions of foods they should add and foods they should delete. They should also calculate their daily energy intake in joules.

2. For several days, have students keep track of their energy expenditures. *(The library can help students find information on energy amounts used for various activities.)* Have students compare their energy intake to their energy expenditures.

Heat 379

Answers to
Challenge Your Thinking

1. Answers will vary, but one response would be to point out that if heat is a fluid, then it should exist in a finite amount. The heat produced by friction is inexhaustible. The third statement can be disputed on the grounds that if the "caloric" were a liquid, it would not be able to move through solid objects. Heat can move through solid objects.

2. One approach would be to burn a sample of each wood, (the same dollar amount for each), using a set amount of water, and then measure the increase in temperature of the water. The wood that gives the greatest temperature increase gives the most heat per dollar.

1. Caloric Quest!

It was only 200 years ago that scientists thought that heat was a weightless fluid called "caloric." It was a neat theory because it explained so many things:

"When you rub two things together the 'caloric' is released and they get hotter."

"When you burn something, it breaks up and the 'caloric' escapes."

"When you heat the end of a metal rod, the 'caloric' flows from the hot end to the cold end."

You are transported back to those days in a time machine. Imagine yourself having an argument with those scientists about what causes burning. Write a report of your experience. This is your chance to become world famous!

2. Softwood or Hardwood?
The price of softwood is $70 a cord and the price of hardwood is $100 a cord. Three friends are trying to decide which to buy.

Daniel: *I think we should buy softwood. You get more energy for your money.*
Lucinda: *No! No! That's not fair! Hardwood is heavier.*
Nestor: *It probably makes no difference.*

But does it? Can you design a simple home experiment to show which type of wood gives more heat per dollar?

7 How Heat Gets Around

Giving Heat a Helping Hand

Dozens of times every day you experience heat moving from one place to another. Sometimes you want to help it on its way. Sometimes you want to slow it down. Let's talk about it!

In the kitchen, for instance, you want heat to move from the stove to the food in the pot. But you do not want heat to move from the pot through the handle to your hands.

In winter, you want heat from the radiator or heater to move throughout the room. However, you do not want to lose heat to the outside through the windows and walls, as you saw in Unit 6.

On a sunny winter day, the sun's rays heat the rooms through the windows, but at night, you close the drapes to keep heat in.

When you go outside on a cold day, you may bundle up in a hat, a coat, and gloves to help retain body heat. In the summer, you tend to wear light-colored clothes to reflect the sun's rays and help keep you cool.

LESSON 7

✳ Getting Started

The lesson begins by having students think about and discuss their daily experiences with the way heat travels from one place or object to another. *Exploration 9* then provides students with an opportunity to observe the three different ways in which heat flows. A discussion of conduction, convection, and radiation follows, in which students are encouraged to apply these concepts to their everyday experiences with heat. The lesson concludes by having students examine an analogy of heat travel to help them clarify and review what they have learned.

Main Ideas

1. Heat always flows from a hotter area to a cooler area.
2. Conduction occurs when heat flows through a substance.
3. Convection occurs when heat travels as a result of the movement of the material that is heated.
4. Radiation occurs when heat travels through empty space or through a transparent material, without heating the space or material between the heat source and the heated object.

✳ Teaching Strategies

Giving Heat a Helping Hand

After students have read page 381, involve them in a discussion of the examples of heat moving from one place to another. Encourage students to offer examples of their own. Help students reach the conclusion that people use the movement of heat in many different ways.
(Continues on next page)

LESSON 7 ORGANIZER

Objectives

By the end of the lesson, students should be able to:
1. Identify the direction in which heat flows.
2. Explain how conduction, convection, and radiation differ.

Process Skills

observing, measuring, investigating, comparing

New Terms

Conduction—heat transfer by direct contact between heated particles.

(Organizer continues on next page)

(Teaching Strategies continued)

After students have read page 382, direct their attention to the illustration at the top of the page. Help them to recognize that the flow of heat and the flow of water are similar in that they both flow through air and fluids. But heat, unlike water, can also flow through solids and empty space.

Introduce the terms *temperature hill* and *temperature valley*. A temperature hill is an area of high temperature. A temperature valley is an area of low temperature. Heat will flow from a temperature hill into a temperature valley, similar to the way water would flow from a hill to a valley.

Heat always flows from hotter areas to cooler areas. How is the flow of heat like the flow of water? What might a "temperature hill" be? Look at the illustration below for clues. How is it different?

Heat can travel through solids, liquids, gases, and even empty space. The way it travels through solids is generally quite different from the way it travels through liquids or gases. And the way it travels through empty space is different from the way it travels through solids, liquids, or gases.

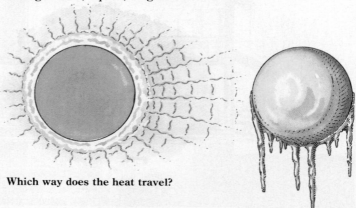

Which way does the heat travel?

(Organizer continued)

Convection—when heat is carried throughout a liquid or a gas by circulation as a result of being heated.

Radiation—heat travel through empty space or through a transparent material, without heating the material that it has passed through.

Materials

Exploration 9
Experiment 1: container of water, metal spoon, craft stick, hot plate, watch or clock with second hand, safety goggles
Experiment 2: spoonful of instant coffee granules, 2 thermometers, container of water, alcohol lamp, matches, safety goggles
Experiment 3: lamp with a 300-watt light bulb, square of glass, square of cardboard the same size as the glass, modeling clay

Science Discovery Videodisc

Disc 2, Image and Activity Bank, 7–7

Time Required

one class period

How Heat Flows

These three experiments investigate the different ways in which heat flows. Observe how heat travels in each of the experiments. In your Journal, write down the differences you see among the three ways that heat travels.

Experiment 1
You Will Need

• a container of water
• a metal spoon
• a craft stick

What to Do

Boil the water. Put the spoon and stick in the boiling water. After 30 seconds, feel the tops of the spoon and the stick. What do you observe? How do you explain your observations?

Experiment 2
You will Need

• a spoonful of instant coffee granules
• 2 thermometers
• a container of water
• an alcohol lamp

What to Do

Arrange the experiment as shown in the illustration below.
Watch the granules.
Watch the thermometer readings. What is happening? How do you explain your observations?

Experiment 3
You Will Need

• a 300-watt light bulb
• a square of glass
• a square of cardboard the same size as the glass

What to Do

Arrange the experiment as shown in the illustration below.
Do you feel the heat of the light bulb through the glass and the cardboard?
Remove the cardboard. Do you feel the heat now?
Does the glass get hot? Have you an explanation for your observations?

Which Type of Heat Travel?

Call on a volunteer to read items *a*, *b*, and *c*. Pause after each one and have students discuss how it relates to the corresponding activity. Have them identify the medium through which the heat flowed. (*Experiment 1, the spoon; Experiment 2, the water; Experiment 3, the air, glass, and cardboard.*)

In response to item *b*: air is a common example of a gas through which heat flows by convection.

Answers to

In-Text Questions

Students should realize that food in a pot gets warm by conduction and convection. Heat flows in an oven by conduction, convection, and radiation; in a toaster by radiation; and in a microwave, food is heated by radiation. A bed becomes warm by the conduction of body heat. Water is made hot by convection.

Answers to

A Problem for Mike and Sue

In the first cartoon, Mike can use the passengers to pass the package to Sue (conduction); in the second cartoon, Mike can take the package to Sue (convection); in the third cartoon, Mike can throw the package to Sue (radiation).

✷ *Follow Up*

Assessment

1. Ask students to prepare posters or a mural to show how conduction, convection, and radiation can be compared to the way a football is moved around a playing field. Hint: students should think of the words passing, kicking, handing off, and running. (*Passing or kicking represents radiation, handing the football from player to player represents conduction, and running with the football represents convection.*)

Which Type of Heat Travel?

In each of the experiments you did, heat traveled in a different way:

(a) In Experiment 1, heat traveled through a solid material. Heat travel from one substance to another is called **conduction.**

(b) In Experiment 2, heat was carried throughout the liquid as the liquid circulated as a result of being heated. This method of heat travel is called **convection.** (Heat can also travel through a gas by convection—can you think of an example?)

(c) In Experiment 3, heat traveled through space or through a transparent material without heating the space or the transparent material. This method of heat travel is called **radiation.**

Now apply these ideas to your everyday experience. How does food in a pot get warm? How do other appliances in the kitchen—oven, toaster, microwave, for example—heat food? How does your bed become warm? How is the water made hot for your bath or shower?

Can you think of other examples where heat flows?

A Problem for Mike and Sue

Here is another way to look at the three methods of heat travel.

Mike, who is at the front of the bus, wants to pass a package to Sue, who is at the back of the bus. However, Mike is blocked by people standing in the aisle. How can Mike get the package to Sue?

In this case, there are no passengers between Mike and Sue. How can Mike get the package to Sue?

Now, the aisle between Mike and Sue is roped off. How can Mike get the package to Sue?

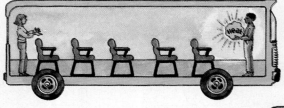

Which cartoon represents:

(a) heat travel by convection?

(b) heat travel by radiation?

(c) heat travel by conduction?

2. Have students make a list of items in their homes that transfer heat. Ask them to identify the ways in which the heat is transferred.

Extension

1. Invite students to research different types of ovens (conventional, convection, and microwave). Ask them to compare how the ovens work and how effective each one is.

2. Challenge students to illustrate the following:
   • Heat traveling from a flame to the food in a frying pan by conduction.
   • A water heater heating water by convection.
   • Infrared rays from a heat lamp warming a person by radiation.

8 Conduction—Heat Travel Through a Material

Scientists think that all matter is made of incredibly tiny particles. The travel of heat along (or through) a material, from the particles of one substance to the particles of the next, is conduction. Does this remind you of Mike and Sue's first situation? Each passenger was like a particle in a solid.

Watching Heat Travel Through a Solid: A Demonstration

1. Cut a strip of aluminum from an aluminum pie plate.

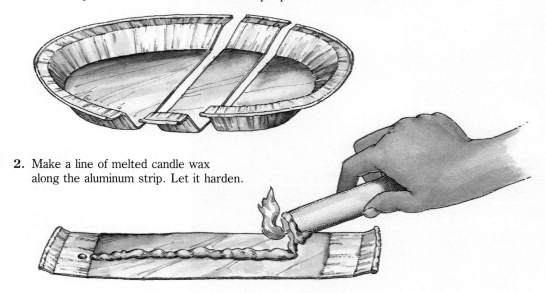

2. Make a line of melted candle wax along the aluminum strip. Let it harden.

3. Hold the aluminum strip with a clothespin. Heat one end of the strip with the candle. Explain what happens next.

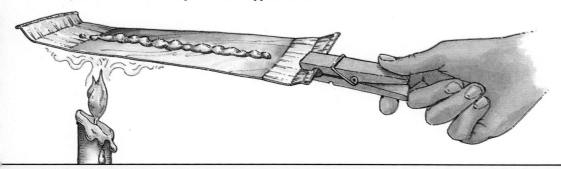

LESSON 8 ORGANIZER

Objectives

By the end of the lesson, students should be able to:
1. Describe the difference between a conductor and an insulator.
2. Identify factors that determine the conduction rate of heat through a solid.
3. Describe ways in which insulators can be made more effective.
4. Identify several materials that are good conductors and several materials that are good insulators.

Process Skills

observing, measuring, predicting, investigating

New Terms

Insulators—materials that slow down the flow of heat.

(Organizer continues on next page)

✳ Getting Started

This lesson takes a more thorough look at how heat travels by conduction. Through a series of activities, students explore the factors that affect the conduction rate of heat. Then they examine a number of materials to determine whether or not they are good conductors. Several seemingly mysterious activities provide students with an opportunity to apply their knowledge of conduction.

Main Ideas

1. Some materials are better conductors of heat than others.
2. The conduction rate of a material is affected by its composition and size, and by the temperature of and distance from the heat source.
3. Increasing the thickness of an insulator increases its effectiveness.

✳ Teaching Strategies

Remind students that in the previous lesson they learned about the three ways heat travels. Write the terms *conduction, convection,* and *radiation* on the chalkboard. Call on volunteers to define each term. Ask them to provide an example of how the term applies to the transfer of heat. Then have students read the lesson introduction.

Watching Heat Travel Through a Solid

Have students perform the demonstration in groups of five or six. As students observe the wax melting, encourage them to explain what they think is happening. *(Heat is being conducted along the aluminum strip from the source of heat.)*

How Fast Is Conduction?

Have students read the paragraphs silently. Then involve them in a discussion of personal experiences with the conduction of heat through different kinds of materials. The factors that affect the travel of heat through a solid include thickness of material and how good a conductor it is.

Exploration 10

Have students work in groups of three or four to complete each of the activities. Then involve them in a discussion of their observations and conclusions.

Station 1

For the most accurate results, the thumbtacks should all be the same distance from the end of the rods. Students should observe that the order of conductivity from the fastest to the slowest is copper, brass, iron, and glass. They should conclude that some materials conduct heat more rapidly than others.

How Fast is Conduction?

Dip a spoon into a cup of hot chocolate. Notice how quickly the heat travels from the hot chocolate up the spoon. Put on a pair of oven mitts, and then remove a hot pan from the oven. The heat still travels from the pan to your fingers but not as quickly this time—otherwise you would burn yourself lifting the pan!

Heat travels at different rates. What factors affect the speed of heat travel in a solid?

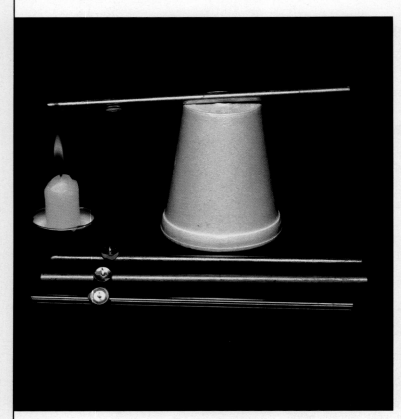

A Closer Look at Conduction

Spend 10 minutes at each of the three stations described on this and the following page. In your Journal, record your observations and then answer the questions for each station.

For each station, write one sentence describing your discovery.

Station 1

Question: Do different materials conduct heat at different rates?

You Will Need

• 4 rods: one each of copper, brass, glass, and iron
• a candle
• thumb tacks
• a Styrofoam cup

What to Do

Attach a thumb tack to each rod with candle wax, and then arrange the apparatus as shown. Make sure each thumb tack is the same distance from the end of the rod. Time how long it takes the thumb tack to drop.

Repeat, using another rod made of glass, brass, or iron. Do all materials conduct heat at the same rate?

(Organizer continued)

Materials

Watching Heat Travel Through a Solid: aluminum pie pan, scissors, candle, matches, clothespin, safety goggles
Exploration 10
Station 1: 4 rods—one each of copper, brass, glass, and iron; candle, thumbtacks, plastic-foam coffee cup, matches, watch or clock with a second hand, safety goggles

Station 2: 2 iron rods of different diameters, 2 plastic-foam cups, 2 candles, 2 thumbtacks, matches, watch or clock with second hand, safety goggles
Station 3: candles, thumbtacks, plastic-foam cups, all sorts of metal rods, matches, a clock or watch with a second hand, safety goggles
The Mystery of the Scorched Paper: a copper rod, a wooden rod of the same diameter, masking tape, an alcohol lamp, matches, safety goggles

Station 2

Question: Does the thickness of the material make a difference?

You Will Need

- 2 iron rods of different thicknesses
- 2 Styrofoam cups
- 2 candles
- 2 thumb tacks

What to Do

Make a setup like that shown below. Before you start, make a prediction. Do you think heat will travel faster along a thick rod or a thin rod? Now try it and find out.

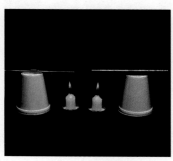

Station 3

Question: Can you make a 30-second timer?

You are stranded on a desert island and the battery in your watch is dying. But you do have a supply of candles, thumb tacks, Styrofoam cups, and all sorts of metal rods.

Compare your timer with those of your classmates.

Thinking About and Using Your Findings

Here are some questions to help you check your understanding. Try them all!

1. On the basis of your observations, which substances are good conductors of heat? Which substances are poor conductors of heat?

2. How can you apply your findings to explain the construction of cooking utensils? What material would you make a pot from? How about the handle?

3. Ten similar rods made of different materials were placed in water at 70 °C. At the end of 1 minute, the top of each rod was felt. Here are the results:

straw	cold
copper	hot
wood	cold
plastic	cold
brass	hot
rubber	cold
iron	hot
lead	hot
glass	cold
aluminum	hot

Which kind of material appears to be a good conductor of heat? There are many everyday products that make use of this kind of material. Can you name five that you have used?

The Mystery of the Extinguished Candle: electrical wire about 40 cm long, candle, matches, jar lid, wire cutters, wire strippers, safety goggles

Two Terrific Tricks to Try
Trick 1: aluminum screen about 8-cm square, candle, clothespin, matches, safety goggles
Trick 2: wooden matches, two forks, safety goggles

A Classroom Demonstration: a number of objects, thermometer for each object, masking tape

Teacher's Resource Binder

Activity Worksheets 7–5 and 7–7
Resource Worksheet 7–6

Science Discovery Videodisc

Disc 2, Image and Activity Bank, 7–8

Time Required

four class periods

Station 2

Again, the most accurate results will be achieved if the thumbtacks are the same distance from the ends of the rods. Have students wait several minutes after the thumbtacks have been attached to the rods to allow the wax to cool and harden. Students should observe that heat is conducted more rapidly through the thick rod than through the thin rod. They should conclude that the thickness of a material affects the rate at which it conducts heat.

Station 3

A timer can be made by determining where to attach a thumbtack to a metal rod using wax so that the wax will melt and the thumbtack will fall in 30 seconds. Students should recognize that the thumbtack will be placed at different positions on rods made of different materials.

Another method of making a timer would be to determine the length of a rod that became heated to a certain temperature in 30 seconds and then cut the rod to that length. You may wish to have students try out their ideas to see which design works the best and produces the most accurate timer.

Answers to

Thinking About and Using Your Findings

You may wish to have students write their responses to the questions in their Journals, or involve the class in a discussion of each one.

1. Good conductors include copper, brass, and iron. Glass is a poor conductor.

2. The container of a cooking utensil is made from a good conductor, such as copper, iron, or aluminum, so that it will easily and quickly transfer heat from the burner to the food that is being cooked. The handle is made from a poor conductor, such as plastic or wood, so that a person can use it to pick up the utensil without being burned.

3. The results of the experiment suggest that metals are good conductors of heat.

   Responses may include: cooking utensils, an iron, a waffle iron, a pancake griddle, a soldering gun, and so on.

(Answers continue on next page)

4. Most students will probably choose the plastic-foam cup as the one they would prefer to hold. How hot a cup is will depend partly on its thickness. Some students may recognize that the more porous the cup is, the less hot it will be. (This is because air is trapped within the pores, and air is a poor conductor of heat.) Students should realize that poor conductors make the best containers for hot liquids. The order for the cups from coolest to hottest (least conductive to most conductive) is: plastic-foam, china, glass, paper, metal.

5. Air is a poor conductor of heat. Small air pockets in wool, fur, and feathers help to keep heat from passing through these materials. As a result, body heat becomes trapped between a person's body and a garment made from wool, fur, or feathers.

6. Students should recognize that some of the heat traveling down the rods would be conducted into the can because the rods are resting on the can as they pass through the holes. Since the rods all touch in the center, heat can travel from one rod to another. Because the thumbtacks are far from the heat source, some of the heat traveling through the rods will be dissipated into the air before it reaches the thumbtacks.

Accept all reasonable ideas for improving Pat's experiment. Some suggestions might include: making a tripod out of a material that does not conduct heat easily, such as wood; not allowing the rods and bars to touch (perhaps by using a larger heat source); and placing the thumbtacks closer to the source of heat.

Answer to caption: Direct students' attention to the picture of the lambs and call on a volunteer to read the question. Help students to recognize that the lambs' coats are very thin. There is too much space between the wool, allowing the lambs' body heat to create convection currents and escape into the air. As a result, the lambs' body heat is carried away.

4. A friend has just made some instant soup for you by pouring boiling water into each of the cups shown at right. Which cup would you prefer to have to hold? Will the thickness of the cup make a difference? What other factors might make a difference? Now list the cups in order of preference. Test your guesses.

5. Woolly sweaters, fur, and feathers are very light yet warm. Why do you think these materials are so warm?

6. To measure conduction rates, Pat made a clever device from a large juice can. She placed rods of different materials, lengths, and thicknesses through a tripod made from the can, so that the ends came together in the center. She used some candle wax to attach a thumb tack to the other end of each rod. Then she placed an alcohol lamp under the tripod so it would heat the inner edge of each rod and bar equally.

Why do you think these lambs need plastic coats to keep warm?

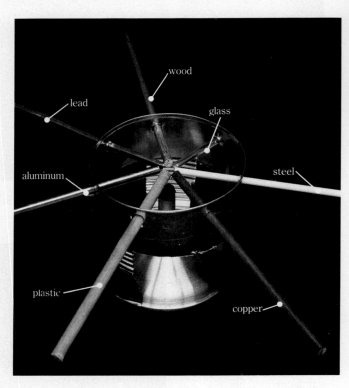

Pat had many difficulties, and her teacher said that the class could not rely on Pat's results. Can you improve Pat's experiment?

Mysterious Events

The Mystery of the Scorched Paper

Join a copper rod or pipe and a wooden rod of the same diameter together by wrapping one layer of paper or masking tape around them. Heat the joint very slowly over an alcohol lamp until the paper is scorched. Which side of the paper is scorched?

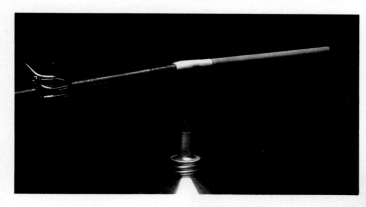

The Mystery of the Extinguished Candle

Strip about 30 cm of the insulation from some electrical wire about 40 cm long. Make the stripped part into a closely spiralling coil, and hold onto the insulated part. Place the coil over a lighted candle. What happens? Light the candle again, but this time hold the coil above the flame until it glows. Now slowly lower it. Explain the results in your Journal.

Two Terrific Tricks to Try

Lower a piece of aluminum screen slowly over the flame. What happens? Why?

Place a wooden match between two prongs of a fork. Light the match. Can you get the whole match to burn? Try other matches, placing them in different positions between the prongs. After observing what happens, can you explain the "trick"?

Mysterious Events

The seemingly mysterious results of these activities provide students with an interesting way to apply their knowledge of conductivity to explain what they are observing.

The Mystery of the Scorched Paper

As an alternative heat source, you may wish to use a hot plate. Caution students to hold the rods well above the heat source so that the paper will not catch on fire. They should observe that the paper next to the wood scorches first. They should conclude that this happens because the copper conducts the heat away from the heat source more rapidly than the wood does.

The Mystery of the Extinguished Candle

Students should observe that the candle goes out when the unheated coil is placed over it, but remains lit when the coil has been heated first. They should conclude that the candle goes out because the copper coil lowers the candle's temperature below its combustion point by conducting heat away from it. When the coil has already been heated, its capacity to conduct more heat is limited.

Two Terrific Tricks to Try

Students should observe that when the screen is placed over the flame, it pushes the flame down. The flame does not burn above the screen. They should conclude that the heat from the flame is being conducted out over the surface of the screen.

It is almost impossible to get the entire match to burn because the prongs of the fork conduct heat away from the flame. However, some students may realize that if you heat the fork first, the match may be able to burn completely.

Would You Believe: The Same Temperature?

A Classroom Demonstration

Pass the objects around the classroom and invite students to hold them against their cheeks for a few seconds. Encourage students to identify which of the objects feel the warmest and which feel the coolest. After 10 minutes have passed, invite some of the students to measure the temperature of the objects. They should discover that all of the objects are the same temperature.

At this point, divide the class into small groups to brainstorm explanations for their observations. Point out that they should be looking for qualities in each item that correlate with their perceived temperatures. That is, metals were perceived to be the coldest; plastic-foam cups were perceived to be the warmest. After students have had time to brainstorm their ideas, reassemble the class. Call on a spokesperson from each group to present the group's ideas. Help students to recognize that good conductors of heat feel colder to the touch than do poor conductors.

Explanation Please

Have students return to their groups to design experiments to test their explanations. At this point, you may wish to allow students to carry out these experiments and then report on their findings.

Answer to

In-Text Question

The following is one possible way of testing the hypothesis.

Heat a variety of materials (a metal cup, a piece of wood, a piece of glass) in an oven set at body temperature (37°C). Remove each object from the oven and hold it against your cheek. Caution students to use care when handling objects from an oven. Record how each object feels. *(All of the objects should feel the same.)* Now repeat the experiment by setting the oven at 50°C. Again, remove the objects and hold them against your

Would You Believe: The Same Temperature?

The activity below looks quite simple. There's really not much to it. However, you may find it to be quite a brain teaser!

A Classroom Demonstration

Leave a number of objects made of different materials in the classroom overnight, so that they all reach the same temperature. For instance, you might use:

- glass (cup or beaker)
- foamed plastic (Styrofoam cup)
- ordinary plastic (pencil case)
- metal (tin can)
- paper (notebook)

You might tape a thermometer to each object to make sure that all are at the same temperature.

Now hold each object against your cheek. Do some feel warmer than others? How is it that some of the objects feel warmer, even though the thermometer shows they are all at the same temperature?

cheek. Allow some time to elapse between different objects so that your cheek will return to its normal temperature. Record how each feels. *(The metal will feel the hottest, followed by the glass and the wood.)* The experiment shows that good conductors transfer heat more readily to the body than do materials that are poor conductors.

Explanation Please

How do you explain the results of the demonstration? What do you think causes this effect?

Design an experiment to test your ideas. Collect the materials you need. Perform the experiment. Record the results in your Journal.

Good luck!

Slowing the Flow of Heat

A Competition: Save the Ice Cube!

Who can prevent an ice cube from melting completely for the longest time?

Invent a way to protect an ordinary ice cube so that it stays frozen for the longest possible time (without using a freezer, of course). Use any materials you wish. Write up your plan. Record the size of your ice cube, the materials you used, the methods you used, and the length of time you were able to save some portion of the ice cube.

┌─────────────────────────────────────┐
│   · Certificate ·   │
│   │
│   'Save the Ice Cube'   │
│   │
│   I hereby certify that   │
│   _____, │
│   NAME   │
│   │
│   on _____ at _____ hours, │
│   DATE   TIME   │
│   │
│   wrapped an ice cube the size of: │
│   │
│   _____ │
│   │
│   and entrusted the same to me for safekeeping. │
│   The last time I witnessed any ice present was │
│   │
│   on _____ at _____ hours │
│   DATE   TIME   │
│   │
│   Signed _____ │
└─────────────────────────────────────┘

You do not always want to improve the flow of heat. Sometimes you want to slow it down. For example, you want to slow down the flow of heat from your house to the outside in the winter. In the summer the reverse is true. You would also want to keep heat from flowing too quickly from a hot pan to your hand when you pick it up. The list goes on and on. Materials that slow down the flow of heat have a name. They are called *insulators*. Think of as many examples of insulators as you can.

A Competition: Save the Ice Cube!

If students perform this activity at home, have them write a report of what they did and what their results were. Invite several students to share their reports with the class. Then involve all class members in a discussion of the procedures and results.

If you wish to hold the competition in the classroom, you may want to make the following materials available: ice cubes, newspaper, paper towels, cotton and wool cloth, plastic-foam, and containers made of different materials (metal, glass, plastic-foam). To make this a fair test, use ice cubes that are about the same size. As students perform their experiments, encourage them to keep careful notes on their procedures and their results.

✳ Follow Up

Assessment

1. Ask students to explain the following situation based on their knowledge of heat:
   Hot water pipes are surrounded by a wrapping of fiberglass wool. Then they are wrapped with an aluminum-foil cover. The aluminum foil feels cool to the touch. *(The fiberglass wrapping keeps in the heat. The aluminum foil feels cool because it conducts heat from your hand.)*
2. Have students imagine that they are going on a hiking trip high in the mountains. The weather will be cold. Have them make a list of things they will take to protect themselves from the weather. Next to each item, ask them to write a brief explanation of how it will slow the flow of heat away from the body, thus helping to keep the body warm.

Extension

Have students take a survey of common, everyday materials to find out which are good conductors of heat and which are poor conductors. Have them share what they discover by organizing their information into a chart.

LESSON 9

✴ Getting Started

Through a series of eight activities, students observe and analyze how heat travels by convection. Also, they solve eight word problems in which they apply what they have learned about convection.

Main Ideas

1. Hot or warm air tends to rise, and cold or cool air tends to fall.
2. In a liquid or gas system, convection currents will occur if the temperature at the top of the system is colder than the temperature at the bottom of the system.

✴ Teaching Strategies

Point out that in this lesson students will learn how heat travels by convection. Ask: Through what kinds of substances does heat travel by convection? *(liquids and gases)* Call on a volunteer to explain how convection works. *(Convection occurs when heat travels as a result of the movement of the material being heated.)*

9

Convection—Heat Travel by Currents

You may recall from page 384 that heat travel in fluids (either liquids or gases) occurs largely by convection. In the Exploration that follows, you will discover more about convection.

Exploring Convection

Form a small group and choose one of the following activities. Practice it, figure out how it works, and then present it to the other groups. Let them ask questions about it until they understand how it works.

Activity 1
You Will Need

- a large beaker or clear bowl of cold water
- a small bottle filled with hot, colored water

- a two-holed stopper with two glass tubes inserted—one tube should almost touch the bottom of the bottle and the other should poke just inside the bottle. **Be Careful:** *Your teacher should be the one who inserts the tubes into the stoppers.*

What to Do

Carefully lower the small bottle into the cold water, keeping your fingers over the ends of the glass tubes as shown in the photo. Take your fingers away. Trace the direction of any currents formed. What do you think causes these currents?

LESSON 9 ORGANIZER

Objectives

By the end of the lesson, students should be able to:
1. Recognize that the flow of heat through a liquid or gas can be accomplished by convection.
2. Explain the formation of convection currents in liquids and gases.
3. Demonstrate that hot air is lighter than cold air.
4. Identify examples of convection currents that occur in nature and in everyday life.

Process Skills

observing, predicting, investigating, illustrating

New Terms

Materials

Exploration 11
Activity 1: beaker or clear bowl, water, small bottle, food coloring, two-holed stopper, 2 glass tubes

Activity 2: large bottle, birthday-type small candle, aluminum foil, 10 cm of natural-fiber rope, watch with a second hand, wire, matches, wire cutters, safety goggles
Activity 3: heavy aluminum foil, straight pin, thread, candle, matches, metric ruler, scissors, lamp with 300-W bulb, safety goggles

---

Activity 2

You Will Need

- a large bottle
- a birthday-type candle
- a T-shaped piece of aluminum foil
- 10 cm of natural-fiber rope
- a watch with a second hand
- wire

What to Do

Use the wire to lower a burning candle into the bottle. Measure how long the candle burns. Allow fresh air to enter the bottle. Repeat, with the foil placed in the mouth of the bottle as in the illustration. Insert the foil quickly after the lighted candle is inserted.

Light your piece of rope and check for currents at points A and B, using the smoke.

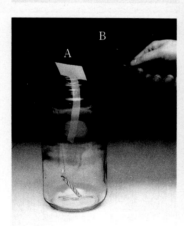

Activity 3

You Will Need

- a circular piece of heavy aluminum foil, 15 cm in diameter
- thread
- a candle

What to Do

Make a pinhole in the center of the foil, then cut it in a spiral. Hang the spiral from a knotted thread.

Place the spiral in several locations: over a candle (not too close!), to the side of the candle, above a lighted light bulb, over a radiator, near the bottom of a window, in different places in the classroom or schoolyard.

Exploration 11

Set up one work station for each of the activities in the Exploration. Assign one activity to each group of students. Have each group demonstrate their activity to the class as a whole.

Activity 1

To avoid injury, you might want to insert the glass tubes in the stoppers for your class. Arrange the glass tubes in the stopper so that one is sticking up higher than the other.

Observation: A current of colored water flowing from the taller tube back into the shorter tube.

Conclusion: The hot liquid in the bottle rises out of the taller tube; the cold liquid in the bowl flows into the shorter tube.

Activity 2

Instruct students to be careful when cutting the rope.

Observation: The burning candle goes out when the foil is not in the neck of the bottle; it stays lit when the foil is in place.

Conclusion: Without the foil, the heated air in the bottle rises quickly, taking the remaining air with it. With the foil in place, the hot air escapes out one side of the foil while colder fresh air flows in on the other side.

Students use the smoke from the rope as a current detector. They can tell which direction the convection current is moving by the direction that the smoke moves.

Activity 3

Observation: The spiral turns clockwise by rising air currents and counterclockwise by falling air currents.

Conclusion: The air pushing on the slanted flat surfaces of the spiral gives a push sideways, causing it to rotate.

Activity 4: 2 beakers, water, ice cube tray, food coloring, wire, wire cutters, freezer

Activity 5: cardboard box, clear plastic wrap, candle, metal lid, 2 corks, 10 cm of natural-fiber rope, matches, scissors, safety goggles

Activity 6: 2 ice cubes, 2 beakers of water, wire, 2 alcohol lamps, matches, wire cutters, safety goggles

Activity 7: 2 equal-sized cans with a hole drilled through the bottom, wooden dowel, string, board, nail, hammer, books, candle, matches, safety goggles

Activity 8: candle, matches, metric ruler, safety goggles

Analysis Please! Journal

Teacher's Resource Binder

Graphic Organizer Transparencies 7–5 and 7–6

Science Discovery Videodisc

Disc 2, Image and Activity Bank, 7–9

Time Required

two class periods

Activity 4

Be sure students understand that they are to place one ice cube in each beaker.

Observation: The water in the beaker with the floating ice cube becomes colored throughout.

Conclusion: This occurs because the cold water from the melting ice cube sinks, and mixes with the water throughout the beaker.

Observation: The water in the beaker with the sunken ice cube becomes colored only at the bottom of the beaker.

Conclusion: This occurs because the cold water from the melting ice is already at the bottom of the beaker and therefore does not mix with the rest of the water.

Activity 5

Students should light the rope so that it gives off smoke and so that it can be used as a convection-current indicator. Encourage them to try different combinations of opened and closed holes.

Observation: The following diagrams show the air currents created by two different combinations of openings in the box.

Conclusion: The hot air above the candle rises and escapes from the box, pulling cold air in to take its place.

Activity 6

You may wish to have students write their predictions on a slip of paper or in their Journals. Then have them complete the activity.

Observation: The floating ice cube melts first.

Conclusion: This happens because the hot water from the bottom of the beaker rises. Ask students to reveal their predictions (and the reasoning behind their predictions) to the class.

Activity 4
You Will Need

- 2 beakers
- 2 ice cube trays
- food coloring
- wire
- water

What to Do

Make a tray of ice cubes using water dyed very dark with food coloring.

Wrap the wire around one of the ice cubes to make it sink. Place each ice cube into a beaker at the same time. Observe how the color spreads. Draw diagrams of the currents that develop.

Activity 5
You Will Need

- a cardboard box (such as a shoe box)
- clear plastic wrap
- a candle
- 2 corks
- 10 cm of natural-fiber rope

What to Do

Arrange the apparatus as shown. Observe the candle flame and the direction of smoke as you remove one or two corks. Try different combinations of open holes. This activity shows one of the most important principles in the formation of convection currents.

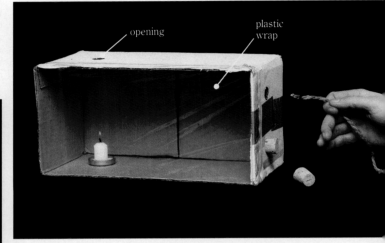

opening   plastic wrap

Activity 6
You Will Need

- 2 ice cubes
- 2 beakers of water
- wire
- 2 alcohol lamps

What to Do

Wrap some wire around one ice cube to make it sink. Place it in a beaker of water along with a plain ice cube as shown on the left. Predict which ice cube will melt first. How do you explain what happens?

Activity 7
You Will Need

• 2 tin cans
• a wooden dowel
• string
• a board with a nail in the end
• a textbook
• a candle

What to Do

Make a simple balance like the one shown on the right. First make sure that your cans are identical, open on one end, and have a hole drilled through the center of the other end. Hang each can from the dowel by threading the string through the hole in one end and tying a knot. Slide the cans back and forth on the dowel until they are balanced.

With a candle, heat the air in one can. Remove the candle. What happens? Let the balance stand for a few moments. Now heat the air under the other can. What happens? Why?

Activity 8
You Will Need

• a candle
• matches

What to Do

Light the candle. Hold your hand 20 cm above it, then hold your hand 20 cm to the side. What do you feel at each position? Try this variation. How close can you put the head of a match to the flame before it catches fire? (**Be Careful:** *Don't burn your fingers!*) Hold matches at different positions around the flame. What is your explanation for what you observe?

Draw a diagram of the candle flame in your Journal. Around it, draw a dotted line showing where the matches caught fire.

Activity 7

Students may substitute a 100-watt bulb for the candle. The cans may be secured to the thread by knotting the ends of the thread so that they will not pass through the holes in the cans.

Observation: As the air in one can becomes heated, the equilibrium of the balance is upset, and the can rises. After the air has had time to return to its original temperature, the balance returns to its original position. The same effect will take place when the air in the other can is heated.

Conclusion: Hot air is lighter than cold air.

Some students may suggest that the hot air rising above the candle pushes up the can. Encourage students to discuss how they could test which conclusion is correct. *(One method would be to suspend the cans, right-side-up, from the string. Hold the candle under the can so that it heats the air inside the can. Another method would be to place the candle inside the upside-down can so that there is practically no current of air rising against the can.)*

Activity 8

Observation: The air is hottest directly above the flame. Students should also observe that matches can be held closest to the bottom of the flame without catching fire.

Conclusion: Cold air is pulled in and around the bottom of the flame as the air that is already there becomes heated and rises.

Answers to
Analysis Please!

You may wish to have students write their responses to the questions in their Journals, or involve the class in a discussion of each question individually.

1. It is probably a good idea for you to demonstrate the activity to students. Student diagrams should look similar to the one below. As shown in the diagram, the air flows more slowly around the bottom of the flame and faster around the top of the flame.

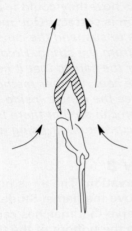

2. You may wish to point out to students that the temperature of water remains more constant than the temperature of land. On a sunny day, the air above the land is warmer than the air above the water. The warmer air above the land rises and cooler air from the water moves in, causing a sea breeze. At night the reverse happens. The land becomes cooler than the water. The warmer air above the water rises and the cooler air from the land moves in to take its place.

3. If the bottle of colored water is cold and the bottle below it is filled with hot water, the colored cold water will sink into the hot water and the color will spread throughout. If the bottle of colored water is hot and the bottle below it is filled with cold water, the hot water will remain where it is and the two will not mix.

Carlo could also have arranged the trick by making the temperature of the water in each bottle the same. In that case, the water will not mix.

Analysis Please!

Hot air rises. Hot liquids rise too. This is why they circulate when heated. You can't always see it happening, however. Here are some problems to help you review what you observed in Exploration 11.

1. In your Journal, draw a diagram showing how you think air flows around a candle. Use longer arrows to show faster air flow and shorter arrows to show slower air flow. Test your model by using a smoking string to reveal the air currents.

2. In the diagram, the air above the ground is heated by the ground, while the air above the water is heated by the water. Copy the diagram into your Journal. Predict the air currents in each scene. How might the pattern change from day to night?

3. Carlo's Trick

Carlo explained to his audience that all four bottles contained water, two of them with blue food coloring added. He then pulled the cards from between the bottles—*abracadabra!* How might he have arranged this trick? In what other way could he have arranged this trick?

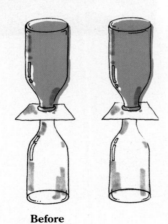

Before   **After**

4. To produce hot water for people in the house to use, water is heated in the boiler and rises to the exchange coil where it gives up its heat to warm the cold water that comes in from the mains. The cooled water in the coil goes back to the boiler where it is heated again.

To heat the house, hot water from the boiler rises to the radiators where it gives up its heat to the air, is cooled, and falls back to the boiler where the water is reheated.

(Answers continue on next page)

4. Here is a model hot water heating system that doesn't need a circulating pump. How does it work?

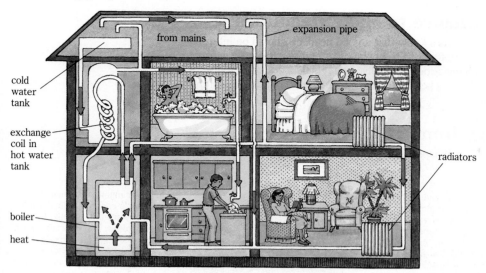

5. Study how this Magic Lamp works. How could you explain to a young child what is happening?

6. Which is the better energy buy: a vertical freezer or a horizontal one? Why?

7. Where would you install an air-conditioning unit: near the floor or near the ceiling?

8. There's a story in the picture below. Can you describe it? What would you do to improve the situation?

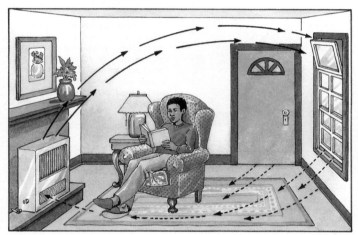

Car Cooling by Convection

Ask an auto mechanic to explain the cooling system of an automobile engine. Then sketch a diagram showing where and how coolant is circulated through the radiator, around the motor, and through the heater of the car.

Car Cooling by Convection

If students do not have access to a mechanic, suggest that they look in an encyclopedia to find out the information.

Answer to

In-Text Question:

The coolant is circulated by a water pump that moves the coolant through the engine where it is heated. It is then taken to the radiator where it is cooled. When the heater is on, a fan forces the air that has been heated by the water around the engine into the car.

☀ *Follow Up*

Assessment

1. Have students make a list of places where convection currents occur in nature and in their lives. *(Answers could include heating a house, cooling a car, and heating the atmosphere.)*
2. Have students draw cartoons to illustrate the difference between conduction and convection. *(Students should convey an understanding that conduction involves heat transfer through direct contact from one heated particle to another, and convection is heat transfer by the spreading out of heated gas or liquid particles.)*

Extension

1. Suggest to students that they make a diagram to show how a ceiling fan is used to distribute heat in a room.
2. Point out to students that when there is a fire in a fireplace, most of the warm air goes up the chimney. Challenge them to think of some improvements in the design of a fireplace so that more of the heat is used to warm the room.

Answers continued

5. The lamp shade rotates as the air heated by the bulb rises and pushes against the vanes attached to the top of the shade.

6. A horizontal freezer is the better energy buy. When a vertical freezer is opened, a large amount of cold air escapes from the bottom while warm air enters at the top. Most of the cold air in a horizontal freezer remains there when the freezer is opened because it is heavier air and does not flow up and out.

7. An air conditioning unit should be installed near the ceiling so that the cold air it generates will sink and spread throughout the room.

8. A convection current has been set up in the room. Cold air enters from around the bottom of the window and door, is heated, rises toward the ceiling, and flows out of the opened window. The situation could be improved by adding insulation around the doors and windows, and by closing the top of the window so that convection currents do not occur.

10 Radiation—Heat in a Hurry

10 Radiation—Heat in a Hurry

Your Chance to Make Headlines!

Newspaper editors know that a good headline should be interesting but also brief and to the point. Pretend you are a newspaper editor. Read this article carefully. Then think of a good headline for each paragraph. The article is about the most important example of radiation.

Energy from a Star

(adapted from *Whence Energy* by Roy Bishop)

_____ ? _____ (1)

We live on a blue and white planet; a small, round, turquoise gem nestled in the black velvet of space. The energy that keeps our planet alive was either present when the earth was formed or has been received from space since that time.

_____ ? _____ (2)

Energy reaches the earth from space in several ways. Meteors streak down through the atmosphere, burning up with great flashes of fire. Cosmic rays bring packets of energy that have traveled far through the universe. At night, we can see the stars sending their light energy to us.

_____ ? _____ (3)

But more than anything else, it is the nearest star that contributes most of the energy we receive from space. Because it is so close, our sun overwhelms the energy contribution from the other stars, so we sometimes forget it is also a star.

_____ ? _____ (4)

On a clear, sunny day, one square meter receives from the sun about the same amount of energy as is given out by a 1000-W electric heater. If you hold your hand up to the heat of the sun, your hand will receive about 14 watts of energy.

_____ ? _____ (5)

The most important immediate use of the sun's energy is the warmth we receive from it. Thanks to the sun, our planet is comfortably warm. Without the sun the temperature of the earth would be almost 300°C lower, or approximately the temperature of the space between the stars. Life could not possibly exist in such intense cold.

THANK YOU!

_____ ? _____ (6)

We also use the sun's energy in many indirect ways, but only after some delay. It can take anywhere from minutes to millions of years for the energy of sunlight to be transformed into a source of energy that can be used to heat our homes. For instance, sunlight causes moisture to evaporate, resulting in rainfall. This rainfall drains into streams and rivers. The rivers are dammed, and the water is forced through turbines to produce electricity. This electricity is used for many purposes: to run motors, to produce light, and to heat our homes, among others.

Getting Started

In this lesson, students examine how heat travels by radiation. They first learn about the sun's energy and its importance to life on earth. The greenhouse effect and the threat it poses to the planet are addressed next. The lesson concludes with a series of activities in which students investigate reflectors, absorbers, and radiators.

Main Ideas

1. The sun is the source of most of the heat energy available to us.
2. The trapping of radiant heat by the earth's atmosphere is called the greenhouse effect.
3. Dark-colored, dull objects are the best absorbers of heat. Light-colored, shiny objects are the poorest absorbers of heat, but they are the best reflectors.
4. Light bulbs and other hot objects radiate heat, which can be reflected and focused.
5. Different colors absorb varying amounts of radiant heat.

Teaching Strategies

Ask students: How is radiation different from conduction and convection? *(Unlike conduction and convection, radiation does not heat the material through which it flows.)* Call on students to suggest examples of radiant heat. *(In Lesson 8, students learned that a light bulb gives off radiant heat. The heat from the sun is also radiant.)*

Primary Source
Description of change: excerpted from *Whence Energy* by Roy Bishop. *Rationale:* adapted to adjust to reading level.

LESSON 10 ORGANIZER

Objectives

By the end of the lesson, students should be able to:
1. Explain how life on earth depends directly and indirectly on the sun's radiant energy.
2. Explain the greenhouse effect and its possible consequences.
3. Identify everyday examples of heat transfer by radiation.
4. Describe radiation, absorption, and reflection in terms of radiant heat.

Process Skills

observing, measuring, investigating, interpreting data

New Terms

Greenhouse effect—the trapping of heat radiated from Earth by atmospheric gases.

Plants also use the energy of the sun to grow. In this form it may take months or longer for the energy of the sun to reach us. Plants are the source of food for many animals. We use both plants and animals as sources of food. People need about 100 J of energy per second, or 2000 nutritional calories per day.

_____?_____ (7)

_____?_____ (8)

When we burn oil, gas, or coal, we are using energy from the sun that was stored long ago. Energy from the sun was captured by plants millions of years ago. These plants were buried and slowly converted into coal, oil, or natural gas. These energy sources will not last forever. There are even fears that most of this energy will be used up within the next century, if not sooner.

_____?_____ (9)

The sun is 150,000,000 kilometers from the earth, but energy from the sun reaches the earth in just 8 minutes! This is heat travel by radiation. As the sun's energy falls on the earth, some heat is reflected back into space—by clouds or snow, for example. But some of the energy is absorbed by the earth, and everything on the surface is warmed. Then, when darkness comes with the setting of the sun, much of this heat is radiated back into space.

The Greenhouse Effect

Have you ever been in a greenhouse on a sunny day? Do you remember noticing how warm it was? Did you wonder why? What happens is that *radiant* energy from the sun passes through the glass of the greenhouse, strikes the ground and the plants, and is absorbed. The plants and ground heat up and then themselves begin to radiate heat energy—but in a slightly different form that cannot easily pass back through the glass, so the heat is trapped!

In many ways the earth behaves like a giant greenhouse. Only in this case, the "glass" of the greenhouse is the earth's atmosphere. Certain atmospheric gases are especially good at slowing the flow of radiant energy from the earth back into space. Carbon dioxide is one of them. Carbon dioxide is produced during burning. In the last 200 years we have released huge amounts of carbon dioxide into the atmosphere. The higher level of carbon dioxide in the atmosphere may be increasing the earth's natural "greenhouse effect." Scientists are concerned that if the current trend continues, the earth could warm up dramatically, with unforeseen and possibly disastrous results.

Look into this issue. Start by reading the "Science and Technology" feature on pages 408–409. Also, read other articles or books about it. Be sure to consider all sides of the issue. Keep the following questions in mind:

1. How serious do scientists consider an increase in the greenhouse effect to be? Is the problem getting worse?

2. What are the major contributors to the greenhouse effect?

3. What are some problems that the greenhouse effect causes? How might it affect agriculture? the climate? the oceans?

4. What are some possible solutions?

Exploration 12

Set up five work stations, one for each activity. Have students move from one station to the next until they have had a chance to investigate each question. Tell students that they should make notes in their Journals as they progress. Then involve the class in a discussion of what they have discovered.

Question 1

To avoid burns, caution students not to put their hands too close to the light bulb. Also caution them not to look directly at the light bulb.

Students should observe that they feel the heat almost immediately when they turn on the light. When they turn off the light, the heat leaves almost as quickly as it came. This can be explained only if the heat generated by the light bulb is the result of radiation, since radiant heat affects only the object it strikes. When the light is turned on, radiant energy immediately strikes the hand and heats it. When the light is turned off, there is no longer any radiant energy, and the hand cools.

When students hold their hand closer to the light, they feel more heat because their hand is directly in the path of more radiant energy (the radiant energy is more concentrated). Students should conclude that the heat felt below the light could not be the result of convection, since hot air rises. Therefore, the heat they feel is the result of their hand getting warmer from radiant energy, not from air heated by convection currents.

Students should find that as the wattage increases, they can feel the heat at greater distances. Based on the results of their investigations, students should conclude that light bulbs and other hot objects radiate heat.

Reflectors, Absorbers, and Radiators

Radiant heat behaves differently than other forms of heat. In the activities that follow, you will conduct experiments in order to answer a few key questions about this form of heat travel.

Heat Travel—Some Questions

Choose one or two questions to investigate, then share your results with your classmates.

Question 1

Do light bulbs and other hot objects radiate heat?

You Will Need

- a lamp
- bulbs of various wattages

What to Do

Turn on the lamp. Do you feel heat immediately? Turn off the lamp. What do you feel? Can you explain this?

Turn the lamp on again. Put your hand closer to it. What do you feel now? Can you explain this?

Could the heat be traveling by convection? (**Hint:** Compare what happens when you put your hand above the bulb, below the bulb, and to the side of the bulb.)

Try this activity with bulbs of various wattages. How far away can you feel the heat of each?

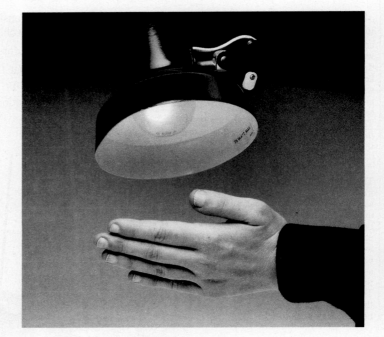

Question 2

Can radiant heat be reflected?

You Will Need

- a lamp (at least 150 W)
- a cardboard square
- a mirror
- a thermometer taped to card-board

What to Do

Hold your hand about 15 cm from the lamp. Now try to reflect more heat onto your hand by using a mirror. Do you notice a difference? Are you sure? Check it with the thermometer.

Next, arrange the lamp, card-board square, and mirror as shown below. Do you feel the reflected radiant heat?

Question 3

Can radiant heat be focused?

You Will Need

- a lamp (at least 150 W)
- a large (thick) magnifying lens
- a thermometer taped to card-board
- a ceramic or metal bowl
- a clothespin
- tissue paper

What to Do

Arrange the lamp and the card-board as shown at right. Move the lens backward and forward, until you can see the image of the light bulb on the cardboard. Once you can see the image, does the temperature of the cardboard rise? Can you explain your observations?

Hold a small piece of tissue pa-per over a ceramic or metal bowl with a clothespin. Try to focus

the sun's rays so that the paper catches fire. **Be Careful:** *The tissue can catch fire and burn quickly.*

Question 2

Suggest that students turn the light on and off a few times to "get the feel" of the amount of heat given off by the light bulb. Then they should place their hand in a direct line with the image in the mirror as shown in the illustration.

Observation: Students' hands be-come warmer as a result of the heat be-ing reflected by the mirror.

Conclusion: The mirror is reflecting the radiant heat emitted from the back of the bulb.

Observation: When the cardboard is used as a reflector, students will not feel any reflected heat.

Conclusion: This is because the cardboard absorbs the heat and is a poor reflector. As a result of their inves-tigations, students should conclude that radiant heat can be reflected.

Question 3

CAUTION: Students should be very careful while focusing the light with the magnifying glass. Point out that con-centrated light can be very hot and may cause serious burns.

Suggest that students focus the light close to, but not on, the bulb of the thermometer.

Observation: The temperature rises as a result of focusing—concentrat-ing—the light from the light bulb.

Conclusion: As the tissue paper bursts into flame, students should rec-ognize that focusing radiant heat con-centrates its energy. As a result of their investigations, students should con-clude that radiant heat can be focused.

Question 4

Observation: The balloon on the black bottle inflates more than the balloon on the white bottle.

Conclusion: The black bottle absorbs more heat.

Have students hold the cards in front of the light for about 1 minute.

Observation: The temperature registers higher on dark-colored cards than on the light-colored ones.

Conclusion: The dark-colored cards absorb more heat than the light-colored ones.

Observation: All of the ice cubes placed on the paper squares melt faster than the ice cube placed on the aluminum foil.

Conclusion: The shiny surface of the foil reflects more radiant heat away from the ice cube than do the dull-colored squares of paper. Another observation could be that the ice cube melts more quickly on the darker paper. This is because dark colors absorb more radiant heat.

As a result of their investigations, students should conclude that dark colors absorb more radiant heat than light colors. Shiny, light surfaces reflect more heat than dull, dark surfaces.

Question 5

Observation: The water in the black can loses the most heat in the shortest amount of time. The water in the unpainted can loses the least amount of heat.

Conclusion: Dark colors radiate more heat than do light colors.

✳ *Follow Up*

Assessment

1. Ask students to summarize the information that they learned from reading the article *Energy from the Sun.* Then have them evaluate the importance of the sun to human survival.

2. Have students create a mural or bulletin board display that shows how radiant heat can be reflected, absorbed, and radiated. Suggest that they include drawings of everyday examples of each kind of phenomenon.

Question 4

Which colors absorb radiant heat the most? the least?

You Will Need

- a bottle, painted white
- a bottle, painted black
- 2 balloons
- a lamp
- a variety of differently colored cards
- a thermometer
- tape
- 5 ice cubes
- a square each of red, green, white, and black paper, and aluminum foil

What to Do

Put a balloon over the mouth of each bottle. Place a lamp halfway between the bottles (or, if it is a sunny day, put the bottles outside for a while). Observe the balloons. How do you explain what happens?

Tape a thermometer to a colored card, then hold it up to the lamp. Repeat, using all the other cards. Remember to keep them the same distance from the lamp. (How long should you wait before reading the thermometer?) In your Journal, record the temperature of each card.

Put an ice cube on each square of paper and aluminum foil. Place them in sunlight. Record in your Journal the order in which the ice cubes melt.

Question 5

Which color radiates the most heat?

You Will Need

- 3 tin cans of the same size, one painted white, one painted black, and the other one unpainted.
- 3 cardboard covers to fit over the tin cans
- 3 thermometers
- hot water

What to Do

Set up the three cans as shown below. Fill each can with the same amount of hot water. Record the temperature of each can at 3-minute intervals.

Extension

1. Suggest that students do some research so that they can write articles about the greenhouse effect. They could use the article *Energy from a Star* as a model. Encourage students to research the long-term problems associated with the greenhouse effect. Invite students to include diagrams. Display the finished articles for others to read.

2. Challenge students to do some research to discover how heat energy, light energy, and radio waves are similar. Ask them to include information on how they are different. Suggest that they share what they have learned by presenting an oral report to the class.

Challenge Your Thinking

1. In your Journal, identify the words that substitute for each of the blanks in the paragraph below. If you can do this quickly, then you are so bright you're radiant!

Ninety percent of the earth's heat comes from the ___?___ in the form of ___?___ energy. This type of energy can be focused by a ___?___. You could also send this type of energy around a corner using a ___?___. If you held your hand a short distance above a candle, most of the heat you would feel would be from ___?___. If you held your hand to one side of the candle, most of the heat you would feel would be from ___?___. Metals at room temperature feel cold to the touch. This is because they ___?___ heat away from your skin very quickly. Materials that carry heat very poorly in this way are known as ___?___.

2. Why is it usually cooler on clear nights than on cloudy nights?

3. Imagine making two blocks of ice that are identical except that one is made from water dyed black, and the other is made from water dyed white. Which would melt faster if both were:
   (a) placed in the sunlight?
   (b) placed in a cool, dark place?
   Why?

4. How would you design a space suit for use on the moon? The temperature of a lunar day is over 100 °C; the temperature of a lunar night is below −150 °C.

5. Do you think that cold can be reflected in the same way as heat? Why or why not?

Summary for

The Big Ideas

Student responses will vary. The following is an ideal summary.

Temperature is a measure of the average heat energy of all the particles of a substance. When most substances take on energy, the particles that make up the substance move, expand, and contract, depending on temperature conditions. A thermometer is calibrated to compare the expansion of a substance (usually a liquid) to a rise in temperature. Temperature is a measure of the *average* heat energy of all the particles of a substance. Heat is the total *amount* of energy in a substance.

People get energy from the food that they eat. When food is broken down, chemical energy is released. The chemical energy contained in foods is measured in joules or calories.

The amount of heat energy in a material depends on its mass and its temperature. The greater the amount of a substance, the more heat energy it is able to absorb.

Heat travels by conduction, convection, and radiation. Heat travels through solids mainly by conduction, in which the energized particles of one substance are in direct contact with the particles of another substance. Heat travels by convection when liquids and gases start to move because of their increased energy. Radiation is energy transfer through space in the form of waves. Radiation comes from any heated object, most notably from the sun. The radiant energy from the sun passes through our atmosphere and heats the air, the water, and the ground. Virtually all of the energy used to run the earth's systems comes from the sun.

The Big Ideas

In your Journal, write a summary of this unit, using the following questions as a guide.
- What are you measuring when you measure temperature?
- How does a thermometer work?
- How do heat and temperature differ? How are they related?
- Where do people get their heat energy? How is this energy measured?
- How are mass and heat related?
- How does heat travel?
- How does heat travel in solids, fluids, and through empty space differ?
- What causes convection?
- How does the earth utilize the sun's heat?

Checking Your Understanding

1. Each example below presents an interesting heat-related problem. Use your understanding of heat and temperature to write brief explanations of each.
   - (a) A match burns my finger but only raises the temperature of 10 mL of water by 7 °C. This doesn't seem to make sense—or does it?
   - (b) The metal lid to a jar is stuck solid. It comes off easily, though, after running the lid under hot water for a few seconds.
   - (c) Glider pilots experience uplift when flying over plowed fields or houses but drop when passing over water or forests.
   - (d) A paper cup is filled with water and placed over an alcohol lamp. The water boils but the paper does not burn.
   - (e) A car is parked in the sunlight with the windows closed. It becomes quite warm inside, yet the glass windows feel cool.
   - (f) On a cold but sunny day a thermometer reads a toasty 25 °C.
   - (g) A motorcycle engine has fins around it.
   - (h) On the way home from the store, Anita keeps the ice cream cold by wrapping it in her sweater!
   - (i) In a room heated by a fireplace, the hot air in the room actually leaves the room and goes up the chimney, yet people in the room feel warm.
   - (j) Five seconds after being removed from a 250 °C oven, a piece of aluminum foil is cool enough to touch.

Answers to

Checking Your Understanding

1. (a) The amount of heat energy is the same, but the heat energy of the match is applied to a much smaller volume when it burns the finger than when it heats a beaker of water. The heat energy of the match is much more concentrated.
(b) The lid comes off because it expands to a greater degree and more quickly than the glass.
(c) Water and forests are capable of absorbing much more heat energy without becoming hot. Plowed fields and houses become hot more quickly, which heats the air above them and causes the air to rise.
(d) The water in the cup absorbs the heat energy so quickly that the paper cannot burn.
(e) Radiant energy passes through the glass and is absorbed by the interior of the car.
(f) If radiant energy from the sun hits a thermometer directly, the thermometer would show a rise in temperature due to radiant heat in sunlight rather than the temperature of the air.

(Answers continue on next page)

2. For the description below of a thermos bottle, fill in the blanks using the words *conduction*, *convection*, and *radiation*.

The plastic cup reduces heat travel by __(a)__.
The cap reduces heat travel by __(b)__.
The double-walled glass bottle reduces heat travel by __(c)__.
The vacuum reduces heat travel by __(d)__.
The silvered surfaces cause heat travel by __(e)__.
The air reduces heat travel by __(f)__.
The plastic case reduces heat travel by __(g)__.

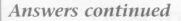

3. Keisha used her homemade calorimeter to test the heat content of various foods. A pecan raised the temperature from 40 °C to 80 °C. A piece of beef fat raised the temperature quickly from 70 °C to 100 °C, where it stopped climbing. Keisha concluded that the pecan had more calories. Was she right? Explain.

4. (a) You are going to bake potatoes in aluminum foil. Aluminum foil has a shiny side and a dull side. Would it make any difference which side is next to the potatoes? Explain.

   (b) Some people prefer their coffee black, others prefer it with cream only, others with sugar only, and still others with both cream and sugar. Of these mixtures, which would cool the fastest? Explain.

5. Construct a concept map using the following terms or phrases: *Conduction*, *heat*, *solids*, *radiation*, *fluids*, *convection*, and *space*.

Reading *Plus*

So far, you have learned quite a bit about temperature and heat. By reading pages S117–S132 in the *SourceBook*, you can take a closer look at how heat is used and how it is measured. You will also learn more about the differences between heat and temperature.

Updating Your Journal

Reread the paragraphs you wrote for this unit's "For Your Journal" questions. Then rewrite them to reflect what you have learned in studying this unit.

About Updating Your Journal

The following are sample ideal answers.

1. Temperature is a measure of the average amount of heat energy of all the particles of a substance. The heat energy of a substance depends on both the temperature and the amount of the substance.

2. Temperature is usually measured by thermometers, which compare the expansion of a substance (usually a liquid) to the rise in temperature.

3. Heat travels from place to place either from one substance to another (conduction), throughout a liquid or gas by circulation (convection), or through space (radiation). *(This transfer of energy is an example of the theme of **Systems and Interactions**.)*

4. Extreme temperature in the material inside the furnace is shown by the light radiating from the furnace and from the protective clothing worn by the workers.

(g) The fins of a motorcycle engine supply much more surface area, so that excess heat can be given off more easily.

(h) The sweater acts as an insulator to keep the heat out.

(i) The people surrounding the fire are warmed by radiant energy.

(j) Because the foil is so thin, the heat that it does absorb is given off quickly to the environment.

2. (a) conduction
   (b) conduction and convection
   (c) conduction
   (d) conduction and convection
   (e) radiation
   (f) conduction
   (g) conduction

3. Keisha should not have concluded that the pecan had more calories. Once the water reached 100 °C, the energy of the burning beef fat does not register as a change in temperature because all of the energy is going into keeping the water boiling.

4. (a) The shiny side reflects heat and should be placed next to the potato. The dull side absorbs heat better.

   (b) If all of the substances start out at the same temperature, the black coffee will cool the fastest because it radiates heat energy the quickest.

5.

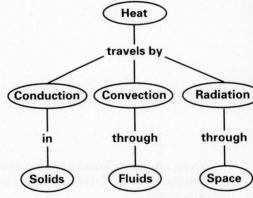

Background

Civil engineering includes the planning, designing, and building of local, state, and federal construction projects. These may encompass a wide range of activities, including the construction of bridges, canals, dams, and tunnels, as well as irrigation, sewage, and water-supply systems. Projects may also include the design and construction of transportation systems such as airports, highways, and railroads. Since many students may not be familiar with this career term, you may wish to explain that the word *civil* means, ''having to do with citizens, the community, or the state.'' The word *engineer* comes from a Latin word which means ''to design.'' Use this information to help students recognize that a civil engineer is a person who designs things for the community. Encourage students to speculate about what some of these structures might be. *(bridges, public buildings, water supply systems, airports, and highways)*

Spotlight on Civil Engineering

Designing structures such as bridges, dams, offshore drilling platforms, towers, and so on is done by civil engineers. Jeanine Sutton is a civil engineer with many years experience working on many different projects.

Q: What do you like most about your work?

Jeanine: I like the variety. Every project is different. Each project has its own unique challenges. The job I have now is stimulating because I spend a fair bit of the time both in the field and here at my desk. I do my design work here, and when I go out into the field, I actually get to see my designs take shape as the project progresses.

Q: What do you do?

Jeanine: I am responsible for various marine structures up and down the coast. By "marine structures" I mean piers, breakwaters, various platforms, wharves, and so on. The ocean is a very tough environment, so these structures are in constant need of repair. Basically my job includes identifying the problem, designing a solution, and supervising the construction of the solution. I work with a wide range of people, from roustabouts to contractors to government committees.

Q: What event of your working life particularly stands out in your mind?

Jeanine: There are so many! Well, one time an offshore platform began to collapse suddenly, without warning. A full-blown gale was raging at the time, but we had a crew (myself included) there within an hour. The first concern, of course, was to see that everyone got off safely, which they did. But then came the hard part. Figuring out what had happened and why.

Q: Did you apply what you learned to future projects?

Jeanine: Definitely. Whenever structures fail, it is because of weaknesses in the design. If we can identify those weaknesses, we can eliminate them in our future designs. Believe me, there is nothing quite so instructive as failure!

Using the Interview

When students finish reading the interview, you may wish to evaluate their understanding by asking questions similar to the following:
- What does Jeanine Sutton like about being a civil engineer? *(She likes the variety and challenge of her work. Each project is different.)*
- What skill does Ms. Sutton feel is most important to a civil engineer? *(the ability to think in an organized fashion—to think a problem through from beginning to end)*
- What does Jeanine Sutton mean when she says that engineering involves team work. *(She means that a civil*

engineer must work well with other people in order to achieve a common goal.)
- What social issues concern Jeanine Sutton as a civil engineer? *(She feels that community safety is a major issue. She is also concerned about what a civil engineer should do if a project is not in the best interest of society, and how the work of a civil engineer may impact the lives of people in the community.)*

After students have finished discussing the interview, ask them to reevaluate whether or not they would like to be a civil engineer. Encourage them to explain the basis for their conclusion.

Q: What advice would you give to a young person interested in engineering?

Jeanine: First the obvious things. Sharpen your skills in math and science. Engineers need to be proficient in all manner of mathematics, as well as sciences such as physics and chemistry. Learn to think analytically. You will have to be able to think through complicated problems from beginning to end. There are other skills that a good engineer should have that are not quite so obvious. Learn to communicate clearly, both orally and in writing. As an engineer you will have to be able to communicate complex ideas clearly and concisely to others. The best ideas in the world are worthless if they cannot be communicated. Learn to work well

with other people. Engineers rarely work alone. You may be one of a team of dozens or even hundreds of people. It's also important for would-be engineers to remember that there's more to life than engineering. Many people become so caught up in preparing for a career that they want to learn about nothing else but what they will need in their careers. This is a mistake. A broad background will serve you well in many ways.

Q: Are there any personal characteristics a good engineer should have?

Jeanine: Some I have already mentioned, but there are others. Stamina. Enthusiasm. A sense of responsibility.

Q: What social issues affect civil engineers?

Jeanine: Safety. In many cases lives will depend on the safety of your designs. If your structure fails, people could be killed. It isn't always the fault of the design when a structure fails, though. If a contractor errs in some way, or tries to cut corners too often, this can lead to a failure. Whenever possible, the engineer has to see to it that the contractor does as directed, otherwise all bets are off. It also concerns me that people are sometimes badly affected by what engineers do. When a dam is built, for example. Someone's home or farm is going to be flooded by the reservoir that forms.

A Project Idea

What structures could be built in your community to make life better? Perhaps a sidewalk, or a footbridge across a ravine, or a playground? A dam to reduce flooding? To get ideas, ask your friends and neighbors what improvements they would like to see.

After you have settled on an idea, then get started on the engineering side of the project. This includes choosing materials, coming up with a design, and making models of the finished design. Depending on your project, doing the actual construction might not be practical.

Some of the questions to consider: Is your design safe? Is it durable? What materials will give the best combination of low cost, safety, and durability?

For Assistance

For advice, talk to a civil engineer in your community. Engineers work for engineering consulting firms, public works and transportation departments, or building contractors. Some engineers also work independently.

◆ Using the Project Ideas

You may wish to divide the class into several groups. Each group participant should interview family members, neighbors, and friends to find out what improvements they would like to see in the community. Then have group members come together and decide on one project idea, determine the best solution, make a design, and if practical, build a model. Encourage the groups to divide the responsibility for the project among the members. When the projects are finished, provide class time for each group to present their ideas to the class. Encourage all class members to ask questions about the project and to become involved in a discussion about the project's practicality, benefits, costs, and safety.

◆ Going Further

To help students gain a greater appreciation of civil engineering, suggest that they work in small groups to think of answers to one or more of the following questions.
- What are some civil engineering projects that have taken place in your community?
- Civil engineers are required to meet building codes and regulations in the structures they help to build and design. What are some of the building codes in the town or city in which you live?

- Jeanine Sutton mentioned the impact of structures on the human community. Structures such as dams, roads, and oil rigs also have an impact on the environment. Do research to find out how engineers determine the effects of their projects on the environment.

Have students share their information with the class by using it to make a bulletin-board display for the classroom.

◆ Background

The earth's greenhouse effect is a naturally occurring phenomenon that causes heat from the sun to be trapped near the earth's surface. Without the greenhouse effect, the average temperature of the earth's surface would drop about 33°C lower than it currently is.

Studies of ice cores suggest that there is a close correlation between average global temperature and the amount of carbon dioxide in the atmosphere. Those periods when the earth has been the coldest match the time in the earth's history when the amount of carbon dioxide in the atmosphere was relatively low—about 200 ppm (parts per million). Warmer periods match those times when the carbon dioxide level was relatively high—about 280 ppm. Ice cores have also shown that the level of carbon dioxide in the atmosphere has risen by 25 percent since 1800.

The level of other atmospheric gases, such as methane and chlorofluorocarbons, is also increasing. Given the current evidence, climatologists predict that the greenhouse effect may continue to steadily push up the average global temperature unless the production of these greenhouse gases due to human activity is cut back quickly and drastically.

The Greenhouse Effect

If you wanted to grow a beautiful tropical plant like an orchid in a cold climate, how would you do it? Or suppose you wanted to grow a summer crop, like tomatoes, in the winter. Obviously, you would need some way of creating a special climate for these plants. The usual way to do this is to build a *greenhouse*, which is a house made mostly of glass.

In a greenhouse, the temperature, humidity, and the amount of light that comes in can be controlled. One important feature of a greenhouse is that the sun's rays can come in to warm the interior of the greenhouse, but the heat produced in this way is held in by the glass. This causes the inside of a greenhouse to stay warm even on a cold day. For this reason, greenhouses are sometimes called *hothouses*.

Greenhouses provide controlled conditions for plants like these.

Global Disaster?

According to some scientists, we are headed for real trouble. The earth, they say, is like a huge greenhouse that is getting hotter all the time. They point out, for example, that the six hottest years on record occurred in the 1980s. If this trend continues, they warn, the consequences could be extremely serious. For starters, there could be changes in the earth's weather patterns, melting of polar ice-caps, and the death of plants and animals that live in coral reefs.

Inside a greenhouse

What's Happening?

The reason for this apparent global warming, these scientists say, is that there has been a buildup of certain gases in the earth's atmosphere. This layer of gases acts like the glass panes of a greenhouse—it holds in the heat of the sun and keeps it from escaping to outer space. The result seems to be that our planet is getting hotter all the time, which the scientists have called the **greenhouse effect.** So far, the situation just seems to be getting worse.

The major gas that is causing the problem, the scientists say, is *carbon dioxide*, and its amount is increasing at an alarming rate. There would be a couple of important reasons for this. One is the use of **fossil fuels** such as coal, petrolem, and natural gas. When these fuels are burned for energy they release carbon dioxide into the atmosphere.

Coral reefs could be damaged by global warming.

◆ Discussion

When students have finished reading the feature, involve them in a discussion of what they have read. You may wish to use questions similar to the following:

1. What is the source of heat for the earth's surface? *(the sun)*
2. Why is the term "greenhouse effect" used to identify what many scientists believe is happening to the earth? *(Like the glass in a greenhouse, gases in the earth's atmosphere hold in the sun's heat and keep it from escaping.)*
3. What do scientists feel is the main cause of the greenhouse effect? *(the increase in the amount of carbon dioxide in the atmosphere)* Why is the level of carbon dioxide in the atmosphere increasing? *(because of deforestation and the use of fossil fuels such as coal, petroleum, and natural gas)*
4. Besides carbon dioxide, what are two other gases that contribute to the greenhouse effect? *(methane and chlorofluorocarbons)* Where do these gases come from? *(Methane comes from the waste of insects, humans, and livestock. Chlorofluorocarbons come from such products as aerosol sprays and from air conditioning and refrigeration systems.)*

Another reason for an increase of carbon dioxide in the atmosphere is **deforestation,** the widespread cutting and killing of trees in our forests. This is particularly a problem in the earth's rain forests. Trees and other plants, you may recall, take in carbon dioxide and give off oxygen. If there were no plants, the level of carbon dioxide would keep increasing. Also, the amount of oxygen would decrease until there wasn't enough left to keep animals alive.

There are other gases that are said to figure into the greenhouse effect. These are primarily *methane* and some chemicals called *chlorofluorcarbons* (CFCs). The methane comes from the waste of insects, humans, and livestock. The CFCs come from such products as aeorosol sprays and from air conditioning systems that use Freon. The amounts of these chemicals in the atmosphere is increasing, as well.

Fossil fuels are a major factor in the greenhouse effect.

Find Out for Yourself

Not everyone agrees that there is a greenhouse effect, or that there is a global warming trend. Do some research to find out what different people are saying. What are some environmental factors that make it difficult to evaluate the effect of gases in the atmosphere on temperature changes on the earth?

Since a greenhouse effect could have such serious consequences, representatives of many countries have met and discussed ways of combatting the greenhouse effect. Find out what agreements have been reached. Do all countries seem willing to take measures that might seem to be necessary? Why might some countries be less willing than others?

The results of deforestation.

◆ *Critical Thinking*

To promote logical-thinking skills, you may wish to ask questions similar to the following:

1. If it continues to get worse, how do you think the greenhouse effect might affect the United States? *(The melting of polar icecaps would cause the coastal areas of the United States to become flooded. Many major cities in these areas would be devastated. Midwestern farm land could turn into desert. Northern areas of the country could become warm all year long, while warm areas of the country would become even warmer.)*

2. Imagine that you had the power to do something about the causes of the greenhouse effect. What would you do? *(Answers will vary, but many students may suggest that laws should be passed to regulate or forbid releasing greenhouse gases into the atmosphere. Students may also suggest that deforestation be stopped.)*

◆ *Going Further*

1. Remind students that deforestation, particularly of the earth's tropical rain forests, is a contributing factor in the increase of carbon dioxide in the atmosphere. Suggest that students do some research to discover how serious the problem of deforestation is.

2. Invite students to do some research to discover what the United States government is doing to control industries from contributing further to the greenhouse effect.

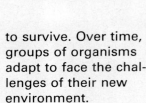

✸ Teaching the Unit

 Unit Overview

In this unit, students are introduced to the long- and short-term changes that shape the surface of the planet. They synthesize their own observations of the world around them into a working model of a changing earth. In the section *The Changeable Planet,* students are encouraged to organize their prior knowledge about the earth in terms of the processes that shaped its landforms over geologic time. In the section *Changes Fast and Slow,* students directly observe physical and chemical weathering processes, and use their observations to infer patterns of erosion taking place on a larger scale. In the section *Water, Wind, and Ice,* students examine the effects of erosion and deposition by running water, wave action, wind, and glaciers.

 Using the Themes

The unifying themes emphasized in this unit are **Scale and Structure, Evolution,** and **Stability.** The following information will help you weave these themes into your teaching plan. A focus question is provided with each theme as a discussion tool to help you tie the information in the unit together.

Scale and Structure is emphasized in the discussion of the various ways the earth's landforms are structured. The concept of scale can be reviewed when introducing the history of the earth and geologic time.

Focus question: *What evidence is used to divide the earth's history into eras and periods?*

Scientists use evidence gained from the study of different rock layers. These rock layers can be distinguished from each other by the fossils they contain and by the type of rock present. Thus each layer acts as a segment on a scale of the earth's history, giving scientists clues to the amount of time that has passed.

Evolution is evident in the discussion of plate tectonic processes and the stages involved in the formation of the modern continents from the single land mass, Pangaea. In section 3, the roles of running water, wind, and ice in shaping the landscape are explored. **Evolution** can be used as a basis for explaining these processes of erosion and deposition.

Focus question: *How might the evolution of the landscape influence the evolution of living things?*

Students should understand that changes within the environment affect the ability of certain organisms to survive. Over time, groups of organisms adapt to face the challenges of their new environment.

Stability is an important theme in the study of geology. The theme is perhaps best expressed by the Principle of Uniformitarianism, which states that the same forces that shape the Earth today are those that shaped the Earth in the past. Throughout this unit, students explore these forces. In Section 1, students also learn how geologists use what they know about the present to construct a history of the Earth's past.

Focus question: *How can scientists predict how rivers will change over time?*

The forces that shape a river are stable and predictable. A river begins when runoff is broken into tiny streams by the rocks and pebbles over which it flows. Tiny streams merge into larger streams, and erosion causes them to widen and deepen. Swift-flowing young rivers cut deep V-shaped valleys. Slow-moving old rivers form wide channels and broad, flat flood plains. Scientists use this knowledge to predict how rivers will change as they age.

 Using the *Science Discovery* Videodiscs

Disc 1 *Science Sleuths, The Missing Beach*
The riverside beach next to a summer home has disappeared. The homeowner thinks it might have been stolen. The Science Sleuths must analyze the evidence for themselves to determine the real reason the beach disappeared.

Disc 2 *Image and Activity Bank*
A variety of still images, short videos, and activities are available for you to use as you teach this unit. See the *Videodisc Resources* section of the **Teacher's Resource Binder** for detailed instructions.

 Using the *SciencePlus SourceBook*

Unit 8 focuses on the natural forces of weathering, erosion, and deposition. Students learn about the varieties of and differences among these geologic activities, as well as how they work together to shape the earth's surface. The specific topographic features resulting from these processes are identified and examined.

PLANNING CHART

SECTION AND LESSON	PG.	TIME*	PROCESS SKILLS	EXPLORATION AND ASSESSMENT	PG.	RESOURCES AND FEATURES
Unit Opener	410		observing, discussing	For Your Journal	411	Science Sleuths: *The Missing Beach* Videodisc Activity Sheets TRB: Home Connection
THE CHANGEABLE PLANET	412			Challenge Your Thinking	427	
1 Seeing the Sights	412	1	observing, inferring, analyzing, summarizing	Exploration 1	413	Image and Activity Bank 8–1 TRB: Activity Worksheet 8–1
2 Unlocking a Planet's Past	416	3	observing, inferring, analyzing, communicating	Exploration 2	420	Image and Activity Bank 8–2 TRB: Resource Worksheet 8–2 Resource Transparencies 8–1 and 8–2 Graphic Organizer Transparency 8–3
CHANGES FAST AND SLOW	428			Challenge Your Thinking	447	
3 Evidence of Change	428	4	observing, analyzing, inferring, recording data	Exploration 3 Exploration 4	429 435	Image and Activity Bank 8–3 TRB: Resource Worksheets 8–3 and 8–4 Graphic Organizer Transparencies 8–4 and 8–5
4 Examining One Type of Change	437	4	observing, predicting, analyzing data, drawing conclusions	Exploration 5 Exploration 6 Exploration 7	438 439 440	Image and Activity Bank 8–4 TRB: Resource Worksheet 8–5 Graphic Organizer Transparency 8–6
5 Gravity—The Great Leveler	442	2	observing, inferring, analyzing, creative writing	Exploration 8	445	Image and Activity Bank 8–5
WATER, WIND, AND ICE	448			Challenge Your Thinking	477	
6 The Power of Water	448	3	problem solving, sequencing, comparing, analyzing	Exploration 9	450	Image and Activity Bank 8–6 TRB: Resource Worksheet 8–6 Resource Transparency 8–7 Graphic Organizer Transparency 8–8
7 Water on the Move	453	2	observing, predicting, analyzing, calculating	Exploration 10	454	Image and Activity Bank 8–7
8 How Rivers Change the Land	456	2 to 3	observing, investigating, inferring, analyzing	Exploration 11 Exploration 12	457 461	Image and Activity Bank 8–8
9 Where Land Meets Sea	462	1 to 2	observing, interpreting, comparing and contrasting, writing			Image and Activity Bank 8–9
10 Wind—An Invisible River	466	1	observing, analyzing, inferring, comparing and contrasting			Image and Activity Bank 8–10
11 Glaciers—Rivers of Ice	468	4 to 5	inferring, analyzing, sequencing, drawing conclusions	Exploration 13 Exploration 14 Exploration 15	470 471 476	Image and Activity Bank 8–11 TRB: Activity Worksheets 8–7 and 8–8 Resource Transparency 8–9 Graphic Organizer Transparencies 8–10 and 8–11
End of Unit	478		applying, analyzing, evaluating, summarizing	Making Connections TRB: Sample Assessment Items	478	TRB: Activity Worksheet 8–9 Resource Worksheet 8–10 Science in Action, p. 480 Science and Technology, p. 482 *SourceBook*, pp. S133–S151

*Time given in number of class periods

✳ Meeting Individual Needs

☀ Gifted Students

1. Have students do some research to make a geologic timeline of their own area. Students will need to consult the library as well as local geologists to get the information they need. Students can extend this activity by focusing on a particular time period of interest and charting the flora and fauna present at that time. Encourage students to illustrate their findings.
2. There is evidence that several mass extinctions took place during the history of life on earth. The most recent mass extinction occurred 65 million years ago and caused the end of the "Age of Dinosaurs." Explain this to students and propose the following fantasy scenario: You can go back in time and stop the mass extinction of the dinosaurs by diverting a comet from its collision course with Earth. What will the world be like in the future if you do this?

☀ LEP Students

1. Have students collect magazine photographs of landforms. Invite them to make scrapbooks or collages with the pictures. Ask students to organize their photographs in sequence or to group them by related phenomena, such as the development of a river valley or a changing coastline. For each group of related images, have students write a few words to identify or explain the processes occurring. If possible, have them work in mixed-language-proficiency cooperative learning groups and develop bilingual or multilingual descriptions.
2. Have students build models of the landforms that are prominent in the local area. They could use clay, papier mâché, wire, construction paper, and many other materials. Ask students to label and define each of the landforms depicted. Display the finished models for other students to look at and enjoy.
3. At the beginning of each unit, give Spanish-speaking students a copy of the *Spanish Glossary* from the *Teacher's Resource Binder*. Also, let Spanish-speaking students listen to the *English/Spanish Audiocassettes*.

☀ At-Risk Students

This unit provides many opportunities for students to observe the processes of weathering and erosion firsthand. However, some students may have difficulty grasping the vastness of time associated with these processes that have shaped the earth. For students who need further practice, have them create their own Geologic Time Scale following the illustration on page 419. Supply them with a long roll of butcher paper. Help them to make a scale relating number of years to a specific length on the timeline. Ask students to create artwork of creatures living at various time periods and organize them on the mural in the appropriate places. Segments of the scale can be divided up among several students.

To get students started on their outdoor explorations of local landforms, take students on a walk or field trip to familiarize them with evidence of changes in the landscape. Try to give them a feeling for where they live geologically. Relate what the students are seeing to the processes of erosion, deposition, and plate tectonics.

☀ Cross-Disciplinary Focus

Creative Writing

The physical setting or location of a story has a great deal to do with its dramatic impact. Authors must research the facts about a setting to give their stories realism. In this unit, students consider a wide variety of landforms and physical environments on the earth's surface. Have a class discussion and brainstorm a list of such settings. Then ask students to think of story ideas that would be appropriate for each setting. Invite them to develop one of these ideas into a short story. Ask students to research the landscape, climate, and so on of their settings to add realistic details to their story. Encourage students to combine their stories into a booklet with illustrations and a cover.

Economics and Architecture

Earthquakes affect the economy, architecture, and many other aspects of life in regions located near the plate boundaries described in this unit. Scientists estimate that hundreds of small earthquakes occur every day and that larger and more dangerous quakes are always a possibility. As a result, cities located in tectonically active areas, such as the Pacific Rim region, have special building codes and other laws designed to minimize possible earthquake damage. Have students do research on the architectural and economic impact of earthquakes on an area. Some possibilities to investigate include costs required to make a building earthquake-safe and architectural strategies for earthquake-safe buildings.

Cross-Cultural Focus

Multilingual Naming

Names for landforms and other earth features come from many different languages. Often, names for unusual or distinctive landforms that occur in one region become known only by their local name throughout the world. One example is the word *tepui*. Tepui was the name used by indigenous people in the area of modern-day Venezuela for very tall, flat-topped mountains located in the tropical rain forest. The tepuis were completely unlike any other known landform in the world. As a result, the native name *tepui* is used when referring to that kind of mountain. Similarly, the native Hawaiian words *aa, pahoehoe,* and *lava* are used to describe volcanic rocks and rock formations. Ask students to research other multilingual names in geology. For example, invite students to research the derivation and meaning of the word *delta*. Encourage them to find out where deltas are located in the United States and to discover how deltas affect the culture of the people that live near deltas.

Students new to this country may be able to report on names for unique landforms in their native countries.

Arctic Cultures

Indigenous people of several different cultural groups make their homes in the glacier-covered regions above the Arctic Circle. Have students do research on one or more of these cultural groups and report on the technological adaptations they have made to life among the glaciers, and the ways in which they utilize the landscape.

 # *Resources*

Bibliography for Teachers

Ballard, Robert D. *Exploring Our Living Planet.* Washington D.C.: National Geographic Society, 1983.

Challand, Helen. *Activities in the Earth Sciences.* Chicago, IL: Children's Press, 1982.

Glenn, W. H. ''The Jigsaw Earth.'' *The Science Teacher*, January 1983.

Glenn, W. H. ''Drifting: Continents on the Move.'' *The Science Teacher*, February, 1983.

Kaufman, Jeffrey S., Robert C. Knott, and Lincoln Bergman. *River Cutters.* Berkeley, CA: Lawrence Hall of Science, 1990.

Skinner, Brian J. *Earth's History, Structure and Materials.* Los Altos, CA: William Kaufmann, 1980.

Bibliography for Students

Aylesworth, Thomas G. *Moving Continents: Our Changing Earth.* Hillside, NY: Enslow Publications, 1990.

Bramwell, Martyn. *Glaciers and Ice Caps.* New York, NY: Franklin Watts Inc., 1986.

Brownstone, David M. and Irene M. Franck. *Natural Wonders of America.* New York, NY: Atheneum, 1989.

Emil, Jane. *All About Rivers.* Mahwah, NJ: Troll Associates, 1984.

Harrington, John W. *Dance of the Continents: Adventures with Rocks and Time.* Boston, MA: J.P. Tarcher, 1983.

Films, Videotapes, Software, and Other Media

Coastlines. Videotape.
Coronet Film & Video
108 Wilmot Road
Deerfield IL 60015
(800) 621-2131

Discovering Our Planet Earth. Videotape.
Focus Media, Inc.
839 Stewart Ave.
Garden City, NY 11530

Dynamic Earth: Changes in its Surface. Videotape.
Coronet Film & Video
108 Wilmot Road
Deerfield IL 60015
(800) 621-2131

The Earth Moves: Folds and Faults. Software.
Grades 3–9.
For Apple II family.
Aquarius People Materials
P.O. Box 128
Indian Rocks Beach, FL 33535
(800) 282-4198

Formations of Continents and Mountains. Videotape.
Focus Media, Inc.
839 Stewart Ave.
Garden City, NY 11530

Geologic Time. Film.
Encyclopedia Britannica Educational Corporation
310 South Michigan Ave.
Chicago, IL 60604
(800) 554-9862

Glacial Landforms. Software.
Grades 5–12.
For IBM PC.
IBM Direct PC Software Department 999
One Culvert Road
Dayton, NJ 08810

Shaping the Earth's Surface. Software.
Grades 7–12.
For Apple II family.
Focus Media, Inc.
839 Stewart Ave.
Garden City, NY 11530

Unit Focus

Pose the following question to students: How does the earth change? There are many possible responses. Students may describe the variation in weather from one day to the next or changes in a familiar landmark such as a mountain, waterfall, or coastline. Other students may describe earthquakes and volcanic eruptions. Write students' suggestions in one column on the chalkboard. Label that column *Changes.* Ask students: How can you tell that these changes have occurred? Label a second column *Evidence* and have students fill it in with the evidence for each of the changes listed. For example, they may know that a mountain has changed because they saw slide areas and rock debris where there had not been any before. Students should be able to provide a great deal of evidence that changes in the earth have taken place.

About the Photograph

The photograph, taken in Africa, reflects many levels of change occurring on the earth's surface. The reddish dune system's dramatic shape is formed by its interaction with the prevailing winds. The sand particles were formed by another type of change—wind erosion of rock and soil.

Unit 8 — Our Changing Earth

For Your Journal

Write a paragraph summarizing your thoughts about each of the following:

1. How old is the earth?
2. Has the earth always looked like it does now?
3. What forces of erosion are constantly wearing away the earth? Why doesn't the earth erode away?
4. Could much of the earth once have been covered by ice? How do we know?
5. What caused the dunes in the photograph to form? How are these dunes like ocean waves?

LESSON 1

✳ *Getting Started*

Through the study of travel brochures, this introductory lesson helps students become aware of the variety of landforms that exist throughout the world. It sets the stage for the rest of the unit by suggesting that the study of geology can provide many explanations for why the land is shaped the way it is.

Main Ideas

1. Many types of landforms exist throughout the world.
2. Geology helps explain the variety of landforms.

✳ *Teaching Strategies*

Where in the World?

Have students read the travel posters on pages 414 and 415. After they have made their travel choices, involve them in a discussion of the reasons for their choices. If some students find none of these locations appealing, allow them to select others. A world map or globe (preferably showing topography), travel magazines, and brochures would be helpful at this point. The purpose of this activity is to have students identify many locations with different geological features.

The World's Full of Different Places

Ask students to read page 412 silently and then discuss the many reasons why people like to visit different scenic locations. Also discuss the questions in the text. Sample answers for
(Continues on next page)

---

① Seeing the Sights

Where in the World?

". . . And now it's time for the big drawing—a trip for two to anyplace in the world! Are you ready? Have your tickets handy. Here we go! The winning number is . . ."

Suppose you won. Where in the world would you go? Read the travel posters on pages 414 and 415. Do any of the places they describe appeal to you?

The World's Full of Different Places

People like to visit new places, if only because they want a "change of scene." You could have many different reasons for wanting to go to a particular place. Your ideal vacation spot might have a certain type of climate or offer certain types of recreational activities. Or you may be interested in seeing wildlife or experiencing different cultures.

Imagine for a moment that the most important consideration for your trip is to go somewhere with spectacular scenery. Carry out the following steps:

1. Read the travel posters again.
2. In a few sentences, summarize the scenery each describes.
3. Suggest reasons (or causes) for the shape and form of the different landscapes.
4. Which scenic landscape would you choose for your trip? What are your reasons?

Some of the answers to how landscapes have been formed can be found in the study of **geology.** In this unit, you will make observations about the landscape around you, much like a geologist would. By examining some of the forces that shape the land, you will gain a better understanding of how the world came to be what it is today.

LESSON ① ORGANIZER

Objectives

By the end of the lesson, students should be able to:
1. Describe some landforms that exist throughout the world.
2. Explain why this variety exists.

Process Skills

observing, inferring, analyzing, summarizing

New Terms

Geology—the study of how the earth formed and how it changes.

Selling Scenery

How good a salesperson are you? Test your skill. Choose *one* of the activities below.

1. You are a travel agent. What would you say to your clients to persuade them to visit the scenic landscape you chose in step 4 on page 412? Write down the main points you would make.

2. Design a travel brochure to persuade vacationers to visit the area you chose. Highlight the area's scenic attractions.

3. You are a travel agent again, but this time your client is a geologist. How would you change your sales pitch?

4. Now you are a geologist, and you are planning an expedition to a place of your choice. Where would you go? What would be your sales pitch to get others to join you?

(The World's Full of Different Places continued)

each location are given in the teacher's material on pages 414 and 415. *(In general, the students should realize that landforms themselves attract travelers.)*

If a slide projector is available, ask students to bring in slides of scenic areas they have visited. Provide class time for a slide show. Encourage students to suggest reasons why the landscape varies. If the word does not come up in discussion, introduce the term *landforms*. Encourage students to use the term as they describe the different land features. This discussion should help you to assess their prior knowledge of geology.

Exploration 1

Remind students of the discussion from the previous page. Whether they choose to write a sales presentation or design a travel brochure, stress that their emphasis should be on geological features. Common tourist attractions such as restaurants, galleries, and museums may also be included. In question 3, students should focus strictly on geological attractions. Since this sales presentation is directed at a geologist, precise, scientific language should be used.

Materials

Exploration 1: construction paper, markers, magazines, scissors, glue

Teacher's Resource Binder

Activity Worksheet 8–1

Science Discovery Videodisc

Disc 2, Image and Activity Bank, 8–1

Time Required

one class period

Mountain Memories

1. Ask a student to read the poster aloud.
2. A sample student description of the scenery: This travel poster describes an area with high, snowy mountains. There are icefields, glacial lakes, and deep rocky valleys.
3. Possible geologic causes of the landforms: This area is at a high elevation. It has a cold climate with much snow and ice. Glaciers cut deep valleys in the land. They left behind many holes that filled with water from the melted snow and ice.
4. Students who choose this location for their trip may enjoy mountain scenery. Related sports include skiing and mountaineering.

Scandinavian Heart

1. Ask a student to read the poster aloud.
2. A sample student description of the scenery: This travel poster describes high mountains that form a dramatic seacoast. Major cities are located next to hilly forest areas. There are many lakes.
3. Possible geologic causes of the landforms: The ocean waters rose to cover an area so that only high mountains are above water. There is much rain and snow, providing plenty of water for lakes.
4. Students who choose this location for their trip may enjoy ocean, lake, and mountain scenery. Related activities include hiking and boating. Tourist attractions of the major cities may also be mentioned.

Arizona's Marvel

1. Ask a student to read the poster aloud.
2. A sample student description of the scenery: This travel poster describes large, deep red rock canyons and the ruins of prehistoric Indian cliff dwellings.
3. Possible geologic causes of the landforms: Rivers flowing in the same location over many thousands of years cut deep canyons into the land. The climate is warm. There is no year-round snow or ice.

4. Students who choose this location for their trip may enjoy colorful and rugged canyon scenery. Related activities include horseback riding, hiking, and camping.

Paradise Islands

1. Ask a student to read the poster aloud.
2. A sample student description of the scenery: This travel poster describes tropical, volcanic islands that are surrounded by coral reefs. There are many sandy beaches.

3. Possible geologic causes of the landforms: Volcanoes erupted in the middle of the Pacific Ocean. The lava from these eruptions built up over time to form these islands. The climate is warm and rainy; the rain wears down the rock to make sand.
4. Students who choose this location for their trip may enjoy tropical beach scenery. Related activities include snorkeling and sunbathing.

ARIZONA'S MARVEL

Thrill to one of the most stunning scenic attractions in the world — the Grand Canyon. This tour makes it easy for you to visit prehistoric Indian cliff dwellings, the gorgeous red rock formations of Oak Creek Canyon, the fabled city of Prescott, and many other places that are unique to Arizona.

TOUR WORLD

PARADISE ISLANDS

The Hawaiian Islands: A splash of coral and volcanic beauty scattered over the blue Pacific. A paradise on Earth. Tropical islands of magical beauty. Golden sands or black lava, verdant valleys. A blessing of friendly people.

TOUR WORLD

CELTIC MAGIC

A week away from the world — see and feel all the magic of Southern Ireland: its meadows as green as they say they are, its quiet lakes ringed by mountains, its rocky coasts and uncrowded bays. Explore the evocative beauty of remote Connemara, Killarney, and the Ring of Kerry.

TOUR WORLD

Assessment

1. Have students prepare a list of landforms from the travel posters. (*Answers include mountains, valleys, lakes, canyons, volcanic islands, icefields, fjords, cliffs, rock formations, and beaches.*)
2. Have students write and design a travel poster describing a nearby area. Posters should include specific geologic descriptions of all landforms.

Extension

1. Have a slide show that highlights prominent geological features. Ask students to write a script that could accompany the slides. (Prepared slides of U.S. National Parks are available and could be used for this activity, or students may wish to use their own vacation slides.)
2. Have students do research to find out how landforms on the ocean floor compare with those on the earth's surface. How are they the same? How are they different? (*Students should conclude that many are similar but that those on land are subject to more weathering.*)

Celtic Magic

1. Ask a student to read the poster aloud.
2. A sample student description of the scenery: This travel poster describes flat, grassy areas surrounded by rocky mountains. There are many lakes. The coastline is very rocky. There are many small bays.

3. Possible geologic causes of the landforms: The rainy climate in Ireland caused meadows and lakes to form on parts of a rocky, mountainous island.
4. Students who choose this location for their trip may enjoy mountain and pastoral scenery. Related activities include hiking, fishing, and boating.

☀ *Getting Started*

This lesson develops the modern theory of plate tectonics. The lesson begins with a presentation of the historical background of Alfred Wegener's theory of continental drift. Using this historical perspective, students learn how geologists build theories based on observations and inferences.

Main Ideas

1. Geologists make inferences about the past based on observations of the present.
2. The theory of continental drift proposes that all the continents were once joined together and have since gradually drifted apart.
3. The theory of plate tectonics proposes that the earth's crust is made up of a number of large and small plates that are continually shifting.
4. Plate tectonics has been useful in explaining phenomena such as volcanoes, earthquakes, and mountain formation.

☀ *Teaching Strategies*

Geologists—The Earth's Historians

If any students have rock collections, ask them to share these collections with the class. Allow students time to observe the different collections and to ask questions about them.

After students have had time to look at the photographs on pages 416 and 417, divide them into discussion groups. Ask them to think of other possible questions for geologists.

2 Unlocking a Planet's Past

Geologists—The Earth's Historians

At one time or another, you may have collected rocks. Chances are, something about these rocks caught your eye. Perhaps they were pretty or oddly shaped. Perhaps they contained the fossil remains of ancient plants or animals. Perhaps you wondered how these rocks formed. Geologists also collect rocks, but they go one step further. By looking closely at rocks and the formations they come from, geologists are able to "read" the earth's history. To the geologist, rocks tell the story of how the earth came to be what it is today, and even what it might be like millions of years from now. The photographs give you an idea of some of the different areas of geological study. Start a class list on the bulletin board of the questions you and your class would like to ask a geologist.

Will the earth ever erode away?

Where do mountains come from?

What causes earthquakes?

Why are fish fossils found in mountains ?

LESSON 2 ORGANIZER

Objectives

By the end of the lesson, students should be able to:
1. Appreciate the different types of work that geologists do.
2. Understand the types of questions that geologists ask.
3. Consider the use of observation and inference in the work of geologists.
4. Distinguish between observation and inference.
5. Know the historical development of the theories of continental drift and plate tectonics.

Process Skills

observing, inferring, analyzing, communicating

Geologists do different tasks. What are some of them?

Will an Ice Age come again?

Why do volcanoes occur only in certain places?

Use the questions on these two pages to guide student thinking. Do not worry about correct answers at this point. However, to provide material for discussion, possible responses are included here.

Will the earth ever erode away?
A given location on the earth will eventually erode away, but there is a constant recycling of earth's materials. This means that the earth in some form will continue to be here.

Why are fish fossils found in mountains?
Parts of the earth's crust, originally formed on the sea floor, can be pushed up when they run into other parts of the crust.

What causes earthquakes?
Movements within the earth's crust cause the plates to shift. When the plates grind together, tension builds. When the stress becomes too great, the rocks along a crustal boundary fracture. This movement causes a sudden release of the built-up stress, causing an earthquake.

Where do mountains come from?
Mountains can be built up by volcanic activity or by direct interactions between pieces of the earth's crust.

Geologists do different tasks. What are some of them?
Specialties within the broad field of geology include volcanology, paleontology, mineralogy, and many others. Related earth sciences include astronomy, meteorology, and oceanography. Specific tasks depend on the particular area of speciality.

Will an Ice Age come again?
The geologic record shows that ice ages have occurred repeatedly in cycles. On the basis of that evidence, another Ice Age will probably occur, although the exact time cannot be predicted.

Why do volcanoes occur only in certain places?
Volcanoes occur where interactions within the earth's crust trap molten magma (from the earth's core) near the earth's surface.

New Terms

Theory of continental drift—Wegener's theory that the continents known today were joined together as one continent 300 million years ago.
Crust—the earth's surface.
Geologic Time Scale—chart used to describe the earth's history through time.
Plate—"islands" of lighter continental rock embedded in the heavier, thinner crust of the ocean floor.

Plate tectonics—theory of how the continents move, based on Wegener's theory of continental drift.

Materials

Exploration 2: tracing or photocopy of the map on page 420 or the Blackline Master entitled "A Continental Jigsaw Puzzle," scissors

(*Organizer continues on next page*)

Our Planet's Long History

Have students study the geologic time scale and identify eras, periods, and epochs.

- *Eras:* Precambrian, Paleozoic, Mesozoic, and Cenozoic
- *Periods:* Cambrian, Ordovician, Silurian, Devonian, Mississippian, Pennsylvanian, Permian, Triassic, Jurassic, Cretaceous, Tertiary, and Quarternary
- *Epochs:* Paleocene, Eocene, Oligocene, Miocene, Pliocene, Pleistocene, and Holocene

Time to Think About Time

On the chalkboard, draw a timeline using 1 m instead of 1000 m. Then divide the line according to the dimensions given in the text.

Animals with skeletons would not appear until after 90.0 cm, dinosaurs after 96.0 cm, and humans not until after 99.9 cm.

Have students use the dates on the geologic time scale to develop their own analogies. They may use outside reference materials if available.

A sample analogy compressing geologic time into one week would be: If the history of the earth were to be compressed into one week, starting at midnight (12:00 a.m.) on Sunday, then the first animals with skeletons appeared at about 7:10 a.m. the next Saturday. The first dinosaurs did not appear until 5:15 p.m. Saturday. The first humans did not appear until after 11:59 p.m. Saturday.

Answer to caption: The Colorado River began forming the Grand Canyon 6 million years ago.

Our Planet's Long History

Over the last 200 years scientists have uncovered much evidence showing, beyond any reasonable doubt, that the earth is very old, and that many different life forms have lived here. Earth scientists use a special kind of scale—the **Geologic Time Scale**—to describe the earth's history through time. This time scale is represented in the drawing on the facing page. At each point on the scale representative plants and animals are shown. The geologic time scale is divided into *eras*, which are large blocks of time marked by certain types of life forms. For example, the first animals to have hard skeletons developed during the Paleozoic (*"old life"*) era. Eras are divided into *periods*, and periods are further divided into *epochs*.

Notice that the Precambrian era takes up almost 90% of the earth's history. During the Precambrian era, only very simple plants and animals existed, most of them single-celled. Fish, reptiles (including dinosaurs), trees, flowering plants, and mammals, are all latecomers on our planet. You have no doubt heard the expression "I wasn't born yesterday, you know." In a very real sense we humans *were* born yesterday. Humans first appeared about 100,000 years ago, a mere eyeblink in geologic time!

Time to Think About Time

Let's represent the earth's history as a journey of 1000 meters, starting at 0. The first animals with skeletons appear at about 900 meters into the journey. The first creatures to live on land appear at about 920 meters. The dinosaurs appear at about 950 meters and disappear at about 985 meters. Humans appear at about 999.8 meters. Civilizations begin to appear at 999.9998 meters.

Now try to think of your own way to summarize the earth's history. Let one week represent the earth's history, for example.

The Grand Canyon, which is more than 1500 meters deep in places, slices deep into the earth's past. Rocks at the bottom of the canyon are more than 2 billion years old. How long do you think the Grand Canyon took to form?

(Organizer continued)

Developing a Theory: Journal
A Familiar Plate Boundary: modeling clay, knife

Teacher's Resource Binder

Resource Worksheet 8–2
Resource Transparencies 8–1 and 8–2
Graphic Organizer Transparency 8–3

Science Discovery Videodisc

Disc 2, Image and Activity Bank, 8–2

Time Required

three class periods

The Geologic Time Scale

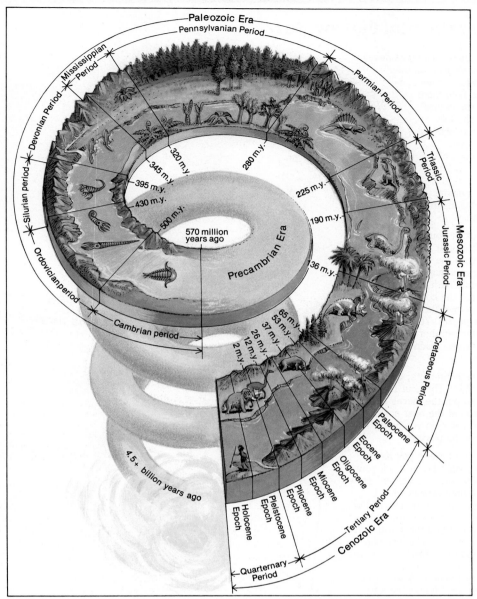

The Geologic Time Scale

The Geologic Time Scale

The chart on page 419 shows a timeline dating back approximately 4.5 billion years, the estimated age of the earth. The chart is presented in the shape of a spiral so that the lengths of the various geologic eras can be represented proportionally on one page.

Highlights of recent fossil finds from throughout geologic time (from most ancient to most recent) are:

- *Precambrian Era:* the first fossil bacteria, some fossil protozoa, sponges, corals, and algae appear
- *Cambrian Period:* abundant invertebrate fossils such as mollusks, crustaceans, and echinoderms; a representative organism was the trilobite (shown on the chart)
- *Ordovician Period:* the first fossil vertebrates are seen (generally armored, jawless fish)
- *Silurian Period:* the first fossil jawed fish appears
- *Devonian Period:* the first fossil amphibians and bony fish appear; first fossils of land plants appear
- *Pennsylvanian Period:* the first fossil conifer trees; first fossil reptiles and insects appear
- *Triassic Period:* the first fossils of primitive dinosaurs appear
- *Jurassic Period:* the first fossil mammals and birds; first fossil flowering plants appear
- *Cretaceous Period:* the first fossil placental mammals; large fossil dinosaurs appear

Fossil finds from epochs of the Tertiary Period are:

- *Paleocene Epoch:* the first fossil prosimians appear
- *Oligocene Epoch:* the first fossil monkeys and apes appear
- *Pliocene Epoch:* the first fossil hominids appear

Fossil finds from the Quaternary Period include:

- *Pleistocene Epoch:* the human species *(Homo sapiens)* appears

Exploration 2

Have students study the world map on page 420. Ask them to make continent cutouts from a tracing, a photocopy of this map, or Resource Worksheet 8–2, "A Continental Jigsaw Puzzle," in the *Teacher's Resource Binder*.

As students work with the cutouts, they should find that there are several possible ways of fitting the continents together.

Instruct students to study the coastlines for clues. One obvious clue for the students to use involves the fit of the coastlines of western Africa and eastern South America. There are other obvious clues in the regions near the Mediterranean Sea and Indian Ocean.

When students find gaps in their fit, discuss what may have happened to the "missing" pieces. *(In many cases, the pieces are actually still there in the form of the continental shelves not shown on this map. Other missing pieces may have moved to unexpected locations or changed shape as they became attached to other land masses.)* The favored fit is pictured on page 424 of the student text.

Students' letters to the Royal Geological Society should express the idea that the continents as they are known today were once part of a larger land mass. It seems logical to conclude that the continents have since moved from their original positions. Have students read some of the letters aloud to the class and display them on a bulletin board.

A Continental Jigsaw Puzzle

As you know, scientists develop inferences based on their observations. These inferences help them explain the natural world. The following Exploration puts you in the shoes of one earth scientist, who used his observations to develop a startling new theory.

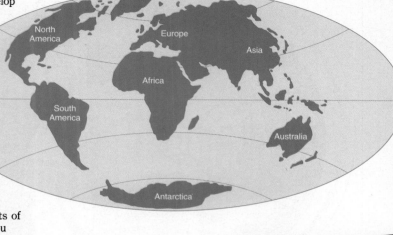

Imagine that you are a young geologist living in Germany in the early 1900s. Looking at a map of the coasts of Africa and South America, you notice that the coastlines appear to fit together like the pieces of a jigsaw puzzle. You then begin to wonder whether all the continents can be made to fit together.

Trace the continents, using the map at right. Then cut them out, and try to put the pieces together to get the best possible fit. What clues do you have? Are there missing pieces?

Finally, you believe you have found the right fit. You ask yourself, "What does this mean? How can I possibly explain what I think happened in the past?" For days you puzzle over the answer. At last you think you have worked out a possible solution. With great excitement you write a letter to the Royal Geological Society in London. What might the letter say? Finish the letter started here, and sign your name as Alfred Wegener.

1143 Bergdorfer Street
Berlin, Germany
April 1, 1911

Royal Geological Society
Holywell House, Worship Street
London, EC2A 2EN

My Esteemed Colleagues,

I wish to bring to your attention a matter of great importance. For several months I have been working on an idea …

Putting the Pieces Together

Read the following history of the development of a theory about the movement of continents. As you read, keep the following questions in mind:

- Who was Alfred Wegener?
- What was Pangaea?
- What is a plate to a geologist?
- According to the plate tectonic theory, what is the earth's crust like?
- What observations led to the development of this theory?

In 1911, Alfred Wegener, a German meteorologist, made a startling proposition. He theorized that about 300 million years ago all the continents we know today were joined together in a single continent which he named "Pangaea" (pronounced Pan JEE uh). Wegener suggested that at some point Pangaea split apart and its pieces began to "drift," or move away from each other.

That continents could once have been joined together was not an entirely new idea. In fact, as early as 1620, the English scientist Francis Bacon had inferred exactly this. Wegener put together his own evidence, as well as material collected by several other scientists to support this **theory of continental drift**.

Wegener's ideas were, at first, very popular. The evidence seemed quite convincing. First, of course, was the fact that the continents seemed to fit together so perfectly. There was other evidence as well. Identical rock formations are found in Africa and South America. Rocks in Newfoundland are of the same kind and age as those found in Scotland and Scandinavia. Coal deposits formed from ancient tropical forests were even found in frigid Antarctica in 1908! Fossils of many similar plants and animals were found on both sides of the Atlantic. These observations all supported the theory that the continents were once joined. Yet a number of observations still remained unexplained. For example, no one could explain what forces caused the continents to move. Because of these remaining problems, Wegener's theory rapidly lost support and continental drift became "just another theory."

Little serious attention was paid to Wegener's ideas for several decades. Then, beginning in the 1950s, geologists began to study the ocean floor, which is part of the earth's *crust* or surface. Until then, scientists actually knew more about the surface of the moon than they knew about the crust between continents! New techniques allowed scientists to unlock some of the mysteries of the ocean floor. Some amazing discoveries eventually came to light. The continents were still moving! Even the ocean floor was drifting. Wegener's theory was looking better and better.

Putting the Pieces Together

The questions on page 421 are intended to encourage students to read the material found on pages 421 through 423 carefully. As students read this material, help them to develop a conceptual understanding of the processes at work.

Answers to

In-Text Questions

The main points that should be gleaned from this material:

- Alfred Wegener, a German meteorologist, theorized that the continents were once joined together in a single continent.
- *Pangaea* was the name given to the continent Wegener described.
- To a geologist, a "plate" is a section of the earth's crust.
- According to the "plate tectonic" theory, the earth's crust is composed of a number of huge plates that move in various directions. A number of smaller plates have also been discovered.

    The interior of the earth consists of hot, molten rock. This hot rock circulates. As it does, it carries the crustal plates with it.

    As the plates move, they interact with each other at their boundaries.

    Plates can separate, converge, and slide past each other.

    As plates move apart, new crust is continuously formed from molten rock from the earth's interior.

- Observations that led to the theory of continental drift:
1. The continents seemed to fit together.
2. Similar rock types are found in Africa and South America.
3. Rocks in Newfoundland are the same type and age as those found in Scotland and Scandinavia.
4. Coal deposits have been found in Antarctica.
5. Similar fossils have been found on the west coast of Africa and the east side of South America.

    Later, scientists learned that the continents and the ocean floor are still moving.

You might want to point out to students that the theory of plate tectonics, like other scientific theories, cannot be proven to be definitely true, but the evidence collected by geologists overwhelmingly supports it.
(Continues on next page)

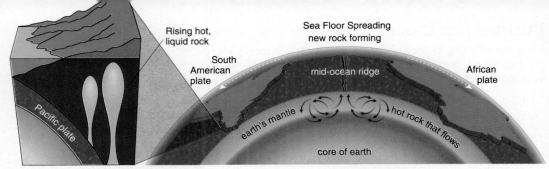

The Causes of Sea Floor Spreading

Rising hot, liquid rock

Sea Floor Spreading new rock forming

South American plate

mid-ocean ridge

African plate

earth's mantle

hot rock that flows

Pacific plate

core of earth

Boundary of South American and Pacific Plates

The text on sea-floor spreading provides the opportunity to emphasize the intertwined nature of scientific knowledge and technological development. Extensive maps of the sea floor have been made possible because of the development of sonar in the 1940s. Involve the class in a discussion of how sonar uses sound waves to measure ocean depth.

Remind students about their study of convection in Unit 7. Ask them to apply that knowledge to explain the movement of the hot molten lava and the earth's plates. Students may be curious about what produces the heat energy inside the earth. Briefly explain that heavy elements in the earth's core are constantly undergoing radioactive decay, and this process produces heat.

The history of the theories of continental drift and plate tectonics is another illustration that scientific discoveries are rarely the work of a single person, but instead are the result of the cumulative efforts of several scientists. Ask students to think of any other examples in the first seven units of this book in which the work of many scientists has led to a new theory or discovery.

Have a map or globe showing land elevations and ocean depths available for students to examine. Explain to students that trenches are found near mountain ranges because colliding plates will force one plate down, forming a trench, and the other plate up, forming a mountain.

During the 1960s, evidence to support the theory continued to accumulate. By the late 1960s geologists were able to develop Wegener's theory further. They theorized that the earth's crust is composed of a number of huge **plates,** moving in various directions. The plates actually float on the hot, dense, semi-liquid rock of the earth's interior—just as ice floats on water. Most of the crustal plates consist of "islands" of lighter continental rock embedded in the heavier, thinner crust that also forms the ocean floor. Scientists disagree today as to the exact number of crustal plates. The map on page 423 shows the six largest plates.

Obviously it must take enormous energy to move these crustal plates. How does this happen?

The interior of the earth consists of hot, molten rock. The earth is always losing a little heat through the crust. Because of this, the hot rock circulates, or *convects,* in much the same way as hot coffee set out to cool, only much more slowly. How slowly? It is thought that a complete convection cycle takes about four hundred million years! As the molten rock circulates, it carries the crustal plates with it. As the plates move across the earth's surface, they interact with one another at their boundaries. There are three basic types of plate boundaries: where plates are separating, where they are converging (approaching each other), and where they are sliding past each other.

The boundary between separating plates is called a *spreading center*. As plates move apart, a gap continuously opens between them. Molten rock from the earth's interior flows into this gap. In this way, new crust is continuously formed. Spreading centers are usually found in mid-ocean. They are marked by rugged mountain chains called *mid-ocean ridges*.

When plates collide, the results can be spectacular. The force of the collision pushes the ocean floor downward to form a deep valley called a *trench*. At the same time the land is folded and thrust upward to form mountains. Look at a map or globe that shows both land elevations and ocean depths. Can you find examples of trenches? Are there also mountain ranges nearby? How do you explain this?

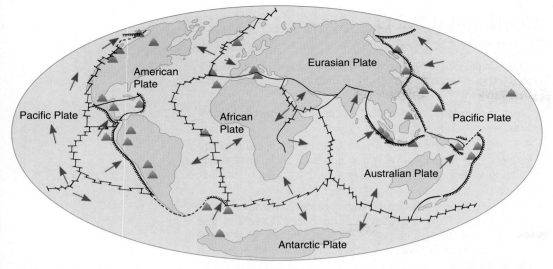

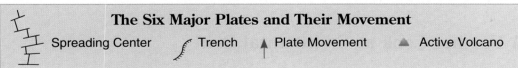

The Six Major Plates and Their Movement

⊥ Spreading Center   ∫ Trench   ▲ Plate Movement   ▲ Active Volcano

The theory of how the continents move, which is based on Wegener's theory of continental drift, is called **plate tectonics.**

Questions

1. What are the names of the six main plates?
2. What do the arrows on the map show?
3. Which plate has no continent on it?
4. What is happening at the mid-ocean ridges? What is the evidence for your answer?
5. To which continents was North America once joined?
6. How can you explain the coal deposits found in Antarctica?
7. Where are most volcanoes found?

By the 1970s, the theory of plate tectonics was almost universally accepted by scientists. It has been useful in explaining earthquakes, volcanoes, and mountains. However, questions remain. As new observations are made about the earth, the theory of plate tectonics is likely to be further refined.

Theories take time to develop. Often, they are the work of many people, each solving a small piece of the puzzle. Complete the timeline at right to compile a brief history of the development of the theory of plate tectonics.

A Developing Theory

In your Journal, fill in the timeline with brief descriptions for each date.

1620
1908
1911
1950s
1960s
1970s
Today

Answers to

Questions

1. The six main plates are the American, African, Antarctic, Pacific, Australian, and Eurasian.
2. The arrows show the direction in which the plates are moving.
3. The Pacific Plate has no continent on it.
4. At the mid-ocean ridges, hot molten rock from the earth's interior flows into the gap formed as the plates move apart. The mid-ocean ridges themselves are evidence, since they contain freshly formed rock.
5. North America was once joined to Africa and Europe.
6. Once, Antarctica must have been located in a warmer climate where trees grew. Eventually, the trees were fossilized and became coal.
7. Volcanoes are found along the boundaries between crustal plates.

Answers to

A Developing Theory

This activity helps students to summarize the information in the reading. *A sample timeline is:*

- 1620—Francis Bacon inferred that continents, at one time, had been joined together.
- 1908—Coal deposits found in Antarctica.
- 1911—Alfred Wegener proposed a single-continent theory; he called the continent *Pangaea*.
- 1950s—Sea-floor exploration; confirmation of continental and ocean-floor movement.
- 1960s—Geologists proposed that the earth's crust is composed of a number of huge plates moving in various directions.
- 1970—The theory of plate tectonics almost universally accepted by scientists.

Continental Facts

Use these facts to conduct a class discussion. Assign one question to each group of students and have each group present its analysis and opinions to the class. Involve the class in a discussion of the implications of each fact and the associated questions.

Do not worry about presenting greater detail on these subjects at this point.

Answers to

In-Text Questions

- North America and Europe began to break apart approximately 180 million years ago. (See diagram 2 on page 425.)
- Earthquakes occur along plate boundaries because the plates are constantly colliding and slipping over and under one another.
- Ocean-floor rocks are younger because new rock is formed from lava flow at the mid-ocean ridges.
- A spreading center can be seen in Africa. The arrows indicate that the plates are moving apart. This spreading center is known as a rift valley.

A Further Look at Continental Drift

For this exercise, students need the continental cutouts they made at the beginning of Lesson 2. Have them compare the arrangement of the continents they made to the one shown on page 424. Discuss and resolve any differences. Ask them if knowing about the underlying process of plate tectonics would have helped them to figure out the placements. *(probably not)* Remind them that Wegener did not have that information either. Explain that Wegener made an inference based on his observations.

Continental Facts

Did you know?

- The Atlantic Ocean between North America and Europe is getting wider by 1 cm each year. How long ago were these continents together?
- Most of the world's earthquakes occur along plate boundaries. Why?
- Scientists estimate that the oldest rocks on the ocean floor are no more than 180 million years old. However, rocks on land may be up to 4 billion (4000 million) years old. Why is the ocean floor younger?
- There is one place where a spreading center is found on a continent. Deep valleys and lakes mark this spreading center. Can you find it on the map on page 423? If the spreading continues here—and there is every indication that it will—an ocean will eventually form.

A Further Look at Continental Drift

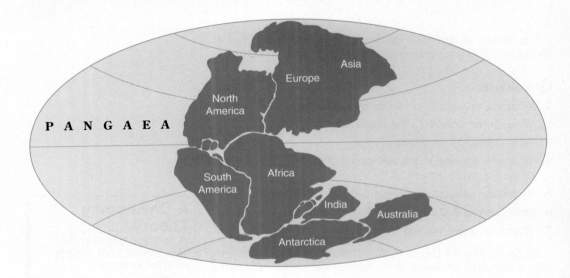

How does your completed continental jigsaw puzzle compare with this one?

On the next page, you will see how some geologists picture the drift of the continents over a period of 225 million years. Try to trace the development of each of the six continents that exist today.

Five Stages in the Breakup of Pangaea

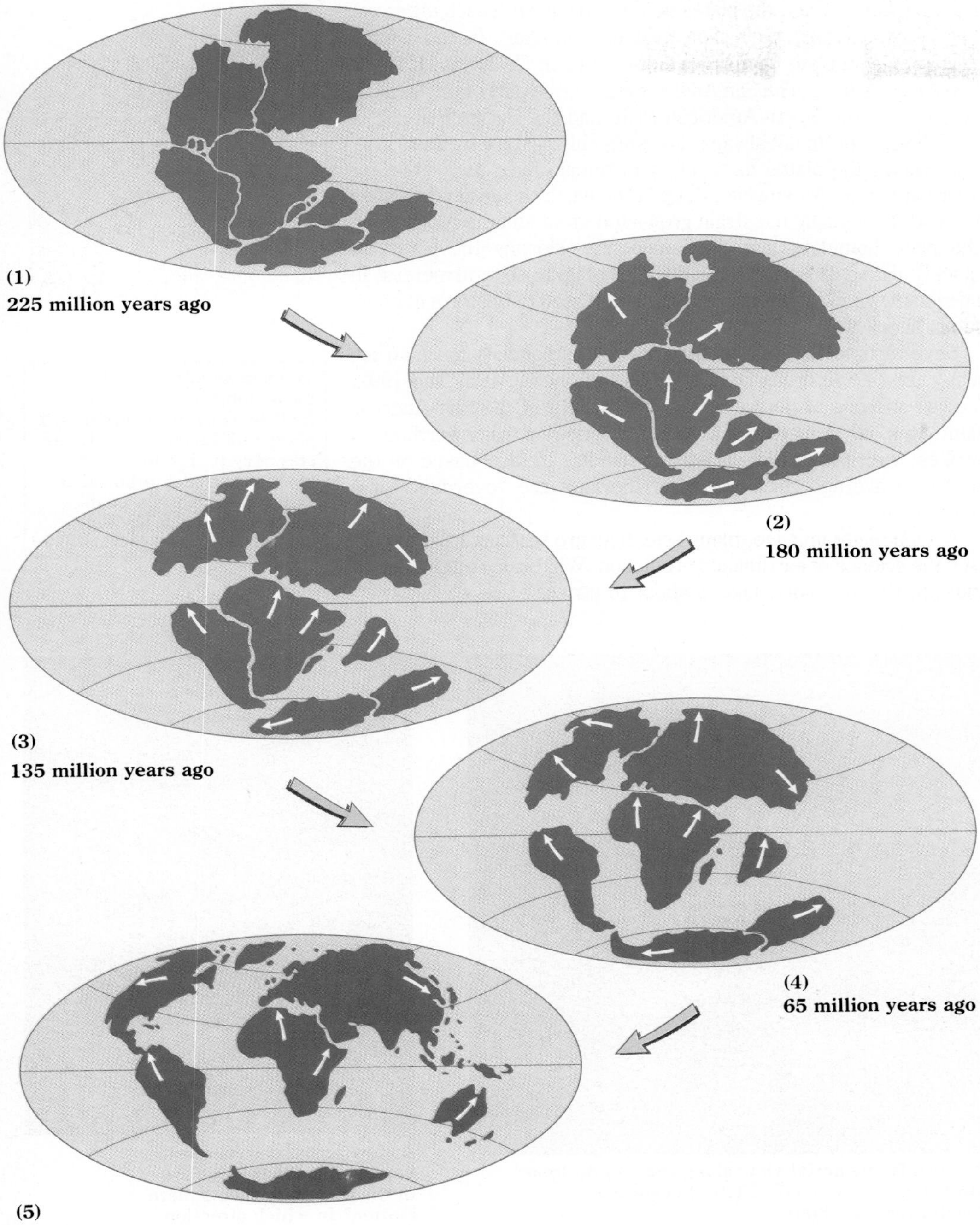

(1)
225 million years ago

(2)
180 million years ago

(3)
135 million years ago

(4)
65 million years ago

(5)
Present

Five Stages in the Breakup of Pangaea

Have students move their continental cutouts apart as indicated in each diagram on page 425 until they have a map of the continents as they exist today. This is a good opportunity to relate the themes of **Evolution** and **Patterns of Change** to the movement of the continents.

Ask students to predict how future drift might change the world as it is known today. Some predictions might include a wider Atlantic Ocean and a more northerly Africa, Australia, and South America. The arrows in diagram 5 on page 425 offer clues to other possible changes.

A Familiar Plate Boundary

Have students read page 426 and study the photographs. If students simulate a fault with modeling clay, they will see that friction causes the pieces to stick together unless the force is so great that the friction is overcome.

Answer to caption: In the photograph at the left, the view is along the San Andreas Fault, looking to the south. The North American Plate is on the left side, and the Pacific Plate is on the right side.

Answer to caption: In the photograph on the right, the view is looking westward from a vantage point on (or over) the North American Plate. Landforms that begin on the North American Plate, such as streambeds and chains of hills, "break" at the fault line and continue on in a more northerly location on the Pacific Plate. This shows that the Pacific Plate is moving north relative to the North American Plate.

 *Follow Up*

Assessment

1. Based on the diagram on page 425, ask students to summarize the history of the continent of North America. *(A possible response might be: 225 million years ago, North America was part of the single continent called Pangaea. It was near the equator and was probably very tropical. The east coast was attached to Eurasia. The south coast was attached to South America and Africa. The west coast faced an enormous ocean. About 180 million years ago, North America started to move away to the northwest. By 135 million years ago, North America's east coast was no longer connected to Africa, but it was still very close to Eurasia. It became fully separated about 65 million years ago and continued to move northwest as Greenland began to separate. North America is still moving west today.)*

A Familiar Plate Boundary

At some boundaries, the plates neither collide with each other nor pull apart. Rather, they slide past one another. In the United States, such a plate boundary can be found in California. It is the San Andreas fault. The San Andreas fault forms part of the boundary between the North American Plate and the Pacific Plate.

These plates do not always slide smoothly past each other. Friction causes the plates to "stick" and remain fixed in position for years at a time. Meanwhile, deep in the earth the strain continues to build. Eventually the strain grows too great and the rocks along the plate boundary give way suddenly, allowing the plates to quickly slide past each other a distance of up to several meters. In an instant, years of pent-up energy is released in the form of enormous shock waves. Earthquake!

Several times in this century major earthquakes have struck along the San Andreas fault, such as the ones in 1989 and 1992. Today, millions of people live in the vicinity of the San Andreas fault. It is only a matter of time before another major earthquake strikes, with potentially disastrous results. In fact, based on the historical average, many parts of the fault are "overdue" for a major quake.

As you might imagine, many scientists are working hard to perfect the science of earthquake prediction. What clues might help to indicate that a major quake is about to strike?

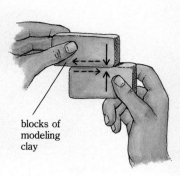

blocks of modeling clay

You can simulate what happens along the San Andreas fault by rubbing together two planed-off blocks of modeling clay. Try it. Try to slide the blocks past each other at the same time that you push them together. What happens?

A south-facing aerial view along the San Andreas fault. Locate the Pacific Plate. Locate the North American Plate.

A view across the San Andreas fault. What evidence in the picture suggests plate motion? In which direction are the plates moving?

2. Ask students to use a map of the world and their knowledge of plate tectonics to identify 10 cities that they predict are likely to experience serious earthquakes in the future. *(Answers may vary, but possible responses include: Los Angeles, Tokyo, San Francisco, Seattle, Anchorage, Mexico City, Manila, Naples, Beijing, and Bombay. All cities along the Pacific Rim are likely candidates.)*

Extension

1. Have students research what their local area was like millions of years ago. They can develop a written report and poster describing the climate, living things, and landforms of their area at different points in time.
2. Have students report on how sonar is used to map the ocean floor. They could make a classroom poster showing how soundings are taken by a ship on the open sea.

1. Locate the Hawaiian Islands on a globe or in an atlas. Notice how these islands "trail off" to the northwest. What might this signify? How might you use the theory of plate tectonics to explain the history of the Hawaiian Islands?

2. Photo mystery!
   Carefully examine the photo on the right. Make an inference about what happened to bring about the scene. Devise a way to test this inference.

3. A friend of yours has discovered what he thinks is a prehistoric cave painting. It is shown below. You realize right away that it couldn't possibly be genuine. How do you convince your friend that the cave painting is not genuine?

4. Imagine that you are a travel agent. You are offering submarine tours of a spreading center at the bottom of the ocean. Write a brochure or sales speech designed to convince an average tourist (not a geologist) to take this tour.

5. Imagine being able to witness the earth's entire history, from beginning to end, played back at one hundred billion times actual speed. Write a story about what you see and experience. First start at the beginning and work up to the present. Then extend the experience into the future. What ultimately happens to the earth?

Answers to
Challenge Your Thinking

1. Activity beneath the earth's surface is causing collected magma to be forced to the surface. This "hot spot" remains in place while the moving plate is carried over it, resulting in a series of islands. The islands "trail off" because once they are formed, the process of erosion begins. Those islands farthest away from the "hot spot" are the older, more eroded islands.

2. The layers in the rock show that the composition of the sediment may have changed over time. The whole area was then uplifted by some force, such as a folding of the landscape that occurs when two plates collide. Water flowing from a higher elevation then flowed through the area, cutting a V-shaped path through the landscape.

3. Humans and dinosaurs did not inhabit the earth at the same time.

4. Answers will vary but should include that molten rock from the earth's interior flows into the gap formed as plates move apart from a spreading center. Students should mention that tourists would see rugged mountain chains called mid-ocean ridges there too. Encourage creativity.

5. Answers will vary. Encourage students to base their story on what they have learned in this unit.

LESSON 3

※ Getting Started

In this lesson, students identify geological features in their schoolyard, from which they can make inferences about the area's geological history. Through a series of activities, students gain insight into the rate and causes of change in the environment.

Main Ideas

1. The geological history of an area can be determined by observing rocks, soil, landforms, and other features.
2. The earth is constantly changing.
3. Change takes place at various rates.
4. Changes may be classified as natural or human-caused.

※ Teaching Strategies

Changes in the Schoolyard

Call on a volunteer to read aloud the first two paragraphs on page 428. Then choose eight people to role-play the parts of the students on page 428. Invite the class to identify the clues mentioned by the students in the story. Possible clues include: fossils, "gravestone" shape of rocks, flatness or hilliness, underground rocks, soil.

Direct students' attention to the photographs shown on pages 428 and 429. Explain what each shows and how the feature was formed. Explain that the sinkhole was formed by the dissolution of minerals by ground water; the dinosaur footprint was formed when the animal made the footprints in soft mud, which became buried and fossilized.

3 Evidence of Change

Changes in the Schoolyard

A science class became curious about the geological history of their area when one of the students saw on television that a well-known geologist planned a public appearance in their town. They decided to invite her to visit their school.

This is how they prepared for the visit. They decided to collect clues that the geologist could use in explaining the forces that shaped the land where they lived and went to school. They started their investigation in the schoolyard. One student suggested that the location of each clue should be marked on a map. To help the geologist, the map would be mailed to her before she arrived. Then the class discussed the types of clues they should look for. The discussion went something like this:

"Let's look for fossils. Maybe we can find a dinosaur footprint," Konrad said.

"We found some fossils at camp one summer, but they weren't footprints, just some kind of plant," answered Dave.

"There are sure a lot of rocks out there. Do fossils form in rocks?" asked Adriana.

"Why do all the rocks look like gravestones?" Tanu'e asked.

"Maybe it's a graveyard," Kim replied with a smile.

Then Paco observed, "There are lots of rocks in front of the school but the playing field is flat."

"Maybe it was bulldozed," suggested Peter. "Maybe the rocks were buried underneath. Let's dig down and see. Maybe we'll find some clues under the ground like archaeologists do. Wouldn't it be something to find some old money?"

"Do you suppose that being on top of a big hill is a clue?" asked Heather. "What about the soil; is it a clue?"

You may not find geological evidence in your schoolyard as spectacular as the examples shown here, but you may be surprised by what you find. Top right: Lava basalt columns; bottom right: sinkholes; bottom left: a petrified tree stump.

LESSON 3 ORGANIZER

Objectives

By the end of the lesson, students should be able to:
1. Identify local geological features that can be used to infer the geological history of the area.
2. Appreciate the methods used by geologists in studying the geological history of an area.
3. Identify changes in the environment.
4. Consider different rates of change.
5. Distinguish between natural and human-caused changes.

Process Skills

observing, analyzing, inferring, recording data

New Terms

Sediments—sand, mud, and other loose material.

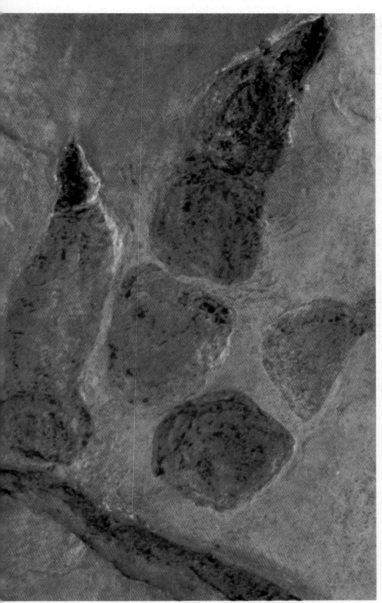

Dinosaur footprint,
Connecticut Valley, Massachusetts

Collecting Clues in the Schoolyard

1. Discuss in class how you would help the geologist. Then draw up a preliminary list of clues.
2. Go outside and observe! Add any other clues you think of to your list.
3. Draw a map. Indicate on the map where you found each clue.
4. Is your evidence complete? Do you have enough clues?

Analyze the clues to see what they can tell you about your area in geological terms. If your class is lucky enough to get a geologist to visit your school, ask for help in inferring the geological history of your schoolyard.

Clues	Possible History
1.	
2.	
3.	
4.	
etc.	

Other classes might be interested in your results, especially after watching your class working outside. Write a "Case Study Report," and describe what you found out about the geology of your schoolyard and the surrounding area. Share your discoveries with other classes.

Exploration 3

Before the activity, arrange for a geologist to visit the class. Also, be sure to check that the schoolyard has observable "clues." Review your knowledge of the general geological history of the local area. (Use a nearby park if there is not a suitable schoolyard.)

Make sure that students understand the threefold purpose of this activity:
1. To find clues that might reveal the geological history of the area.
2. To draw a map to identify the locations of the clues.
3. To make inferences from these clues about the geological history of the area.

Before going outside, start a list of possible clues on the chalkboard. Ask students to copy the list in their Journals to refer to when in the schoolyard. You may also wish to suggest that students collect soil, rock, and vegetation samples. They can look at these and study them following the activity in the schoolyard.

Materials

Exploration 3: Journal, shovels, meter sticks, and metric rulers
Gauging the Change: Journal
The Niagara Story: Journal
People and Change: magazines and newspapers

Teacher's Resource Binder

Resource Worksheets 8–3 and 8–4
Graphic Organizer Transparencies 8–4 and 8–5

Science Discovery Videodisc

Disc 2, Image and Activity Bank, 8–3

Time Required

four class periods

A Case Study in Change

James Hutton, a Scottish physician, was born in 1726. He is credited with providing geologists with a framework for thinking about the earth's history. His method was to learn all that he could about modern deposits of sediments and the processes that formed them. Then he compared them to any ancient deposits he discovered. In so doing, he made many valuable inferences regarding the earth's geological history. Have students read silently the first two paragraphs on page 430. Involve them in a discussion of their perceptions of local geological history. For example, do they think that their home community was ever under water or buried under ice? Discuss any evidence students have observed for these changes. Other changes students may want to discuss include changes from earthquakes and volcanic eruptions. If these are a part of the history in your area, ask students to describe any evidence of these changes.

The following is a list of questions you can use to help students evaluate the evidence they obtained in *Exploration 3*.

1. Is the land flat, sloping, or hilly? How can you tell?
2. Is the school at sea level? What proof do you have?
3. Are there a lot of rocks, or just a few? How large are they? What do they look like? Can you identify them? Are there rocks below the surface? If so, how far below? Do some stick out part-way?
4. Is the soil rocky or even, dense or thin? Can you tell what it is made of?
5. How many living things can you find growing in the schoolyard? Are they large, medium, or small?
6. Is there running water on or near the schoolyard?
7. What human-made features contribute to the environment?

A visiting geologist could help students collect clues in the schoolyard and then assist with the interpretation of these clues. The geologist could also give a short talk about the nature of his or her work.

If possible, bring in samples of sedimentary rocks, such as coarse-grained sandstones and mud shales. Let students examine the rock samples and hypothesize about how they were formed. Discuss the changes that occurred to turn loose sand or mud into rock.

If rock samples are not readily available, color photographs from a field guide on rocks and minerals can serve the same purpose.

A Case Study in Change

Do you find it hard to believe that the area in which you live was once buried under a thick layer of ice, or was once at the bottom of the sea? It is difficult to imagine the landscape being any different from the way it is now. In fact, it wasn't until the late 1700s that scientists began to explore some of the processes of change that must have taken place to produce the landscapes that exist today.

A Scottish medical doctor, James Hutton, made careful observations of the Scottish countryside in the late 1700s. He concluded that layers of rock are in fact hardened layers of sand, mud, and other loose material called **sediments.** Hutton is often called the "Father of Geology" because he developed a method of working out the earth's geologic history. Hutton believed that earth processes at work today have also been at work throughout time, and that the evidence of this could be seen in the rocks around us. "The present," Hutton said, "is the key to the past."

Flashback—Niagara Falls, 1678

In 1678 Father Louis Hennepin was the first European explorer to reach Niagara Falls. Read his description of what he saw and heard.

This wonderful downfall is compounded of two great cross-streams of water, and two falls, with an isle sloping along the middle of it. The waters that fall from this vast height do foam and boil after the most hideous manner imaginable, making an outrageous noise, more terrible than that of thunder, for when the wind blows, from off the south, their dismal roaring may be heard fifteen leagues off.

Compare the sketch based on Father Hennepin's description of Niagara Falls with this contemporary photograph. Both pictures feature a portion of the Falls now known as Horseshoe Falls. Look carefully at the right-hand side of each picture. What differences do you observe between the sketch and the photo?

Primary Source
Description of change: excerpted from *A New Discovery of a Vast Country in America,* by Louis Hennepin.
Rationale: excerpted to focus on Hennepin's description of Niagara Falls.

Flashback—Niagara Falls, 1678

Have students read the description of Niagara Falls written by Father Hennepin. Ask them to carefully study the sketch on page 430 and the photograph on page 431. Have students compare them and state any differences they observe. Answers may vary, but possible responses include:

- One is a drawing; the other is a photograph.
- The angle at which the observer is standing is different.
- The shape of the Falls seen in the photograph is considerably different than in the sketch. There are more curves and they are more exaggerated than those in the sketch.
- The sketch was made years ago; the photograph was taken recently.
- Highways, railroads, and a bridge are visible in the photograph.

Gauging the Change

Call on a volunteer to read the first paragraph and then direct students' attention to the diagram. The water is flowing over the waterfalls and into the Niagara River. Help students visualize the paths of the two waterways. Point out that the measurements made in 1678 and 1842 were to mark the position of the rock under the waterfall.

Have students notice that the recession of the Falls represents a fairly rapid change. Explain that recession, in this case, refers to the wearing away of the rock. Ask the class to name some causes for this change. *(Answers may vary, but possible responses include the type of rock and the force of the water.)* Involve the class in a discussion of why the rate of change has slowed since 1842. *(Answers may vary, but possible responses include that the volume of water going over the falls now has decreased and that the type of rock which is now exposed is more resistant to erosion.)*

Answers to

In-Text Questions

- In the illustration, the water is flowing from south to north, or from the top to the bottom.
- The rock under Horseshoe Falls is more deeply indented than that under the American Falls. This is because the water has been flowing over the top of Horseshoe Falls for a longer period.
- Horseshoe Falls receded about 340 m between 1678 and the present (measured at the curve of the falls). The rate of recession between 1678 and the present in meters per year is 340/313 = 1.1 m per year. American Falls has receded about 25 m since 1842 (0.17 m per year).
- The erosion has occurred at different rates because of differences in rock type, volume of water, or speed of the water.
- Over the past 300 years, the water has eroded the rocks to create an elongated shape. The shape has changed from a gentle curve to a deep horseshoe and then to a "bent" horseshoe.
- No, the type of rock and force of the water would vary along the crest,

Gauging the Change

Niagara Falls has changed since Father Hennepin first saw it in 1678. Study the diagram below. Each broken line represents a survey carried out during the year indicated. How have the Falls changed over the years?

Answer the following questions in your Journal.

- Which way is the water flowing in the illustration?

- How do Horseshoe Falls and the American Falls differ? What accounts for the difference?

- How far did Horseshoe Falls recede (wear away) between 1678 and the present? How far has the American Falls receded since 1842? What is the rate of recession in meters per year for each of the Falls?

- Why have Horseshoe Falls and the American Falls eroded at different rates?

- How has the shape of the Falls changed in the last 300 years?

- Do all parts of the crestline (edge of the cliff) change at the same rate? Why or why not?

- What do you infer will happen to the shape of the Falls in the future?

- Where do you predict the Falls will be in 50 years? in 5000 years?

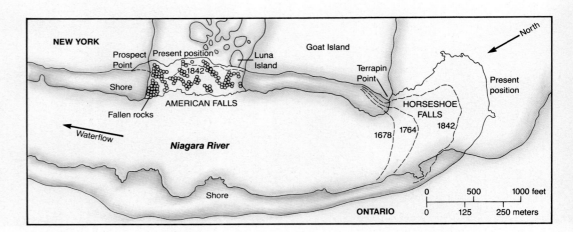

creating differences in recession rates. Students can quantify these differences by measuring the distance between recession lines at different points and calculating the recession rate for those points.
- The shape of the Falls will continue to curve and elongate.
- In 50 years, the Falls will probably have receded an additional 50 m, and will not appear very different from the way it looks now. In 5000 years it will have receded possibly as much as 5000 m, and it will be much farther upriver.

The Niagara Story

Niagara Falls has not always existed. In fact, in geologic terms Niagara Falls are extremely young—only about 12,000 years old! The Falls formed at the end of the last ice age as the huge glaciers that covered the continent retreated northward. Meltwaters caused the newly formed Lake Erie to overflow, forming the Niagara River.

What you have just read is "Chapter 1" of the Niagara Story. The illustrations below tell more of the story. Your job is to use these illustrations, along with your knowledge of earth processes, to bring the story up to date. Write the next chapter of the Niagara Story in your Journal. Then answer the questions below.

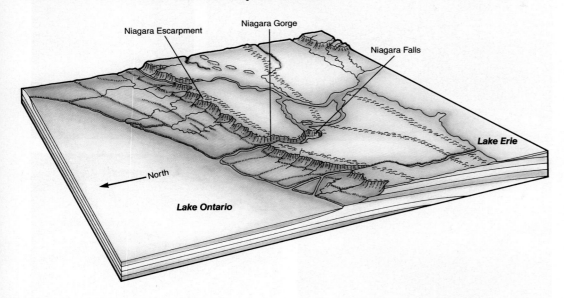

Points to Ponder

1. How did the Niagara Gorge form?
2. Why do the Falls not erode away?
3. What will happen to the Falls in the future?
4. If the present trend continues, what might eventually happen to Niagara falls?
5. What might eventually happen to Lake Erie?

Now write the final chapter of the Niagara Story in your Journal.

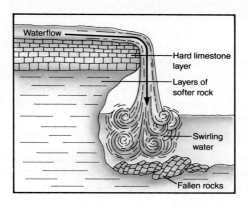

Answers to

Points to Ponder

1. The flow of water wore away the softer rock beneath the surface limestone. The surface then collapsed. This process, occurring over and over again, formed the Niagara Gorge.
2. The limestone wears down more slowly than the rock beneath, forming a "lip" for the waterfall.
3. The location of the Falls will continue to shift upriver.
4. Eventually, it will move so far upriver that it will actually cease to exist. Instead there will be a deep gorge reaching from Lake Erie to Lake Ontario.
5. • Eventually, Lake Erie might merge with Lake Ontario.
   • A final chapter for Niagara Falls might be:
   Eventually, there will be a straight channel between Lake Erie and Lake Ontario. All the rock will have been worn down and eroded away.

The Niagara Story

Call on a volunteer to read aloud the first two paragraphs to the class. Then direct students' attention to the illustration. Point out the location of Lake Erie, the overflow water from Lake Erie, and the Niagara River. Be sure students visualize this path. Ask them to pinpoint the Falls and the Gorge. Ask them to explain those terms in reference to the diagram. Explain the meaning of *Niagara Escarpment* to students if they cannot infer its meaning from the diagram. An escarpment is a steep cliff formed by erosion or by faulting between plates. Remind students about the process of erosion and its effects on rock. Then suggest that they continue the Niagara Story in their Journals.
A possible entry might be:

The Niagara River flowed over the hard limestone for many thousands of years. At the edge of the limestone, there was softer rock. As the water fell over the edge, the softer rock beneath the limestone wore away. With nothing to support it, the edge of the hard limestone collapsed. This happened over and over again for many thousands of years. Finally, the Niagara Gorge was formed. The edge of the Falls continues to move upriver at the rate of approximately 1 m per year.

What Caused the Change?

This exercise gives students an opportunity to review the terms *erosion* and *weathering*. These concepts will be considered in more depth in the next few lessons.

Discuss the agent of change in each photograph. Encourage free discussion and new ideas.

Answers to

In-Text Questions

Sample answers for the table can be found below.

Arranging the changes in order from fastest to slowest may lead to some debate. The most likely order is: roadcut; river in flood; gravestone weathering; and horizontal layering of rock.

Humans can have the following effects on these changes:

1. They can speed up or slow down the bulldozing of the land.
2. They can prevent weathering by applying protective materials to the gravestone; keeping it clean; and/or preventing the effects of acid rain.
3. They can slow down shore erosion by building breakwaters and retaining walls.
4. Humans cannot affect the horizontal layering of rock.

What Caused the Change?

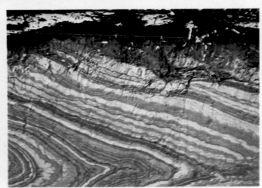

In each picture above a change has occurred or is taking place. Your tasks are (a) to identify the change, (b) to suggest what has caused the change, and (c) to decide whether the change was caused by natural or human forces. Record your conclusions in a table using these headings:

Change   Cause   Natural   Human

Now, arrange the changes in order from the fastest to the slowest. Which changes could humans speed up, slow down, or affect in some other way?

Answer to Table, In-Text Questions

	Photo	Change	Cause	Natural	Human
1.	Roadcut	alteration of landscape	person and machine	no	yes
2.	Gravestone	weathering	gases in air, air pollution, and moisture	yes	yes
3.	River in flood	erosion of shore	moving water	yes	no
4.	Rock layers	horizontal layering of rock	pressure within the earth	yes	no

A Science Project: Recognizing Change

Look for a feature in your backyard, on the way to school, or around your town that seems to show a change taking place. It might be a crack in a rock, a piece of bare ground, or a gully formed in a hill by running water.

Once you have found a suitable feature, prove that a change is occurring. The following ideas will help you conduct your project scientifically.

Before you begin your investigation, plan ahead. Observe the condition of the feature over a period of time. Compare its condition before you started your investigation with its condition afterward. Write down what you see in your Journal; it's easy to forget details after a while. (Sketches and diagrams often help.) When you have completed your observations, prepare a report using the following headings:

1. Results of the Investigation. (Write down what change you observed.)
2. Investigating the Change. (Give details of how you collected your information.)
3. Results Obtained. (Include drawings, photos, data sheet, etc.)
4. Inferences and Summary. (What caused the change? Will change continue to take place? What will eventually result? Can the change be reversed? Can humans have any effect on the change?)

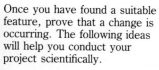

Exploration 4

This Exploration can be assigned as a long-term science project to be done at home. To be sure that students understand what they are expected to do, spend part of a class period discussing the organization of the project. Have students think about the *purpose of their project, the specific research methods they will use, the raw data they plan to collect,* and *what analysis needs to be done.*

Have students check with you as each phase is completed. In this way, you can review their progress and suggest improvements. If some students are unable to think of an investigation of their own, they can duplicate Chuck's investigation described on page 436.

People and Change

Divide the class into small discussion groups. Ask each group to discuss and classify the 10 changes listed. When the groups have finished, reassemble the class to discuss their classifications. Students can assemble photos and illustrations of man-made changes in a poster or folder. Ask students to briefly describe the changes as harmful or beneficial and to give their reasons.

Answers to

In-Text Questions

The following are general answers and should vary according to the points raised.

Change for the Better
(although students may correctly observe that some environmental damage is possible)
1. Irrigation of the desert
3. Building dams to control floods
5. Draining swamps to make farmland
8. Using the tides to generate electric power
9. Constructing breakwaters along the seacoast

Change for the Worse
4. Strip mining coal

Difficult to Classify
2. Clearing land to build houses. Clearing large tracts of land destroys animal habitat and can lead to problems such as flooding and soil damage. However, people need housing.
6. Clear-cutting the forest. If reforestation is being practiced, the harm to the environment is lessened. Otherwise, problems similar to those mentioned in number 2 can occur.
7. Plowing land for crops. This depends on whether wise farming methods are being practiced. If not, soil can be seriously depleted.
10. Damming rivers for hydroelectric power. Although hydroelectric power is a natural way to meet energy needs, it is still controversial because of the attendant changes imposed on people and the environment.

EXPLORATION 4—CONT.

One Student's Investigation

Chuck decided to watch for a change under a downspout at the corner of his house. First, he took a photo and made a drawing of the area directly under the downspout. Then he observed the area closely. He noticed that a change occurred after a rainfall. He made measurements of the changed area. Chuck also made notes about some features of the area: the number of rocks, their appearance, size, and position, as well as any living things nearby. After each rainfall, he made further observations and measurements. Finally, Chuck summarized his findings in a brief report.

People and Change

Most of the changes examined in this unit are changes brought about by natural causes such as glaciers, earthquakes, flowing water, and gravity. Yet changes in our environment that are caused by humans also occur all the time. Some would be classified by most people as "improvements," others would not. Look over the list below. In your Journal classify each change as either *for the better, for the worse,* or *difficult to classify.* Try to see the positive and negative aspects of each situation. Briefly explain your classification of each change.

1. Irrigating the desert
2. Clearing land to build houses
3. Building dams to control floods
4. Strip mining for coal
5. Draining swamps to make farmland
6. Clear-cutting the forest
7. Plowing land for crops
8. Using the tides to generate electric power
9. Constructing breakwaters along the seacoast
10. Damming rivers for hydroelectric power

Can you find specific examples of changes such as these in newspapers and magazines? Look for articles and photographs showing the effects of human-caused changes.

✹ *Follow Up*

Assessment

Have students examine a building such as their home or school and analyze what has been done in the design and construction to help it resist changes due to processes such as flooding and weathering. *(Answers will vary but may describe drainage systems, exterior paint or siding, caulking, and weatherstripping.)*

Extension

1. Have students do some research to identify other landforms that give clues to the geological history of their area. They may do library research or contact a local museum or college.
2. Have students interview older members of the community in regards to changes in landforms they may have witnessed. *(the effects of erosion, weathering, and man-made changes)* After the interviews have been completed, suggest that students use the information to write a feature story for a newspaper.

4 Examining One Type of Change

Detecting Change

Change is taking place in each of these pictures. Can you figure out what it is?

Agents of Change

Were you able to detect that the rocks in each of the photos were being broken or worn down? This process is known as **weathering.** Water, wind, and ice all work to cause weathering. Human-caused phenomena, such as acid rain, can accelerate the weathering process. Living things such as lichens and mosses can also contribute to weathering.

All exposed materials weather, not just rocks. Housepaint, concrete, glass, brick—even steel—all undergo change because of the action of weathering agents. Some materials merely take longer than others to show the effects of weathering.

LESSON 4 ORGANIZER

Objectives

By the end of the lesson, students should be able to:

1. Identify examples and causes of weathering.
2. Appreciate that weathering occurs at various rates.
3. Identify factors that determine the rate of weathering.
4. Relate these factors to weathering in the local environment.

Process Skills

observing, predicting, analyzing data, drawing conclusions

New Terms

Weathering—the process by which exposed surfaces are broken and worn down.

(Organizer continues on next page)

LESSON 4

✳ *Getting Started*

In this lesson, students identify examples of weathering and consider whether it is a helpful or harmful process. Through a variety of activities, students determine factors that affect the rate of weathering and relate these findings to their local environment.

Main Ideas

1. Weathering is a process by which rocks are worn down and broken by water, ice, air, pollutants, and the activities of plants and animals.
2. The amount and rate of weathering is determined by a variety of factors.

✳ *Teaching Strategies*

Detecting Change

Ask students to identify the change that is taking place in each photograph. The first photograph shows how differences in rock composition affect rates of erosion, causing this strange structure. The lichens on the rocks produce acids that break down rock surfaces. The headstone has worn away due to cracks formed by wind, water, and ice. Ice in the freezing stream causes the waterway to expand and erode more of the surrounding land.

Agents of Change

Have students read silently the bottom half of page 437. Ask them about the causes of weathering and the materials that are usually affected by the weathering process. *(causes: water, wind, ice; materials: any exposed surfaces, not just rocks)*
(Continues on next page)

(Agents of Change continued)

You might want to point out to students that weathering can be classified as physical or chemical. Physical weathering breaks down rocks but does not change their mineral composition. Chemical weathering occurs when chemical reactions occur between the exposed material and the environment. Water, frozen and unfrozen, is the main agent of physical weathering. Plants and animals are also involved in physical weathering. Such human activities as irrigation, dam and highway building, mining, and quarrying also break down rocks.

Chemical weathering breaks down rocks and, in the process, changes their minerals into new products such as soil. Most chemical weathering changes are brought about by the action of carbon dioxide, water, and oxygen. Carbon dioxide combines with water to produce a weak acid which reacts chemically with the rock to break it down. Rocks can also be oxidized to form new minerals. Iron-bearing rocks are good examples of this process.

Exploration 5

Divide the class into small groups. Ask them to make their tables in their Journals before they go outside. Instruct students to choose three different locations and to complete their tables with the information they discover. Comments on the rate of change and suggestions as to how the weathering process could be slowed or prevented could also be included. Reassemble the groups when the activity is completed and involve students in a discussion of their results.

Investigating Rock-Breaking Forces

Do you know how much force you would need to break a rock? Have you ever tried to do so? Some rocks break easily, but usually it requires tremendous force. However, though you may not realize it, rock-breaking forces are present in your schoolyard and are acting at this very instant. Think of all the places where there is rock, brick, or concrete. Check out some of them on your way home from school. Can you find evidence that forces of change are at work?

Choose three different locations to investigate. Consider the suggestions made below as you carry out your study.

1. If your school is made of brick, check for rounded corners, cracks, chips, or rough surfaces in the brick. Does the mortar stick out or recede? Does the brick look old? If your school is made of something other than brick, can you find evidence of weathering?

2. Check the foundation of your school. Are there any rough and irregular surfaces, cracks, or broken corners? Compare each side of the foundation. Do you notice any difference in the amount of weathering?

3. Find a rock. Break away a portion to expose a fresh surface. Compare exposed and fresh surfaces.
   Be Careful: *Wear safety goggles when chipping or breaking rock.*

4. Look for moss or lichen growing on exposed rocks. Gently peel away the lichen and feel the rock surface underneath. Compare this surface to that of a rock that is free of moss or lichen.

5. Examine sidewalks, stone fences, or concrete pillars. Is the concrete cracking, breaking, or crumbling? Are there trees or other plants growing nearby whose root systems may be affecting the concrete in some way?

Keeping a Record

Summarize your findings in your Journal in a table like this:

Location	Evidence of Weathering	Cause(s)	Comments
sidewalk	cracks, broken corners	frost, tree roots	Sidewalk built in 1985—only a few cracks

---

(Organizer continued)

Materials

Exploration 5: hammer, safety goggles, Journal

Exploration 7
Simulation 1: rock samples (granite, limestone, sandstone, brick, piece of concrete), magnifying glass, containers for soaking rocks, trays, freezer, water, watch or clock with second hand

Simulation 2: one whole piece of chalk, 200 mL dilute hydrochloric acid, two 250-mL beakers, graduated cylinder, paper towels, safety goggles, gloves, apron
Simulation 3: 100 g marble chips, water, 2 containers with lids, 100 g quartzite, balance scale, clock or watch

Teacher's Resource Binder

Resource Worksheet 8–5
Graphic Organizer Transparency 8–6

Science Discovery Videodisc

Disc 2, Image and Activity Bank, 8–4

Time Required

four class periods

Monuments to Change

If there is a graveyard in your community that is over 100 years old, you have the makings of an interesting project.

Problem 1

What is the relationship between the amount of weathering and the length of time a monument has been exposed?
Hint: Find stones of different ages made from the same kind of rock. Look for newer ones (0–100 years old), older ones (over 150 years old), and some in between. Compare the amount of weathering.

Problem 2

Do different types of stones weather at different rates?
Hint: Find several gravestones of approximately the same age but made of different kinds of rock. Compare the amount of weathering in each.
What do you conclude from your study?

How Are They Affected?

If you worked at one of the jobs below, how would weathering affect you?

How are these gentlemen affected by weathering?

Exploration 6

This activity could be assigned as an individual project or reserved for a class field trip. Remind students that they should treat the land and gravestones with respect.

Problem 1

Generally, the longer a gravestone has been exposed, the greater the amount of weathering. Remind students to keep a list of the ages of the stones and the amount of weathering as they proceed.

Problem 2

Harder rock, such as granite, will probably show less weathering than rock made of marble, even if the age of the rocks are the same. Again, remind students to take careful notes of their findings. Encourage them to make sketches of their observations as well.

Students may conclude from *Exploration 6* that gravestones exposed for longer periods will show more weathering. However, harder rocks, such as granite, weather more slowly than softer rocks, such as marble.

Weathering: How Fast?

Ask students to read silently the material on the left side of page 440. Involve them in a discussion of the places in which weathering would be the least harmful. Ask them to support their predictions with reasons. Weathering does not occur at the same rate all over the world. The desert and moon locations would be the best choices. *(the desert, because of its low humidity; the moon, because it has no atmosphere)*

Exploration 7
Simulation 1

Divide the class into small groups, with one set of rock samples for each. Label each rock with a number. (Samples of the local bedrock could be examined in addition to the rocks named in the text.) Allow several class periods for them to examine the rocks. Students should record any changes they observe.

After the simulation is finished, involve students in a discussion of the effects of temperature changes on rocks. Ask students to name which type of climate they think has the slowest rate of weathering. *(a hot, dry climate or a cold, dry climate)* Discuss with students the importance of water and climatic change in weathering rates. *(Water contributes to weathering from ice formation and contributes to chemical reactions with the rock.)* Point out to students that water seeps into the cracks in rocks. If the water freezes, its volume expands by 10 percent. Every time the water thaws and refreezes, it wedges farther into the rock. More rock surface is then exposed to chemical weathering. Emphasize that changes in the climate cause stress in the rocks, which increases weathering.

Weathering: How Fast?

What Is Your Prediction?

Does weathering occur at the same rate all over the world? If you were in the business of selling gargoyles, where could you offer the longest guarantee on your product? Make a prediction.

1. Polar regions
2. Tropics
3. Desert
4. Mountains
5. Prairies
6. Coastal regions
7. On the moon
8. Where you live

Three Simulations

It is very difficult to determine the speed of weathering through actual observation (not to mention very time-consuming). Real rocks take a very long time to break down. Sometimes, however, laboratory activities can *simulate* (imitate) what happens in the environment. Three factors that might affect the speed of weathering are investigated in the simulations that follow.

Simulation 1

What effect do freezing and thawing have on rocks? Make a prediction.

You Will Need

- a magnifying glass
- rock samples (granite, limestone, sandstone, brick, a piece of concrete)
- a tray
- a freezer

What to Do

1. Examine your samples using the magnifying glass. Can you find any cracks where water might enter?
2. Take a sample of each type of rock and soak it in water. After several minutes, remove it and place it in a tray in the freezer overnight.
3. The next day, remove the samples from the freezer, and allow the rocks to heat up to room temperature.
4. Examine the samples for any changes. Then repeat the process of soaking, freezing, and thawing. If time allows, repeat the freezing/thawing cycle several times.

Answers to

Questions

1. Students should have found that the greatest change occurred with sandstone and concrete, the least change with granite.
2. The activity simulates the repeated processes of freezing and thawing.

Questions

1. Compare what happens to the different samples. Which sample shows the greatest change? the least change?
2. How does this simulation relate to conditions in the environment?

Simulation 2

Do small pieces of rock weather faster than large pieces? Make a prediction.

You Will Need

- A whole piece of chalkboard chalk
- dilute hydrochloric acid
- two 250-mL beakers

What to Do

1. Break a piece of chalkboard chalk in half. Put aside one half and break the other half into several small pieces. (You can wrap it in a paper towel and hit it with a hammer.)
2. Carefully pour 200 mL of dilute hydrochloric acid into each beaker.
3. Place the larger piece of chalk in one beaker, and the smaller pieces in the other.

Questions

1. In which beaker did the bubbling last the longest?
2. What happened to the chalk in each beaker?
3. What comparison can you make between this investigation and the natural weathering process?

Simulation 3

Do some kinds of rocks resist weathering better than others? One class investigated this problem by using pre-soaked marble chips and quartzite. They weighed out 100 g of each rock and placed each in a container about half full of water. After putting on the cover, they shook each container for 5 minutes at a rate set before the experiment. After draining each container, they weighed and recorded the mass of the chips and quartzite. They repeated the procedure three more times, weighing each sample after each 5 minute shaking, for a total of 20 minutes. Their results are recorded in the table.

Time (min)	Mass of Marble Chips Remaining (g)	Mass of Quartzite Chips Remaining (g)
0	100.0	100.0
5	98.5	99.7
10	96.9	99.6
15	95.3	99.3
20	92.7	99.2

How Fast Does Weathering Occur in Your Community?

Weathering occurs at different rates, depending on the conditions in the environment. Suggest conditions in the environment that affect the speed of weathering (other than those you have already dealt with, of course.)

Make a list of all the factors in your area that might help determine the speed of weathering.

Questions

1. Which kind of rock lost the greatest amount of mass?
2. What inferences can you make about the resistance of marble to weathering? the resistance of quartzite to weathering?
3. During which time period did the greatest loss of mass from the marble chips occur? Can you explain this?
4. What do you think might happen if you shook each sample for 1 hour?
5. How does this investigation simulate the weathering process?

Simulation 3

This experiment shows that quartzite resists weathering more than marble does. It simulates both weathering and erosion as one piece of material hits another. Students should conclude that some materials resist change better than others.

Answers to

Questions

1. The marble lost the greatest amount of mass.
2. Quartzite is more resistant to weathering than marble is.
3. The greatest loss of mass from the marble chips occurred between 15 and 20 minutes. The reason is that more surface area was being exposed as the rock broke into smaller pieces.
4. The mass of each would continue to decrease.
5. It simulates the weathering process by showing how rocks can be eroded when they are shaken and when they collide with each other and with water.

Assessment

Present students with the following situation: You have been asked to design a statue for a park in Butte, Montana. What kind of research would you have to do before you could decide on the type of stone to use? *(Investigate the climate of the area: amount of rainfall, humidity, temperature variation, and ice formation.)*

Extension

Moisten some steel wool and place it in a closed plastic container. Ask students to observe it for several days. Ask: What changes can be seen? Is the "weathered" steel wool as strong as the original? Explain. Is this an example of physical or chemical weathering? *(Chemical: the iron is combining with oxygen to produce iron oxide, or rust. "Weathered" steel would not be as strong as the original because the fibers weaken due to corrosion.)*

Simulation 2

Set up the materials needed by each group at separate work stations. Since dilute hydrochloric acid is used, this activity provides an excellent opportunity to discuss laboratory safety.

Answers to

Questions

1. the beaker with the smaller pieces of chalk
2. In both beakers, some chalk may disappear. More chalk disappears in the beaker with smaller pieces.
3. Small rocks weather faster than large rocks.

✳ *Getting Started*

In this lesson, students are introduced to the concept of erosion. They learn that the force of gravity is ultimately responsible for all erosion. Students use a model to explore landslides. The lesson concludes with a discussion of mudslides and avalanches.

Main Ideas

1. Erosion is a type of weathering in which parts of the earth's surface are carried away primarily by wind and water.
2. Gravitational force is ultimately responsible for all erosion.
3. Downslope movements include landslides, mudslides, and avalanches.

✳ *Teaching Strategies*

Weathering Wonders

After students have read page 442, ask them to carefully observe the photographs. The photographs should help students conclude that weathered materials are removed in various ways, primarily by wind and water. Examples of clues: grooves formed by running water and visible dust clouds. Bryce Canyon, Utah, was formed from many tiny streams, which caused both chemical and physical weathering. The weathered materials were then removed by both wind and water.

⑤ Gravity—The Great Leveler

Weathering Wonders

Where does the debris from weathering go? Imagine how the earth would look if the debris of billions of years of weathering were piled up where it had formed. Why do you think this doesn't happen?

In these photographs, what indications are there that loose weathered material has been removed?

LESSON ⑤ ORGANIZER

Objectives

By the end of the lesson, students should be able to:
1. Understand changes caused by erosion.
2. Realize that the force of gravity underlies the erosion caused by water, ice, and wind.
3. Distinguish between different types of downslope movements.

Process Skills

observing, inferring, analyzing, creative writing

New Terms

Erosion—the carrying away of weathered soil, rock, and other materials. The agents of erosion are gravity, wind, glaciers, and moving water.

Erosion and Gravitational Force

The weathering and carrying away of soil, rock, and other materials is known as **erosion.** Erosion is caused by many natural agents. Flowing water, wind, waves, and glaciers all continually wear away the land. The most important source of erosion, though, is the flowing water in streams and rivers. Water carries away more rock and soil than all the other causes of weathering put together. Consider this fact: The Yellow River in China moves over 2000 million tons of sediment per year!

Gravity plays a role in all types of erosion. The earth exerts a pull on everything on or near the planet's surface. The result of this is that things tend to move downhill until they can move no farther. Boulders and other loose rocks roll or slide downhill. Rivers and streams flow downhill. Glaciers grind their way slowly downhill. Water vapor carried to high elevations by the air eventually falls as rain or snow. Wind redistributes fine particles by picking them up one place and then dropping them somewhere else. None of these erosive processes could happen without gravity.

Erosion and Gravitational Force

Call on a volunteer to read aloud the two paragraphs on page 443. Ask another student to explain the term *erosion.* Call on a volunteer to name the causes of erosion. *(gravity, flowing water, wind, waves, and glaciers)* Invite another student to explain the term gravity and how it affects erosion. *(The pull of gravity tends to force things to move downhill.)* Emphasize the role of gravity in the process of erosion, and continue to draw attention to it in subsequent lessons.

This is a good opportunity to discuss students' personal observations of erosion in action. Discuss the appearance of rivers from afar. The sediment they carry is often visible and gives the river a distinctive color or a muddy appearance.

Some rivers have been named for the color of the sediments they carry. For example, the Yellow River in China actually carries sediments that give it a distinctive yellowish color for part of its length. The Colorado River, which runs through the southwestern United States and formed the Grand Canyon, gets its name from the reddish sediments it carries. The word *colorado* is colloquial Spanish for "red." The Red River, which runs through the states of Texas, Arkansas, and Louisiana, received its name for the same reason.

If there are local or regional parks with hiking trails nearby, suggest that students visit these areas. If it is possible, invite a ranger or naturalist to talk to the class about the impact of erosion in park areas.

Materials

Exploration 8: board, sand, water, tray, wood blocks or bricks to prop up the board, pitcher

Science Discovery Videodisc

Disc 2, Image and Activity Bank, 8–5

Time Required

two class periods

"Landslide Claims 66"

After students have read the newspaper account of the Frank slide, help them to visualize the scene during and after the landslide. Ask them to look at the photograph and imagine tons of rocks sliding down the mountain. This will help them to appreciate the effects of this disaster on human life. Remind them that the account of the 1903 disaster would have been communicated by newspapers, since television had not yet been invented.

A possible activity to accompany this article could be to have students role-play on-the-spot reporters. They could report orally, or develop written copy describing what they found at the scene.

Use this opportunity to discuss students' personal observations of landslides. Ask: How can you tell if an area is likely to have slides? *(Disrupted vegetation, loose rocks, and visible debris are usually seen in slide-prone areas.)*

Answers to

Analyzing the Frank Slide

1. Rocks, gravel, soil, and water, as well as living things, can slide down a slope.
2. These materials can be loosened by water between soil particles, by the alternate freezing and thawing of water, and by earthquake vibrations.
3. Huge rocks could easily move down a steep hill once they were dislodged.
4. The slide itself could not have been prevented. However, if its warning signs are detected early enough, people can be evacuated from the area. Cracks in the ground or in walls and foundations, trees at an angle in the ground, and breaking underground pipes are all signs of potential slides.
5. Slides can occur wherever the incline is steep enough and where soil and rocks are not held firmly in place by vegetation.
6. The force of the rocks and other material breaking loose caused a compression wave to form in the air, like one that forms when a bomb goes off.

Landslide Claims 66

FRANK, ALTA., CANADA— April 29, 1903

At 4:10 A.M. this morning, seventy million tons of Turtle Mountain broke loose without warning and plummeted into the valley below, cutting a swath of total destruction through the heart of this small rural community and killing 66 people as they slept. Eyewitnesses report that the slide moved at tremendous speed, leaving no time for escape.

A few lucky survivors were hurled to safety by a blast of air that preceded the slide as it raced downhill.

Rescue operations are underway as police, firemen, and members of the community dig through up to 100 feet of soil and rock strewn across the valley floor for a distance of 2 miles. Officials admit the chance of finding any survivors is very slim.

It is believed that the slide was triggered by unusually heavy spring rains.

Analyzing the Frank Slide

1. What types of materials slide down a slope?
2. What might cause them to come loose?
3. Have you ever tried to move a large rock? How easily might a large rock move down a steep hill?
4. Do you think that the Frank slide could have been prevented?
5. Where else might slides also occur?
6. What caused the blast of air that preceded the Frank slide?

A Model Landslide

Each year one of the projects in Mrs. Jefferson's class is to build a model and do an experiment with it. Pam and Sanjay decided to build a model that would help them figure out what causes slides. Pam and Sanjay thought of three ways to get the sand to slide:

1. Pour water on the sand.
2. Pile the sand deeper.
3. Make the angle of the board steeper.

damp sand

What other methods might Pam and Sanjay have tried? Do all these methods cause the sand to slide down the board? Test them and find out. Can you think of any natural occurrences that parallel your investigations?

Exploration 8

Review the concept of a *fair test* with students. Discuss how to control the variables in this experiment in order to make the comparisons valid. Emphasize that only one factor or variable can be investigated, or changed, at a time, and that the others must be controlled, or kept constant. For example, the sand must be piled to the same height each time, unless the effect of depth of sand is being investigated. Similarly, the angle of the board must be kept constant, unless board angle is the variable that is being studied.

Divide the class into small groups. Ask each group to investigate a different variable and to demonstrate it to the rest of the class.

Answers to

In-Text Questions

1. Other methods of causing the sand to slide include: jarring the board, pushing on the sand, or even using material other than sand on the board (clay, topsoil, or a mixture of sand and gravel).
2. Students will probably answer in the affirmative.
3. Natural occurrences that parallel the investigations:
   - Pouring water on sand parallels soil saturation after a rain.
   - Piling on more sand parallels the buildup of snow or loose rocks.
   - Changing the angle of the board parallels the natural differences that exist in the degree of slope.
   - Changing type of material parallels the natural differences among the materials that are present on a slope.
   - Jarring the board parallels naturally occurring earthquake vibrations.
   - Pushing on the sand parallels the natural occurrence of a small slide starting a larger one.

Answers to

Other Downslope Movements

A Mudslide:
A heavy rainfall can cause mud to slide. The water between the soil particles loosens the mud.

An Avalanche:
Avalanches are easily started. Depending on snowfall and weather conditions, the slightest added weight (such as a clump of snow falling off a tree), or even a sudden sound (such as a gunshot), can start the slide. Sometimes, avalanches are started deliberately by means of explosives. This is done in order to prevent an unexpected slide. Avalanche speeds can range up to 160 km/h. The most serious avalanches occur on slopes of 30° to 40°.

Answers to

Summing Up

1. Encourage students to write about the sights and sounds of a landslide or avalanche in their story. Instruct them to avoid an over-emotional or "horror story" approach. (Accounts have been published of people who were found alive after being buried by avalanches. A library search might provide a model.)

2. This word list should help students to connect all the concepts they have encountered in their study of downslope movements.

✳ Follow Up

Assessment

From the information learned in *Exploration 8,* suggest that students design a device that could prevent landslides.

Other Downslope Movements

Each photograph shows a type of downslope movement.

Above, a *mudslide*—What triggered this event?

Above, an *avalanche*—What causes an avalanche? Sometimes avalanches are deliberately started. Why do you think this is done?

Summing Up

1. Write a human interest magazine article entitled "I Survived the Frank Slide," or "Buried Alive in an Avalanche!"

2. Write an explanatory paragraph entitled "Downslope Movements." Use as many of the following words as you can in your description: *weathering, air, debris, water, angle, rockfall, glacier, erosion, creep, slide, snow, earthquake, slowly, avalanche, mountain, rain, gravity, downhill, boulder,* and *mud.*

Extension

1. Have students research areas where avalanches occur. Ask them to find out how avalanches can be predicted. They can prepare a written report or a poster report for classroom display.

2. Have students research the impact of soil erosion on farm communities in their state or region. Sources could include agricultural extension stations, newspaper accounts, or interviews.

1. You are a sculptor, and you have been asked to design a monument that will be placed in downtown New York City. How would you go about determining what type of stone would be the best to use? What would you have to know?

2. Weathering processes fall into two categories: physical and chemical. Limestone dissolving to form caves is an example of chemical weathering. The cracking of rock during a freeze-thaw cycle is an example of physical weathering. Classify the following examples of weathering as "chemical," "physical," or "not enough information to say."

   • A rock splits open after a day in the hot sun.

   • A block of sandstone grows soft and crumbly after being exposed to water for a period of time.

   • A rock breaks into pieces when it is heated.

   • A rock develops a grayish color after being left outside.

   • A rock is ground down during a flash flood.

   • A rock's surface is crumbly where a lichen grew on it.

3. After a twenty year absence, Rip returns to his hometown. He is dumbfounded. "Why it's just as I left it. It hasn't changed a bit. Look—the sidewalk still has my initials scratched in it. The old sycamore tree we used to have the tire swing on is still there by the old stone church. It hasn't changed and neither has the church. The creek is still crystal clear. It hasn't changed..." Were things truly "just as Rip left them," or should he take a closer look? What would Rip see if he looked more closely?

LESSON 6

☀ Getting Started

In this lesson, students are introduced to the power of water as an agent of erosion. They learn about rainfall, runoff, porosity, permeability, and water distribution. Students apply these concepts to three practical situations.

Main Ideas

1. Raindrops strike the earth with great force, breaking off fragments of rock and creating runoff.
2. The volume of water absorbed by the ground is a measure of soil porosity.
3. The rate at which water can pass through a porous material is a measure of the material's permeability.

☀ Teaching Strategies

Use the diagram to open a discussion of the possible places that rain might go. List student answers on the board. Possible responses include: rocks and soil, the stream, the lake, the well, the plants, and the building.

Answers to

A Numbers Game

Review the concept of area with students. Calculators are suggested.
- Students should determine what fraction of a hectare their head represents and then multiply this by the number of raindrops. This number can then be multiplied by the time needed to walk home.

(Answers continue on next page)

---

6 The Power of Water

"Rain, rain, go away;
Come again some other day."

Have you ever spoken these words as you watched the rain fall? No doubt you wished that the rain would stop, but think of the rhyme in another way. Rain really does go away. Even the heaviest downpour seems to disappear shortly after it strikes the ground. Where does it go? Look closely at the diagram. How many different places might a raindrop go?

A Numbers Game

Fact: In an average rainfall, over 12 million raindrops fall on every hectare (10,000 square meters) of land or surface every second!

- Calculate the number of raindrops that fall on your head as you walk home from school.
- Find out the area of your schoolyard. Then calculate the number of raindrops that would fall on the schoolyard in an hour.
- How large an area does your community cover? How many raindrops fall on your community during an average rainstorm?

Fact: In an average rainfall, half a centimeter (5 mm) of rain falls every 15 minutes.

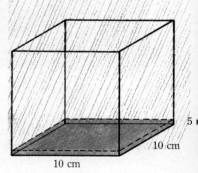

- How many raindrops would it take to fill a 10-cm-square container to a depth of half a centimeter?
- What is the volume of one raindrop?

LESSON 6 ORGANIZER

Objectives

By the end of the lesson, students should be able to:
1. Describe the effects of erosion caused by falling rain.
2. Compare soil types on the basis of their porosity and permeability.

Process Skills

problem solving, sequencing, comparing, analyzing

New Terms

Runoff—excess water that is prevented from sinking into the ground and thus collects and runs over the surface.
Porosity—the volume of water a volume of rock or soil can hold.
Permeability—how easily water can pass through the open spaces in rock or soil.
Ground water—water that collects beneath the surface of the earth.

Runoff

What effect do all these raindrops have when they strike the earth?

Rain wears away the earth's surface with astonishing force. Each raindrop is like a miniature hammer, pounding the soil with a force of nearly 1 kilogram per square centimeter. This is enough force to break tiny fragments from solid rock. Each raindrop that strikes loose soil gouges a miniature crater. A muddy mixture of water and undissolved particles forms that clogs the surface pores of the ground, preventing water from sinking in. Gradually, puddles form as more and more rain is prevented from sinking into the ground. Excess water, or **runoff**, begins to collect and flow over the surface. In a hard rain, almost all of the water becomes runoff. The runoff quickly collects into rivulets, which dislodge soil and rock as they flow. These materials, in turn, add to the water's erosive power, scraping the ground like sandpaper. The runoff carries its sediment load with it as it flows into the nearest stream. The stream, swollen with runoff, tears away at the land as it flows to the river, where it dumps its load. The river itself, swollen with the runoff of many streams, flows toward the sea, continuing the erosive process on a much larger scale.

Make a "flow chart" of runoff. The illustration will get you off and running.

A Flow Chart of Runoff

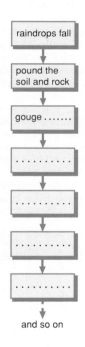

A raindrop explodes as it strikes the earth, creating a tiny crater in the soil.

Materials

Exploration 9: several identical transparent containers, different soil samples (sand, clay, garden, and so on), water, measuring cup, watch or clock with a second hand, Journal

Teacher's Resource Binder

Resource Worksheet 8–6
Resource Transparency 8–7
Graphic Organizer Transparency 8–8

Science Discovery Videodisc

Disc 2, Image and Activity Bank, 8–6

Time Required

three class periods

Answers continued

- Students must convert land areas that are in square miles to square meters. Roughly, one square mile equals 1600 m². As a hint, tell students that the rate is 12 drops per square decimeter per second.
- Have students use the scale on a road map to determine the area in their community. For ease, have them think of their community as a rectangle on the map. Again, they will need to convert miles to meters by multiplying 1600 meters times the length and the width of the rectangle. Then they can follow the same procedure as in question 2.
  Have students use the rate 12 drops/dm²/second to calculate answers to the last two questions.
- If the container has an area of 1 dm², then 10,800 drops (60 × 12 drops × 15 minutes) fall into the container in 15 minutes.
- 100 mm × 100 mm × 5 mm = 50,000 mm³. Volume of one rain drop = 50,000/10,800 = 4.6 mm³.

Answers to

Runoff

Ask students to make a flow chart of the path of a raindrop from the time it falls from the sky until it is deposited in the sea. Ask volunteers to write their flow charts on the chalkboard. Have students compare them and resolve any differences. Sample flow chart:
1. Raindrops fall.
2. They pound the soil and rock.
3. They gouge holes and splash particles.
4. Mud is created.
5. The mud clogs the pores on the surface of the ground.
6. Water collects in sheets on the surface of the ground.
7. Raindrops churn the sheets of water.
8. Soil and rock are dislodged and moved by the sheets of water.
9. Pieces of rock scrape the ground.
10. Runoff carries the pieces and scrapings to streams.
11. Streams carry this load and erode the land further.
12. Streams deposit their load in rivers.
13. Rivers carry this load and erode land further on the way to the sea.

Exploration 9

Divide the class into groups of three or four students. Soil samples may be collected from the schoolyard or brought from home by students. If possible, sand and clay should be included. Four different samples should be adequate. Calibrate the transparent containers in deciliters. (100 mL = 1 dL) This will make it easier for students to measure equal amounts of soil. Each student should have a chance to add water to a soil sample and to measure the time it takes to reach the bottom of the container.

Attention should be paid to how the water is added to the soil (slowly, middle of sample, and so on) so that all procedures are similar. Timing should start when the water begins to move through the soil, and it should stop when the water reaches the bottom of the container. The water may reach the bottom by taking a route between the soil and the container.

Generally, the larger the soil particles, the faster the water will flow through. This is because the larger particles do not pack together as tightly as smaller ones, thereby leaving larger spaces.

Answers to

Making Sense of Your Results

Reassemble the groups. Ask students to read the material silently. Then involve them in a discussion of the terms *porosity* and *permeability.* Call on volunteers to explain the results of the Exploration in regards to the porosity and permeability of the various soil samples:

- stored the greatest amount of water: garden soil
- greatest porosity: garden soil
- least porous: clay
- greatest permeability: sand
- least permeable: clay
- would allow the most runoff during a rainstorm: clay

Investigating the Movement of Water in the Earth

Do some soils hold more water than others? How fast does water move through the soil?

You Will Need

- several identical transparent containers
- soil samples
- water
- a measuring cup
- a watch with a second hand

What to Do

1. Fill each container to the same height with soil taken from several locations (sand, clay, garden soil, etc.) Be careful not to pack the soil.

2. Look carefully at each sample. Predict which will hold the most water. Also, predict which sample the water will move through the fastest.

3. Fill the measuring cup to the 100 mL mark. Slowly add water to each soil sample until it can hold no more. At the same time, measure the time it takes for the water to reach the bottom of each container.

4. Copy the following table into your Journal. Fill it in as you make your observations.

Type of Soil	Time for Water to Pass Through	Volume of Water Absorbed

Making Sense of Your Results: Porosity and Permeability

Under the influence of gravity, rainwater moves downward into tiny openings in soil and rock. The spaces between the soil or rock particles are called "pores." The greater the volume of water that a type of soil can hold, the more *porous* the soil is. Therefore, measuring the volume of water that a soil can hold is measuring its **porosity.**

Which sample stored the greatest amount of water? Which sample had the greatest porosity? Which was the least porous?

Certain soils allow water to pass through them faster than others do. In other words, some soils are more *permeable* than others. When you measured the time it took for water to reach the bottom of the container, you were measuring the **permeability** of the soil.

Which sample had the greatest permeability? Which sample was the least permeable? Which type of soil would allow the most runoff during a rainstorm?

Water Below!

When the pores in the soil are filled, any additional water filters to lower and lower levels. How far down does it go? At a certain point, the spaces in the rock become completely filled with water, so it begins to collect. Water that collects beneath the surface of the earth is known as **ground water**. Ground water is a vital source of fresh water for human use. Streams and springs are fed by ground water, as are the wells of towns and farms and the reservoirs of cities. Does your community rely on ground water? What causes a well to "go dry?"

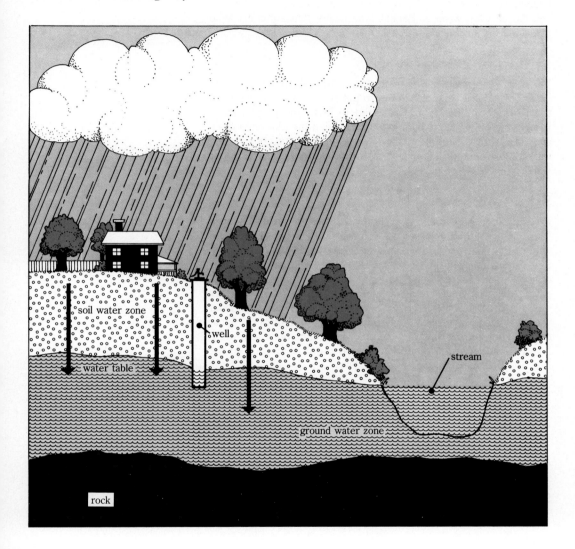

Water Below!

Have a student read aloud the paragraph on page 451. Call on a volunteer to describe the term *ground water*. Then direct students' attention to the diagram. Point out the *soil water zone*, the *water table,* and the *ground water zone*. The information below will help you explain the different areas.

- *soil water zone:*
  Area where water percolates through the soil and filters down into the water table. The soil here is not saturated with water.
- *water table:*
  The top surface of the ground water in which all of the open spaces are filled with water.
- *ground water zone:*
  Water will continue to travel downward in the soil until it reaches an impermeable layer of rock or clay. Water will collect and pool on top of this impermeable layer, filling all of the open spaces with water.

Drinking water is supplied in a variety of ways. Some communities get their water supply directly from a nearby river. Others use water from a lake or reservoir. Still other communities tap ground water supplies by digging wells.

Water wells may be many hundreds of meters deep if the local water table is very far below the surface. To get water from such a deep well requires the use of pumps.

A well "goes dry" when the water table drops below the bottom of the well.

This might be a good opportunity to open a discussion of problems with our water supply. At the present time, there is great concern over the extent and safety of ground water supplies in the United States. For many years, garbage and toxic materials have been buried in landfill sites. These sites are natural or human-made depressions in the soil that are sealed at the bottom, filled with waste materials, and then covered over by soil. Unfortunately, the techniques used to seal the bottom of these landfill sites have proven to be inadequate in many cases. This means that toxic materials can contaminate ground water supplies.

Another problem is the vast interconnectedness of groundwater. Because rivers literally flow under the ground, a leaky landfill could contaminate well water in communities many hundreds of kilometers away.

Water, Wind, and Ice   451

Divide the class into three groups. Assign one situation to each group to discuss. Then reassemble the groups and involve the class in a discussion of the situations.

Situation 1

The better decision was to put the rows across the hill. Since gravity pulls water downhill, gullying and soil erosion occurs between rows that go up and down a slope. You could demonstrate this in class by using a stream table.

Situation 2

The better decision was to use the straw. Straw absorbs the impact of raindrops, thereby preserving the large pores in the soil. Hence, moisture is retained rather than lost in runoff.

Situation 3

The mayor made the wrong decision. Heavy snowfall and spring rain increase the chance of flooding, and the concrete parking lot did not allow the water to soak into the soil. Therefore, the runoff to the already swollen river would increase dramatically.

Follow Up

Assessment

1. Have students compare and contrast the qualities of sand, clay, and garden soil. They should describe the characteristics of each type of soil and compare how each interacts with water. The terms *porosity* and *permeability* should be included in their answers.

2. Have students make a flow chart like the one on page 449 for each alternative in one of the *You Be the Judge* situations. Then they should explain how the flow chart illustrates the correct decision.

You Be the Judge

Apply what you have discovered to the following three situations. See if you can judge who made the right decision.

Situation 1

Two gardeners were sharing a garden plot on the side of a hill. When it was time to prepare the rows, an argument arose. One gardener insisted that the rows should go straight up and down the hill, while the other argued that the rows should cut across the hill, following its contours. To settle the argument they divided the plot and did as they wished. Rainfall was heavy that summer. Who made the better decision? Explain.

Situation 2

The next year, another argument arose. After the plants began to grow well, one gardener wanted to put layers of straw between the rows, while the other preferred to leave the ground bare. Unable to settle their argument, they divided the plot once again and did as they wished. It was a very dry summer, except for a few thunderstorms with heavy rain. Who made the better decision? Explain.

Situation 3

An application for a shopping mall came before the Town Council of Mesopotamia, a community built on a plain between two rivers. One of the features of the plan was a huge concrete parking lot. Several members of the Council were concerned that the chances of flooding in the area would be greater if the shopping center and parking lot were built. Others argued that the town needed the tax money the project would generate. A vote was taken. The result was a tie. The Mayor cast the deciding vote—in favor of the application. The summer following the project's completion there was a heavy thunderstorm, with 15 cm of rain in only 2 hours. Did the Mayor make the right decision? Explain.

Extension

1. Have students research the source of their community's drinking water. Ask them to find out what is done to the water to make it safe for drinking before it is piped into their homes. Students could discuss the characteristic taste and smell of local drinking water and relate the characteristics of the local water to its source and processing.

2. After a rainstorm, have students examine the drainage pattern that carries away rainwater from the schoolyard. Invite students to make a map of the patterns observed.

7 Water on the Move

Rain or snow falling on the land eventually drains away. Streams and rivers catch the water and funnel it downhill. Falling water has energy, and so it causes changes as it flows downhill. Rivers change dramatically as they flow from their beginnings to their ends. On this page a number of streams and rivers are shown. Make as many observations as you can about each stream. Compare them to one another. Rate each stream in terms of its ability to affect its surroundings. Which appears to have the most energy? Which appears to have the least? What is the connection between the speed of the stream and its ability to erode its bed and banks?

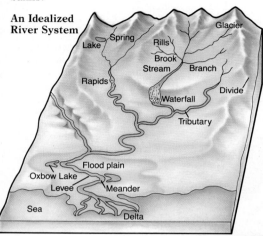

An Idealized River System

LESSON 7 ORGANIZER

Objectives

By the end of the lesson, students should be able to:
1. Identify the factors that determine the speed of a river or stream.
2. Relate the energy of moving water to the process of erosion.

Process Skills

observing, predicting, analyzing, calculating

New Terms

(Organizer continues on next page)

✳ Getting Started

This lesson provides students with an opportunity to observe how runoff forms rivers and streams. Students relate slope of the land and volume of water to stream speed and amount of erosion.

Main Ideas

1. Water picks up, sorts, and moves earth materials as it flows downhill.
2. The faster the water moves in a stream, the more power it has to erode the surface over which it travels.
3. The rate of flow of a stream is influenced by a variety of factors.

✳ Teaching Strategies

Call on a volunteer to read aloud page 453. Then have students study the stream diagram. Ask students to record their observations of the streams in their Journals. Observations should include a description of each stream's point of origin, branches, and subsequent paths. All streams, whether small or large, affect their surroundings. Have students discuss their impressions of the effects of each of the streams in the diagram.

Generally the stream that travels the steepest slope with the greatest volume of water will have the most energy. The small stream traveling on ground that is level or nearly so will have the least energy. Generally, greater stream speed means greater ability to erode.

Exploration 10

Have students make their predictions before performing any of the steps of this activity. This Exploration may also be done as a class demonstration. If performed by students, it is important to demonstrate the procedure first. Do not allow students to start their siphons by suction. Instead, demonstrate the method of starting a siphon by first immersing it in water. When the siphon is filled with water, hold your finger over the free end and immerse the other end in your water source, which is higher than the pan. Release your finger, and the siphon will start flowing.

Divide the class into small groups. They will need to work together to operate the device and time the results accurately.

Encourage students to use a table like the one below to record their results.

Activity 1

Slope	Travel Time(s)
4 cm	
8 cm	

Activity 2

Volume	Travel Time(s)
1 siphon	
2 siphons	

The results of *Activities 1* and *2* should confirm that greater slope and water volume both produce greater stream speed.

Factors Affecting Flow Rate

Call on a volunteer to read the material. Ask students to list in their Journals the factors that affect the speed of water in a stream. Make a composite list on the chalkboard. Responses should include: the slope of the land, the volume of water, the shape of the stream bed, and the roughness of the bottom of the stream bed.

Observations of a neighborhood stream will vary, but students should conclude that the speed of the water varies in different parts of the stream.

Fast or Slow Streams

What determines whether a stream flows quickly or slowly? Do the following activities to find out.

You Will Need

• a set-up such as the one shown below (Be sure that there is a drain at the lower end of the pan.)

Activity 1

What effect does changing the slope of a stream have on the speed of the water?

What to Do

1. First, write down a prediction to the above question in your Journal.
2. Set up the pan of water and the siphons as illustrated. Adjust the trough so that the upper end is 4 cm high.
3. With a wax pencil, mark a starting line 8 cm from the upper end of the trough.
4. Open one siphon. Add a drop of food coloring to the water as it flows past the starting line.
5. Time how long it takes the dye to reach the end of the trough.
6. Change the slope of the stream to 8 cm. Then repeat steps 3 to 5 above. Record and compare the results.

Activity 2

What effect does changing the volume of the water flowing in a stream have on the speed of the water?

What to Do

1. Write down a prediction to the above question in your Journal.
2. Follow the directions described in steps 2 to 5 of Activity 1. But this time, open the second siphon as well, *before* adding the food coloring. Record and compare your results with those obtained earlier.

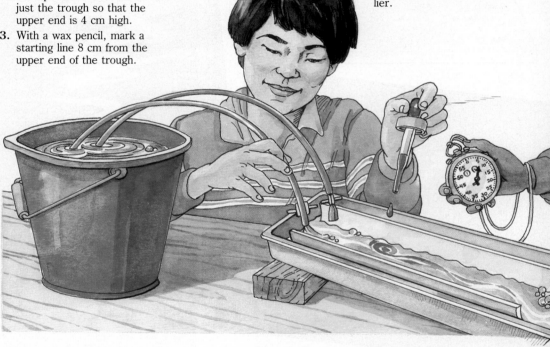

(Organizer continued)

Materials

Exploration 10: clock or watch with a second hand, metric ruler, trough (made from a cardboard tube), large pan with drain, pail for run off, food coloring, pail of water, wooden block, eyedropper, wax pencil, rubber tubing or siphon, large paper clips or clamps

Science Discovery Videodisc

Disc 2, Image and Activity Bank, 8–7

Time Required

two class periods

Factors Affecting Flow Rate

Slope and volume both affect the speed of water in a stream. The shape of the stream is another factor. A narrow, deep stream flows faster than a wide, shallow stream. The roughness of the bottom is also a factor. Boulders and rocks can slow down the rate at which water flows. If you have a stream in your neighborhood, check to see whether it flows quickly or slowly. Also find out whether the rate at which the water flows is the same in all parts of the stream.

Believe It or Not

Did you know that as a result of erosion by flowing water:

- each year, one square kilometer of land loses between 20 and 1000 T (metric tons) of rock and soil?
- every 300 years, 1 cm of thickness is eroded from the land?
- 4 billion T of sediment are carried to the ocean each year?

How big is your state? From the first item above, figure out the smallest and the greatest amount of material that could be removed each year. Which figure do you think is closer to the truth?

Presenting the Evidence

Look at the predictions you made. Does the data you recorded support your predictions? Write a paragraph in your Journal summarizing your data and presenting your conclusions.

 # Follow Up

Assessment

Give students the following situation: Imagine that there was a flash storm in your area. Your school is located near part of a stream. What predictions could you make about how the water would move near your school? *(On a hill with a large slope, the water would move very fast; on an area that is not too sloped, the water would form a lake.)*

Extension

Have students conduct an outdoor investigation of the rate of flow and slope of a nearby stream or river. Have them research and design some measurement methods on their own. Students could make posters and present oral reports to the class.

Believe It or Not

The following factors must be considered in estimating the amount of soil lost to rivers and streams each year: average rainfall, number of rivers, type of soil, amount and type of underlying rock, and the amount of vegetation.

To perform the calculation of the material removed each year from a particular state, have students determine the approximate dimensions of their state by measuring the length and width of the state on a map drawn to a known scale. (Approximate a rectangle for irregularly shaped states.) Students may have to convert from the length and width in miles to that in kilometers. One mile equals approximately 1.6 km. The amount lost each year would be a result of the factors listed by the students.

LESSON 8

✳ Getting Started

In this lesson, students investigate and observe how materials are eroded and deposited in a river system.

Main Ideas

1. A stream or river slows down and deposits sediments when it reaches a bend, when it widens, or when its slope decreases.
2. Water moves faster on the outside edge of a bend and erodes the river bank.
3. The age of a river is determined by the degree to which the land around it has been worn down and eroded.
4. Young rivers have steep banks and straight channels; old rivers have low banks and travel sideways in a curved path.

✳ Teaching Strategies

Involve students in a discussion of the situation presented on page 456. Direct their attention to the diagram. Invite them to choose one of the pieces of land and then to explain their choice.

- Lot B is the best choice since there is little chance of erosion or deposition occurring here.
- Lot D is also a good choice because deposition, not erosion, will occur.
- Lots A and C are on the outside of the curve where water tends to move faster; therefore, erosion will occur. In fact, lot C may disappear if the stream cuts a new channel.
- Lot G is poor because the river could take a shortcut here and leave an island.
- Lots E and F will have additional erosion from wave action of the lake.

8 How Rivers Change the Land

Imagine that you have won the grand prize in a contest: the plot of land of your choice. The choices are shown in the illustration below. Which lot would you choose? Collect evidence to support your choice by using a stream table in the way described in the next Exploration.

LESSON 8 ORGANIZER

Objectives

By the end of the lesson, students should be able to:
1. Explain how materials are eroded and deposited in a river system.
2. Identify the stages of development of a river.

Process Skills

observing, investigating, inferring, analyzing

New Terms

Watershed—an area that a river drains.
Gullies—ditches carved out by moving water.
Tributaries—streams that feed into a main stream.

A Stream Table Experiment

You Will Need

- a set-up as shown in the illustration below

What to Do

1. Place sand to a depth of 5 cm in the stream table.
2. Wet the sand so that it can be shaped. Form the sand into a gentle slope.
3. Trace a path with your finger almost to the bottom of the sand.
4. Adjust the flow of water so that it moves slowly into the tray.
5. Allow the water to flow down the path for 20 minutes.
6. Turn off the water, but leave the sand in place.

While the water is flowing, watch for the following:

(a) places where the water slows down or speeds up (food coloring may help here),
(b) places where banks are being eroded,
(c) places where sand build-up occurs,
(d) changes in the course of the stream.

Pretend that a friend was absent from school during the stream table experiment. Describe for him or her exactly what you saw during the experiment. Do your observations support your choice of lots?

cliff 5 m

lake

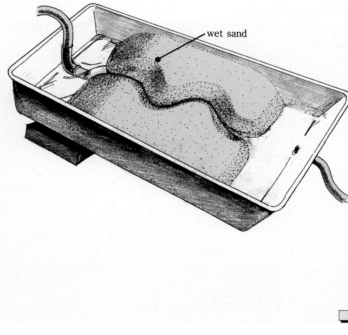

wet sand

Exploration 11

Divide the class into small groups. Distribute the necessary materials. Suggest that students keep the volume of water low so that the changes occur slowly. Have groups set up their stream tables by a sink or use at least two buckets under the table to catch the overflow. Suggest that students take notes in their Journals as they make their observations.

Instruct students to watch carefully for the four points (a to d) mentioned in the text.

(a) *water slows down:* at curves; *water speeds up:* along straight areas and at the steep, downhill places

(b) *banks are being eroded:* on the outside of the curves where the water is flowing the fastest

(c) *sand build-up occurs:* on the inside of the curves where water is moving more slowly

(d) *the stream changes course:* the longer the water runs, the wider the bends will become, and the stream bed will deepen and widen; the meanders will become more exaggerated

Point out to students that in the real world, a stream or river slows down when it reaches a bend, when it gets wider, or when its slope decreases. Slower water lacks the energy needed to carry its load, so it drops what it has been transporting. Over time, this process exaggerates the curves of the river. When a curve becomes extremely exaggerated, the river may cut across it, thereby forming an island.

Materials

Exploration 11: sand, aluminum tray or stream table, rubber tubing, metric ruler, water, pail (for runoff), block of wood, clock or watch, food coloring **Do Rivers Have Age?** Journal

Science Discovery Videodisc

Disc 2, Image and Activity Bank, 8–8

Time Required

two to three class periods

Caught in the Act of Change

Have students study the photographs on pages 458 and 459. Involve students in a discussion of their observations and inferences. You can use the following information to help you in your discussion.

The Mississippi River and feeder streams

The Mississippi is an old river that has been eroding its banks and widening its channel for many thousands of years. Sediment is constantly building up on the inside of the river's curves, and land is being eroded on the outside of the curves. (Remind students that they observed this in the Stream Table Experiment.) This creates the deep meanders usually seen in photographs of the Mississippi. Sometimes, a meandering river will take a "shortcut" on a downhill slope, with the result that a section of a meander is cut off. Eventually, the section may be cut off entirely to form an "oxbow" lake. This process has happened repeatedly along the Mississippi River. (Help students to relate the processes described here to the features shown in the photograph.)

The Mouth of the Eel River

Many changes in the coastline have occurred as a result of the deposition of sediment by the Eel River. The photograph shows an extensive sediment plume at the mouth of the river. Wave action has moved sediment in both directions along the coastline to form a long beach and a sand bar. A break in the sand bar, probably kept open by dredging, serves as the entrance to Humboldt Bay.

The rough triangular area (delta) visible around the river's mouth was formed by sediments deposited by the river over thousands of years. The main river channel has probably shifted positions several times. It appears that it may be trying to shift position again, since the river channel divides and rejoins again near the coastline. (Help students to relate the processes described here to the features shown in the photograph.)

(Continues on next page)

Caught in the Act of Change

What kinds of changes do these photographs reveal?

The Mississippi River and feeder streams

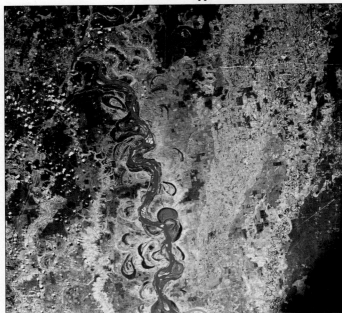

The Mouth of the Eel River in Northern California (false-color photograph)

A Challenge

1. Look carefully at the photograph of the Eel River. What's going on in this picture? What time of year do you think this picture was taken?

2. What evidence do you see that the Mississippi has changed course over the years? Do you also see this in its feeder streams?

3. Name as many differences as you can between the Mississippi and the Colorado River.

The Grand Canyon, carved by the Colorado River

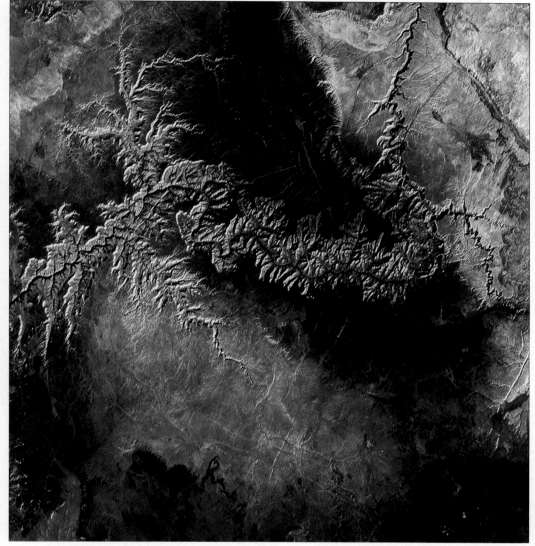

(Caught in the Act of Change continued)
The Grand Canyon, carved by the Colorado River

Have students study the photograph of the Grand Canyon. Involve them in a discussion of their observations.

The photograph, taken from space, shows the Colorado River system along the entire length of the Grand Canyon. The dark area in the photograph is the forested Kaibab Plateau on the Canyon's North Rim. The large lake at one end of the canyon is Lake Mead, a reservoir created by the building of Hoover Dam.

The Colorado River flows through an area that has a hot and dry climate. As a result, the effects of weathering occur slowly. The river cuts a deep, steep-walled channel because the canyon walls are not being eroded away quickly.

Answers to

A Challenge

1. The Eel River is transporting large amounts of light-colored sediment. Because of the amount of sediment and the volume of water in the river, it can be inferred that the photograph was probably taken during the rainy season.

2. There are many islands and oxbow lakes visible along the course of the Mississippi. These features, along with the wide, meandering river bed, indicate that the river has changed course repeatedly over many thousands of years.

3. Answers may vary, but possible responses include: The Mississippi River is wider, longer, and follows a more twisting path than the Colorado River. The Mississippi also has more meanders, islands, and lakes along its path. The Colorado River has formed a much deeper channel (valley) than that of the Mississippi. The Colorado River region is much drier, and the local rocks are red. The weathered rock particles that the Colorado River carries give the river a reddish color.

Do Rivers Have Age?

Call on a volunteer to read the verse from "The Negro Speaks of Rivers." Students may find it simpler to start this exercise with the third question.

Answers to

In-Text Questions (page 461)

1. The stages of river development shown in each figure are:
   A—maturity
   B—infancy (youngest)
   C—old age (oldest)
   D—youth
2. Statements may apply to more than one figure, and students should be reminded that the process of river development is very slow. The figures represent "snapshots" of different stages in the river's life, similar to snapshots taken of human development.
3. Answers will vary, but possible responses include:
   A. This figure shows a mature river. The distinctive V-shaped valley can still be recognized. There are long tributaries and deep valleys. The river's path is beginning to develop curves. This shows that it is eroding its banks and enlarging its valley.
   B. This figure shows a river in its infancy. It is just beginning to form. The flow of water is starting to carve gullies and form a river channel.
   C. This figure shows an old river. It travels slowly from side to side. It moves in a highly curved path.
   D. This figure shows a youthful river. It has carved, deep, V-shaped valleys with mountains on all sides. It does not bend or curve much. It has not begun to widen and erode its banks.

Primary Source
Description of change: excerpted from "The Negro Speaks of Rivers" by Langston Hughes.
Rationale: excerpted to focus on the age of rivers.

Do Rivers Have Age?

The Negro Speaks of Rivers
by Langston Hughes

I've known rivers:

I've known rivers ancient
   as the world and older than
   the flow of human blood in
   human veins.

My soul has grown deep
   like rivers.
...

In this poem, rivers are said to be old and to have grown deep. You might wonder how can a river be old? How does a river grow?

About 100 years ago, an American geologist, William Davis, proposed that rivers follow a distinct pattern of development. Davis likened rivers to living organisms, noting that both change markedly as they age. But the age of a river is not measured in years. The age of a river is a measure of how completely the river has eroded its **watershed,** that is, the area that it drains. Young rivers have steep banks and narrow valleys and fall in elevation quickly (1). Old rivers (2) fall very slowly, have low banks and wide valleys and tend to meander (travel an S-shaped course).

The life cycle of a river begins when a huge block of flat land is slowly lifted above sea level. Rainwater running down the fresh slopes carves out *gullies,* or ditches (3). These gullies run together to form larger channels, which in turn run together to form still larger channels. Over long periods, rivers carve valleys into the uplifted land. The river continues to develop as its **tributaries** (feeder streams) deepen their channels and cut downward to form steep-sided V-shaped valleys (4). As the river matures, new tributaries form and existing tributaries grow.

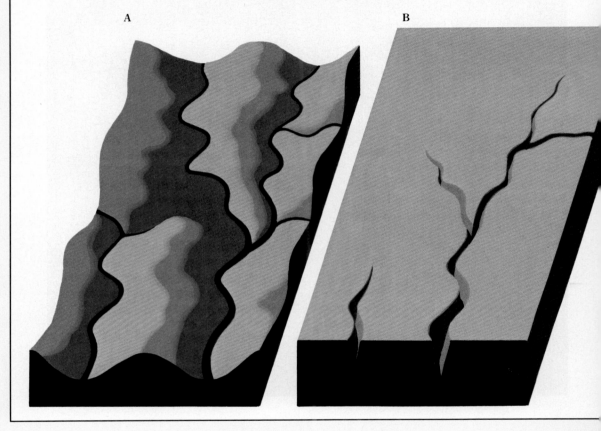

A

B

A young river carries little water because it has few tributaries. It quickly erodes downward. As a river matures and the amount of water it carries increases, it begins to erode its valley as well as its bed. Erosion wears away at the valley walls, causing them to become less steep (5). After much time, erosion wears down the river valley so thoroughly that it is almost the same elevation as the river. At this point, the river can no longer erode downward, so it begins to erode sideways (meander). The river meanders back and forth across its valley, continually changing course (6).

Eventually the river wears down its watershed into a featureless plain near sea level. The river is now in a state of old age. It flows slowly and carries little sediment.

The figures below illustrate the four stages of river development. Trace each one into your Journal. Can you identify the features described?

1. Identify the stage shown in each figure: infancy, youth, maturity, or old age.

2. Match the features or terms numbered in the text above to one or more of the figures.

3. Write a descriptive sentence about each figure using your own words.

Check It Out

1. Is there a river near you? What stage is it in?

2. Many states contain well-known valleys or canyons. Find out about areas such as these in your state. Then use a map to find out whether or not rivers flow through them. Try to answer these questions:

- Which came first, the valley or canyon, or the river?

- What is the relationship of each to the other?

- Even if the valley or canyon does not have a river flowing through it, might it have at one time? How might you tell?

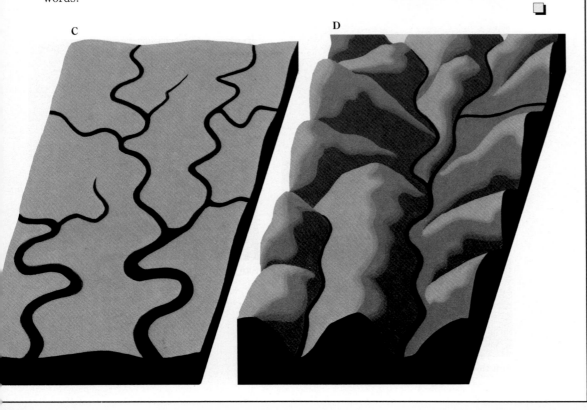

C   D

✷ Follow Up

Assessment

1. Have students review the rivers shown in the illustrations and photographs on pages 456 to 459. Ask them to classify them as rivers in their infancy, youth, maturity, or old age. Request that students support their answers with reasons. *(The rivers on pages 456 and 457 and the Mississippi River on page 458 are in their old age because they have deep meanders. The Eel River on page 458 is a mature river because of the mountains, V-shaped canyons, and its curving river bed. The Colorado River on page 459 could be considered a youthful river because of the deep, V-shaped valley.)*

2. Based on their work in *Exploration 12*, have students write an essay predicting the future of the land around the local river they studied. (This will help to develop their ability to see **Patterns of Change** and **Evolution** of the landscape in their local area.)

Extension

1. Many attempts have been made to change or control the course of rivers. Have students investigate some of the methods that have been used, such as building canals, levees, and dams. (Possible sources of information include the Army Corps of Engineers, state or local flood control agencies, and water districts.)

2. Have students locate historic maps of their city. The maps will probably show rivers or streams that are no longer evident above ground. Ask students to do some research to find out what happened to these streams. To summarize their findings, have them develop a poster or map of their area for classroom display.

Answers to

Exploration 12

This activity is intended to draw students' attention to their local area. Suggest that students talk to available resource people or use reference books at the library to answer these questions. Generally, a river comes first and creates the valley or canyon. If the river has changed course, it may no longer be present, but the valley or canyon remains.

LESSON 9

Deltas and Estuaries

Eventually, rivers reach the sea. The meeting place of river and ocean is a dynamic environment where many forces interact. The kind of geologic features that develop in such a setting depend on many factors: how much sediment the river carries, how strong the waves, tides, and currents are, and how quickly the sea floor drops off, to name a few. Look at the photographs on these pages. Do you see different types of meeting places between river and ocean?

Many rivers deposit a fan-shaped wedge of sediment at their mouths. These deposits are called **deltas**. Why do you think they form? As the photographs on these pages show, deltas come in many different forms. How do they differ?

Mouth of the Mississippi, USA

San Francisco Bay

Mouth of the Nile, Egypt

✳ Getting Started

In this lesson, students explore the features of shorelines. They learn about the development of deltas, estuaries, and beaches.

Main Ideas

1. Coastlines or shorelines are eroded by the action of ocean waves and currents.
2. The mouth of a river can be in the form of a delta or an estuary.
3. Beaches are not permanent features of a landscape. They are deposits of sediments and rock fragments that move with the action of water.

✳ Teaching Strategies

Deltas and Estuaries

Call on a volunteer to read aloud page 462. Then direct students' attention to the photographs on the page. Involve them in a discussion so that they can compare their observations. (Mention that all of these photographs were taken from space.)

The top photograph on page 462 shows the Mississippi delta. Over many thousands of years, deposited sediment has enlarged the Mississippi delta and pushed it out into the Gulf of Mexico.

The photograph on the bottom left side of page 462 shows the Nile delta in Egypt. The wedge shape is readily apparent from space.

The photograph on the right side of page 462 shows San Francisco Bay, which was formed by the Sacramento River. Its estuary takes the form of a long bay with a distinct shoreline.
(Continues on next page)

LESSON 9 ORGANIZER

Objectives

By the end of the lesson, students should be able to:
1. Identify deltas and estuaries and explain how they are formed.
2. Understand how ocean waves erode the shoreline and build beaches.
3. Relate their knowledge of beach formation to beaches in their local area.

Process Skills

observing, interpreting, comparing and contrasting, writing

New Terms

Deltas—fan-shaped deposits of sediment at the mouths of rivers.
Estuary—a wide river mouth that is submerged by ocean water and extends far inland.

There is another type of meeting place between river and ocean. Most of these formed during the last ice age, when so much water was locked up in huge glaciers that the sea level dropped by as much as 150 meters. Rivers had to cut new courses to the sea through the exposed seabed. When the oceans rose again at the end of the ice age, these river valleys were flooded by the rising waters. The result was wide, shallow mouths that usually extend well inland. This type of river mouth is known as an **estuary**. The mouths of most of the rivers along the Atlantic Coast of the U.S. are estuaries.

Estuaries nurture a wide variety of fish, shellfish, and crustaceans. Thus, they are a valuable source of food for humans and wildlife alike. Many species prized by humans for food require an estuary setting to reproduce.

Mouth of the Betsiboka, Madagascar

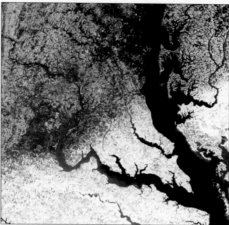
Chesapeake Bay

Questions

1. What is a delta? How does it form?

2. How do the Nile and Mississippi deltas differ? What conditions might account for their different appearances?

3. Do you think that the Mississippi delta has always been where it is today? (Look carefully at the photo before answering.) Explain.

4. Look at the photograph of the Betsiboka river. This river once flowed clear. Now it definitely does not. What kind of human activities might have caused this?

5. Suppose a dam were to be built somewhere upstream on any of the rivers shown on page 462. How would the deltas be affected?

6. Which photographs show estuaries? How can you tell?

Materials

Science Discovery Videodisc

Disc 2, Image and Activity Bank, 8–9

Time Required

one to two class periods

(Deltas and Estuaries continued)

Have a volunteer read aloud the two paragraphs on the top of page 463. Ask students to study the photographs on this page and then compare them to each other and to the photographs on page 462.

The photograph on the left of page 463 shows the delta of the Betsiboka River on the Island of Madagascar. The reddish streaks show large amounts of silt that have eroded from recently deforested areas.

The photograph on the right on page 463 shows Chesapeake Bay, a large estuary in the eastern part of the United States. It was formed by the Potomac, Susquehanna, and Patuxent Rivers. The estuary takes the form of a long bay with a distinct shoreline.

Answers to

Questions

1. A delta is a fan-shaped wedge of sediment deposited at the mouth of a river. It forms from the buildup of sediment carried by the river.

2. The Nile delta is more fan-shaped; the Mississippi delta is more elongated. Perhaps the sea floor is more shallow and the sand builds up more quickly in the Mississippi area.

3. No. It can be inferred from the photograph that the Mississippi delta has been moving outward into the Gulf of Mexico.

4. Cutting down many trees may have exposed more land to erosion.

5. If a dam were built upstream, sediment would be trapped there. The delta would not be replenished, and it would eventually be washed away.

6. The photographs of Chesapeake Bay and San Francisco Bay show estuaries. The rivers open into wide shallow mouths extending far inland.

On the Waterfront

Have a volunteer read aloud the top of page 464. Involve students in a discussion of their experiences with ocean waves at the beach. Ask students to focus on their experiences of the force and movement of waves as they break onto a beach. Point out that they may have observed sediments and sand suspended in the curl of a breaking wave.

Mention that not all beaches are made of sand. Direct students' attention to the photographs. They show a variety of dramatically different beaches and coastlines.

Answers to

In-Text Questions

Have students study the photographs and propose answers to the questions on this page.

- Coastlines develop through the interaction of the sea and the land.
- The way a coastline will look in the future depends on many factors. One factor involving the land includes the movement of tectonic plates that can cause uplift and faulting. Factors involving interaction with the sea include changes in water level, erosion, and storms.
- Beaches differ because of local differences in wave action and the types of rocks or sediments present. Beaches are composed of rock, sand, or gravel. These materials can be derived from many kinds of parent rock, or in some cases, coral.
- Beaches are rocky when the adjacent waters are rough. Strong wave action carries away the smaller sand particles, leaving only large rocks and boulders.

Coastlines are sandy when the adjacent waters are gentle. The small waves do not move enough to keep the tiny sand grains suspended. They drop out onto the coastline, thereby forming a sandy beach.

On the Waterfront

Have you ever played in the ocean waves? Think about the experience. Describe how the force of the waves felt. Did this give you an appreciation for the power of waves?

Day after day, year after year, the shore is constantly being eroded by the sea, endlessly shaped and reshaped by the power of the ocean waves and currents. The shore is narrow and rocky in some places, wide and sandy in others. Some shores are bordered by high, rugged cliffs; others slope gently to the sea.

How do coastlines develop? What will they look like in the future? Why do beaches differ? Why are some rocky and others sandy?

Think About it

Before you read the following page, think about each of the questions below.

- Which of these beaches probably experiences gentle waves most of the time?
- Which of these beaches probably experiences many fierce storms?
- Which of these beaches is probably eroding at a very fast rate?

What causes a sand beach to form? Where does the sand come from?

Answers to

Think About It

- The tropical beach, with its fine-grained sand, probably experiences gentle waves most of the time.
- Any beach with little or no sand visible, such as the cobble beach and rocky coastline, experiences fierce storms.
- The sea cliffs, without a beach to absorb the impact of the waves, are probably eroding at a very fast rate.
- A sand beach forms when sand and sediment (either carried out to sea by a nearby river or formed by wave action) wash up and settle out of the waves along the shoreline.

Location is an important factor in the way a beach develops. Rocky beaches are common along ocean coastlines, especially at northern latitudes. Ocean beaches frequently experience large waves. Winter storms may lash the beach with waves 5 or more meters high.

Depending on the size of the waves, materials are either removed from or returned to a beach. Large waves attack a beach, shifting sand out to sea and exposing the rocks along the shore. Gentle waves gradually shift sand back onto a beach, where it can pile up to a depth of several meters.

Think of the land that borders on water in your state. Can you locate both sandy and rocky beaches?

Waves can also cause other shoreline features to develop. Can you explain how the formations shown in the accompanying photographs might have come about?

✳ *Follow Up*

Assessment

1. Give students the following situation: You have been assigned to write an article for a surfing magazine about the beaches shown in the photographs on pages 464–465. What would you say about the waves in each of the places shown? *(Articles should be based on the principle that rocky beaches have larger and stronger waves than do sandy beaches.)*
2. Many cities are located near the mouths of rivers. Have students write an essay discussing the pros and cons of building a city near a river delta or an estuary.

Extension

Have students research the problem of "disappearing" beaches. Ask them to make a diagram to explain the situation.

An important point to stress is that beaches are dynamic, constantly changing places. The appearance of a beach gives students a "snapshot" they can use to infer the type of wave action that has been taking place there. A rocky beach indicates that the area is subject to strong wave action. Sand formed or carried there is washed away immediately. A sandy beach occurs when wave action is not strong enough to carry away the sand.

A winter visit to a beach can illustrate this point. Many beaches are changed completely by winter storms. A fine-grained sandy beach in summer may become a pebbly, rocky beach in winter. These differences are due to changes in wave action.

The force of ocean waves can cause the development of the shoreline features shown in the photographs. For example, wave action can bore caves in cliffs. If such caves are in a headland, tunnels will appear and eventually collapse, leaving a sea stack (a landform that looks like a chimney). Recession of the coastline increases the distance of the stack from the shore. Wave action causes cliffs to recede. Each time seawater rushes into a crack in the rocks, the air in the crack is compressed. The force of compression enlarges the cracks until parts of the cliff begin to wash away.

Getting Started

In this lesson, students study photographs of landforms created by wind erosion. Then they make inferences about the processes involved in producing these landforms.

Main Ideas

1. Wind is a major agent of erosion in dry areas.
2. Sand dunes formed by different wind patterns have distinctive shapes.
3. Human activities can cause an increase in wind erosion.

Teaching Strategies

Have students silently read page 466 and study the photographs on pages 466 and 467. Involve them in a discussion of the landforms shown.

The dune photographs show the effects of different wind patterns on sand. The dune photograph on the left side of page 466 shows transverse dunes. These dunes were formed in areas where there was abundant sand and where the wind blew in the same direction for a long period of time. The photograph on the right side of page 466 shows linear dunes.

The dune photograph on the left side of page 467 shows star dunes. These dunes form when the wind direction is frequently changing.

Have students silently read page 467, study the photographs, and answer the questions. Generally, sand that accumulates in deserts is formed through direct erosion of bare rock or soil by particle-bearing winds. When the wind slows down, the load of sand drops out onto the land.

10 Wind—An Invisible River

What comes to mind when you think of the desert? If you are like most people you think of sand dunes stretching to the horizon. In most people's minds, deserts are always sandy wastelands. Most of the world's great dunes are, in fact, found in deserts. Why is this so? How does so much sand come to be concentrated in one place?

We don't normally think of the wind as a major agent of erosion, and most of the time it is not. In most places, enough rain falls to keep streams and rivers flowing year round and these do most of the eroding. But deserts, by definition, have little water, therefore water is less important as an agent of erosion. Wind is an important agent of erosion in deserts, where the soil is loose and dry, with little vegetation to hold it in place. When the wind blows, it easily picks up the loose soil. If the wind blows hard enough, it can pick up enough soil to become a powerful erosive force. (Think of the technique of sandblasting.)

An unusual wind-formed rock formation

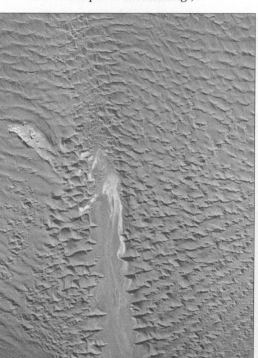

Photos of dunes taken from space (left and below)

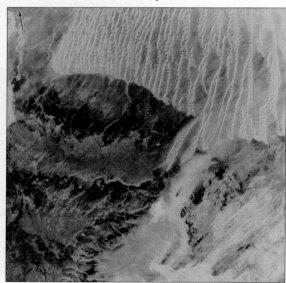

LESSON 10 ORGANIZER

Objectives

By the end of the lesson, students should be able to:
1. Identify examples of wind erosion.
2. Compare and contrast wind and water erosion.
3. Relate the shape of sand dunes to the process of dune formation.
4. Explain how human practices can increase wind erosion.

Process Skills

observing, analyzing, inferring, comparing and contrasting

New Terms

Deserts are not the only places where sand dunes are found. Most of us are familiar with the sand dunes commonly found along the seashore. How do you think these form? Dunes actually take many different forms. How do the dunes pictured on these pages differ? Try to identify each picture with the following conditions.

- The wind blows the same direction almost all the time.

- The wind changes direction frequently.

All dunes tend to *migrate* (move) in the direction the wind is blowing. The harder the wind blows, the faster the dunes migrate. It is almost impossible to stop them. On occasion, whole communities have had to be abandoned due to migrating dunes.

Strong winds blowing long distances across plains and farmland can pick up large amounts of soil, causing an unpleasant phenomenon known as a *dust storm*. Have you ever experienced a dust storm? A bad one can raise a suffocating cloud of soil and dust some 3000 meters high and can move millions of tons of topsoil. In parts of the midwest in the 1930s, dust storms were especially frequent and violent. Many people were forced to abandon their farms and ranches. In some places the soil consists entirely of wind-blown material.

Photo of a dune taken from space

Questions

1. Why does wind erosion occur primarily in the desert?
2. How do erosion and deposition by wind differ from erosion and deposition by water? How are they similar?
3. What human practices increase or reduce the effects of wind erosion?
4. Why is it difficult to stop migrating dunes?

Answers to
Questions

1. Desert soil is loose and dry, with little vegetation to hold it in place.
2. Water is a stronger agent of erosion and deposition than wind. However, both water and wind erode the land by carrying away small pieces of the landscape.
3. Humans can remove the natural covering of vegetation. This exposes bare soil, increasing the chances of wind (and water) erosion.
4. To stop migrating dunes, you would have to stop the prevailing winds in an area.

 *Follow Up*

Assessment

Have students write a descriptive story about living in a town that is trying to fight migrating sand dunes.

Extension

1. Have students research the problem of desertification.
2. Have students make and use a wind direction indicator to determine local wind patterns.

Materials

Science Discovery Videodisc

Disc 2, Image and Activity Bank, 8–10

Time Required

one class period

11 Glaciers—Rivers of Ice

On the night of April 14, 1912, while on its maiden voyage from Southhampton, England to New York, the luxury liner *Titanic* struck an iceberg. In less than three hours the pride of the White Star Fleet, a ship that was advertised as unsinkable, went to the bottom—taking over 1500 of its passengers with it. Where in the world could such a huge chunk of ice have come from?

Icebergs come from thick sheets of ice called **glaciers**. Glaciers cover cold areas like northern Canada, Greenland, and Antarctica as well as certain high mountains. The iceberg that sank the Titanic most likely originated in Greenland. Both Greenland and Antarctica are almost completely buried by ice to a depth in places of over 3000 meters! The ice flows slowly outward and downward from the center. Eventually it spills over the edge of the land, into the sea. This is how icebergs are born. The massive glaciers covering Greenland and Antarctica are remnants of the last ice age, which ended about 10,000 years ago. At its peak, about 20,000 years ago, about a third of the earth's land area was covered by ice many hundreds of meters thick.

Titanic Strikes Iceberg!

☀ Getting Started

In this lesson, students learn about the origin and movement of glaciers. First, a historical perspective is presented on the evidence of glaciers. Then, physical features resulting from glacial action are described.

Main Ideas

1. Glaciers are thick sheets of ice that cover cold areas such as polar regions and high mountains.
2. Glaciers are formed when snow accumulates, compacts, and gradually changes to ice.
3. Glaciers flow at different rates. These rates can be measured.
4. As glaciers move, they carry loose, eroded materials and rock fragments scraped from valley walls and floors.
5. Glacial action has created many physical features throughout the world.

☀ Teaching Strategies

Ask a volunteer to read aloud the story of the *Titanic.* At this point, you may wish to discuss the use of robotic submarines, which have been used to locate and film the wreckage of the *Titanic* in its deep resting place at the bottom of the north Atlantic.

Pose the question asked at the end of the first paragraph to ascertain students' prior knowledge about icebergs, glaciers, and their origins. Accept all reasonable responses.
(Continues on next page)

LESSON 11 ORGANIZER

Objectives

By the end of the lesson, students should be able to:
1. Describe the origin and locations of glaciers.
2. Explain the formation and movement of glaciers.
3. Provide evidence of past glaciers.
4. Describe formations resulting from glacial action.

Process Skills

inferring, analyzing, sequencing, drawing conclusions

New Terms

Glaciers—thick sheets of flowing ice.
Till—unsorted sediment left behind by glaciers.
Terminal moraine—till that has been deposited and forms a ridge at the end of a glacier.

An aerial view of a valley glacier

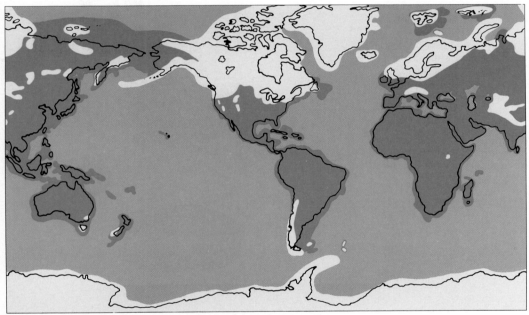

Maximum extent of glacial ice, approximately 20,000 years ago

(Teaching Strategies continued)

Use the text and the glaciation map on page 469 to provide background information on *continental glaciers.* At present, only about 10 percent of the world's total land area is covered by continental glaciers, or ice caps. The continental glacier of Antarctica comprises 85 percent of that total. The continental glacier of Greenland involves another 10 percent, and the remaining 5 percent is located throughout the Arctic regions of northern Canada, central Asia, and Iceland.

In addition to the continental glaciers described on page 468, there are also *valley glaciers* like those shown in the aerial photograph on the top of page 469. Have students study this photograph and develop an explanation of how these glaciers formed independently in these mountain valleys. This exercise will serve as a conceptual preview of the material in *Exploration 13.* *(A possible student explanation: Valley glaciers form in areas where the snow does not melt from year to year. After several years, the layers of snow pack together to form ice. The weight of the ice causes it to spread out. When the ice reaches a slope, gravity causes it to move downward.)*

Meltwater—a stream of water carrying a large load of sediment that flows down from the foot of a glacier.
Névé—rounded grains of snow found on the upper end of a glacier.
Outwash—a deposit of sediment carried by meltwater, found down the valley from a terminal moraine.

Materials

Exploration 14: water, 1-cm deep tray (ice tray with no dividers), wire, wire cutters, several masses of varying sizes, freezer, 2 blocks of wood
Developing a Theory of Glaciation: Journal

Teacher's Resource Binder

Activity Worksheets 8–7 and 8–8
Resource Transparency 8–9
Graphic Organizer Transparencies 8–10 and 8–11

Science Discovery Videodisc

Disc 2, Image and Activity Bank, 8–11

Time Required

four to five class periods

Exploration 13

Have students read the material and study the illustration on this page. The pictures should start them thinking about the processes that form glacial ice from snow.

If your school is located in an area that receives winter snow, you can use the characteristics of an actual snowdrift to help students visualize the process described in this Exploration. If it is not winter, or if your school is in an area without winter snow, obtain a photograph of a cut snowbank at the side of a freshly cleared road or highway. The photograph should show distinct layering.

The layering in a snowdrift provides a model for the different stages that snow goes through in the formation of a glacier. Have students observe this layering in the photograph or by making a vertical cut through an actual snowdrift. Encourage them to examine the exposed layers and observe the differences among the layers (in color and compaction, for example). Compare the formation of layers in the snowdrift to the five steps of glacier formation listed on page 470.

Answers to

In-Text Questions

The correct order:

(d) Star-shaped flakes collect in a fluffy mass with a lot of air between them.

(b) Evaporation and melting cause the flakes to lose their shape.

(a) The snow particles become rounded pellets due to the added weight of accumulating snow.

(c) As the snow builds up, the pressure from the top layers squeezes out the air between the rounded grains of snow. Icy particles called *névé* are formed.

(e) The névé undergoes further packing and melting until it gradually changes into solid ice.

How Do Glaciers Form?

Can you turn snow into ice? How would you do it? It happens all the time in glaciers, although it takes quite a while.

To understand the process by which glaciers form, read the sentences below. Beware, though—their order is scrambled! Try to rearrange them into proper order. Use the accompanying diagram as a guide.

(a) The snow particles become rounded pellets due to the added weight of accumulating snow.

(b) Evaporation and melting cause the flakes to lose their shape.

(c) As the snow builds up, the pressure from the top layers squeezes out the air between the rounded grains of snow. Icy particles called *névé* (NAY vay) are formed.

(d) Star-shaped flakes collect in a fluffy mass with a lot of air caught between them.

(e) The névé undergoes further packing and melting until it gradually changes into solid ice.

Did you get the sentences in the right order? If you did, then you can truthfully say that you have got glaciers down cold!

Glaciers on the Move

In the summer of 1956, the perfectly-preserved body of a man was ejected from a glacier at the foot of the Weisshorn, a mountain in the Swiss Alps. At first, the body was believed to be that of a Swiss man who had fallen into a crack in the glacier in 1946. Later, however, the body was correctly identified as that of a young German mountain climber, George Winkler, who had fallen from the Weisshorn in 1888. In 68 years, the ice had carried Winkler approximately 1.5 km, from the upper part of the glacier to its end.

It may seem impossible, but ice can flow! Glaciers move at different speeds, though. The speed depends on several factors: the steepness of the slope on which it lies, the depth of the ice, the load of ice and snow at the glacier's source, and the temperature and general weather conditions in the area. Gravity, however, is what makes the glacier flow. The force of gravity acting on a glacier's huge mass causes the glacier to sag under its own weight and slowly "ooze" downhill.

One way to measure a glacier's speed is to place stakes in a straight line across it at several points. The stakes are then examined sometime later to gauge the glacier's flow. Examine the diagram below to see how this works. Two sets of stakes were driven into the ice of the Rhone Valley glacier in the Alps in 1874. Their positions were mapped every two years until 1882. Compare the speed of this glacier with the speed of the glacier that carried George Winkler's body for 68 years.

EXPLORATION 14

Can Ice Really Flow?

Can you design an experiment proving that ice can change its shape or flow without melting? Perhaps you could try this idea. Freeze a layer of ice about 1 cm thick in a tray. Once it has frozen, remove the ice from the tray. In a freezer, support the layer of ice as shown below. Hang a good-sized mass from its middle with a wire. Observe what happens during the next few days. Explain what you observe. Repeat the experiment with different size masses. Can you apply your findings to explain how glaciers move?

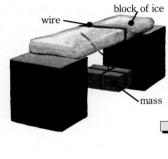

wire

block of ice

mass

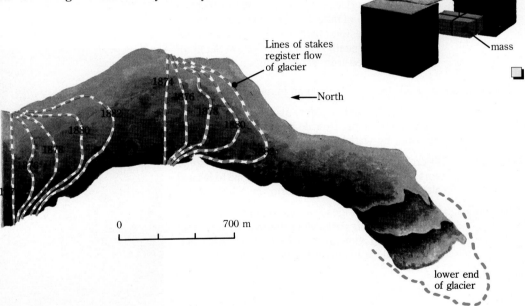

Lines of stakes register flow of glacier

1874

1876

1882

1878

1880

← North

0   700 m

lower end of glacier

Glaciers on the Move

Involve students in a discussion of the origin of the body and its speed of movement. Stress the fact that glacial movement is not regular. The speed can vary from glacier to glacier, within the same glacier, from season to season and from year to year.

Ask students to study the diagram at the bottom of the page and consider the following questions:
- Which parts of the glacier move the fastest? Why do you think this is so? *(The middle part of the glacier moves the fastest. Friction with the walls and floor of the valley slows down the sides and bottom of the glacier.)*
- Estimate how far the glacier in the diagram moved between 1874 and 1882. On average, how far did it move each year? *(700 m between 1874 and 1882; an average of 87.5 m per year)*
- What is happening at the lower end of the glacier? Why? *(The glacier is receding. It is melting because of an increase in temperature from the heat of the earth, lower elevation, and changes in climate.)*

Point out to students that glacial flow has two components: *basal slip* and *internal flow. Basal slip* occurs when the ice at the bottom of a glacier is always at or near its melting point as a result of the weight of the snow above and the heat of the earth below. The thin film of water that forms at the base lubricates the glacier, allowing it to slip over its bed in much the same way that skates allow a skater to glide over the ice. *Internal flow* is a slow creep that occurs within a glacier as ice crystals slip over one another.

The fastest-moving glaciers (in Greenland) move at about 60 m per day in summer but slow to a few meters per day in winter. In contrast, the flow of most alpine glaciers averages between 5 and 15 m per year.

Exploration 14

Encourage students to try this activity at home or to design an experiment of their own. Ask them to write a report based on their findings.

You can demonstrate the effect of pressure on ice by taking two similar ice cubes, placing one under a brick, and comparing their melting times. *(If the weight is heavy enough, the ice will flow.)*

Developing a Theory of Glaciation

Charpentier and Agassiz

The "icy argument" between Agassiz and Charpentier lends itself to several different teaching approaches. One approach could be to perform it as a class dramatization. One student could act as the narrator, while two others play the parts of the two scientists. As an alternative, the class could hold a debate. You could assign a group of students to present each point of view and have the rest of the class listen, discuss, and evaluate the arguments.

It is possible that some students (who may never have visited a mountain area) may find it difficult to visualize the evidence that Agassiz and Charpentier are discussing. Building a diorama or making three-dimensional props to use in a dramatization may make Agassiz' and Charpentier's arguments clearer.

Emphasize that both Charpentier and Agassiz adopted a scientific attitude. They based their ideas on inferences and observations rather than unfounded opinions. (Remind students about their studies of scientific attitudes from Unit 1 of this book.)

Take this opportunity to discuss the role of different types of thinking in science. Science is based on collecting evidence, but intuitive thinking and questioning based on the evidence also play an important role.

(Overall, Charpentier had the stronger argument; he presented more real evidence. Agassiz theorized too much about what might have happened.)

Students may suggest many possible rejoinders to Charpentier's last argument on page 473. *(Answers may vary, but one possible response might include: "If the ground here was once covered by ice, what happened to it? If it melted away, why didn't the water carry away the till?")* There are many other possibilities. Encourage students do examine the evidence and explore all the possibilities.
(Continues on next page)

Developing a Theory of Glaciation

Charpentier and Agassiz

In the summer of 1836, Louis Agassiz, a young Swiss naturalist, visited Bex, a small town in the Alps. His plan was to search for fish fossils in limestone beds high in the mountains near Bex. He had been invited to Bex by Johann von Charpentier, the director of the local mine, whom Agassiz had met 20 years earlier. Charpentier wanted to show Agassiz evidence for a theory that he had been developing for some time. Charpentier believed that a type of sediment called *till,* which lay throughout the region on hills, mountains, and lowlands, was left there by glaciers. To Agassiz, though, the idea that huge sheets of ice had once covered Europe seemed like a fairy tale. However, since his mind was really on fossils, he didn't argue the point.

Imagine accompanying these men on their first expedition into the mountains. Charpentier starts to present the evidence to support his theory. As they stand beside a large outcrop of rock, Agassiz argues stubbornly against Charpentier's theory.

Agassiz: "It's quite obvious the till formed right where it is, by weathering. You can see that these rocks have been shattered."

Charpentier: "If weathering is the cause, then why don't the rocks *look* weathered? These rocks have fresh, unweathered surfaces. Moreover, all the rocks in this outcrop are of different types: there's granite, basalt, and limestone, and who knows what else. The rock underneath is sandstone. How can granite be weathered from sandstone?"

Continuing up the trail, they come upon an immense boulder.

Charpentier: "Look at that huge boulder, many kilometers from where it should be. How do you think it got here—by wind, by water? It's far too heavy."

Agassiz: "Perhaps there was a violent explosion of some sort which bounced the boulders from hill to hill and also churned up the soil to form the till."

Charpentier: "Nonsense! That idea is about as good as suggesting that these big rocks were dropped by huge icebergs drifting about in some huge flood. What evidence is there to support such an idea?"

A glacial boulder

Scratches in bedrock

Till

Agassiz: "I believe the till is excellent evidence. It could have been deposited by a flood that once covered the entire earth. This explains why till is found everywhere, from lowlands to mountains."

Charpentier: "How can you say that? Haven't you read Hutton? Do you not believe him when he says that the present is the key to the past? Do the sea deposits formed today bear any resemblance to the till all around us? Absolutely not! Here's more evidence for glaciation. Look at the scratches and grooves on this bedrock. What forces could have done such a thing? There's only one answer. Rocks caught in the ice gouged out these deep grooves. Have you ever seen bedrock look like it has been polished? How do you explain that? Only a glacier could have done that! There's only one explanation: The ground we are standing on was once covered by ice!"

And so the argument continued. How might Agassiz have answered Charpentier? Now play the referee in their debate. Make two columns in your Journal: Agassiz's Evidence, and Charpentier's Evidence. List the evidence each presented. Who do you think had the strongest case? Why?

(Charpentier and Agassiz continued)
The following is background information on Louis Agassiz that you can share with your students. In his later years, Agassiz became so intrigued with glaciation that he abandoned his study of fossil fish and spent 10 years studying alpine glaciation and till. His studies led him to propose that glacial ice once covered Eurasia from the North Pole to the Mediterranean Sea. In 1840 he published a book on his research, entitled *Studies on Glaciers.* The book presented evidence for continental glaciation. The detailed, circumstantial evidence presented in his book began to convince many people who had formerly doubted his theory. In 1846, Agassiz left Europe for the United States, where he studied North American glacial evidence.

Answers to

In-Text Questions

Have students compare the evidence by making lists in their Journals as suggested on page 473. *Sample lists of evidence:*

Agassiz' Evidence
1. Till was formed from weathered rocks; the rocks appear shattered.
2. A violent explosion churned up the soil to form till and threw immense boulders about.
3. Till was deposited by a flood that covered the earth. Thus, till is found everywhere, from lowlands to mountains.

Charpentier's Evidence
1. The rocks have fresh, unweathered faces.
2. The underlying rock is sandstone; the outcrop is granite, basalt, limestone, and others.
3. Granite cannot be formed from weathered sandstone.
4. Sea deposits do not bear any resemblance to present-day till.
5. Scratches and grooves can be seen on the bedrock.
6. The bedrock looks polished.

Glacial Calling Cards

Call on a volunteer to read aloud page 474. Ask students to explain in their own words the meanings of the terms *terminal moraine, meltwater,* and *outwash.* Direct their attention to the diagram of the glacier. Point out the locations of the different glacial features. Be sure that students understand the terms and how they are shown on the diagram. It may be difficult for students to visualize how glaciers can change the land so dramatically. To demonstrate this, freeze a layer of water in which rocks, pebbles, and gravel have been submerged. Allow the ice to melt until the materials protrude. Then push the ice over some soil in a stream table or across a slab of modeling clay. Finally, allow the ice to melt completely to let students see how glaciers drop their load of assorted rocks and gravel.

To help students understand how rocks can become embedded in solid ice, try the following activity. Place two ice cubes in a shallow pan with a key, coin, or heavy nail on one of them. Put both cubes in the freezer overnight. Have students observe what happens to the piece of metal. *(If the object is heavy enough, it will become embedded in the ice.)* Analogous to this process is the embedding of leaves in ice, a phenomenon students may have seen if they live in an area that reaches freezing temperatures in the winter.

Identify glacial deposits in the local area if they exist. A field trip to an appropriate site would be an ideal way to build understanding.

Glacial Calling Cards

A glacier consists of more than just ice. As a glacier moves, it scrapes off and carries along huge amounts of soil and rock. Even after loose material is scraped off, the enormous grinding weight of the glacier wears down any projecting parts of the valley sides or floor. Sometimes, too, boulders fall from the valley walls onto the glacier, which then carries them great distances before dropping them. Remember how Charpentier used the large boulder as evidence to convince Agassiz?

A glacier is like a giant bulldozer pushing a huge pile of debris before it. When a glacier stops advancing (terminates), it dumps whatever rock fragments it has been carrying or pushing. This deposit forms a ridge called a **terminal moraine.** Terminal moraines are a mishmash of soil and rock fragments of all sizes, from microscopic particles to boulders.

At the same time, a stream of **meltwater** flows down from the foot of the glacier carrying a large load of sediment with it. This sediment is deposited in formations called **outwash.** Outwash is found down the valley from the terminal moraine.

Now look at the diagram. Notice where the terminal moraine is formed.

Questions

1. What happens to the projecting bedrock as the glacier continues to move?
2. Where might the glacier pick up "hitchhikers"?
3. Why are moraines composed of rocks of different sizes and type?
4. Think back to your stream studies. Why does glacial meltwater carry away only the smaller rock fragments?
5. Why are glacial outwash deposits layered?

Glacial Deposits

Glacier

Projecting bedrock

Till

Terminal Moraine

Outwash stream

Outwash deposits

Answers to

Questions

1. As the glacier continues to move, it wears away at any projecting bedrock.
2. "Hitchhikers" fall from the valley walls, are plucked from the bedrock, and are gouged from the softer parts of rocks and soil.
3. The rocks carried by the glacier come from different sources, such as stream deposits, soil, weathered rock, and bedrock scraped from valley walls. This material is all dumped together when the glacier terminates.
4. There is too much material for the meltwater to carry it all away, and some of the fragments are too heavy.
5. Meltwater flows from the glacier at its point of termination and carries the smaller fragments along. The meltwater deposits sorted beds of pebbles, sand, and clay. The amount varies with the stream flow, causing layers of outwash deposits to form.

Glacial Landforms

Glaciers leave many changes in their wake. On this page are a few of the many varied landforms that glaciers can cause, some baffling, some beautiful.

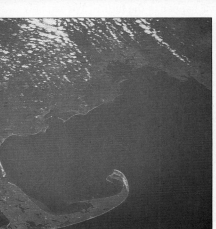

How might you account for each of these features?
Which is a terminal moraine?

- *Striations*—long, parallel scratches in rocks. Striations are caused by rock fragments embedded in moving ice, scraping over the rocks on the surface.
- *Kettle lakes*—round, water-filled depressions in the outwash plain. They formed when buried blocks of ice melted.
- *Fjords*—glacial valleys that have been filled with water. In many cases, the glaciers were so heavy that they became submerged at the edge of the sea and continued to gouge out an underwater valley.
- *Erratic*—A large boulder of a different type of rock than is generally found in the surrounding area. It was carried and left by a glacier.

Point out to students that these are just some of the landforms caused by glaciers. Cirques, hanging falls, finger lakes, and shore bluffs can also be added to the list. Additional examples can be found in the argument between Charpentier and Agassiz.

To make students' understanding of these processes more concrete, use models. For example, the process of forming a kettle lake can be illustrated by burying a large chunk of ice in a stream table, allowing it to melt, and observing the depression that results.

Answer to

In-Text Question

The photograph on the top left was formed by a glacier that carved out U-shaped valleys and sharp ridges. The photo on the top right is a fjord, formed when glaciers gouged out a U-shaped valley. Later, when the glacier melted and the sea level rose, the valley was flooded. The photo on the bottom left is a terminal moraine. It shows the debris piled up at the far end of a continental glacier. The photo on the bottom right is an esker, formed by meltwater that ran in channels beneath the glacier and that deposited sediments.

Glacial Landforms

This page shows photographs of a variety of glacial landforms. Have students study the photographs and identity those features that they think might have been formed by glacial activity. A list of glacial landforms and the process by which they were formed follows:

- *Glaciated valleys*—valleys with a distinct U-shape, gouged out by a glacier. Yosemite Valley is an outstanding example of this landform.
- *Outwash deposits*—formed of material left behind by the meltwater that comes from the end of the glacier.
- *Braided streams*—formed in a braided pattern as meltwater from the end of a glacier travels over loose deposits of rock and gravel.
- *Drumlins*—elongated teardrop-shaped hills formed from glacial sediment. They were probably formed when material left behind by a previous glacier was "run over" by a later glacier.
- *Eskers*—long, winding ridges deposited by glaciers. They are formed by meltwater running in channels beneath the glaciers and depositing sediments.

Exploration 15

If a field trip is not possible, invite a geologist to come to the class to discuss glacial landforms. Slides of glacial formations may be available from a state or national park.

What Causes Ice Ages?

Have students read the material. Involve them in a discussion of the possible causes of ice ages. Several theories follow. Ask students which theory they think makes the most sense and why.

- *Astronomical theories*—focus on the geometry of the earth's orbital path, the tilt of the earth, the variations in the sun's output of flares, and the occurrence of sunspots.
- *Atmospheric theories*—focus on the earth's atmosphere. The buildup of dust blocks the sun's rays.
- *Geological theories*—focus on mountain uplifting and changes in ocean currents that blocked the relatively warm water from the equator from reaching the poles. *(If glaciers began melting, the sea level would rise, causing greater weathering and erosion. Continuing to pollute the atmosphere with carbon dioxide and ozone-depleting chemicals would cause the greenhouse effect to worsen.)*

✳ *Follow Up*

Assessment

1. Give students the following situation: You have been sent to explore an area where no one has ever been before. What kinds of evidence would you look for to determine if the area had once been covered by a glacier? *(Students should describe glacial landforms discussed in the lesson.)*

2. Have students write a story describing local and worldwide changes that would precede another ice age. *(Answers may vary, but responses might include: volcanoes erupting and blocking the sun's rays, a significant drop in temperature, the interior of continents becoming covered with ice, and a change in the sun's energy output.)*

Glaciers in Your Neighborhood

Look back at the map on page 469. Do you live within the area once covered by glaciers? If so, then you can probably find evidence of glaciation in your area. Organize a field trip to try to find that evidence.

Depending on your area, you may be able to find several different types of glacial features. Consult your teacher, reference material or a geologist to find out what types of glacial features, if any, you are likely to find.

Next, prepare a field guide for use on your trip. It should include descriptions of typical evidence of glacial activity in the past.

Then, after studying a site, make complete notes and several sketches.

Finally, write up a "field report" to sum up your findings.

A Final Note on the Glacial Scientists

Like any good scientist, Agassiz considered Charpentier's new ideas very carefully. Eventually, he came to accept Charpentier's theory. He even went further by becoming an important researcher of the role of glaciers in shaping the landscape.

What Causes Ice Ages?

Four times within the last 1,300,000 years, glaciers advanced over large areas of the continents and then mysteriously melted away. Other ice ages have also happened in the distant past. Why? What conditions caused this to happen? What might cause another glacial episode?

So far, many theories have been proposed to explain the causes of ice ages, but none clearly has all the answers. Certainly, a significant drop in the earth's average yearly temperature, about 6 °C, would bring on another "deep freeze." Such a drop in temperature might result from a change in the sun's energy output; from an alteration in the rotation of the earth on its axis; from major changes in the arrangement of the continental plates; or from volcanic dust thrown up into the atmosphere, cutting off the heat from the sun.

If, on the other hand, the greenhouse effect worsens, the earth's glaciers could begin to melt. What would be the effect of this? What could cause the greenhouse effect to worsen?

Many scientists point out that the ice age has never really ended. We are simply in an "interglacial period"—a kind of global warm spell. As long as the earth has polar ice caps, they say, we are in an ice age. The ice could come surging back at any time. No one can say for certain what will happen in the future. We can only wait and see.

Extension

1. Have students give a presentation to younger students based on their field report from the activity *Glaciers in Your Neighborhood.*

2. Have students build a model of a glacial landscape based on a topographical map of the area.

1. If you follow a river upstream, it forks again and again, until finally the headwaters are reached; but rivers almost never split into different forks as they flow downstream. Why is this the case?

2. Consider the following statements: "The more eroded a landscape is, the slower it erodes. The less eroded a landscape is, the faster it erodes." Does this make any sense? Explain.

3. How good a geologist are you? To find out, take the following test.

   A list of observations is given below. Write down each one and give one or more possible explanations for it. Check your answers with your teacher to find out how you did.

Super Geologist	7 or 8
Geologist	5 or 6
Geologist of the Future	4 or less

   (a) You find rocks in your backyard that had to have come from another county.

   (b) Deep scratches are discovered in the surface of highly polished bedrock.

   (c) You find fish fossils high in the Rocky Mountains.

   (d) Over a period of five years, a beach disappears.

   (e) A crack large enough to put your foot into runs the length of a huge boulder lying next to the highway.

   (f) The fossil plant Glossopteris has been found in Australia, India, and Antarctica.

   (g) A huge granite boulder stands alone at the edge of a lake.

   (h) Rocks found in France are similar to rocks found in Maine.

Answers to
Challenge Your Thinking

1. The many forks at the headwaters of a river are caused by runoff of excess water. As the waters accumulate to form a river, a deeper and wider valley forms. The waters of the main stream do not fork downstream, due to the forces of gravity.

2. The statement makes sense because the light, fine particles of a less-eroded landscape would be carried off quickly at first.

3. Answers will vary. The following are possible responses.
   (a) During the last ice age, glaciers traveled from another county through yours, depositing rocks in your backyard.
   (b) The scratches on the polished surface of the rock indicate that the rock was scoured by ice, probably during the last ice age.
   (c) The rock forming the mountains was originally under water and, when one crustal plate collided with another, was pushed up to form a mountain.
   (d) Several causes might explain the disappearance of a beach, but tidal encroachment and erosion from wave action are probably the major causes.
   (e) The boulder was probably deposited by a glacier. The crack might be the result of weathering from ice wedging into cracks, or from blasting during highway construction.
   (f) The discovery of this fossil plant on three continents provides evidence for the theory that the continents were once joined together.
   (g) As a glacier moved across the area, the lake could have been gouged out and the boulder deposited.
   (h) The occurrence of similar rocks on different continents suggests that these pieces of land were once joined.

UNIT 8
Making Connections

Summary for

The Big Ideas

Student answers will vary. The following is an ideal summary.

Geology is the study of the history of the earth, the forces that have shaped its history, and the forces that will shape its future. Geologists use the clues found in the earth's landforms to deduce the forces and changes that led to these formations.

For example, the evidence that supports the theory of continental drift comes directly from observing the earth's features. This evidence includes the way in which the outlines of the continents seem to fit together like pieces of a puzzle. Also, fossil evidence shows identical plants and animals occurring on widely separated land masses. The organisms could have been in both places only if the continents had once been joined. Similarities in age and type of rocks, as well as continuity of landforms, indicate that the continents were once joined.

The earth is changed by many forces. One of the most important forces is that of weathering. The primary agents of weathering are water, wind, ice, and gravity. Water wears down the landscape both physically and chemically. The force of moving water carries away loose debris. This carried debris then acts as sandpaper, eroding even more of the landscape. Water also breaks down the landscape in chemical reactions. When water freezes, the ice that forms within cracks in rocks expands and widens the already existing cracks. Portions eventually break off. When glaciers move, they carry a great deal of sediment. Gravity causes the water to flow downhill, rocks to slide, and ice to move. With the downward movement of material, erosion occurs.

Glaciers move due to the force of gravity on their own weight. As they move, they carry along with them pieces of loose rock. The glacier polishes the rock surface (bedrock) left behind. The debris carried along with

The Big Ideas

In your Journal, write a summary of this unit, using the following questions as a guide.

- What is geology all about?
- What does the expression "the present is the key to the past" mean?
- How do geologists use inferences and observations?
- What is some evidence to support the theory of continental drift?
- What are some agents of weathering?
- What role does water play in the weathering process? What role does gravity play?
- What is the evidence for widespread glaciation in the past?
- Is the ice age over for good?

Checking Your Understanding

1. Most words have more than one meaning. Read each sentence below and explain what is meant by the underlined word. Then rewrite the sentence showing that you understand the geological or scientific meaning of the underlined word as it is used in this unit.

   Example: Betty and Sergei were in the <u>runoff</u> race.
   Heavy rains can cause great damage due to <u>runoff</u>.

   (a) He is in big trouble for having his hand in the <u>till.</u>
   (b) How are you <u>weathering</u> the storm?
   (c) Why not <u>meander</u> over to my house after supper?
   (d) Her election win was a <u>landslide</u> victory.
   (e) She received an <u>avalanche</u> of phone calls after she won the trophy.
   (f) The baseball missed home <u>plate</u> by a country mile.
   (g) Is a <u>water table</u> like a water bed?

   Find other examples of words used in this unit that have both a scientific and a common meaning.

2. How do you think the process of erosion would be affected if:
   (a) the force of gravity was doubled?
   (b) the average temperature went up by 5 °C?
   (c) the atmosphere vanished?
   (d) the boiling point of water suddenly changed to 10 °C?
   (e) there were no gravity?
   (f) water froze at 25 °C?
   (g) water were four times as heavy (for a given volume)?

   Explain each answer.

the glacier often leaves deep scratches in this polished surface. When the glacier deposits its load of debris, many different types of rock are then found together. Some of these "foreign" rocks are much too large to have been moved by any force other than that of an immense glacier.

The geologic record shows that ice ages have occurred repeatedly in cycles. On the basis of that evidence, it is thought another ice age will probably occur, although the exact time cannot be predicted. Forces that caused the earth to cool in the past could conceivably cause the earth to cool in the future.

Answers to

Checking Your Understanding

1. (a) "Hand in the till" means stealing from a cash drawer. *Geological meaning:* The *till* deposited by the glacier consists of many different types of rock.
   (b) "Weathering the storm" suggests surviving a difficult situation. *Geological meaning:* The *weathered* landscape had only large boulders in it that could not be carried off by the wind.

(Answers continue on next page)

3. A famous saying related to geology is written in code below. Here is how to crack the code. One letter simply stands for another.

AXYDLBAAXR
LONGFELLOW

Use the example to get started. Can you decipher this famous saying?

PDA   LNAOAJP   EO   PDA   GAU
PK   PDA   LWOP—FWIAO   DQPPKJ

4. Imagine that all tectonic activity suddenly comes to a grinding halt. What might the earth be like in 10 million years? a hundred million years? a billion years?

5. Make a concept map using the following terms or phrases: *waves, ice, gravity, erosion, wind,* and *flowing water.*

Reading *Plus*

Now that you have been introduced to earth-shaping processes, let's take a closer look at the forces that change the face of our planet. By reading pages S133–S151 of the *SourceBook,* you will learn about different causes of weathering, how soil is formed, about different agents of erosion, how humans minimize erosion, and how the products of erosion are transported and deposited.

Updating Your Journal

Reread the paragraphs you wrote for this unit's "For Your Journal" questions. Then rewrite them to reflect what you have learned in studying this unit.

About Updating Your Journal

The following are sample ideal answers.
1. Most scientists believe that the earth came into existence about 4.5 billion years ago.
2. The earth has gone through many changes. *(Evidence of these **Patterns of Change** can be seen in the present landforms on the earth.)*
3. Flowing water, wind, ice, and gravity are constantly wearing away the earth. The earth doesn't erode away because the particles eroded are simply moved to another part of the landscape.
4. Evidence that much of the earth was once covered with ice can be seen in the polished and scratched surfaces of the bedrock and in the transportation of the loose surface layer of rock to distant places.
5. The dunes in the photograph could have been formed when drought caused all the vegetation to die, which led to the erosion of the soil. The dunes are like waves in that they move and flow due to force of the wind.

(c) "Meander" here refers to a slow walk. *Geological meaning:* Many *meanders* had developed in the old river.

(d) "Landslide" here refers to a victory by a large majority. *Geological meaning:* The earthquake triggered the *landslide.*

(e) "Avalanche" here suggests a great number. *Geological meaning:* The *avalanche* was started on purpose by an explosion.

(f) Home "plate" is home base in a baseball game. *Geological meaning:* The earth's crust is broken up into many *plates.*

(g) *Geological meaning:* The *water table* is like a table because it is the upper surface of the layer of ground where all the pores are filled with water.

2. **(a)** Gravity is the force behind moving water, moving ice, and moving rocks. Doubling its force would greatly increase erosion.

(b) This might cause more moisture to accumulate in the atmosphere, which would cause greater weathering and erosion.

(c) Weathering and erosion would greatly decrease because there would be no wind or water.

(d) Except in areas with temperatures below 10 °C, there would be no natural bodies of water, as they would have boiled away. This would decrease the amount of erosion.

(e) Erosion would cease because gravity is the force behind all erosion.

(f) Most of the earth's surface would be covered by ice. This would increase the amount of erosion.

(g) Erosion would greatly increase due to the increase in the force of gravity.

3. The quote reads as follows: *The present is the key to the past—* James Hutton

4. If all tectonic activity stops, the earth would probably remain much as it is at this time.

5. See page S170 for concept map.

Science in *Action*

Spotlight on Geophysics

✦ Background

Marine geophysicists generally perform research work for universities, governmental organizations, or the petroleum industry. Marine geophysics research is designed to further knowledge about the physical processes and phenomena taking place in the world's oceans.

Marine geophysicists may perform some of their work in a laboratory, but data gathering and experimentation take place largely at sea. Sediment samples and measurements of underwater topography are examples of data gathered and analyzed by marine geophysicists.

To become a marine geophysicist, a college degree in geology, physics, or oceanography is required, and higher-level degrees are preferred. A person with a Bachelor's or Master's degree could work as part of a research team led by a marine geophysicist holding a doctorate degree.

Marianne Spence is a marine geophysicist. Geophysics applies the science of physics to the study of the earth, especially the interior of the earth, which cannot be observed directly. We visited her in her laboratory.

Q: What does your current work involve?

Marianne: My area of research is the continental margin off the east coast of North America. Continental margins are the edges of continents, between the continental shelf and the deep ocean where the sea floor slopes very steeply down to the ocean bottom. Depths along the continental margin range from 100 or 200 meters to several thousand meters. I am chiefly interested in finding out exactly how the continental margin formed. We know in general how this happened—sediments that eroded from the continent piled up over millions of years—but the details still elude us. It's really much more complicated and interesting than it sounds. For example, North America, Africa, and Europe

were once "welded" together. What effect did this continental breakup have on the formation of the continental margins? Though my interests in this field are purely scientific—I just want to know what happened—there are practical applications of the knowledge we gain. Sandwiched in between the thick layers of

sediments making up the continental margin are world-class oil and gas deposits.

Q: How does a geophysicist go about collecting information?

Marianne: Using special techniques we can actually "see" underground.

✦ Using the Interview

Have students read the interview silently or ask volunteers to read it aloud. Afterwards, involve the class in a discussion about the kind of work done in the marine geophysics field. To evaluate student understanding of the interview, ask questions similar to the following:

- Why did Marianne Spence feel that the continental margin off the east coast of North America was an interesting area to study? *(It is an area where the edge of the continent drops off suddenly into a deep ocean basin. She wants to find out why it drops off in this way, and why it is located in its present position and not somewhere else.)*

- What kind of evidence is she looking for to help her answer her research questions? *(She is studying the layers of sediments found at the continental margins for clues.)*
- How can studying the sediments help her to determine what took place? *(Sediments form layers that can be dated. Materials found in a sediment layer give information about conditions in the ocean at a particular time. Using this information, a marine geophysicist can reconstruct a series of geologic events.)*

Geophysicists examining core samples brought up from the ocean floor.

Some Project Ideas

Locate geologic maps of your area. See if you can recognize some of the structures and rock types shown on the map. How long ago were the local rocks formed? Using the map and reference materials, try to piece together a brief geologic history of your area.

Locate a seismic profile and a geologic map of an area. Describe and interpret what you see. How do the two compare? How do you think geologists and geophysicists use seismic profiles when they prepare geologic maps?

Prepare a geologic map of your own for a small area. Try to find an area with lots of exposed rock, for easy mapping. Use an actual geologic map as a guide.

For Assistance

Check your local library for geologic maps or books with geologic maps and seismic profiles. State or county agencies may also prove helpful. Ask a geologist or geophysicist for help if necessary. These people can help you locate geologic maps, seismic profiles, and reference materials. Geologists can be found on the staffs of colleges and universities, and at state and local agencies (especially those dealing with environmental-, land-, or water-related matters.)

The process is called *seismic profiling*. How this works, in brief, is that you create a shock wave (either by setting off explosives or by using a special air gun). This shock wave goes down to the ocean floor. Some of it bounces back, but much of it penetrates into the subsurface. Every time this shock wave hits a new rock layer, some of it is reflected back. We record all of the returning echoes and feed the information into a computer. It processes the information and then spits out a cross-section of the subsurface. Then comes the fun part, trying to interpret these seismic profiles.

Q: Earth sciences are fairly well dominated by men. Has this caused you any problems?

Marianne: What you say is really not true any more. I would estimate that 35 to 40 percent of the students in earth science fields are female. This will almost certainly increase in the future. However, one problem I have had is balancing my professional and family lives. Perhaps for men this problem is not as severe. Unfortunately, the tasks of rearing children and making a home still fall largely on the wife, whether she works or not.

Background

Earthquakes result from the release of built-up stresses within the earth's crust. Convection processes in the molten core are thought to be the cause. Stress-releasing events that produce earthquakes include sudden fault movements and volcanic activity.

At the focus of an earthquake (in the crust or mantle), stress energy changes to wave energy, producing seismic waves. Seismic waves occur as compression waves (P-waves) and transverse waves (S-waves and L-waves). P-waves move rapidly in all directions and actually pass all the way through the center of the earth. Since P-waves slow down as they pass through soft or liquid materials, measurements of their speed provide information about the interior of the earth. S-waves (sometimes called shear waves) move through the solid subsurface layers, causing adjacent points in the ground to move in opposite directions. P-waves and S-waves set up surface waves known as L-waves. L-waves cause rippling motions that can topple buildings and open cracks in the ground.

Seismographs measure seismic-wave activity. Since P-waves travel the fastest, they reach a seismograph first. They are followed by S-waves and finally, by L-waves, which arrive last because they travel along the surface.

The distance from the seismograph station to the point on the earth's surface closest to the focus of the quake (the epicenter) can be calculated by measuring the difference between the arrival times of P-waves and S-waves. The epicenter can be located more precisely by comparing data from several seismograph locations. The distance to the epicenter (the surface point closest to the focus) is calculated for each location and used as the radius of a circle. The point where the circles from each seismograph station intersect is the epicenter location.

Science and Technology

Earthquake!

Imagine a raft composed of logs tied together by rope. The raft can move around as a single unit, but as it does, the individual logs will rub against each other.

As stable as it may seem, the surface of the earth is actually made up of a number of separate plates that can rub against one another like the logs in the raft. Tremendous pressure and friction may build up along the lines where the plates touch. These lines are known as **faults.** If the plates suddenly slip, the result is an earthquake.

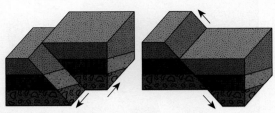

This drawing illustrates the two types of faults: a strike-slip fault (left) and a dip-slip fault (right).

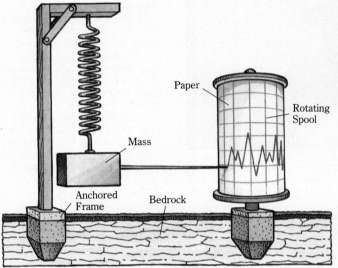

Paper

Rotating Spool

Mass

Anchored Frame

Bedrock

Predicting Earthquakes

From past records, we know that earthquakes are more likely to occur in some places than in others. Also, in certain areas, earthquakes occur with a fairly definite regularity. For example, a medium-sized earthquake strikes about every twenty years in the Cholame Valley of California. To predict an earthquake to the nearest day or hour, however, much more information would be needed.

Detection and Measurement

The energy released by an earthquake travels in waves along the surface of the earth. These **seismic waves** can be measured by a device known as a **seismograph,** which is illustrated at the left.

An earthquake is measured on the **Richter Scale.** Each number in the scale represents a tenfold increase in the size of the seismic waves. An earthquake measuring 8 on the Richter scale has seismic waves ten times as great as an earthquake measuring 7. Earthquakes measuring greater than 6 or 7 on the Richter Scale are considered major.

Discussion

When students have finished reading the feature, involve them in a discussion of what they have read. You may wish to use questions similar to the following:

1. Why is it difficult to measure an earthquake? *(When the earth is moving, there are no fixed reference points.)*
2. Although earthquake prediction is generally seen as a positive thing, there are possible drawbacks. What might some drawbacks be? *(Many experts worry that false alarms produce needless panic and may cause economic losses.)*

To get information about exactly what happens before an earthquake, the most advanced equipment would need to be at the right place at the right time. For instance, there is an instrument known as a *color laser geodimeter,* which can measure ground movements within a millimeter. A number of other things can be studied for clues to upcoming earthquakes, including tilting of the land near the fault zone, the resistance to electrical flow in rocks, flashes of colored light in the sky, and perhaps even the behavior of animals.

Earthquake Protection

The major danger during earthquakes is from collapsing buildings and other large structures such as freeways and tunnels. To withstand an earthquake, such structures must be designed with a certain amount of flexibility. One way to do this is to use shock-absorbing devices in the structure of a building. Such devices, which are often composed of layers of rubber and steel, permit a building to sway during an earthquake instead of breaking.

Find Out for Yourself

Do some research to find out about the movements of the plates of the earth's surface. What are the two main kinds of faults? Where are some of the major faults in the earth's surface? What are some of the most earthquake–prone areas on the earth?

Do a report on how architects and engineers design buildings and other structures to withstand earthquakes.

A Way to Bring Ideas Together

What Is a Concept Map?

Have you ever tried to tell someone about a book or a chapter you've just read, and you find that you can remember only a few isolated words and ideas? Or maybe you've memorized facts for a test and then weeks later, you're not even sure what topic those facts are related to.

In both cases, you may have understood the ideas or concepts *by themselves,* but not in relation to one another. If you could somehow link the ideas together, you would probably understand them better and remember them longer. This is something a concept map can help you do. A concept map is a visual way of showing how ideas or concepts fit together. It can help you see the "big picture."

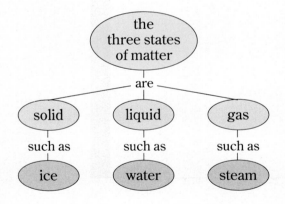

How to Make a Concept Map

1. **Make a list of the main ideas or concepts.**
   It might help to write each concept on its own slip of paper. This will make it easier to rearrange the concepts as many times as you need to before you've made sense of how the concepts are connected. After you've made a few concept maps this way,
   you can go directly from writing your list to actually making the map.

2. **Spread out the slips on a sheet of paper and arrange the concepts in order from the most general to the most specific.**
   Put the most general concept at the top and circle it. Ask yourself, "How does this concept relate to the remaining concepts?" As you see the relationships, arrange the concepts in order from general to specific.

3. **Connect the related concepts with lines.**

4. **On each line, write an action word or short phrase that shows how the concepts are related.**

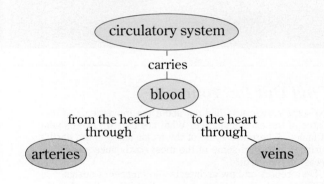

Look at the concept maps on this page and then see if you can make one for the following terms: *plants, water, photosynthesis, carbon dioxide,* and *sun's energy.* The answer is provided below, but don't look at it until you try the concept map yourself.

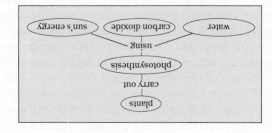

SourceBook™

This *SourceBook* is designed as a handy reference so you may learn more about many of the concepts you have discovered in your reading of Science*Plus*. For each unit of Science*Plus*, you will find a corresponding unit in the *SourceBook*. Questions on the first page of each unit will help direct your thinking as you read the material.

Contents

Unit 1

In This Unit

Reading *Plus*

Now that you have been introduced to science and its methods, you might want to know more about the different areas of science and how practicing scientists use scientific methods while doing research. Read pages S2 to S20 and prepare a brief feature for a newspaper about what science is and the methods scientists use in their investigations. The following questions will help you.

1. What is "science"? What does this term suggest to you?

2. How is the study of science helped by separating it into different subject areas?

3. How would you describe the career of a scientist to a younger person interested in becoming a scientist?

4. How do experiments demonstrate the use of scientific methods? What are some examples of how you use some of the skills of science in everyday living?

1.1 SCIENCE IS CURIOSITY

Curiosity, the desire to know, is the hallmark of intelligence. Of all the life forms on earth, humans have the highest degree of intelligence and so the greatest amount of curiosity. People have always asked questions about things they have seen and experienced. They ask questions such as: "Why did that happen?" "Where did it come from?" "Will it make a good tool?" "How can I improve it?"

These kinds of questions lead to more questions, which lead to even *more* questions. Asking questions and finding answers is at the heart of **science**. The following are examples—one from each of the three major branches of science—of curious events that have caused people to ask questions.

Science The asking and answering of questions in order to satisfy curiosity about the natural world.

Asking Questions

■ In 1977, scientists were on board the research submarine *Alvin* exploring the bottom of the Pacific Ocean near the Galapagos Islands. The scientists were studying the hot-water springs that escape from cracks in the ocean floor. These cracks are called *vents*. The scientists were surprised to discover a large community of creatures living around the hot springs. Among these they found blood-red tube worms up to three meters long. See Figure 1-1. They also saw several other types of *organisms*, or living things, that they had never seen before.

The sun had long been thought to be the source of energy for all living things on earth. The organisms around the hot springs, however, must have had a different source of energy since sunlight does not reach the ocean bottom.

For the first time, a whole community of living things had been discovered that did not get its energy from the sun. How can living things exist in the darkness of the deep ocean floor? What do living things need to exist anywhere? Could life exist on other planets?

Figure 1-1 *Giant tube worms were discovered in the hot water around ocean vents.*

■ It was a place for camping, hunting, and fishing. There were green forests, meadows, and lakes. Such was the area around Mount St. Helens in the state of Washington. At 8:32 A.M. on May 18, 1980 the mountain blew its top. About 250 billion kilograms of rock and dust were blasted out by the eruption. The forests, meadows, lakes, and surrounding area were turned into a landscape that resembled the surface of the moon. See Figure 1-2. Since that May morning, scientists have been studying Mount St. Helens, searching for answers to many questions.

Figure 1-2 Mount St. Helens before it erupted (left). *Mount St. Helens after it erupted* (right).

Our planet is always being changed by powerful forces. Almost every day the news tells us of volcanoes, earthquakes, storms, floods, and droughts. At some time, these forces will touch the life of every person. Why do volcanoes erupt? What causes weather and earthquakes? Can earthquakes and volcanic eruptions be predicted? Finding answers to questions like these can save lives and property.

■ Suppose you are caught outside in a sudden rainstorm. As the rain comes down, your eyes begin to sting. You notice that the rainwater has a sour taste. The falling rain is not pure water. Instead, it seems more like vinegar or lemon juice than water.

Scientists now call this kind of rain *acid rain*. What causes acid rain? Scientists are trying to find answers to this question. But understanding the cause of acid rain is only the beginning. Many more questions must be answered. How can we protect our soil from acid rain? What does acid rain do to our water supplies? What effect does acid rain have on the health of plants, animals, and people? See Figure 1-3.

Finding Answers

One of the ways to find answers to the types of questions asked above is by doing scientific research. Through *observation*, scientists have learned that the water around the hot-spring vents is rich in tiny organisms that are able to use

Figure 1-3 The scientist in the photograph above is testing the acidity of lake water.

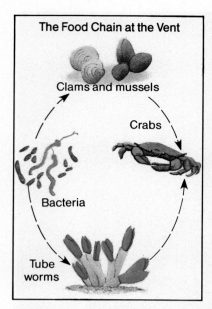

The Food Chain at the Vent

Clams and mussels

Crabs

Bacteria

Tube worms

Figure 1-4 *Chemicals provide a source of energy for a whole community.*

Technology The application of knowledge, tools, and materials to solve practical problems.

Scientist A person who is curious about the natural world. Professional scientists are trained in certain techniques and methods.

chemicals in the hot water as a source of energy. Larger organisms then get their energy by feeding on these tiny organisms. See Figure 1-4. Through *analysis*, the composition of acid rain has been determined. By its composition, the sources of acid rain production can be identified.

Many other questions have been answered and much has been learned. By doing research, our understanding of the universe increases daily, helping us to better answer even harder questions. Much more, however, remains to be learned. Many answers need to be found; answers to questions that have not even been asked yet. The research of scientists can help provide these answers.

Gathering knowledge, through observations and asking questions, is part of the process of science. The application of knowledge in improving the quality of life involves **technology**. Although technology is displayed by other species, science is a uniquely human endeavor.

Summary

Curiosity is the desire to know and learn about things. Because of curiosity, people ask questions which lead to more questions. Science results from curiosity and questioning. Technology is the application of the knowledge gathered through science.

1.2 WHO IS A SCIENTIST?

Look at the two people in Figure 1-5. Which person do you think is a **scientist**? How can you tell? You might think of a scientist as a person who wears a white coat and works in a laboratory. However, scientists do not always dress the same, and not all of them work in laboratories. All scientists *do* have one thing in common—they are all curious about nature. They ask questions and then try to answer their questions.

Are *you* a scientist? Do you ask questions? Are you curious about the world around you? If so, then you could be considered a scientist. Professional scientists, however, have studied the *techniques* of science for many years, and they follow certain *methods* when they ask and answer their questions.

Since the world is so large, and there are so many things to ask questions about, scientists have organized their investigations into three major areas: *life science, earth science,* and *physical science.* The scientists that spend most of their time asking questions in each of these areas are likewise called life scientists, earth scientists, and physical scientists.

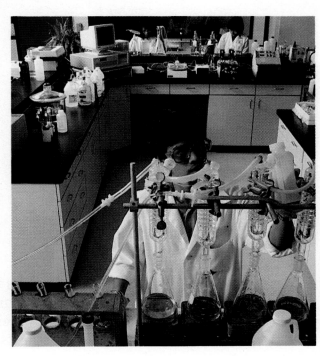

Figure 1-5 Most people think of a scientist as a person who works in a laboratory. But people like Dr. Sally Ride, the former NASA astronaut, are also scientists, even though they may work in places that are very far from a laboratory.

What Do Life Scientists Do?

Why would anyone want a job like the one listed at the right? To a scientist, it might be a rewarding opportunity. To a marine biologist, a scientist who studies life in the oceans, it might be the best chance to observe the ocean bottom.

Life scientists are people who are involved with *biology,* the study of living things. Most life scientists are called biologists. There are many specialized fields of study in biology. Two of the major areas are *botany* and *zoology.* Botanists are biologists that study plants, while zoologists study animals.

There are many other specialized fields of study in the life sciences. For example, *entomology* is the study of insects. Over 75 percent of all the animal species are insects. Entomologists are the life scientists who study, identify, and classify insects. *Ecology* is the study of the environment and its effect on plants and animals. An animal ecologist may, for instance, study the effect of a severe drought on an animal population.

Genetics is the study of heredity. The work that geneticists do ranges from answering theoretical questions about

WANTED: Men and women willing to work $9\frac{1}{2}$ hours at a time inside a small, metal sphere on the ocean bottom. Must have a background in biological sciences. Duties include measuring water depth and temperature, taking water samples, and photographing and collecting living things from the ocean floor. Must be able to withstand cramped areas, cold, and long periods of crouching.

Figure 1-6 *A biologist may further specialize in microbiology.*

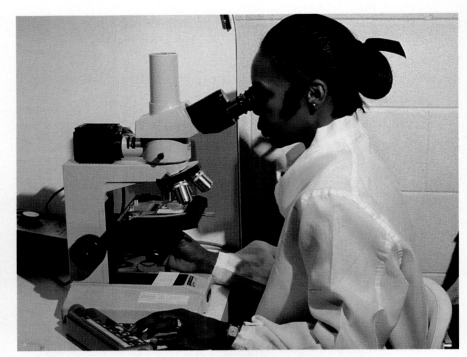

Figure 1-7 *An entomologist studies and classifies insects.*

inheritance to applying genetic principles to practical matters of economic value. Geneticists study animals as well as plants and microorganisms to learn how genes transfer traits from generation to generation. Geneticists have also made great contributions to the quality of human life in the fields of medical research and food production.

Figure 1-8 *An ecologist studies the relationships among animals, plants, and their surroundings.*

Figure 1-9 *A geneticist studies how traits are inherited by animals, plants, and micro-organisms.*

Figure 1-10 *This plant geneticist is applying her knowledge to the production of better food plants.*

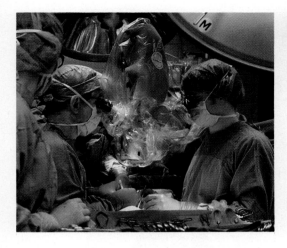

Figure 1-11 Careers in surgery (left) and nursing (right) require a background in biology.

All of the careers in health care and medicine are part of the life sciences. Their work emphasis ranges from trying to understand how the body actually works and treating it for the various problems it encounters, to building devices, such as artificial hearts and knees, to help the body work better.

What Do Earth Scientists Do?

The job in the ad to the right is one type of work that an earth scientist might do. Figure 1-12 shows an earth scientist taking samples of lava. Lava is the melted rock that comes from volcanoes. By studying these samples of lava and other details of the mountain, earth scientists can learn much about volcanoes.

Earth science, the study of our planet, can be divided into four branches. One branch—called *geology*—is the study of the rocky surface of the earth and the earth's interior. Geologists study the matter and the structure of the planet. They do this to find out how the earth was formed and how it changes through time. Some geologists study volcanoes because volcanoes change the surface of the earth. They also give hints as to what lies beneath the surface. Other geologists search for natural resources, such as oil. Oil is important to modern technology since it provides energy, plastics, and solvents for our use. Almost all of the things we use daily come from the earth. Understanding the earth can improve the way we live.

The earth is surrounded by a layer of gases that make up its atmosphere. *Meteorology* is the branch of earth science that studies this atmosphere. The scientists who work in the field of meteorology are called meteorologists. They also observe weather and study climates.

> **WANTED:** Men and women for dangerous work on active volcanoes. Must be able to work in extreme heat and be able to lift heavy objects. Backpacking and/or helicopter-piloting experience a plus. Duties include collecting and studying lava to find the source of melted rock.

Figure 1-12 This volcanologist is wearing protective clothing and a mask to shield himself from the intense heat of the lava. He is using a steel pipe to collect a sample of the molten lava.

Figure 1-13 *A laser range finder is being used by a geologist to measure the movements of parts of Mount St. Helens.*

Figure 1-14 *Oil geologists study the earth's features to find oil deposits.*

Figure 1-15 *Meteorologists study the weather.*

Oceans cover most of the earth's surface. *Oceanography* is the branch of earth science that studies the oceans of the world. Oceanography also includes the study of the earth's surface below the oceans, the sea floor. The scientists who make these studies are called oceanographers, or marine scientists.

Wastes from human activity cause pollution of both air and water. By studying the atmosphere and the oceans, scientists can begin to understand how pollution affects them and to come up with methods of controlling pollution.

Astronomy, sometimes called space science, is the study of the universe beyond the earth. Astronomy is included as a branch of earth science because it shares many of the same questions with other earth sciences. Astronomers study other planets, the sun and stars, and many other objects in space. Also, from space we can see the earth itself as never before. Already, pictures of the earth from orbiting spacecraft have helped locate valuable deposits of minerals, as well as pinpointing sources of pollution.

Figure 1-16 Oceanographers study the oceans.

Figure 1-17 Astronomers study the universe.

What Do Physical Scientists Do?

Physical science includes the study of both matter and energy. The two main branches of physical science are *chemistry* and *physics*. Chemistry is the study of all forms of matter and its interactions. Physics is the study of energy, its changes, and its relationship to matter. Both of these branches include many special areas of study. Chemists and physicists also work in the life sciences and earth sciences.

In chemistry, for example, many biochemists—scientists who study the chemistry of life—work in the medical industry. Their research may find answers to how different disease organisms affect the body and provide information

WANTED: Men and women for challenging jobs in the physical sciences. Must be imaginative, detail oriented, and good problem-solvers. Laboratory and field positions available. Duties may include smashing atoms, perfecting musical sounds, or developing new ways to improve the flavor and shelf life of canned foods.

Figure 1-18 This biochemist works in a medical laboratory.

Figure 1-19 Organic chemists may study chemicals obtained from refining crude oil.

Figure 1-20 *This chemist is taking air samples that will be analyzed in a laboratory for pollutants.*

Figure 1-21 *Laser light is a form of radiant energy. This concentrated energy can be used to cut metal, or to perform delicate surgery.*

Figure 1-22 *Physical oceanographers apply the principles of physics to their study of the oceans.*

that can lead to a cure. Other biochemists develop new drugs and test their effectiveness for the pharmaceutical industry.

Many chemists work in the chemical manufacturing industry. Some chemists specialize in organic chemistry, the study of compounds containing carbon, and many work for the oil industry doing research on crude oil and other petroleum products. Other chemists might test air samples for a variety of environmental pollutants, as shown in Figure 1-20. Most chemists work in university, private, or government research laboratories.

Physicists study things such as light, mechanical forces, sound, and the structure of and the forces inside of atoms, the tiny particles that make up all matter. The physicist in Figure 1-21 is studying *laser* light—a highly concentrated form of light. Lasers are used in space science and medicine, as well as in the entertainment industry. A physical oceanographer might study the physical properties of ocean water (such as density and temperature) and ocean forces (such as waves, currents, and tides).

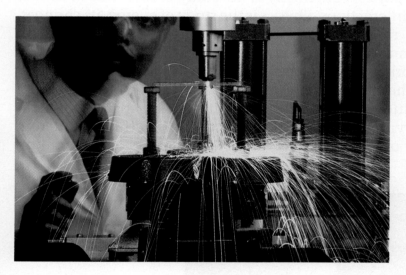

Some physicists study sounds—sounds we hear and sounds we cannot hear. Concert halls and theaters are designed by engineers using the findings of these physicists. These engineers work with sound, making sure sound waves combine in pleasing ways. *Sonar* equipment can be used to detect objects underwater. *Ultrasound* is used by doctors to study the inside of the human body. Both sonar and ultrasound use rapidly vibrating (high-frequency) sound waves that are above our range of hearing, but that can be detected by special instruments.

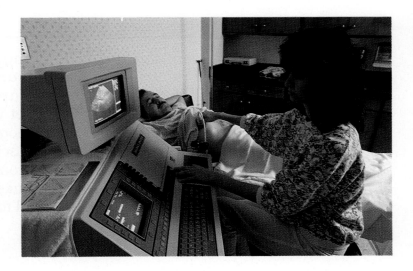

Figure 1-23 Doctors use ultrasound waves to form images of the inside of a human body.

Another important branch of physics involves the study of the structure and internal forces of the atom. Physicists who study the atom have identified even smaller particles held together by forces within the atom. The presence of these particles can be detected by devices such as the cloud chamber, as shown in Figure 1-24.

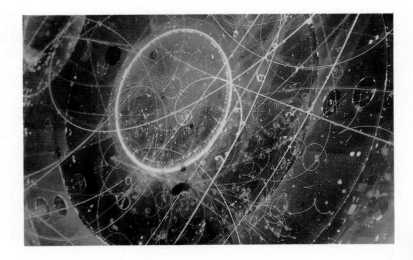

Figure 1-24 The cloud chamber was invented by C.T.R. Wilson. He shared the 1927 Nobel Prize in physics for his discovery. Each of the tracks in this photograph was made by a particle from an atom.

Energy within the atom can be released through the processes of *fission* and *fusion*. Fission, the splitting of an atom, is the source of nuclear energy currently used in the production of useful electric power. The tremendous amount of energy that fission releases is demonstrated by the destructive power of atomic weapons. Fusion, the joining together of two atoms to form a new kind of atom, is thought to be the source of the sun's heat and light. See Figure 1-25. Someday, perhaps, people will be able to control fusion reactions on earth to provide a safer and cheaper form of nuclear energy.

Figure 1-25 The fusion of hydrogen atoms to form a helium atom is thought to be the main source of the sun's energy.

Summary

People who work as life scientists study living things. They are called biologists, and may specialize in a variety of areas. Two major branches of biology are botany and zoology. Earth scientists study the complex planet we live on. The main branches of earth science are geology, meteorology, oceanography, and astronomy. Physical scientists study chemistry and physics, both of which are composed of many specialized areas. Chemists study the make up of matter and its interactions, and physicists study all forms of energy.

1.3 USING SCIENTIFIC METHODS

Modern experimental science began about 400 years ago. An Italian scientist named Galileo Galilei (1564–1642) performed experiments to test ideas about nature. Galileo tried to find basic rules that explain the way things happen in the natural world. Today we call Galileo's way of finding answers a **scientific method**. It is not, however, a *technique* for always getting the right answer to a problem. Rather, it is a *way of thinking* about and investigating nature to discover more about it.

Scientific Method A way of thinking about nature involving the use of certain skills to solve problems in an orderly manner.

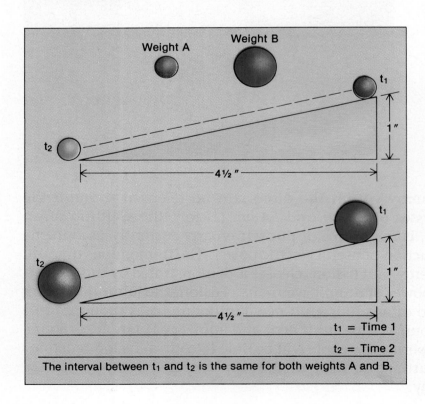

Figure 1-26 *Galileo used ramps as a way of studying falling objects. He showed that two heavy balls of different weights will roll down the same ramp in the same amount of time.*

Weight A Weight B

t_1

1"

t_2

4½"

t_1

1"

t_2

4½"

t_1 = Time 1

t_2 = Time 2

The interval between t_1 and t_2 is the same for both weights A and B.

Galileo used one scientific method to study the motion of falling objects. See Figure 1-26. He believed that scientific understanding of the natural world comes from making **observations** and doing experiments. He refused to blindly accept the ideas about falling objects that people had believed for thousands of years. He therefore let various objects fall, made observations of their fall, and recorded his observations. He then carried out experiments to further understand his observations.

Modern scientists also use scientific methods to study all types of problems. However, not all scientists use all of the same steps, nor do they necessarily use them in the same order. These steps are better thought of as skills that are common to all scientists. These skills can also be used by anyone who solves problems in an orderly, thoughtful way.

Scientists tackle different problems in different ways. Some problems lead to specific solutions. For example, a new type of disease might appear. Its cause must be found and a cure developed. At other times, the purpose of research is to find out more about a general subject, such as the nature of gravity. The following paragraphs detail the steps or skills involved in using scientific methods.

Observation Any information that we gather by using our senses.

Defining the Problem

The mournful howl of a lone coyote, like the one in Figure 1-27, breaks the stillness of the night. At a distant sheep ranch, a rancher hears the howl and reaches for his rifle. "That pest won't kill any of my sheep tonight!" he mutters.

For over a century, the coyote has been the focus of a dispute. Ranchers and farmers claim it kills domestic animals, such as sheep and poultry, for food. Environmental groups say that this does not happen very often. In fact, very little is known about coyotes. If more could be learned about them, perhaps the dispute could be settled.

Marc Bekoff and Michael Wells are scientists. They are trying to learn about the behavior of coyotes. As part of this effort, they carried out a three-year study. One of their goals was to learn why some coyotes live alone and others form packs. Bekoff and Wells suspected that some coyotes in the wild switched back and forth from one type of living to the other.

First, they stated the problem as a clearly worded question: What makes some coyotes live alone and others live in packs? Their next step was to find out what information was already known. Bekoff and Wells went to a

Figure 1-27 While other large North American animals are disappearing, coyotes seem to be thriving.

library. They found some earlier studies done by scientists on coyotes. They also read about the behavior of animals such as jackals and hyenas. These animals are similar to coyotes. The information from these earlier studies, based on the observations of other scientists, was a starting point from which Bekoff and Wells could find answers to their questions.

Forming Hypotheses

After collecting basic information, scientists usually suggest an answer to the problem they have defined. This is done by forming a **hypothesis**. A hypothesis is a possible answer to a question. It is sometimes called an "educated guess." A hypothesis is based on the information the scientist has already gathered. It should be the best possible solution to the problem that the scientists can think of. More than one hypothesis may be formed from the same information. Each possible solution must then be tested.

Hypothesis A possible answer to a question based on gathered information.

Bekoff and Wells made a hypothesis: Food sources available to coyotes determine whether they live alone or in packs. This statement specified what they felt would be a good answer to their question.

Stating a hypothesis is only one step in using a scientific method. Demonstrating that a hypothesis is correct or incorrect is another. Scientists *test* their hypotheses by making observations and doing experiments.

Making Observations

When you think of scientific research, do you think of a scientist in a laboratory mixing chemicals? Science *is* done in the laboratory, but there are also other ways to do scientific research. Imagine that you are an astronomer trying to find out how stars form. There is not much that you could do in a laboratory. Your investigation would involve making many observations of stars. The coyote study also involved making many oberservations. See Figure 1-28. The two scientists would have to watch the coyotes over a long period of time.

To test their hypothesis, Bekoff and Wells went to Grand Teton National Park, Wyoming. From the top of a hill, they could observe the behavior of several lone coyotes. They could also see packs of coyotes in the valley below.

Observations of the coyotes were made over several years. During the summer months, the coyotes' main foods were field mice, gophers, and ground squirrels. They hunted and killed these small animals. See Figure 1-29. During the

Figure 1-28 Dr. Marc Bekoff uses a spotting scope to observe coyotes in the wild.

Figure 1-29 In summer, a lone coyote hunts for small animals.

winter months, however, they ate the remains of deer, elk, and moose. These larger animals had died from other causes. Throughout the study, coyotes were never seen attacking any live, large animal. This, however, does not *prove* that they never do.

The information gathered by Bekoff and Wells showed several things. In the summer, the coyotes hunted and killed small animals for food, and there were fewer coyotes in packs. More were hunting alone over wider areas. In the winter, the weather was very cold and snowy, and there were more large, dead animals available. More coyotes could feed on the same food source. The coyotes came together in packs.

Where the winter supply of large, dead animals was plentiful, the pack size was larger. See Figure 1-30. Where the food was scarce, the packs were smaller. These observations tended to support the scientists' hypothesis that food supply determines whether coyotes live alone or in packs.

Figure 1-30 In winter, a pack of coyotes feeds on the carcass of a mule deer.

Performing Experiments

Bekoff and Wells were interested in another aspect of coyote behavior. They wanted to find out how lone coyotes find and capture their prey. The two scientists believed that coyotes used all of their senses while hunting. But were some senses more important than others? How could the importance of sight be compared to the importance of hearing, or smell?

The scientists would have liked to watch the animals from their hilltop spot. But the range of a lone coyote may be more than 30 square kilometers. The scientists would not be able to observe animals that traveled over such a large area to find food. They also realized that just watching the animals would not give them enough information to answer their questions. They decided to run **experiments** under more controllable conditions.

To do this, several coyotes were captured and brought to a university for study. Each coyote was placed in a large, fenced-in outdoor area. Somewhere in that area was a hidden rabbit. The coyotes were able to use all of their senses to find the rabbit. The amount of time it took each coyote was measured and recorded. Since the times recorded were for the coyotes using all of their senses, the relative importance of *one* sense could not be identified. This part of the experiment is called the **control**. The control conditions were as close to the natural setting as possible. All other parts of an experiment are compared to the control.

The part of an experiment that is different from the control is called the **variable**. Scientists change only one part of an experiment at a time. In this way, they know that the different results probably are caused by one specific variable. For example, the scientists wanted to check how important sight is to coyotes. To do this, the test was done on a dark night when there was no moonlight. Infrared photography was used to track the coyotes' movements in the dark. See Figure 1-31. In this case, the tested variable was the sense of sight.

To eliminate the variable of sound, dead rabbits were hidden. There would be no noise to help the coyotes locate the rabbit. To eliminate the variable of smell, the coyotes' nostrils were flushed with a nasal spray. The spray temporarily stopped the coyotes' sense of smell.

One at a time, each of the three variables was tested. The time it took for each coyote to find the rabbit was measured and recorded. Each part of the experiment was run many times. This was done to find an average time. Repeating an experiment several times improves the reliability of its results.

Experiment An activity designed to test a hypothesis.

Control The part of an experiment that serves as a standard to which variables are compared.

Variable Any factor in an experiment that could affect the results and is therefore tested separately.

Figure 1-31 Coyotes were tracked at night to test the importance of vision.

Analyzing Data

Once all of the **data** from an experiment are collected, the data must be organized. This organized information can then be studied. Data, in the form of measurements, can be organized in data tables. Table 1-1 is a data table that could have been used in the coyote experiment.

Data Information collected from observation and experiment.

Coyote Number	Sight Only		Hearing Only		Smell Only	
	Trials	Avg.	Trials	Avg.	Trials	Avg.
1						
2						
3						
etc.						

Table 1-1

Once the data are collected and averaged, the results can be analyzed. The results of the coyote experiment showed that sight is most important in locating food. The sense of smell is second in importance, followed by hearing.

Sometimes results are more easily analyzed and understood in the form of *graphs*. Figure 1-32 illustrates the results of the coyote experiment in the form of a *bar graph*. The average time in seconds is given on the left side of the graph. Bar **A** shows the average time it took the coyotes to find the rabbits while using all three senses. This was about 30 seconds. This is the control time against which the other parts of the experiment are compared.

Bar **B** shows the average time using sight only. The variables of sound and smell had been removed. Using sight only, the time increased to about 55 seconds. This indicated that coyotes use more senses than sight to find their food.

When the coyotes were able to use only smell, as shown by Bar **C**, their average time was more than double the control time—about 73 seconds.

Bar **D** shows the results when using hearing only. The time increased to 209 seconds. This is almost seven times as long as the control situation.

Finally, all three senses were removed. Now it took the coyotes an average of 22 *minutes* to find the rabbit. The bar representing 22 minutes would be too long to fit on the graph. It had to be broken and labeled so that readers would understand that it should really be much longer.

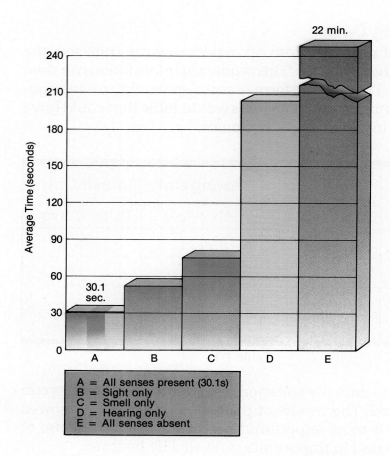

22 min.

Average Time (seconds)

240

210

180

150

120

90

60

30.1
sec.

30

0

A   B   C   D   E

A = All senses present (30.1s)
B = Sight only
C = Smell only
D = Hearing only
E = All senses absent

Figure 1-32 *What does the height of the bars mean on this graph?*

You can see from the graph that the loss of smell and hearing only slightly increased the times. Therefore, Bekoff and Wells concluded that vision is the most important sense. Could this be because the wind can distort sounds and disperse smells? Again you can see how questions can lead to more questions.

Drawing Conclusions

After data are collected and analyzed, conclusions can be made. The results may lead the scientist to believe that the hypothesis is a good one. On the other hand, they may not. If not, the scientist must make a decision. Was there an error in the experimental set-up? Or was the hypothesis not correct to begin with? In either case, experiments are run many times to check the results. If the hypothesis is not supported by the results, it must be changed. Sometimes it is thrown out. Then new hypotheses must be developed.

The hypothesis made by Bekoff and Wells will have to be tested again and again. The experiment will be done with other coyotes, by other researchers, in other places. Only when these additional experiments verify the original results can the hypothesis be considered reliable.

Communicating Results

From their results, Bekoff and Wells were able to make several general statements. They said that the social behavior of coyotes seems to be related to the food supply. They found that sight was the most important factor in locating food. Their results were reported in an article in a scientific magazine. Experimental results are also presented at scientific meetings and in one-on-one discussions with other scientists.

This sharing of results is an important part of science. See Figure 1-33. In this way, other scientists learn what has been done. Then they can decide what still needs to be studied. These scientists can also repeat the experiments the original scientists did to check their reliability. They may see ways to apply other scientists' results to their own work.

Figure 1-33 *A scientist discusses the results of an experiment with other scientists.*

The Changing Nature of Science

As demonstrated by the investigations of Bekoff and Wells, a scientific method is not a "straight line" of steps. It contains loops in which several of its steps may be repeated over and over. See Figure 1-34. A hypothesis may also be extended to include related areas of questioning. The hypothesis by Bekoff and Wells might be applied to similar animals like wolves, jackals, and hyenas. If these other animals also show the same behavior, the hypothesis may be accepted by scientists as evidence in support of a **scientific theory**.

A scientific theory is an explanation of why things work the way they do. Theories are used to *explain* the results of different kinds of experiments and also to *predict* the outcome of other experiments. In this way, scientific theories actually guide the process of science. Theories are always tested. In fact, they sometimes turn out to be wrong. For

Scientific Theory A general statement of why things work based on hypotheses that have been tested many times.

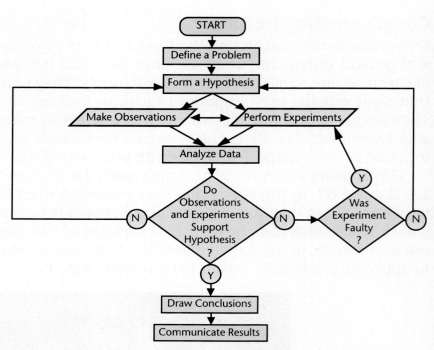

Figure 1-34 *Some of the steps involved in a scientific method.*

Scientific Law A statement of what happens in a certain event based on verified observations and experiments.

example, the theory that the sun is the only source of energy for life on earth was shown to be wrong. It had to be changed when communities around the ocean's hot-water vents were discovered.

Scientific theories are often confused with **scientific laws**. A scientific law describes *what* happens during a certain event, not *why* it happens. Scientific laws are summaries of the results of many, many experiments and observations. When results of sets of experiments are always the same, they no longer need to be tested. For example, Newton's law of gravity can be used to describe the effect of gravity on any object without further testing. Galileo's studies of the motion of falling objects contributed to the development of Newton's laws of gravity and motion.

Even scientific laws, however, can sometimes undergo change. A scientist once said that science moves ahead by correcting errors it made earlier. The body of information we call scientific knowledge is always changing.

Summary

All scientists answer questions with a sequence of problem-solving skills called a scientific method. Some of these skills include defining the problem, forming a hypothesis, making observations, performing experiments, analyzing data, drawing conclusions, and communicating results. The answers to questions may change as scientists design better experiments and make new observations.

Reading *Plus*

Now that you have learned about some of the characteristics of living things, you might want to know more about the fundamental units of life and how they combine to form larger living things. Read pages S22 to S40 and write a report you could give to a meeting of scientists about the basic characteristics of life. Your report should include answers to the following questions.

1. What are the three major points of the cell theory? Describe an experiment that could demonstrate these points.

2. What are the main parts of cells, and how do they function?

3. What are the five major categories of living things, and how do these groups differ?

2.1 CELLS: THE STUFF OF LIFE

Have you ever seen anything smaller than you could see with your own eyes? If you have ever looked through a magnifying glass or a light microscope, your answer is probably "Yes." But before the late 1600s, people had never imagined there were living things smaller than the naked eye could see.

The Cell Theory

Very little was known about the structure of living matter until the development of the light microscope. Then Robert Hooke, an English scientist, made an important discovery in 1665 while using a simple microscope that he designed. He observed tiny, orderly, but empty spaces in a thin slice of *cork*, a type of dead plant material. These spaces reminded him of the spaces in a honeycomb. He called these spaces "cells." See Figure 2-1.

Microscopes were used to study all kinds of plant and animal material. Careful examination of these materials revealed that they were all composed of small units. These units were named **cells**, after the term Robert Hooke first used to describe the spaces in cork.

Studies using microscopes also revealed a world of previously unseen organisms. Some of these tiny creatures were observed to reproduce themselves. This observation and other observations caused many scientists to doubt the long held belief that some living organisms came from nonliving substances. By this process, called *spontaneous generation*, maggots were thought to come from rotting meat and mice from old rags and wheat. Although it took another 200 years, scientific experiments and microscope observations showed that all living things come from other living things.

By the late 1830s, a formal theory about the structure and function of all life had been developed. This theory, called the Cell Theory, may be stated as follows.

1. All living things are made up of cells.

2. The cell is the basic unit of all living things.

3. Only living cells can produce new living cells.

What Are Cells Made Of?

Robert Hooke's cork "cells" were empty because they were taken from dead plants. The same early investigators who studied different types of living material with their microscopes found that living cells are not empty. They contain a thick, jelly-like fluid.

Cells The basic units of all living organisms.

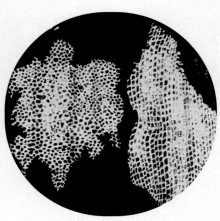

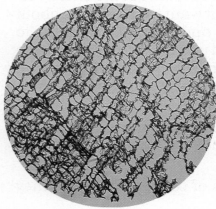

Figure 2-1 *Robert Hooke drew these cork cells.*

This fluid was found to be mostly water, with molecules of many other substances dissolved or suspended in it. Some of these materials are the gases oxygen and carbon dioxide. Also present are a variety of minerals. Most of the molecules are of the following types: carbohydrates, sugars and starches, which are sources of energy; fats, which store energy; proteins, which serve as building materials; and DNA and RNA, which determine how organisms grow and develop. These substances are related only to the activities of living things.

Summary

The cell theory states that the cell is the basic unit of life and that all life comes from other living cells. Cells contain a thick jelly-like substance, which is a mixture of water and several other substances.

2.2 THE STRUCTURE OF CELLS

Cells are the building blocks of living organisms and come in many shapes and sizes. They carry on the activities necessary for life. Some cells are very simple in their structure. All of the materials necessary to run and reproduce these cells are scattered throughout the cell's jelly-like substance, which is surrounded by a covering.

Other cells, however, do contain many specialized structures that perform the various functions of cell activity. Complex cells, such as those that make up animals and plants, have the following basic parts.

1. Surrounding each cell is a covering called the **cell membrane**. See Figure 2-2. The cell membrane limits what materials enter or leave the cell.

2. All cells have a jelly-like substance called **cytoplasm**. Many of the activities of a cell are carried out in the cytoplasm.

Cell membrane The part of the cell that determines what enters and leaves the cell.

Cytoplasm The jelly-like substance surrounding the nucleus of the cell. The cell's activities are carried on here.

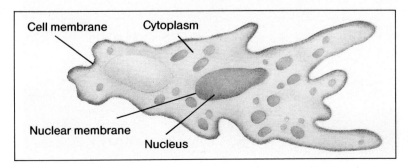

Cell membrane   Cytoplasm

Nuclear membrane

Nucleus

Figure 2-2 The major parts of all cells are identified on this amoeba.

Nucleus The "control center" of the cell that directs all the cell's activities.

3. Near the center of most cells is a structure called the **nucleus**. The nucleus is the "control center" of the cell. All of the activities of the cell, including reproduction, are directed from the nucleus. It, too, is surrounded by a membrane called the *nuclear membrane*.

Plant and animal cells have many of the same structures. These structures have the same functions in both plants and animals. However, these cells are different in a few important ways.

Animal Cells

It may help you to understand the function of each part of a cell if we compare the cell to a factory, such as the one in Figure 2-3. Fuel and raw materials delivered to a factory enter through gates in its security fence. The factory workers follow a set of directions from the main office as they do their jobs. Fuel is burned to operate generators that provide electrical energy. This energy is used to transform the raw materials into finished products. During the manufacturing process, wastes are produced and need to be removed. Some wastes are given off into the air, while others are stored in containers and then removed through the exit gate. Finished products are packed and stored until they can be shipped out of the factory.

The activities of a factory may be compared to the life processes that are carried out by cells. The finished products of cells are the compounds they use to maintain themselves. These products are also used to form the parts of other cells.

The Nucleus The nucleus is the main office and planning department of our cell factory. It controls everything that

Figure 2-3 What part of a cell is similar to the fence around this factory?

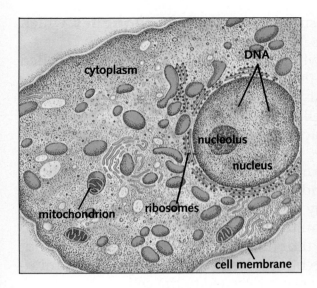
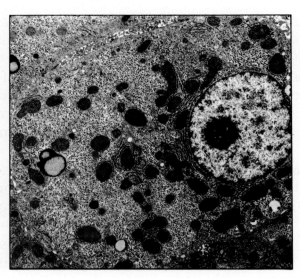

Figure 2-4 *Compare the electron micrograph (magnified 5000 times) and the drawing of a typical animal cell.*

goes on inside the cell. Contained in the nucleus are the genetic materials—**DNA** and **RNA**. These complex organic molecules contain, transport, and interpret the instructions for the reproduction, growth, and development of all living organisms.

The microscopes in most schools are not powerful enough to show many details inside the nucleus. You may see a dark spot called the *nucleolus* inside the nucleus. The nucleolus is rich in RNA and functions in the making of proteins. See Figure 2-4.

Throughout the nucleus are structures called **chromosomes**. The chromosomes are made of DNA and contain the instructions for the manufacture of the finished products of the cell. The chromosomes can be compared to the files of blueprints in the factory's main office. Some blueprints contain the plans for the factory. Another identical factory could be built from them. Blueprints also show how the finished product of the factory are produced and what they will look like.

In a factory, the original blueprints never leave the office. Instead, copies are made and sent from the office into the work area. In a cell, RNA molecules make copies of instructions found in the DNA and carry them out of the nucleus to be used in making the various products of the cell.

The Cytoplasm   The cell's manufacturing processes are carried out in the cytoplasm. In our factory model of a cell, the cytoplasm is the "shop floor." There are many specialized structures located in the cytoplasm. They perform the processes needed to carry out the instructions sent from the

DNA and RNA The genetic materials that determine how all organisms grow and develop.

Chromosomes Rod-shaped structures found in the nucleus of the cell that are made of coiled DNA.

Organelles Tiny specialized structures within a cell that perform cell functions.

Vacuoles Storage areas located in the cytoplasm.

Mitochondria Structures in the cytoplasm that release energy from food.

Ribosomes Structures in the cytoplasm where proteins are made.

nucleus. These tiny structures are called **organelles**, which means "little organs."

The organelles which serve as storage areas are called **vacuoles**. Some of these vacuoles store food for future use. Some store chemicals. Others store wastes until they can be removed from the cell. Vacuoles are sometimes large enough to see with a light microscope. In animal cells, they resemble tiny air bubbles.

The power generators of the cell are called **mitochondria**. The mitochondria are also located in the cytoplasm. They produce energy for cell activities by *cellular respiration*, a process that is similar to burning. Foods, like sugar and starch, are the fuels that are "burned" in the mitochondria. After sugar and starch have been broken down in the mitochondria, usable energy is released to the cell.

Some of this energy provided by the mitochondria is used by tiny round structures called **ribosomes**. The ribosomes, which contain RNA, are attached to a long, winding network in the cytoplasm. They can be compared to the machines in a factory that manufacture the finished products. Ribosomes are the places where proteins are made. These proteins are one of the final products made from the raw materials brought into the cell.

The Cell Membrane The cell membrane that surrounds the cytoplasm acts like the fence that surrounds a factory. It allows only certain substances to enter. See Figure 2-5. Like a

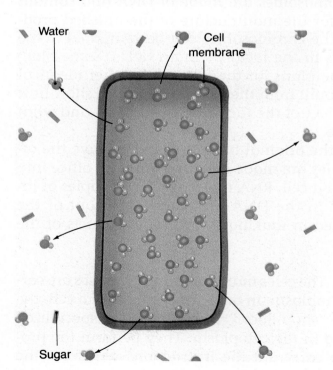

Figure 2-5 The movement of water molecules into and out of a cell takes place freely while sugar molecules must be transported across the boundary.

Water

Cell membrane

Sugar

fence, a cell membrane has tiny spaces in it that allow very small molecules, like water and oxygen, to pass through freely. Larger particles, like food molecules, are transported into a cell by "pathways" that require energy. These pathways can be compared to the gates in a fence through which workers enter and leave. Trucks bring in raw materials and take out finished products and wastes through these gates. In both cases, energy is used.

Plant Cells

Plant cells contain all the structures that are found in animal cells. See Figure 2-6. But there are several differences that are unique to plant cells. One of the most obvious of these differences is the size of the vacuoles. Vacuoles in plant cells are very large. Like the vacuoles in animal cells, the plant cell vacuole also acts as a storage area. It is filled with a clear fluid that is mostly water, but also contains sugar, starch, and protein molecules.

Figure 2-6 Compare the photo and drawing of a plant cell (below) *to the animal cell in Figure 2-4.*

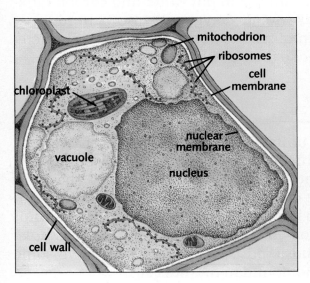
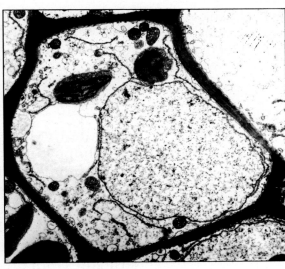

Plant cells also have a thick, firm, outer boundary called the **cell wall**. The cell wall supports and protects the cell. These thick walls were the outlines of the "cells" that Robert Hooke saw in his thin slice of cork. Animal cells do not have a cell wall, just a cell membrane. The cell membrane in a plant cell is pressed up against the inside of the cell wall.

The thick, rigid cell walls will remain long after the plant cell dies. In trees, many of these cell walls remain behind in layers. Eventually, these layers form the rigid material we call wood.

The ability to make food is the major functional difference between plant and animal cells. In the cytoplasm of

Cell wall The rigid, protective structure that surrounds the plant cell.

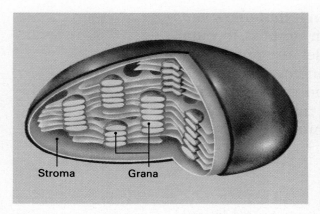

Figure 2-7 *Chloroplasts, found in the leaves of green plants, are the location of photosynthesis.*

Chloroplasts Oval-shaped structures in plant cells that contain chlorophyll.

Chlorophyll Organic material in green plants that absorbs sunlight for making food.

some plant cells, usually those which make up the leaves, there are many small, green structures called **chloroplasts**. See Figure 2-7. These chloroplasts contain molecules of **chlorophyll**. Chlorophyll enables a plant cell to make its own food by a process called *photosynthesis*. *Photo* means "light" and *synthesis* means "to put together." Photosynthesis uses energy from sunlight to put water and carbon dioxide together to make food. Oxygen is also a product of photosynthesis. Animal cells do not have chlorophyll. Therefore, they cannot make their own food.

Summary

Cells are the basic units of life. Even though cells vary in size, shape, and contents, they all have certain basic parts in common. A living cell is similar to a factory. The "machines" of both use energy to turn raw materials into finished products. Both have a "main office" that controls what happens in the "shop" areas. Plant and animal cells have some of the same basic parts; but, plant cells have some structures that are not found in animal cells.

2.3 LEVELS OF ORGANIZATION

We have just compared the workings of a cell to the workings of a factory. Now, let's take a quick look at the purpose of a factory. Factories make something—produce a product. Different kinds of factories produce different products. In other words, they specialize. For example, car factories produce cars, shoe factories produce shoes, and still other factories process and package food. Each uses special machinery to produce a certain product. How many different kinds of factories can you think of?

There are many other examples of specialization with which you may be familiar. Schools specialize in education. Retail stores sell factory products. Military and police forces specialize in protecting us. Doctors and hospitals help us get well. Governments organize communities, states, and countries by making laws and providing services. Is all of this specialization necessary? In a very large society like ours, it is.

Humans once lived in very small groups where all of the individuals participated in many of the activities necessary for survival—food gathering, finding or making shelter, making shoes and clothing, treating wounds, and protecting the group from attack. But over a period of time, one hunter could learn to kill enough game for many individuals, and one individual could make more than enough clothing for themselves. Specializing was found to be more efficient. The hunter could share his food with the clothesmaker, who would in turn share clothing with the hunter. This specialization allowed groups to become larger which, in turn, allowed more forms of specialization, like organizing groups of individuals responsible for protection. Today we live in a highly specialized world in which millions of people are organized into cooperative and functioning groups. See Figure 2-8.

Figure 2-8 Cooperation has allowed the specialization of firefighters who help protect our lives and property.

Single-celled organisms are similar to those early human groups. Each single cell must perform all the life functions by itself. But in *multicellular* organisms, those organisms made up of many cells, the cells are specialized. Each cell has a special function that benefits the other cells. In this way, the cells of a multicellular organism depend on one another for survival.

Cells began to specialize as organisms became multicellular. The specialized cells of multicellular organisms are commonly grouped together into larger organized structures for carrying out the life processes more efficiently. Biologists identify five levels of this specialized organization in living things.

Cells

The cell itself is the first level of organization. Most specialized cells have a certain size and shape related to their purpose. See Figure 2-9. For example, in humans there are two types of blood cells and three types of muscle cells. There are also covering cells, nerve cells, bone cells, and fat cells. Each cell has a special shape that allows it to perform its task.

In plants, there are specialized cells for absorbing water from the soil. Plants also have specialized cells for covering and protecting, transporting, and growing.

Figure 2-9 *The shapes of cells vary with their functions: muscle cells* (left), *blood cells* (middle), *and plant transport cells* (right).

 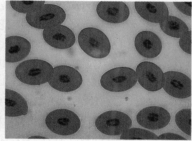 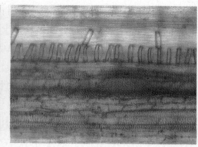

Tissues

Tissue A group of similar cells with similar functions.

Specialized cells of the same type are grouped together to perform their functions. These cell groups are called **tissues**. For example, some groups of cells form tissues that are specialized for movement. Other tissues provide protection. Another group of cells forms structures that support the organism. Groups of cells that look alike and perform similar functions make up a tissue. Tissues are the second level of organization.

There are four main types of animal tissue. They are covering, muscle, nervous, and connective tissues. Covering tissue covers and protects internal and external surfaces of the organism. Muscle tissue provides movement. Nervous tissue helps organisms respond to stimuli in the environment and also helps to coordinate their movement. One type of connective tissue, blood, helps distribute oxygen and food. Other forms of connective tissue include fat, bone, and cartilage.

Plant cells also form specialized tissues. There is a covering tissue that covers and protects the parts of a plant. On the leaves it functions to let in sunlight and control the movement of oxygen, carbon dioxide, and water vapor into and out of the leaf. Tissues under the covering layer perform photosynthesis and store energy. Plants also have transporting tissues and tissues responsible for growth.

Organs

Organs represent the third level of organization. An organ is made up of different tissues that work together to perform a special task. The heart is an organ that is made up of muscle, nerve, covering, and connective tissues. These tissues work together to pump blood throughout the body. The lungs, which exchange oxygen for carbon dioxide, are organs that contain muscle and connective tissues. See Figure 2-10. Another organ, the stomach, carries out its function of digestion with the aid of strong muscle tissue and covering tissue. The brain is composed of nervous, covering, and connective tissues. The skin, the largest organ, covers almost the entire body. It also is composed of all four tissue types. Its major function is protection.

Organ A group of different tissues working together to perform a specific function.

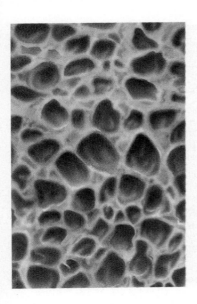
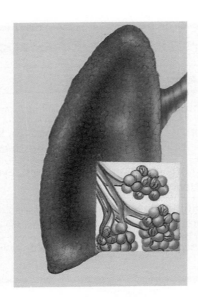
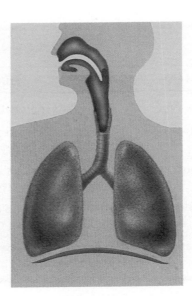

Figure 2-10 Spongy tissue makes up the tiny air sacs that form the lungs, an organ. The lungs, in turn, are part of the respiratory system.

Some organs have more than one function. The male and female reproductive organs—the *testes* and *ovaries*—are examples of organs with more than one function. They produce reproductive cells as well as chemical messengers called *hormones.*

Plants also have structures similar in function to animal organs. Leaves are plant organs that make food and exchange gases. The tissues of a leaf include the covering tissues, tissues that make food by photosynthesis, and tissues that conduct water and other materials. Roots and stems are plant organs that conduct water and provide support. They contain conducting tissues, covering tissue, and growth tissue. Plants also have reproductive organs. The *pistil* is the female reproductive organ and the *stamen* is the male organ in flowering plants.

Organ Systems

Organ System A group of related organs performing a major function for an organism.

A group of organs working together is known as an **organ system**. Organ systems are the fourth level of organization of life. Examples of human organ systems include the circulatory, digestive, nervous, reproductive , and respiratory systems. See Table 2-1 for a comparison of the functions and organs of each system. All animals have these same basic systems. However, the organs involved may be different.

Plants also have organ systems. The roots, stems, and leaves compose the transport system. Roots and stems both function as a support system. Cones and flowers are highly specialized plant structures. They contain the reproductive organs and are thus a part of the reproductive system for most plants.

ORGAN SYSTEMS OF THE HUMAN BODY		
System	**Function**	**Organs**
Circulatory	Transports materials throughout the body	Heart, Arteries, Capillaries, Veins
Digestive	Changes food into simpler compounds that can be used by the cells	Mouth, Esophagus, Stomach, Intestines, Pancreas, Liver, Gall Bladder
Nervous	Receives, coordinates, and acts upon information from the environment	Brain, eyes, ears, nose, tongue, skin
Reproductive	Enables humans to continue their own kind by producing more humans	Ovaries, Uterus, Vagina, Testes, Prostate gland, Penis
Respiratory	Exchanges gases between outside and inside the body	Nose, Windpipe, Bronchial tubes, Lungs

Table 2-1

Organism

Organism The highest level of cell organization. An organism is the combination of its cells, tissues, organs, and organ systems.

The fifth, and highest, level of organization of life is the multicelled **organism**. Multicellular organisms are composed of the combination of all its cells, tissues, organs, and organ systems. Many organisms do not show all of these levels of organization.

Summary

The cells in multicellular organisms are specialized for certain jobs. Specialization enables each job to be performed better. There are five levels of organization: cells, tissues, organs, organ systems, and the organism itself.

2.4 SCIENTIFIC CLASSIFICATION

People tend to place things together in groups. The groups are usually based on certain similarities shared by the members of the group. These similarities may have to do with what an object is made of, what it looks like, or even how an object is used. Things that are different are placed in separate groups. For example, in a grocery store, all fresh fruits and vegetables are grouped together on the shelves of one department. They are then separated by the individual kind of fruit or vegetable. The dairy products are found together in another area of the store and are also arranged according to kind. This organization of things into groups by their similarities and differences is called **classification**.

Scientists also group things together. They *classify* many things: rocks and minerals, stars and galaxies, chemical elements and compounds, as well as living organisms. Scientists use classification to understand how objects are related to each other. Thus, they have arranged all organisms, past and present, into groups in order to demonstrate these relationships.

Classification The organization of things into groups according to ways in which they are alike and not alike.

Organizing Organisms

Putting living things into related groups is not a new idea. Over 2000 years ago, a Greek scientist and philosopher named Aristotle tried to explain how things in nature are related. He divided living things into two large groups—plants and animals. Then he divided these into smaller groups. He classified animals by whether they were land, water, or air animals. His plant categories included herbs, shrubs, and trees. See Figure 2-11.

Figure 2-11 What characteristics did Aristotle use to classify plants and animals?

LIVING THINGS

PLANTS — Herbs, Trees, Shrubs

ANIMALS — Land, Water, Air

Kingdom The level of the classification system with the largest number of living things that are alike in some basic ways.

Species A group of related organisms that are alike in many ways. They can mate and produce living young.

Genus A group of related species differing in only a few ways.

Figure 2-12 All people belong to the same species (left). The seven levels of classification (right). The size of the box indicates the relative number of organisms each category contains.

Later scientists tried other systems of classification. At one time, animals were classified as useful, harmful, or unnecessary. Plants were once grouped by whether they produced fruits, vegetables, fibers, or wood. The system used today began by comparing similarities of form and structure. It was developed in the mid-1700s by a Swedish botanist named Carolus Linnaeus.

Linnaeus established categories into which he grouped organisms based on the degree to which they appeared to be related. As Aristotle had done, Linnaeus also based his classification system on similarities. However, outward appearance was only one of the similarities. In addition, he used similarities of the internal organs and the way the body systems perform their functions.

Linnaeus used two **kingdoms** in his system—the Plant Kingdom and the Animal Kingdom. These are the largest groups of organisms in his classification system. They contained the organisms that shared only the few characteristics that distinguish plants from animals.

Linnaeus established two new categories that he called **species** and **genus**. He placed organisms that were the most similar to each other into the species category. Organisms of the same species have the same basic characteristics. However, they may vary in size, shape, color, and in other ways. People, for example, are all the same species, even though they may be different in appearance. See Figure 2-12 (left). Since some species groups were very similar to one another and differ only in a few characteristics, Linnaeus placed those similar species into a larger group—a genus.

After Linnaeus, other categories were added to his classification system until there were a total of seven. See Figure 2-12 (right). They are, in order from the largest group to the

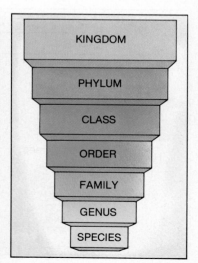

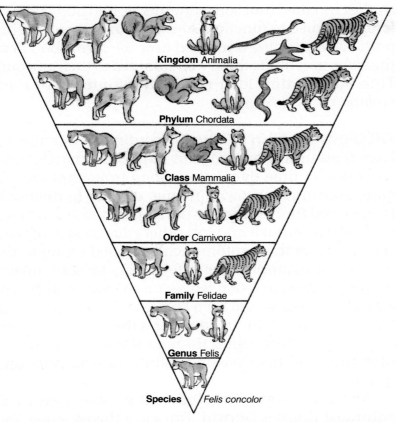

Figure 2-13 *This upside-down pyramid shows how a category gets more specific as the number of living things in the category decreases.*

Kingdom Animalia

Phylum Chordata

Class Mammalia

Order Carnivora

Family Felidae

Genus Felis

Species | *Felis concolor*

smallest group: Kingdom, Phylum, Class, Order, Family, Genus, and Species. A kingdom includes the largest number of different organisms. In most cases, each of the other categories contains a smaller number of living things than the one above it. See Figure 2-13.

Modern Classification

Two discoveries—that living organisms change over time and that traits are transmitted to offspring by means of cellular instructions called *genes*—have affected the way organisms are classified today. Modern classification systems now include both living and extinct forms of life. Organisms are grouped according to how closely they are related to one another and how they are related to one another through life forms that once lived. These relationships are determined by careful studies of the fossil remains of once-living organisms, the biochemicals that make up organisms, their reproductive habits, and the structure of their DNA.

The idea that living organisms change over time—a process called **evolution**—is a fundamental concept in biology. The study of fossils has revealed life forms from the past that were different than those of today. It also revealed creatures that have no apparent living relatives. Other

Evolution The process whereby living organisms change over time.

studies revealed that some organisms had body parts that no longer seemed to function. The human appendix is one such part. Scientists also wondered how life forms had developed the traits that made them well-adapted to their surroundings. This information lead to the development of *theories of evolution.*

THEORIES OF EVOLUTION   According to one theory, by a French naturalist named Jean Baptiste Lamarck, organisms change over time by passing along traits that they had acquired during their own lifetime, directly to their offspring. He believed that organisms developed new traits in response to a need to survive and lost others due to lack of use. These changes were then automatically passed along to their offspring. For example, a giraffe's neck, he said, grew longer from stretching to reach leaves on the top of trees. This trait for its long neck would then be passed on to the next generation. See Figure 2-14. In Lamarck's theory, changes occur by acquiring characteristics through the use or disuse of body structures and then passing those characteristics on to offspring.

Another theory of evolution was developed by English naturalist Charles Darwin. Darwin's theory states that over many generations, the characteristics of organisms change as individuals with certain pre-existing traits are "selected" by nature for survival. See Figure 2-15. Darwin spent many years observing the variations in traits among organisms of the same species. He noticed that organisms with certain traits were better suited for surviving in their environment than others that did not have that particular trait. Individuals with

Figure 2-14 Lamarck believed that traits gained during a lifetime could be passed on to offspring.

Figure 2-15 Two forms of the Peppered moth. How does their color affect their survival?

the advantage of this trait would survive and pass those traits on to their offspring. For example, the giraffes that already had long necks, and thus were able to reach higher for food, would most likely survive to produce more offspring. Their offspring would also carry the trait for longer necks. In Darwin's theory, all changes are the result of this *natural selection*. It is this theory of evolution that is the currently accepted theory of how life evolves on this planet.

GENETICS The science of genetics provides the missing information needed to explain how characteristics are passed along from one generation to the next, and how new variations arise. Units of inherited information, called **genes**, carry the instructions to duplicate certain traits. Genes are segments of chromosomes that are made of DNA. During reproduction, copies of genes are made and passed to offspring. From these genes, the same traits develop in the next generation. Some of these genes, however, are found to undergo changes—a process called *mutation*. The ability of a gene to change helps to explain the appearance of new variations in organisms.

Changes in living things have been very slow because a single gene contains only a small amount of information. It takes many genes to make up a single trait in most organisms. For example, there are over 100,000 genes in the 23 sets of human chromosomes. This was determined by a special project of the National Institute of Health called the *Human Genome Project*. This project is attempting to make a map of the chromosomes showing the location of all human genes.

Gene A segment of a chromosome that carries hereditary information.

How Many Kingdoms Are There?

Another reason classification schemes have changed so much is that new organisms, both living and fossil forms, are constantly being discovered. Often new groups are named or old groups rearranged to accommodate these new findings. For a long time, the Animal Kingdom and the Plant Kingdom remained the only two kingdom groups. However, new methods of studying organisms have lead to the addition of more kingdoms.

A five-kingdom classification system is used by most biologists today. The five kingdoms are: Monera, Protista, Fungi, Plantae, and Animalia. Each group shares a distinct *set* of characteristics that are different from those of the other four groups. See Table 2-2.

A FIVE-KINGDOM CLASSIFICATION SYSTEM		
Kingdom	**Description**	**Examples**
Monera	*Monerans* are all single-celled organisms that do not have nuclei.	bacteria; blue-green bacteria
Protista	*Protists* are one-celled or many-celled organisms that do have nuclei.	algae; protozoa
Fungi	Mostly many-celled. *Fungi* absorb food directly from living or dead organisms.	yeasts; molds; mushrooms
Plantae	Many-celled. *Plants* make their own food using chlorophyll and sunlight.	ferns; conifers; seed plants
Animalia	Many-celled. *Animals* cannot make their own food. They eat other organisms and digest them.	insects; reptiles; birds; mammals

Table 2-2

Kingdom Monera Members of this kingdom, called *monerans*, are single-celled organisms. Their cells are very simple and *do not* have nuclei or organelles. Some absorb food molecules from their surroundings, while others make their own food by photosynthesis or by *chemosynthesis*. Many can live in environments where there is no oxygen. Included in this kingdom are bacteria and blue-green bacteria.

Kingdom Protista Called *protists*, the members of this kingdom *do* have nuclei and cell organelles. Most are single-celled, but some are multicellular organisms. Multicellular forms show no organization above the tissue level. Some absorb food molecules or ingest small food particles, while others make food by photosynthesis. Included in this kingdom are algae and protozoans.

Kingdom Fungi Fungi can be either single-celled or multi-cellular organisms. Their cells also have nuclei and organelles. The bodies of multicellular forms develop specialized reproductive structures. None of the fungi can make their own food and must *absorb* food from their surroundings. Included in this kingdom are yeasts, molds, and mushrooms.

Kingdom Plantae All plants are multicellular. Their cells have nuclei, organelles, and *cell walls*. Their bodies are organized into organs, and most plants have organ systems. All members make their own food by photosynthesis. Included in this kingdom are ferns, cone-bearing plants, and flowering plants.

Kingdom Animalia All animals are multicellular organisms. Their cells have nuclei and organelles. All but the simplest forms show the organ system level of organization. All members obtain energy by *ingesting* and digesting food. Included in this kingdom are sponges, worms, insects, fish, reptiles, birds, and mammals.

As more organisms are discovered and new ways of studying living things are found, ideas about classification will continue to change. As we look closer, more kingdoms may be needed. Perhaps another classification category may have to be established to better define the evolutionary relationships among living organisms. Scientists are constantly increasing our body of knowledge. In doing so, existing theories and ways of looking at things also change.

Naming Living Things

Linnaeus made another major contribution to science by establishing a new naming system for living organisms, one that is still used today. He gave each different type of plant and animal a two-part name. The two-part name of an organism is called its *scientific name* or species name. He used the Latin language because, at that time, it was understood by educated people throughout Europe.

The scientific name of an organism has two parts. The first part is taken from the genus name, while the second part is a term that describes the specific species. The "species" name, therefore, always contains two words. See Figure 2-16. For example, the sugar maple is called *Acer*

Figure 2-16 The twin flower, Linnaea borealis, *was Linnaeus's favorite. The term* borealis *means "northern."*

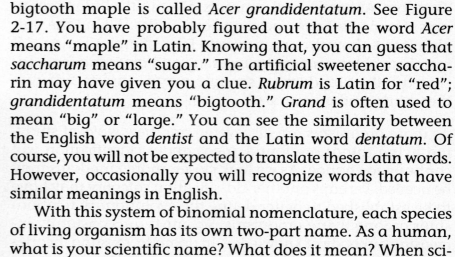

Figure 2-17 *Two types of maple tree leaves are shown here—sugar maple (right) and bigtooth maple (left).*

saccharum, the red maple is called *Acer rubrum*, and the bigtooth maple is called *Acer grandidentatum*. See Figure 2-17. You have probably figured out that the word *Acer* means "maple" in Latin. Knowing that, you can guess that *saccharum* means "sugar." The artificial sweetener saccharin may have given you a clue. *Rubrum* is Latin for "red"; *grandidentatum* means "bigtooth." *Grand* is often used to mean "big" or "large." You can see the similarity between the English word *dentist* and the Latin word *dentatum*. Of course, you will not be expected to translate these Latin words. However, occasionally you will recognize words that have similar meanings in English.

With this system of binomial nomenclature, each species of living organism has its own two-part name. As a human, what is your scientific name? What does it mean? When scientists want to discuss a particular organism, they use its scientific name because it means the same to all, regardless of their native language or dialect. See Figure 2-18.

Figure 2-18 *Many small seed-eating birds are commonly called sparrows. The house sparrow shown above, Passer domesticus, is related more to weaver-finches than to other sparrows. Sometimes called the English sparrow, it is actually found worldwide.*

Summary

Scientists classify living things. It helps them understand how organisms are related. Once classified only by similarities and differences in form and appearance, organisms are now classified by genetic and biochemical makeup to show their evolutionary relationships. There are seven levels of classification categories for organisms. The highest category is called the kingdom. There are presently five kingdoms in the modern classification system. Each kind of organism has a two-part scientific name made up of its genus and species names.

Reading *Plus*

Now that you know something about microorganisms and how they can be both harmful and helpful in food preparation, let's take a look at diseases and the microorganisms that cause them. Read pages S42 to S56 and write a column for a health magazine about disease, the microorganisms that cause disease, and how your body defends itself against them. The main points highlighted in your column should deal with the following questions.

1. What are infectious diseases and how are they spread?

2. How are viruses different from other microorganisms?

3. What are the body's levels of defense and what happens at each level to protect the body from illness?

3.1 MICROORGANISMS AND DISEASE

In Ireland in the 1800s, many people lived on small farms. Potatoes were a major crop because they were easy to grow, were a good food source, and could be stored over the winter. In both 1845 and 1846, however, a potato disease called *late blight* destroyed almost the entire potato crop of Ireland in just a few short weeks. Because of this, over one million people died of starvation. Many others left their homeland and came to America. See Figure 3-1.

Many other tragedies have been caused by diseases that affect food sources or cause illnesses in people themselves. One of the most tragic was the plague of the 1300s called the Black Death, which wiped out one-fourth of Europe's entire population! This deadly disease was spread by rats that infested the villages and towns. But the rats were only a means of transporting the actual cause of the plague—microorganisms.

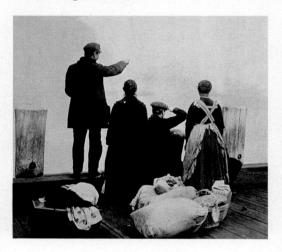

Figure 3-1 *The disease of a plant forced many people to face the unknown in search of a new life.*

Linking Microorganisms to Disease

The idea that microorganisms can cause disease was developed by a French chemist named Louis Pasteur in the mid nineteenth century. This idea is often called the *germ theory of disease*. A **germ** is any microorganism that can cause disease. At first this theory, like many others, was not taken seriously. However, the idea soon gained the support of some famous scientists and physicians of the day.

Joseph Lister, an English surgeon, was one of the first to see the importance of Pasteur's work. Lister used chemicals that killed germs to make his operating rooms safe. He made sure that everything that touched his patients was very clean. His methods prevented infections after surgery. An **infection** is the growth of disease organisms in the body

Germ Any microorganism that can cause disease.

Infection The growth of disease microorganisms in the body of a host.

of a host. The chemicals that Lister used are called **disinfectants**. Disinfectants kill many of the germs that cause disease.

Robert Koch, a German physician, was the first to show that microorganisms can cause disease. He studied a disease called anthrax, which affects horses, cows, sheep, and humans. During his investigations, Koch developed a set of rules, or steps, for proving that a specific microorganism is the cause of a specific disease. This set of rules, called *Koch's postulates*, is still used today. Koch's postulates, below, are a fine example of a scientific method in use. See Figure 3-2.

1. Show that the microorganism believed to cause the disease is present in the diseased organism.

2. Grow the microorganism in laboratory cultures.

3. Inject microorganisms from the laboratory culture into a healthy animal. Examine the animal for the disease.

4. If the animal gets the disease, grow the suspected microorganism in a laboratory culture. Check to make sure that they are the same as the microorganisms that were in the original culture.

Disinfectant A chemical capable of killing many of the germs that cause disease.

Figure 3-2 Scientists still follow Koch's procedure today.

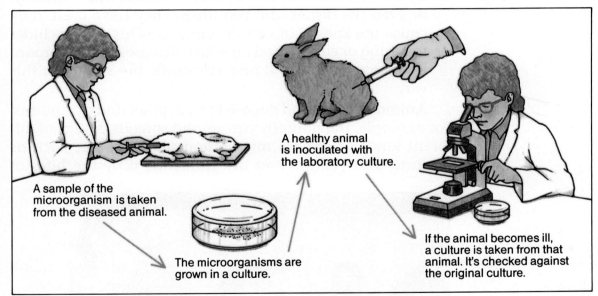

A sample of the microorganism is taken from the diseased animal.

The microorganisms are grown in a culture.

A healthy animal is inoculated with the laboratory culture.

If the animal becomes ill, a culture is taken from that animal. It's checked against the original culture.

Infectious Disease

What exactly is disease? A *disease* is a condition in which some part of a living thing is not working properly. Some types of disease are caused by genetic and environmental factors. Other types of disease are caused by microorganisms. When a disease-causing microorganism lives in a host plant or animal, it may attack and destroy the host's tissues and make it ill. Some microorganisms make poisons that kill their hosts.

Most diseases caused by microorganisms can be transmitted to other individuals. This type of disease is called an **infectious disease**. Infectious diseases are spread when the microorganisms that cause them are transferred from one host to another. These diseases can be spread in three basic ways:

Infectious disease A disease caused by a microorganism that can spread from one organism to another.

1. By water. Some disease-causing microorganisms can live in water and are spread through the water supply. This happens if wastes from humans and animals are not kept far enough away from the water supply. If people drink that water, they may get one of these diseases. Typhoid is a disease that spreads in this way.

2. By air. Many diseases are spread by tiny droplets of water in the air. For example, suppose you have a cold and you sneeze. Millions of the microorganisms that caused your cold leave your mouth on tiny water droplets. Anyone who inhales them could catch your cold. Diphtheria and tuberculosis are also spread in this way. See Figure 3-3.

3. By direct contact. Touching an individual with a disease, or even the dishes and bed linens they have used, may cause the spread of certain diseases. This also includes touching or eating food on which disease-causing organisms grow. Colds, flu, and *salmonella* are spread in this way.

Animals can spread disease to each other and to humans. For example, the housefly carries and spreads dozens of different kinds of disease microorganisms. Diseases such as malaria and yellow fever are transmitted by the bites of

Figure 3-3 *The force of a sneeze sends germs into the air.*

certain mosquitos. Dogs, cats, wolves, cattle, squirrels, and bats are among the animals that can spread rabies by direct contact.

Some people that do not show symptoms of a disease can still spread a disease. Such people are called *carriers*. Carriers can be just as infectious as those who are ill with the disease. Infections caused by *Staphylococcus* bacteria, such as a sore throat, can be spread by carriers, for example.

Causes of Infectious Disease

The organism identified by Koch as causing anthrax was a certain type of bacteria. However, bacteria are only one kind of microorganism that can cause infectious disease. By using Koch's postulates for isolating agents of disease, viruses, protozoa, and fungi have also been identified as disease-causing microorganisms.

Bacteria Bacteria can affect a human body in different ways. The bacteria that causes tuberculosis kills the cells and tissues of the host. Other types of bacteria do damage by releasing **toxins**, or strong poisons, into the host. The bacteria that cause *tetanus* live on the host where the skin is broken. These bacteria make a toxin that is carried to the brain by the bloodstream. There, it does enough damage to the brain to cause death in humans.

Toxin A poison produced by a microorganism that causes harm to the host.

Bacteria are responsible for a long list of human diseases. See Table 3-1. Lists just as long or longer could be made of the diseases caused by bacteria in other animals or in plants.

BACTERIAL DISEASES	VIRAL DISEASES
bacterial dysentery	chicken pox
bacterial pneumonia	the common cold
boils	fever blisters
bubonic plague	influenza (flu)
gonorrhea	measles
strep throat	mumps
syphilis	polio
tetanus	rabies
tuberculosis	some types of pneumonia

Table 3-1

Viruses Viruses are another major cause of disease. They are also the smallest of the disease-causing microorganisms. Even the largest virus can just barely be seen with a light microscope. This is one of the reasons viruses were not discovered until the 1930s. Nevertheless, doctors have been treating diseases caused by viruses for over 200 years. These diseases include the common cold, influenza ("flu"), cold sores, warts, smallpox, rabies, and AIDS. See Table 3-1 again.

Protozoans Amebic dysentery, malaria, and sleeping sickness are examples of diseases caused by *protozoa*. Amebic dysentery is caused by a species of amoeba. Malaria is spread by the bite of a certain type of mosquito that injects a parasitic protozoan into the bloodstream. Sleeping sickness is caused by a protozoan that is passed from host to host by the bite of the *tsetse* fly.

Fungi Fungi can also cause diseases in humans, such as athlete's foot. See Figure 3-4. Other examples of fungal disease are ringworm and histoplasmosis. Histoplasmosis is a sometimes serious disease affecting the lungs, throat, liver, and lymph system. It is caused by a fungus that grows in soil containing bird or bat droppings. Cells of the fungus can enter the body through the digestive or respiratory systems.

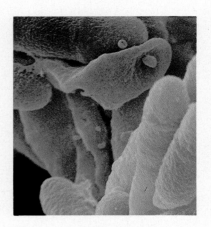

Figure 3-4 The moisture in athletic lockers and shower rooms can be ideal for the growth and spread of the fungus responsible for athlete's foot.

Diseases in Plants

The story about the potato famine in Ireland shows that animals are not the only living things that can have a disease. Microorganisms also cause diseases in plants. Plant diseases that are caused by microorganisms are spread in the same ways as infectious animal diseases. The control of plant diseases is of great economic and social importance. Recall the effect of Ireland's potato disease!

Bacteria are responsible for many plant diseases. House plants and greenhouse-grown crops commonly wilt in moist or wet soil because of a disease called bacterial wilt. Bacteria also cause soft rot to occur on many vegetables and fruits. Fresh fruits and vegetables cannot be stored for long periods of time due to rotting diseases. For long-term storage, they must be processed—frozen, dried, cooked, or canned.

A disease of tobacco, which causes the destruction of chlorophyll in a leaf, was found to be caused by a virus. The result is an irregular pattern (mosaic) on the leaf. Much early work on viruses was done on the cause of tobacco-mosaic disease. Many plants are affected by the same type of virus. Since these viruses cannot be destroyed by burning, mosaic diseases are often spread among greenhouse crops, such as tomatoes, by people who smoke tobacco.

Fungi also cause very serious plant diseases. Wheat rusts, a type of fungi, have caused large losses in wheat crops.

A disease caused by another fungus wiped out the chestnut tree in this country in the early part of this century. More recently, thousands of elm trees have been dying from the Dutch elm disease fungus, which is transmitted by two different species of beetle. See Figure 3-5.

Summary

Microorganisms have been shown to be the cause of various diseases. A disease is a condition in which some part of a living thing is not working properly. Infectious diseases are caused by microorganisms and are spread in several ways. Microorganisms cause infectious diseases in plants as well as in animals and humans.

3.2 MORE ABOUT BACTERIA AND VIRUSES

What do you see in the picture in Figure 3-6? Is it an abstract design printed on a piece of fabric? Is it a group of animals gathered around a watering hole as seen from a helicopter? Is it a squadron of alien spacecraft about to land on earth in the middle of the night?

Actually, it *is* the beginning of an invasion. But it is the invasion of a single bacterium by a virus. Bacteria and viruses are the smallest and most numerous of the disease-causing microorganisms. They each are unique and interesting in their own way.

Bacteria

Bacteria are among the smallest living things. Some 50,000 bacteria could fit on the head of a pin. Even at a magnification of 1000 times, only their general shape can be seen. Bacteria, like the ones in Figure 3-7, are everywhere. They have been found in many places where other life forms cannot exist. Some bacteria have been detected eight to ten kilometers up into the atmosphere. Others thrive in the hot-water vents on the ocean floor, and some even live inside other living things. Fossil evidence indicates that bacteria have been on earth for a very long time. See Figure 3-8.

Besides being adapted to various unusual environments, some bacteria have ways to survive extremely unfavorable conditions. They often do this by surrounding themselves with a hard coat and becoming inactive. When conditions

Figure 3-5 *Dutch Elm disease has nearly wiped out one of North America's favorite shade trees.*

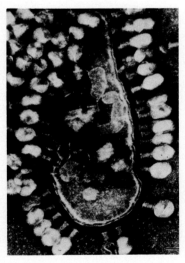

Figure 3-6 *What is this? How big do you think these objects are?*

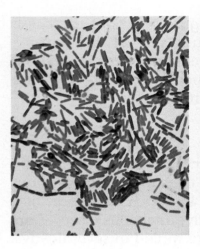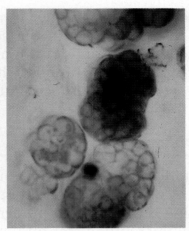

Figure 3-7 *These bacteria (left), magnified 400 times, cause botulism (food poisoning).*

Figure 3-8 *Fossilized bacteria from ancient times (right).*

are better, they become active once again. Some types of bacteria can survive over 50 years in this way. In Figure 3-9 you can see a diagram of a bacterial cell with a protective capsule and many *flagella*. The flagella are whiplike structures that help the bacterium to move. However, not all bacteria have these structures.

Classifying Bacteria   Bacteria are simple, one-celled organisms. They were once classified as simple plants because they have cell walls. However, it has since been determined that their cell walls are different from the cell walls of plants. Bacterial cells do not have a nucleus or any other cell organelles. Reproduction in bacteria is almost always a simple splitting of one cell into two cells. Many biologists now place the bacteria in a separate category—the Kingdom Monera.

Bacteria are further classified according to their shapes and whether they form chains or clusters. Bacteria come in three basic shapes—rods, spheres, and spirals. A rod-shaped

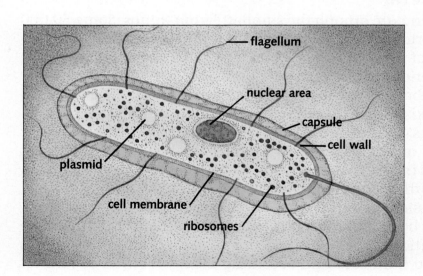

Figure 3-9 *The structure of a typical bacterial cell. Most bacteria have a rigid cell wall, covered by the capsule.*

bacterium is called a *bacillus*. Bacilli may stick together after they divide to form long chains. The bacteria in your intestines are this type. The bacteria that cause strep throat are round, or spherical. A spherical bacterium is called a *coccus*. Cocci may form either long chains, or they may gather in clusters. A spiral, or corkscrew-shaped, bacterium is called a *spirillum*. Most of the spirilli are harmless, aquatic organisms. See Figure 3-10 for an example of each of these types of bacteria.

Figure 3-10 Bacillus (left); coccus (middle); and spirillum (right). All are magnified about 200 times.

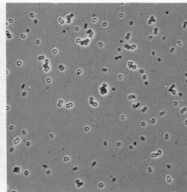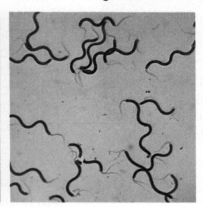

How Bacteria Obtain Food   Differences in the way bacteria make or obtain food may also be used to classify them. Most bacteria get their food from other living or dead organisms. Some bacteria are **parasites**. Parasites live in or on another living organism. They obtain their food from it. Parasites are usually harmful to the "host." Parasitic bacteria are often a cause of disease. In some cases, bacteria live in a host without causing harm. They may even help. For example, termites could not digest the wood they eat without the help of bacteria in their bodies. Cows also need bacteria to help them digest the grasses they eat. Bacteria that get their food from dead organisms are called **saprophytes**. Many of these types of bacteria are very useful. Saprophytes break down the tissues of dead organisms, thus releasing their chemicals back into the air and soil.

Many bacteria make their own food. One major group of bacteria, called blue-green bacteria, can produce its own food by photosynthesis. The color of blue-green bacteria comes from the fact that they contain chlorophyll, which enables them to use the sun's energy to make food. Most of these bacteria live in fresh water. Some contain gas bubbles, so they can float near the water's surface in order to receive more sunlight. They produce oxygen and also serve as food for other organisms. Other bacteria make their own food

Parasite An organism that lives in or on another living organism and usually causes harm to its host.

Saprophytes Organisms that get food from dead or decaying organisms.

S49

Figure 3-11 *Cheddar cheese begins as a soupy mixture that includes milk and bacteria.*

without using the energy of the sun. These bacteria get their energy from chemical reactions. The bacteria in the hot-water vents on the ocean floor are in this group. So are some of the bacteria found in the soil.

Bacteria and Humans Bacteria have an important role in the lives of humans. They are everywhere! In fact, bacteria are living in and on you right now. Many bacteria live on your skin and in your nostrils, mouth, and large intestine. Though some bacteria do cause diseases in humans, most of the bacteria we come in contact with are harmless.

Some bacteria are useful in a variety of ways. For example, bacteria can be added to milk to produce yogurt, sour cream, cottage cheese, and hard cheeses. See Figure 3-11. Sauerkraut, sour pickles, and vinegar are also made by the action of bacteria. One type of bacterium found in soil is used to make medicines that help our bodies fight other, attacking bacteria. Bacteria are also useful in the mass production of substances such as human insulin. Human genes for insulin synthesis are isolated and spliced into the DNA strand of a bacterium. Since bacteria reproduce rapidly, the new instructions will produce the desired product in amounts that can be used by doctors in the treatment of human patients with diabetes.

Bacteria are in all the foods we eat. They cause rotting and spoilage as they break down these foods for their own

Figure 3-12 *Unrestricted growth of blue-green bacteria can cover a lake.*

consumption. Because of this, bacteria can cause heavy losses in stored food. Fortunately, refrigeration slows down the growth of bacteria. The heat of cooking also reduces the number of bacteria.

Blue-green bacteria can signal environmental pollution. They reproduce very rapidly in water that contains chemical fertilizers, making the water pea green and smelly. See Figure 3-12. When these bacteria die, other bacteria feed on their remains. This cycle may use up all the oxygen in the water, causing fish that may also be in the water to die from lack of oxygen.

Viruses

Years ago, smallpox was an easily spread and often fatal disease. It caused severe chills, headaches, fever, nausea, and pains in the back, arms, and legs. Pink-red blisters appeared all over the body, and once they dried up, they left hollow pockmarks. For a long time, scientists could not find the microorganisms that caused diseases such as smallpox.

What are Viruses?

In his work, Pasteur found that the bacteria that caused milk to turn sour could be captured by fine filters. Eventually, all the disease-causing bacteria that scientists identified were known to be stopped by very fine filters. However, the agents that caused smallpox and other mysterious illnesses, such as rabies, were so small that they were able to pass through these filters. They came to be known as *filterable viruses*, or simply viruses, from a Latin word that means "poison." However, not much was known about viruses themselves until after the invention of the electron microscope in 1933.

Modern equipment makes it easier to study viruses. Photographs of viruses enlarged over 300,000 times have been made with the help of the electron microscope. See Figure 3-13. These photographs show that viruses come in many

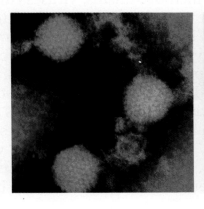 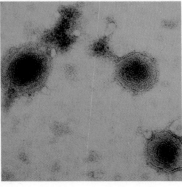

Figure 3-13 *These viruses, photographed with an electron microscope, are magnified 80,000 times (left) and 27,000 times (right). The virus at right causes measles.*

Nucleic acid A chemical that controls activities in a cell and passes on traits to new cells.

shapes and sizes. They may be round or shaped like rods, needles, or cubes. They may have many-sided shapes as well.

Being able to see viruses revealed that they are not cells. They do not have a nucleus, cytoplasm, or a cell membrane. The simplest viruses seem to be made simply of a **nucleic acid** (DNA or RNA) with a coating of protein. See Figure 3-14. Remember, nucleic acids control the activities in a cell and are the means by which traits are passed on to new cells.

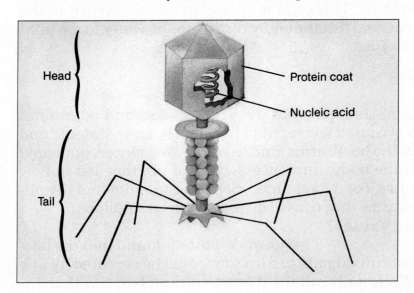

Figure 3-14 *The structure of a measles virus like the ones shown in Figure 3-13.*

Are Viruses Alive? It is difficult to decide if viruses are alive or not. They do not carry on life processes in the way that living cells do. They do not take in food or give off wastes and can only reproduce inside the cells of living organisms. The mumps virus, for example, only becomes active when it comes in contact with the gland cells near a person's jaw. The polio virus multiplies only in one kind of nerve cell in the brain and spinal cord.

Since scientists do not consider them to be *alive*, viruses are not included in the five-kingdom system of classification. However, they are often included in the study of microorganisms because, like microorganisms, viruses cannot be seen or identified without the use of a powerful microscope. Viruses can be grouped by the kinds of organisms they affect, as well as by the type of nucleic acid (DNA or RNA) they contain and the shape and the size of the virus.

Scientists have learned much about viruses by studying a type that attacks bacteria. When this type of virus attacks a bacterium, the protein coat of the virus attaches to the bacterium's cell surface. The nucleic acid of the virus is then injected into the cell. Sometimes the whole virus enters the cell. Once this happens, the nucleic acid may become

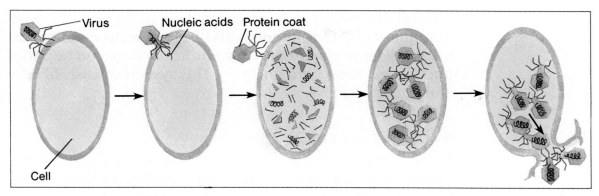

Figure 3-15 *A virus multiplies by using the host cell's energy and chemicals.*

active, or it may instead enter into an inactive, or *dormant*, state.

How Viruses Function   If the nucleic acid remains inactive, it can be passed from cell to cell as the host cell divides. Later, a change in conditions may cause the virus' nucleic acid to become active. When the nucleic acid is active, it may cause changes in the cell. These changes may harm the cell and cause it to die. Many viruses change the cell but do not kill it. Some cells lose control over their rate of division and multiply very rapidly. Thus, they cannot do the jobs they did before the virus entered them. To reproduce, a virus' nucleic acid takes over a cell's nucleus and causes it to make hundreds of new viruses. Soon the cell bursts, and new viruses are released. See Figure 3-15. These, in turn, attack other cells and repeat the process. In this way, additional viruses are formed and spread from cell to cell.

Summary

Bacteria are single-celled organisms that lack nuclei and other organelles. Their shape and the different ways they obtain food are used to classify bacteria. Bacteria are both harmful and helpful to other organisms. Viruses seem to be made only of a nucleic acid covered with protein. Viruses do not appear to carry on all the life processes. Therefore, viruses are not usually classified as living organisms. Viruses reproduce only in the cells of living things.

Figure 3-16 *This boy must be protected from all germs—even those from his family. He has no immunity to disease.*

3.3 THE BODY'S DEFENSES

The boy in Figure 3-16 has spent his entire life inside a plastic bubble. He is not allowed to touch anyone, not even his mother or father. The reason is that he was born with no natural defense against infectious disease. As a result, even a simple cold could endanger his life. Fortunately, most of us have a defense system that automatically fights off bacteria and viruses that could harm us. This system consists of several lines of defense.

Skin and Mucus

The first line of defense is the skin. Under normal conditions, the skin stops microorganisms from entering the body. However, when the skin is broken, cut, or damaged, germs can enter. That is why it is very important to clean cuts and scrapes. The bark on a tree protects the plant from disease organisms in much the same way. Large wounds on a tree should be closed with tree paint.

Mucus is a thick, sticky fluid that covers many surfaces inside the body and inside the natural openings of the body. Mucus stops germs from attacking tissue not covered by skin. For example, the inside of the nose is covered by tiny hairs and a mucus lining. These hairs trap dust and germs from the air you breathe. The trapped germs are swallowed with the mucus and travel down the food tube to the stomach. In the stomach, strong acids kill the microorganisms. These stomach acids also kill most germs brought into the body with food.

Sometimes extra mucus is made in response to the presence of foreign substances such as dust, pollen, or germs. If there is a lot of mucus in your nose, you should try to blow it out. Blowing your nose and sneezing helps get rid of any trapped microorganisms. That is why it is important to cover your mouth and nose when you sneeze. See Figure 3-17.

White Blood Cells

What happens if you cut your skin and germs enter the cut? Then your second line of defense, the *white blood cells*, becomes active.

White blood cells are one part of our blood. See Figure 3-18. They are made in the center part of some bones. Many of them are found in the lymph nodes and in the tonsils. Some are found between the cells in your tissues.

If microorganisms get past the skin, the white blood cells take over. It is believed that damaged tissue, such as a cut, and invading germs both release chemicals. These chemicals attract white blood cells. When this happens, the area around the cut becomes warm and appears red. The cut has become infected.

Mucus A thick, sticky fluid covering many surfaces inside of the body and in its natural openings.

Figure 3-17 *Blowing your nose helps clean out the mucus that traps disease-carrying microorganisms.*

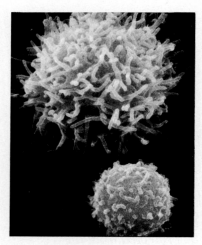

Figure 3-18 *Two types of white blood cells are visible here.*

White blood cells surround and destroy germs and damaged tissue. Their action is similar to an amoeba surrounding its food. This stops infection and cleans the area so that proper healing can take place.

The Immune System

In the body, white blood cells have still another way of fighting disease. Some kinds of white blood cells help make special chemicals called **antibodies**. Each antibody fights a particular type of microorganism or foreign chemical, as shown in Figure 3-19.

The production of antibodies is a fast process. A few days after the invader has entered, a large number of antibodies can usually be found in the blood. These antibodies seek out and destroy the invading microorganisms. This process is a function of the **immune system**. It is the body's third line of defense.

When a disease like chicken pox is over, most of the antibodies that fought against it leave the body. There is a group of white blood cells remaining, however, that "remembers" how to make the antibody. If the virus that causes chicken pox enters the body again, these cells will make new antibodies very quickly. They will eliminate the virus before it can do any damage. That is why a person usually gets diseases like measles, mumps, whooping cough, scarlet fever, and chicken pox only once. This resistance to a disease is called **acquired immunity**. Acquired immunity to some diseases lasts a lifetime.

Immune System Disorders

Not all so-called "diseases" are caused by microorganisms. Some of the conditions we call disease, such as some types of heart disease and diabetes, are caused by malfunctions of the body itself. Like other systems in the body, the immune

Antibodies Chemicals made by the body to fight germs or other foreign bodies.

Immune system The body's natural resistance to disease involving antibody production.

Acquired immunity Resistance to reinfection with a disease after the body has once recovered from the disease.

Figure 3-19 White blood cells can make antibodies.

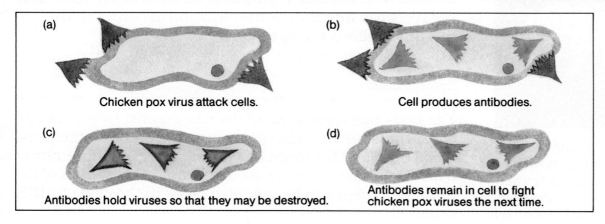

(a) Chicken pox virus attack cells.

(b) Cell produces antibodies.

(c) Antibodies hold viruses so that they may be destroyed.

(d) Antibodies remain in cell to fight chicken pox viruses the next time.

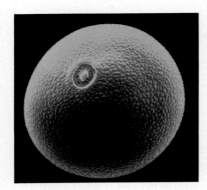

Figure 3-20 *An airborne pollen grain is one foreign substance that may trigger an allergic reaction.*

Autoimmune disorder
A condition in which the immune system produces antibodies that attack the body's own tissues.

Immune deficiency disorder A condition in which the immune system breaks down, leaving the body unprotected from disease.

AIDS An immune deficiency disorder that leaves the body defenseless against microorganisms.

Figure 3-21 *The green "dots" in the photograph are human immunodeficiency viruses. They are shown attacking a T-lymphocyte cell.*

system can malfunction or even break down altogether. Such a breakdown is called an immune disease or disorder. There are three basic types of *immune disorders*: allergies, autoimmune disorders, and immune deficiency disorders.

An *allergy* is a condition in which the immune system reacts to a normally harmless foreign substance, such as pollen or certain foods. See Figure 3-20. In an allergic reaction, the immune system antibodies attack the foreign substance, causing a variety of symptoms: runny nose, sneezing, red and watery eyes, swelling, rashes, and so on. In a few cases, severe allergic reactions can be fatal.

An **autoimmune disorder** is a condition in which the body attacks its own tissues. There are many different types of autoimmune disorders. Some are mild, and some are serious—even life-threatening. Some examples of autoimmune disorders are rheumatoid arthritis, multiple sclerosis, and Grave's disease. Some of these diseases are caused by genetic factors and some by exposure to certain chemicals. Still others develop after the body has fought off a viral infection.

An **immune deficiency disorder** is a condition in which the body is unable to defend itself against invading microorganisms. This condition causes its victims to suffer from repeated infections. Severe cases of immune deficiency may completely disable the immune system. Such cases are almost always fatal. Some immune deficiencies are inherited. Others are acquired during a person's lifetime.

AIDS (Acquired Immune Deficiency Syndrome) is an example of an immune deficiency disorder. AIDS is caused by a virus called the human immunodeficiency virus, or *HIV*. This virus attacks T_4 cells, which are white blood cells that are vital to the body's immune system. See Figure 3-21. People with AIDS suffer a variety of diseases as their immune systems are gradually destroyed, leaving their bodies defenseless against viruses, bacteria, and cancers. Not all people infected with HIV show symptoms of AIDS. Many years may pass between infection by the virus and the onset of AIDS. At this time, there is no cure for AIDS.

Summary

The body has three lines of defense against infectious disease. These are the skin and mucus membranes, the white blood cells, and the immune system. A natural immunity to a disease often follows a case of the disease. Disorders of the immune system can be inherited or, as in the case of AIDS, acquired.

Unit 4

Reading *Plus*

Now that you have been introduced to the properties of matter, let's take a closer look at the particles that make up matter and how they are combined. Read pages S58 to S72 and prepare a demonstration on matter, including its properties, particles, changes, and relationships. Your demonstration should pay special attention to the concepts indicated by one of the following questions.

1. What happens to matter during physical changes and chemical changes? Give examples of each.

2. How are mixtures of matter, such as solutions and compounds, made? And how are they separated into the parts they are made of?

3. How are the particles of matter related to each other? And how are they related to elements, compounds, and solutions?

4.1 MATTER AND MOLECULES

Imagine that you are a skydiver. With your parachute strapped on securely, you jump from an airplane. For a short time you fall freely. Then at a certain height, the parachute opens and you float gently down to the ground.

What might you see on such a jump? At first you would see the whole landscape beneath you. You might see fields, highways, even whole towns. Coming down closer, you would see a smaller area in greater detail. You would be able to see trees, cars on the highway, and individual houses. Finally, on landing you would see grass, soil, and twigs on the ground around you. See Figure 4-1.

Figure 4-1 *This photograph of Baltimore was taken from a satellite far overhead. Closer to the ground, you would be able to see trees and houses.*

Matter Anything that has mass and takes up space.

Let's look at matter in a way similar to the falling skydiver. **Matter** is defined simply as anything that takes up space and has mass. However, just as the details on earth's surface become clearer to a falling skydiver, a closer look at matter shows that it is made up of smaller parts.

All kinds of matter are made up of particles that are in constant motion. The amount of motion of the particles determines the structure of matter. Different kinds of matter have different properties.

Particles of Matter

Try dividing a glass of water as many times as you can. First pour out half the water. You still have half a glass of water. Then divide that in half, and so on. What would happen if you could keep on dividing the remaining amount of water in half? Imagine that you could keep pouring out more and more water. You would finally have one tiny particle that could still be called water. That small particle of water is called a **molecule**.

The word *molecule* comes from the Latin word *molecula,* meaning "little mass." A water molecule is the smallest particle of water that is still water. Generally speaking, all water molecules are alike. A water molecule in a rain drop is the same as a water molecule in the ocean.

Actually, it would be impossible for you to separate out just one water molecule. Water molecules are small. It would take about 60 million water molecules side by side to reach across a penny!

What would happen if you could divide a solid such as sugar in the same way as you imagined you did with water? Eventually, you would come to the smallest particle that is still sugar. This particle would be called a molecule of sugar.

Properties of Matter

You can tell the difference between different kinds of matter by their different properties. For example, suppose you have two cups, each partly filled with a liquid. One cup contains water, while the other contains vinegar. You could easily tell which cup contains the vinegar because vinegar has a different odor than water. By carefully sniffing each liquid, you would be able to identify the vinegar. If the vinegar also happened to be red, its color would be an obvious indication that there was a difference between the two liquids.

Properties of matter, such as odor and color, that you can observe or measure without changing the identity of the material are called **physical properties**. See Figure 4-2. Other examples of physical properties are taste, hardness, density, melting point, and boiling point. You can observe any physical property of matter by using only your senses. See Figure 4-3.

Chemical properties, on the other hand, can be observed only when one kind of matter reacts with another. For example, when you add baking soda to vinegar, a gas is released. If you slowly add baking soda to vinegar until no more gas is produced, you will find that you can no longer observe the odor and other physical properties of the vinegar.

Molecule The smallest particle of a substance, such as water, that is still identified as that substance.

Figure 4-2 This scientist is investigating the physical properties of a material.

Physical Property A property of matter that can be observed by your senses without altering the identity of the matter.

Chemical Property A description of how one kind of matter behaves in the presence of another kind of matter.

Figure 4-3 *How many different physical properties can you identify in this photograph?*

A chemical property describes how one substance reacts with other substances. The behavior of vinegar with baking soda is an example of a chemical property of the vinegar. Water does not share this chemical property with vinegar. If you mixed baking soda with water, no gas would be produced. Thus, you could also use chemical properties to distinguish between water and vinegar.

Vinegar contains water molecules and acetic acid molecules. These molecules, however, are different from sugar molecules. Molecules of the same substance are all the same. Molecules of different substances differ from each other. They do not have the same physical and chemical properties.

States of Matter

At ordinary temperatures, all matter exists in one of three *states*: solid, liquid, or gas. In each of these three states, the molecules of the material behave in different ways. In a *solid*, the molecules are in a fixed pattern, like the people sitting in rows in a theater. In a *liquid*, the molecules can change position and move past each other. This is like people milling about the lobby of the theater during intermission. In a *gas*, the molecules are spread apart, like people leaving the theater after the performance. See Figure 4-4.

At very high temperatures, substances enter a fourth state of matter called a *plasma*. In a plasma, the molecules have been separated into electrically charged particles. Matter on the sun and other stars is in the plasma state. Some scientists are trying to use plasmas of hydrogen to release energy by nuclear fusion. This is the process by which the stars are thought to produce tremendous amounts of electromagnetic

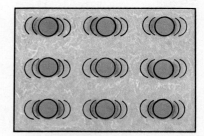
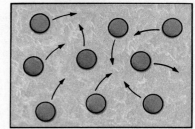
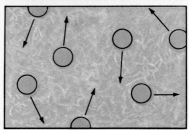

Figure 4-4 *The motion of molecules is different in a solid* (top), *a liquid* (middle), *and a gas* (bottom).

energy. The big problem is that fusion reactions require temperatures of millions of degrees to start.

Changes in Matter

You know from experience that water is not always a liquid. You can freeze liquid water to make solid ice. You can also boil water and change it into a gas. See Figure 4-5.

Figure 4-5 *Water can exist as a liquid, a solid (ice), and a gas (steam).*

Physical Changes   Melted ice has the same physical properties as water before it is frozen. The molecules in water, ice, and steam are all alike. The changes of water from a liquid to a solid or a gas are each examples of a **physical change**. After a physical change, each of the molecules in a substance is the same as it was before the change.

A physical change is any change in a property of matter that does not change the identity of the matter. Boiling, melting, and freezing are examples of physical changes. Any change in matter from one state to another is, therefore, a physical change. Other examples of a physical change are cutting, grinding, pulverizing, compressing, or expanding.

Physical Change Any change in matter that does not change the identity of the matter.

Chemical Change A change in matter in which one substance is changed into another substance.

Chemical Changes Not all changes in matter are physical changes. Suppose an iron nail lies on the ground until it becomes rusty. Where did the rust come from? Does the rust have the same properties as iron? If you compare rust with iron, you will find out that they have many different properties. For example, the color, hardness, and melting points of rust and iron are different. Therefore, rust must be made of a different kind of matter than iron. The rusting of iron is an example of a chemical change. When one substance changes into another substance, a **chemical change** takes place. The new substance has new properties. For example, when vinegar is mixed with baking soda, both the vinegar and the baking soda are chemically changed. One of the new substances produced by this chemical change is the gas that is given off.

Summary

Matter is made of small particles called molecules. The molecules that make a substance determine its physical and chemical properties. A physical change in matter takes place when the molecules are arranged differently but are not changed in any other way. A chemical change causes one substance to become another substance.

4.2 MIXTURES AND SOLUTIONS

The next time you pour yourself a bowl of cereal, look at the package. Somewhere on the box you will find a label that tells you what went into making the cereal. You will find that your cereal, like most foods, is made of different substances.

Figure 4-6 Many different foods are mixtures. All mixtures contain more than one substance.

Mixtures

If you read the labels on packages of food, you will find that they contain different substances such as sugar and salt. Any kind of matter that contains more than one substance is called a **mixture**. Most foods are mixtures. See Figure 4-6.

There are many different kinds of mixtures, but they all have three things in common.

1. A mixture is always made of at least two substances.

2. The substances are not chemically changed when they are mixed together. This means that you can still identify each substance in the mixture.

3. The substances can be put together in any proportion.

The substances in a mixture can be separated by a physical change. A physical change does not change the identity of the substances as they are separated. For example, in a mixture of salt and pepper, the grains of salt and pepper can be seen and separated. You can separate the dark pepper grains from the light salt grains simply by picking them out one by one. Pepper and salt each have their own properties. These properties do not change when pepper and salt are mixed and then separated.

Solutions

Suppose that you dissolve a spoonful of sugar in a glass of water. Would you be able to separate the sugar and water easily? When you dissolve sugar in water, the solid sugar crystals disappear in the water. You cannot see the sugar. However, you know that the sugar is mixed with the water because the mixture tastes sweet. Sugar molecules are no longer in the form of a crystal. Now individual sugar molecules are mixed with the water molecules. See Figure 4-7.

Mixture Any matter that contains more than one substance and that can be separated by a physical change.

Figure 4-7 When sugar dissolves in water, the sugar molecules are mixed with the water molecules. Sugar is the solute and water is the solvent.

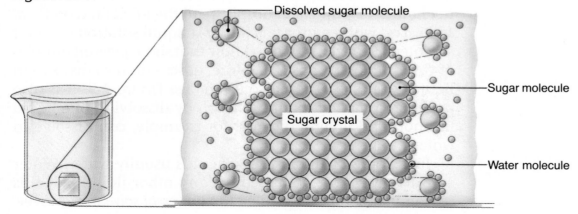

Dissolved sugar molecule

Sugar molecule

Sugar crystal

Water molecule

Solution A mixture formed when one substance mixes evenly with another substance.

Solute The part of a solution that is dissolved.

Solvent The part of a solution that does the dissolving.

A mixture that forms when one substance, such as sugar, mixes evenly with another substance, such as water, is called a **solution**. Solutions are uniform mixtures of separate substances.

Something that dissolves to make a solution is called a **solute**. In a solution of sugar and water, the sugar is the solute. The water is called the **solvent**. A solvent is a substance in a solution that does the dissolving.

Solutions can be separated by heating the mixture. In a salt solution, the water will boil away, and the salt will then be left in the form of solid crystals. See Figure 4-8. The solid salt is the same substance it was before it dissolved. The steam from the boiling solution can be captured, cooled, and changed back into liquid water. The water will also be the same as before it was mixed with salt.

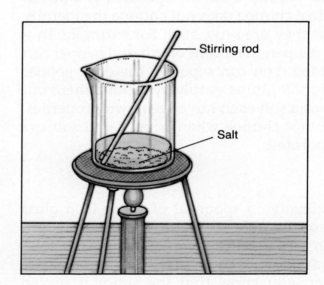

Figure 4-8 If a salt solution is boiled, the water will evaporate, leaving behind the solid salt. Like all mixtures, a salt-water solution can be broken down by a physical change.

Liquid Solutions Using a liquid solvent such as water makes a *liquid solution*. Usually, a solid solute is dissolved in the liquid solvent. For example, read the label on a bottle of soda. You will see that it is partly a liquid solution of sugar in water. However, you also know that soda gives off bubbles of carbon dioxide gas. Therefore, gases can also dissolve in liquids to make a liquid solution. See Figure 4-9. It is also possible to make a liquid solution by dissolving one liquid in another. Rubbing alcohol, for example, can dissolve in water.

In a liquid solution, the solvent is usually water. Water can dissolve more solutes than any other liquid. For this reason, it is sometimes called the *universal solvent*. However, you also know that some things will not dissolve in water. For example, cooking oil and water will not make a solution. When a substance dissolves in water, its particles are mixed very closely with the water molecules. The two kinds of molecules attract each other. This is why they can be mixed together so closely. Oil will not mix with water because the molecules of water do not attract oil molecules strongly enough.

Gaseous Solutions Because their molecules are far apart, one gas will easily mix with another to make a *gaseous solution*. Air is an example of a gaseous solution. There is more nitrogen gas than any other gas in air, and thus nitrogen is said to be the solvent. The material that is more abundant in a solution is usually called the solvent. The second most abundant gas in air is oxygen. Air also contains small amounts of many other gases.

Solid Solutions Many solids are really *solid solutions*. For example, steel is a solid solution in which carbon is dissolved in iron. The carbon dissolves in the iron when the iron is melted. When the iron cools and changes back into a solid, the carbon remains dissolved in the solid steel. Solid solutions are often called *alloys*. Liquids and gases can also be dissolved in solids in the same way.

Figure 4-9 A gas can be dissolved in a liquid. Bubbles of carbon dioxide gas can be seen coming out of solution and escaping from the soda in this glass.

Summary

A mixture contains more than one kind of substance. A solution is a mixture in which a solute is dissolved in a solvent. In all mixtures, even solutions, the different substances can be separated by a physical change. Liquids, gases, and solids can all be solutions.

4.3 COMPOUNDS AND ELEMENTS

Like most mixtures, solutions can be broken down by a physical change. Some substances, however, cannot be broken down into simpler parts by a physical change. For example, aspirin is a compound. If you crushed an aspirin tablet, you would have only smaller particles of aspirin. A physical change, such as crushing, cannot separate the aspirin into

Compound A substance that can only be broken down into simpler parts by a chemical change.

different substances. See Figure 4-10. Pure water also cannot be broken down or separated by any physical change. Such substances are called **compounds**.

The properties of a compound are usually different from the properties of the elements that make up the compound. For example, sodium is a solid that reacts violently with water. Chlorine is a poisonous gas. When they combine chemically, they form crystals of ordinary table salt.

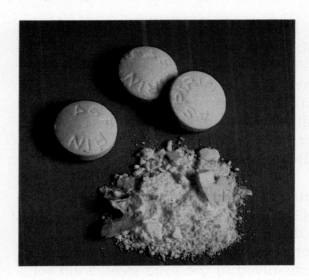

Figure 4-10 *Aspirin is a compound. Like all compounds, it can only be broken down by a chemical change.*

Separating Compounds

You already know that water cannot be broken down by a physical change, but what about a chemical change? A procedure called *electrolysis* can bring about a chemical change in water. Using equipment such as that shown in Figure 4-11, an electric current can be passed through the water. Bubbles of gas form around the ends of the wires where the current enters and leaves the water. These gases then bubble up into one or the other of the two test tubes. Tests reveal that one gas is hydrogen and the other is oxygen. Both hydrogen and oxygen are substances completely different from water.

Figure 4-11 *When an electric current passes through the solution in the beaker, it breaks water down into the two gases: hydrogen and oxygen. The hydrogen and oxygen are collected in the test tubes.*

Other compounds can also be broken down chemically into two or more different substances. Sugar can be broken down into carbon, oxygen, and hydrogen. You may have seen this happen when sugar burns. The sugar turns into solid black carbon, while hydrogen and oxygen escape as water vapor. Salt can be broken down into sodium and chlorine. Sulfuric acid is composed of sulfur, oxygen, and hydrogen.

When a compound is broken down, it always yields the same substances in the same amounts. For example, water is always made up of 11 percent hydrogen and 89 percent oxygen by mass. This means that a sample of water with a mass of 10.0 grams could be broken down into 1.1 grams of hydrogen and 8.9 grams of oxygen. Hydrogen peroxide, another compound of hydrogen and oxygen, is 6 percent hydrogen and 94 percent oxygen. Ten grams of hydrogen peroxide would yield 0.6 grams of hydrogen and 9.4 grams of oxygen.

Examining Elements

As we have seen, water is made up of water molecules. A water molecule is the smallest particle of water that can still be called water. It, however, is composed of simpler forms of matter—hydrogen and oxygen. What happens if a sample of oxygen is repeatedly divided in the same way as we imagined previously for water? A small particle that is still oxygen would remain. When a substance can no longer be divided into simpler substances by either physical or chemical changes, it is called an **element**.

An element is the simplest form of matter that cannot be chemically changed into anything else. Up to the present, more than 100 elements have been identified. The most common elements in nature are listed in Table 4-1. All

Element A substance that cannot be broken down by either physical or chemical changes.

COMMON ELEMENTS FOUND IN THE EARTH'S CRUST AND IN THE HUMAN BODY			
Most Common Elements in the Earth's Crust		**Most Common Elements in the Human Body**	
Oxygen	46.60%	Oxygen	65.0%
Silicon	27.72%	Carbon	18.0%
Aluminum	8.13%	Hydrogen	10.0%
Iron	5.00%	Nitrogen	3.0%
Calcium	3.63%	Calcium	2.0%
Sodium	2.83%	Phosphorus	1.0%
Potassium	2.59%	Potassium	0.3%
Magnesium	2.09%	Sulfur	0.2%
Titanium	0.44%	Sodium	0.15%
Hydrogen	0.14%	Chlorine	0.15%
All others	0.83%	Iron	0.04%
		All others	0.15%

Table 4-1

known matter in the universe is made up of these and other elements, either alone or in different combinations.

Summary

Compounds cannot be broken down by a physical change. They can, however, be broken down by a chemical change. Each compound is composed of the same substances in the exact same amounts. Elements are substances that cannot be broken down by either physical or chemical changes.

4.4 ATOMS AND PARTICLES

Look at any of the colored photographs in this book with a strong magnifying glass. You will see that each picture is made up of many small colored dots, as shown in Figure 4-12. Suppose that you could look at a compound, such as water, in the same way. You would see that the water is also made up of very small identical molecules. If you look even closer, you would discover that each water molecule is made up of still smaller particles—hydrogen and oxygen.

Figure 4-12 *A colored picture is made up of small dots of color. Matter is also made up of smaller particles.*

Atom The smallest particle of an element.

The smallest particle of an element is called an **atom**. The element oxygen, for example, is made up of only oxygen atoms. Hydrogen contains only hydrogen atoms and carbon contains only carbon atoms. See Figure 4-13. All elements are composed of particles called atoms. Since there are over 100 elements, there are also over 100 kinds of atoms.

Figure 4-13 The lump of graphite in the photograph on the left looks very different from the diamond in the photograph on the right. But both graphite and diamond are made of carbon atoms.

The Atomic Theory

How big is the smallest thing you can think of? It is probably many times bigger than an atom. For example, think about soap bubbles. They are very thin and break easily. A bubble's thickness is much less than the thickness of a human hair. Yet the surface of some soap bubbles is over several thousand times thicker than the diameter of an atom.

Early Theories About Atoms About two thousand years ago, two ideas about the composition of matter were being taught by the scholars of ancient Greece. Democritus, one Greek thinker, believed that matter was made up of small objects called "atoms" (from the Greek word *atomos,* meaning "cannot be divided"). To Democritus, atoms were hard, solid balls.

On the other hand, the famous Greek philosopher and teacher Aristotle held to an ancient belief that all matter was made up of four materials—earth, air, fire, and water. See Figure 4-14. Wood, for example, was said to be made of fire and earth. When wood burned, *fire* escaped and *earth* remained as ashes. Since Aristotle was a very respected teacher, his ideas won out over those of Democritus. The idea that matter was made up of earth, air, fire, and water prevailed for the next 2000 years.

Development of Modern Atomic Theory During the 1600s and 1700s, however, scientists began to consider the old

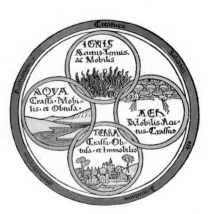

Figure 4-14 The four basic elements of the ancient Greeks—fire, water, air, and earth. The Greeks thought that all matter was made of combinations of these "elements."

ideas of Democritus once again. In 1808 an English schoolteacher and chemist named John Dalton presented an atomic theory that combined the findings of several researchers, along with some of his own. His theory of matter stated:

1. All matter is composed of tiny particles called atoms.
2. Each element is made up of atoms of the same kind, and the atoms of one element are different from the atoms of another element.
3. Atoms cannot be divided, created, or destroyed.
4. Atoms of elements combine in certain ratios to form compounds.

For example, water is made from the atoms of two elements, hydrogen and oxygen. The atoms of hydrogen are different from the atoms of oxygen. The compound water is always made of two parts hydrogen and one part oxygen.

Several of the ideas of John Dalton are still used today. But, his belief that *all* matter is composed of atoms and the idea that atoms could not be divided have since been shown to be not completely accurate in all situations.

Particle Physics

Three twentieth-century physicists were responsible for the discovery that atoms were not the smallest particles of matter. All three scientists received Nobel Prizes for their work. Nobel Prizes are awarded to those who make significant contributions to humanity in various fields of science and the arts. The prizes were established by Alfred Nobel, the inventor of dynamite.

Atomic Particles Through various experiments with electricity, it was becoming clear to scientists by the end of the 1900s that there might be particles of matter smaller than atoms. Then in 1897, J.J. Thomson of England demonstrated that cathode rays were composed of negatively charged particles. Cathode rays are a special form of electricity that flows through low-pressure gases in tubes such as a television tube. These particles eventually came to be called **electrons**. See Figure 4-15. Through other experiments, electrons were found to be much smaller than the smallest atom—hydrogen. This confirmed that

Electron The negatively charged particle discovered in cathode rays that is much smaller than a hydrogen atom.

there existed particles of matter that were not composed of atoms. Electrons became the first of many so-called *subatomic particles*.

Figure 4-15 Rays in a cathode tube are bent in a magnetic field. This indicates the rays are made of electrically charged particles.

The discovery of two other subatomic particles soon followed. In 1919 Ernest Rutherford announced the discovery of the **proton**, which has a positive charge equal in force to the negative charge of an electron. The proton was found to be 1,836 times as massive as an electron, but still smaller than an atom of hydrogen. In fact, the hydrogen atom was determined to contain about the same mass as that of a proton and an electron combined.

Proton The subatomic particle that has a positive charge equal in force to the negative charge of an electron.

The last particle, called a **neutron**, was discovered in 1932 by James Chadwick, a former student and colleague of Rutherford. The existence of such a particle had been predicted by Rutherford in 1920. A neutron has no electrical charge and has about the same mass as a proton.

Neutron The subatomic particle with no electric charge and about the same mass as the proton.

Particle Accelerators You may have heard of the proposed particle accelerator—the SSC—to be built in Texas. The SSC, or Superconducting Super Collider, will be the largest "atom smasher" in the world. It will be a circular ring of scientific instruments with a circumference 87 kilometers around.

The SSC is just the latest in a series of huge machines, called particle accelerators, designed by physicists to investigate the world of subatomic particles. By shooting particles such as electrons, protons, and neutrons at each other, scientists have been able to detect particles even smaller than these three. These strange new particles have been given even stranger names, such as *quarks* and *leptons*. At

Figure 4-16 Artist's rendering of the end of a superconducting dipole magnet. It will be used in the Superconducting Super Collider particle accelerator to guide beams of protons.

present, there have been over 200 such subatomic particles identified. With the SSC, scientists hope to answer many of the questions that still exist about the nature of matter and energy. See Figure 4-16.

How far matter can be subdivided is one of those questions. The existence of so many subatomic particles, however, would seem to indicate that there might be something wrong with the way we view the fundamental makeup of matter. Remember, science is always changing as new discoveries are made. Perhaps a future Nobel Prize winner may now be sitting in your classroom—perhaps in your very seat!

Summary

Ideas about atoms have evolved from the idea that matter was composed of earth, air, fire, and water, to the idea that all matter is composed of atoms. Atoms, the basic units of all the elements, however, are not necessarily the smallest form of matter. The electron, proton, and neutron were discovered in the late 1800s and early 1900s, demonstrating the existence of matter smaller than the atom. Other, even smaller subatomic particles have been identified through the use of large particle accelerators.

Unit 5

Reading *Plus*

Now that you have learned about the differences between physical and chemical changes and have learned to carefully observe these changes, you might want to know more about the elements and why they behave the way they do. Read pages S74 to S98 and prepare an oral report about your discoveries. Your report should be based on answers to the following questions.

1. What are the basic parts of atoms, and how are they arranged?

2. How is the Periodic Table arranged, and how can it be used to predict the chemical activity of an element? Give examples.

3. How do chemical changes occur? Give examples of each way.

5.1 ATOMIC STRUCTURE

An atom is a very, very small object. A typical atom has a diameter of about 0.0000002 millimeters. In fact, it would take more than a million atoms side by side to equal the thickness of this page. An atom is much too small to be seen clearly. Therefore scientists cannot study atoms directly. Instead, they use **scientific models** of atoms.

Scientific Model A theoretical representation of something that cannot be directly observed.

Models are developed by scientists to represent what they cannot actually see. The earliest scientific models of atoms showed them as tiny solid balls. But the discovery of electrons and other subatomic particles showed that these early models were not completely correct. Models, like theories, can change over time as we learn more about the world around us.

Developing an Atomic Model

If you were given the parts of a watch, could you put them all together to make a watch that works? A similar problem faced scientists studying the atom in the early part of this century. By 1900 scientists knew that atoms were not the smallest particles of matter. Could these particles possibly be the parts of an atom? And if so, how do they fit together?

Early Models of the Atom   In 1897, physicist J. J. Thomson concluded from his study of cathode rays that matter contains negatively charged particles. These particles came to be called *electrons*. Since most matter has no charge, positive charges were also thought to be part of matter. (Remember, a positive charge cancels an equal negative charge.) However, no one knew *how* these particles were related to atoms. Thomson thought that an atom might be a ball of positive electricity with negative electrons scattered throughout—much like raisins in a muffin. See Figure 5-1.

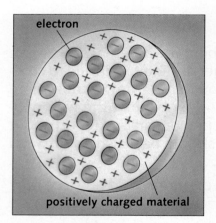

electron

positively charged material

Figure 5-1 *J. J. Thomson believed that the atom was a ball of positive electricity with negative charges scattered throughout.*

Then in 1911 Ernest Rutherford, a scientist from New Zealand working in England, reported the results of a brilliant experiment. These results led to the first modern scientific model of the atom.

In this experiment, a beam of fast-moving, positively charged particles was aimed at a very thin sheet of gold. Gold foil was used as a target because it can be made into sheets that are only a few hundred atoms in thickness. The original purpose of the experiment was to see how the paths of the particles would be changed when they hit the gold atoms. The results of the experiment, however, were very surprising. They showed that most of the particles went straight through the gold foil as if nothing were there. Yet a few of the particles bounced off the gold atoms as if they were solid. See Figure 5-2. Rutherford said, "It was as though you had fired a 15-inch shell at a piece of tissue paper, and it came back and hit you."

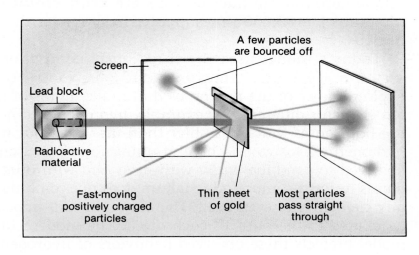

Figure 5-2 *This drawing shows the setup of Rutherford's famous experiment from which the existence of the nucleus was inferred.*

This experiment can be compared to what happens if you throw pebbles at a wire fence. Most of the pebbles go right through the fence because it is mostly empty space. However, a few pebbles may hit wires and bounce back.

Rutherford concluded that most of the mass of an atom is found in a very small core at its center. This central core is called the **nucleus**. Protons and neutrons were later described as particles making up the nucleus of an atom. The region around the nucleus of an atom, where the electrons were located, was thought to be mostly empty space.

In 1913 Niels Bohr, a Danish scientist who worked in Rutherford's laboratory, designed a model to explain how electrons move around atomic nuclei. According to Bohr's theory, electrons moving around a nucleus travel only in certain orbits, much as planets orbit the sun. Each electron moves in an orbit that is a certain distance from the nucleus. For every element, the electrons of its atoms always follow the same basic orbits. Bohr drew his model using circles to represent the paths of the electrons. See Figure 5-3. We call this representation of the atom the *Bohr model* of the atom.

Although some of Bohr's ideas were correct, his model did not adequately describe all of the observed properties of electrons. By 1928 Austrian and German scientists had worked out an arrangement for electrons using complex

Nucleus The central core of an atom in which most of the mass is concentrated.

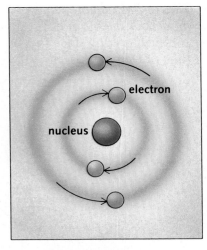

Figure 5-3 *The Bohr model of the atom indicates that electrons are arranged in electron shells.*

mathematics. This arrangement better explains the chemical behavior of atoms.

The Atomic Model Today The current model of the atom states that all the protons and neutrons are found in the nucleus. The nucleus has a positive charge because it contains the positive protons. The electrons are found in a "cloud" around the nucleus. This **electron cloud** is approximately 100,000 times greater in diameter than the nucleus.

Today's model uses the three basic components of an atom—protons, neutrons, and electrons—to help explain many of the properties that make atoms of different elements different. For example, hydrogen and helium are both gases that are lighter than air. But what makes hydrogen explosive and helium unburnable? Hydrogen is observed to combine easily with itself and with other elements to form compounds. Helium does not combine with any element, not even itself. The reason for this appears to be related to the parts of each atom. The modern atomic model predicts these observed behaviors of hydrogen and helium.

By using the modern atomic model, scientists have had much success in describing the properties of elements and in predicting how they will combine to form compounds. However, the current model uses complex mathematical formulas to describe how electrons are arranged. It is very hard to represent this electron arrangement with physical shapes. See Figure 5-4. In introductory science classes, therefore, we tend to use a modified version of the Bohr model to talk about some of the characteristics of atoms. This older model is still useful for showing the numbers of protons,

Electron Cloud The area surrounding the nucleus in which the electrons can be found.

Figure 5-4 *Theoretical models of the atom have changed greatly since the time of Democritus.*

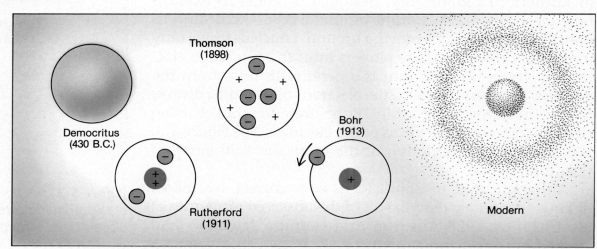

Democritus
(430 B.C.)

Thomson
(1898)

Rutherford
(1911)

Bohr
(1913)

Modern

neutrons, and electrons in an atom, and for demonstrating how atoms combine.

Electric Charge and Nuclear Force Atoms normally do not have an overall electric charge. The positive charges of the protons in the nucleus exactly cancel the negative charges of the electrons moving around the nucleus. Therefore, the number of electrons around the nucleus would have to be the same as the number of protons in the nucleus. For example, all hydrogen atoms have one proton in the nucleus. Every hydrogen atom also has one electron moving around its nucleus. Thus, hydrogen atoms are electrically neutral. Oxygen atoms have eight protons and eight electrons. Oxygen atoms are also neutral.

This means that a seemingly impossible situation exists in the nucleus. Since the only charged particles in the nucleus are the positive protons, their like electrical charges should repel one another. A great deal of force, therefore, is needed to hold the protons in a nucleus so close together. The energy providing such a force is released when the nucleus of an atom is split, or undergoes fission. This energy is called *nuclear energy*.

Using the Atomic Model

Each element can be described by the number of protons in its atoms. For example, atoms with only one proton in their nuclei are hydrogen atoms. Atoms with eight protons are oxygen atoms. See Figure 5-5. The number of protons in the nucleus is called the **atomic number** of the element. Hydrogen has an atomic number of 1 because all hydrogen atoms have one proton in the nucleus. Since oxygen has eight protons, oxygen has an atomic number of 8. Table 5-1 lists the atomic numbers of the first 20 elements. Since an equal number of negative charges is needed to balance the positive charges of the protons, the atomic number of

FIRST 20 ELEMENTS	
Element	Atomic Number
hydrogen	1
helium	2
lithium	3
beryllium	4
boron	5
carbon	6
nitrogen	7
oxygen	8
fluorine	9
neon	10
sodium	11
magnesium	12
aluminum	13
silicon	14
phosphorus	15
sulfur	16
chlorine	17
argon	18
potassium	19
calcium	20

Table 5-1

Atomic Number The number of protons in the nucleus of an atom.

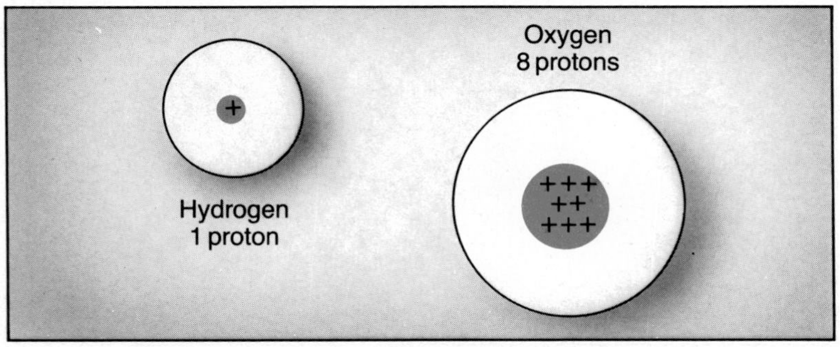

Figure 5-5 Each element has a different number of protons in its nucleus.

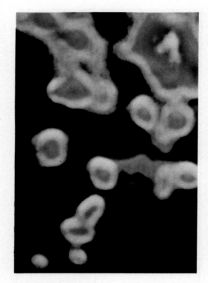

Figure 5-6 *This is an actual picture of uranium atoms enlarged 10,000,000 times. It was made by a scientist at the University of Chicago.*

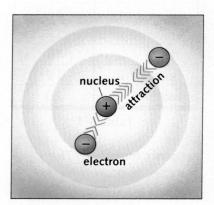

Figure 5-7 *Electrical attraction between the positive nucleus and the negative electrons keeps the electrons in orbit around the nucleus.*

Figure 5-8 *Each energy level can hold only a certain number of electrons.*

an element also tells you the number of electrons that its atoms have.

Electron Arrangement The first photographs of atoms showed them as fuzzy shapes. See Figure 5-6. The fuzziness is thought to be the cloud of electrons whirling around the nucleus at high speeds. Each electron makes billions of trips around the nucleus in one second. Electric forces between the negative electrons and the positive nucleus keep the electrons moving around the nucleus. See Figure 5-7. These electrons buzz around the nucleus somewhat like a swarm of bees around a hive. But unlike bees, each electron must be part of an *energy level*. An energy level describes the most likely location in which electrons can be found. They move around a nucleus within an energy level at a certain average distance from the nucleus. See Figure 5-8.

Only a limited number of electrons may be in each energy level. The one electron in a hydrogen atom ordinarily moves around the nucleus in the first level. The two electrons in helium also usually move in the first level. Two electrons are the limit for this first level. The next energy level can hold eight electrons. Figure 5-9 shows the electron arrangement of the first 12 elements. This diagram shows the electrons in circles where each circle represents an energy level. Keep in mind that the levels are not flat, as shown in the drawings; they are *shells* that completely surround the nucleus. These shells represent *average* positions for electrons. Table 5-2 shows all the energy levels of the first 20 elements.

The number of electrons in the electron cloud is different for each kind of atom. To describe any atom, you must know its atomic number. The atomic number tells you how many electrons are moving around the nucleus. Electrons fill the energy levels in order. The first level (closest to the nucleus)

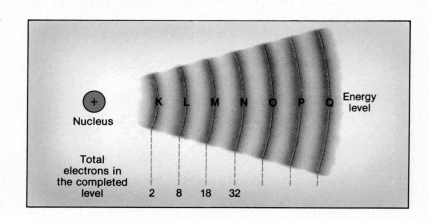

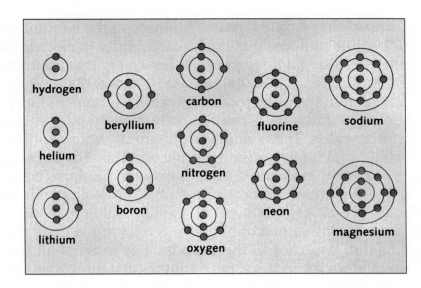

Figure 5-9 *Bohr models showing the electron arrangement of the first 12 elements.*

is filled first. Then the second level is filled. This goes on until all the electrons are in place. For example, a sodium atom with atomic number 11 has 11 electrons. In most cases, two of these electrons are found in the first level. Eight more are in the second level. The remaining one is found in the third level.

Atomic Number	Element	Number of Electrons		
1	hydrogen	1		
2	helium	2		
3	lithium	2	1	
4	beryllium	2	2	
5	boron	2	3	
6	carbon	2	4	
7	nitrogen	2	5	
8	oxygen	2	6	
9	fluorine	2	7	
10	neon	2	8	
11	sodium	2	8	1
12	magnesium	2	8	2
13	aluminum	2	8	3
14	silicon	2	8	4
15	phosphorus	2	8	5
16	sulfur	2	8	6
17	chlorine	2	8	7
18	argon	2	8	8
19	potassium	2	8	8	1
20	calcium	2	8	8	2

Table 5-2

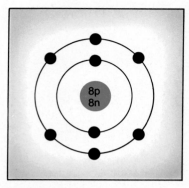

Figure 5-10 *This Bohr model of an oxygen atom shows that oxygen has eight protons and eight neutrons in its nucleus. Oxygen has an atomic mass of 16 u.*

Atomic Mass Unit Unit of mass approximately the mass of one proton or one neutron.

Mass Number Number of protons *and* neutrons in the nucleus of an atom.

Determining Atomic Mass All three of the subatomic particles that compose our model atom differ in electric charge and in mass. All three particles have very small masses. For example, about 600,000,000,000,000,000,000,000 protons have a mass of only about one gram. A neutron has nearly the same mass as a proton, but an electron has a much smaller mass. These values are so small that scientists use a special unit for the mass of atomic particles. This unit is called the **atomic mass unit** (u). Protons and neutrons each have a mass of about 1 atomic mass unit, while electrons have a mass of only 1/1,837 u.

Most of the mass of an atom is thus made up of the protons and neutrons in the nucleus. The mass of all the electrons in an atom is so small that it can usually be ignored. Since atoms are made up of atomic particles, the masses of atoms are also given in atomic mass units. Ignoring the electrons, the mass of an atom depends on the number of protons and neutrons it contains. For example, an ordinary oxygen atom has eight neutrons in its nucleus, as shown in Figure 5-10. Thus the mass of this oxygen atom is 16 u. The mass of an atom, in atomic mass units, is equal to the number of its protons plus its neutrons.

The number of protons and neutrons in a nucleus is called the **mass number** of the atom. You can use the mass number to find the number of neutrons in the nucleus. For example, if you know that the atomic number of oxygen is 8 and its mass is 16 u, you could find the number of neutrons in an oxygen nucleus as follows:

$$
\begin{array}{ccc}
\text{mass number} & - & \text{atomic number} & = & \text{neutrons} \\
(\text{protons} + \text{neutrons}) & - & (\text{protons}) & = & \text{neutrons} \\
16 & - & 8 & = & 8
\end{array}
$$

Figure 5-11 shows an atom of fluorine. In this case, the fluorine atom has 9 protons and 10 neutrons. This gives a mass number of 19 u.

Actually, the masses of atoms have been carefully measured to a much greater precision than is indicated by the total number of protons and neutrons present. You may see on various periodic tables that the atomic mass of oxygen is given as 15.9994 u and that of fluorine is 18.998403 u. For our purposes, however, the rounded-off values indicated by 16 u and 19 u are sufficient.

Iron has an atomic number of 26 and an atomic mass of 56 u. Therefore, it has 30 neutrons in its nucleus. Notice, as in the case of fluorine, that the number of neutrons does not have to equal the number of protons. The higher the atomic

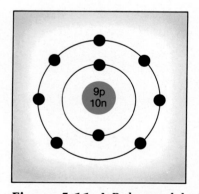

Figure 5-11 *A Bohr model of a fluorine atom. The atomic mass of fluorine is 19 u.*

number is, the greater the difference between the number of protons and neutrons.

Isotopes of Atoms   Scientists have also found that not all atoms of some elements have the same number of neutrons. A hydrogen atom, for example, may have any one of three arrangements in its nucleus. Most hydrogen atoms have only one proton in the nucleus and no neutrons. However, some hydrogen atoms have one proton and one neutron, while a few hydrogen atoms have one proton and two neutrons in the nucleus. The element known as hydrogen is made up of atoms with *all* three types of nuclei. Each type of nucleus produces an atom which is called an **isotope** of hydrogen. Hydrogen has three isotopes: hydrogen-1 (*protium*), hydrogen-2 (*deuterium*), and hydrogen-3 (*tritium*). See Figure 5-12.

Isotope Atoms of the same element that have different masses.

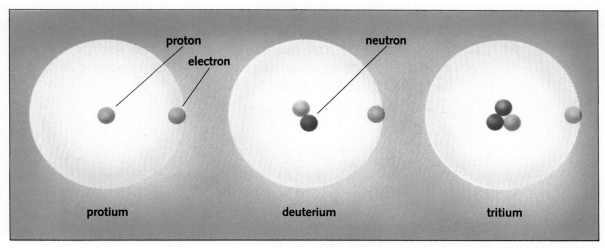

protium   deuterium   tritium

Because they have different numbers of neutrons, isotopes have different masses. Almost all elements have isotopes. For example, lithium exists as lithium-6 and lithium-7. The **atomic mass** of an element is actually the *average* of the masses of all the isotopes of that element as they are found in nature. For example, the atomic mass of the mixture of lithium-6 and lithium-7 found in nature is 6.94 u. It is the average of the atomic masses for the mixture of both isotopes of lithium. This is because 93 percent of all lithium atoms in nature have a mass of 7 u. Only seven percent have a mass of 6 u. The atomic mass of the mixture of hydrogen atoms found in nature is 1.008 u.

Often, the atomic mass of an element is rounded off to the nearest whole number. This is equal to the mass number of the element. The number 6.94 can be rounded off to 7. Thus the mass number of most lithium atoms is 7. The mass

Figure 5-12 *The three isotopes of hydrogen. Protium (H-1) has no neutrons and an atomic mass of 1 u. Deuterium (H-2) has one neutron and an atomic mass of 2 u. Tritium (H-3) has two neutrons and an atomic mass of 3 u. Notice that all of these isotopes have only one proton.*

Atomic Mass The average mass of an element as it is found in nature.

number of an atom is always equal to the sum of its protons and neutrons. For lithium, the mass number 7 equals 3 protons plus 4 neutrons.

Radioactivity   Most isotopes are made of stable forms. Some isotopes, however, are unstable. The structure of the nucleus and the nature of the forces that hold it together are responsible for this phenomenon.

Protons and neutrons are crowded together in an extremely small amount of space inside the nucleus. Of the particles in the nucleus, neutrons are neutral, but protons each carry a positive charge. The positive charge on the protons makes them repel each other. As a result, it seems like the nucleus should fly apart. Since it doesn't, there must be some other force holding the nucleus together. This force is called the *strong nuclear force.*

A nucleus, which contains a certain number of protons, needs just the right number of neutrons to make it stable. If it has too many neutrons or too few neutrons, it will *decay*, or release some of the particles in its nucleus. An atom whose unstable nucleus changes to become more stable is said to be *radioactive*. See Figure 5-13.

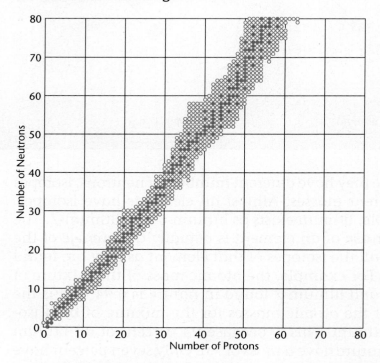

Figure 5-13 The ratio of neutrons to protons affects nuclear stability. Stable nuclei are shown by solid circles. If a nucleus has too many or too few neutrons, it will be unstable. Open circles represent unstable nuclei.

Radioactivity was discovered by the French scientist Henri Becquerel in 1896. Becquerel observed that substances containing uranium gave off rays that could pass through paper and affect photographic film. Marie Curie and her husband Pierre became interested in the strange new rays detected by Becquerel. After several years of work, they discovered two previously unknown radioactive elements. They named these elements *radium* and *polonium*. Following the pioneering work of Becquerel and the Curies, other radioactive elements were found. The radioactive isotopes of elements are made up of atoms with unstable nuclei.

Summary

Because atoms are too small to study directly, scientists use models to describe them. According to the current model, atoms consist of a nucleus that is made up of protons and neutrons, surrounded by clouds of electrons that move in energy levels around the nucleus. These energy levels can contain only a specific number of electrons. Most of the mass of an atom is found in the nucleus. The atomic mass is the sum of the protons and neutrons. Different atoms of the same element may have different numbers of neutrons and are called isotopes. Some isotopes are unstable and are radioactive.

5.2 ATOMS AND CHEMICAL ACTIVITY

At one time, hydrogen gas was commonly used to fill airships. In order to stay in the air, an airship must be filled with a gas that is lighter than air. Since hydrogen gas is lighter than air, the airship floats in the air in the same way that a piece of wood floats in water. But hydrogen is a dangerous gas. It can burn or explode when it combines with oxygen. Some early airships using hydrogen were destroyed when their hydrogen supply exploded. See Figure 5-14.

Helium, on the other hand, is a much safer gas to use in airships. Like hydrogen, helium is also much lighter than air. Unlike hydrogen, however, helium does not burn because

Figure 5-14 *In 1937 the explosion of highly reactive hydrogen gas destroyed the Hindenburg, the largest airship ever built.*

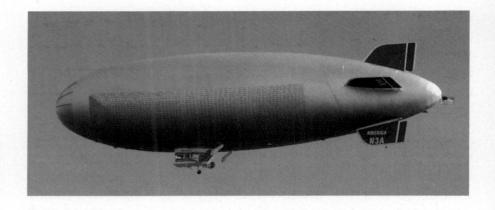

Figure 5-15 *Helium, which does not burn, is used in all modern airships such as this blimp.*

it does not combine with oxygen. It is therefore safe to use in large amounts. See Figure 5-15. Helium is a very stable element. In fact, helium will not take part in any chemical changes. Helium atoms exist separately, and they are never part of a molecule. Why do you think helium does not take part in chemical changes?

Chemically Active Atoms

Chemical Activity The way an atom reacts with atoms of other elements.

The way an atom reacts with atoms of other elements is called its **chemical activity**. Hydrogen, which reacts readily with other elements, is chemically active. Helium, which does not react with other elements, is not chemically active. For this reason, helium is called a *noble* gas. It does not associate with "common" elements.

Hydrogen and helium are the only two elements that have only a single occupied energy level. See Figure 5-16. This level can hold only two electrons. Since helium already has two electrons, it has a completely filled energy level. It does not join with other atoms to form molecules. Hydrogen, on the other hand, has only one electron. It needs one more electron to fill the energy level. Therefore, unlike helium, hydrogen reacts with many other atoms to form molecules.

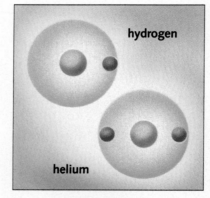

Figure 5-16 *Helium, a noble gas, is stable. Hydrogen, with just a single electron in its outer level, is highly reactive.*

Is it possible that hydrogen and helium behave so differently because of the different number of electrons in their outer energy levels? If this is true, then the behavior of atoms with the same number of outer electrons should be alike. Atoms with a complete outer energy level, or a stable number of electrons, do not easily lose or gain electrons. If an atom has one, two, or three electrons *less* than a stable number, it will tend to add electrons until a stable number is reached. If an atom has one, two, or three electrons *more* than a stable number, it will tend to lose electrons until a stable number is reached.

For example, think about a lithium atom. The atomic number of lithium is 3. Therefore, a lithium atom has three electrons. There are two electrons in the first energy level and one electron in the second level. See Figure 5-17. Thus, lithium will tend to lose that one electron to reach the stable number of two. Table 5-3 lists five other elements that can also be expected to lose one electron. This group of elements is called the **alkali metals**.

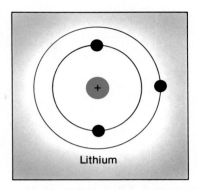

Lithium

Figure 5-17 *Lithium has three electrons: two in its first energy level and one in its second level. Lithium tends to lose the one outer electron.*

THE ALKALI METALS		
Atoms that lose 1 electron easily	Atomic number	Stable electron number after losing 1 electron
lithium	3	2
sodium	11	10
potassium	19	18
rubidium	37	36
cesium	55	54
francium	87	86

Table 5-3

Alkali Metals The group of elements that have only one electron in their outermost energy level.

Now think about a fluorine atom. The atomic number of fluorine is 9. Therefore, fluorine has a total of nine electrons. As shown in Figure 5-11 on page S80, fluorine has two electrons in its first level and seven electrons in its outer level. Fluorine thus has one electron less than the stable number of eight in its outer level. Fluorine must add one electron to have a stable electron arrangement. Table 5-4 lists four other elements that will gain one electron to become stable. These elements are called the **halogens**.

Halogens The group of elements that have seven electrons in their outermost energy level.

THE HALOGENS		
Atoms that gain 1 electron easily	Atomic number	Stable electron number after gaining 1 electron
fluorine	9	10
chlorine	17	18
bromine	35	36
iodine	53	54
astatine	85	86

Table 5-4

Elements, like the alkali metals and the halogens, that lose or gain electrons readily are chemically active. In other words, they take part readily in chemical changes.

Noble Gases

Scientists can determine how much energy is needed to remove an electron from the outer level of an atom. These amounts of energy, ranging from hydrogen (atomic number 1) to calcium (atomic number 20), form a pattern. The graph in Figure 5-18 shows that the atoms of the elements helium, neon, and argon need the highest amounts of energy to remove electrons.

Figure 5-18 A graph of the energy required to remove an electron from an atom of the first 20 elements.

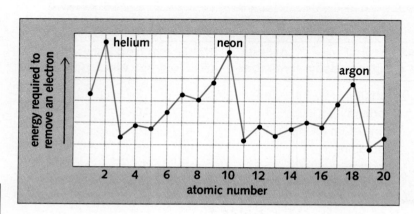

Helium, neon, and argon have a tighter hold on their electrons than do other atoms. Helium (atomic number 2) has a total of two electrons. Neon has 10 electrons and argon has 18 electrons. Recall how many electrons fill each energy level around the nucleus of an atom. The first level is full with two electrons. The second level is full with eight electrons. Thus helium has all of its electrons in one completely filled level. Neon has filled the first and second levels (2 + 8). Argon has a stable number of electrons with two in its first level, eight in its second level, and eight in its third level. See Figure 5-19. Energy levels above the second can hold more than eight electrons. However, eight is the largest number that the *outermost* energy level of an atom may have.

Atoms that have completely filled energy levels—or that have eight electrons in their outermost energy level—do not easily lose electrons. Their electron arrangement is stable. Experiments have shown that there are a total of six noble gases among the known elements. In addition to helium, neon, and argon, the other noble gases are krypton, xenon, and radon.

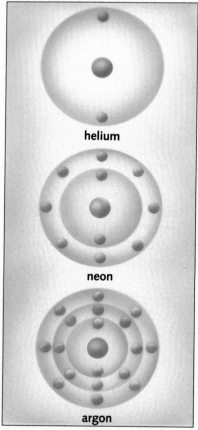

Figure 5-19 The stability of helium, neon, and argon is the result of a full set of electrons in their outer energy levels.

Classifying the Elements

Scientists have discovered a total of 91 naturally occurring elements. Several other elements have been made by artificial means as well. As scientists were discovering more elements, they began to search for ways to organize these elements. It was also becoming more difficult to use the full names of these elements when referring to them in writing.

Symbols of the Elements   Up until now, the name of each chemical element in this book has been written out (hydrogen, helium, and so forth). For many years, chemists did the same thing. But then the Swedish chemist Jöns Jakob Berzelius suggested that, since symbols were being used in algebra and physics, scientists also should use symbols for the chemical elements. He established a system by which elements were referred to with letters.

The system Berzelius suggested is still used today, with new symbols being assigned as new elements are discovered. These symbols consist of one or two letters, frequently from the element's name. For example, the symbol for hydrogen is H. The symbol for helium is He. When there are two letters in a symbol, the first letter is capitalized, while the second is not.

Some symbols, however, seem to be unrelated to their names. For example, Hg is the symbol for mercury and Au is the symbol for gold. These symbols represent the Latin names for these elements, since Latin was the language of science when they were identified as elements. Thus, Hg stands for *hydrargyrum* and Au stands for *aurum*, the same elements we know as mercury and gold. Table 5-5 is a list of some common elements and their symbols.

More recently discovered elements tend to be named after famous people or places, for example, einsteinium and californium. Names of newly discovered elements and their symbols are decided by an international committee of scientists.

Chemical Families   You probably know members of the same family who look somewhat alike. Sometimes these family members even behave alike. One way to classify elements is by placing them in families. The chemical properties of the atoms of an element determine the family to which that element belongs.

You already know that some groups of atoms have the same outer electron arrangements. The atoms in the alkali group all have one outer electron. Alkali metals have similar chemical properties. The halogens all lack one electron in their outer levels. They also have similar chemical

SYMBOLS OF SOME COMMON ELEMENTS	
hydrogen	H
boron	B
carbon	C
nitrogen	N
oxygen	O
fluorine	F
phosphorus	P
sulfur	S
iodine	I
helium	He
lithium	Li
aluminum	Al
silicon	Si
calcium	Ca
nickel	Ni
bromine	Br
magnesium	Mg
chlorine	Cl
zinc	Zn
sodium (natrium)	Na
potassium (kalium)	K
copper (cuprum)	Cu
gold (aurum)	Au
silver (argentum)	Ag
iron (ferrum)	Fe
lead (plumbum)	Pb
tin (stannum)	Sn
antimony (stibium)	Sb

Table 5-5

Chemical Family A group of elements with similar chemical properties.

properties. The noble gases, likewise, are similar in that they all have complete outer electron levels. A group of elements with similar chemical properties is called a **chemical family**. The alkali metals, halogens, and noble gases are examples of chemical families.

The Periodic Table

By the mid 1800s, scientists had discovered and described the properties of many elements using newly developed methods. The atomic masses of most known elements had also been determined. Scientists observed that several elements shared similar physical and chemical properties. It was found that when the elements were listed by increasing atomic mass, elements with similar properties occurred *periodically*, or at regular intervals.

In 1869 a Russian chemist named Dmitri Mendeleev announced that he had developed a chart of the elements that reflected the similarities in their properties. He listed the elements by increasing atomic mass but placed them in columns. He noticed that elements with similar properties appeared next to each other. He left gaps in the table in order to make elements with similar properties

Figure 5-20 *Mendeleev's original manuscript is shown at the top. His findings were first published in a journal as shown below.*

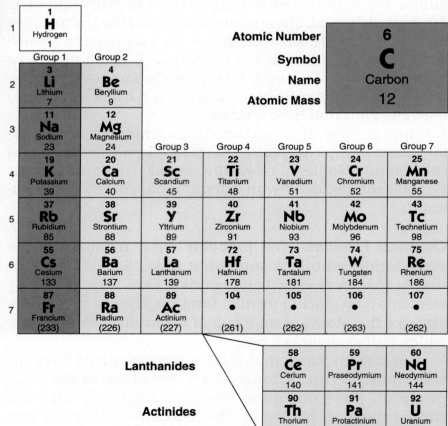

S88

fall in the same row. Mendeleev predicted that new elements would be discovered to fill these blank spaces. His chart was developed further and eventually became known as the **Periodic Table** of the elements. See Figure 5-20.

Modern periodic tables are slightly different from the original one made by Mendeleev. In the 1920s, it was discovered that the elements of the Periodic Table should actually be arranged by increasing atomic number rather than by atomic mass. This caused only small changes from Mendeleev's original order. The table itself has also been turned so that Mendeleev's rows are now columns in the Periodic Table. Compare Figure 5-21 to Figure 5-20.

Using the Periodic Table

A street map is helpful if you have to find your way around an unfamiliar city. In the same way, the Periodic Table is useful in learning about the chemical elements. Due to its periodic arrangement, elements that display similar physical and chemical properties will be found in the same area of the Periodic Table.

Elements with the most similar properties (the chemical families) are listed in the vertical columns of the table. For

Periodic Table Chart of the elements arranged according to periodic properties of the elements.

Figure 5-21 Periodic Table of the Elements. The columns are referred to as groups and the rows are referred to as periods.

METALS
- Alkali Metals
- Other metals

NONMETALS
- Noble Gases
- Halogens
- Other nonmetals

					Group 13	Group 14	Group 15	Group 16	Group 17	Group 18
										2 **He** Helium 4
					5 **B** Boron 11	6 **C** Carbon 12	7 **N** Nitrogen 14	8 **O** Oxygen 16	9 **F** Fluorine 19	10 **Ne** Neon 20
					13 **Al** Aluminum 27	14 **Si** Silicon 28	15 **P** Phosphorus 31	16 **S** Sulfur 32	17 **Cl** Chlorine 35	18 **Ar** Argon 40

Group 8	Group 9	Group 10	Group 11	Group 12						
26 **Fe** Iron 56	27 **Co** Cobalt 59	28 **Ni** Nickel 59	29 **Cu** Copper 64	30 **Zn** Zinc 65	31 **Ga** Gallium 70	32 **Ge** Germanium 73	33 **As** Arsenic 75	34 **Se** Selenium 79	35 **Br** Bromine 80	36 **Kr** Krypton 84
44 **Ru** Ruthenium 101	45 **Rh** Rhodium 103	46 **Pd** Palladium 106	47 **Ag** Silver 108	48 **Cd** Cadmium 112	49 **In** Indium 115	50 **Sn** Tin 119	51 **Sb** Antimony 122	52 **Te** Tellurium 128	53 **I** Iodine 127	54 **Xe** Xenon 131
76 **Os** Osmium 190	77 **Ir** Iridium 192	78 **Pt** Platinum 195	79 **Au** Gold 197	80 **Hg** Mercury 201	81 **Tl** Thalium 204	82 **Pb** Lead 207	83 **Bi** Bismuth 209	84 **Po** Polonium (209)	85 **At** Astatine (210)	86 **Rn** Radon (222)
108 •	109 •									

• Elements synthesized, but not officially named

61 **Pm** Promethium (145)	62 **Sm** Samarium 150	63 **Eu** Europium 152	64 **Gd** Gadolinium 157	65 **Tb** Terbium 159	66 **Dy** Dysprosium 163	67 **Ho** Holmium 165	68 **Er** Erbium 167	69 **Tm** Thulium 169	70 **Yb** Ytterbium 173	71 **Lu** Lutetium 175
93 **Np** Neptunium 237	94 **Pu** Plutonium (244)	95 **Am** Americium (243)	96 **Cm** Curium (247)	97 **Bk** Berkelium (247)	98 **Cf** Californium (251)	99 **Es** Einsteinium (252)	100 **Fm** Fermium (257)	101 **Md** Mendelevium (258)	102 **No** Nobelium (259)	103 **Lr** Lawrencium (262)

Group A set of elements arranged vertically, in columns, in the Periodic Table.

Period A row, or horizontal line of elements, in the Periodic Table.

Figure 5-22 What characteristics of metals are demonstrated by this copper tea kettle?

example, the noble gases are found in a single column at the right side of the table. Next to the noble gases is the column containing the halogens. The alkali metals are found in a single column at the far left of the table. All the columns in the table, likewise, list elements with similar properties. Each column of elements is referred to as a **group**. There are 18 groups in the modern Periodic Table, numbered from left to right.

Each horizontal row is called a **period**. The periods contain the elements with the same number of occupied energy levels. The length of a row indicates the additional number of electrons needed to fill the energy levels of the elements in that row. Each row, except the first, begins with an alkali metal and ends with a noble gas. Notice how hydrogen is separated from the first period. Even though hydrogen has only one electron in its outermost energy level, it is not considered an alkali metal.

This trend, from alkali metal to noble gas, continues for seven rows. Thus there are seven periods in the Periodic Table. The last period, however, is not complete because these elements have not yet been identified. The two rows of elements located below the table should actually be included in periods 6 and 7, between groups 3 and 4. They are placed below the table to save space.

The zig-zag line to the right of center in the Periodic Table represents a boundary between two major types of elements: the *metals* and the *nonmetals*. Physical properties common to the elements in each group determine their classification. Metals are good conductors of heat and electricity, can be hammered into different shapes, and are shiny. See Figure 5-22. All metals, except mercury, are solids at normal room temperatures. Mercury is a liquid at ordinary temperature and pressure.

Nonmetals, on the other hand, tend to be poor conductors of heat and electricity, are brittle, and do not have a metallic shine. Some nonmetals, such as chlorine, oxygen, and nitrogen, are gases under ordinary conditions, while bromine is a dark red liquid. Solid nonmetals, such as carbon and sulfur, are brittle. They break if pulled or hammered.

By inventing the Periodic Table, Mendeleev discovered a valuable tool for scientific research. Each element has its own position on the Periodic Table; if you know the chemical properties of two or three elements, you can predict the properties of a neighboring element. You could even predict the chemical behavior of elements not yet discovered. Mendeleev himself predicted the general properties of several elements that had not yet been discovered. When the elements were later discovered, they were found to behave almost exactly as Mendeleev had predicted.

Summary

Unstable atoms tend to gain or lose electrons by reacting chemically with other elements. Atoms with the same number of electrons in their outer energy levels have similar characteristics and belong to the same chemical family. In the Periodic Table of the elements, the members of a chemical family are found in the same vertical column.

5.3 PUTTING ATOMS TOGETHER

Have you ever put a jigsaw puzzle together? The separate pieces seem to have no pattern. But you know that the different pieces will fit together if you can match them properly. In this manner, atoms are somewhat like the pieces of a puzzle. Atoms join together, but only in certain ways.

What Holds Atoms Together?

Diamond is the hardest naturally-occurring substance known. A diamond crystal is made only of carbon atoms. Carbon is also found in other forms besides diamond. The hardness of a diamond is a result of the strength with which the individual carbon atoms cling to each other. Compare carbon, in the form of diamond, with helium. As you know, helium is a very light gas. In order to change helium into a liquid, its temperature must drop to 4.2 kelvins (–268.8 °C). See Figure 5-23. This temperature is only a few degrees above **absolute zero**. This means that helium atoms can cling together only when they are almost motionless.

Why do carbon atoms hold so tightly to their neighbors, while helium atoms do not? To find an answer to questions like this, we will take a closer look at hydrogen atoms because they are the simplest of all atoms. We will see how hydrogen atoms combine to form a molecule of hydrogen.

Suppose that two hydrogen atoms come close to each other. Hydrogen atoms have only one electron in one energy level. Each atom needs another electron to become stable. Both hydrogen atoms can become stable by *sharing* their one electron with the other atom. When two hydrogen atoms share electrons, the shared electrons move about

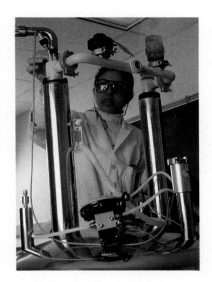

Figure 5-23 *Liquid helium has many uses in the laboratory due to its low temperature.*

Absolute Zero The temperature at which molecular motion is at a minimum (0 K on the Kelvin scale, –273 °C on the Celsius scale, and –460 °F on the Fahrenheit scale).

both nuclei. Then the two hydrogen atoms are joined to form a hydrogen molecule. The steps by which they join are shown in Figure 5-24. No more than two hydrogen atoms can combine because each energy level can only hold two electrons. In a hydrogen molecule, the energy level of each atom is completely filled by the shared electrons.

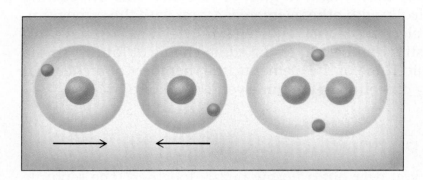

Figure 5-24 *Two hydrogen atoms share their electrons to form a hydrogen molecule.*

Chemical Bond A link between atoms resulting from the mutual attraction of their nuclei for electrons.

When each of the two hydrogen atoms shares its electron with the other, the two atoms are joined by a **chemical bond**. A chemical bond is a link between atoms resulting from the mutual attraction of their nuclei for electrons. One way in which atoms are held together by a chemical bond is when their electrons are attracted to, and move around, the nuclei of both atoms. Figure 5-25 shows how the electrons in a hydrogen molecule are attracted to both nuclei to form a chemical bond.

Now, compare the behavior of two hydrogen atoms with two helium atoms. The outermost energy level of each helium atom is filled with two electrons. Thus a helium atom does not need to share electrons to become stable. In other words, helium atoms will not form a chemical bond. In nature, helium atoms do not combine with other atoms to form molecules. The same is true for the other members of the noble-gas family of elements. They are the only elements that exist in nature *only* as free atoms.

Types of Chemical Bonds

Atoms form chemical bonds in two general ways. They either *share* electrons to become stable, or they *gain* or *lose* electrons to become stable. For example, a hydrogen atom has only one electron. Since two electrons are needed to fill hydrogen's only energy level, a single hydrogen atom often shares one electron, as in the example above. Sometimes, however, it loses its one electron in order to form a more stable compound.

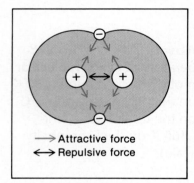

Figure 5-25 *Two hydrogen atoms are held together in a hydrogen molecule because the shared electrons are attracted to the nuclei of both atoms.*

Sharing Electrons   Elemental hydrogen almost always exists as molecules. Each atom of this element is missing only one electron to complete its outer energy level. As a result, two hydrogen atoms share one electron with the other to form a molecule made up of two atoms. When atoms share electrons to fill their outer levels, the chemical bond that forms is called a **covalent bond**. The bond between two hydrogen atoms is a covalent bond. Some other atoms that form covalent bonds are chlorine, oxygen, nitrogen, and fluorine. These gases are found in nature as covalently-bonded molecules.

Because these molecules each contain two atoms, they are known as **diatomic molecules**. Most diatomic molecules are not very reactive. All of the gases found in nature, except the noble gases, exist as diatomic molecules.

Atoms may share more than one pair of electrons to form a covalent bond. For example, a sulfur atom has six outer electrons. Each sulfur atom needs two electrons to complete its outer level. Thus a sulfur atom could share two pairs of electrons to form a sulfur molecule. Carbon atoms have four outer electrons, which they can share to form covalent bonds. However, these substances are rarely found as diatomic molecules. Atoms with more than one electron to share, like sulfur, carbon, and silicon, form molecules with six, eight, or more atoms. Diamonds are so hard because they are composed of carbon atoms in which every carbon atom shares an electron with four other carbon atoms that surround it. See Figure 5-26.

Atoms of two different types also form covalent bonds between themselves. For example, two hydrogen atoms and an oxygen atom can be joined by covalent bonds to make a water molecule. The oxygen atom's outer level is filled by sharing an electron from each of the two hydrogen atoms, and each hydrogen atom fills its outer level by sharing one oxygen electron.

Losing and Gaining Electrons   Sodium atoms have 11 electrons (2 + 8 + 1). Thus each sodium atom has one outer electron. Rather than sharing its outer electron, sodium tends to lose one electron completely to become stable. When a sodium atom gives up an electron, the sodium atom becomes a positive **ion**. An ion is an atom that has an electrical charge because it does not have equal numbers of electrons and protons. See Figure 5-27.

Suppose that a sodium atom and a chlorine atom come together. The chlorine atom, having 17 electrons (2 + 8 + 7),

Covalent Bond A chemical bond resulting from the sharing of electrons.

Diatomic molecule A molecule consisting of only two atoms.

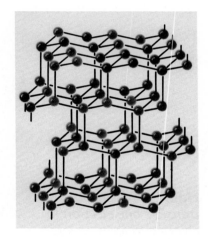

Figure 5-26 In diamond, each carbon atom is bonded to four other carbon atoms.

Ion An atom with an electrical charge due to having unequal numbers of electrons and protons.

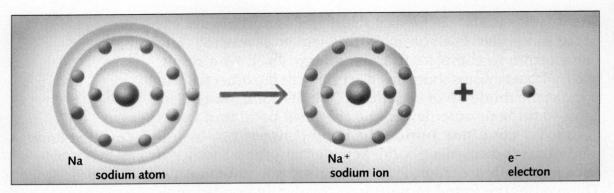

Na
sodium atom

Na⁺
sodium ion

e⁻
electron

Figure 5-27 *Sodium has a full complement of electrons in its outer level only after it loses one electron. The resulting ion has an electric charge of 1+.*

needs to gain one electron to become stable. The sodium atom needs to lose one electron. Therefore, for both of the atoms to become stable, the sodium atom will lose one outer electron to the chlorine atom. See Figure 5-28. The sodium atom becomes a positive sodium ion, and the chlorine atom becomes a negative chloride ion. The two oppositely charged ions are then electrically attracted to each other. This attraction forms another kind of chemical bond and holds the sodium and chloride ions together.

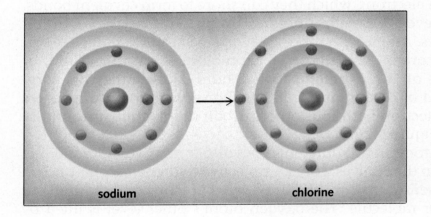

sodium   chlorine

Figure 5-28 *Sodium transfers one electron to chlorine to form an ionic bond.*

Ionic Bond A chemical bond resulting from the attraction between two ions.

Bonds that are formed between atoms as a result of this *transfer* of electrons are called **ionic bonds**. Sodium and chlorine form an ionic bond to become sodium chloride, which is common table salt. An ionic compound, like salt, always contains atoms of two or more elements. Since one atom must lose an electron and one must gain an electron, an ionic bond cannot form between two atoms of the same element.

Describing Chemical Compounds

When you mix lemonade, you may make it too sweet by adding too much sugar or too sour by adding too much lemon juice. Like all mixtures, the composition of a solution is not always the same. However, chemical compounds are always made up of the same elements in the same proportions. A pure compound, such as water or sodium chloride, will always be exactly the same no matter how it is made. See Figure 5-29.

Chemical Formulas Every atom can be represented by its symbol. Thus a compound can be described by using the symbols for the atoms in the compound. For example, water contains hydrogen atoms and oxygen atoms. The symbols H for hydrogen and O for oxygen can be used to describe water.

However, you have seen that certain numbers of hydrogen and oxygen atoms combine to make water molecules. Because oxygen atoms need two electrons to fill their outer energy level, two hydrogen atoms combine with each oxygen atom. These numbers must be included in a correct description of water. Thus the symbol for a molecule of water is H_2O. The number 2 written below the symbol for hydrogen is called a *subscript*. This indicates that there are two atoms of hydrogen in each molecule of water. A description of a chemical compound using symbols and numbers is called a **chemical formula**. Every chemical compound can be described by a chemical formula.

The subscript number 1 is never used as part of a chemical formula. If no subscript number is given after the symbol of an atom, it means that the molecule contains one atom of that element. For example, the correct formula for common table salt is NaCl. This formula says that a unit of salt is always made of one atom of sodium for each atom of chlorine.

Formulas can also be used to describe diatomic molecules. Remember that two hydrogen atoms can form a diatomic molecule by sharing electrons. The formula for a hydrogen molecule is H_2. Hydrogen gas consists of diatomic molecules. Oxygen gas, O_2, is also made up of diatomic molecules. Many elements actually exist as diatomic molecules rather than as single atoms. Other diatomic molecules include chlorine (Cl_2), nitrogen (N_2), fluorine (F_2), bromine (Br_2), and iodine (I_2).

Figure 5-29 *When you make a mixture, you can add the components in different proportions. The elements in a compound, however, always combine in the same ratio.*

Chemical Formula A description of a chemical compound using symbols and numbers.

Describing Chemical Changes

You have already learned that a chemical change is different from a physical change. For example, chopping wood is a physical change, while burning the wood in a fireplace is

Figure 5-30 *A chemical reaction takes place during the burning of charcoal.*

Chemical Reaction A process in which a chemical change occurs: reactants yield products.

Chemical Equation A description of a chemical reaction using chemical formulas.

a chemical change. In a chemical change, the atoms in the molecules of one or more substances are rearranged or exchanged to form one or more new substances.

Chemical Reactions How would you describe charcoal burning in a barbecue grill? Burning charcoal, or any other material, produces a chemical change. See Figure 5-30. When a chemical change takes place, the substances that are present before the change are called *reactants*. The reactants are the substances that react or change. The new substances formed as a result of the chemical change are called *products*. Thus a general description of a chemical change could be written as: reactants yield products. For example, charcoal is made up mostly of carbon atoms. When charcoal burns, it combines with oxygen to form carbon dioxide. Carbon and oxygen are the reactants and carbon dioxide is the product. The burning of charcoal can be described as follows:

carbon plus oxygen yields carbon dioxide

The combination of any element, such as carbon, with oxygen is called *oxidation*. The combining of iron and oxygen to form rust is another example of oxidation. Oxidation is one kind of **chemical reaction**. A chemical reaction is a process in which a chemical change takes place. Burning charcoal is a chemical reaction because the carbon and oxygen are chemically changed into the compound carbon dioxide.

You can usually observe some evidence that a chemical reaction has taken place. For example, many chemical reactions result in an increase or a decrease in the temperature of the reactants. Energy is involved in making and breaking chemical bonds. A change in temperature indicates that energy, in the form of heat, is being released or used up as a reaction takes place.

Chemical Equations Another way of writing the reaction of carbon with oxygen is with the formulas for carbon and oxygen.

$$C + O_2 \rightarrow CO_2$$

This description of a chemical reaction is called a **chemical equation**. The chemical equation for the burning of charcoal says that one atom of carbon reacts with one molecule of oxygen to form one molecule of carbon dioxide.

In a chemical equation, the formulas for all reactants are written on the left side. Each reactant is separated from the others by a plus (+) sign. The formulas for the products are written on the right. Reactants and products are separated by an arrow that means "produces" or "yields."

The following word equation represents the reaction of hydrogen and oxygen to form water.

hydrogen plus oxygen yields water

Using formulas, the chemical equation is:

$$H_2 + O_2 \rightarrow H_2O$$

However, this equation is not complete. Look at the number of oxygen atoms on each side of the equation. There are two oxygen atoms on the left of the arrow but only one oxygen atom on the right. See Figure 5-31. One oxygen atom seems to have disappeared. But scientists have determined that matter cannot be destroyed—only rearranged—during chemical reactions. The same number and types of atoms exist after a chemical reaction as before the reaction. The fact that matter cannot be created or destroyed is called the **law of conservation of mass**.

Law of Conservation of Mass Matter cannot be created or destroyed.

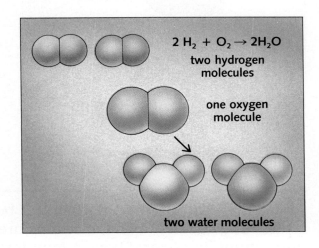

$$2 H_2 + O_2 \rightarrow 2H_2O$$
two hydrogen molecules

one oxygen molecule

two water molecules

Figure 5-31 The equation, as well as the illustration, is not complete. The unbalanced equation does not account for a missing oxygen atom.

To correct the above equation, you must *balance* it. Since there are two oxygen atoms on the left of the arrow, there must also be two on the right.

$$H_2 + O_2 \rightarrow 2H_2O$$

Now the oxygen atoms are balanced but the hydrogen atoms are not. There are four hydrogen atoms on the right, but there are only two hydrogen atoms on the left. The problem must not be solved by changing the formulas H_2, O_2, or H_2O. Each of these formulas correctly describes the molecules of hydrogen, oxygen, and water. The problem can be solved by placing a 2 in front of H_2. A number written in front of a formula is called a *coefficient*. A coefficient tells how many molecules are used or made. With the coefficient 2 added, the equation now reads:

$$2H_2 + O_2 \rightarrow 2H_2O$$

The equation now says that two molecules of H_2 react with one molecule of O_2 to yield two molecules of H_2O. See Figure 5-32. Now there are four hydrogen atoms and two oxygen atoms on either side of the equation. The equation is now correctly balanced. A balanced equation demonstrates the law of conservation of mass—atoms are neither created nor destroyed in a reaction.

Figure 5-32 *This equation is balanced and correctly describes the formation of water from hydrogen and oxygen.*

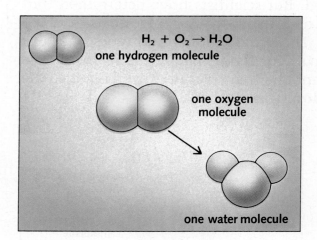

$H_2 + O_2 \rightarrow H_2O$
one hydrogen molecule

one oxygen molecule

one water molecule

Summary

Atoms are held together by chemical bonds to form molecules. In a covalent bond, electrons are shared by two or more atoms. In an ionic bond, atoms lose or gain electrons. By sharing, losing, or gaining electrons, atoms achieve a stable number of electrons in the outermost energy level. Chemical formulas are used to represent the number and kinds of atoms that combine to form a compound. Chemical changes occur when the atoms of substances are rearranged to form new substances. Chemical reactions are events in which chemical changes occur. Chemical equations are used to describe chemical reactions.

Unit 6

Reading *Plus*

Now that you have been introduced to several forms and uses of energy, let's take a closer look at what energy is and how we can harness it to do work. Read pages S100 to S116 and write an article for an environmental journal about energy and how we produce it. Your article should deal with the following questions.

1. What is energy, and in what forms is it observed?

2. How can a bouncing ball be used to show how energy is conserved and how it decreases in its usefulness?

3. In what ways is energy from the sun harnessed by humans to do work?

6.1 WHAT IS ENERGY?

Energy is everywhere! Every time a bolt of lightning cracks the evening sky, nature is showing us some of its energy. Water rushing over waterfalls and crashing down on the rocks below, as in Figure 6-1, is another demonstration of energy. Not all displays of energy, however, are as dramatic. A stone rolling down a hill, a star shining in space, a leaf blowing in the wind, and ice melting in a pond are also displays of energy.

Defining Energy

Our universe is rich in energy. But it is hard to say just what energy really is. We do know, however, what energy does—it causes change. Almost all of the changes you see in the world are the result of energy.

Energy can be defined as "the ability to cause change." One type of change is a change in position, or *motion*. For example, soft, summer breezes and cold, icy winds occur because energy from the sun heats our atmosphere and causes air molecules to move. The energy in wind causes the motion of a sailboat when the wind pushes against its sails. See Figure 6-2.

When energy causes matter to change positions, we say

Figure 6-1 *The potential energy of the water at the top of the falls is converted into kinetic energy by the time it reaches the bottom.*

Energy The ability to cause change or do work.

Figure 6-2 *These billowing sails capture the wind's energy to push the boats forward.*

Figure 6-3 *Work is the result of these horses exerting a force to move this wagon through a distance.*

that **work** has been done. In fact, energy is also described as "the ability to do *work.*" For example, the horses in Figure 6-3 are doing work. The amount of work done is equal to the strength of the *force* that moves an object, multiplied by the *distance* the object is moved.

Another term that is often confused with energy and work is **power**. Power is the *rate* at which work is done. The two horses in Figure 6-3 would have more power than a single horse because they can do the same amount of work faster.

Forms of Energy

Unless you know what to look for, energy can be hard to recognize because it takes many forms. As you know, the two basic types of energy are *kinetic* and *potential.* Kinetic energy, the energy of motion, is energy that can be used directly to do work. Potential energy, the energy stored in an object or system, is the energy that can be transformed into kinetic energy by physical or chemical changes. Energy is constantly changing from one form to another.

Scientists classify energy into several different forms that describe energy as we see it. They include: mechanical energy, electrical energy, chemical energy, nuclear energy, radiant energy, and thermal energy. These six forms of energy are described below.

Mechanical Energy   Energy that is due to the position and/ or motion of an object is called **mechanical energy**. The bowling ball and pins in Figure 6-4 have mechanical energy. The moving parts of a machine have mechanical energy, as does falling water and a hammer hitting a nail. All of these objects have potential energy: the bowling ball when it is held in someone's hand; the pins while they are standing; the water before it falls; the hammer when it is poised above the head of the nail. When they are put in motion, this potential energy becomes kinetic energy.

Electrical Energy   The energy of a stream of electrons moving through a substance is called **electrical energy**. A negative charge develops in a place where electrons collect. A place that has too few electrons takes on a positive charge. In this situation, electric potential energy exists between the two positions.

If a connection is made between the negative and positive positions, electrons will "flow" from one position to the other, resulting in an electric current. Thus electric potential

Work The product of a force on an object and the distance the object is moved.

Power The rate at which work is done.

Figure 6-4 The bowling ball has mechanical energy because it is rolling. Once the pins are hit, they also have mechanical energy.

Mechanical Energy Energy of an object due to its position, motion, or both.

Electrical Energy Energy of electrical charges as a result of their position or motion.

Figure 6-5 *Lightning is an example of electrical energy.*

Chemical Energy Energy stored in the chemical bonds of molecules.

Figure 6-6 *The chemical energy stored in the match is released through chemical reactions.*

energy is converted into kinetic energy of moving electrons. Substances through which electrical energy can flow are called conductors. Metals, air, and even your body can conduct electrons.

Power plants use generators to produce large quantities of electrical energy. A battery also has the ability to produce electrical energy. The batteries that you are familiar with have chemicals that react in certain ways, moving electrons in one direction and not another. When a battery is connected to a radio, for example, electrons from the negative pole are conducted through a wire to the radio and back to the positive pole of the battery. The electrical energy is used to make the radio play.

A bolt of lightning, like the one in Figure 6-5, is a release of electrical energy that we can see. In nature, electrons build up in the bottom of a storm cloud. The earth's surface tends to have an excess positive charge, which is located at the tops of pointed objects like trees, chimneys, and even people. A huge spark is generated when the cloud's electrons flow through moist air to a positively charged object. This spark is the lightning we see. The same thing happens when you become electrically charged by dragging your feet across a nylon carpet. A spark jumps if you get very close to an object, such as a doorknob, that can conduct electrons away from you. Of course, this spark is much smaller than lightning.

Chemical Energy **Chemical energy** is the energy stored in chemical bonds that holds molecules together. This energy may be released if the chemical bonds are broken. Chemical energy is either released or added during chemical changes. For example, the match in Figure 6-6 has chemical potential energy. The head of a match is made of chemicals that react to produce a flame when the match is struck. When a match burns, many chemical bonds are broken, while others are formed. Excess chemical energy is released in the form of heat and light. Burning releases chemical energy from many substances, such as wood and oil. These substances are called fuels.

The food we eat also has chemical energy. Your body releases this energy by slowly breaking chemical bonds in the food and forming others. This process is called *cellular respiration*. Some of the chemical energy released from your food becomes the heat that keeps your body temperature constant. Some of the energy is used to enable you to think and do work.

Nuclear Energy   The forces that act on the protons and neutrons in the nucleus of an atom are responsible for **nuclear energy**. Nuclear energy is by far the most concentrated and powerful form of energy. It is released in large amounts by either splitting atomic nuclei through the process of *fission*, as demonstrated by Figure 6-7, or by forcing nuclei together through the process of *fusion*.

The energy that makes the sun shine is thought to come from the fusion of hydrogen nuclei to make helium. Heat, light, and other radiation are also produced. In the process of fission, radioactive isotopes change into isotopes of other elements. Both particles and radiation are given off during fission. Particles released by nuclear reactions have a tremendous amount of kinetic energy—enough to split other nuclei and continue the reaction. Another characteristic of nuclear reactions is that they convert some matter into energy.

Radiant Energy   Sunlight is a familiar example of **radiant energy**. Radiant energy is transmitted in the form of special waves called *electromagnetic waves*, which can even pass through the near vacuum of space. These waves travel at an extremely rapid speed—about 300,000 kilometers per second—taking only eight minutes to travel from the sun to the earth. Radiant energy is produced as a result of complex processes that take place deep inside the sun. About 90 percent of the radiant energy given off by the sun is either visible light or *infrared* rays. Infrared rays cannot be seen, but they can be felt as heat.

Other types of radiant energy that you might recognize are X rays, microwaves, and television and radio waves. These waves form the *electromagnetic spectrum*. The electromagnetic spectrum, shown in Figure 6-8, is the whole range of radiant energy waves. It is arranged in order from the waves with

Nuclear Energy Energy that is released by either splitting atomic nuclei or by forcing the nuclei of atoms together.

Figure 6-7 An uncontrolled fission reaction results in a nuclear explosion.

Radiant Energy Energy in the form of electromagnetic waves.

Figure 6-8 The electromagnetic spectrum of radiant energy.

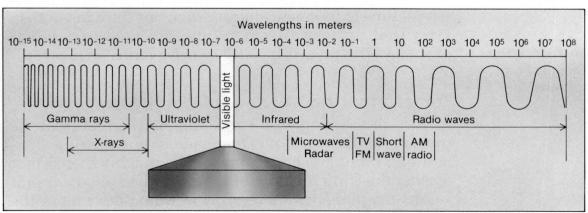

Wavelengths in meters

10^{-15} 10^{-14} 10^{-13} 10^{-12} 10^{-11} 10^{-10} 10^{-9} 10^{-8} 10^{-7} 10^{-6} 10^{-5} 10^{-4} 10^{-3} 10^{-2} 10^{-1} 1 10 10^{2} 10^{3} 10^{4} 10^{5} 10^{6} 10^{7} 10^{8}

Gamma rays   Ultraviolet   Visible light   Infrared   Radio waves

X-rays

Microwaves / Radar   TV / FM   Short wave   AM radio

Figure 6-9 *Thermal energy is associated with the motion of the particles that make up matter.*

Thermal Energy Energy due to the vibration of molecules.

Heat Energy transferred between two substances because of a difference in temperature.

Energy Transformation A change in energy from one form to another.

the shortest *wavelength* to the waves with the longest wavelength. Wavelength is the distance between the peaks of two adjacent waves.

Thermal Energy As you know, the molecules of a substance are constantly moving. **Thermal energy** is the total potential and kinetic energy of moving molecules in a material. See Figure 6-9. *Temperature* is a measure of the average amount of kinetic energy the molecules of a substance have. When a group of molecules gains kinetic energy, the substance they are a part of becomes hotter; and when the molecules lose kinetic energy, the substance becomes cooler. **Heat** is thermal energy that is *transferred* between two substances because of a difference in temperature. Heat can be transferred to other substances when some of their molecules collide. Heat always *flows* from warmer objects to cooler objects. The distinctions among thermal energy, heat, and temperature will be discussed in Unit 7.

Summary

Energy is the ability to cause change or do work. All energy is either kinetic energy (energy in motion) or potential energy (stored energy). Energy can come in many different forms, among which are mechanical energy, electrical energy, chemical energy, nuclear energy, radiant energy, and thermal energy.

6.2 ENERGY TRANSFORMATIONS

Scientists know that all physical and chemical changes involve energy. Energy itself constantly changes from its potential state to its kinetic state, or from one form to another. Every change that occurs in the universe involves a change of energy. This process is called **energy transformation**.

Transformation of Energy from the Sun

Almost all the energy on earth originally comes from the sun. See Figure 6-10. Matter in the sun is converted into thermal and radiant energy. Some of the radiant energy that reaches the earth as sunlight is transformed into heat that warms the planet's surface. This warming determines the earth's climate.

Green plants use sunlight to convert carbon dioxide and water into food, which stores energy in chemical bonds. A warm-blooded animal that eats plants transforms part of the chemical energy in the food into heat to maintain its body temperature. Some of the chemical energy is transformed into mechanical energy when the animal moves. In some cases, this mechanical energy can be transferred to other objects, for example, when a horse carries a rider or pulls a wagon.

Some plants and animals that lived and died long ago have become the coal and oil we now use as fuels. The chemical energy of these fuels was stored in the organisms while they lived and is transformed into heat and light by the process of burning. This energy can then be transformed into mechanical energy by an engine, or into electrical energy by a generator.

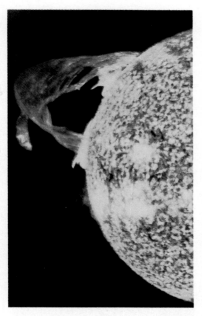

Figure 6-10 *The sun is the source for almost all of the energy found on earth.*

The Conservation of Energy

When an automobile engine converts the chemical energy of gasoline into heat, only 30 percent of the energy in the gasoline actually becomes the mechanical energy of a moving automobile. What happens to the other 70 percent? Is it used up in the change? No. The chemical energy of gasoline is first transformed into light, sound, and heat as it is burned. Only some of the heat is then transformed into mechanical energy.

During any energy transformation, the total amount of energy involved remains the same. In other words, the energy is *conserved*. All of the energy is still there—it is just in different forms. These observations are summed up by a scientific law called the **law of conservation of energy**. This law states: *Energy can be changed from one form to another, but it cannot be created or destroyed.*

The law of conservation of energy may seem to defy common sense. For example, a bouncing ball does not continue to bounce up to the same height. See Figure 6-11 on the next page. It loses some height with each bounce. If energy is conserved, shouldn't the potential energy be the same at the top of each bounce?

A bouncing ball does not continue to bounce up to the same height because some of its kinetic energy is changed into sound and thermal energy. The ball makes a noise as it hits the floor. It also gets warm. Therefore, it loses energy with each bounce and, as a result, does not bounce as high. The energy is not destroyed; it is simply transformed into other forms of energy.

Law of Conservation of Energy Energy cannot be created or destroyed but may be changed from one form to another.

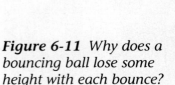

Figure 6-11 *Why does a bouncing ball lose some height with each bounce?*

Figure 6-12 *Some of the work used to pump up this bicycle tire is converted into waste heat.*

Decrease in the Usefulness of Energy

Every time energy in a system changes from one form to another, the amount of *useful* energy decreases. In the example of the automobile above, only 30 percent of the energy contained in the chemical bonds of gasoline becomes mechanical energy to make the car move. The other 70 percent is wasted, in a sense, because it cannot be used to move the car. Part of this energy is heat that merely warms parts of the car and the air around it.

In any transformation of energy from one form to another, some of the energy becomes *waste heat*—heat that cannot be used to do work. You can observe this heat by touching any of the following: a ball after you have bounced it several times, a nail after you have hammered it into a piece of wood, or a bicycle pump and tire after you have pumped up the tire. See Figure 6-12. All of these activities involve changing potential energy into kinetic energy.

Summary

Energy exists in several different forms and can be changed from one form to another. When energy is transformed, the total amount of energy in a system is conserved. Energy cannot be created or destroyed. Some of the energy in a transformation, however, is changed into heat that does no work. The total amount of useful energy in a system, therefore, decreases as energy transformations occur.

6.3 ENERGY FOR SOCIETY

Today's society uses great quantities of energy. We use energy to produce light and heat; to produce food, clothing, and other products; and to transport people, raw materials, and products from place to place. Most of the energy we use comes from oil, coal, and natural gas. These fuels are burned to produce heat, which can be used to drive engines and generators. Energy also comes from other sources, such as the internal heat of the earth, wind, and moving water. As you know, most of the energy we use came originally from the sun. This energy, however, may have undergone several transformations before it is used to operate a car or heat a home.

A History of Energy Use

Humans first relied on their own muscles to do work. Then animals, such as oxen, camels, and horses, were domesticated and harnessed to do work. See Figure 6-13. The fuel that provided energy for humans and animals to do this work was the food that they ate. Burning wood, of course, was used for heating and cooking. As other sources of energy were developed, societies grew larger, and more energy was used to do more work.

Figure 6-13 *In some areas of the world, animals are still used on a daily basis to do work.*

Moving Water   The energy of moving or falling water was once used to turn waterwheels. These wheels first turned mill stones and were later connected to pulleys, belts, or ropes to drive machines. Falling water was eventually used to run turbines. A *turbine* is a fan-shaped disk or wheel that spins when water pushes on it. See Figure 6-14. A turbine operates much like a pinwheel in a breeze. Turbines run generators

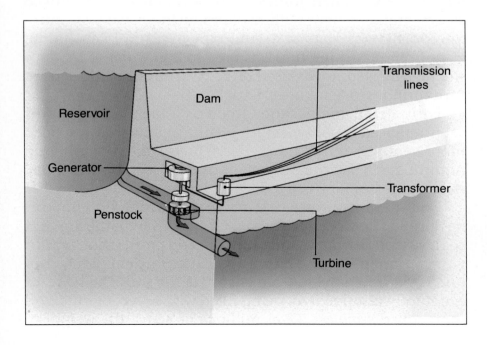

Figure 6-14 *In a hydroelectric dam, water flows from a reservoir through turbines. Each turbine, in turn, operates a generator to produce electricity.*

that produce electricity. *Hydroelectric energy* comes from the energy of falling water and is still a major source of energy today. Very large dams, such as the Hoover Dam on the Colorado River and the Grand Coulee Dam on the Columbia River, store large reservoirs of water. When some of this water is allowed to flow through the dam and past turbines, hydroelectricity is generated.

Wind Energy The wind was also harnessed to do work. Winds are currents that form when the sun heats some parts of the atmosphere more than others. Wind transfers some of its kinetic energy to other objects. For example, sailing ships were built to capture kinetic energy from the wind to propel them across the seas.

Windmills were also invented to capture the kinetic energy of the wind. When wind strikes the blades of a windmill, the wind's kinetic energy is converted into spinning motion. This motion is used to turn shafts and gears to do various kinds of work.

Windmills were first used to pump water from the ground and to grind corn and other dried grains. Later, windmills were connected to generators and used to generate electricity. In the early part of this century, thousands of American farms used wind power for pumping water and generating electricity. Some of these windmills are still at work, as shown in Figure 6-15.

Figure 6-15 Windmills, such as this one, pump water or generate electricity on many American farms today.

Fossil Fuels When James Watt developed an improved steam engine, a new method of producing power was introduced. This was a major event in the Industrial Revolution. Heat from a burning fuel was used to boil water to produce steam. The steam was used directly to run machines or to turn turbines to generate electricity.

Early steam engines used wood as a fuel. But wood was soon replaced by other, more plentiful fuels that provided more heat per unit of mass. These fuels were coal, oil, and natural gas. They are referred to as *fossil fuels* because they were formed millions of years ago.

Coal is a dark brown or black rock-like material that can be burned like wood for energy. Geologists hypothesize that coal was made from the remains of dead plants that lived in vast swamps millions of years ago. These ancient plants captured and stored the radiant energy of the sun. The swamps eventually disappeared, being filled with layers of mud and sand called *sediment*. Over millions of years, the weight of this sediment compressed the dead and decaying plant material into coal. See Figure 6-16.

The development of coal as a fuel made available larger amounts of energy. Unfortunately, coal is a very "dirty" fuel. Once cities like Pittsburgh, Pennsylvania literally became black with the pollution from burning coal. Coal still provides about 23 percent of the energy used in the United States. Although soot is now controlled, the burning of coal is thought to be one of the major causes of acid rain.

By the late 1940s, oil and natural gas had replaced coal as the major fuels for industry. Oil and natural gas are also made from decaying organisms—the small plants and microorganisms that were abundant in ancient warm shallow seas. Like coal, the energy in these organisms came originally from the sun. Oil and natural gas are superior to coal because they provide more heat, are easier to handle, burn cleaner, and cost less. At the present time, oil provides about 41 percent and natural gas about 24 percent of all the energy used in the United States.

It took millions of years to form the world's deposits of coal, oil, and natural gas. Once they are used up, they are gone. We cannot make any more of these fuels. For this reason, fossil fuels are called *nonrenewable resources*. Scientists are not sure just how much coal, oil, and natural gas we have left.

Figure 6-16 *This piece of coal contains a fossil of a fern that lived millions of years ago.*

Nuclear Energy During the 1960s, nuclear energy was added to the world's energy sources. When atoms are split in a *fission reactor,* such as the one shown in Figure 6-17, great amounts of energy are released as heat. This heat is used to create steam, which is used to operate turbines. The turbines then drive generators, which make electricity. Radioactive uranium is the fuel for fission reactors.

In nuclear fission, nuclei of uranium atoms are split by free neutrons. When each nucleus is split, it releases heat and additional neutrons. These neutrons go on to split other nuclei to cause a *chain reaction*. This chain reaction must be carefully regulated with special equipment and materials.

Using nuclear fission to make electricity has major environmental problems. One problem is that it produces radioactive wastes that will be dangerous for thousands of years. The safe disposal of these wastes is a major concern. Another problem is the danger of a nuclear accident, which could release tons of radioactive materials into the environment. The radioactivity in these materials can cause immediate death to humans and other organisms. A long term

Figure 6-17 *Nuclear reactors, such as this one, use fission reactions to produce electricity. Currently only 8 percent of the electricity used in the United States is produced by nuclear reactors.*

Figure 6-18 *A computer simulation of the distribution of radioactivity ten days after the accident at the Chernobyl atomic power station.*

effect is an increase in cases of cancer. The worst nuclear accident to date occurred in 1986 at Chernobyl in the Soviet Union. See Figure 6-18.

Nuclear energy can also be thought of as a non-renewable energy source because the uranium needed for fission reactors is not limitless. Sooner or later, we will be forced to use other, *renewable resources* for energy production. Renewable resources are available in an almost unlimited supply. Some are also much cleaner than fuels currently in use. The old sources of wind and moving water are two renewable resources that we must use to replace nonrenewable energy sources. Other sources of energy, including solar energy, geothermal energy, nuclear fusion, and hydrogen fuel must also be developed as alternative energy sources.

More Energy from the Sun

You have already learned that energy from the sun travels through space as radiant energy. It provides the earth with both light and heat. It also provides the energy source for photosynthesis. Photosynthesizing organisms, like plants and algae, use carbon dioxide and water to produce food and release oxygen. Without plants and algae, which support the food chain and provide most of the oxygen in the atmosphere, there would be no life on earth.

Energy from the sun controls the climate on earth. The uneven heating of different parts of the earth drives the winds and the ocean currents. It also causes water to evaporate, which then cools and falls as rain or snow. Life on earth is adapted to the climate as it is. If the climate were to change drastically, most life forms on earth would probably die. As you can see, life on earth depends on energy from the sun for its very existence.

All of the energy sources mentioned so far in this unit contain energy that came originally from the sun. Even so, more energy strikes the earth than is needed for basic life and climate purposes. This excess energy may become an important energy source for society's needs, such as heating buildings and producing electricity.

Passive Solar Heating
Systems that use simple absorption of radiant energy to heat buildings or other structures.

Solar Energy Energy that we use directly from the sun is called *solar energy*. Solar energy systems convert the incoming radiant energy from the sun directly into a useable form, such as heat or electricity.

Solar heating systems are either *passive* or *active*. **Passive solar heating** systems use the natural absorption of radiant energy to heat buildings or other structures. For an example of passive solar heating, think of a time when you sat in a sunny window. It was warm. The house in Figure 6-19 is being heated passively by solar energy. The many windows of the house let in sunlight, thus heating the house naturally.

Figure 6-19 This passive solar home collects the sun's energy through strategically placed windows and skylights.

Active Solar Heating
Systems that use solar collectors to gather sunlight and convert it to heat.

Active solar heating systems use *solar collectors* to gather sunlight and convert it to heat. The heat is absorbed by air or water and then distributed by a mechanical device, such as a fan or a pump. Excess heat is stored in insulated containers so it can be used at night or on cloudy days.

Solar energy can also be used to make electricity. With devices called *solar cells*, sunlight can be converted directly into electrical energy. See Figure 6-20. However, each cell produces only a small amount of electricity. Solar cells are very useful for special purposes or where only small amounts of electricity are needed. For example, they are used on spacecraft where other sources of electricity are not practical. They are also used to power a variety of small appliances that do not use much electricity, such as calculators, radios, and even telephones.

While the sun's radiant energy is free, using solar collectors and solar cells for large-scale energy production is expensive and not practical at this time. For one thing, solar

Figure 6-20 Each solar cell that makes up a solar panel has the ability to generate electricity directly from sunlight.

collectors and solar cells are both expensive to produce. In addition, to produce enough electricity for a city, large areas of sunny land must be covered with these devices. See Figure 6-21. It is also important to note that the present technology by which solar cells are made produces toxic wastes, which become a disposal problem.

Figure 6-21 *This array of solar collectors is designed to produce enough heat to generate steam.*

Figure 6-22 *Many wind turbines grouped together are called wind farms. This wind farm is located in California.*

Wind Turbines Even though windmills have long been used to generate electricity for individual farms, more modern-looking wind turbines are now being used to generate electricity on a larger scale. A typical wind turbine works on the same principle as the older windmills to produce electricity from the kinetic energy of the wind. Wind turbines can be used to generate electricity for individual homes. On wind farms, there are groups of many wind turbines with giant, propeller-shaped blades that catch the wind and generate electricity for use by many customers. See Figure 6-22. Currently, research is being done to find more efficient designs for these new "wind mills."

Like all other sources of energy, wind energy has disadvantages. The major disadvantage is that wind turbines are intermittent—they only work when the wind is blowing. Therefore, they are practical only in areas where the wind blows most of the time. Wind turbines may also be considered unattractive additions to the neighborhood and are noisy during operation.

Energy from Ocean Water Water flowing down a river is not the only way to use the energy of moving water to make electricity. Another method uses the ocean tides, which involves large masses of moving water. Tides are caused by the gravitational pull of the moon and the sun acting on the surface of the earth. Ocean water is the most affected by this pull. In a few locations around the world, special dams are used to trap water within a bay area during high tide. Then at low tide, the water is allowed to drain through turbines located inside of the dams to produce hydroelectric energy. See Figure 6-23.

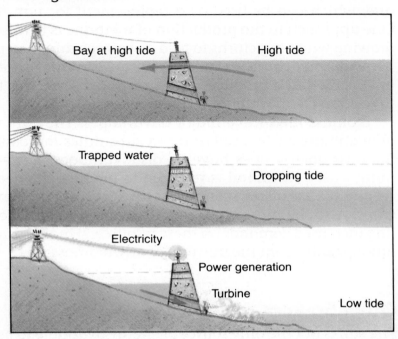

Figure 6-23 *The principle of a tidal dam is illustrated here.*

Research is being conducted to produce hydroelectric energy in still another way—from the movement of ocean waves. Some scientists and engineers believe the up-and-down motion of the waves could be used to compress air or a fluid and force it through turbine generators to produce electricity. Though there are still many technical difficulties to be worked out, this energy source may have great potential.

The oceans also represent a source of energy that is not based on water movement. Instead, this energy source is based on water temperature. The water at the surface of the oceans absorbs large amounts of solar energy. As a result, surface water is much warmer than deeper water. Power plants of the future may extend from the surface into deep water to use *temperature differences* to generate electricity.

Biomass Fuels   Plant and animal materials are referred to as *biomass*. The firewood in Figure 6-24 is a form of biomass. In this case, the biomass (wood) can be burned directly as a fuel to provide heat. In other instances, the biomass must be

Figure 6-24 *Firewood is a readily available form of biomass. However, firewood takes many years to grow and produces pollution when burned.*

converted into another fuel before it is used. For example, plants like corn, sugar beets, and potatoes can be converted into alcohol. The alcohol can then be mixed with gasoline and burned in automobiles. This mixture is called *gasohol*.

Methane, or swamp gas, is another fuel that is a product of biomass. The decomposition of garbage, sewage, or practically any other kind of organic matter will produce methane, which can be used as a replacement for natural gas. One approach to the production of methane is to allow fast-growing water hyacinths to feed on sewage and then process the water hyacinths to collect methane. In this process, not only is methane produced, but unwanted sewage is treated to reclaim clean water at the same time.

Biomass fuels have major advantages. They are renewable and are easily used as direct substitutes for fossil fuels. Biomass energy does have its disadvantages, however. In many cases, farmland is required to produce the necessary crops. This use of land competes with its use for growing food crops. Also, biomass crops require water and fertilizer, putting increased demands on these resources. Finally, some pollution results from the burning of any biomass fuel.

Other Sources of Energy

The sun is not the only source of energy available to us. Heat is produced inside the earth and can be tapped for energy production. It may be possible that an unlimited supply of energy could one day come from controlled nuclear fusion, the most intensive energy-producing process that we presently know. Hydrogen, due to its abundance, is also a promising source of fuel for future energy needs.

Geothermal Energy Deep in the earth's core, radioactive nuclei produce heat as they decay. The pressure of thousands of kilometers of rock also results in heat. This natural heat within the earth is called *geothermal energy*. In some places, geological forces push large pools of melted rock, or *magma*, to within 4 to 6 kilometers of the earth's surface, forming geothermal "hot spots." If the earth above these hot spots allows water to seep in, the water becomes very hot. Sometimes this hot water forces its way back to the earth's surface, forming geysers or hot springs. See Figure 6-25.

Steam turbines in electric generating plants work just as well on steam from under the earth's surface as they do on steam from a boiler. Therefore, a plant located above a hot spot can use steam directed through its turbines to generate

Figure 6-25 *Geysers, such as this one, are produced by geothermal energy.*

electricity. In some cases, subsurface rocks above hot spots do not already contain water and steam. In these situations, water can be pumped down into the earth to produce the necessary steam to operate the turbines.

Many countries, including the United States, already have electric generating plants that operate on geothermal energy. Like solar energy, geothermal energy is free. Unfortunately, it is only available in a limited number of locations. Many of these locations are not near places where people live. Also, the water from some hot spots is slightly radioactive and must be disposed of carefully. Geothermal energy currently supplies less than 0.3 percent of the energy used in the United States.

Nuclear Fusion In addition to the fission of atoms like uranium, nuclear energy can be obtained by the process of nuclear fusion. Nuclear energy is released when hydrogen nuclei fuse to make helium. A tremendous amount of energy is released when this happens. Being able to control the energy of nuclear fusion and use it to generate electrical power has been a goal of scientists for many years.

Two isotopes of hydrogen, *deuterium* and *tritium*, are used as fuel in a nuclear fusion reaction. See Figure 6-26. However, extremely high temperatures are necessary to start the fusion reaction. Fusion occurs when temperatures are millions of degrees—like the temperatures inside the sun. However, reaching these temperatures on earth is very difficult.

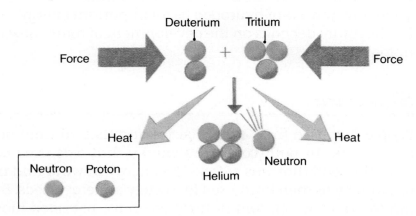

Figure 6-26 *In a fusion reaction, deuterium and tritium are forced together to form helium and a free neutron. Great amounts of heat are released during this reaction.*

Unfortunately, the amount of energy required to produce, control, and contain a fusion reaction is still many times greater than the amount of electrical energy generated. It cannot, at this time, be used as an efficient energy source. There is hope that by using laser technology, the process of nuclear fusion might someday be achieved and put to practical use.

Hydrogen Fuel   The element hydrogen could be the ultimate energy source. For example, hydrogen in either its liquid or solid state will be the fuel for energy production by nuclear fusion once the technology for controlling a fusion reaction is developed. Hydrogen, in its liquid state, is presently used as a rocket fuel. In the main engines of the Space Shuttle, liquid hydrogen (the fuel) and liquid oxygen (an oxidizer) combine explosively in a chemical reaction that powers the vehicle into space. See Figure 6-27. Some power plants use hydrogen fuel to generate electrical energy. There are also working models of engines for cars and buses that burn hydrogen fuel.

Once produced only by electrolysis of water, there are now newer technologies for producing large quantities of hydrogen. Most commercially produced hydrogen is made by combining methane gas and water to form hydrogen gas and carbon monoxide. The hydrogen gas produced is either compressed into metal cylinders or liquefied by high-tech refrigeration for storage and transportation.

Scientific research has made possible the uses we have for hydrogen today. But there are still many problems to be overcome. Although it is a clean fuel, one problem with using hydrogen for fuel relates to the water vapor that is formed in the process. If released into the atmosphere, this excess water vapor could drastically change the climate of the earth. The water vapor must be captured somehow and, perhaps, recycled. Cheaper methods of production must also be found. Therefore, the use of hydrogen as an important energy source for the future depends on the development of many new technologies.

Figure 6-27 *Liquid hydrogen is the fuel used to lift the Space Shuttle into orbit.*

Summary

People first used their own muscles and then animal power to do work. In both cases, the energy that was used came from the food that was eaten. The energy in wind and moving water was then harnessed for society's energy needs. Burning wood, coal, oil, and natural gas have provided most of our energy needs up to now. New sources of energy include solar energy, biomass fuels, ocean water, and modern wind turbines. All of these forms of energy can be traced back to the sun as the original source. Other sources of energy are also being developed for the future. They include geothermal energy, nuclear fission and fusion, and hydrogen.

Unit 7

Reading *Plus*

Now that you have studied the concepts of temperature and heat, let's take a closer look at how heat is used to do work and how it can be measured. Read pages S118 to S132 and then prepare a laboratory investigation about heat. Your investigation should include a hypothesis based on one of the following questions.

1. What is heat, and how is it related to thermal energy?

2. How does heat move from place to place?

3. In what ways is heat measured, and how do these methods differ?

7.1 THERMAL ENERGY

Thermal energy can be obtained by the transformation of other kinds of energy. For example, radiant energy can be changed into thermal energy by solar collectors. Thermal energy can be produced by mechanical, chemical, nuclear, and electrical energy. But what exactly is thermal energy? And what is its relationship to heat?

Thermal Energy is Motion

As you learned in Unit 4, matter is made up of small particles, called molecules, that are too small to see. These molecules vibrate in a constant motion, and when heat is added to an object, these small particles vibrate faster. For example, a drop of water contains a huge number of individual water molecules, all of which are vibrating. When water is heated, its molecules vibrate faster and bump into each other more often. See Figure 7-1.

You cannot watch one water molecule to see if heating or cooling changes its speed; only the results of the motion of a large number of water molecules can be seen. For example, if you put a drop of food coloring into a glass of water that has been standing still for a while, you will notice that the coloring slowly spreads throughout the water. It is the motion of the water molecules that causes the coloring to spread evenly throughout the water in the glass.

A bar of iron may look as if none of its parts are moving, but the atoms of iron are also in constant motion. When the iron is heated, its atoms move faster and spread apart. The solid piece of iron will expand because the increase in thermal energy increases the average distance between its atoms and molecules. When the iron cools, this distance decreases and the iron shrinks. See Figure 7-2. All kinds of matter expand when heated because their particles move faster and the distance between their particles increases.

Thermal Energy or Heat?

Just what is the difference between thermal energy and heat? Since they are both defined as forms of energy, why do we use two terms? As described above, thermal energy refers to the *internal* energy of a substance. The motion of its molecules, measured by temperature, determines this internal, or thermal, energy. The word "heat," on the other hand, is used when we talk about the transfer of energy that occurs because of a temperature difference between two places or

Figure 7-1 When the water in this pan is heated, the water molecules begin to vibrate faster. They bump into each other more often and the water begins to boil.

Figure 7-2 The expansion joint on a bridge, as shown here, allows for the expansion and contraction of the metal as it is heated and cooled.

two substances. For example, the heat that you feel on your shoulders when you sit in the sunshine is due to the radiant energy of the sun being transferred to your skin. The thermal energy of your skin increases as its temperature rises. If you touch your shoulder, this thermal energy can be felt as heat as it transfers from your shoulder to your hand.

Thermal energy is a result of the transfer of energy from another source of energy, such as radiant energy or chemical energy. Heat, on the other hand, is simply the movement of thermal energy from an object at one temperature to an object at another temperature. A hot object contains more thermal energy than a cold object of the same size and composition. If they are brought into contact, heat will flow from the hot object to the cold object until the temperature of both is the same. Therefore, heat refers to thermal energy in motion. This flow of energy can be used to do work.

Heat and Work

Certain machines, called **heat engines**, change thermal energy into mechanical energy that can be used to do work. For example, a *steam engine* uses the thermal energy of steam to push against a metal plate called a *piston*. The piston moves back and forth inside a tube called a *cylinder*. See Figure 7-3. As the engine works, steam from a boiler enters the cylinder through a sliding valve and pushes the piston, first in one direction and then in the opposite direction. It is the transfer of the thermal energy of the steam to the engine parts that gives motion to the engine.

The steam engine was an important machine during the Industrial Revolution of the late 18th and early 19th centuries. Today, however, steam engines have largely been replaced by the *steam turbine*. In a steam turbine, the steam pushes against a fan-like turbine, causing it to spin like a high-speed windmill. See Figure 7-4.

Heat engine A machine that changes thermal energy into mechanical energy.

Figure 7-3 In a steam engine, the sliding valve above the cylinder directs the steam first to one side and then to the other side of the piston.

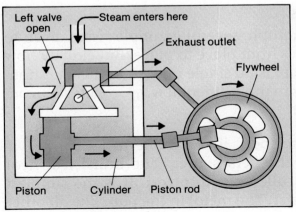

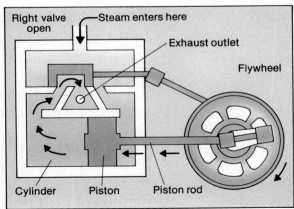

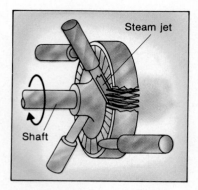

Figure 7-4 *The wheel of a turbine turns when steam pushes against the blades.*

Automobile engines also use thermal energy. A burning fuel produces hot gases inside the cylinders to push pistons that turn a crankshaft. The motion of the crankshaft eventually is used to turn the wheels of the car. Jet engines also use hot gases produced by burning fuels. However, in a jet engine, the hot gases run a turbine that forces hot air at high speed out the back of the engine. The engine then works in the same way as a rocket. The hot gases leaving the rear of the engine cause an unbalanced reaction force that pushes the engine ahead.

Summary

Thermal energy is an important form of energy. When a substance is heated, energy is added to its particles. This causes the particles to move faster and become farther apart, increasing the internal energy of the substance. Heat is thermal energy in motion. Heat flows from warmer objects to cooler objects. Heat engines are machines that change some of the energy of moving particles into mechanical energy, and thus motion.

7.2 METHODS OF HEAT TRANSFER

A metal cooking pan put on top of an electric stove acquires some of the thermal energy from the heating coils of the stove. Liquids can be heated, or food can be cooked in the pan. Cooking can also be done over an open fire or glowing hot coals. If you stand near a stove or hot coals, you can feel the heat they produce. When a meal is cooked in your kitchen, the entire kitchen becomes warmer. If it is daytime and the kitchen has windows, some of this heat may have originated from the sunlight coming through the windows.

How Heat Moves

In the previous paragraph, several examples were given to show how heat moves from place to place. But exactly how does heat move? There is no single answer to this question. Actually, heat moves in three different ways: *conduction, convection,* and *radiation.*

Conduction Transfer of heat by direct contact.

Conduction A metal pan, like the one in Figure 7-5, is heated by touching the heat source. The transfer of heat by direct contact is called **conduction**. It is the simplest method of heat transfer. The metal in the pan, like all other

Figure 7-5 This pan is being heated by conduction.

substances, is made up of atoms. The rapidly moving atoms of the hot coils of the stove bump the atoms in the metal pan, making them vibrate faster. Each atom of metal bumps its neighbors in the cooler parts of the pan. This continues until all the atoms in the pan are moving about an equal amount. If you touch the pan, you will be burned. Heat is also transferred from the pan to your skin by conduction.

The metal in a pan conducts heat very well. However, not all materials conduct heat as well as metals. Wood, for example, is a poor conductor of heat. That is why the handles of pans and other metal objects are often made of wood. Liquids, gases, and non-metallic solids are poor conductors of heat and are called insulators.

The vacuum bottle in Figure 7-6 shows several ways that an object can be insulated. Inside the outer covering of the bottle there is a double-walled glass bottle. The space

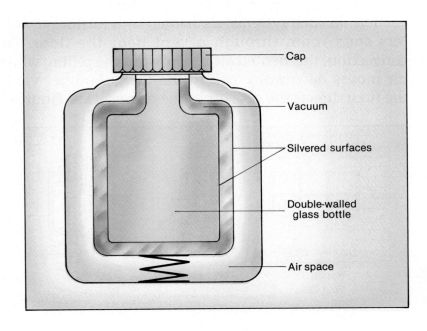

Cap

Vacuum

Silvered surfaces

Double-walled glass bottle

Air space

Figure 7-6 A vacuum bottle can keep liquids hot or cold because it is well insulated.

between the two glass walls contains a vacuum. Since there are no molecules of any kind present in a vacuum, heat cannot be conducted across the vacuum. Glass itself is a nonmetal, and therefore a poor conductor of heat. Also notice that the inner surfaces of the glass are silvered. They reflect heat inward, thus preventing it from moving out of the bottle. Between the glass bottle and the outer walls, there is an air space. Air is another poor conductor of heat. Finally, the bottle is covered by a cap with a rubber plug that is also a poor conductor of heat.

Convection How does heat from a fire or hot coals reach the food you are cooking on your outdoor grill? The answer depends on the way air acts when it is heated. The air over the fire becomes hot. This hot air expands because its molecules start to move faster. Thus each molecule collides with its neighbors with greater force. These collisions cause the average distance between the molecules to increase. Therefore, the hot air takes up more space than the surrounding cooler air. Expansion of the heated air makes it less dense than the surrounding air because there is more empty space between its particles. Because the hot air is less dense, it moves up toward the food. Transfer of heat by the movement of a heated gas or liquid is called **convection**. Convection occurs when a gas (such as air) or a liquid (such as water) is heated unevenly. The heated part of the gas or liquid becomes less dense and floats upward. Heat transfer by convection can take place only in gases or liquids.

An open fireplace is usually a poor source of heat for a room. Convection carries most of the heat up the chimney. Many heating systems, however, do take advantage of convection. In such systems, air heated by a furnace usually enters each room through a vent near the floor. Due to convection, this heated air rises toward the ceiling while cool air moves downward toward the floor. Another vent near the floor directs the cool air to the furnace. See Figure 7-7.

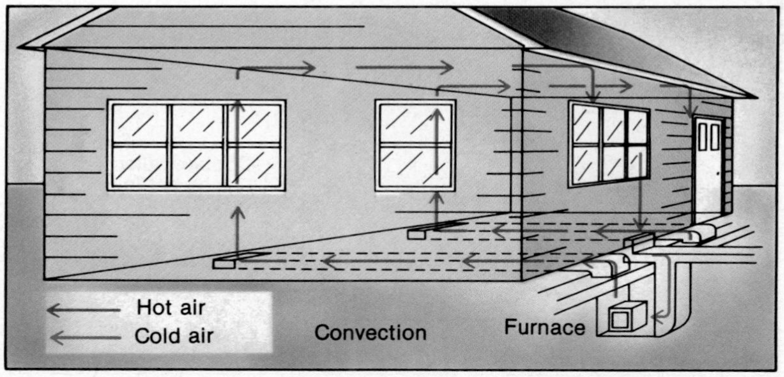

Convection Transfer of heat by movement of a heated gas or liquid.

Figure 7-7 *This diagram shows how a hot-air heating system heats a home by means of convection.*

Radiation The third method of heat transfer, **radiation**, is very different from either conduction or convection. Radiation transfers heat through space by electromagnetic waves. The particular electromagnetic waves that transfer heat from one location to another are called *infrared* waves. Sources of heat, such as a hot stove or a fire, send out these invisible infrared waves. Infrared waves are responsible for some of the warmth you feel when you are near a hot object. When the waves reach your skin or other material, the energy of the infrared waves increases the motion of the molecules in the material they meet, and therefore, increases its temperature. Thus heat is transferred from the original source to the object. See Figure 7-8.

Radiation Transfer of heat through space by infrared waves.

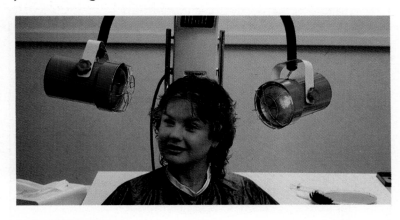

Figure 7-8 Infrared heat lamps, such as those shown here, can be used as hair dryers.

Heating the Earth

Radiation is also how the earth receives heat from the sun. Since approximately 150 million kilometers of mostly empty space separates the sun from the earth, heat cannot be transferred by either conduction or convection. You feel warm while sitting in the sun because you are receiving its heat by radiation.

Absorbing Radiation The air, land, and water of the earth are warmed by absorbing radiant energy. The atmosphere allows radiant energy to enter, but prevents it from leaving. Some of this energy is reflected by the land and water, and sent back into the air in a less energetic state. The reflected waves cannot pass out of the atmosphere. This energy is blocked and absorbed by carbon dioxide and water vapor in the air. The trapped energy heats the air molecules of the atmosphere. By adding more carbon dioxide to the atmosphere, more heat will be trapped. Burning fossil fuels has already put large amounts of carbon dioxide into the air. For this reason, the earth may be getting warmer. This warming of the earth is referred to as the *greenhouse effect*. This

Figure 7-9 *The greenhouse effect occurs in a greenhouse* (top) *because the glass windows trap heat. The same thing happens to a city* (bottom), *but the heat is absorbed by the atmosphere.*

term is used because the atmosphere acts like the glass in a greenhouse. See Figure 7-9.

Using Convection Because of the shape of the earth, its atmosphere and surface are not heated evenly. If the earth were flat, all areas would receive the same amount of energy from the sun; but because the earth's surface is curved, polar regions receive less energy than the regions near the equator. See Figure 7-10. Regions around the equator receive direct rays from the sun that provide concentrated energy, while polar regions receive slanting rays that spread the energy over a larger area than direct rays do. Therefore, the air near the equator gets hotter than it does at the poles. Without some way to transfer the heat from the equator to the poles, the equator would only become hotter and the poles would become colder.

But convection causes air to move between the earth's poles and the equator. Air near the poles is cooler, and therefore heavier. As this cold, heavy air settles downward, it moves

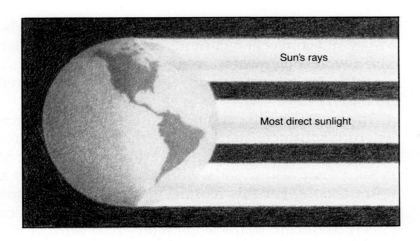

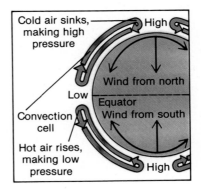

Figure 7-10 *Areas near the equator receive direct sunlight, while areas near both poles receive indirect sunlight.*

Figure 7-11 *Cold air moves toward the equator and warm air moves toward the poles.*

Convection Cell A complete circle of moving air caused by temperature differences.

from the polar regions toward the equator. Warmed air near the equator is less dense and lighter. The warmer air rises and streams from the equator toward the poles. See Figure 7-11. Thus the sun's energy is spread more evenly over the earth. Convection has made it possible for life to exist on much of the land surface of the earth.

When air moves horizontally, it is called wind. Wind almost always is caused by differences in temperature in the atmosphere. Because it is warm, the air near the ground is less dense than the air above. Warm air rises and cool air sinks. As the warm air rises, it is cooled. It sinks back toward the ground and is warmed again. The complete cycle of moving air is called a **convection cell**. Movement of air in convection cells causes winds along the ground to flow from areas of high pressure to areas of low pressure.

Storing Thermal Energy   Large amounts of heat can be absorbed by water without changing the temperature of the water very much. You could confirm this by heating water in a metal pot. The metal of the pot and its handle will soon become too hot to touch, while the water inside is only warm. However, once the water is heated and removed from the heat source, the pan will cool quickly, while the water remains warm for a long period of time. Similarly, because water heats slowly, air near oceans and lakes stays cool during the day. The air in these areas also remains warm at night because water cools slowly. But the land is like the metal pot. When the sun is out, land heats quickly. At night, land quickly loses the heat it absorbed during the day. Thus the air around land areas is warm during the day and cool at night.

The oceans absorb nearly 75 percent of the energy that reaches the earth through rays from the sun. However, since these rays do not reach more than a few meters into the water, only the water very close to the surface can be heated. Waves and convection currents cause the warm water to be mixed with cooler water from below to form a *surface layer* in which the temperature of the water generally remains the same.

The ocean acts like a storage tank for thermal energy on the earth's surface. There is more thermal energy stored in the upper three meters of the sea than in the entire atmosphere. Water also absorbs and releases heat much slower than air does. For this reason, the sea affects climates all over the world. In the winter, the water does not cool as quickly as the air, so the water tends to be warmer than the air. Thus, water has a warming effect on the atmosphere in the winter. In the summer, the water does not heat as quickly as the air, so the water is usually cooler than the air. Because of this, the ocean tends to cool the atmosphere in the summer.

The warmest surface waters are found near the equator, where the sun's rays strike the earth most directly. High temperatures cause the evaporation of large amounts of sea water into the atmosphere. The evaporation of water from tropical seas has two important effects on the atmosphere. First, the air becomes very moist. The warm, moist air masses formed over the oceans near the equator have a strong influence on the world's weather and climates. The second effect of the evaporation of water from the sea is the addition of heat to the atmosphere. The water vapor leaving the surface removes heat from the sea and adds it to the atmosphere. This heat is distributed by hurricanes and other storms that form over the warm parts of the ocean and then move into cooler waters. See Figure 7-12.

Figure 7-12 *Different colors* (left) *show the different temperatures of a hurricane. Clouds can be seen circling the "eye"* (right).

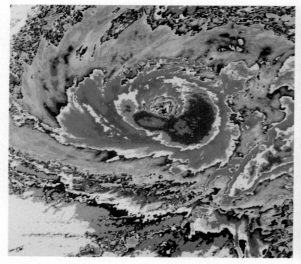

Heat from the Earth

Not all of the earth's heat comes from radiant energy from the sun. The earth itself contains thermal energy. Some of this energy may be left over from the formation of the earth over 4.5 billion years ago. Much of it is produced inside the earth by the tremendous pressure caused by the weight of the rocks of the earth. More heat comes from the decay of the many radioactive elements in the *mantle* and *crust*. This heat may cause rocks to melt inside the earth. Because it is cooler near the surface of the earth and hotter near the center, convection currents are formed. See Figure 7-13. These convection currents distribute the heat inside the earth and also cause the melted rock to flow.

By drilling deep holes in the earth's surface, it has been determined that the temperature of the earth rises about 30 °C for every kilometer of depth. The center of the earth is estimated to be about 5000 °C. Some of this heat is conducted outward, but not very readily. The rocks near the surface of the earth are poor conductors of heat. We do not really feel the heat from inside the earth except where some of the materials warmed by that heat come to the surface. Hot lava from erupting volcanoes and steam from geysers are two examples of materials that are very hot because of the thermal energy inside the earth. These hot materials are sources of geothermal energy.

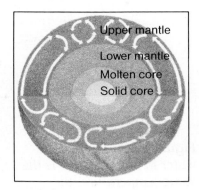

Figure 7-13 *Convection currents in the mantle are believed to cause the crustal plates to move.*

Summary

Heat is transferred in three ways. Heat transfer by direct contact is called conduction. Heat transfer by circulating currents is called convection. Radiation transfers heat by electromagnetic waves called infrared waves. People, houses, and even the earth itself are warmed in all of these ways. Radiant energy from the sun is absorbed by air, land, and water, which in turn, store and transfer heat, affecting weather and climates all over the world.

7.3 TEMPERATURE AND HEAT

Thermal energy and temperature are related, but they are not the same thing. Look at Figure 7-14 on the next page. Which do you think has more thermal energy, a small beaker of water at a temperature of 40 °C or a large beaker of water at the same temperature?

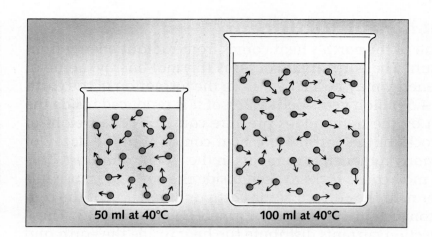

Figure 7-14 *Though the water in both beakers is the same temperature, the larger beaker contains more thermal energy.*

50 ml at 40°C   100 ml at 40°C

As you have learned, thermal energy refers to the *total* energy, both potential and kinetic, of the molecules in an object. The more thermal energy a substance contains, the faster its molecules move. In any material, different molecules are moving at different speeds—some faster, some slower.

Temperature is the "hotness" or "coldness" of a substance. It is a measure of the average *kinetic* energy of the molecules of a substance. An object with a high amount of kinetic energy has a high temperature. Likewise, an object with a low amount of kinetic energy has a low temperature. The average kinetic energy of the molecules in two different quantities of the same substance may be the same, while the total number of molecules differs. Two beakers of different sizes may both be filled with water at the same temperature. But because the larger beaker holds more water molecules, the water contains a greater amount of thermal energy.

The beaker with the larger quantity of water, and therefore more thermal energy, could give off more heat. In other words, it could melt more ice than the water in the small beaker. Looking at it in another way, it takes more ice to cool a large glass of water at room temperature, than it does to cool a small glass of water. The heat available to do work is related to the temperature and amount of the material, as well as to the composition of the material.

Measuring Temperature

How hot is "hot"? How cold is "cold"? If someone were to ask you what the outside temperature was today, could you give an accurate answer? If you stuck your hand outside a window, could you estimate the temperature of the air? Do you think that everyone in the class would agree with your estimate? If you had to report the temperature to the weather station, could you do so accurately without a measuring instrument?

As you know, a *thermometer* is an instrument used for measuring temperature, and it works by undergoing physical changes. These changes result from the increase or decrease in the kinetic energy of molecules in the materials that form the thermometer. Most materials expand when heated and contract when cooled. The most commonly used type of thermometer is based on such a change. When a liquid, such as mercury or alcohol, is sealed in a glass tube, it can be used as a thermometer. These two liquids are commonly used because they expand and contract at a uniform rate and do not boil or freeze over the range of normal temperatures. When a thermometer is heated, its liquid expands and rises in the tube. Cooling causes the liquid to contract and fall.

To measure the amount of this change, the thermometer must have a scale. You already know that, on the Celsius scale, water (at sea level) freezes at 0 °C and boils at 100 °C. Another scale you may be familiar with from weather reports is the Fahrenheit scale. The symbol °F is placed after temperatures measured on this scale. On the Fahrenheit scale, water freezes at 32 °F and boils at 212 °F. A third scale, called the Kelvin scale, is the official SI temperature scale. It is used by scientists all over the world. See Figure 7-15 for a

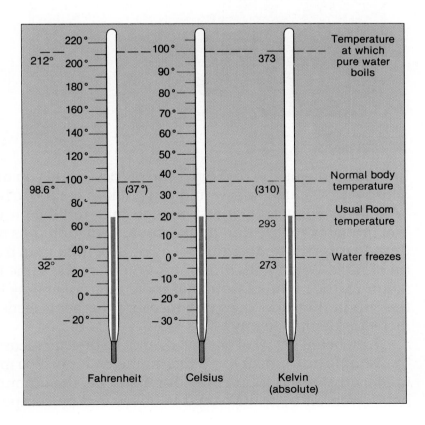

Figure 7-15 *The Fahrenheit, Celsius, and Kelvin temperature scales. This diagram allows you to compare temperatures on the three scales.*

Figure 7-16 *As the bimetallic strip inside this thermostat becomes warm, it coils. As the strip becomes cool, it uncoils. This action causes a drop of mercury to move back and forth inside a vial turning an air conditioner or heater on and off.*

comparison of these three temperature scales. The unit of temperature on the Kelvin, or absolute, scale is the *kelvin* (K). Notice that the degree symbol is not used for Kelvin scale temperatures. On the Kelvin scale, water freezes at 273 K and boils at 373 K. On this scale 0 K, or *absolute zero*, is the temperature at which molecular motion is at a minimum. Notice also that a change in 1 K is equal to a change in 1°C.

Not all thermometers use liquid in a glass tube. A *thermostat*, for example, uses a coiled strip made of two different metals sandwiched together. This strip is called a *bimetallic strip*. The two metals expand and contract by a slightly different amount when the temperature changes. This causes the metal strip to wind or unwind. See Figure 7-16. Another kind of thermometer, called a *thermocouple*, measures temperature by its effect on an electric current. Thermocouples are now used by many medical professionals to take patients' temperatures because they react very quickly. See Figure 7-17.

Figure 7-17 *This nurse is taking a patient's temperature by using an electric thermometer (thermocouple).*

Measuring Heat

Imagine that you are making a cup of cocoa, and you are in a hurry. How much milk would you put into the pot to heat? Would you fill it or heat just enough milk to fill your cup? You probably realize that it takes more heat, and thus more time, to raise the temperature of a potful of milk than a cupful of milk. When both amounts of milk are the same temperature, the potful of water has more internal energy than the cupful. But how does one measure the heat needed to increase thermal energy?

Heat, being a flow of energy, cannot be directly measured by a simple instrument like a thermometer. It must be measured by the effects it produces. For example, the amount of heat given off by a fuel could be measured by comparing the temperature change of a quantity of water that it could heat. If one type of fuel warms a certain amount of water by 1°C and another type of fuel warms the same amount of water by 2°C, the second fuel produces twice as much heat.

Scientists may measure heat in units called *calories* (cal). A calorie is the amount of heat needed to raise the temperature of 1 g of water by 1°C. Thus to raise the temperature of 100 g of water by 1°C, 100 cal are required. Raising the temperature of 100 g of water 20°C requires 2000 cal. It takes about 20,000 cal to heat a cup of water from room temperature to boiling. As you can see, a calorie is a very small quantity of heat. Scientists sometimes use the unit called a *kilocalorie* (kcal) to measure heat. One kilocalorie is equal to 1000 calories. It is the amount of heat needed to raise the temperature of 1 kg of water by 1°C. The kilocalorie is sometimes written "Calorie," with a capital C, to distinguish it from the smaller calorie. It is this larger unit that you refer to when "counting Calories." The energy supplied by food is measured in Calories.

Now that heat is understood in terms of energy, most scientists usually measure heat in units called *joules* (J). This is the same unit that they use to measure other forms of energy, as well as work. By definition, 1 cal now equals 4.19 joules. An instrument known as a *calorimeter* is used to determine how much heat is exchanged between substances.

Specific Heat

Heat does not affect the temperature of all materials in the same way. See Figure 7-18. For example, if 100 cal (419 J) of heat were added to 100 g of water, the temperature of the water would be raised by 1°C; however, if 100 cal (419 J) of

Figure 7-18 All of these materials have the same mass and were heated to the same temperature (left). However, they each melt wax at a different rate (right).

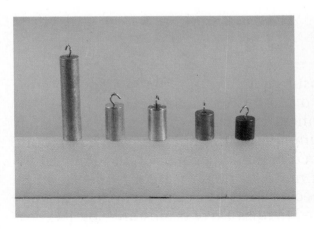
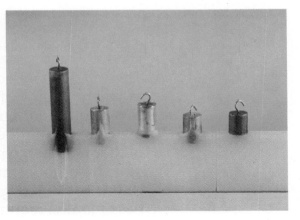

Specific Heat The amount of heat needed to raise the temperature of one gram of a substance by one Celsius degree.

SPECIFIC HEAT CAPACITY OF SOME COMMON MATERIALS		
	(cal/g·°C)	(J/g·°C)
water	1.00	4.19
ice	0.50	2.09
wood	0.42	1.76
aluminum	0.22	0.92
iron	0.11	0.46
copper	0.09	0.39

Table 7-1

heat were transferred to 100 g of iron, the temperature of the iron would be raised by a little over 9°C. To compare the effects of heat on different materials, scientists calculate the specific heat of the substance. **Specific heat** is the amount of heat needed to raise the temperature of 1 g of a substance by 1°C. The specific heat of water is, by definition, 1.0 cal/g·°C (4.19 J/g·°C). This reads: one calorie per gram per degree Celsius. The specific heats of some other materials are given in Table 7-1.

Note that water has the highest specific heat on the list. In fact, only a few substances have a higher specific heat than water. This means that it takes a lot more heat to raise the temperature of a certain amount of water than the same amount of another material. The heat needed to change the temperature of a substance depends on the mass of the substance, its specific heat, and the amount of change in the temperature.

When exposed to the same amount of heat, water heats more slowly than most other materials because it has a higher specific heat. Have you ever felt the difference in temperature between water in an outdoor pool and the concrete walk around it on a hot summer day? Concrete has a lower specific heat than water. Even though the amount of sunlight per square meter of surface may be the same, the concrete gets too hot to walk on, while the water stays cool. Water also cools off more slowly than most other materials. This is because the water must give up more heat per gram to cool off each Celsius degree than other materials. This explains why areas near a lake or ocean stay cooler in the summer and warmer in the winter than inland areas. The water has such a high capacity for heat that the air above it stays cool in summer. In winter, the water gives off so much heat that the air above it stays warmer. The nearby shore benefits from this moderating influence.

Summary

Thermometers measure temperature, the average amount of kinetic energy of a substance's molecules, in degrees Celsius, degrees Fahrenheit, or kelvins. They cannot be used to measure the total amount of thermal energy. The amount of thermal energy in a material depends on its temperature and the amount of material present. Heat is measured in calories or joules. Specific heat is the amount of heat, in calories or joules, required to raise 1 g of a substance by 1°C.

Unit 8

In This Unit

Reading *Plus*

Now that you have been introduced to the forces that alter the shapes of continents, let's take a closer look at some of these processes. Read pages S134 to S151 and then construct a diorama (model) on the effects of weathering, erosion, and deposition. Your diorama should indicate one or more of the ideas expressed by the following questions.

1. What are the processes of weathering, erosion, and deposition, and how are they related to one another?

2. How are the following features different? an alluvial fan and a talus slope, a V-shaped valley and a U-shaped valley, a sand dune and a sand bar.

3. In what ways do the processes of weathering, erosion, and deposition affect people?

Figure 8-1 Mt. Pinatubo in the Philippines erupted in June 1991, sending tons of rock and ash into the atmosphere.

Weathering All of the processes that break rock into smaller pieces.

Erosion All of the processes that cause pieces of weathered rock to be carried away.

Deposition All of the processes by which eroded materials are dropped.

Figure 8-2 After long periods of weathering and erosion, the youthful mountains on the left may one day look like the mature mountains on the right.

8.1 WEATHERING

The earth's surface is constantly changing. Sometimes the changes are sudden, like the explosive eruption of Mt. Pinatubo shown in Figure 8-1. More often, however, the changes take place slowly, like the wearing down of jagged mountains into gently rolling hills. See Figure 8-2. No matter where you look on the surface of the earth, you see the results of a constant battle between two kinds of forces—forces that cause the land to be built up and forces that wear the land down.

On one side of this battle are forces that result from movements of the earth's mantle and crust. As you learned in Unit 7, the earth's internal heat causes convection currents within the mantle. These currents, in turn, can result in movement in the upper mantle and crust. Movements of the crust produce powerful forces that have determined the basic shapes of the continents and their location on earth. These forces also build mountains by breaking, folding, and lifting the earth's crust.

On the other side of the battle are the processes that wear down the earth's crust: **weathering** and **erosion**. These processes work together to break down solid rock and carry it away, thus reshaping the surface of the continents. Broken rock particles also reshape the surface features of the earth through another process called **deposition**.

The term *weathering* includes all of the processes that break rock into small pieces. Rock material is usually formed below the surface of the crust where it is not exposed to the forces of weathering. As long as it remains buried, no weathering takes place. Only rocks that are exposed at the earth's surface can be acted upon by the processes of weathering. In general, weathering occurs where the solid

part of the earth's crust comes into contact with either water or air.

Physical Weathering

There are several processes by which rocks can undergo weathering. One type of weathering is called **physical weathering**. By physical weathering, rocks are broken down mechanically into smaller and smaller pieces. Mechanical forces apply pressures that force rocks to split apart. Physical weathering does not cause any change in the composition of the rock. It simply breaks the rock into smaller pieces. Some of the ways by which physical weathering occurs are discussed below.

Frost Action   The effect of *frost action* on a rock is one type of physical weathering. Frost action takes place when water enters cracks in rock and freezes. Water expands when it freezes and, by doing so, produces great pressure. This pressure pushes the sides of the crack apart, making it larger. During the course of cold weather, water inside the crack may freeze and melt many times. Each time the crack gets a little larger until the rock finally cracks completely apart. See Figure 8-3. Because this "cracking" process happens so slowly, it is not very noticeable. But when water freezes inside of a pipe, the results can be very dramatic—and wet!

Root Action   Plants can be agents of physical weathering. Plant roots, from the largest of trees to the smallest of weeds, work their way through small cracks in the rock. As the roots grow in length and diameter, they apply constant pressure and eventually break apart the rock.

Thermal Expansion   Heating and cooling can also cause rock to break apart. Rocks, like other solid materials, expand when heated and contract when cooled. Most kinds of rock are made up of many different substances called *minerals*. When heated or cooled, these different minerals in a rock expand and contract by different amounts, causing the rock to crack. Over a long period of time, heating during the day and cooling at night can make the outer layers of the rock break into smaller pieces.

Rebounding   Another kind of physical weathering begins with rock that is buried deep underground. Rock deep beneath the surface is under great pressure from the weight of

Physical Weathering The ways rock breaks up into smaller pieces without any change in the materials in the rock.

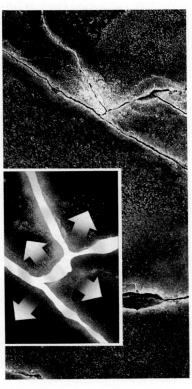

Figure 8-3 *Ice acts as a wedge that breaks rock apart, as shown in the inset. Frost action is responsible for much of the shattering seen in the photograph.*

the layers of rock above. This buried rock *rebounds*, or expands, when it is exposed by the process of erosion. Its outer layers may be loosened and peel off like the layers of an onion by a process called *exfoliation*. See Figure 8-4. Once the weight of an outer layer is removed, pressure is again released from the inner layers below. These layers may then peel off as well.

Exfoliation also results from frost action and the repeated expansion and contraction of rocks as they are heated and cooled. Weathering by exfoliation causes rocks to take on a rounded shape as the layers peel off.

Figure 8-4 *Half Dome in Yosemite National Park is an example of a large dome of rock produced by exfoliation.*

Figure 8-5 *As the rocks in a flowing stream tumble and bump into each other, sharp edges are rounded off.*

Abrasion When rocks come into contact with other rocks, they tend to knock off sharp edges, breaking up larger rocks and producing rounded fragments. The longer that rock fragments undergo this process, called *abrasion*, the smaller, smoother, and more round they become. See Figure 8-5.

Chemical Weathering

Chemical Weathering
The ways rock breaks down by changing some of the materials in the rock.

Chemical weathering changes the composition of rock through chemical action instead of by mechanical force. Chemical weathering takes place when minerals in rock are either removed or chemically altered by water, certain gases in the air, or other substances. Let's look at some of the agents of chemical weathering.

Water There are three ways in which water chemically weathers rocks. Many minerals in rocks can be dissolved in and carried away by water that washes over them. Often, the minerals being dissolved were holding or "cementing" small pieces of rock, such as sand, together. Once this cement is removed, the rock crumbles into the pieces from which it was made. Some minerals that make up rock are able to absorb water the way a sponge does. This absorbed water increases the size of those parts, straining and weakening the rock. The weakened rock is then more easily broken apart. Water can also combine with certain minerals to form new compounds by a process called *hydration*. Micas and feldspars, for instance, are changed into clay by hydration.

Oxygen A small amount of oxygen from the air can join with some minerals in rock when they are wet. These minerals are then chemically changed into new substances through the process of *oxidation*. For example, oxygen can cause the oxidation of wet iron to form rust. As shown in Figure 8-6, objects made by humans can also be weathered by oxidation. Rocks often contain iron that can rust just like an old iron chain or car bumper. The red, yellow, and orange colors often seen in weathered rock may be the result of oxidation.

Figure 8-6 *Rust is caused by oxygen and water acting on iron.*

Carbon Dioxide Carbon dioxide in the air can react with water to form a weak acid called *carbonic acid*. This acid is able to dissolve some of the minerals in rock. The degree of chemical weathering that can be accomplished by carbonic acid is represented dramatically by limestone caves. See Figure 8-7.

Living Organisms Chemical weathering can also be caused by acids from living organisms. Lichens, which consist of fungi and algae, grow on rock surfaces and produce an acid that dissolves some of the materials in the rock. Lichens are often called "pioneer plants" because they are one of the first types of living things to grow in a rocky area. By

Figure 8-7 *Limestone caves are formed by the action of carbonic acid.*

Figure 8-8 *When lichens grow on rocks, they produce a type of acid that dissolves the minerals in the rocks.*

breaking up rock, they prepare the ground for plant life. See Figure 8-8.

The Formation of Soil

Physical and chemical weathering work in combination to break down rocks into other, smaller products. One of the end products of such weathering is called *soil*. Soil contains rock particles and other materials, which form a mixture that supports plant life. The type of parent rock being weathered determines what type of particles a soil contains.

Soil contains small pieces of weathered rock in various sizes. The larger pieces of rock are called *gravel*, smaller grains are called *sand*, while the smallest pieces are called *silt* and *clay*. Silt and clay may be as fine as flour or dust. Soil also contains the decaying remains of dead plants and animals. Decayed plants and animals are changed into *humus* by bacteria.

Humus is a very important part of the soil and is one of the main sources of the nutrients needed for the growth of new plants. Without a supply of the nutrients supplied by humus, soil is not *fertile* and is unable to support plant life. Soils differ in the amount of humus they contain. For example, the soil in swamps may be made almost entirely of humus. In deserts, on the other hand, the soil usually has only a small amount of humus.

Summary

The earth's land surfaces are the result of two opposing forces. Movements of the crust raise the land to form features such as mountains. At the same time, the agents of weathering and erosion work to wear down the land features. Rocks are broken down into smaller pieces by physical and chemical weathering. Soil is formed from small pieces of weathered rock and the remains of plants and animals.

8.2 EROSION

What happens to all of the particles of rock that are formed by the processes of weathering? Once rock has been broken down by weathering, rock particles and soil can be moved by several means: gravity, streams, ice, wind, or waves. Everything that happens to cause pieces of rock or soil to be carried away is called *erosion*. Erosion is mostly a slow, gradual process that plays a major role in shaping the land-forms of the earth.

Erosion by Gravity

Broken rock pieces can fall from a cliff or slide down a slope. A pile of such broken material at the bottom of a cliff or steep slope is called *talus*. Figure 8-9 shows talus on the side of a canyon wall. Gravity is the agent of erosion here because it pulls pieces of rock down to the bottom of a slope.

Gravity can also move large amounts of loose, weathered rock and soil in the sudden movement of a landslide. The rock and soil may come from part of a slope or the side of a mountain. Landslides are very dangerous because they can occur in areas where people live. See Figure 8-10. Earthquakes often cause landslides, as does excess moisture from heavy rains or melting snow. Landslides throughout the world have cost many lives. Entire towns and villages have been wiped out. Sudden floods sometimes occur when large landslides block rivers or raise the level of lakes so that water spills over dams.

Figure 8-9 A pile of talus has collected at the bottom of these cliffs.

Figure 8-10 Landslides can be caused when heavy rains or earthquakes loosen material on a steep slope.

The movement of weathered rock by gravity is not always sudden. Sometimes the movement of weathered rock is only about one to two centimeters a year. Slow downhill movement of loose rock or soil is called *creep*. It is often hard to tell that creep is taking place since there is usually no change in the way the slope looks. However, careful observation of trees, telephone poles, or fence posts can show evidence of creep. Creep is the most common kind of erosion caused by gravity. It is the main way weathered rock moves downhill. See Figure 8-11.

Sometimes part of a slope may slide down more or less in one piece called a *slump*. A slump usually takes place where

Figure 8-11 The surface of this sloping field shows extensive soil creep.

Figure 8-12 *A slump usually occurs on a curved surface. The edge of this spoon-shaped surface is visible at the top of the slump.*

the slope of the land has been changed due to erosion. For example, the banks of streams often slump into the eroded stream channel. See Figure 8-12. Slumping is also seen along cliffs at the shore where waves have cut into the base of the cliff.

Erosion by Streams

Water moving over the earth's surface moves soil, rocks, and even boulders, thus shaping the land. Stream erosion is responsible for many familiar land forms including valleys, hills, plateaus, mesas, and buttes. Suppose the photograph shown in Figure 8-13 could have been made about nine million years ago. It would not show the exposed layers of rock that you now see. The San Juan River flowing along the bottom of this twisting channel carved out this great valley over millions of years. Another example of stream erosion is the Grand Canyon, which is about 1.6 km deep and 14 to 29 kilometers wide. It shows the power of flowing water to erode the earth's surface.

Flowing water erodes the land surface in three ways. One way is when soil and rock materials dissolve in water and are carried away. But the water does not change the rock very much since this process takes many years. Most erosion by streams is done in a second way: when particles of rock and soil are carried away by the water's current. As these particles are carried by the water, they wear away the channel through which the stream flows—just like sandpaper wears away wood. A third way is when pieces of rock too large to be carried by the stream are rolled and bounced along the channel. They chip and wear away the rock of the channel. Thus streams are able to move loose materials and, at the same time, erode deeper channels in the solid rock.

Figure 8-13 *The San Juan River has created Gooseneck Canyon in Utah.*

From Runoff to Rivers Erosion by flowing water begins with raindrops that come down on exposed soil. Erosion takes place rapidly where the soil is loosely packed or where the slope is steep. Raindrops break up lumps of loose soil and thus stir up the soil. During heavy rainfall, soil cannot absorb all of the rain as it falls. Therefore, only some of the rain sinks into the soil, while the rest moves over the soil surface. Water that moves over the surface of the land is called **runoff**.

Runoff may come from melting snow and ice as well as from rain. It begins as a shallow layer, or sheet, of water flowing downhill. Pebbles and rocks on the surface quickly break the sheet into tiny streams that form shallow *channels*. These channels come together and are widened and deepened by the water flowing through them. Small streams join others, forming larger streams. All the streams from an area finally flow into one large stream or river. Streams that flow into a river are called *tributaries*. The large area from which a major river and its tributaries collect runoff is called a *drainage basin*, or **watershed**.

A river system is usually large enough to drain the average runoff from its watershed. When the amount of runoff is greater than usual, and the river is not large enough to handle the extra water, a flood results. Heavy rain or fast-melting snow can cause floods. Most rivers have a small flood once in a while; major floods occur less often. Unfortunately, these floods often cause disasters in which lives may be lost and buildings, roads, and crops destroyed.

Rate of Erosion Rivers are often described as young or old. Young rivers flow swiftly in deep, often narrow, V-shaped canyons. They have rocky beds and may have many rapids and waterfalls. See Figure 8-14. Young rivers are very energetic and erode rock rapidly. Old rivers, on the other hand, flow very slowly across broad expanses of primarily flat land. Their channels are wide and flat, and they curve in large bends called *meanders*. See Figure 8-15. The rate of erosion by old rivers is much slower. They primarily distribute the materials that were brought into them by younger tributaries.

Careless use of the land by humans speeds the rate of erosion. Plants protect the soil from washing away. When the natural plant cover is removed by human activity, such as farming or construction, or by natural processes, the soil is exposed and eroded. Since nature needs about 1000 years to make only 2.5 cm of soil, it can take a long time to replace

Runoff Water running downhill over the land surfaces.

Watershed The land area that is drained by a stream or river.

Figure 8-14 Young rivers flow in rocky V-shaped valleys.

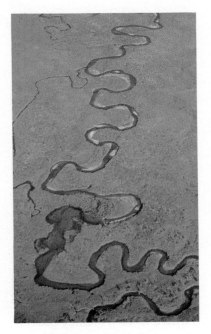

Figure 8-15 Old, slow-flowing rivers have many meanders.

the lost soil. Grass and trees planted along roadways and overpasses help to hold soil in place. Many farmers use *contour plowing* to reduce soil erosion in their fields. See Figure 8-16.

Erosion by Glaciers

Most snow that falls on land eventually melts to form runoff, which returns to the sea in rivers. There are places on earth, however, where it is too cold for all the snow to melt. As the snow falls, year after year, it piles up. The snowflakes are squeezed together and become ice. When the weight becomes great enough, the body of ice and snow begins to move.

Types of Glaciers   Some of the greatest rivers on earth are made of solid ice. Like huge plows, they carve and shape large parts of the earth's surface. These large bodies of moving ice and snow are called *glaciers*. There are two basic types of glaciers: *valley glaciers* and *continental glaciers*.

Valley glaciers are found in mountainous areas all over the world. See Figure 8-17. They look like rivers of dirty ice filling mountain valleys. Valley glaciers are fed from snow that builds up on their upper ends. They are able to move because the pull of gravity causes their great mass to slide downhill, sometimes at speeds up to one meter per day. Valley glaciers also move because parts of the ice are under pressure and thus creep slowly. As glaciers move, the ice near the surface breaks and forms numerous cracks. Large cracks often appear near the edges of a glacier when some of its parts move faster than others. These great cracks are called *crevasses*. When valley glaciers reach the sea, huge pieces fall off of the cracked ice and float away as *icebergs*.

Continental glaciers, also called *icecaps*, are giant sheets of ice that may cover thousands of square kilometers. Twenty thousand years ago, continental glaciers covered almost 30 percent of the earth's land area. Such a period of extensive glaciation is called an *ice age*. Continental glaciers greatly affect the land they cover. The Great Lakes, for example, were formed by their action.

Today, two such glaciers cover most of Antarctica and Greenland. In places, the Antarctic icecap is over 4500 meters thick. See Figure 8-18. It covers great mountain ranges that run across the continent. Ninety percent of the world's ice is in the Antarctic icecap. Antarctic ice also contains 75 percent of the world's fresh water. Edges of icecaps also break off when they reach the sea, producing many icebergs.

Figure 8-16 Contour plowing follows the shape of the land surface to help prevent rapid runoff with heavy erosion.

Figure 8-17 A valley glacier descends from snowfields located at the top of mountains.

Figure 8-18 Continental glaciers may be hundreds of meters thick and may cover areas as large as Antarctica.

Landforms Carved by Glaciers   Glaciers are responsible for the appearance of much of the earth's surface at high altitudes and latitudes. Sharp mountain peaks, wide valleys, level plains, and lakes have been made by glaciers. Rocks buried in the ice at the bottom and sides of a glacier act like the teeth of a file. As glaciers move, the rocks scrape and dig into the land, grinding away solid rock and often leaving deep scratches. See Figure 8-19. Given enough time, glaciers can eventually grind down the land to a nearly level surface.

Glaciers that form in mountains greatly change the shape of those mountains. The changes begin in pockets, called *snowfields*, where snow and ice collect. Frost action breaks rock off of mountainsides, and the pieces are carried along when the ice begins to move downhill, carving away more rock. By this process, the mountainside under a snowfield is changed into a rounded, steep-walled basin called a *cirque*. As a glacier grows, it moves down a valley wearing away its floor and walls. In time, mountain valleys that are originally V-shaped are changed into U-shaped valleys. See Figure 8-20.

Figure 8-19 What evidence is found on these rocks to show that they were once covered by a glacier?

Figure 8-20 The rugged landscape of this typical U-shaped valley was formed by alpine glaciers.

Erosion by Wind

Have you ever felt a strong wind? See Figure 8-21. Sometimes the wind can blow you over unless you lean against its force or hold onto something. It is the wind's energy that you feel. This energy is also able to erode rock and soil.

Figure 8-21 *Some places in the world can have very strong winds.*

Like flowing water, the wind can carry pieces of rock, causing changes on the earth's surface. However, the wind moves only small rock particles like sand and dust. Its effect is greatest in dry, desert climates where many small particles are exposed to the wind. Particles in moist soils cling together, making it hard for the wind to pick them up. In deserts there is little or no moisture in the soil and very few plants to cover and protect it from the wind. Therefore, the unprotected soil and sand is blown away. This means that most deserts are covered by large patches of solid and broken rock—a type of surface, called *desert pavement*. See Figure 8-22. Deserts are

Figure 8-22 *The area from which the sand is removed is often left barren, resulting in a hard surface called desert pavement.*

not, as many think, covered by sand dunes. Sand dunes occur only in limited areas in most deserts.

Flood plains, plowed ground, and beaches may also be exposed to much erosion by the wind. In dry regions or during droughts, strong winds may cause huge dust storms. During a large dust storm, a cubic kilometer of air may carry as much as 900,000 kilograms of dust. A storm covering a large area is able to move many billions of kilograms of dust. In the 1930s several years of severe drought allowed wind storms to blow away massive amounts of soil from mid-western farms. At that time, this area was known as the "dust bowl."

Larger particles, like sand, can only move short distances through the air. Sand particles are moved across beaches and deserts by a rolling and bouncing motion called *saltation*. By this motion, sand particles are lifted no higher than a couple of meters above the ground. Wind-blown sand causes erosion by abrasion when the sharp edges of sand grains scrape at and wear away objects they come in contact with. Since wind-blown sand particles stay close to the ground, their greatest effect is to abrade and polish larger rocks left on the ground. See Figure 8-23.

Figure 8-23 Wind helps to shape unusual rock formations in deserts.

Erosion by Waves

Wind is also able to move water and thereby cause erosion. Winds blowing across oceans or lakes create waves that travel across the water surface toward the shoreline. When waves reach a shoreline, they pound against it. During storms, large waves hit with great force. The constant pounding of waves erodes the rocks along a shoreline.

Waves break up rocks in two ways. First, waves force water and air into cracks, applying pressure that forces the rock apart. Over time, large blocks of rock are broken up in this

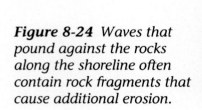

Figure 8-24 Waves that pound against the rocks along the shoreline often contain rock fragments that cause additional erosion.

way. These rocks may be moved by further wave action and aid in the second method of wave erosion. Broken rocks cause additional erosion when they are smashed against the shore by the waves. See Figure 8-24. As the rock fragments are thrown around by waves, they also grind and rub against each other, thus becoming smaller and smaller.

The effect of waves depends on the force of the waves and the type of rock that makes up the shoreline. Interesting structures form in places where some rocks are broken down faster than others. Unequal erosion produces sea stacks as shown in Figure 8-25. Sea stacks are columns of rock that stand on a beach or a short distance offshore. They are formed when the softer rock is worn away, leaving harder rock standing in columns. Figure 8-26 shows a sea cliff that has been eroded by waves that come straight into the shore and continually wear away softer rocks at the base of the cliff. The rocks at the top of the cliff eventually tumble down and are ground up by wave action. Waves may also hollow out soft rock in a sea cliff to form sea caves.

Figure 8-25 A sea stack on a shoreline.

Summary

Gravity can cause landslides, creep, or slumps, thus moving large amounts of rock and soil. Water flowing across the land causes erosion by carrying or rolling rock and soil. This run-off water eventually enters a river system. Rivers age as the speed of water moving through their channels becomes slower. Large amounts of snow and ice may build up in mountain valleys and over land near the poles, forming glaciers. Materials carried along by moving glaciers erode the land. Wind can cause erosion in dry regions by picking up small particles of sand. These moving particles may strike against and wear away solid rock. Waves wear away the land along the shore, forming many interesting structures in the rock.

Figure 8-26 The White Cliffs of Dover, in England, are one of the world's most famous sea cliffs.

8.3 DEPOSITION

Picture the shore of a river, lake, or ocean. Do you see beaches, sandbars, and dunes? All of these features can be traced back to solid rock that was broken down by weathering and then carried to the shore by erosion. Eventually, the rock particles were dropped by a process called *deposition*. The deposition of eroded materials creates new and constantly changing landforms, thus playing a role in shaping the continents.

Stream Deposits

Streams and rivers deposit the rock and soil they erode in many places as they flow toward the ocean. The largest quantity of material is deposited where the water flow slows down. The most noticeable stream and river deposits are found at the base of mountains, at the edge of stream channels, and where rivers meet a lake or ocean.

Fast-moving mountain streams slow down drastically when they reach the floor of a valley. Most of the rock and soil they carry are deposited there in triangle-shaped deposits called *alluvial fans*. Since the smallest particles continue to be carried on downstream and are deposited elsewhere, alluvial fans are composed mainly of coarse sand and gravel. Alluvial fans are distinctive features of the mountains in arid areas of the western United States. See Figure 8-27. Several alluvial fans may grow together to form the gently sloping "skirt" of a mountain.

Figure 8-27 Runoff from slopes in desert regions deposits sediment in an alluvial fan.

Sometimes a river overflows its banks and causes a flood. Flood waters carry rock particles and soil onto the land beside a river channel where they are deposited on both sides of the channel. Repeated flooding builds up layer upon layer of rich soil, eventually forming a flat area called a *flood plain*. Older rivers often have wide, flat flood plains that are commonly used for farming because of their rich, deep soil.

Streams and rivers eventually empty into lakes or an ocean. In lakes, the material brought by streams settles throughout the entire body of water. A lake may become completely filled with this material, first forming a swamp, and then dry land. Where a large river flows into an ocean, another triangle-like structure, called a delta, may form. See Figure 8-28. A delta may extend many miles into an ocean. For example, the delta formed by the Mississippi River reaches far into the Gulf of Mexico. The deposits found in old river deltas are made of very fertile soils and also make excellent farmland.

Figure 8-28 When a river meets an ocean or a gulf, the materials carried by the river are deposited in a delta.

Figure 8-29 Glacial deposits, such as those shown here, are called till.

Glacial Deposits

Moving glaciers pick up broken and ground up rock. When the ice melts, all of this material is deposited. Glaciers deposit two kinds of materials. One kind of glacial deposit consists of the rocks, sand, and dust dropped directly by the melting ice. This unsorted material is called *till*. See Figure 8-28. Mounds of till, called *moraines*, can be deposited in ridges along the sides of a glacier or at its front edge when it stops advancing. If meltwater collects behind such a moraine, a lake will form.

A second type of material deposited by glaciers is that left by streams of *meltwater* flowing out from a glacier. These bits of broken rock are called *outwash deposits*. Outwash deposits are layered according to size. If the meltwater streams flow out onto level ground, the material is deposited in wide, even sheets to form an *outwash plain*. See Figure 8-30. Sometimes blocks of ice break off of a retreating glacier and are buried in outwash deposits. When these blocks melt, large water-filled holes, called *kettle lakes* are left. See Figure 8-31.

Figure 8-30 *The flood of water from a melting glacier often deposits a thick blanket of eroded material on an outwash plain.*

Wind Deposits

The sand, silt, and dust carried by the wind are deposited as the wind slows down. For example, a bush or a large rock can cause the wind to slow down. Such a barrier is called a *windbreak*. A mound of rock particles often builds up around such windbreaks. Once the deposit is started, it forms a larger barrier that acts to block the wind further. In time, the mound grows and becomes a *dune*. Dunes are commonly found along beaches where the wind carries sand back from the beach and drops it around nearby plants or other windbreaks. In deserts, dry, loose material is easily lifted from unprotected ground and moved by the wind. Thus many deserts also have dunes.

Dunes can take many shapes, but all dunes have two things in common. Every dune has a gentle slope that faces the wind and a steep slope that faces away from the wind. Sand moves up to the top of a dune by the rolling and bouncing motion of saltation and then slips down the other side. See Figure 8-32. This causes dunes to move slowly

Figure 8-31 *Kettle lakes are one of the distinct features of continental glaciers.*

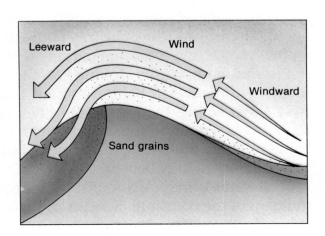

Leeward   Wind

Windward

Sand grains

Figure 8-32 *A dune has a gentle slope facing the wind and a steeper side away from the wind.*

in the direction that the wind blows. Dunes can move over roads, railroad tracks, farmland, and even buildings. Plants and fences are often used to block the movement of dunes.

Not all the particles carried by the wind are deposited as dunes. Smaller and lighter particles of dust are carried farther than the dune-building sand and soil. When this light dust eventually comes to rest, it covers the land like a blanket. Thick layers of wind-blown dust are called *loess*. See Figure 8-33. Deposits of loess are usually tan in color and can be up to 30 meters thick, covering hills and valleys. Loess deposits are soft and easily eroded.

Figure 8-33 A deposit of loess.

Deposition by Ocean Waves and Currents

Wave action also deposits broken rock particles that were either eroded directly from a shoreline or brought to a shore by streams. Waves, and the currents they produce, deposit broken rock to form *beaches*. Beaches are deposits of sand and larger materials, such as pebbles and cobblestones, that are found along the shoreline.

Beaches made of pebbles and cobblestones occur along rocky coastlines where exposed cliffs are being eroded by high-energy waves. These beaches are characteristic of shorelines with sea caves, sea cliffs, and sea stacks. Wide sandy beaches are found along gently sloping coastlines that are covered by soft sediments left behind by slow-moving rivers. Large river systems, like the Mississippi River system, carry huge amounts of sand and fine soil particles into coastal waters. Some of these materials are brought back to the shore by waves to form sandy beaches.

The kinds of deposits found on a beach depend on the makeup of the coastline. Beach sand may be light- or dark-colored, depending on the original source of the sand.

See Figure 8-34. For example, the white sand beaches of northern Florida and other southeastern coastal states come from the erosion of the light-colored sedimentary rocks of the Appalachian Mountains. The black sand and cobblestone beaches along the northern Pacific Coast come from the erosion of the dark volcanic rocks of the Cascade Mountains.

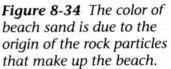

Figure 8-34 The color of beach sand is due to the origin of the rock particles that make up the beach.

Elongated ridges, called *sand bars*, are usually found along sandy beaches. Sand bars are built up by wave action. They form in the shallow zone near the beach where the waves gradually dissipate their energy. Depending on the slope of the beach and the average wave energy, there may be up to several sand bars, all running parallel to the beach at various distances from it. Sand bars shift constantly due to tides and changes in wave action.

Sand along the beach is also moved parallel to the shore by these currents. Sometimes this movement forms a *spit*, which is a long, narrow deposit of sand that remains attached to the beach at one end. A spit that becomes separated from the beach may become a *barrier island*, which is a long, narrow island of sand that runs parallel to a coastline. See Figure 8-35. Barrier islands, like other features of a sandy shoreline, are constantly being changed due to the movement of sand by waves and currents.

Figure 8-35 Barrier islands are usually long and narrow.

Summary

Streams and rivers deposit the rock and soil they erode in alluvial fans, flood plains, and deltas. Glaciers deposit materials when they melt, leaving both sorted and unsorted materials. Deposits of sand and dust collect when wind slows down and drops the material it carries. Many familiar coastal features are formed by the action of waves and currents.

GLOSSARY

A

Acids a class of chemicals with similar properties. They have a sour taste, turn litmus paper red, and react with bases to form a salt and water **(265)**

Adaptations changes that help a living thing survive in a different environment **(98)**

Air exchange the movement of air between the inside and the outside **(327)**

Algae (singular, alga) a large group of primitive plants having chlorophyll, but lacking true roots, flowers, stems, and leaves. Algae are the chief marine and fresh-water plants, ranging in size from pond scum to kelp **(128)**

Alloy a mixture of two or more metals, or of a metal with some other substance **(253)**

Animalcules the name given to the first microorganisms seen by von Leuweenhoek. The word means "little animals" **(123)**

Antibiotic a chemical produced by certain microorganisms, capable of killing or stopping the growth of some bacteria **(152)**

B

Bacteria a large class of single-celled microorganisms, considered neither plant nor animal, belonging to Kingdom Monera. Their actions cause a number of diseases and many processes including decay, fermentation, and soil enrichment **(129)**

Bases a class of chemicals with similar properties. They have a bitter taste, turn litmus paper blue, and react with acids to form a salt and water **(265)**

Biological properties characteristics that distinguish living things from nonliving things **(184)**

Boiling point the temperature at which a substance in its liquid state changes rapidly into a gas **(212)**

Bomb calorimeter measures the amount of energy in food by burning it in a closed chamber (the "bomb") **(377)**

C

Calorie a unit of measure of heat energy used to describe the energy content of food **(378)**

Calorimeter a device that measures the amount of heat in a substance **(375)**

Cancer a harmful, uncontrolled growth in human tissues **(80)**

Cells the smallest units of living things **(104)**

Chemicals substances produced by or used in chemical reactions, such as water, salt, and sugar **(230)**

Chemical change a change resulting in the formation of a new chemical, as in burning **(242)**

Chemical properties characteristics of a substance that describe how the substance behaves in chemical changes **(185)**

Cold-blooded having body temperatures that change and that stay close to the temperature of the surroundings **(96)**

Combustion burning; chemically combining a substance with oxygen so rapidly that heat and light are produced **(271)**

Compost a mixture of decomposing matter **(136)**

Compounds substances that could be broken down into elements during a chemical reaction **(260)**

Compressed squeezed into a smaller space **(207)**

Conduction heat traveling through a solid material **(384)**

Controlled experiment an experiment in which variables are controlled to make the experiment fair and the results reliable **(31)**

Convection heat traveling throughout a liquid as it is circulated as a result of being heated **(384)**

Corrosion a type of chemical change such as the one that takes place when iron reacts with oxygen in the process of rusting **(271)**

Crust the earth's surface **(421)**

Cryptogram a message in a secret code **(11)**

Culture to grow microorganisms by providing the living conditions that will allow them to grow best **(125)**

D

Dead once alive but no longer having any of the signs of life **(56)**

Delta a triangular or fan-shaped wedge of sediment deposited at the mouth of a river **(462)**

Dew point the temperature at which moisture first forms **(212)**

Displacement method a method of finding the volume of an object by submerging it in water **(198)**

Dormancy a sleep-like state that may be triggered by changes in the environment **(97)**

Ductile able to be drawn out thin, as when aluminum is drawn into wire **(253)**

E

Electrolysis the passing of an electrical current through certain substances in order to break them down, such as when water is broken down into hydrogen and oxygen gases **(258)**

Elements substances that cannot be broken down during a chemical reaction. They combine with other elements to form compounds. No element can be changed into another element by means of chemical reactions **(260)**

Energy the ability to do work **(299)**

Erosion the weathering and carrying away of soil, rock, and other materials **(443)**

Estuary a wide, shallow river mouth that usually extends well inland **(463)**

Evaporation the change from a liquid to a gas **(210)**

F

Freezing point the temperature at which a substance in its liquid state changes to a solid **(211)**

Fungi (singular, fungus) a kingdom, neither plant nor animal, of organisms adapted to absorb food from living or dead matter; includes yeasts, molds, mushrooms, and puffballs **(136)**

G

Gall a harmful growth in the tissues of plants **(80)**

Geologic time scale a special kind of time scale that scientists use to describe the earth's history through time **(418)**

Geology science that studies the earth and the changes brought about by natural processes **(412)**

Germinate to sprout; to begin to grow from a seed **(73)**

Glacier huge moving masses of ice on land **(468)**

Ground water water that collects beneath the surface of the earth **(451)**

Gullies ditches carved out by rainwater **(460)**

H

Hyphae (singular, hypha) thread-like or stem-like parts of a fungus **(148)**

Hypothesis an assumption to be tested **(31)**

I

Indicators natural dyes that have one color in acids and another in bases **(265)**

Inferences conclusions drawn from observations that attempt to explain or make sense of the observations **(22)**

Infusion a preparation obtained by steeping a substance in a liquid **(125)**

Insulin a chemical produced by a small gland called the pancreas. It is used to break down sugars during the process of digestion, and in the treatment of diabetes **(7)**

Insulators materials that slow down the flow of heat **(391)**

Interface the boundary between two different substances **(207)**

Interpret to explain the meaning of something **(22)**

Irritability the ability of an organism to respond to stimuli **(82)**

J

Joule a unit of energy, about equal to the amount of energy required to raise a 100-g mass 1 meter **(375)**

K

Karst landscape type of terrain consisting of limestone hills pocked with caves and sinkholes **(238)**

Kinetic energy energy in motion **(296)**

Kingdom the most general category scientists use for classifying organisms **(127)**

L

Living presently alive **(56)**

Locomotion an animal moving on its own **(58)**

Lung capacity the amount of air the lungs can hold **(199)**

M

Malleable able to be easily shaped into many useful products **(253)**

Mass the measure of the amount of matter of a thing **(201)**

Matter anything that has volume and mass **(183)**

Melting point the temperature at which a substance in its solid state changes to a liquid **(212)**

Meltwater water from a melting glacier **(474)**

Meniscus the curvature of the surface of a liquid **(194)**

Microbiology the study of microorganisms **(123)**

Microorganisms tiny living things that can be seen only with the aid of a microscope **(120)**

Mid-ocean ridges underwater mountain chains formed in connection with spreading centers **(422)**

Migration movement from one place or climate to another in response to a change of seasons **(91)**

Model a picture or representation of the real thing, supported by observations and inferences **(28)**

Monera a kingdom, neither plant nor animal, consisting of bacteria **(129)**

Multicelled composed of more than a single cell **(122)**

N

Neutralization reaction a reaction in which an acid neutralizes a base to form a salt and water **(266)**

Névé (Nay VAY) rounded grains of snow found on the upper end of a glacier **(470)**

Nonliving never having been alive **(56)**

Nonrenewable resources energy sources that cannot be replaced once they have been used up **(333)**

O

Observation seeing, feeling, hearing, tasting, or smelling **(16)**

Outwash a formation created from sediment deposits of meltwater streams **(474)**

P

Pangaea the theorized continent from which all continents stem, according to Wegener **(421)**

Particle model of matter a model in which all matter is made of particles **(215)**

Pasteurization heating a substance to kill unwanted microorganisms while sparing beneficial ones **(140)**

Periodic table a list of symbols of every known element arranged by families (columns of elements with similar chemical properties) and periods (rows of elements whose properties resemble each other more closely than those that are far apart) **(262)**

Permeability a measure of the ease with which a liquid flows through a porous material **(450)**

Perpetual motion machine a hypothetical machine that would run forever once started, without any additional input of energy **(306)**

Perspire to sweat; to secrete water from small glands through the skin **(96)**

Physical change a change, such as boiling, freezing, or breaking, that does not result in the formation of a new chemical **(242)**

Physical properties characteristics of matter that do not involve chemical changes. Examples of physical properties are shape, length, mass, and boiling point **(185)**

Plate tectonics the theory of how the continents move, based on Wegener's theory of continental drift **(423)**

Plates large masses of the earth's crust moving in various directions **(422)**

Porosity a measure of the empty space in a material, as determined by the volume of water that can be absorbed by the material **(450)**

Potential energy stored energy **(296)**

Precipitate a solid formed as the result of a chemical change **(246)**

Prediction telling about something in advance **(30)**

Product new substances formed during a chemical change **(256)**

Properties characteristics that distinguish one thing from another **(17)**

Protista a kingdom, neither plant nor animal, consisting of the protists **(127)**

Protists certain one-celled organisms, such as the euglena and the paramecium, with plant-like or animal-like characteristics—or both (127)

Q

Qualitative observations observations that do not involve measurement or numbers (17)

Quantitative observations observations that involve measurements and numbers (17)

R

Radiation heat traveling through empty space or through a transparent material—without heating the empty space or the transparent material between the heat source and the heated object (384)

Reactants the starting substances of a chemical change (256)

Refining purifying a substance by a chemical process (231)

Regeneration the growth of new body parts to replace those lost or damaged (76)

Renewable resources energy sources that can be replaced naturally, if wisely used (333)

Reproduction plants or animals producing offspring of their own kind (80)

Response a reaction to a stimulus (82)

Runoff excess water that begins to collect and flow over the surface (449)

S

Science knowledge about the natural world derived from observations and experiment (42)

Sediments deposits of loose material such as sand, mud, and small bits of gravel; usually deposited by water (430)

Segments sections or parts into which a body is divided (66)

Spore cases swellings or spheres that contain spores (148)

Spreading center the boundary between separating plates (422)

Stimulus anything that causes a living thing to react (82)

Strip mining the removal of ores found close to the earth's surface by laying them bare instead of sinking a shaft (338)

Supernova an exploding star (6)

Système International d'Unités the international system of metric units, SI (190)

T

Technology the scientific application of knowledge to solve practical problems and to make new inventions (42)

Terminal moraine the ridge formed by the rock fragments a glacier was carrying or pushing before the glacier stopped advancing (474)

Theory of continental drift the theory that at some point Pangaea (a single continent) split apart and its pieces began to "drift" away from each other (421)

Thermal resistance the R-value of insulating material that measures how effective the materials are at preventing heat from getting through them (328)

Toxins poisons produced by certain organisms; they are harmful to normal cell functions (148)

Trench a deep valley formed by the pushing down of the ocean floor by the force of colliding plates (423)

Tributaries streams or rivers that flow into a larger river or lake (460)

V

Variables factors in an experiment that may change or have different values (31)

Virus crystal-like particles that border between living and nonliving material; they cause symptoms of disease when they contact living material (130)

Volume the amount of space something occupies (193)

W

Warm-blooded having body temperatures that do not change and that are usually above the temperature of the surroundings (92)

Watt-hour a unit of measure for the total amount of electrical energy consumed (311)

Watershed the area that a river drains (460)

Weathering the process of rock being broken down or worn down by water, wind, or ice (437)

Word equation a chemical equation that shows the reactants and products of a reaction in terms of words and symbols (256)

Abbreviated as follows: (t) top; (b) bottom; (l) left; (r) right; (c) center.

Table of Contents: iii(t), The Telegraph Colour Library/FPG International; iii(b), HRW Photo by John Langford; iv(t), Johnathan Blair/Woodfin Camp & Associates; iv(c), The Telegraph Colour Library/FPG International; iv(b), HRW Photo by John Langford; v(t), Myron J. Dorf/The Stock Market; v(b), M. E. Walker/Science Source/Photo Researchers; vi(t), Larry Ulrich/Adventure Photo; vi(b), Custom Medical Stock Photo; vii(t), Tom Ives/The Stock Market; vii(b), HRW Photo by John Langford; viii(t), The Telegraph Colour Library/FPG International; viii(b), Doug Allan/Science Library Photo/Photo Researchers; ix, HRW Photo by John Langford.

Unit 1: Pages 2, NASA: 4(t), H. Mark Weidman; 4(c), Department of Regional Industrial Expansion; 4(b), H. Mark Weidman; 5(t), Martin Rogers/FPG International; 5(c), Canapress Photo Service; 5(b), Ross Lewis/Medichrome/The Stock Shop; 6(t), George Brown College; 6(bl), David Malin/Canapress Photo Service; 6(br), Steven Lee/Canapress Photo Service; 7(l), John Mahoney/Canapress Photo Service; 7(r), Banting Best Department of Medical Research, University of Toronto; 13(both), SSC Photo Centre; 44(t), Metro Toronto Reference Library, Picture Collection; 45(tl), Metro Toronto Reference Library, Picture Collection; 45(tr), Metro Toronto Reference Library, Picture Collection; 45(b), AT&T Photo Service; 49, NASA; 50(l), Bachmann/The Stock File; 50(r), Blair Seitz/Photo Researchers; 51(t), Ontario Ministry of Education; 51(b), Pat Lanza/Bruce Coleman, Inc.; 52(t), Roger Ressmeyer; 52(b), U.S. Department of Commerce, National Bureau of Standards; 53(t), Courtesy of EC & G Energy Measurements, Inc., Las Vegas, NV; 53(b), Courtesy Space Industries, Inc., Houston, TX.

Unit 2: 54, Mitch Reardon/TSW; 56, 57, Michael P. Gadomski/Bruce Coleman, Inc.; 58(all), Bill Ivy; 60(tl), Bill Ivy; 60(c), Bill Ivy; 60(bl), Bill Ivy; 60(tr), A. Schmidecker/Miller Services; 60(br), Dr. Aubrey Crich; 61(tl), Roland Weber/Masterfile; 60(cr), Bill Ivy; 64, Runk/Schoenberger/Grant Heilman Photography; 72(l), Holt Studios Ltd/Earth Scenes; 72(r), D. R. Specker/Earth Scenes; 75(tl), (tc), (tr), Bill Ivy; 75(cl) Jack Dermid/Bruce Coleman, Inc.; 75(bl), Bill Ivy; 75(br), Barbara K. Deans/Masterfile; 77, Scala/Art Resource, New York; 78(t), E. R. Degginger/Animals Animals; 78(b), Bill Ivy; 79(t), 79(bl), Runk/Schoenberger/Grant Heilman Photography; 79(br), Denise Tackett/Tom Stack & Associates; 80(tr), J. H. Robinson/Photo Researchers; 80(cr), James Stevenson/Science Photo Library/Photo Researchers; 80(b), Jane Burton/Bruce Coleman, Inc.; 85(all), Bill Ivy; 90, Tom Bean/Allstock; 92(t), Bill Ivy; 92(c), Stephen J. Krasemann/Photo Researchers; 92(b), S. R. Maglione/Photo Researchers; 93(tl), Carleton Ray/Photo Researchers; 93(tr), Merlin D. Tuttle/Bat Conservation International/Photo Researchers; 93(b), Grant Heilman/Grant Heilman Photography; 98(l), Cameron; 98(r), M.P.L. Fogden/Bruce Coleman, Inc.; 99(t), E. S. Ross; 99(b), Davidson; 99(cr), Bill Ivy; 99(br), Harold Lambert; 107(l), Hugh Spencer/Photo Researchers; 107(r), M. I. Walker/Photo Researchers; 108(l to r), Manfred Kage/Peter Arnold, Inc.;108, Biophoto Associates/Science Source/Photo Researchers; 108, Gennaro/Grillone/Photo Researchers; 108, Biophoto Associates/Photo Researchers; 108, Biophoto Associates/Photo Researchers; 108, Biophoto Associates/Photo Researchers; 108, Patrick Lynch/Photo Researchers; 108, Michael Abbey/Science Source/Photo Researchers; 108, Chuck Brown/Science Source/Photo Researchers; 111, Tony Reardon/TSW; 112(t), Ryan Beyer/Allstock; 112(b), David R. Frazier; 113(t), David R. Frazier; 113(b), Nicholas DeVore III/Bruce Coleman, Inc.; 114(t), The Granger Collection, New York; 114(b), John James Audubon, National Audubon Society/Photo Researchers; 115, John James Audubon "Birds of America"/Photo Researchers.

Unit 3: Biophoto Associates/Science Source/Photo Researchers; 123(both), The Bettmann Archive; 128(all), Carolina Biological Supply Co.; 129(all), Manfred Kage/Peter Arnold, Inc.; 130(tr), E. R. Degginger/Bruce Coleman, Inc.; 130(bl), Custom Medical Stock Photo; 130(br), NIBSC/Science Photo Library/Custom Medical Stock Photo; 131 (l),(r), From *The World Book Encyclopedia.* © 1992 World Book, Inc. By permission of the publisher; 133, Dr. Jeremy Burgess/Science Photo Library; 135, Faculty of Medical Arts, University of Toronto; 137, Carolina Biological Supply Co.; 140, The Bettmann Archive; 143(all), David R. Frazier; 147, David Scharf/Peter Arnold, Inc.; 148(l), Martin M. Rotker/Taurus Photos; 148(r), Carolina Biological Supply Co.; 150, Dr. Kwang Shing Kim/Peter Arnold, Inc.; 151(all), Dr. Tony Brain and David Parker/Science Photo Library/Photo Researchers; 152, The Bettmann Archive; 153, Martin M. Rotker/Taurus Photos; 160, The Metro Toronto Library Board; 162, D. M. Phillips/Taurus Photos; 175, Biophoto Associates/Science Source/Photo Researchers; 176, HRW Photo by Ken Lax; 177(l), Harry J. Przekop, Jr./The Stock Shop; 177(r), Custom Medical Stock Photo; 178(t), B. Nations/Sygma; 178(b), Odyssey Productions/Woodfin Camp & Associates; 179(t), ICI Americas ; 179(b), University of Mass. News Services.

Unit 4: Spencer Swanger/Tom Stack & Associates; 184(tl), USDA Photo; 184(tr), State of Michigan Department of Conservation; 184(b), HRW Photo by William Hubbell; HRW Photo by Russell Dian; 187(tr), Ontario Ministry of Natural Resources; 187(l), Department of Regional Industrial Expansion; 187(br), The Telegraph Colour Library/FPG International; 188(t), Abitibi-Price, Inc.; 188(b), Department of Regional Industrial Expansion; 197, 198, HRW Photo by John Langford; 209(t), Spencer Swanger/Tom Stack & Associates; 209(b), P. Degginger/H. Armstrong Roberts; 210, Tim Clark; 216(t), Jeannie Taylor/TexaStock; 216(b), David Madison; 217, Michael Melford; 218(t), Mark Moldaver; 218(b), Grant Heilman Photography; 221, Spencer Swanger/Tom Stack & Associates; 222, Standford Linear Accelerator Center/Science Photo Library/Photo Research-ers; 223, Tom Carroll/Phototake; 224(t), David Madison; 224(b), Howard Boylan/Allsport; 225(t), Leif Skoogfors/Woodfin Camp & Associates; 225(b), Sullivan/TexaStock.

Unit 5: 226, SuperStock International; 238, Michael Mitchell; 243, Art Wolfe/The Image Bank; 245, 246(all), Michael Mitchell; 247(all), Michael Mitchell; 248, Michael Mitchell, 253(t), (c), (br), Alcan Aluminum Limited; 253(bl), Peter Girdley/FPG International; 254, Michael Mitchell; 255, Michael Mitchell; 258(t), From the picture by Marcus Stone; 258(b), William R. Wilson/FPG International; 260, Buck Miller/SuperStock International; 261(t), Chris Schwarz/Canapress; 261(b), SSC/Canadian Photo Centre; 275, SuperStock International; 276, Tom Tracy/The Stock Shop; 277(l), Birgitte Nielson; 277(c), OMAF; 278(t), International Museum of Photography at George Eastman House; 278, Paul Franz Moore; 279, Scott Barrow.

Unit 6: 280, TSW; 282, Larry J. Pierce/ The Image Bank; 283(tr), John Terence Turner/FPG International; 283(bl), Peter Turner/The Image Bank; 283(br), A&J Verkaik/The Stock Market; 291(tl), The Granger Collection, New York; 291(bl), The Bettmann Archive; 291(br), Historical Picture Service; 292(tl), The Granger Collection, New York; 292(tr), The Granger Collection, New York; 292(bl), The Bettmann Archive; 292(br), Wide World Photos; 293(tl), AT&T Bell Laboratories; 293(tr), UPI/Bettmann Newphotos; 293(bl), Stone Flower Studio/ DPI; 298(t), Yoav Levy/Phototake; 298(b), SSC Photo Centre; 299(tl), Julian Baum/ Bruce Coleman, Inc.; 299(tr), SSC Centre Photo; 299(br), HRW Photo by Eric Beggs; 304(tr), Nick Pavloff/The Image Bank; 304(br), Comstock, Inc.; 305(l), E. R. Degginger/Bruce Coleman, Inc.; 305(r), Per Ervik; 329, Daedulus Enterprises, Inc.; 332, Comstock, Inc.; 333, John Elk III/ Bruce Coleman, Inc.; 335(l), Ken Graham/ Bruce Coleman, Inc.; 335(r), Michael P. Gadomski/Bruce Coleman, Inc.; 336(tr), R. Phillips/The Image Bank; 335(bl), Lowell J. Georgia/Photo Researchers; 337(tr), Per Ervik; 337(bl), Ford Motor Company of Canada; 338(t), Ontario Hydro; 338(b), Wendell Metzen/Bruce Coleman, Inc.; 345, TSW; 346, Craig Hodge/Canapress; 347, Larry Ghiorsi/Brooklyn Image Group; 348(t), Larry Hamill; 348(b), Hank Morgan/Science Source/Photo Researchers; 349, T. Matsumoto/Sygma.

Unit 7: 350, Charles Thatcher/TSW; 353(l), Photri; 353(r), D. Luria/FPG International; 378, HRW Photo by Dennis Fagan; 386, Michael Mitchell; 387(all), Michael Mitchell; 388(l), Michael Mitchell; 388(tr), HRW Photo by Lance Schriner; 388(br), Canapress; 389(all), Michael Mitchell; 390, Michael Mitchell; 392, Michael Mitchell; 393(all), Michael Mitchell; 394(all), Michael Mitchell; 395(all), Michael Mitchell; 400, Michael Mitchell; 401(all), Michael Mitchell; 402(all), Michael Mitchell; 405, Charles Thatcher/TSW; 406, Travelpix/FPG International; 407(bl), Michael George/ Bruce Coleman, Inc.; 407(r), Richard T. Nowitz/Photri; 408(t), Loren McIntyre/ Woodfin Camp & Associates; 408(c), Bill Sallaz/Timberland Nursery/Gamma-Liaison; 408(b), Ussel/Sipa Press; 409(t), Larry Lee/Woodfin Camp & Associates; 409(b), Stephanie Maze/Woodfin Camp & Associates.

Unit 8: 410, TSW; 412, HRW Photo by John Langford; 414(both), Birgitte Nielson; 415(tl), Ted Yarwood; 415(tr), David Muench/The Image Bank; 415(b), Birgitte Nielson; 416(l), David Falconer/ West Stock; 416(r), HRW Photo by John Langford; 417(tc), Tom Tracy/After Image; 417(cr), B. F. Boher/U.S.G.S.; 417(br), Terraphotographics/BPS; 418, Trevor Wood/The Image Bank; 426(l), Kevin Schafer/Allstock; 426(r), George Hall/Woodfin Camp & Associates; 427, Ward's Natural Science Establishment; 428(l), GSC 1609; 428(tr), GSC 1484; 428(br), GSC 1484; 429, Ward's Natural Science Establishment; 430, Hennepin's First Sight of Niagara Falls, December 1678, Charles William Jefferys, pen and black ink over pencil, Acc. No. 1972-26-597X, C-70245, National Archives of Canada; 431, Dallas & John Heaton/Stock Boston; 434(tl), Kathleen O'Donnell/The Image Bank; 434(tr), Ontario Ministry of Natural Resources; 434(bl), Keith Gunnar/FPG International; 434(br), Ontario Science Centre; 435(t), GSC 92274; 435(c), John Gerlach/Earth Scenes; 435(bl), E. R. Degginger/Earth Scenes; 435(bc), GSC 70288; 435(br), Robert P. Carr/Bruce Coleman, Inc.; 437(l), Doris Dewitt/TSW/Click/Chicago; 437(tr), Michael Markew/Bruce Coleman, Inc.; 437(cr), Ontario Ministry of Natural Resources; 437(br), Ward's Natural Science Establishment; 439(tl), Peter Menzel/Stock Boston; 439(tr), Peter M. Miller/The Image Bank; 439(c), Jaime Villaseca/The Image Bank; 439(b), Photri; 442(l), Joseph Holmes; 442(r), Pete Turner/The Image Bank; 443(b), SCS Photo; 444, AP/Wide World Photos, Inc.; 445(l), Doug Menuez/Stock Boston; 446(r), Tom Ericson/Mountain Stock; 447, Townsend P. Dickinson/Photo Researchers; 449, Official U.S. Navy Photograph; 453(tr), Thomas Wanstall/ The Image Works; 453(bl), Jeffry W. Myers; 453(br), Nathan Benn/Stock Boston; 458(t), Photri; 458(b), Grant Heilman Photography; 459, Photri; 462(all), NASA; 463(l), NASA; 463(r), Photri; 464(l), Joseph Holmes; 464(tr), Joseph Holmes; 464(cr), Hank Morgan/ Rainbow; 465(t), Baron Wolman/Woodfin Camp & Associates; 465(c), HRW Photo by Ken Lax; 465(b), Thomas Wanstall; 466(bl), NASA; 466(tr), Lillian N. Bolstad/ Peter Arnold, Inc.; 466(br), Photri; 467(tl), Photri; 467(c), John Elk III/Bruce Coleman, Inc.; 468, The Granger Collection, New York; 469(t), National Air Photo Library, Department of Energy Mines and Resources, Canada; 472, Rhoda Sidney/ Stock Boston; 473(both), Ward's Natural Science Establishment; 475(tl), Gene Ahrens/Bruce Coleman, Inc.; 475(tr), Julius Fekete/FPG International; 475(bl), Photri; 475(br), Tom Bean; 479, TSW; 480(tl), Michael Salas/The Image Bank; 480(br), Kennedy/TexaStock; 481, Kenneth Garrett/Woodfin Camp & Associates; 483, Paul Scott/Sygma.

SOURCEBOOK

Unit 1: S1, NASA; S3(l), James Sugar/ Black Star; S3(r), John Marshall; S3(br), E. R. Degginger; S5(l), Frank Pedrick/ The Image Works; S5(r), NASA; S6(tl), HRW Photo by Yoav Levy; S6(tr), Baxter Travenol Laboratories/Frost Publishing; S6(bl), HRW Photo by Yoav Levy; S6(bc), Erich Hartmann/Magnum Photos; S6(br), Phototake; S7(tl), Dan McCoy/Rainbow; S7(tr), Richard Laird/Medichrome; S7(br), B. F. Bohor/USGS; S8(tl), John De Visser/ Black Star; S8(tr), Ralph Perry/Black Star; S8(bl), HRW Photo by Russell Dian; S9(tl), Bill Curtsinger/Photo Researchers; S9(tr), Alan Carey/The Image Works; S9(bl), R. S. Uzzell/Woodfin Camp & Associates; S9(br), Michael Heron/Woodfin Camp & Associates; S10(t), Michael Heron/ Woodfin Camp & Associates; S10(cr), A. Howarth/International Stock Photo; S10(b), Michael Heron/Woodfin Camp & Associates; S11(t), Joseph Lynch/Medical Images, Inc.; S11(c), Dan McCoy/Rainbow; S11(b), NASA; S13, E. R. Degginger/ Animals Animals; S14, Michael Wells; S15(t), C. Lockwell/Animals Animals; S15(b), Tom McHugh; S19, Tom Tracy/ The Stock Shop.

Unit 2: S21, Tony Reardon/TSW; S22(t), The Bettmann Archive; S22(b), Runk–Schoenberger/Grant Heilman Photography; S24, John Paul Kay/Peter Arnold, Inc.; S25, Pfizer, Inc.; S27, Karen Klomparens/Michigan State University; S29, Peter Beck/The Stock Market; S30(l), M.I. Walker/Photo Researchers; S30(c), Eric V. Grave/Photo Researchers; S30(r), Runk/Schoenberger/Grant Heilman Photography; S35, D. Klesenski/International Stock Photo; S37(l),(r), Breck Kent; S39, Dee Wilder; S40(tl), E. R. Degginger; S40(tr), Susan Gibler; S40(bl), E. Duscher/Bruce Coleman, Inc.

Unit 3: S41, Biophoto Associates/Science Source/Photo Researchers; S42, Photri; S44, HRW Photo by Russell Dian; S46, Manfred Kage/Peter Arnold, Inc.; S47(t), Peter Ward/Bruce Coleman, Inc.; S47(b), Lee D. Simon/Photo Researchers, Inc.; S48(l), M. Abbey/Photo Researchers, Inc. S48(r), Andrew H. Knoll; S49(l) (c), M. Abbey/Photo Researchers, Inc.; S48(r), Runk/Schoenberger/Grant Heilman, Photography; S50(t), Hank Morgan/Rainbow; S50(b), Daniel Brody/Stock Boston; S51(l), Heather Davis/Photo Researchers; S51(r), Dr. Gopal Murti/Photo Researchers; S53, Diane Koos Gentry/Black Star; S54(t), Michael Heron/Monkmeyer Press; S54(b), D. Fawcett/E. Shelton/Photo Researchers; S56(t), Jeremy Burgess/Photo Researchers; S56(b), NIBSC/Science Photo Library/Photo Researchers.

Unit 4: S57, Spencer Swanger/Tom Stack & Associates; S58, NASA; S59, Wally Emerson/MIDWESTOCK; S60, HRW Photo by Richard Haynes; S61(l), David Pollack/The Stock Market; S61(r), Robin Lehman/The Stock Market; S62, HRW Photo by Ken Karp; S65, HRW Photo by Ken Karp; S66(l), HRW Photo by Ken Karp; S66(b), HRW Photo by Dennis Fagan; S68(l)(r), Antonio Cusmao/Black Star; S69(l), Breck Kent; S69(r), Willie Rivelli/The Image Bank; S71, Kodansha Ltd.; S72, Universities Research Association, Inc.

Unit 5: S73, SuperStock International; S78, Dr. Albert V. Crewe/University of Chicago; S83, Wide World Photos, Inc.; S84, Robert Brenner/PhotoEdit; S90, HRW Photo by Richard Haynes; S91, Lisa Davis; S95, HRW Photo by Russell Dian; S96, HRW Photo by Russell Dian.

Unit 6: S99, TSW; S100(t), J. Messerschmidt/Bruce Coleman, Inc.; S100(bl), Sharon Greer/The Stock Market; S100(br), Bob Firth/International Stock Photo; S101, Ben Rose/The Image Bank; S102(t), Bob McKeever; S102(b), HRW Photo by Yoav Levy; S103, Courtesy of the U.S. Department of Energy; S104, Dick Durrance/Woodfin Camp & Associates; S105, NASA; S106(t), Richard Megna/Fundamental Photographs; S106(c), HBJ Photo by Sam Joosten; S107, Michael Sullivan/TexaStock; S108, Spencer Swanger/Tom Stack & Associates; S109(t), Manfred Kage/Peter Arnold, Inc.; S109(b), Gary R. Zahm/Bruce Coleman, Inc.; S110(tl), Photo Researchers; S111(t), Alan Weitz/Black Star; S111(b), Douglas Kirkland/Contact Stock Images; S112(t), Peter Menzel; S112(c), Lowell Georgia/Science Source/Photo Researchers; S113, Kevin Schafer/Peter Arnold, Inc.; S114, Keith Gunnar/Bruce Coleman, Inc.; S116, Frank P. Rossotto/The Stock Market.

Unit 7: S117, Charles Thatcher/TSW; S118, Richard Choy/Peter Arnold, Inc.; S121, Park Street Photography; S123, HRW Photo by Richard Haynes; S126(l)(r), NOAA; S130(t), E. R. Degginger; S130(c), HRW Photo by Rhoda Neal; S131(l)(r), World Book Inc.

Unit 8: S133, TSW; S134(t), Reuters/Bettmann Newsphotos; S134(bl), Gerry Ellis/Manhattan Views; S134(br), Ruth Dixon; S135, Nancy Simmerman/Click/Chicago; S136(c), Manuel Rodriguez; S136(bl), E. R. Degginger; S137(c), Michael Markew/Bruce Coleman, Inc.; S137(br), Robert Knowles/Photo Researchers; S138, G. R. Roberts; S139(tr), Manuel Rodriguez; S139(c), Bart Bartholomew/Black Star; S139(br), Jeff Gnass/The Stock Market; S140(t), Jacques Janeoux/Peter Arnold, Inc.; S140(b), Manuel Rodriguez; S141(t), Stephen Fuller/Peter Arnold, Inc.; S141(b), Earth Scenes; S142(t), Grant Heilman Photography; S142(b), Leo Touchet/Woodfin Camp & Associates; S143(t), W. Curtsinger/Photo Researchers; S143(c), Leland Brown/Photo Researchers; S143(b), Jack Wilburn/Earth Scenes; S144(t), Sabine Weiss/Photo Researchers; S144(b), E. R. Degginger; S145, Charles Ott/Photo Researchers; S146(t), Loraine Wilson/Robert Harding Picture Library; S146(b), D. C. Lowe/Alaska Photo/Aperture; S147(t), Paolo Koch/Photo Researchers; S147(b), G. R. Roberts; S148(l), Steve Coombs/Photo Researchers; S148(r), G. R. Roberts; S149(t), E. R. Degginger; S149(b), Michael Giannechini/Photo Researchers; S150, Grant Heilman Photography; S151(tl), Dwight R. Kuhn/Bruce Coleman, Inc.; S151(tr), Phil Degginger/Click/Chicago; S151(br), Robert Perron/Nawrocki Stock Photo.

ART CREDITS

Boston Graphics   432, 433, 453

Les Case   482

Heather Collins   21, 23, 25, 30, 31, 41, 46, 62, 63, 67, 69, 73, 81, 82, 83, 86, 87, 88, 89, 95, 96, 103, 182, 192, 193, 194, 195, 196, 211, 212, 230, 272, 298, 299, 309, 311, 319, 320, 321, 322, 323, 324, 325, 326, 327, 328, 329, 330, 343, 360, 361, 364, 368, 369, 374, 381, 382, 394, 398, 399, 436, 450, 451, 477, 478

Holly Cooper   189, 200, 205, 215, 219, 220, 229, 231, 233, 234, 236, 237, 246, 249, 251, 252, 257, 267, 273, 324, 340, 341, 342, 343, 344, 352, 358, 359, 362, 366, 369, 370, 374, 380, 381, 383, 396, 403

Howard Friedman   110

Don Gauthier   132, 144

David Griffin   62, 63, 66, 100, 101, 106, 107, 201, 295, 313, 357, 361, 362, 365, 366, 376, 382, 383, 384, 385, 397, 405, 426, 482

Linda Hendry   200, 210, 214, 314

Robert Johannsen   32, 35, 36, 231, 296, 297, 316

Chuck Joseph   20, 81, 157

Michael Krone   15, 18, 23, 24 ,34, 38, 40, 46, 47, 48, 59, 66, 68, 69, 70, 71, 122, 129, 131, 154, 161, 291, 295, 296, 297, 310, 311, 312, 313, 317, 318, 322, 331, 369, 427, 440, 454, 477

Vesna Krstanovich   234, 354, 355, 396, 397

Suzanna Krykorka   12, 371

Ligature, Inc.   459

Jimmy Longacre   33

Michael Martchenko   16, 20, 22, 29, 186,
197, 206, 207, 208, 259, 268, 269, 270, 271, 284, 323, 324, 372, 373, 438

John McKee   120, 121, 163

Paul McCusker   118, 119, 134, 141, 170

Julian Mulock   8, 9, 10, 11, 17, 39, 42, 43, 104, 105, 183, 204, 284, 285, 286, 287, 288, 289, 290, 300, 301, 302, 303, 309, 326, 336, 363, 364, 367, 456, 457, 470, 471, 474

Avril Orloff   171

Ric Riordon   21, 24, 27, 448

Steve Schindler   19, 26, 28, 142, 156, 164, 165, 235, 265, 266, 267, 307, 380

Maureen Shaughnessy   365, 445

David Simpson   199, 356, 357

Gary Undercuffler   172

Peter Van Gulik   64, 65, 74, 76, 78, 79, 94, 97, 100, 101, 102, 124, 125, 126, 138, 145, 146, 148, 153, 156, 160, 166, 167, 168, 174, 202, 203, 358, 375, 377

Henry Vander Linde   228, 236, 237

ACKNOWLEDGMENTS

For permission to reprint copyrighted material, grateful acknowledgment is made to the following sources:

Harcourt Brace Jovanovich, Inc.: From *HBJ Physical Science* by William G. Lamb, et al. Copyright © 1989 by Harcourt Brace Jovanovich, Inc.

Holt, Rinehart and Winston, Inc.: From *Holt Earth Science* by William L. Ramsey, et al. Copyright © 1986, 1982, 1978 by Holt, Rinehart and Winston, Inc. From *Holt General Science* by William L. Ramsey, et al. Copyright © 1988, 1983, 1979 by Holt, Rinehart and Winston, Inc. From *Holt Life Science* by William L. Ramsey, et al. Copyright © 1986, 1982, 1978 by Holt, Rinehart and Winston, Inc. From *Holt Physical Science* by William L. Ramsey, et al. Copyright © 1988, 1986, 1982, 1978 by Holt, Rinehart and Winston, Inc.

Houghton Mifflin Company: From "Riddles in the Dark" from *The Hobbit* by J. R. R. Tolkien. Copyright © 1966 by J. R. R. Tolkien. All rights reserved.

Alfred A. Knopf, Inc.: "January" from *A Child's Calendar* by John Updike. Copyright © 1965 by John Updike and Nancy Burkert.

Alfred A. Knopf, Inc.: From "The Negro Speaks of Rivers" from *Selected Poems of Langston Hughes.* Copyright © 1926 by Alfred A. Knopf, Inc. and copyright renewed © 1954 by Langston Hughes.

T–13, David Young Wolff/PhotoEdit; T–14(t), HRW Photo; T–14(c), Art Montes de Oca/FPG International; T–14(b), HRW Photo by Tomás Pantin; T–15(tr), A. Mercieca/SuperStock International; T–15(b), Carl Rosenstein/Viesti Associates; T–16(t), David F. Malin/Anglo–Australian Telescope Board; T–16(b), HRW Photo by Ken Lax; T–17(tl), HRW Photo; T–17(tr), SuperStock International; T–17(b), HRW Photo by Tomás Pantin; T–18(tl), HRW Photo by Richard Weiss; T–18(tr), HRW Photo; T–18(b), D. Northcott/SuperStock International T–20(tl), SuperStock International; T20(b), HRW Photo by Greg Schaler; T–21(t), HRW Photo by Tomás Pantin; T–21(b), David Young Wolff/PhotoEdit; T–22, David Young Wolff/PhotoEdit; T–23, Larry Hamill; T–24(t), HRW Photo; T–24(b), HRW Photo by Tomás Pantin; T–25(t), HRW Photo by Russell Dian; T–25(b), HBJ Photo by Sam Joosten; T–26, HRW Photo by Russell Dian; T–27(t), Diamond Promotion Service; T–27(bl), Myron J. Dorf/The Stock Market; T–27(br), David Young Wolff/PhotoEdit; T–28(t), Kenneth Hayden/Black Star; T–28(b), David Young Wolff/PhotoEdit; T–29(l), HRW Photo; T–29(tr), Telegraph Colour Library/FPG International; T–29(b), David Young Wolff/PhotoEdit; T–30(t), David Young Wolff/PhotoEdit; T–30(bl), HRW Photo by Martha Cooper; T–30(br), David Young Wolff/PhotoEdit; T–31(t), HRW Photo by Dennis Fagan; T–31(b), HRW Photo by Dennis Fagan; T–32(t), HRW Photo by Yoav Levy/Phototake; T–32(c), SuperStock International; T–32(b), Roger Ressmeyer/Starlight; T–33(tl), NASA; T–33(tr), HRW Photo by Russell Dian; T–33(b), Tom Till DRK Photo; T–34(t), David Young Wolff/PhotoEdit; T–34(c), Hans Pfetschinger/Peter Arnold, Inc.; T–34(b), HRW Photo by Tomás Pantin; T–36(t), HRW Photo; T–36(c), Michael D. Sullivan/TexaStock; T–37(t), Michael Powers/Adventure Photos; T–39(b), HRW Photo by Tomás Pantin; T–38(t), SuperStock International; T–38(c), National Optical Astronomy Observatories; T–38(b), HRW Photo by Tomás Pantin; T–39(tl), NASA/JPL Photo; T–39(tr), Roger Allyn Lee/SuperStock International; T–39(b), Peter Vandermark/Stock Boston; T–40(t), HRW Photo by Russell Dian; T–40(b), Tony Freeman/PhotoEdit; T–41(t), HRW Photo; T–41(b), David Young Wolff/PhotoEdit; T–42(t), HRW Photo, T–42(b), NASA;

T–43(t), HRW Photo by Stephen McCarroll; T–43(c), HRW Photo by Russell Dian; T–43(b), David Young Wolff/PhotoEdit; T–44(t), HRW Photo by Dennis Fagan; T–44(b), HRW Photo by Richard Haynes; T–45, HRW Photo; T–46(t), HRW Photo by Russell Dian; T–46(b), HRW Photo by Tim Pannell; T–47, HRW Photo by Dennis Fagan; T–48(t), NASA; T–48(b), HRW Photo by Dennis Fagan; T–49(tl), HRW Photo; T–49(tr), HRW Photo by Dennis Fagan.

Unit 1: 1A, Telegraph Colour Library/FPG International; 1B, HRW Photo by Russell Dian; 1C, HRW Photo by ; 1D, HRW Photo by William Hubbell.

Unit 2: 53A, HRW Photo by William Hubbell; 53B, A. Schmidecker/FPG International; 53C, Myron J. Dorf/The Stock Market; 53D, James L. Amos/Superstock International.

Unit 3: 115A, Ted Horowitz/ The Stock Market; 115B, NCI/Science Source/Photo Researchers, Inc.; 115C, David Sharf/Peter Arnold, Inc.; 115D, Rannels/Grant Heilman Photographers, Inc.

Unit 4: 179A, Blair Seitz/Science Source/Photo Researchers, Inc.; 179B, Larry West/FPG International; 179C, Science Source/Photo Researchers, Inc.; 179D, Science Source/Photo Researchers, Inc.

Unit 5: 225A, HRW Photo by Greg Schaler; 225B, HRW Photo by Paul Wilson; 225C, HRW Photo by Yoav Levy; 225D, HRW Photo by Dennis Fagan.

Unit 6: 279A, HRW Photo by Ken Karp; 279C, Telegraph Colour Library/FPG International; 279D, HRW Photo by Coranado.

Unit 7: 349A, Runk/Schoeberger/Grant Heilman Photography, Inc.; 349B (l), HRW Photo by Rodney Jones; (r), HRW Photo by Rodney Jones; 349C, Howard Sochurek/The Stock Market; 349D, Michael D. Sullivan/TexaStock.

Unit 8: 409A, Tom McHugh/Photo Researchers, Inc.; 409B, Roger Allyn Lee/Superstock International; 409C, Robert Cassell/The Stock Market; 409D, Geraldine Prentice/Tony Stone Worldwide.

Answers to Tables and Graphs

Unit 2, *Checking Your Understanding,*
page 110, question 4.

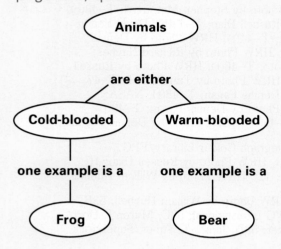

Unit 3, *Checking Your Understanding,*
page 175, question 4.

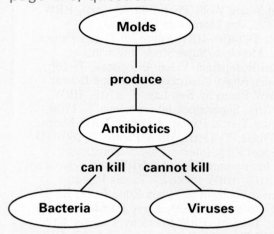

Unit 4, *Some Problems to Solve,*
page 203, question 3.

Volume	Mass of Sand	Mass of Water	Mass of Sawdust
1000 mL	2800 g	1000 g	700 g
500 mL	1400 g	500 g	350 g
200 mL	560 g	200 g	140 g
100 mL	280 g	100 g	70 g

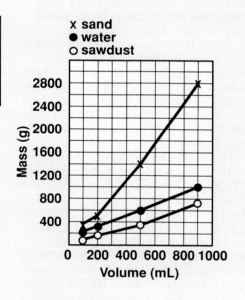

Unit 4, *What Have You Learned?,*
page 208, question 1.

Characteristics of States

	Has a boundary with air and cannot be noticeably compressed	Has no boundary with air and can be noticeably compressed
Apparently rigid	solids	--------
Flows	liquids	gases

Unit 4, *Challenge Your Thinking,* page 219.

Word	Scientific Meaning	Common Meaning
(a) melted	changed from a solid to a liquid	collapsed
(b) boiling	(process of) rapidly changing from a liquid to a gas	bubbling over, out of control
(c) freeze	change from a liquid to a solid	don't move, stand still
(d) evaporated	changed from a liquid to a gas	disappeared unexpectedly
(e) crystallized	changed to a solid from a gas or a liquid	became clear
(f) solidify	change into a solid	make sure of, establish
(g) condensed	changed from a gas into a liquid	shortened

Unit 5, *Physical and Chemical Words,* page 243.

Physical Words		Chemical Words	
grinding	wheat, rocks	burning	wood, oil
breaking	plates, egg-shells	rotting	wood
eroding	soil, sand on a beach, a cliff	rusting	tools, a car
evaporating	water from a lake, per-spiration	reacting	vinegar and baking soda
melting	ice, wax	digesting	food
condensing	water in a terrarium	respiration	living things
drying	clothes	photosyn-thesis	plants
freezing	fish, meat, water		
cutting	grass		

Unit 5, *Exploration 2,* page 245.

The Reactants	The Change	Physical	Chemical	Reasons or Evidence
1. Copper sulfate, water, and iron	blue solution turns paler, bits of copper metal fall out of solution		√	1. Color change occurs. 2. A new substance is formed. 3. Not easily reversible.
2. Vinegar and milk	milk turns lumpy		√	1. A precipitate forms.
3. Eggshell and vinegar	eggshell dissolves, carbon dioxide is released		√	1. Bubbles form. 2. Change is not reversible.
4. Candle wax and heat	wax melts	√		1. Change is reversible.
5. Breath and limewater	calcium carbonate forms		√	1. Color change.
6. Water, cobalt chloride, and heat	blue cobalt chloride turns solution red		√	1. Color change.
7. Lemon juice and heat	clear liquid turns brown		√	1. Color change. 2. Change not easily reversible.
8. Iodine and starch	starch turns purple		√	1. Color change.
9. Water and baking powder	bubbles form		√	1. Gas is produced.

Unit 5, *Challenge Your Thinking,*
page 273, question 3(a).

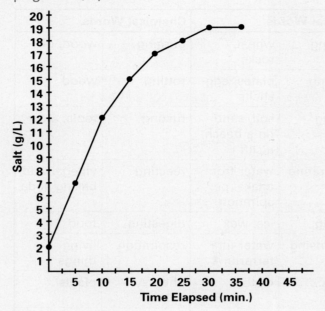

Unit 5, *Challenge Your Thinking,*
page 273, question 3(c).

Time Elapsed (Min.)	Salt (g/L)
0	2
5	7
10	12
15	15
20	17
25	18
30	19
35	19

Unit 6, *Checking Your Understanding,*
page 345, question 3.

Machine	Efficiency	Desired Energy Form	Waste Energy Forms
Toaster	90%	Heat	Light, excess heat
Steamboat	10%	Mechanical	Excess heat
Hair dryer	85%	Heat	Friction
Car engine	30%	Mechanical	Excess heat

Unit 8, *Checking Your Understanding,*
page 479, question 5.

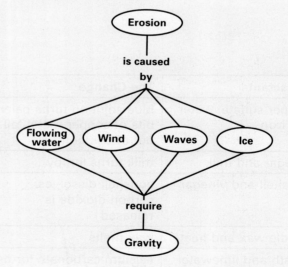